Student Solutions Manual

to accompany

Chemistry
The Molecular Nature of Matter and Change

Canadian Edition

Prepared by:

Sophie Lavieri
Simon Fraser University

Rashmi Venkateswaran
University of Ottawa

McGraw-Hill Ryerson

McGraw-Hill
Ryerson

Student Solutions Manual to accompany
Chemistry: The Molecular Nature of Matter and Change
Canadian Edition

ISBN-13: 978-1-25-907773-9
ISBN-10: 1-25-907773-X

1 2 3 4 5 6 7 8 9 10 WEB 1 9 8 7 6 5 4 3

Printed and bound in Canada.

Director of Product Management: Rhondda McNabb
Group Product Manager: Leanna MacLean
Senior Product Manager: James Booty
Executive Marketing Manager: Joy Armitage Taylor
Product Developer: Chris Cullen
Supervising Editor: Jessica Barnoski
Production Coordinator: Scott Morrison
Cover Design: Michelle Losier
Page Layout: Brian Lehen Graphic Design Ltd.
Printer: Webcom

CONTENTS

PREFACE

WELCOME TO YOUR STUDENT SOLUTIONS MANUAL!

Your Student Solutions Manual (SSM) includes detailed solutions for highlighted End-of-Chapter Problems in the Canadian Edition of Silberberg, Lavieri, and Venkateswaran's *Chemistry: The Molecular Nature of Matter and Change*.

You should use the SSM in your study of chemistry as a study tool:
- To better understand the reasoning behind problem solutions. The plan-solution-check format illustrates the problem-solving thought process for selection End-of-Chapter Problems.
- To better understand the concepts through their application in problems. Explanations and hints for problems are in response to questions from students in general chemistry courses.
- To check your problem solutions. Solutions provide comments on the solution process as well as the answer.

To succeed in general chemistry you must develop skills in problem solving. Not only does this mean being able to follow a solutions path and reproduce it on your own, but also to analyze problems you have never seen before and develop a solution strategy. Chemistry problems are story problems that bring together chemistry concepts and mathematical reasoning. The analysis of new problems is the most challenging step for general chemistry students. You may face this in the initial few chapters or not until later in the year when the material is less familiar. When you find you are having difficulty starting problems, do not be discouraged. This is an opportunity to learn new skills that will benefit you in future courses and your future career. The following two strategies, tested and found successful by many students, may help you develop the skills you need.

The first strategy is to become aware of your own thought processes as you solve problems. As you solve a problem, make notes in the margin concerning your thoughts. Why are you doing each step and what questions do you ask yourself during the solution? After you complete the problem, review your notes and make an outline of the process you used in the solution while reviewing the reasoning behind the solution. It may be useful to write a paragraph describing the solution process you used.

The second strategy helps you develop the ability to transfer a solution process to a new problem. After solving a problem, rewrite the problem to ask a different question. One way to rewrite the problem is to ask the question backwards—find what has been given in the problem from the answer to the problem. Another approach is to change the conditions—for instance, ask yourself what if the temperature is higher or there is twice as much carbon dioxide present? A third method is to change the reaction or process taking place—what if the substance is melting instead of boiling?

At time, you may find slight differences between your answer and the one in the SSM. Two reasons may account for the differences. First, SSM calculations do not round answers until the final step to this may impact the exact numerical answer. Note the in preliminary calculations extra significant figures are retained and shown in the intermediate answers. The second reason for discrepancies may be that your solutions route was different from the one given in the SSM. Valid alternate paths exist for many problems, but the SSM does not space to show all alternate solutions. So, trust your solution as long as the discrepancy is small, and use the different solution route to understand the concepts used in the problem. Some answers have more than one correct answer. For example, if you are asked to name a metal, there over 80 correct answers.

Good luck with your studies!

CHAPTER 1 KEYS TO THE STUDY OF CHEMISTRY

END–OF–CHAPTER PROBLEMS

1.2   Plan: Apply the definitions of the states of matter to a container. Next, apply these definitions to the examples. Gas molecules fill the entire container; the volume of a gas is the volume of the container. Solids and liquids have a definite volume. The volume of the container does not affect the volume of a solid or liquid.
        Solution:
        a) The helium fills the volume of the entire balloon. The addition or removal of helium will change the volume of a balloon. Helium is a **gas**.
        b) At room temperature, the mercury does not completely fill the thermometer. The surface of the **liquid** mercury indicates the temperature.
        c) The soup completely fills the bottom of the bowl, and it has a definite surface. The soup is a **liquid**, though it is possible that solid particles of food will be present.

1.4   Plan: Define the terms and apply these definitions to the examples.
        Solution:
        Physical property – A characteristic shown by a substance itself, without interacting with or changing into other substances.
        Chemical property – A characteristic of a substance that appears as it interacts with, or transforms into, other substances.
        a) The change in color (yellow–green and silvery to white), and the change in physical state (gas and metal to crystals) are examples of **physical properties**. The change in the physical properties indicates that a chemical change occurred. Thus, the interaction between chlorine gas and sodium metal producing sodium chloride is an example of a **chemical property**.
        b) The sand and the iron are still present. Neither sand nor iron became something else. Colors along with magnetism are **physical properties**. No chemical changes took place, so there are no chemical properties to observe.

1.6   Plan: Apply the definitions of chemical and physical changes to the examples.
        Solution:
        a) Not a chemical change, but a **physical change** — simply cooling returns the soup to its original form.
        b) There is a **chemical change** — cooling the toast will not "un–toast" the bread.
        c) Even though the wood is now in smaller pieces, it is still wood. There has been no change in composition, thus this is a **physical change**, and not a chemical change.
        d) This is a **chemical change** converting the wood (and air) into different substances with different compositions. The wood cannot be "unburned."

1.8   Plan: A system has a higher potential energy before the energy is released (used).
        Solution:
        a) The exhaust is lower in energy than the fuel by an amount of energy equal to that released as the fuel burns. The **fuel** has a higher potential energy.
        b) **Wood**, like the fuel, is higher in energy by the amount released as the wood burns.

1.13   Lavoisier measured the total mass of the reactants and products, not just the mass of the solids. The total mass of the reactants and products remained constant. His measurements showed that a gas was involved in the reaction. He called this gas oxygen (one of his key discoveries).

1.16   A well-designed experiment must have the following essential features:
        1) There must be two variables that are expected to be related.
        2) There must be a way to control all the variables, so that only one at a time may be changed.
        3) The results must be reproducible.

1.19   <u>Plan:</u> Review the table of conversions in the chapter or inside the back cover of the book. Write the conversion factor so that the unit initially given will cancel, leaving the desired unit.
<u>Solution:</u>

a) To convert from cm^2 to m^2, use $\dfrac{(1\ m)^2}{(100\ cm)^2}$

b) To convert from km^2 to m^2, use $\dfrac{(1000\ m)^2}{(1\ km)^2}$; to convert from m^2 to cm^2, use $\dfrac{(100\ cm)^2}{(1\ m)^2}$

c) This problem requires two conversion factors: one for distance (km to m) and one for time (h to s). It does not matter which conversion is done first and alternate methods may be used.
To convert distance, km to m, use:
$$\left(\frac{1000\ m}{1\ km}\right) = 10^3\ m/km$$
To convert time, h to s, use:
$$\left(\frac{1\ h}{60\ min}\right)\left(\frac{1\ min}{60\ s}\right) = \frac{1\ h}{3600\ s}$$
Therefore, the complete conversion factor is:
$$\left(\frac{1000\ m}{km}\right)\left(\frac{1\ h}{3600\ s}\right) = \frac{1\ m \cdot h}{3.6\ km \cdot s}$$
Do the units cancel when you start with units of km/h?

d) To convert from kg/m^3 to g/cm^3 requires two conversion factors:
To convert mass, kg to g:
$$\left(\frac{1000\ g}{1\ kg}\right) = 10^3\ \frac{g}{kg}$$

To convert volume from cm^3 to m^3 use, $\left(\dfrac{(1\ m)^3}{(100\ cm)^3}\right) = 10^{-6}\ \dfrac{m^3}{cm^3}$.

The complete conversion is: $\left(10^3\ \dfrac{g}{kg}\right)\left(10^{-6}\ \dfrac{m^3}{cm^3}\right) = 10^{-3}\ \dfrac{g \cdot m^3}{kg \cdot cm^3}$

Do the units cancel when you start with units of kg/m^3?

1.21   <u>Plan:</u> Review the definitions of extensive and intensive properties.
<u>Solution:</u>
An extensive property depends on the amount of material present. An intensive property is the same regardless of how much material is present.
a) Mass is an **extensive property**. Changing the amount of material will change the mass.
b) Density is an **intensive property**. Changing the amount of material changes both the mass and the volume, but the ratio (density) remains fixed.
c) Volume is an **extensive property**. Changing the amount of material will change the size (volume).
d) The melting point is an **intensive property**. The melting point depends on the substance, not on the amount of substance.

1.23   <u>Plan:</u> Density $= \dfrac{mass}{volume}$. An increase in mass or a decrease in volume will increase the density. A decrease in density will result if the mass is decreased or the volume increased.
<u>Solution:</u>
a) Density **increases**. The mass of the chlorine gas is not changed, but its volume is smaller.
b) Density **remains the same**. Neither the mass nor the volume of the solid has changed.
c) Density **decreases**. Water is one of the few substances that expands on freezing. The mass is constant, but the volume increases.

d) Density **increases**. Iron, like most materials, contracts on cooling; thus the volume decreases while the mass does not change.

e) Density **remains the same**. The water does not alter either the mass or the volume of the diamond.

1.26   Plan: Use conversion factors from the inside back cover: 1 pm = 10^{-12} m; 10^{-9} m = 1 nm.
Solution:

$$\text{Radius (nm)} = \left(1430 \text{ pm}\right)\left(\frac{10^{-12} \text{ m}}{1 \text{ pm}}\right)\left(\frac{1 \text{ nm}}{10^{-9} \text{ m}}\right) = \textbf{1.43 nm}$$

1.28   Plan: Use conversion factors: 1 m = 10^{-9} nm
Solution:

$$\text{Length (nm)} = \left(100. \text{ m}\right)\left(\frac{10^{9} \text{ nm}}{1 \text{ m}}\right) = 10^{11} \text{ nm}$$

1.30   Plan: Use conversion factors $(1 \text{ cm})^2 = (0.01 \text{ m})^2$; $(1000 \text{ m})^2 = (1 \text{ km})^2$ to express the area in km^2. To calculate the cost of the patch, use the conversion factor: $(2.54 \text{ cm})^2 = (1 \text{ in})^2$.
Solution:

$$\text{a) Area (km}^2) = \left(20.7 \text{ cm}^2\right)\left(\frac{(0.01 \text{ m})^2}{(1 \text{ cm})^2}\right)\left(\frac{(1 \text{ km})^2}{(1000 \text{ m})^2}\right) = \textbf{2.07x10}^{-9} \textbf{ km}^2$$

$$\text{b) Cost} = \left(20.7 \text{ cm}^2\right)\left(\frac{(10 \text{ mm})^2}{(1 \text{ cm})^2}\right)\left(\frac{\$3.25}{1 \text{ mm}^2}\right) = \textbf{\$6.73} \times \textbf{10}^3$$

1.34   Plan: Mass in g is converted to kg in part a) with the conversion factor 1000 g = 1 kg; mass in g is converted to mg in part b) with the conversion factors 1000 mg = 1 g. Volume in cm^3 is converted to m^3 with the conversion factor $(1 \text{ cm})^3 = (0.01 \text{ m})^3$ and to mm^3 with the conversion factors $(10 \text{ mm})^3 = (1 \text{ cm})^3$. The conversions may be performed in any order.
Solution:

$$\text{a) Density (kg/m}^3) = \left(\frac{5.52 \text{ g}}{\text{cm}^3}\right)\left(\frac{(1 \text{ cm})^3}{(0.01 \text{ m})^3}\right)\left(\frac{1 \text{ kg}}{1000 \text{ g}}\right) = \textbf{5.52x10}^3 \textbf{ kg/m}^3$$

$$\text{b) Density (mg/mm}^3) = \left(\frac{5.52 \text{ g}}{\text{cm}^3}\right)\left(\frac{(1 \text{ cm})^3}{(10 \text{ mm})^3}\right)\left(\frac{1000 \text{ mg}}{1 \text{ g}}\right) = \textbf{5.52 mg/mm}^3$$

1.36   Plan: Use the conversion factors $(1 \text{ μm})^3 = (1\text{x}10^{-6} \text{ m})^3$; $(1\text{x}10^{-3} \text{ m})^3 = (1 \text{ mm})^3$ to convert to mm^3. To convert to L, use the conversion factors $(1 \text{ μm})^3 = (1\text{x}10^{-6} \text{ m})^3$; $(1\text{x}10^{-2} \text{ m})^3 = (1 \text{ cm})^3$; $1 \text{ cm}^3 = 1 \text{ mL}$; $1 \text{ mL} = 1\text{x}10^{-3} \text{ L}$.
Solution:

$$\text{a) Volume (mm}^3) = \left(\frac{2.56 \text{ μm}^3}{\text{cell}}\right)\left(\frac{(1\text{x}10^{-6} \text{ m})^3}{(1 \text{ μm})^3}\right)\left(\frac{(1 \text{ mm})^3}{(1\text{x}10^{-3} \text{ m})^3}\right) = \textbf{2.56x10}^{-9} \textbf{ mm}^3\textbf{/cell}$$

$$\text{b) Volume (L)} = \left(10^5 \text{ cells}\right)\left(\frac{2.56 \text{ μm}^3}{\text{cell}}\right)\left(\frac{(1\text{x}10^{-6} \text{ m})^3}{(1 \text{ μm})^3}\right)\left(\frac{(1 \text{ cm})^3}{(1\text{x}10^{-2} \text{ m})^3}\right)\left(\frac{1 \text{ mL}}{1 \text{ cm}^3}\right)\left(\frac{1\text{x}10^{-3} \text{ L}}{1 \text{ mL}}\right)$$

$$= 2.56\text{x}10^{-10} = \textbf{10}^{-10} \textbf{ L}$$

1.38   Plan: The mass of the mercury in the vial is the mass of the vial filled with mercury minus the mass of the empty vial. Use the density of mercury and the mass of the mercury in the vial to find the volume of mercury and thus the volume of the vial. Once the volume of the vial is known, that volume is used in part b. The density of water is used to find the mass of the given volume of water. Add the mass of water to the mass of the empty vial.
Solution:
a) Mass (g) of mercury = mass of vial and mercury – mass of vial = 185.56 g – 55.32 g = 130.24 g

$$\text{Volume (cm}^3\text{) of mercury = volume of vial} = (130.24 \text{ g})\left(\frac{1 \text{ cm}^3}{13.53 \text{ g}}\right) = 9.626016 = \textbf{9.626 cm}^3$$

b) Volume (cm^3) of water = volume of vial = 9.626016 cm^3

$$\text{Mass (g) of water} = (9.626016 \text{ cm}^3)\left(\frac{0.997 \text{ g}}{1 \text{ cm}^3}\right) = 9.59714 \text{ g water}$$

Mass (g) of vial filled with water = mass of vial + mass of water = 55.32 g + 9.59714 g = 64.91714 = **64.92 g**

1.40   Plan: Calculate the volume of the cube using the relationship Volume = (length of side)^3. The length of side in mm must be converted to cm so that volume will have units of cm^3. Divide the mass of the cube by the volume to find density.
Solution:

$$\text{Side length (cm)} = (15.6 \text{ mm})\left(\frac{10^{-3} \text{ m}}{1 \text{ mm}}\right)\left(\frac{1 \text{ cm}}{10^{-2} \text{ m}}\right) = 1.56 \text{ cm} \quad \text{(convert to cm to match density unit)}$$

Al cube volume (cm^3) = (length of side)^3 = (1.56 cm)^3 = 3.7964 cm^3

$$\text{Density (g/cm}^3) = \frac{\text{mass}}{\text{volume}} = \frac{10.25 \text{ g}}{3.7964 \text{ cm}^3} = 2.69993 = \textbf{2.70 g/cm}^3$$

1.42   Plan: Use the equations given in the text for converting between the three temperature scales.
Solution:
a) T (in K) = T (in °C) + 273.15 = 18°C + 273.15 = 291.15 = **291 K**
b) T (in K) = T (in °C) + 273.15 = –164°C + 273.15 = 109.15 = **109 K**
c) T (in °C) = T (in K) – 273.15 = 0 K – 273.15 = –273.15 = **–273°C**

1.45   Plan: Use 1 nm = 10^{-9} m to convert wavelength in nm to m. To convert wavelength in pm to nm, use 1000 pm = 1 nm.
Solution:

$$\text{a) Wavelength (m)} = (247 \text{ nm})\left(\frac{10^{-9} \text{ m}}{1 \text{ nm}}\right) = \textbf{2.47x10}^{-7} \textbf{ m}$$

$$\text{b) Wavelength (nm)} = (6760 \text{ pm})\left(\frac{1 \text{ nm}}{1000 \text{ pm}}\right) = \textbf{6.76 nm}$$

1.52   Plan: Review the rules for significant zeros.
Solution:
a) No significant zeros (leading zeros are not significant)
b) No significant zeros (leading zeros are not significant)
c) 0.041<u>0</u> (terminal zeros to the right of the decimal point are significant)
d) 4.<u>0100</u>x10^4 (zeros between nonzero digits are significant; terminal zeros to the right of the decimal point are significant)

1.54   Plan: Review the rules for rounding.
Solution: (significant figures are underlined)
a) 0.0003<u>5</u>54: the extra digits are 54 at the end of the number. When the digit to be removed is 5 and that 5 is followed by nonzero numbers, the last digit kept is increased by 1: **0.00036**
b) 35.<u>8</u>348: the extra digits are 48. Since the digit to be removed (4) is less than 5, the last digit kept is unchanged: **35.83**

c) 22.4555: the extra digits are 555. When the digit to be removed is 5 and that 5 is followed by nonzero numbers, the last digit kept is increased by 1: **22.5**

1.56   Plan: Review the rules for rounding.
        Solution:
        19 rounds to 20: the digit to be removed (9) is greater than 5 so the digit kept is increased by 1.
        155 rounds to 160: the digit to be removed is 5 and the digit to be kept is an odd number, so that digit kept is increased by 1.
        8.3 rounds to 8: the digit to be removed (3) is less than 5 so the digit kept remains unchanged.
        3.2 rounds to 3: the digit to be removed (2) is less than 5 so the digit kept remains unchanged.
        2.9 rounds to 3: the digit to be removed (9) is greater than 5 so the digit kept is increased by 1.
        4.7 rounds to 5: the digit to be removed (7) is greater than 5 so the digit kept is increased by 1.

$$\left(\frac{20 \times 160 \times 8}{3 \times 3 \times 5}\right) = 568.89 = \mathbf{6x10^2}$$

Since there are numbers in the calculation with only one significant figure, the answer can be reported only to one significant figure. (Note that the answer is 560 using the original numbers.)

1.58   Plan: Use a calculator to obtain an initial value. Use the rules for significant figures and rounding to get the final answer.
        Solution:
        a) $\dfrac{(2.795 \text{ m})(310 \text{ m})}{6.48 \text{ m}} = 133.71 = \mathbf{134 \text{ m}}$ (maximum of 3 significant figures allowed since two of the original

numbers in the calculation have only 3 significant figures)

b) $V = \left(\dfrac{4}{3}\right)\pi(17.282 \text{ mm})^3 = 21,620.74 = \mathbf{21,621 \text{ mm}^3}$ (maximum of 5 significant figures allowed)

c) 1.110 cm + 17.3 cm + 108.2 cm + 316 cm = 442.61 = **443 cm** (no digits allowed to the right of the decimal since 316 has no digits to the right of the decimal point)

1.60   Plan: Review the procedure for changing a number to scientific notation. There can be only 1 nonzero digit to the left of the decimal point in correct scientific notation. Moving the decimal point to the left results in a positive exponent while moving the decimal point to the right results in a negative exponent.
        Solution:
        a) $\mathbf{1.310000x10^5}$ (Note that all zeros are significant.)
        b) $\mathbf{4.7x10^{-4}}$ (No zeros are significant.)
        c) $\mathbf{2.10006x10^5}$
        d) $\mathbf{2.1605x10^3}$

1.62   Plan: Review the examples for changing a number from scientific notation to standard notation. If the exponent is positive, move the decimal back to the right; if the exponent is negative, move the decimal point back to the left.
        Solution:
        a) **5550**   (Do not use terminal decimal point since the zero is not significant.)
        b) **10070.**   (Use terminal decimal point since final zero is significant.)
        c) **0.000000885**
        d) **0.003004**

1.64   Plan: In most cases, this involves a simple addition or subtraction of values from the exponents. There can be only 1 nonzero digit to the left of the decimal point in correct scientific notation.
        Solution:
        a) $\mathbf{8.025x10^4}$ (The decimal point must be moved an additional 2 places to the left: $10^2 + 10^2 = 10^4$)
        b) $\mathbf{1.0098x10^{-3}}$ (The decimal point must be moved an additional 3 places to the left: $10^3 + 10^{-6} = 10^{-3}$)
        c) $\mathbf{7.7x10^{-11}}$ (The decimal point must be moved an additional 2 places to the right: $10^{-2} + 10^{-9} = 10^{-11}$)

1.66   Plan: Calculate a temporary answer by simply entering the numbers into a calculator. Then you will need to round the value to the appropriate number of significant figures. Cancel units as you would cancel numbers, and place the remaining units after your numerical answer.
Solution:

a) $\dfrac{\left(6.626 \times 10^{-34}\ \text{J} \cdot \text{s}\right)\left(2.9979 \times 10^{8}\ \text{m/s}\right)}{489 \times 10^{-9}\ \text{m}} = 4.062185 \times 10^{-19}\ \text{J}$

4.06×10^{-19} J (489×10^{-9} m limits the answer to 3 significant figures; units of m and s cancel)

b) $\dfrac{\left(6.022 \times 10^{23}\ \text{molecules/mol}\right)\left(1.23 \times 10^{2}\ \text{g}\right)}{46.07\ \text{g/mol}} = 1.6078 \times 10^{24}\ \text{molecules}$

1.61×10^{24} molecules (1.23×10^{2} g limits answer to 3 significant figures; units of mol and g cancel)

c) $\left(6.022 \times 10^{23}\ \text{atoms/mol}\right)\left(2.18 \times 10^{-18}\ \text{J/atom}\right)\left(\dfrac{1}{2^{2}} - \dfrac{1}{3^{2}}\right) = 1.82333 \times 10^{5}\ \text{J/mol}$

1.82×10^{5} J/mol (2.18×10^{-18} J/atom limits answer to 3 significant figures; unit of atoms cancels)

1.68   Plan: Exact numbers are those which have no uncertainty. Unit definitions and number counts of items in a group are examples of exact numbers.
Solution:
a) The height of Horseshoe Falls is a measured quantity. This is **not** an exact number.
b) The number of planets in the solar system is a number count. This **is** an exact number.
c) The number of grams in a pound is not a unit definition. This is **not** an exact number.
d) The number of millimeters in a meter is a definition of the prefix "milli–." This **is** an exact number.

1.70   Plan: Observe the figure, and estimate a reading the best you can.
Solution:
The scale markings are 0.2 cm apart. The end of the metal strip falls between the mark for 7.4 cm and 7.6 cm. If we assume that one can divide the space between markings into fourths, the uncertainty is one-fourth the separation between the marks. Thus, since the end of the metal strip falls between 7.45 and 7.55 we can report its length as **7.50 ± 0.05 cm**. (Note: If the assumption is that one can divide the space between markings into halves only, then the result is 7.5 ± 0.1 cm.)

1.72   Plan: Calculate the average of each data set. Remember that accuracy refers to how close a measurement is to the actual or true value while precision refers to how close multiple measurements are to each other.
Solution:

a) $I_{avg} = \dfrac{8.72\ \text{g} + 8.74\ \text{g} + 8.70\ \text{g}}{3} = 8.7200 = \textbf{8.72 g}$

$II_{avg} = \dfrac{8.56\ \text{g} + 8.77\ \text{g} + 8.83\ \text{g}}{3} = 8.7200 = \textbf{8.72 g}$

$III_{avg} = \dfrac{8.50\ \text{g} + 8.48\ \text{g} + 8.51\ \text{g}}{3} = 8.4967 = \textbf{8.50 g}$

$IV_{avg} = \dfrac{8.41\ \text{g} + 8.72\ \text{g} + 8.55\ \text{g}}{3} = 8.5600 = \textbf{8.56 g}$

Sets **I** and **II** are most accurate since their average value, 8.72 g, is closest to the true value, 8.72 g.
b) To get an idea of precision, calculate the range of each set of values: largest value – smallest value. A small range is an indication of good precision since the values are close to each other.
I_{range} = 8.74 g – 8.70 g = 0.04 g
II_{range} = 8.83 g – 8.56 g = 0.27 g
III_{range} = 8.51 g – 8.48 g = 0.03 g
IV_{range} = 8.72 g – 8.41 g = 0.31 g
Set III is the most precise (smallest range), but is the least accurate (the average is the farthest from the actual value).

c) **Set I** has the best combination of high accuracy (average value = actual value) and high precision (relatively small range).
d) **Set IV** has both low accuracy (average value differs from actual value) and low precision (has the largest range).

1.74   <u>Plan:</u> If it is necessary to force something to happen, the potential energy will be higher.
        <u>Solution:</u>
        a)   b)

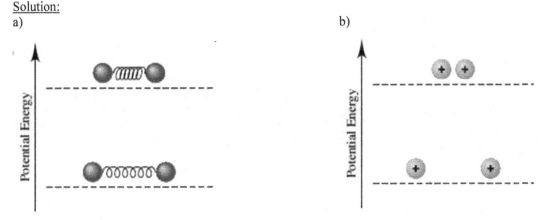

a) The balls on the relaxed spring have a lower potential energy and are more stable. The balls on the compressed spring have a higher potential energy, because the balls will move once the spring is released. This configuration is less stable.
b) The two + charges apart from each other have a lower potential energy and are more stable. The two + charges near each other have a higher potential energy, because they repel one another. This arrangement is less stable.

1.76   <u>Plan:</u> Use the concentrations of bromine given.
        <u>Solution:</u>
        $$\frac{\text{Mass bromine in Dead Sea}}{\text{Mass bromine in seawater}} = \frac{0.50 \text{ g/L}}{0.065 \text{ g/L}} = \textbf{7.7 / 1}$$

1.78   <u>Plan:</u> In each case, calculate the overall density of the ball and contents and compare to the density of air. The volume of the ball in cm^3 is converted to units of L to find the density of the ball itself in g/L. The densities of the ball and the gas in the ball are additive because the volume of the ball and the volume of the gas are the same.
        <u>Solution:</u>
        a) Density of evacuated ball: the mass is only that of the sphere itself:
        $$\text{Volume of ball (L)} = \left(560 \text{ cm}^3\right)\left(\frac{1 \text{ mL}}{1 \text{ cm}^3}\right)\left(\frac{10^{-3} \text{ L}}{1 \text{ mL}}\right) = 0.560 = 0.56 \text{ L}$$

        $$\text{Density of evacuated ball} = \frac{\text{mass}}{\text{volume}} = \frac{0.12 \text{ g}}{0.560 \text{ L}} = \textbf{0.21 g/L}$$

        The evacuated ball will **float** because its density is less than that of air.
        b) Because the density of CO_2 is greater than that of air, a ball filled with CO_2 will **sink**.
        c) Density of ball + density of hydrogen = 0.0899 + 0.21 g/L = 0.30 g/L
        The ball will **float** because the density of the ball filled with hydrogen is less than the density of air.
        d) Because the density of O_2 is greater than that of air, a ball filled with O_2 will **sink**.
        e) Density of ball + density of nitrogen = 0.21 g/L + 1.165 g/L = 1.38 g/L
        The ball will **sink** because the density of the ball filled with nitrogen is greater than the density of air.

        f) To sink, the total mass of the ball and gas must be $\left(\frac{0.560 \text{ L}}{}\right)\left(\frac{1.189 \text{ g}}{1 \text{ L}}\right) = 0.66584 \text{ g}$

        For the evacuated ball:
        0.66584 – 0.12 g = 0.54585 = **0.55 g**. More than 0.55 g would have to be added to make the ball sink.
        For ball filled with hydrogen:

Mass of hydrogen in the ball $= (0.56 \text{ L})\left(\dfrac{0.0899 \text{ g}}{1 \text{ L}}\right) = 0.0503 \text{ g}$

Mass of hydrogen and ball $= 0.0503 \text{ g} + 0.12 \text{ g} = 0.17 \text{ g}$

$0.66584 - 0.17 \text{ g} = 0.4958 = \textbf{0.50 g}$. More than 0.50 g would have to be added to make the ball sink.

1.80   <u>Plan:</u> Convert the surface area to m^2 and then use the surface area and the depth to determine the volume of the oceans (area x depth = volume) in m^3. The volume is then converted from cubic metres to litres, and finally to the mass of gold using the density of gold in g/L. Once the mass of the gold is known, its density is used to find the volume of that amount of gold. The mass of gold is converted to troy oz and the price of gold per troy oz gives the total price.
<u>Solution:</u>

a) Area of ocean $(m^2) = (3.63 \times 10^8 \text{ km}^2)\left(\dfrac{(1000 \text{ m})^2}{(1 \text{ km})^2}\right) = 3.63 \times 10^{14} \text{ m}^2$

Volume of ocean $(m^3) = (\text{area})(\text{depth}) = (3.63 \times 10^{14} \text{ m}^2)(3800 \text{ m}) = 1.3794 \times 10^{18} \text{ m}^3$

Mass of gold (g) $= \left(1.3794 \times 10^{18} \text{ m}^3\right)\left(\dfrac{1 \text{ L}}{10^{-3} \text{ m}^3}\right)\left(\dfrac{5.8 \times 10^{-9} \text{ g}}{\text{L}}\right) = 8.00052 \times 10^{12} = \textbf{8.0} \boldsymbol{\times} \textbf{10}^{\textbf{12}} \textbf{ g}$

b) Use the density of gold to convert mass of gold to volume of gold:

Volume of gold $(m^3) = \left(8.00052 \times 10^{12} \text{ g}\right)\left(\dfrac{1 \text{ cm}^3}{19.3 \text{ g}}\right)\left(\dfrac{(0.01 \text{ m})^3}{(1 \text{ cm})^3}\right) = 4.14535 \times 10^5 = \textbf{4.1} \boldsymbol{\times} \textbf{10}^{\textbf{5}} \textbf{ m}^{\textbf{3}}$

c) Value of gold $= \left(8.00052 \times 10^{12} \text{ g}\right)\left(\dfrac{1 \text{ tr. oz.}}{31.1 \text{ g}}\right)\left(\dfrac{\$1611.46}{1 \text{ tr. oz.}}\right) = 4.14551 \times 10^{14} = \boldsymbol{\$}\textbf{4.1} \boldsymbol{\times} \textbf{10}^{\textbf{14}}$

1.82   <u>Plan:</u> Use the equations for temperature conversion given in the chapter. The mass of nitrogen is conserved when the gas is liquefied; the mass of the nitrogen gas equals the mass of the liquid nitrogen. Use the density of nitrogen gas to find the mass of the nitrogen; then use the density of liquid nitrogen to find the volume of that mass of liquid nitrogen.
<u>Solution:</u>
a) T (in °C) $= T$ (in K) $- 273.15 = 77.36 \text{ K} - 273.15 = \textbf{–195.79°C}$
b)

Mass of liquid nitrogen = mass of gaseous nitrogen $= (895.0 \text{ L})\left(\dfrac{4.566 \text{ g}}{1 \text{ L}}\right) = 4086.57 \text{ g N}_2$

Volume of liquid $N_2 = (4086.57 \text{ g})\left(\dfrac{1 \text{ L}}{809 \text{ g}}\right) = 5.0514 = \textbf{5.05 L}$

1.83   <u>Plan:</u> For part a), convert km to m and h to s. For part b), time is converted from h to min and length stays in km. For part c), use the average speed in km/h to find the time necessary to cover the given distance.
<u>Solution:</u>

a) Speed (m/s) $= \left(\dfrac{9.4 \text{ km}}{\text{h}}\right)\left(\dfrac{1000 \text{ m}}{1 \text{ km}}\right)\left(\dfrac{1 \text{ h}}{3600 \text{ s}}\right) = 2.611 = \textbf{2.6 m/s}$

b) Distance (km) $= (98 \text{ min})\left(\dfrac{1 \text{ h}}{60 \text{ min}}\right)\left(\dfrac{9.4 \text{ km}}{\text{h}}\right) = 15.353 = \textbf{15 km}$

c) Time (h) $= (14.5 \text{ km})\left(\dfrac{1 \text{ h}}{9.4 \text{ km}}\right) = 1.5426 = 1.5 \text{ h}$

If she starts running at 11:15 am, 1.5 hours later the time is **12:45 pm**.

1.85   Plan: In visualizing the problem, the two scales can be set next to each other.
        Solution:
        There are 50 divisions between the freezing point and boiling point of benzene on the °X scale and 74.6 divisions
        (80.1°C – 5.5°C) on the °C scale. So $°X = \left(\dfrac{50°X}{74.6°C}\right)°C$

        This does not account for the offset of 5.5 divisions in the °C scale from the zero point on the °X scale.

        So $°X = \left(\dfrac{50°X}{74.6°C}\right)(°C - 5.5°C)$

        Check: Plug in 80.1°C and see if result agrees with expected value of 50°X.

        So $°X = \left(\dfrac{50°X}{74.6°C}\right)(80.1°C - 5.5°C) = 50°X$

        Use this formula to find the freezing and boiling points of water on the °X scale.

        $fp_{water}°X = \left(\dfrac{50°X}{74.6°C}\right)(0.00°C - 5.5°C) = -3.68°X = \mathbf{-3.7°X}$

        $bp_{water}°X = \left(\dfrac{50°X}{74.6°C}\right)(100.0°C - 5.5°C) = \mathbf{63.3°X}$

1.86   Plan: Determine the total mass of Earth's crust in metric tonnes (t) by finding the volume of crust (surface area x
        depth) in km^3 and then in cm^3 and then using the density to find the mass of this volume, using conversions from
        the inside back cover. The mass of each individual element comes from the concentration of that element
        multiplied by the mass of the crust.
        Solution:
        Volume of crust (km^3) = area x depth = $(35 \text{ km})(5.10 \times 10^8 \text{ km}^2) = 1.785 \times 10^{10} \text{ km}^3$

        Volume of crust (cm^3) = $\left(1.785 \times 10^{10} \text{ km}^3\right)\left(\dfrac{(1000 \text{ m})^3}{(1 \text{ km})^3}\right)\left(\dfrac{(1 \text{ cm})^3}{(0.01 \text{ m})^3}\right) = 1.785 \times 10^{25} \text{ cm}^3$

        Mass of crust (t) = $\left(1.785 \times 10^{25} \text{ cm}^3\right)\left(\dfrac{2.8 \text{ g}}{1 \text{ cm}^3}\right)\left(\dfrac{1 \text{ kg}}{1000 \text{ g}}\right)\left(\dfrac{1 \text{ t}}{1000 \text{ kg}}\right) = 4.998 \times 10^{19} \text{ t}$

        Mass of oxygen (g) = $\left(4.998 \times 10^{19} \text{ t}\right)\left(\dfrac{4.55 \times 10^5 \text{ g oxygen}}{1 \text{ t}}\right) = 2.2741 \times 10^{25} = \mathbf{2.3 \times 10^{25} \text{ g oxygen}}$

        Mass of silicon (g) = $\left(4.998 \times 10^{19} \text{ t}\right)\left(\dfrac{2.72 \times 10^5 \text{ g silicon}}{1 \text{ t}}\right) = 1.3595 \times 10^{25} = \mathbf{1.4 \times 10^{25} \text{ g silicon}}$

        Mass of ruthenium = mass of rhodium = $\left(4.998 \times 10^{19} \text{ t}\right)\left(\dfrac{1 \times 10^{-4} \text{ g element}}{1 \text{ t}}\right)$

        $= 4.998 \times 10^{15} = \mathbf{5 \times 10^{15} \text{ g each of ruthenium and rhodium}}$

CHAPTER 2 THE COMPONENTS OF MATTER

TOOL OF THE LABORATORY BOXED READING PROBLEMS

B2.1   Plan: There is one peak for each type of Cl atom and peaks for the Cl_2 molecule. The m/e ratio
equals the mass divided by 1+.
Solution:
a) There is one peak for the ^{35}Cl atom and another peak for the ^{37}Cl atom. There are three peaks for the three
possible Cl_2 molecules: $^{35}Cl^{35}Cl$ (both atoms are mass 35), $^{37}Cl^{37}Cl$ (both atoms are mass 37), and $^{35}Cl^{37}Cl$ (one
atom is mass 35 and one is mass 37). So the mass of chlorine will have **5 peaks.**

b) Peak m/e ratio
^{35}Cl **35**   **lightest particle**
^{37}Cl 37
$^{35}Cl^{35}Cl$ 70 (35 + 35)
$^{35}Cl^{37}Cl$ 72 (35 + 37)
$^{37}Cl^{37}Cl$ **74** (35 + 37)   **heaviest particle**

B2.3   Plan: Review the discussion on separations.
Solution:
a) Salt dissolves in water and pepper does not. Procedure: add water to mixture and filter to remove solid pepper.
Evaporate water to recover solid salt.
b) The water/soot mixture can be filtered; the water will flow through the filter paper, leaving the soot collected
on the filter paper.
c) Allow the mixture to warm up, and then pour off the melted ice (water); or, add water, and the glass will sink
and the ice will float.
d) Heat the mixture; the alcohol will boil off (distill), while the sugar will remain behind.
e) The spinach leaves can be extracted with a solvent that dissolves the pigments. Chromatography can be used to
separate one pigment from the other.

END–OF–CHAPTER PROBLEMS

2.1   Plan: Refer to the definitions of an element and a compound.
Solution:
Unlike compounds, elements cannot be broken down by chemical changes into simpler materials. Compounds
contain different types of atoms; there is only one type of atom in an element.

2.4   Plan: Remember that an element contains only one kind of atom while a compound contains at least two different
elements (two kinds of atoms) in a fixed ratio. A mixture contains at least two different substances in a
composition that can vary.
Solution:
a) The presence of more than one element (calcium and chlorine) makes this pure substance a **compound**.
b) There are only atoms from one element, sulfur, so this pure substance is an **element**.
c) This is a combination of two compounds and has a varying composition, so this is a **mixture**.
d) The presence of more than one type of atom means it cannot be an element. The specific, not variable,
arrangement means it is a **compound**.

2.12   Plan: Restate the three laws in your own words.
Solution:
a) The law of mass conservation applies to all substances — **elements, compounds, and mixtures**. Matter
can neither be created nor destroyed, whether it is an element, compound, or mixture.
b) The law of definite composition applies to **compounds** only, because it refers to a constant, or definite,
composition of elements within a compound.
c) The law of multiple proportions applies to **compounds** only, because it refers to the combination of elements to
form compounds.

2.14   Plan: Review the three laws: law of mass conservation, law of definite composition, and law of multiple proportions.
Solution:
a) **Law of Definite Composition** — The compound potassium chloride, KCl, is composed of the same elements and same fraction by mass, regardless of its source (Chile or Poland).
b) **Law of Mass Conservation** — The mass of the substances inside the glass bulb did not change during the chemical reaction (formation of magnesium oxide from magnesium and oxygen).
c) **Law of Multiple Proportions** — Two elements, O and As, can combine to form two different compounds that have different proportions of As present.

2.16   Plan: Review the definition of percent by mass.
Solution:
a) **No**, the <u>mass percent</u> of each element in a compound is fixed. The percentage of Na in the compound NaCl is 39.34% (22.99 u/58.44 u), whether the sample is 0.5000 g or 50.00 g.
b) **Yes**, the <u>mass</u> of each element in a compound depends on the mass of the compound. A 0.5000 g sample of NaCl contains 0.1967 g of Na (39.34% of 0.5000 g), whereas a 50.00 g sample of NaCl contains 19.67 g of Na (39.34% of 50.00 g).

2.18   Plan: Review the mass laws: law of mass conservation, law of definite composition, and law of multiple proportions. For each experiment, compare the mass values before and after each reaction and examine the ratios of the mass of white compound to the mass of colourless gas.
Solution:
Experiment 1: mass before reaction = 1.00 g;   mass after reaction = 0.64 g + 0.36 g = 1.00 g
Experiment 2: mass before reaction = 3.25 g;   mass after reaction = 2.08 g + 1.17 g = 3.25 g
Both experiments demonstrate the **law of mass conservation** since the total mass before reaction equals the total mass after reaction.
Experiment 1: mass white compound/mass colourless gas = 0.64 g/0.36 g = 1.78
Experiment 2: mass white compound/mass colourless gas = 2.08 g/1.17 g = 1.78
Both Experiments 1 and 2 demonstrate the **law of definite composition** since the compound has the same composition by mass in each experiment.

2.20   Plan: Fluorite is a mineral containing only calcium and fluorine. The difference between the mass of fluorite and the mass of calcium gives the mass of fluorine. Mass fraction is calculated by dividing the mass of element by the mass of compound (fluorite) and mass percent is obtained by multiplying the mass fraction by 100.
Solution:
a) Mass (g) of fluorine = mass of fluorite – mass of calcium = 2.76 g – 1.42 g = **1.34 g fluorine**

b) Mass fraction of Ca = $\dfrac{\text{mass Ca}}{\text{mass fluorite}} = \dfrac{1.42 \text{ g Ca}}{2.76 \text{ g fluorite}} = 0.51449 = \textbf{0.514}$

Mass fraction of F = $\dfrac{\text{mass F}}{\text{mass fluorite}} = \dfrac{1.34 \text{ g F}}{2.76 \text{ g fluorite}} = 0.48551 = \textbf{0.486}$

c) Mass percent of Ca = 0.51449 x 100 %= 51.449 %= **51.4%**
Mass percent of F = 0.48551 x 100 %= 48.551 %= **48.6%**

2.22   Plan: Dividing the mass of magnesium by the mass of the oxide gives the ratio. Multiply the mass of the second sample of magnesium oxide by this ratio to determine the mass of magnesium.
Solution:
a) If 1.25 g of MgO contains 0.754 g of Mg, then the mass ratio (or fraction) of magnesium in the oxide

compound is $\dfrac{\text{mass Mg}}{\text{mass MgO}} = \dfrac{0.754 \text{ g Mg}}{1.25 \text{ g MgO}} = 0.6032 = \textbf{0.603}.$

b) Mass (g) of magnesium = $\left(534 \text{ g MgO}\right)\left(\dfrac{0.6032 \text{ g Mg}}{1 \text{ g MgO}}\right) = 322.109 \text{ g} = \textbf{322 g magnesium}$

2.24   Plan: Since copper is a metal and sulfur is a nonmetal, the sample contains 88.39 g Cu and 44.61 g S. Calculate the mass fraction of each element in the sample by dividing the mass of element by the total mass of compound. Multiply the mass of the second sample of compound in grams by the mass fraction of each element to find the mass of each element in that sample.
Solution:
Mass (g) of compound = 88.39 g copper + 44.61 g sulfur = 133.00 g compound

$$\text{Mass fraction of copper} = \left(\frac{88.39 \text{ g copper}}{133.00 \text{ g compound}} \right) = 0.664586$$

$$\text{Mass (g) of copper} = \left(5264 \text{ kg compound}\right)\left(\frac{10^3 \text{ g compound}}{1 \text{ kg compound}} \right)\left(\frac{0.664586 \text{ g copper}}{1 \text{ g compound}} \right)$$

$$= 3.49838 \times 10^6 \text{ g} = \mathbf{3.498 \times 10^6 \text{ g copper}}$$

$$\text{Mass fraction of sulfur} = \left(\frac{44.61 \text{ g sulfur}}{133.00 \text{ g compound}} \right) = 0.335414$$

$$\text{Mass (g) of sulfur} = \left(5264 \text{ kg compound}\right)\left(\frac{10^3 \text{ g compound}}{1 \text{ kg compound}} \right)\left(\frac{0.335414 \text{ g sulfur}}{1 \text{ g compound}} \right)$$

$$= 1.76562 \times 10^6 \text{ g} = \mathbf{1.766 \times 10^6 \text{ g sulfur}}$$

2.26   Plan: The law of multiple proportions states that if two elements form two different compounds, the relative amounts of the elements in the two compounds form a whole-number ratio. To illustrate the law we must calculate the mass of one element to one gram of the other element for each compound and then compare this mass for the two compounds. The law states that the ratio of the two masses should be a small whole-number ratio such as 1:2, 3:2, 4:3, etc.

Solution:

Compound 1: $\dfrac{47.5 \text{ mass \% S}}{52.5 \text{ mass \% Cl}} = 0.90476 = 0.905$

Compound 2: $\dfrac{31.1 \text{ mass \% S}}{68.9 \text{ mass \% Cl}} = 0.451379 = 0.451$

Ratio: $\dfrac{0.905}{0.451} = 2.0067 = 2.00 : 1.00$

Thus, the ratio of the mass of sulfur per gram of chlorine in the two compounds is a small whole-number ratio of 2:1, which agrees with the law of multiple proportions.

2.29   Plan: Determine the mass percent of sulfur in each sample by dividing the grams of sulfur in the sample by the total mass of the sample and multiplying by 100. The coal type with the smallest mass percent of sulfur has the smallest environmental impact.
Solution:

$$\text{Mass \% in Coal A} = \left(\frac{11.3 \text{ g sulfur}}{378 \text{ g sample}} \right)(100\%) = 2.9894 \% = 2.99\% \text{ S (by mass)}$$

$$\text{Mass \% in Coal B} = \left(\frac{19.0 \text{ g sulfur}}{495 \text{ g sample}} \right)(100\%) = 3.8384 \% = 3.84\% \text{ S (by mass)}$$

$$\text{Mass \% in Coal C} = \left(\frac{20.6 \text{ g sulfur}}{675 \text{ g sample}} \right)(100\%) = 3.0519 \% = 3.05\% \text{ S (by mass)}$$

Coal A has the smallest environmental impact.

2.31   Plan: This question is based on the law of definite composition. If the compound contains the same types of atoms, they should combine in the same way to give the same mass percentages of each of the elements.
Solution:
Potassium nitrate is a compound composed of three elements — potassium, nitrogen, and oxygen — in a specific ratio. If the ratio of these elements changed, then the compound would be changed to a different compound, for example, to potassium nitrite, with different physical and chemical properties. Dalton postulated that atoms of an element are identical, regardless of whether that element is found in India or Italy. Dalton also postulated that compounds result from the chemical combination of specific ratios of different elements. Thus, Dalton's theory explains why potassium nitrate, a compound comprised of three different elements in a specific ratio, has the same chemical composition regardless of where it is mined or how it is synthesized.

2.32   Plan: Review the discussion of the experiments in this chapter.
Solution:
Millikan determined the minimum *charge* on an oil drop and that the minimum charge was equal to the charge on one electron. Using Thomson's value for the *mass/charge ratio* of the electron and the determined value for the charge on one electron, Millikan calculated the mass of an electron (charge/(charge/mass)) to be 9.109×10^{-28} g.

2.36   Plan: Re-examine the definitions of atomic number and the mass number.
Solution:
The atomic number is the number of protons in the nucleus of an atom. When the atomic number changes, the identity of the element also changes. The mass number is the total number of protons and neutrons in the nucleus of an atom. Since the identity of an element is based on the number of protons and not the number of neutrons, the mass number can vary (by a change in number of neutrons) without changing the identity of the element.

2.39   Plan: The superscript is the mass number, the sum of the number of protons and neutrons. Consult the periodic table to get the atomic number (the number of protons). The mass number – the number of protons = the number of neutrons. For atoms, the number of protons and electrons are equal.
Solution:

Isotope	Mass Number	# of Protons	# of Neutrons	# of Electrons
^{36}Ar	36	18	18	18
^{38}Ar	38	18	20	18
^{40}Ar	40	18	22	18

2.41   Plan: The superscript is the mass number (A), the sum of the number of protons and neutrons; the subscript is the atomic number (Z, number of protons). The mass number – the number of protons = the number of neutrons. For atoms, the number of protons = the number of electrons.
Solution:
a) $^{16}_{8}O$ and $^{17}_{8}O$ have the **same number of protons and electrons** (8), but different numbers of neutrons.

$^{16}_{8}O$ and $^{17}_{8}O$ are isotopes of oxygen, and $^{16}_{8}O$ has $16 - 8 = 8$ neutrons whereas $^{17}_{8}O$ has $17 - 8 = 9$ neutrons.
Same Z value

b) $^{40}_{18}Ar$ and $^{41}_{19}K$ have the **same number of neutrons** (Ar: $40 - 18 = 22$; K: $41 - 19 = 22$) but different numbers of protons and electrons (Ar = 18 protons and 18 electrons; K = 19 protons and 19 electrons). **Same N value**

c) $^{60}_{27}Co$ and $^{60}_{28}Ni$ have different numbers of protons, neutrons, and electrons. Co: 27 protons, 27 electrons, and $60 - 27 = 33$ neutrons; Ni: 28 protons, 28 electrons and $60 - 28 = 32$ neutrons. However, both have a mass number of 60. **Same A value**

2.43   Plan: Combine the particles in the nucleus (protons + neutrons) to give the mass number (superscript, A). The number of protons gives the atomic number (subscript, Z) and identifies the element.
Solution:
a) $A = 18 + 20 = 38$; $Z = 18$; $^{38}_{18}\textbf{Ar}$

b) $A = 25 + 30 = 55$; $Z = 25$; $^{55}_{25}\textbf{Mn}$

c) $A = 47 + 62 = 109$; $Z = 47$; $^{109}_{47}\textbf{Ag}$

2.45   Plan: Determine the number of each type of particle. The superscript is the mass number (A) and the subscript is the atomic number (Z, number of protons). The mass number – the number of protons = the number of neutrons. For atoms, the number of protons = the number of electrons. The protons and neutrons are in the nucleus of the atom.
Solution:

a) $_{22}^{48}\text{Ti}$ b) $_{34}^{79}\text{Se}$ c) $_{5}^{11}\text{B}$

22 protons   34 protons   5 protons
22 electrons   34 electrons   5 electrons
48 – 22 = 26 neutrons   79 – 34 = 45 neutrons   11 – 5 = 6 neutrons

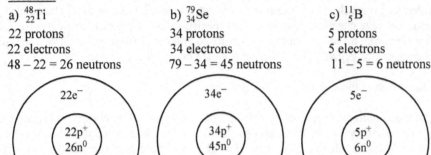

2.47   Plan: To calculate the atomic mass of an element, take a weighted average based on the natural abundance of the isotopes: (isotopic mass of isotope 1 x fractional abundance) + (isotopic mass of isotope 2 x fractional abundance).
Solution:

$$\text{Atomic mass of gallium} = \left(68.9256 \text{ u}\right)\left(\frac{60.11\%}{100\%}\right) + \left(70.9247 \text{ u}\right)\left(\frac{39.89\%}{100\%}\right) = 69.7230 \text{ u} = \textbf{69.72 u}$$

2.49   Plan: To find the percent abundance of each Cl isotope, let x equal the fractional abundance of ^{35}Cl and $(1 - x)$ equal the fractional abundance of ^{37}Cl since the sum of the fractional abundances must equal 1. Remember that atomic mass = (isotopic mass of ^{35}Cl x fractional abundance) + (isotopic mass of ^{37}Cl x fractional abundance).
Solution:
Atomic mass = (isotopic mass of ^{35}Cl x fractional abundance) + (isotopic mass of ^{37}Cl x fractional abundance)

$35.4527 \text{ u} = 34.9689 \text{ u}(x) + 36.9659 \text{ u}(1 - x)$
$35.4527 \text{ u} = 34.9689 \text{ u}(x) + 36.9659 \text{ u} - 36.9659 \text{ u}(x)$
$35.4527 \text{ u} = 36.9659 \text{ u} - 1.9970 \text{ u}(x)$
$1.9970 \text{ u}(x) = 1.5132 \text{ u}$
$x = 0.75774$ and $1 - x = 1 - 0.75774 = 0.24226$
% abundance $^{35}\text{Cl} = \textbf{75.774\%}$ % abundance $^{37}\text{Cl} = \textbf{24.226\%}$

2.52   Plan: Review the section in the chapter on the periodic table.
Solution:
a) In the modern periodic table, the elements are arranged in order of increasing atomic **number**.
b) Elements in a **column or group** (or family) have similar chemical properties, not those in the same period or row.
c) Elements can be classified as **metals**, metalloids, or nonmetals.

2.55   Plan: Review the properties of these two columns in the periodic table.
Solution:
The alkali metals (Group 1) are metals and readily lose one electron to form cations whereas the halogens (Group 17) are nonmetals and readily gain one electron to form anions.

2.56   Plan: Locate each element on the periodic table. The Z value is the atomic number of the element. Metals are to the left of the "staircase," nonmetals are to the right of the "staircase," and the metalloids are the elements that lie along the "staircase" line.
Solution:
a) Germanium   Ge   14   metalloid

b) Phosphorus	P	15	nonmetal
c) Helium	He	18	nonmetal
d) Lithium	Li	1	metal
e) Molybdenum	Mo	6	metal

2.58   Plan: Review the section in the chapter on the periodic table. Remember that alkaline earth metals are in Group 2, the halogens are in Group 17, and the metalloids are the elements that lie along the "staircase" line; periods are horizontal rows.
Solution:
a) The symbol and atomic number of the heaviest alkaline earth metal are **Ra** and **88**.
b) The symbol and atomic number of the lightest metalloid in Group 14 are **Si** and **14**.
c) The symbol and atomic mass of the coinage metal whose atoms have the fewest electrons are **Cu** and **63.55 u**.
d) The symbol and atomic mass of the halogen in Period 4 are **Br** and **79.90 u**.

2.60   Plan: Review the section of the chapter on the formation of ionic compounds.
Solution:
Reactive metals and nometals will form **ionic** bonds, in which one or more electrons are transferred from the metal atom to the nonmetal atom to form a cation and an anion, respectively. The oppositely charged ions attract, forming the ionic bond.

2.63   Plan: Assign charges to each of the ions. Since the sizes are similar, there are no differences due to the sizes.
Solution:
Coulomb's law states the energy of attraction in an ionic bond is directly proportional to the *product of charges* and inversely proportional to the *distance between charges*. The *product of charges* in MgO (+2 x –2 = –4) is greater than the *product of charges* in LiF (+1 x –1 = –1). Thus, **MgO** has stronger ionic bonding.

2.66   Plan: Locate these groups on the periodic table and assign charges to the ions that would form.
Solution:
The monatomic ions of Group 1 have a +1 charge (e.g., Li^+, Na^+, and K^+) whereas the monatomic ions of Group 17 have a –1 charge (e.g., F^-, Cl^-, and Br^-). Elements gain or lose electrons to form ions with the same number of electrons as the nearest noble gas. For example, Na loses one electron to form a cation with the same number of electrons as Ne. The halogen F gains one electron to form an anion with the same number of electrons as Ne.

2.68   Plan: A metal and a nonmetal will form an ionic compound. Locate these elements on the periodic table and predict their charges.
Solution:
Potassium sulfide (K_2S) is an ionic compound formed from a metal (potassium) and a nonmetal (sulfur). Potassium atoms transfer electrons to sulfur atoms. Each potassium atom loses one electron to form an ion with +1 charge and the same number of electrons (18) as the noble gas argon. Each sulfur atom gains two electrons to form an ion with a –2 charge and the same number of electrons (18) as the noble gas argon. The oppositely charged ions, K^+ and S^{2-}, attract each other to form an ionic compound with the ratio of two K^+ ions to one S^{2-} ion. The total number of electrons lost by the potassium atoms equals the total number of electrons gained by the sulfur atoms.

2.70   Plan: Locate these elements on the periodic table and predict what ions they will form. For cations (metals), ion charge = group number; for anions (nonmetals), ion charge = group number minus 18 .
Solution:
Barium in Group **2** forms a +2 ion: $\mathbf{Ba^{2+}}$. Selenium in Group **16** forms a –2 ion: $\mathbf{Se^{2-}}$ (16 –18 = –2).

2.72   Plan: Use the number of protons (atomic number) to identify the element. Add the number of protons and neutrons together to get the mass number. Locate the element on the periodic table and assign its group and period number.
Solution:
a) Oxygen (atomic number = 8)   mass number = 8p + 9n = 17   Group 16   Period 2
b) Fluorine (atomic number = 9)   mass number = 9p + 10n = 19   Group 17   Period 2

c) Calcium (atomic number = 20)   mass number = 20p + 20n = 40   Group 2 Period 4

2.74   Plan: Determine the charges of the ions based on their position on the periodic table. For cations (metals), ion charge = group number; for anions (nonmetals), ion charge = group number minus 18. Next, determine the ratio of the charges to get the ratio of the ions.
Solution:
Lithium [Group 1] forms the Li^+ ion; oxygen [Group 16] forms the O^{2-} ion (16 - 18 = -2). The ionic compound that forms from the combination of these two ions must be electrically neutral, so two Li^+ ions combine with one O^{2-} ion to form the compound Li_2O. There are twice as many Li^+ ions as O^{2-} ions in a sample of Li_2O.

$$\text{Number of } O^{2-} \text{ ions} = (8.4 \times 10^{21} \text{ } Li^+ \text{ ions}) \left(\frac{1 \text{ } O^{2-} \text{ ion}}{2 \text{ } Li^+ \text{ ions}} \right) = \textbf{4.2} \times \textbf{10}^{\textbf{21}} \textbf{ } \textbf{O}^{\textbf{2-}} \textbf{ ions}$$

2.76   Plan: The key is the size of the two alkali metal ions. The charges on the sodium and potassium ions are the same as both are in Group 1, so there will be no difference due to the charge. The chloride ions are the same in size and charge, so there will be no difference due to the chloride ion.
Solution:
Coulomb's law states that the energy of attraction in an ionic bond is directly proportional to the *product of charges* and inversely proportional to the *distance between charges*. The *product of the charges* is the same in both compounds because both sodium and potassium ions have a +1 charge. Attraction increases as distance decreases, so the ion with the smaller radius, Na^+, will form a stronger ionic interaction (**NaCl**).

2.78   Plan: Review the definition of molecular formula.
Solution:
The subscripts in the formula, MgF_2, give the number of ions in a formula unit of the ionic compound. The subscripts indicate that there are two F^- ions for every one Mg^{2+} ion. Using this information and the mass of each element, we could calculate the percent mass of each element.

2.80   Plan: Review the concepts of atoms and molecules.
Solution:
The mixture is similar to the sample of hydrogen peroxide in that both contain 20 billion oxygen atoms and 20 billion hydrogen atoms since both O_2 and H_2O_2 contain 2 oxygen atoms per molecule and both H_2 and H_2O_2 contain 2 hydrogen atoms per molecule. They differ in that they contain different types of molecules: H_2O_2 molecules in the hydrogen peroxide sample and H_2 and O_2 molecules in the mixture. In addition, the mixture contains 20 billion molecules (10 billion H_2 molecules + 10 billion O_2 molecules) while the hydrogen peroxide sample contains 10 billion molecules.

2.84   Plan: Locate each of the individual elements on the periodic table, and assign charges to each of the ions. For cations (metals), ion charge = group number; for anions (nonmetals), ion charge = group number minus 18. Find the smallest number of each ion that gives a neutral compound. To name ionic compounds with metals that form only one ion, name the metal, followed by the nonmetal name with an -ide suffix.
Solution:
a) Sodium is a metal that forms a +1 (Group **1**) ion and nitrogen is a nonmetal that forms a −3 ion (Group **15**, 15 - 18 = −3).

                                        +3 −3
             +1 −3   +1
             Na N Na_3N The compound is **Na_3N, sodium nitride**.
b) Oxygen is a nonmetal that forms a −2 ion (Group **16**, 16 - 18 = −2) and strontium is a metal that forms a +2 ion (Group **2**).   +2 −2
                          Sr O   The compound is **SrO, strontium oxide**.
c) Aluminum is a metal that forms a +3 ion (Group **3**) and chlorine is a nonmetal that forms a −1 ion (Group 17, 17-18 = −1).   +3 −3
             +3 −1   +3 −1
             Al Cl $AlCl_3$ The compound is **$AlCl_3$, aluminum chloride**.

2.86   <u>Plan:</u> Based on the atomic numbers (the subscripts) locate the elements on the periodic table. Once the atomic numbers are located, identify the element and based on its position, assign a charge. For cations (metals), ion charge = group number; for anions (nonmetals), ion charge = group number minus 18. Find the smallest number of each ion that gives a neutral compound. To name ionic compounds with metals that form only one ion, name the metal, followed by the nonmetal name with an -ide suffix.
<u>Solution:</u>
a) $_{12}$L is the element Mg ($Z = 12$). Magnesium [Group **2**] forms the Mg^{2+} ion. $_9$M is the element F ($Z = 9$). Fluorine [Group 17] forms the F^- ion ($17\text{-}18 = -1$). The compound formed by the combination of these two elements is **MgF_2, magnesium fluoride**.
b) $_{30}$L is the element Zn ($Z = 30$). Zinc forms the Zn^{2+} ion (see Table 2.3). $_{16}$M is the element S ($Z = 16$). Sulfur [Group 16] will form the S^{2-} ion ($16\text{-}18 = -2$). The compound formed by the combination of these two elements is **ZnS, zinc sulfide**.
c) $_{17}$L is the element Cl ($Z = 17$). Chlorine [Group 17] forms the Cl^- ion ($17\text{-}18 = -1$). $_{38}$M is the element Sr ($Z = 38$). Strontium [Group 2] forms the Sr^{2+} ion. The compound formed by the combination of these two elements is **$SrCl_2$, strontium chloride**.

2.88   <u>Plan:</u> Review the rules for nomenclature covered in the chapter. For ionic compounds, name the metal, followed by the nonmetal name with an -ide suffix. For metals, like many transition metals, that can form more than one ion each with a different charge, the ionic charge of the metal ion is indicated by a Roman numeral within parentheses immediately following the metal's name.
<u>Solution:</u>
a) tin(IV) chloride = **$SnCl_4$** The (IV) indicates that the metal ion is Sn^{4+} which requires 4 Cl^- ions for a neutral compound.
b) $FeBr_3$ = **iron(III) bromide** (common name is ferric bromide); the charge on the iron ion is +3 to match the –3 charge of 3 Br^- ions. The +3 charge of the Fe is indicated by (III).   +6 –6
c) cuprous bromide = **CuBr** (cuprous is +1 copper ion, cupric is +2 copper ion).   +3 –2
d) Mn_2O_3 = **manganese(III) oxide** Use (III) to indicate the +3 ionic charge of Mn: Mn_2O_3

2.90   <u>Plan:</u> Review the rules for nomenclature covered in the chapter. For ionic compounds, name the metal, followed by the nonmetal name with an -ide suffix. For metals, like many transition metals, that can form more than one ion each with a different charge, the ionic charge of the metal ion is indicated by a Roman numeral within parentheses immediately following the metal's name. Hydrates, compounds with a specific number of water molecules associated with them, are named with a prefix before the word hydrate to indicate the number of water molecules.
<u>Solution:</u>
a) **cobalt(II) oxide** Cobalt forms more than one monatomic ion so the ionic charge must be indicated with a Roman numeral. Since the Co is paired with one O^{2-} ion, the charge of Co is +2.
b) **Hg_2Cl_2** The Roman numeral I indicates that mercury has an ionic charge of +1; mercury is an unusual case in which the +1 ion formed is Hg_2^{2+}, not Hg^+.
c) **lead(II) acetate trihydrate** The $C_2H_3O_2^-$ ion has a –1 charge (see Table 2.5); since there are two of these ions, the lead ion has a +2 charge which must be indicated with the Roman numeral II. The •$3H_2O$ indicates a hydrate in which the number of H_2O molecules is indicated by the prefix tri-.   +3 –2   +6 –6
d) **Cr_2O_3** "chromic" denotes a +3 charge (see Table 2.4), oxygen has a –2 charge: $CrO \rightarrow Cr_2O_3$

2.92   <u>Plan:</u> Review the rules for nomenclature covered in the chapter. For metals, like many transition metals, that can form more than one ion each with a different charge, the ionic charge of the metal ion is indicated by a Roman numeral within parentheses immediately following the metal's name. Compounds must be neutral.
<u>Solution:</u>
a) Barium [Group 2] forms Ba^{2+} and oxygen [Group 16] forms O^{2-} ($16 \text{-} 18 = -2$) so the neutral compound forms from one Ba^{2+} ion and one O^{2-} ion. Correct formula is **BaO**.
b) Iron(II) indicates Fe^{2+} and nitrate is NO_3^- so the neutral compound forms from one iron(II) ion and two nitrate ions. Correct formula is **$Fe(NO_3)_2$**.
c) Mn is the symbol for manganese. Mg is the correct symbol for magnesium. Correct formula is **MgS**. Sulfide is the S^{2-} ion and sulfite is the SO_3^{2-} ion.

2.94   Plan: Acids donate H^+ ion to the solution, so the acid is a combination of H^+ and a negatively charged ion. Binary acids (H plus one other nonmetal) are named hydro- + nonmetal root + -ic acid. Oxoacids (H + an oxoanion) are named by changing the suffix of the oxoanion: -ate becomes -ic acid and -ite becomes -ous acid.
Solution:
a) Hydrogen sulfate is HSO_4^-, so its source acid is H_2SO_4. Name of acid is **sulfuric acid** (-ate becomes -ic acid).
b) HIO_3, **iodic acid** IO_3^- is the iodate ion: -ate becomes -ic acid.
c) Cyanide is CN^-; its source acid is **HCN hydrocyanic acid** (binary acid).
d) H_2S, **hydrosulfuric acid** (binary acid).

2.96   Plan: Use the formulas of the polyatomic ions. Recall that oxoacids are named by changing the suffix of the oxoanion: -ate becomes -ic acid and -ite becomes -ous acid. Compounds must be neutral.
Solution:
a) ammonium ion = NH_4^+ ammonia = NH_3
b) magnesium sulfide = MgS magnesium sulfite = $MgSO_3$ magnesium sulfate = $MgSO_4$
Sulfide = S^{2-}; sulfite = SO_3^{2-}; sulfate = SO_4^{2-}.
c) hydrochloric acid = HCl chloric acid = $HClO_3$ chlorous acid = $HClO_2$
Binary acids (H plus one other nonmetal) are named hydro- + nonmetal root + -ic acid. Chloric indicates the polyatomic ion ClO_3^- while chlorous indicates the polyatomic ion ClO_2^-.
d) cuprous bromide = $CuBr$ cupric bromide = $CuBr_2$
The suffix -ous indicates the lower charge, +1, while the suffix -ic indicates the higher charge, +2.

2.98   Plan: This compound is composed of two nonmetals. The element with the lower group number is named first. Greek numerical prefixes are used to indicate the number of atoms of each element in the compound.
Solution:
disulfur tetrafluoride S_2F_4 Di- indicates two S atoms and tetra- indicates four F atoms.

2.100   Plan: Review the nomenclature rules in the chapter. For ionic compounds, name the metal, followed by the nonmetal name with an -ide suffix. For metals, like many transition metals, that can form more than one ion each with a different charge, the ionic charge of the metal ion is indicated by a Roman numeral within parentheses immediately following the metal's name. Binary acids (H plus one other nonmetal) are named hydro- + nonmetal root + -ic acid.
Solution:
a) Calcium(II) dichloride, $CaCl_2$: The name becomes **calcium chloride** because calcium does not require "(II)" since it only forms +2 ions. Prefixes like di- are only used in naming covalent compounds between nonmetal elements.
b) Copper(II) oxide, Cu_2O: The charge on the oxide ion is O^{2-}, which makes each copper a Cu^+. The name becomes **copper(I) oxide** to match the charge on the copper.
c) Stannous fluoride, SnF_4: Stannous refers to Sn^{2+}, but the tin in this compound is Sn^{4+} due to the charge on the fluoride ion. The tin(IV) ion is the stannic ion; this gives the name **stannic fluoride or tin(IV) fluoride**.
d) Hydrogen chloride acid, HCl: Binary acids consist of the root name of the nonmetal (chlor in this case) with a hydro- prefix and an -ic suffix. The word acid is also needed. This gives the name **hydrochloric acid**.

2.102   Plan: Break down each formula to the individual elements and count the number of atoms of each element by observing the subscripts. The molecular (formula) mass is the sum of the atomic masses of all of the atoms.
Solution:
a) There are **12 atoms of oxygen** in $Al_2(SO_4)_3$. The molecular mass is:

Al	=	2(26.98 u)	=	53.96 u
S	=	3(32.07 u)	=	96.21 u
O	=	12(16.00 u)	=	<u>192.0 u</u>
				342.2 u

b) There are **9 atoms of hydrogen** in $(NH_4)_2HPO_4$. The molecular mass is:

N	=	2(14.01 u)	=	28.02 u
H	=	9(1.008 u)	=	9.072 u
P	=	1(30.97u)	=	30.97 u
O	=	4(16.00 u)	=	<u>64.00 u</u>
				132.06 u

c) There are **8 atoms of oxygen** in $Cu_3(OH)_2(CO_3)_2$. The molecular mass is:

Cu	=	3(63.55 u)	=	190.6 u
O	=	8(16.00 u)	=	128.0 u
H	=	2(1.008 u)	=	2.016 u
C	=	2(12.01 u)	=	24.02 u
				344.6 u

2.104   Plan: Review the rules for nomenclature covered in the chapter. For ionic compounds containing polyatomic ions, name the metal, followed by the name of the polyatomic ion. The molecular (formula) mass is the sum of the atomic masses of all of the atoms.
Solution:
a) **$(NH_4)_2SO_4$**   ammonium is NH_4^+ and sulfate is SO_4^{2-}

N	=	2(14.01 u)	=	28.02 u
H	=	8(1.008 u)	=	8.064 u
S	=	1(32.07 u)	=	32.07 u
O	=	4(16.00 u)	=	64.00 u
				132.15 u

b) **NaH_2PO_4**   sodium is Na^+ and dihydrogen phosphate is $H_2PO_4^-$

Na	=	1(22.99 u)	=	22.99 u
H	=	2(1.008 u)	=	2.016 u
P	=	1(30.97 u)	=	30.97 u
O	=	4(16.00 u)	=	64.00 u
				119.98 u

c) **$KHCO_3$**   potassium is K^+ and bicarbonate is HCO_3^-

K	=	1(39.10 u)	=	39.10 u
H	=	1(1.008 u)	=	1.008 u
C	=	1(12.01 u)	=	12.01 u
O	=	3(16.00 u)	=	48.00 u
				100.12 u

2.106   Plan: Convert the names to the appropriate chemical formulas. The molecular (formula) mass is the sum of the masses of each atom times its atomic mass.
Solution:
a) dinitrogen pentoxide N_2O_5 (di- = 2 and penta- = 5)

N	=	2(14.01 u)	=	28.02 u
O	=	5(16.00 u)	=	80.00 u
				108.02 u

b) lead(II) nitrate $Pb(NO_3)_2$ (lead(II) is Pb^{2+} and nitrate is NO_3^-)

Pb	=	1(207.2 u)	=	207.2 u
N	=	2(14.01 u)	=	28.02 u
O	=	6(16.00 u)	=	96.00 u
				331.2 u

c) calcium peroxide CaO_2 (calcium is Ca^{2+} and peroxide is O_2^{2-})

Ca	=	1(40.08 u)	=	40.08 u
O	=	2(16.00 u)	=	32.00 u
				72.08 u

2.108   Plan: Use the chemical symbols and count the atoms of each type to give a molecular formula. Use the nomenclature rules in the chapter to derive the name. The molecular (formula) mass is the sum of the masses of each atom times its atomic mass.

Solution:
a) Formula is **SO_3**. Name is **sulfur trioxide** (the prefix tri- indicates 3 oxygen atoms).

S	=	1(32.07 u)	=	32.07 u
O	=	3(16.00 u)	=	48.00 u
				80.07 u

b) Formula is **C₃H₈**. Since it contains only carbon and hydrogen it is a hydrocarbon and with three carbons its name is **propane**.

$$
\begin{array}{lllll}
\text{C} & = & 3(12.01\ \text{u}) & = & 36.03\ \text{u} \\
\text{H} & = & 8(1.008\ \text{u}) & = & \underline{8.064\ \text{u}} \\
& & & & \mathbf{44.09\ u}
\end{array}
$$

2.112   Plan: Review the discussion on separations.
Solution:
Separating the components of a mixture requires physical methods only; that is, no chemical changes (no changes in composition) take place and the components maintain their chemical identities and properties throughout. Separating the components of a compound requires a chemical change (change in composition).

2.115   Plan: Review the definitions of homogeneous and heterogeneous. The key is that a homogeneous mixture has a uniform composition while a heterogeneous mixture does not. A mixture consists of two or more substances physically mixed together while a compound is a pure substance.
Solution:
a) Distilled water is a **compound** that consists of H_2O molecules only.
b) Gasoline is a **homogeneous mixture** of hydrocarbon compounds of uniform composition that can be separated by physical means (distillation).
c) Beach sand is a **heterogeneous mixture** of different size particles of minerals and broken bits of shells.
d) Wine is a **homogeneous mixture** of water, alcohol, and other compounds that can be separated by physical means (distillation).
e) Air is a **homogeneous mixture** of different gases, mainly N_2, O_2, and Ar.

2.117   Plan: Review the discussion on separations.
Solution:
a) Filtration — separating the mixture on the basis of differences in particle size. The water moves through the holes in the colander but the larger pasta cannot.
b) **Extraction** — The coloured impurities are extracted into a solvent that is rinsed away from the raw sugar (or **chromatography**). A sugar solution is passed through a column in which the impurities stick to the stationary phase and the sugar moves through the column in the mobile phase.

2.119   Plan: Use the equation for the volume of a sphere in part a) to find the volume of the nucleus and the volume of the atom. Calculate the fraction of the atom volume that is occupied by the nucleus. For part b), calculate the total mass of the two electrons; subtract the electron mass from the mass of the atom to find the mass of the nucleus. Then calculate the fraction of the atom's mass contributed by the mass of the nucleus.
Solution:

a) Volume (m^3) of nucleus = $\dfrac{4}{3}\pi\, r^3 = \dfrac{4}{3}\pi \left(2.5\times10^{-15}\ \text{m}\right)^3 = 6.54498\times10^{-44}\ \text{m}^3$

Volume (m^3) of atom = $\dfrac{4}{3}\pi\, r^3 = \dfrac{4}{3}\pi \left(3.1\times10^{-11}\ \text{m}\right)^3 = 1.24788\times10^{-31}\ \text{m}^3$

Fraction of volume = $\dfrac{\text{volume of Nucleus}}{\text{volume of Atom}} = \dfrac{6.54498\times10^{-44}\ \text{m}^3}{1.24788\times10^{-31}\ \text{m}^3} = 5.2449\times10^{-13} = \mathbf{5.2\times10^{-13}}$

b) Mass of nucleus = mass of atom – mass of electrons
$$= 6.64648\times10^{-24}\ \text{g} - 2(9.10939\times10^{-28}\ \text{g}) = 6.64466\times10^{-24}\ \text{g}$$

Fraction of mass = $\dfrac{\text{mass of Nucleus}}{\text{mass of Atom}} = \dfrac{\left(6.64466\times10^{-24}\ \text{g}\right)}{\left(6.64648\times10^{-24}\ \text{g}\right)} = 0.99972617 = \mathbf{0.999726}$

As expected, the volume of the nucleus relative to the volume of the atom is small while its relative mass is large.

2.120 **Plan:** Use Coulomb's law which states that the energy of attraction in an ionic bond is directly proportional to the *product of charges* and inversely proportional to the *distance between charges*. Choose the largest ionic charges and smallest radii for the strongest ionic bonding and the smallest ionic charges and largest radii for the weakest ionic bonding.
Solution:
Strongest ionic bonding: **MgO**. Mg^{2+}, Ba^{2+}, and O^{2-} have the largest charges. Attraction increases as distance decreases, so the positive ion with the smaller radius, Mg^{2+}, will form a stronger ionic bond than the larger ion Ba^{2+}.
Weakest ionic bonding: **RbI**. K^+, Rb^+, Cl^-, and I^- have the smallest charges. Attraction decreases as distance increases, so the ions with the larger radii, Rb^+ and I^-, will form the weakest ionic bond.

2.124 **Plan:** Determine the percent oxygen in each oxide by subtracting the percent nitrogen from 100%. Express the percentage in u and divide by the atomic mass of the appropriate elements. Then divide each amount by the smaller number and convert to the simplest whole-number ratio. To find the mass of oxygen per 1.00 g of nitrogen, divide the mass percentage of oxygen by the mass percentage of nitrogen.

Solution:
a)   I $(100.00 - 46.69 \text{ N})\% = 53.31\%$ O

$$\left(\frac{46.69 \text{ u N}}{14.01 \text{ u N}}\right) = 3.3326 \text{ N} \qquad\qquad \left(\frac{53.31 \text{ u O}}{16.00 \text{ u O}}\right) = 3.3319 \text{ O}$$

$$\frac{3.3326 \text{ N}}{3.3319} = 1.0002 \text{ N} \qquad\qquad \frac{3.3319 \text{ O}}{3.3319} = 1.0000 \text{ O}$$

The simplest whole-number ratio is **1:1 N:O.**

    II $(100.00 - 36.85 \text{ N})\% = 63.15\%$ O

$$\left(\frac{36.85 \text{ u N}}{14.01 \text{ u N}}\right) = 2.6303 \text{ N} \qquad\qquad \left(\frac{63.15 \text{ u O}}{16.00 \text{ u O}}\right) = 3.9469 \text{ O}$$

$$\frac{2.6303 \text{ N}}{2.6303} = 1.0000 \text{ mol N} \qquad\qquad \frac{3.9469 \text{ O}}{2.6303} = 1.5001 \text{ O}$$

The simplest whole-number ratio is 1:1.5 N:O = **2:3 N:O.**

    III $(100.00 - 25.94 \text{ N})\% = 74.06\%$ O

$$\left(\frac{25.94 \text{ u N}}{14.01 \text{ u N}}\right) = 1.8515 \text{ N} \qquad\qquad \left(\frac{74.06 \text{ u O}}{16.00 \text{ u O}}\right) = 4.6288 \text{ O}$$

$$\frac{1.8515 \text{ N}}{1.8515} = 1.0000 \text{ N} \qquad\qquad \frac{4.6288 \text{ O}}{1.8515} = 2.5000 \text{ O}$$

The simplest whole-number ratio is 1:2.5 N:O = **2:5 N:O.**

b)   I $\left(\dfrac{53.31 \text{ u O}}{46.69 \text{ u N}}\right) = 1.1418 = \mathbf{1.14 \text{ g O}}$

    II $\left(\dfrac{63.15 \text{ u O}}{36.85 \text{ u N}}\right) = 1.7137 = \mathbf{1.71 \text{ g O}}$

    III $\left(\dfrac{74.06 \text{ u O}}{25.94 \text{ u N}}\right) = 2.8550 = \mathbf{2.86 \text{ g O}}$

2.128 **Plan:** To find the mass percent divide the mass of each substance in mg by the amount of seawater in mg and multiply by 100. The percent of an ion is the mass of that ion divided by the total mass of ions.
Solution:

a) Mass (mg) of seawater $= \left(1 \text{ kg}\right)\left(\dfrac{1000 \text{ g}}{1 \text{ kg}}\right)\left(\dfrac{1000 \text{ mg}}{1 \text{ g}}\right) = 1\times10^6$ mg

$$\text{Mass \%} = \left(\frac{\text{mass of substance}}{\text{mass of seawater}} \right) (100\%)$$

$$\text{Mass \% Cl}^- = \left(\frac{18,980 \text{ mg Cl}^-}{1 \times 10^6 \text{ mg seawater}} \right) (100\%) = \textbf{1.898\% Cl}^-$$

$$\text{Mass \% Na}^+ = \left(\frac{10.560 \text{ mg Na}^+}{1 \times 10^6 \text{ mg seawater}} \right) (100\%) = \textbf{1.056\% Na}^+$$

$$\text{Mass \% SO}_4^{2-} = \left(\frac{2650 \text{ mg SO}_4^{2-}}{1 \times 10^6 \text{ mg seawater}} \right) (100\%) = \textbf{0.265\% SO}_4^{2-}$$

$$\text{Mass \% Mg}^{2+} = \left(\frac{1270 \text{ mg Mg}^{2+}}{1 \times 10^6 \text{ mg seawater}} \right) (100\%) = \textbf{0.127\% Mg}^{2+}$$

$$\text{Mass \% Ca}^{2+} = \left(\frac{400 \text{ mg Ca}^{2+}}{1 \times 10^6 \text{ mg seawater}} \right) (100\%) = \textbf{0.04\% Ca}^{2+}$$

$$\text{Mass \% K}^+ = \left(\frac{380 \text{ mg K}^+}{1 \times 10^6 \text{ mg seawater}} \right) (100\%) = \textbf{0.038\% K}^+$$

$$\text{Mass \% HCO}_3^- = \left(\frac{140 \text{ mg HCO}_3^-}{1 \times 10^6 \text{ mg seawater}} \right) (100\%) = \textbf{0.014\% HCO}_3^-$$

The mass percents do not add to 100% since the majority of seawater is H_2O.
b) Total mass of ions in 1 kg of seawater
$$= 18,980 \text{ mg} + 10,560 \text{ mg} + 2650 \text{ mg} + 1270 \text{ mg} + 400 \text{ mg} + 380 \text{ mg} + 140 \text{ mg} = 34,380 \text{ mg}$$

$$\text{\% Na}^+ = \left(\frac{10,560 \text{ mg Na}^+}{34,380 \text{ mg total ions}} \right) (100) = 30.71553 = \textbf{30.72\%}$$

c) Alkaline earth metal ions are Mg^{2+} and Ca^{2+} (Group 2 ions).
Total mass % = 0.127% Mg^{2+} + 0.04% Ca^{2+} = 0.167%
Alkali metal ions are Na^+ and K^+ (Group 1 ions). Total mass % = 1.056% Na^+ + 0.038% K^+ = 1.094%

$$\frac{\text{Mass \% of alkali metal ions}}{\text{Mass \% of alkaline earth metal ions}} = \frac{1.094\%}{0.167\%} = 6.6$$

Total mass percent for alkali metal ions is **6.6 times greater** than the total mass percent for alkaline earth metal ions. Sodium ions (alkali metal ions) are dominant in seawater.
d) Anions are Cl^-, SO_4^{2-}, and HCO_3^-.
Total mass % = 1.898% Cl^- + 0.265% SO_4^{2-} + 0.014% HCO_3^- = 2.177% anions
Cations are Na^+, Mg^{2+}, Ca^{2+}, and K^+.
Total mass % = 1.056% Na^+ + 0.127% Mg^{2+} + 0.04% Ca^{2+} + 0.038% K^+ = 1.2610 = 1.26% cations
The mass fraction of **anions** is larger than the mass fraction of cations. Is the solution neutral since the mass of anions exceeds the mass of cations? Yes, although the mass is larger, the number of positive charges equals the number of negative charges.

2.130   Plan: First, count each type of atom present to produce a molecular formula. The molecular (formula) mass is the sum of the atomic masses of all of the atoms. Divide the mass of each element in the compound by the molecular mass and multiply by 100 to obtain the mass percent of each element.
Solution:
The molecular formula of succinic acid is $\textbf{C}_4\textbf{H}_6\textbf{O}_4$.

C	=	4(12.01 u)	=	48.04 u
H	=	6(1.008 u)	=	6.048 u
O	=	4 (16.00 u)	=	64.00 u
				118.09 u

$$\% \text{ C} = \left(\frac{48.04 \text{ u C}}{118.088\,\text{u}}\right)100\% = 40.6815 = \mathbf{40.68\% \text{ C}}$$

$$\% \text{ H} = \left(\frac{6.048 \text{ u H}}{118.088 \text{ u}}\right)100\% = 5.1216 = \mathbf{5.122\% \text{ H}}$$

$$\% \text{ O} = \left(\frac{64.00 \text{ u O}}{118.088 \text{ u}}\right)100\% = 54.1969 = \mathbf{54.20\% \text{ O}}$$

Check: Total = (40.68 + 5.122 + 54.20)% = 100.00% The answer checks.

2.133   Plan: List all possible combinations of the isotopes. Determine the masses of each isotopic composition. The molecule consisting of the lower abundance isotopes (N-15 and O-18) is the least common, and the one containing only the more abundant isotopes (N-14 and O-16) will be the most common.
Solution:
a)   b)

Formula	Mass (u)	
$^{15}N_2{}^{18}O$	2(15 u N) + 18 u O = **48**	**least common**
$^{15}N_2{}^{16}O$	2(15 u N) + 16u O = **46**	
$^{14}N_2{}^{18}O$	2(14 u N) + 18 u O = **46**	
$^{14}N_2{}^{16}O$	2(14 u N) + 16 u O = **44**	**most common**
$^{15}N^{14}N^{18}O$	1(15 u N) + 1(14 u N) + 18 u O = **47**	
$^{15}N^{14}N^{16}O$	1(15 u N) + 1(14 u N) + 16 u O = **45**	

2.135   Plan: To find the formula mass of potassium fluoride, add the atomic masses of potassium and fluorine. Fluorine has only one naturally occurring isotope, so the mass of this isotope equals the atomic mass of fluorine. The atomic mass of potassium is the weighted average of the two isotopic masses: (isotopic mass of isotope 1 x fractional abundance) + (isotopic mass of isotope 2 x fractional abundance).
Solution:
Average atomic mass of K =
        (isotopic mass of ^{39}K x fractional abundance) + (isotopic mass of ^{41}K x fractional abundance)

$$\text{Average atomic mass of K} = (38.9637 \text{ u})\left(\frac{93.258\%}{100\%}\right) + (40.9618 \text{ u})\left(\frac{6.730\%}{100\%}\right) = 39.093 \text{ u}$$

The formula for potassium fluoride is KF, so its molecular mass is (39.093 + 18.9984)u = **58.091 u**

2.137   Plan: One molecule of NO is released per atom of N in the medicine. Divide the total mass of NO released by the molecular mass of the medicine and multiply by 100 for mass percent.
Solution:
NO = (14.01 + 16.00) u = 30.01 u
Nitroglycerin:
$C_3H_5N_3O_9$ = 3(12.01 u C) + 5(1.008 u H) + 3(14.01 u N) + 9(16.00 u O) = 227.10 u
In $C_3H_5N_3O_9$ (molecular mass = 227.10 u), there are 3 atoms of N; since 1 molecule of NO is released per atom of N, this medicine would release 3 molecules of NO. The molecular mass of NO = 30.01 u.

$$\text{Mass percent of NO} = \frac{\text{total mass of NO}}{\text{mass of compound}}(100\%) = \frac{3(30.01 \text{ u})}{227.10 \text{ u}}(100\%) = 39.6433\% = \mathbf{39.64\%}$$

Isoamyl nitrate:
$C_5H_{11}NO_3$ = 5(12.01 u C) + 11(1.008 u H) + 1(14.01 u N) + 3(16.00 u O) = 133.15 u
In $(CH_3)_2CHCH_2CH_2ONO_2$ (molecular mass = 133.15 u), there is one atom of N; since 1 molecule of NO is released per atom of N, this medicine would release 1 molecule of NO.

$$\text{Mass percent of NO} = \frac{\text{total mass of NO}}{\text{mass of compound}}(100\%) = \frac{1(30.01 \text{ u})}{133.15 \text{ u}}(100\%) = 22.5385 \% = \mathbf{22.54\%}$$

2.138   Plan: First, count each type of atom present to produce a molecular formula. Determine the mass fraction of each element. Mass fraction = $\dfrac{\text{total mass of the element}}{\text{molecular mass of TNT}}$. The mass of TNT multiplied by the mass fraction of each element gives the mass of that element.

Solution:
The molecular formula for TNT is $C_7H_5O_6N_3$. The molecular mass of TNT is:

C	=	7(12.01 u)	=	84.07 u
H	=	5(1.008 u)	=	5.040 u
O	=	6(16.00 u)	=	96.00 u
N	=	3(14.01 u)	=	42.03 u
				227.14 u

The mass fraction of each element is:

$$C = \frac{84.07 \text{ u}}{227.14 \text{ u}} = 0.3701 \text{ C} \qquad\qquad H = \frac{5.040 \text{ u}}{227.14 \text{ u}} = 0.02219 \text{ H}$$

$$O = \frac{96.00 \text{ u}}{227.14 \text{ u}} = 0.4226 \text{ O} \qquad\qquad N = \frac{42.03 \text{ u}}{227.14 \text{ u}} = 0.1850 \text{ N}$$

Masses of each element in 1.00 kg of TNT = mass fraction of element x 1.00kg.
Mass (kg) C = 0.3701 x 1.00 kg = **0.370 kg C**
Mass (kg) H = 0.02219 x 1.00 kg = **0.0222 kg H**
Mass (kg) O = 0.4226 x 1.00 kg = **0.423 kg O**
Mass (kg) N = 0.1850 x 1.00 kg = **0.185 kg N**

2.143   Plan: A change is physical when there has been a change in physical form but not a change in composition. In a chemical change, a substance is converted into a different substance.

Solution:
1) Initially, all the molecules are present in blue-blue or red-red pairs. After the change, there are no red-red pairs, and there are now red-blue pairs. Changing some of the pairs means there has been a **chemical change**.
2) There are two blue-blue pairs and four red-blue pairs both before and after the change, thus no chemical change occurred. The different types of molecules are separated into different boxes. This is a **physical change**.
3) The identity of the box contents has changed from pairs to individuals. This requires a **chemical change**.
4) The contents have changed from all pairs to all triplets. This is a change in the identity of the particles, thus, this is a **chemical change**.
5) There are four red-blue pairs both before and after, thus there has been no change in the identity of the individual units. There has been a **physical change**.

CHAPTER 3 STOICHIOMETRY OF FORMULAE AND EQUATIONS

END–OF–CHAPTER PROBLEMS

3.2   Plan: The molecular formula of sucrose tells us that 1 mole of sucrose contains 12 moles of carbon atoms. Multiply the amount (mol) of sucrose by 12 to obtain amount (mol) of carbon atoms; multiply the amount (mol) of carbon atoms by Avogadro's number to convert from amount (mol) to atoms.
Solution:

a) Amount (mol) of C atoms $= \left(1 \text{ mol } C_{12}H_{22}O_{11}\right)\left(\dfrac{12 \text{ mol C}}{1 \text{ mol } C_{12}H_{22}O_{11}}\right) = \textbf{12 mol C}$

b) C atoms $= \left(2 \text{ mol } C_{12}H_{22}O_{11}\right)\left(\dfrac{12 \text{ mol C}}{1 \text{ mol } C_{12}H_{22}O_{11}}\right)\left(\dfrac{6.022 \times 10^{23} \text{ C atoms}}{1 \text{ mol C}}\right) = \textbf{1.445} \times \textbf{10}^{\textbf{25}} \textbf{ C atoms}$

3.7   Plan: The relative atomic masses of each element can be found by counting the number of atoms of each element and comparing the overall masses of the two samples.
Solution:
a) The element on the **left** (green) has the higher molar mass because only 5 green balls are necessary to counterbalance the mass of 6 yellow balls. Since the green ball is heavier, its atomic mass is larger, and therefore its molar mass is larger.
b) The element on the **left** (red) has more atoms per gram. This figure requires more thought because the number of red and blue balls is unequal and their masses are unequal. If each pan contained 3 balls, then the red balls would be lighter. The presence of 6 red balls means that they are that much lighter. Because the red ball is lighter, more red atoms are required to make 1 g.
c) The element on the **left** (orange) has fewer atoms per gram. The orange balls are heavier, and it takes fewer orange balls to make 1 g.
d) **Neither** element has more atoms per mole. Both the left and right elements have the same number of atoms per mole. The number of atoms per mole (6.022×10^{23}) is constant and so is the same for every element.

3.8   Plan: Locate each of the elements on the periodic table and record its atomic mass. The atomic mass of the element multiplied by the number of atoms present in the formula gives the mass of that element in one mole of the substance. The molar mass is the sum of the masses of the elements in the substance expressed in g/mol.
Solution:
a) $\mathcal{M} = (1 \cdot \mathcal{M} \text{ of Sr}) + (2 \cdot \mathcal{M} \text{ of O}) + (2 \cdot \mathcal{M} \text{ of H})$
        $= (1 \cdot 87.62 \text{ g/mol Sr}) + (2 \cdot 16.00 \text{ g/mol O}) + (2 \cdot 1.008 \text{ g/mol H})$
        $= \textbf{121.64 g/mol of Sr(OH)}_2$
b) $\mathcal{M} = (2 \cdot \mathcal{M} \text{ of N}) + (3 \cdot \mathcal{M} \text{ of O})$
        $= (2 \cdot 14.01 \text{ g/mol N}) + (3 \cdot 16.00 \text{ g/mol O})$
        $= \textbf{76.02 g/mol of N}_2\textbf{O}_3$
c) $\mathcal{M} = (1 \cdot \mathcal{M} \text{ of Na}) + (1 \cdot \mathcal{M} \text{ of Cl}) + (3 \cdot \mathcal{M} \text{ of O})$
        $= (1 \cdot 22.99 \text{ g/mol Na}) + (1 \cdot 35.45 \text{ g/mol Cl}) + (3 \cdot 16.00 \text{ g/mol O})$
        $= \textbf{106.44 g/mol of NaClO}_3$
d) $\mathcal{M} = (2 \cdot \mathcal{M} \text{ of Cr}) + (3 \cdot \mathcal{M} \text{ of O})$
        $= (2 \cdot 52.00 \text{ g/mol Cr}) + (3 \cdot 16.00 \text{ g/mol O})$
        $= \textbf{152.00 g/mol of Cr}_2\textbf{O}_3$

3.10   Plan: Locate each of the elements on the periodic table and record its atomic mass. The atomic mass of the element multiplied by the number of atoms present in the formula gives the mass of that element in one mole of the substance. The molar mass is the sum of the masses of the elements in the substance expressed in g/mol.
Solution:
a) $\mathcal{M} = (1 \cdot \mathcal{M}$ of Sn$) + (1 \cdot \mathcal{M}$ of O$)$
        $= (1 \cdot 118.7$ g/mol Sn$) + (1 \cdot 16.00$ g/mol O$)$
        = **134.7 g/mol of SnO**
b) $\mathcal{M} = (1 \cdot \mathcal{M}$ of Ba$) + (2 \cdot \mathcal{M}$ of F$)$
        $= (1 \cdot 137.3$ g/mol Ba$) + (2 \cdot 19.00$ g/mol F$)$
        = **175.3 g/mol of BaF$_2$**
c) $\mathcal{M} = (2 \cdot \mathcal{M}$ of Al$) + (3 \cdot \mathcal{M}$ of S$) + (12 \cdot \mathcal{M}$ of O$)$
        $= (2 \cdot 26.98$ g/mol Al$) + (3 \cdot 32.07$ g/mol S$) + (12 \cdot 16.00$ g/mol O$)$
        = **342.17 g/mol of Al$_2$(SO$_4$)$_3$**
d) $\mathcal{M} = (1 \cdot \mathcal{M}$ of Mn$) + (2 \cdot \mathcal{M}$ of Cl$)$
        $= (1 \cdot 54.94$ g/mol Mn$) + (2 \cdot 35.45$ g/mol Cl$)$
        = **125.84 g/mol of MnCl$_2$**

3.12   Plan: Determine the molar mass of each substance, then perform the appropriate molar conversions. To find the mass in part a), multiply the amount (mol) by the molar mass of the substance. In part b), first convert mass of compound to amount (mol) of compound by dividing by the molar mass of the compound. The molecular formula of the compound tells us that 1 mole of compound contains 6 moles of oxygen atoms; use the 1:6 ratio to convert amount (mol) of compound to amount (mol) of oxygen atoms. In part c), convert mass of compound to amount (mol) of compound by dividing by the molar mass of the compound. Since 1 mole of compound contains 6 moles of oxygen atoms, multiply the amount (mol) of compound by 6 to obtain amount (mol) of oxygen atoms; then multiply by Avogadro's number to obtain the number of oxygen atoms.
Solution:
a) $\mathcal{M}$ of KMnO$_4 = (1 \cdot \mathcal{M}$ of K$) + (1 \cdot \mathcal{M}$ of Mn$) + (4 \cdot \mathcal{M}$ of O$)$
        $= (1 \cdot 39.10$ g/mol K$) + (1 \cdot 54.94$ g/mol Mn$) + (4 \cdot 16.00$ g/mol O$) = 158.04$ g/mol of KMnO$_4$

$$\text{Mass of KMnO}_4 = \left(0.68 \text{ mol KMnO}_4\right)\left(\frac{158.04 \text{ g KMnO}_4}{1 \text{ mol KMnO}_4}\right) = 107.467 \text{ g} = \mathbf{1.1 \times 10^2 \text{ g KMnO}_4}$$

b) $\mathcal{M}$ of Ba(NO$_3$)$_2 = (1 \cdot \mathcal{M}$ of Ba$) + (2 \cdot \mathcal{M}$ of N$) + (6 \cdot \mathcal{M}$ of O$)$
        $= (1 \cdot 137.3$ g/mol Ba$) + (2 \cdot 14.01$ g/mol N$) + (6 \cdot 16.00$ g/mol O$) = 261.3$ g/mol Ba(NO$_3$)$_2$

$$\text{Amount (mol) of Ba(NO}_3)_2 = \left(8.18 \text{ g Ba(NO}_3)_2\right)\left(\frac{1 \text{ mol Ba(NO}_3)_2}{261.3 \text{ g Ba(NO}_3)_2}\right) = 0.031305 \text{ mol Ba(NO}_3)_2$$

$$\text{Amount (mol) of O atoms} = \left(0.031305 \text{ mol Ba(NO}_3)_2\right)\left(\frac{6 \text{ mol O atoms}}{1 \text{ mol Ba(NO}_3)_2}\right)$$

$$= 0.18783 \text{ mol} = \mathbf{0.188 \text{ mol O atoms}}$$

c) $\mathcal{M}$ of CaSO$_4$•2H$_2$O $= (1 \cdot$ of Ca$) + (1 \cdot \mathcal{M}$ of S$) + (6 \cdot \mathcal{M}$ of O$) + (4 \cdot \mathcal{M}$ of H$)$
        $= (1 \cdot 40.08$ g/mol Ca$) + (1 \cdot 32.07$ g/mol S$) + (6 \cdot 16.00$ g/mol O$) + (4 \cdot 1.008$ g/mol H$)$
        $= 172.18$ g/mol
(Note that the waters of hydration are included in the molar mass.)

$$\text{Amount (mol) of CaSO}_4\text{•2H}_2\text{O} = \left(7.3 \times 10^{-3} \text{ g CaSO}_4\text{•2H}_2\text{O}\right)\left(\frac{1 \text{ mol CaSO}_4\text{•2H}_2\text{O}}{172.18 \text{ g CaSO}_4\text{•2H}_2\text{O}}\right)$$

$$= 4.239749 \times 10^{-5} \text{ mol}$$

$$\text{Amount (mol) of O atoms} = \left(4.239749 \times 10^{-5} \text{ mol CaSO}_4\text{•2H}_2\text{O}\right)\left(\frac{6 \text{ mol O atoms}}{1 \text{ mol CaSO}_4\text{•2H}_2\text{O}}\right)$$

$$= 2.54385 \times 10^{-5} \text{ mol O atoms}$$

$$\text{Number of O atoms} = \left(2.54385 \times 10^{-4} \text{ mol O atoms}\right)\left(\frac{6.022 \times 10^{23} \text{ O atoms}}{1 \text{ mol O atoms}}\right)$$

$$= 1.5319 \times 10^{20} \text{ atoms} = \mathbf{1.5 \times 10^{20} \text{ O atoms}}$$

3.14   Plan: Determine the molar mass of each substance, then perform the appropriate molar conversions. To find the mass in part a), multiply the amount (mol) by the molar mass of the substance. In part b), first convert the mass of compound in kg to mass in g and divide by the molar mass of the compound to find amount (mol) of compound. In part c), convert mass of compound in mg to mass in g and divide by the molar mass of the compound to find amount (mol) of compound. Since 1 mole of compound contains 2 moles of nitrogen atoms, multiply the amount (mol) of compound by 2 to obtain amount (mol) of nitrogen atoms; then multiply by Avogadro's number to obtain the number of nitrogen atoms.

Solution:

a) $\mathcal{M}$ of $MnSO_4$ = (1 •$\mathcal{M}$ of Mn) + (1 •$\mathcal{M}$ of S) + (4 •$\mathcal{M}$ of O)
= (1 •54.94 g/mol Mn) + (1 •32.07 g/mol S) + (4 •16.00 g/mol O) = 151.01 g/mol of $MnSO_4$

Mass (g) of $MnSO_4$ = $\left(6.44\text{x}10^{-2} \text{ mol } MnSO_4\right)\left(\dfrac{151.01 \text{ g } MnSO_4}{1 \text{ mol } MnSO_4}\right)$ = 9.725044 g= **9.73 g $MnSO_4$**

b) $\mathcal{M}$ of $Fe(ClO_4)_3$ = (1 •$\mathcal{M}$ of Fe) + (3 •$\mathcal{M}$ of Cl) + (12 •$\mathcal{M}$ of O)
= (1 •55.85 g/mol Fe) + (3 •35.45 g/mol S) + (12 •16.00 g/mol O)
= 354.20 g/mol of $Fe(ClO_4)_3$

Mass (g) of $Fe(ClO_4)_3$ = $\left(15.8 \text{ kg } Fe(ClO_4)_3\right)\left(\dfrac{10^3 \text{ g}}{1 \text{ kg}}\right)$ = 1.58 x 10^4 kg $Fe(ClO_4)_3$

Amount (mol) of $Fe(ClO_4)_3$ = $\left(1.58\text{x}10^4 \text{ g } Fe(ClO_4)_3\right)\left(\dfrac{1 \text{ mol } Fe(ClO_4)_3}{354.20 \text{ g } Fe(ClO_4)_3}\right)$

= 44.6076 mol= **44.6 mol $Fe(ClO_4)_3$**

c) $\mathcal{M}$ of NH_4NO_2 = (2 •$\mathcal{M}$ of N) + (4 •$\mathcal{M}$ of H) + (2 •$\mathcal{M}$ of O)
= (2 •14.01 g/mol N) + (4 •1.008 g/mol H) + (2 •16.00 g/mol O) = 64.05 g/mol NH_4NO_2

Mass (g) of NH_4NO_2 = $\left(92.6 \text{ mg } NH_4NO_2\right)\left(\dfrac{10^{-3} \text{ g}}{1 \text{ mg}}\right)$ = 0.0926 g NH_4NO_2

Amount (mol) of NH_4NO_2 = $\left(0.0926 \text{ g } NH_4NO_2\right)\left(\dfrac{1 \text{ mol } NH_4NO_2}{64.05 \text{ g } NH_4NO_2}\right)$ = $1.44575\text{x}10^{-3}$ mol NH_4NO_2

Amount (mol) of N atoms = $\left(1.44575\text{x}10^{-3} \text{ mol } NH_4NO_2\right)\left(\dfrac{2 \text{ mol N atoms}}{1 \text{ mol } NH_4NO_2}\right)$ = $2.8915\text{x}10^{-3}$ mol N atoms

Number of N atoms = $\left(2.8915\text{x}10^{-3} \text{ mol N atoms}\right)\left(\dfrac{6.022 \times 10^{23} \text{ N atoms}}{1 \text{ mol N atoms}}\right)$

= 1.74126 x 10^{21} atoms= **1.74 x 10^{21} N atoms**

3.16   Plan: The formula of each compound must be determined from its name. The molar mass for each formula comes from the formula and atomic masses from the periodic table. Determine the molar mass of each substance, then perform the appropriate molar conversions. In part a), multiply the amount (mol) by the molar mass of the compound to find the mass of the sample. In part b), divide the number of molecules by Avogadro's number to find amount (mol); multiply the amount (mol) by the molar mass to obtain the mass. In part c), divide the mass by the molar mass to find amount (mol) of compound and multiply amount (mol) by Avogadro's number to find the number of formula units. In part d), use the fact that each formula unit contains 1 Na ion, 1 perchlorate ion, 1 Cl atom, and 4 O atoms.

Solution:

a) Carbonate is a polyatomic anion with the formula, CO_3^{2-}. Copper(I) indicates Cu^+. The correct formula for this ionic compound is Cu_2CO_3.

$\mathcal{M}$ of Cu_2CO_3 = (2 •$\mathcal{M}$ of Cu) + (1 •$\mathcal{M}$ of C) + (3 •$\mathcal{M}$ of O)
= (2 •63.55 g/mol Cu) + (1 •12.01 g/mol C) + (3 •16.00 g/mol O) = 187.11 g/mol of Cu_2CO_3

Mass (g) of Cu_2CO_3 = $\left(8.35 \text{ mol } Cu_2CO_3\right)\left(\dfrac{187.11 \text{ g } Cu_2CO_3}{1 \text{ mol } Cu_2CO_3}\right)$ = 1562.4 = **$1.56\text{x}10^3$ g Cu_2CO_3**

b) Dinitrogen pentaoxide has the formula N_2O_5. Di- indicates 2 N atoms and penta- indicates 5 O atoms.
$\mathcal{M}$ of $N_2O_5 = (2 \cdot \mathcal{M}$ of N) $+ (5 \cdot \mathcal{M}$ of O)

$$= (2 \cdot 14.01 \text{ g/mol N}) + (5 \cdot 16.00 \text{ g/mol O}) = 108.02 \text{ g/mol of } N_2O_5$$

Amount (mol) of $N_2O_5 = \left(4.04 \times 10^{20} \ N_2O_5 \text{ molecules}\right)\left(\dfrac{1 \text{ mol } N_2O_5}{6.022 \times 10^{23} \ N_2O_5 \text{ molecules}}\right) = 6.7087 \times 10^{-4} \text{ mol } N_2O_5$

Mass (g) of $N_2O_5 = \left(6.7087 \times 10^{-4} \text{ mol } N_2O_5\right)\left(\dfrac{108.02 \text{ g } N_2O_5}{1 \text{ mol } N_2O_5}\right) = 0.072467 \text{ g} = \textbf{0.0725 g } N_2O_5$

c) The correct formula for this ionic compound is $NaClO_4$; Na has a charge of +1 (Group 1 ion) and the perchlorate ion is ClO_4^-.
$\mathcal{M}$ of $NaClO_4 = (1 \cdot \mathcal{M}$ of Na) $+ (1 \cdot \mathcal{M}$ of Cl) $+ (4 \cdot \mathcal{M}$ of O)

$$= (1 \cdot 22.99 \text{ g/mol Na}) + (1 \cdot 35.45 \text{ g/mol Cl}) + (4 \cdot 16.00 \text{ g/mol O}) = 122.44 \text{ g/mol of } NaClO_4$$

Amount (mol) of $NaClO_4 = \left(78.9 \text{ g } NaClO_4\right)\left(\dfrac{1 \text{ mol } NaClO_4}{122.44 \text{ g } NaClO_4}\right) = 0.644397 \text{ mol} = \textbf{0.644 mol } NaClO_4$

Formula units of $NaClO_4 = \left(0.644397 \text{ mol } NaClO_4\right)\left(\dfrac{6.022 \times 10^{23} \text{ formula units } NaClO_4}{1 \text{ mol } NaClO_4}\right)$

$$= 3.88056 \times 10^{23} \text{ formula units} = \textbf{3.88} \times \textbf{10}^{\textbf{23}} \textbf{ formula unit } NaClO_4$$

d) Number of Na^+ ions $= \left(3.88056 \times 10^{23} \text{ formula units } NaClO_4\right)\left(\dfrac{1 \ Na^+ \text{ ion}}{1 \text{ formula unit } NaClO_4}\right)$

$$= \textbf{3.88} \times \textbf{10}^{\textbf{23}} \ Na^+ \textbf{ ions}$$

Number of ClO_4^- ions $= \left(3.88056 \times 10^{23} \text{ formula units } NaClO_4\right)\left(\dfrac{1 \ ClO_4^- \text{ ion}}{1 \text{ formula unit } NaClO_4}\right)$

$$= \textbf{3.88} \times \textbf{10}^{\textbf{23}} \ ClO_4^- \textbf{ ions}$$

Number of Cl atoms $= \left(3.88056 \times 10^{23} \text{ formula units } NaClO_4\right)\left(\dfrac{1 \text{ Cl atom}}{1 \text{ formula unit } NaClO_4}\right)$

$$= \textbf{3.88} \times \textbf{10}^{\textbf{23}} \textbf{ Cl atoms}$$

Number of O atoms $= \left(3.88056 \times 10^{23} \text{ formula units } NaClO_4\right)\left(\dfrac{4 \text{ O atoms}}{1 \text{ formula unit } NaClO_4}\right)$

$$= \textbf{1.55} \times \textbf{10}^{\textbf{24}} \textbf{ O atoms}$$

3.18   Plan: Determine the formula and the molar mass of each compound. The formula gives the relative number of amount (mol) of each element present. Multiply the amount (mol) of each element by its molar mass to find the total mass of element in 1 mole of compound. Mass percent $= \dfrac{\text{total mass of element}}{\text{molar mass of compound}}(100)$.

Solution:
a) Ammonium bicarbonate is an ionic compound consisting of ammonium ions, NH_4^+ and bicarbonate ions, HCO_3^-. The formula of the compound is NH_4HCO_3.
$\mathcal{M}$ of $NH_4HCO_3 = (1 \cdot \mathcal{M}$ of N) $+ (5 \cdot \mathcal{M}$ of H) $+ (1 \cdot \mathcal{M}$ of C) $+ (3 \cdot \mathcal{M}$ of O)

$$= (1 \cdot 14.01 \text{ g/mol N}) + (5 \cdot 1.008 \text{ g/mol H}) + (1 \cdot 12.01 \text{ g/mol C}) + (3 \cdot 16.00 \text{ g/mol O})$$
$$= 79.06 \text{ g/mol of } NH_4HCO_3$$

There are 5 moles of H in 1 mole of NH_4HCO_3.

Mass (g) of H $= \left(5 \text{ mol H}\right)\left(\dfrac{1.008 \text{ g H}}{1 \text{ mol H}}\right) = 5.040 \text{ g H}$

Mass percent $= \dfrac{\text{total mass H}}{\text{molar mass of compound}}(100) = \dfrac{5.040 \text{ g H}}{79.06 \text{ g } NH_4HCO_3}(100) = 6.374905 \% = \textbf{6.375\% H}$

b) Sodium dihydrogen phosphate heptahydrate is a salt that consists of sodium ions, Na^+, dihydrogen phosphate ions, $H_2PO_4^-$, and seven waters of hydration. The formula is $NaH_2PO_4 \cdot 7H_2O$. Note that the waters of hydration are included in the molar mass.

$\mathcal{M}$ of $NaH_2PO_4 \cdot 7H_2O = (1 \cdot \mathcal{M}$ of Na$) + (16 \cdot \mathcal{M}$ of H$) + (1 \cdot \mathcal{M}$ of P$) + (11 \cdot \mathcal{M}$ of O$)$

$\qquad = (1 \cdot 22.99$ g/mol Na$) + (16 \cdot 1.008$ g/mol H$) + (1 \cdot 30.97$ g/mol P$) + (11 \cdot 16.00$ g/mol O$)$

$\qquad = 246.09$ g/mol $NaH_2PO_4 \cdot 7H_2O$

There are 11 moles of O in 1 mole of $NaH_2PO_4 \cdot 7H_2O$.

$$\text{Mass (g) of O} = \left(11 \text{ mol O}\right)\left(\frac{16.00 \text{ g O}}{1 \text{ mol O}}\right) = 176.00 \text{ g O}$$

$$\text{Mass percent} = \frac{\text{total mass O}}{\text{molar mass of compound}}(100\%) = \frac{176.00 \text{ g O}}{246.09 \text{ g } NaH_2PO_4 \cdot 7H_2O}(100\%)$$
$$= 71.51855\% = \textbf{71.52\% O}$$

3.20   Plan: Determine the formula and the molar mass of each compound. The formula gives the relative amount (mol) of each element present. Multiply the amount (mol) of each element by its molar mass to find the total mass of element in 1 mole of compound. Mass fraction $= \dfrac{\text{total mass of element}}{\text{molar mass of compound}}$.

Solution:

a) Cesium acetate is an ionic compound consisting of Cs^+ cations and $C_2H_3O_2^-$ anions. (Note that the formula for acetate ions can be written as either $C_2H_3O_2^-$ or CH_3COO^-.) The formula of the compound is $CsC_2H_3O_2$.

$\mathcal{M}$ of $CsC_2H_3O_2 = (1 \cdot \mathcal{M}$ of Cs$) + (2 \cdot \mathcal{M}$ of C$) + (3 \cdot \mathcal{M}$ of H$) + (2 \cdot \mathcal{M}$ of O$)$

$\qquad = (1 \cdot 132.9$ g/mol Cs$) + (2 \cdot 12.01$ g/mol C$) + (3 \cdot 1.008$ g/mol H$) + (2 \cdot 16.00$ g/mol O$)$

$\qquad = 191.9$ g/mol of $CsC_2H_3O_2$

There are 2 moles of C in 1 mole of $CsC_2H_3O_2$.

$$\text{Mass (g) of C} = \left(2 \text{ mol C}\right)\left(\frac{12.01 \text{ g C}}{1 \text{ mol C}}\right) = 24.02 \text{ g C}$$

$$\text{Mass fraction} = \frac{\text{total mass C}}{\text{molar mass of compound}} = \frac{24.02 \text{ g C}}{191.9 \text{ g } CsC_2H_3O_2} = 0.125169 = \textbf{0.1252 mass fraction C}$$

b) Uranyl sulfate trihydrate is is a salt that consists of uranyl ions, UO_2^{2+}, sulfate ions, SO_4^{2-}, and three waters of hydration. The formula is $UO_2SO_4 \cdot 3H_2O$. Note that the waters of hydration are included in the molar mass.

$\mathcal{M}$ of $UO_2SO_4 \cdot 3H_2O = (1 \cdot \mathcal{M}$ of U$) + (9 \cdot \mathcal{M}$ of O$) + (1 \cdot \mathcal{M}$ of S$) + (6 \cdot \mathcal{M}$ of H$)$

$\qquad = (1 \cdot 238.0$ g/mol U$) + (9 \cdot 16.00$ g/mol O$) + (1 \cdot 32.07$ g/mol S$) + (6 \cdot 1.008$ g/mol H$)$

$\qquad = 420.1$ g/mol of $UO_2SO_4 \cdot 3H_2O$

There are 9 moles of O in 1 mole of $UO_2SO_4 \cdot 3H_2O$.

$$\text{Mass (g) of O} = \left(9 \text{ mol O}\right)\left(\frac{16.00 \text{ g O}}{1 \text{ mol O}}\right) = 144.0 \text{ g O}$$

$$\text{Mass fraction} = \frac{\text{total mass O}}{\text{molar mass of compound}} = \frac{144.0 \text{ g O}}{420.1 \text{ g } UO_2SO_4 \cdot 3H_2O} = 0.3427755 = \textbf{0.3428 mass fraction O}$$

3.23   Plan: Determine the formula of cisplatin from the figure, and then calculate the molar mass from the formula. Divide the mass given by the molar mass to find amount (mol) of cisplatin. Since 1 mole of cisplatin contains 6 moles of hydrogen atoms, multiply the amount (mol) given by 6 to obtain amount (mol) of hydrogen and then multiply by Avogadro's number to obtain the number of atoms.

Solution:

The formula for cisplatin is $Pt(Cl)_2(NH_3)_2$.

$\mathcal{M}$ of $Pt(Cl)_2(NH_3)_2 = (1 \cdot \mathcal{M}$ of Pt$) + (2 \cdot \mathcal{M}$ of Cl$) + (2 \cdot \mathcal{M}$ of N$) + (6 \cdot \mathcal{M}$ of H$)$

$\qquad = (1 \cdot 195.1$ g/mol Pt$) + (2 \cdot 35.45$ g/mol Cl$) + (2 \cdot 14.01$ g/mol N$) + (6 \cdot 1.008$ g/mol H$)$

$\qquad = 300.1$ g/mol of $Pt(Cl)_2(NH_3)_2$

a) Amount (mol) of cisplatin $= \left(285.3 \text{ g cisplatin}\right)\left(\dfrac{1 \text{ mol cisplatin}}{300.1 \text{ g cisplatin}}\right) = 0.9506831$ mol$= \textbf{0.9507 mol cisplatin}$

b) Amount (mol) of H atoms = $(0.98 \text{ mol cisplatin})\left(\dfrac{6 \text{ mol H}}{1 \text{ mol cisplatin}}\right) = 5.88$ mol H atoms

Number of H atoms = $(5.88 \text{ mol H atoms})\left(\dfrac{6.022 \times 10^{23} \text{ H atoms}}{1 \text{ mol H atoms}}\right) = 3.540936 \times 10^{24}$ atoms= **3.5x10²⁴ H atoms**

3.25 Plan: Determine the molar mass of rust. Convert mass in kg to mass in g and divide by the molar mass to find the amount (mol) of rust. Since each mole of rust contains 1 mole of Fe_2O_3, multiply the amount (mol) of rust by 1 to obtain amount (mol) of Fe_2O_3. Multiply the amount (mol) of Fe_2O_3 by 2 to obtain amount (mol) of Fe (1:2 Fe_2O_3:Fe mole ratio) and multiply by the molar mass of Fe to convert to mass.
Solution:
a) $\mathcal{M}$ of $Fe_2O_3 \cdot 4H_2O$ = (2 • $\mathcal{M}$ of Fe) + (7 • $\mathcal{M}$ of O) + (8 • $\mathcal{M}$ of H)
    = (2 •55.85 g/mol Fe) + (7 •16.00 g/mol O) + (8 •1.008 g/mol H) = 231.76 g/mol

Mass (g) of rust = $(45.2 \text{ kg rust})\left(\dfrac{10^3 \text{ g}}{1 \text{ kg}}\right) = 4.52 \times 10^4$ g

Amount (mol) of rust = $\left(4.52 \times 10^4 \text{ g rust}\right)\left(\dfrac{1 \text{ mol rust}}{231.76 \text{ g rust}}\right) = 195.029$ mol= **195 mol rust**

b) The formula shows that there is 1 mole of Fe_2O_3 for every mole of rust, so there are also **195 mol of Fe_2O_3**.

c) Amount (mol) of iron = $(195.029 \text{ mol Fe}_2\text{O}_3)\left(\dfrac{2 \text{ mol Fe}}{1 \text{ mol Fe}_2\text{O}_3}\right) = 390.058$ mol Fe

Mass (g) of iron = $(390.058 \text{ mol Fe})\left(\dfrac{55.85 \text{ g Fe}}{1 \text{ mol Fe}}\right) = 21784.74$ g= **2.18x10⁴ g Fe**

3.27 Plan: Determine the formula and the molar mass of each compound. The formula gives the relative amount (mol) of nitrogen present. Multiply the amount (mol) of nitrogen by its molar mass to find the total mass of nitrogen in 1 mole of compound. Divide the total mass of nitrogen by the molar mass of compound and multiply by 100 to

determine mass percent. Mass percent = $\dfrac{(\text{mol N})(\text{molar mass N})}{\text{molar mass of compound}}(100\%)$. Then rank the values in order of

decreasing mass percent N.
Solution:

Name	Formula	Molar Mass (g/mol)
Potassium nitrate	KNO_3	101.11
Ammonium nitrate	NH_4NO_3	80.05
Ammonium sulfate	$(NH_4)_2SO_4$	132.15
Urea	$CO(NH_2)_2$	60.06

Mass % N in potassium nitrate = $\dfrac{(1 \text{ mol N})(14.01 \text{ g/mol N})}{101.11 \text{ g/mol}}$ x 100% = 13.856196 %= **13.86% N**

Mass % N in ammonium nitrate = $\dfrac{(2 \text{ mol N})(14.01 \text{ g/mol N})}{80.05 \text{ g/mol}}$ x 100% = 35.003123% = **35.00% N**

Mass % N in ammonium sulfate = $\dfrac{(2 \text{ mol N})(14.01 \text{ g/mol N})}{132.15 \text{ g/mol}}$ x 100% = 21.20318 %= **21.20% N**

Mass % N in urea = $\dfrac{(2 \text{ mol N})(14.01 \text{ g/mol N})}{60.06 \text{ g/mol}}$ x 100% = 46.6533 %= **46.65% N**

Rank is **$CO(NH_2)_2$ > NH_4NO_3 > $(NH_4)_2SO_4$ > KNO_3**

3.28   Plan: The volume must be converted from cubic metres to cubic centimetres. The volume and the density will give the mass of galena which is then divided by molar mass to obtain amount (mol). Part b) requires a conversion from cubic decimetres to cubic centimetres. The density allows a change from volume in cubic centimetres to mass which is then divided by the molar mass to obtain amount (mol); the amount in moles is multiplied by Avogadro's number to obtain formula units of PbS which is also the number of Pb atoms due to the 1:1 PbS:Pb mole ratio.
Solution:
Lead(II) sulfide is composed of Pb^{2+} and S^{2-} ions and has a formula of PbS.
$\mathcal{M}$ of PbS = (1 $\cdot \mathcal{M}$ of Pb) + (1 $\cdot \mathcal{M}$ of S) = (1 $\cdot$207.2 g/mol Pb) + (1 $\cdot$32.07 g/mol S) = 239.3 g/mol

a) Volume (cm^3) = $\left(1.00 \ m^3 \ PbS\right)\left(\dfrac{100 \ cm}{1 \ m}\right)^3$ = 1,000,000 cm^3

Mass (g) of PbS = $\left(1 \times 10^6 \ cm^3 \ PbS\right)\left(\dfrac{7.46 \ g \ PbS}{1 \ cm^3}\right)$ = 7.46×10^6 g PbS

Amount (mol) of PbS = $\left(7.46 \times 10^6 \ g \ PbS\right)\left(\dfrac{1 \ mol \ PbS}{239.3 \ g \ PbS}\right)$ = 31,174.26 mol = $\mathbf{3.12 \times 10^4}$ **mol PbS**

b) Volume (cm^3) = $\left(1.00 \ dm^3 \ PbS\right)\left(\dfrac{(0.1 \ m)^3}{(1 \ dm)^3}\right)\left(\dfrac{(1 \ cm)^3}{(10^{-2} \ m)^3}\right)$ = $1.00 \times 10^3 \ cm^3$

Mass (g) of PbS = $\left(1.00 \times 10^3 \ cm^3 \ PbS\right)\left(\dfrac{7.46 \ g \ PbS}{1 \ cm^3}\right)$ = 7460 g PbS

Amount (mol) of PbS = $\left(7460 \ g \ PbS\right)\left(\dfrac{1 \ mol \ PbS}{239.3 \ g \ PbS}\right)$ = 31.17426 mol PbS

Amount (mol) of Pb = $\left(31.17426 \ mol \ PbS\right)\left(\dfrac{1 \ mol \ Pb}{1 \ mol \ PbS}\right)$ = 31.17426 mol Pb

Number of lead atoms =
$\left(31.17426 \ mol \ Pb\right)\left(\dfrac{6.022 \times 10^{23} \ Pb \ atoms}{1 \ mol \ Pb}\right)$ = 1.87731×10^{25} atoms= $\mathbf{1.88 \times 10^{25}}$ **Pb atoms**

3.32   Plan: Remember that the molecular formula tells the *actual* amount (mol) of each element in one mole of compound.
Solution:
a) No, this information does not allow you to obtain the molecular formula. You can obtain the empirical formula from the f amount (mol) of each type of atom in a compound, but not the molecular formula.
b) Yes, you can obtain the molecular formula from the mass percentages and the total number of atoms.
Plan:
        1) Assume a 100.0 g sample and convert masses (from the mass % of each element) to amount (mol) using molar mass.
        2) Identify the element with the lowest f amount (mol) and use this number to divide into the number of amount (mol) for each element. You now have at least one elemental mole ratio (the one with the smallest number of moles) equal to 1.00 and the remaining mole ratios that are larger than one.
        3) Examine the numbers to determine if they are whole numbers. If not, multiply each number by a whole-number factor to get whole numbers for each element. You will have to use some judgment to decide when to round. Write the empirical formula using these whole numbers.
        4) Check the total number of atoms in the empirical formula. If it equals the total number of atoms given then the empirical formula is also the molecular formula. If not, then divide the total number of atoms given by the total number of atoms in the empirical formula. This should give a whole number. Multiply the number of atoms of each element in the empirical formula by this whole number to get the molecular formula. If you do not get a whole number when you divide, return to step 3 and revise how you multiplied and rounded to get whole numbers for each element.

Road Map

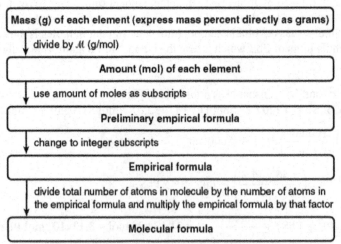

c) Yes, you can determine the molecular formula from the mass percent and the number of atoms of one element in a compound. <u>Plan:</u>
        1) Follow steps 1–3 in part b).
        2) Compare the number of atoms given for the one element to the number in the empirical formula. Determine the factor the number in the empirical formula must be multiplied by to obtain the given number of atoms for that element. Multiply the empirical formula by this number to get the molecular formula.

Road Map
(Same first three steps as in part (b).)

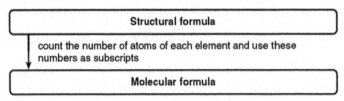

d) No, the mass % will only lead to the empirical formula.

e) Yes, a structural formula shows all the atoms in the compound. <u>Plan:</u> Count the number of atoms of each type of element and record as the number for the molecular formula.
Road Map

      Structural formula

      count the number of atoms of each element and use these
      numbers as subscripts

      Molecular formula

3.34   <u>Plan:</u> Examine the number of atoms of each type in the compound. Divide all atom numbers by the common factor that results in the lowest whole-number values. Add the molar masses of the atoms to obtain the empirical formula mass.
    <u>Solution:</u>
    a) C_2H_4 has a ratio of 2 carbon atoms to 4 hydrogen atoms, or 2:4. This ratio can be reduced to 1:2, so that the empirical formula is CH_2. The empirical formula mass is 12.01 g/mol C + 2(1.008 g/mol H) = **14.03 g/mol**.
    b) The ratio of atoms is 2:6:2, or 1:3:1. The empirical formula is CH_3O and its empirical formula mass is 12.01 g/mol C + 3(1.008 g/mol H) + 16.00 g/mol O = **31.03 g/mol**.

c) Since, the ratio of elements cannot be further reduced, the molecular formula and empirical formula are the same, N_2O_5. The formula mass is 2(14.01 g/mol N) + 5(16.00 g/mol O) = **108.02 g/mol**.
d) The ratio of elements is 3 atoms of barium to 2 atoms of phosphorus to 8 atoms of oxygen, or 3:2:8. This ratio cannot be further reduced, so the empirical formula is also **$Ba_3(PO_4)_2$**, with a formula mass of 3(137.3 g/mol Ba) + 2(30.97 g/mol P) + 8(16.00 g/mol O) = **601.8 g/mol**.
e) The ratio of atoms is 4:16, or 1:4. The empirical formula is **TeI_4**, and the formula mass is 127.6 g/mol Te + 4(126.9 g/mol I) = **635.2 g/mol**.

3.36   Plan: Use the chemical symbols and count the atoms of each type to obtain the molecular formula. Divide the molecular formula by the largest common factor to give the empirical formula. Use nomenclature rules to derive the name. This compound is composed of two nonmetals. The naming rules for binary covalent compounds indicate that the element with the lower group number is named first. Greek numerical prefixes are used to indicate the number of atoms of each element in the compound. The molecular (formula) mass is the sum of the atomic masses of all of the atoms.
Solution:
The compound has 2 sulfur atoms and 2 chlorine atoms and a molecular formula of S_2Cl_2. The compound's name is **disulfur dichloride**. Sulfur is named first since it has the lower group number. The prefix di- is used for both elements since there are 2 atoms of each element. The empirical formula is $S_{\frac{2}{2}}Cl_{\frac{2}{2}}$ or **SCl**.

$\mathcal{M}$ of S_2Cl_2 = (2 • $\mathcal{M}$ of S) + (2 • $\mathcal{M}$ of Cl) = (2 •32.07 g/mol S) + (2 •35.45 g/mol Cl) = **135.04 g/mol**

3.38   Plan: Determine the molar mass of each empirical formula. The subscripts in the molecular formula are whole-number multiples of the subscripts in the empirical formula. To find this whole number, divide the molar mass of the compound by its empirical formula mass. Multiply each subscript in the empirical formula by the whole number.
Solution:
Only approximate whole-number values are needed.
a) CH_2 has empirical mass equal to 12.01 g/mol C + 2(1.008 g/mol C) = 14.03 g/mol

$$\text{Whole-number multiple} = \frac{\text{molar mass of compound}}{\text{empirical formula mass}} = \left(\frac{42.08 \text{ g/mol}}{14.03 \text{ g/mol}} \right) = 3$$

Multiplying the subscripts in CH_2 by 3 gives **C_3H_6**.

b) NH_2 has empirical mass equal to 14.01 g/mol N + 2(1.008 g/mol H) = 16.03 g/mol

$$\text{Whole-number multiple} = \frac{\text{molar mass of compound}}{\text{empirical formula mass}} = \left(\frac{32.05 \text{ g/mol}}{16.03 \text{ g/mol}} \right) = 2$$

Multiplying the subscripts in NH_2 by 2 gives **N_2H_4**.
c) NO_2 has empirical mass equal to 14.01 g/mol N + 2(16.00 g/mol O) = 46.01 g/mol

$$\text{Whole-number multiple} = \frac{\text{molar mass of compound}}{\text{empirical formula mass}} = \left(\frac{92.02 \text{ g/mol}}{46.01 \text{ g/mol}} \right) = 2$$

Multiplying the subscripts in NO_2 by 2 gives **N_2O_4**.
d) CHN has empirical mass equal to 12.01 g/mol C + 1.008 g/mol H + 14.01 g/mol N = 27.03 g/mol

$$\text{Whole-number multiple} = \frac{\text{molar mass of compound}}{\text{empirical formula mass}} = \left(\frac{135.14 \text{ g/mol}}{27.03 \text{ g/mol}} \right) = 5$$

Multiplying the subscripts in CHN by 5 gives **$C_5H_5N_5$**.

3.40   Plan: The empirical formula is the smallest whole-number ratio of the atoms or moles in a formula. All data must be converted to amount (mol) of an element by dividing mass by the molar mass. Divide each mole number by the smallest mole number to convert the mole ratios to whole numbers.
Solution:
a) 0.063 mol Cl and 0.22 mol O: preliminary formula is $Cl_{0.063}O_{0.22}$
Converting to integer subscripts (dividing all by the smallest subscript):

$$Cl_{\underset{0.063}{0.063}}O_{\underset{0.063}{0.22}} \rightarrow Cl_1O_{3.5}$$

The formula is $Cl_1O_{3.5}$, which in whole numbers (x 2) is **Cl_2O_7**.

b) Find amount (mol) of elements by dividing by molar mass:

$$\text{Amount (mol) of Si} = (2.45 \text{ g Si})\left(\frac{1 \text{ mol Si}}{28.09 \text{ g Si}}\right) = 0.08722 \text{ mol Si}$$

$$\text{Amount (mol) of Cl} = (12.4 \text{ g Cl})\left(\frac{1 \text{ mol Cl}}{35.45 \text{ g Cl}}\right) = 0.349788 \text{ mol Cl}$$

Preliminary formula is $Si_{0.08722}Cl_{0.349788}$

Converting to integer subscripts (dividing all by the smallest subscript):

$$Si_{\underset{0.08722}{0.08722}}Cl_{\underset{0.349788}{0.349788}} \rightarrow Si_1Cl_4$$

The empirical formula is **$SiCl_4$**.

c) Assume a 100 g sample and convert the masses to amount (mol) by dividing by the molar mass:

$$\text{Amount (mol) of C} = (100 \text{ g})\left(\frac{27.3 \text{ parts C by mass}}{100 \text{ parts by mass}}\right)\left(\frac{1 \text{ mol C}}{12.01 \text{ g C}}\right) = 2.2731 \text{ mol C}$$

$$\text{Amount (mol) of O} = (100 \text{ g})\left(\frac{72.7 \text{ parts O by mass}}{100 \text{ parts by mass}}\right)\left(\frac{1 \text{ mol O}}{16.00 \text{ g O}}\right) = 4.5438 \text{ mol O}$$

Preliminary formula is $C_{2.2731}O_{4.5438}$

Converting to integer subscripts (dividing all by the smallest subscript):

$$C_{\underset{2.2731}{2.2731}}O_{\underset{2.2731}{4.5438}} \rightarrow C_1O_2$$

The empirical formula is **CO_2**.

3.42   Plan: The percent oxygen is 100% minus the percent nitrogen. Assume 100 grams of sample, and then the amount (mol) of each element may be found by dividing the mass of each element by its molar mass. Divide each of the moles by the smaller value, and convert to whole numbers to get the empirical formula. The subscripts in the molecular formula are whole-number multiples of the subscripts in the empirical formula. To find this whole number, divide the molar mass of the compound by its empirical formula mass. Multiply each subscript in the empirical formula by the whole number.

Solution:

a) % O = 100% − % N = 100% − 30.45% N = 69.55% O

Assume a 100 g sample and convert the masses to moles by dividing by the molar mass:

$$\text{Amount (mol) of N} = (100 \text{ g})\left(\frac{30.45 \text{ parts N by mass}}{100 \text{ parts by mass}}\right)\left(\frac{1 \text{ mol N}}{14.01 \text{ g N}}\right) = 2.1734 \text{ mol N}$$

$$\text{Amount (mol) of O} = (100 \text{ g})\left(\frac{69.55 \text{ parts O by mass}}{100 \text{ parts by mass}}\right)\left(\frac{1 \text{ mol O}}{16.00 \text{ g O}}\right) = 4.3469 \text{ mol O}$$

Preliminary formula is $N_{2.1734}O_{4.3469}$

Converting to integer subscripts (dividing all by the smallest subscript):

$$N_{\underset{2.1734}{2.1734}}O_{\underset{2.1734}{4.3469}} \rightarrow N_1O_2$$

The empirical formula is **NO_2**.

b) Formula mass of empirical formula = 14.01 g/mol N + 2(16.00 g/mol O) = 46.01 g/mol

$$\text{Whole-number multiple} = \frac{\text{molar mass of compound}}{\text{empirical formula mass}} = \left(\frac{90 \text{ g/mol}}{46.01 \text{ g/mol}}\right) = 2$$

Multiplying the subscripts in NO_2 by 2 gives **N_2O_4** as the molecular formula.

Note: Only an approximate value of the molar mass is needed.

3.44   Plan: The amount (mol) of the metal is known, and the amount (mol) of fluorine atoms may be found in part a) from the M:F mole ratio in the compound formula. In part b), convert amount (mol) of F atoms to mass and subtract the mass of F from the mass of MF_2 to find the mass of M. In part c), divide the mass of M by amount (mol) of M to determine the molar mass of M which can be used to identify the element.
Solution:
a) Determine the amount (mol) of fluorine.

$$\text{Amount (mol) of F} = (0.600 \text{ mol M})\left(\frac{2 \text{ mol F}}{1 \text{ mol M}}\right) = \mathbf{1.20 \ mol \ F}$$

b) Determine the mass of M.

$$\text{Mass of F} = (1.20 \text{ mol F})\left(\frac{19.00 \text{ g F}}{1 \text{ mol F}}\right) = 22.8 \text{ g F}$$

$$\text{Mass (g) of M} = MF_2(g) - F(g) = 46.8 \text{ g} - 22.8 \text{ g} = \mathbf{24.0 \ g \ M}$$

c) The molar mass is needed to identify the element.

$$\text{Molar mass of M} = \frac{24.0 \text{ g M}}{0.600 \text{ mol M}} = 40.0 \text{ g/mol}$$

The metal with the closest molar mass to 40.0 g/mol is **calcium**.

3.47   Plan: The empirical formula is the smallest whole-number ratio of the atoms or moles in a formula. Assume 100 grams of cortisol so the percentages are numerically equivalent to the masses of each element. Convert each of the masses to moles by dividing by the molar mass of each element involved. Divide each mole number by the smallest mole number to convert the mole ratios to whole numbers. The subscripts in the molecular formula are whole-number multiples of the subscripts in the empirical formula. To find this whole number, divide the molar mass of the compound by its empirical formula mass. Multiply each subscript in the empirical formula by the whole number.
Solution:

$$\text{Amount (mol) of C} = (69.6 \text{ g C})\left(\frac{1 \text{ mol C}}{12.01 \text{ g C}}\right) = 5.7952 \text{ mol C}$$

$$\text{Amount (mol) of H} = (8.34 \text{ g H})\left(\frac{1 \text{ mol H}}{1.008 \text{ g H}}\right) = 8.2738 \text{ mol H}$$

$$\text{Amount (mol) of O} = (22.1 \text{ g O})\left(\frac{1 \text{ mol O}}{16.00 \text{ g O}}\right) = 1.38125 \text{ mol O}$$

Preliminary formula is $C_{5.7952}H_{8.2738}O_{1.38125}$
Converting to integer subscripts (dividing all by the smallest subscript):

$$C_{\frac{5.7952}{1.38125}} H_{\frac{8.2738}{1.38125}} O_{\frac{1.38125}{1.38125}} \rightarrow C_{4.2}H_6O_1$$

The carbon value is not close enough to a whole number to round the value. The smallest number that 4.20 may be multiplied by to get close to a whole number is 5. (You may wish to prove this to yourself.) All three ratios need to be multiplied by five: $5(C_{4.2}H_6O_1) = C_{21}H_{30}O_5$.
The empirical formula mass is = 21(12.01 g/mol C) + 30(1.008 g/mol H) + 5(16.00 g/mol O) = 362.45 g/mol

$$\text{Whole-number multiple} = \frac{\text{molar mass of compound}}{\text{empirical formula mass}} = \left(\frac{362.47 \text{ g/mol}}{362.45 \text{ g/mol}}\right) = 1$$

The empirical formula mass and the molar mass given are the same, so the empirical and the molecular formulas are the same. The molecular formula is **$C_{21}H_{30}O_5$**.

3.49   Plan: In combustion analysis, finding the amount (mol) of carbon and hydrogen is relatively simple because all of the carbon present in the sample is found in the carbon of CO_2, and all of the hydrogen present in the sample is found in the hydrogen of H_2O. Convert the mass of CO_2 to moles and use the ratio between CO_2 and C to find the amount (mol) and mass of C present. Do the same to find the amount (mol) and mass of H from H_2O. The amount (mol) of oxygen are more difficult to find, because additional O_2 was added to cause the combustion reaction. Subtracting the masses of C and H from the mass of the sample gives the mass of O. Convert the mass

of O to moles of O. Take the moles of C, H, and O and divide by the smallest value to convert to whole numbers to get the empirical formula. Determine the empirical formula mass and compare it to the molar mass given in the problem to see how the empirical and molecular formulas are related. Finally, determine the molecular formula.
Solution:

$$\text{Amount (mol) of C} = \left(0.449 \text{ g CO}_2\right)\left(\frac{1 \text{ mol CO}_2}{44.01 \text{ g CO}_2}\right)\left(\frac{1 \text{ mol C}}{1 \text{ mol CO}_2}\right) = 0.010202 \text{ mol C}$$

$$\text{Mass (g) of C} = \left(0.010202 \text{ mol C}\right)\left(\frac{12.01 \text{ g C}}{1 \text{ mol C}}\right) = 0.122526 \text{ g C}$$

$$\text{Amount (mol) of H} = \left(0.184 \text{ g H}_2\text{O}\right)\left(\frac{1 \text{ mol H}_2\text{O}}{18.02 \text{ g H}_2\text{O}}\right)\left(\frac{2 \text{ mol H}}{1 \text{ mol H}_2\text{O}}\right) = 0.020422 \text{ mol H}$$

$$\text{Mass (g) of H} = \left(0.020422 \text{ mol H}\right)\left(\frac{1.008 \text{ g H}}{1 \text{ mol H}}\right) = 0.020585 \text{ g H}$$

$$\text{Mass (g) of O} = \text{Sample mass} - (\text{mass of C} + \text{mass of H})$$
$$= 0.1595 \text{ g} - (0.122526 \text{ g C} + 0.020585 \text{ g H}) = 0.016389 \text{ g O}$$

$$\text{Amount (mol) of O} = \left(0.016389 \text{ g O}\right)\left(\frac{1 \text{ mol O}}{16.00 \text{ g O}}\right) = 0.0010243 \text{ mol O}$$

Preliminary formula = $C_{0.010202}H_{0.020422}O_{0.0010243}$
Converting to integer subscripts (dividing all by the smallest subscript):

$$C_{\frac{0.010202}{0.0010243}} H_{\frac{0.020422}{0.0010243}} O_{\frac{0.0010243}{0.0010243}} \rightarrow C_{10}H_{20}O_1$$

Empirical formula = $C_{10}H_{20}O$
Empirical formula mass = 10(12.01 g/mol C) + 20(1.008 g/mol H) + 1(16.00 g/mol O) = 156.26 g/mol
The empirical formula mass is the same as the given molar mass so the empirical and molecular formulas are the same. The molecular formula is **$C_{10}H_{20}O$**.

3.50   A balanced chemical equation describes:
1) The identities of the reactants and products.
2) The molar (and molecular) ratios by which reactants form products.
3) The physical states of all substances in the reaction.

3.53   Plan: Examine the diagram and label each formula. We will use A for red atoms and B for green atoms.
Solution:
The reaction shows A_2 and B_2 diatomic molecules forming AB molecules. Equal numbers of A_2 and B_2 combine to give twice as many molecules of AB. Thus, the reaction is $A_2 + B_2 \rightarrow 2$ AB. This is the balanced equation in **b**.

3.54   Plan: Balancing is a trial-and-error procedure. Balance one element at a time, placing coefficients where needed to have the same number of atoms of a particular element on each side of the equation. The smallest whole-number coefficients should be used.
Solution:
a) __Cu(s) + __ S$_8$(s) → __Cu$_2$S(s)
Balance the S first, because there is an obvious deficiency of S on the right side of the equation. The 8 S atoms in S$_8$ require the coefficient 8 in front of Cu$_2$S:
__Cu(s) + __S$_8$(s) → 8Cu$_2$S(s)
Then balance the Cu. The 16 Cu atoms in Cu$_2$S require the coefficient 16 in front of Cu:
16Cu(s) + S$_8$(s) → 8Cu$_2$S(s)
b) __P$_4$O$_{10}$(s) + __H$_2$O(l) → __H$_3$PO$_4$(l)
Balance the P first, because there is an obvious deficiency of P on the right side of the equation. The 4 P atoms in P$_4$O$_{10}$ require a coefficient of 4 in front of H$_3$PO$_4$:
___P$_4$O$_{10}$(s) + __H$_2$O(l) → 4H$_3$PO$_4$(l)
Balance the H next, because H is present in only one reactant and only one product. The 12 H atoms in 4H$_3$PO$_4$ on the right require a coefficient of 6 in front of H$_2$O:

___ $P_4O_{10}(s) + \underline{6}H_2O(l) \rightarrow \underline{4}H_3PO_4(l)$

Balance the O last, because it appears in both reactants and is harder to balance. There are 16 O atoms on each side:

$P_4O_{10}(s) + 6H_2O(l) \rightarrow 4H_3PO_4(l)$

c) __$B_2O_3(s)$ + __ $NaOH(aq) \rightarrow$ __$Na_3BO_3(aq)$ + __$H_2O(l)$

Balance oxygen last because it is present in more than one place on each side of the reaction. The 2 B atoms in B_2O_3 on the left require a coefficient of 2 in front of Na_3BO_3 on the right:

__$B_2O_3(s)$ + __$NaOH(aq) \rightarrow \underline{2}Na_3BO_3(aq)$ + __$H_2O(l)$

The 6 Na atoms in $2Na_3BO_3$ on the right require a coefficient of 6 in front of NaOH on the left:

__$B_2O_3(s)$ + $\underline{6}NaOH(aq) \rightarrow \underline{2}Na_3BO_3(aq)$ + __$H_2O(l)$

The 6 H atoms in 6NaOH on the left require a coefficent of 3 in front of H_2O on the right:

__$B_2O_3(s)$ + $\underline{6}NaOH(aq) \rightarrow \underline{2}Na_3BO_3(aq)$ + $\underline{3}H_2O(l)$

The oxygen is now balanced with 9 O atoms on each side:

$B_2O_3(s) + 6NaOH(aq) \rightarrow 2Na_3BO_3(aq) + 3H_2O(l)$

d) __$CH_3NH_2(g)$ + __$O_2(g) \rightarrow$ __$CO_2(g)$ + __$H_2O(g)$ + __$N_2(g)$

There are 2 N atoms on the right in N_2 so a coefficient of 2 is required in front of CH_3NH_2 on the left:

$\underline{2}CH_3NH_2(g)$ + __$O_2(g) \rightarrow$ __$CO_2(g)$ + __$H_2O(g)$ + __$N_2(g)$

There are now 10 H atoms in $2CH_3NH_2$ on the left so a coefficient of 5 is required in front of H_2O on the right:

$\underline{2}CH_3NH_2(g)$ + __$O_2(g) \rightarrow$ __$CO_2(g)$ + $\underline{5}H_2O(g)$ + __$N_2(g)$

The 2 C atoms on the left require a coefficient of 2 in front of CO_2 on the right:

$\underline{2}CH_3NH_2(g)$ + __$O_2(g) \rightarrow \underline{2}CO_2(g)$ + $\underline{5}H_2O(g)$ + __$N_2(g)$

The 9 O atoms on the right (4 O atoms in $2CO_2$ plus 5 in $5H_2O$) require a coefficient of 9/2 in front of O_2 on the left:

$\underline{2}CH_3NH_2(g)$ + $\underline{9/2}O_2(g) \rightarrow \underline{2}CO_2(g)$ + $\underline{5}H_2O(g)$ + __$N_2(g)$

Multiply all coefficients by 2 to obtain whole numbers:

$4CH_3NH_2(g) + 9O_2(g) \rightarrow 4CO_2(g) + 10H_2O(g) + 2N_2(g)$

3.56   <u>Plan:</u> Balancing is a trial-and-error procedure. Balance one element at a time, placing coefficients where needed to have the same number of atoms of a particular element on each side of the equation. The smallest whole-number coefficients should be used.

<u>Solution:</u>

a) __$SO_2(g)$ + __$O_2(g) \rightarrow$ __$SO_3(g)$

There are 4 O atoms on the left and 3 O atoms on the right. Since there is an odd number of O atoms on the right, place a coefficient of 2 in front of SO_3 for an even number of 6 O atoms on the right:

__$SO_2(g)$ + __$O_2(g) \rightarrow \underline{2}SO_3(g)$

Since there are now 2 S atoms on the right, place a coefficient of 2 in front of SO_2 on the left. There are now 6 O atoms on each side:

$2SO_2(g) + O_2(g) \rightarrow 2SO_3(g)$

b) __$Sc_2O_3(s)$ + __$H_2O(l) \rightarrow$ __ $Sc(OH)_3(s)$

The 2 Sc atoms on the left require a coefficient of 2 in front of $Sc(OH)_3$ on the right:

__$Sc_2O_3(s)$ + __$H_2O(l) \rightarrow \underline{2}Sc(OH)_3(s)$

The 6 H atoms in $2Sc(OH)_3$ on the right require a coefficient of 3 in front of H_2O on the left. There are now 6 O atoms on each side:

$Sc_2O_3(s) + 3H_2O(l) \rightarrow 2Sc(OH)_3(s)$

c) __$H_3PO_4(aq)$ + __$NaOH(aq) \rightarrow$ __$Na_2HPO_4(aq)$ + __$H_2O(l)$

The 2 Na atoms in Na_2HPO_4 on the right require a coefficient of 2 in front of NaOH on the left:

__$H_3PO_4(aq)$ + $\underline{2}NaOH(aq) \rightarrow$ __$Na_2HPO_4(aq)$ + __$H_2O(l)$

There are 6 O atoms on the right (4 in H_3PO_4 and 2 in 2NaOH); there are 4 O atoms in Na_2HPO_4 on the right so a coefficient of 2 in front of H_2O will result in 6 O atoms on the right:

__$H_3PO_4(aq)$ + $\underline{2}NaOH(aq) \rightarrow$ __$Na_2HPO_4(aq)$ + $\underline{2}H_2O(l)$

Now there are 4 H atoms on each side:

$H_3PO_4(aq) + 2NaOH(aq) \rightarrow Na_2HPO_4(aq) + 2H_2O(l)$

d) __$C_6H_{10}O_5(s)$ + __$O_2(g) \rightarrow$ __$CO_2(g)$ + __$H_2O(g)$

The 6 C atoms in $C_6H_{10}O_5$ on the left require a coefficient of 6 in front of CO_2 on the right:

$\_\_C_6H_{10}O_5(s) + \_\_O_2(g) \rightarrow \underline{6}CO_2(g) + \_\_H_2O(g)$

The 10 H atoms in $C_6H_{10}O_5$ on the left require a coefficient of 5 in front of H_2O on the right:

$\_\_C_6H_{10}O_5(s) + \_\_O_2(g) \rightarrow \underline{6}CO_2(g) + \underline{5}H_2O(g)$

There are 17 O atoms on the right (12 in $6CO_2$ and 5 in $5H_2O$); there are 5 O atoms in $C_6H_{10}O_5$ so a coefficient of 6 in front of O_2 will bring the total of O atoms on the left to 17:

$$C_6H_{10}O_5(s) + 6O_2(g) \rightarrow 6CO_2(g) + 5H_2O(g)$$

3.57   Plan: Balancing is a trial-and-error procedure. Balance one element at a time, placing coefficients where needed to have the same number of atoms of a particular element on each side of the equation. The smallest whole-number coefficients should be used.

Solution:

a) $\_\_As_4S_6(s) + \_\_O_2(g) \rightarrow \_\_As_4O_6(s) + \_\_SO_2(g)$

The 6 S atoms in As_4S_6 on the left require a coefficient of 6 in front of SO_2 on the right:

$\_\_As_4S_6(s) + \_\_O_2(g) \rightarrow \_\_As_4O_6(s) + \underline{6}SO_2(g)$

The 18 O atoms on the right (6 in As_4O_6 and 12 in $6SO_2$) require a coefficient of 9 in front of O_2 on the left:

$\_\_As_4S_6(s) + \underline{9}O_2(g) \rightarrow \_\_As_4O_6(s) + \underline{6}SO_2(g)$

There are 4 As atoms on each side:

$$As_4S_6(s) + 9O_2(g) \rightarrow As_4O_6(s) + 6SO_2(g)$$

b) $\_\_Ca_3(PO_4)_2(s) + \_\_SiO_2(s) + \_\_C(s) \rightarrow \_\_P_4(g) + \_\_CaSiO_3(l) + \_\_CO(g)$

The 4 P atoms in P_4 require a coefficient of 2 in front of $Ca_3(PO_4)_2$ on the left:

$\underline{2}Ca_3(PO_4)_2(s) + \_\_SiO_2(s) + \_\_C(s) \rightarrow \_\_P_4(g) + \_\_CaSiO_3(l) + \_\_CO(g)$

The 6 Ca atoms in $2Ca_3(PO_4)_2$ on the left require a coefficient of 6 in front of $CaSiO_3$ on the right:

$\underline{2}Ca_3(PO_4)_2(s) + \_\_SiO_2(s) + \_\_C(s) \rightarrow \_\_P_4(g) + \underline{6}CaSiO_3(l) + \_\_CO(g)$

The 6 Si atoms in $6CaSiO_3$ on the right require a coefficient of 6 in front of SiO_2 on the left:

$\underline{2}Ca_3(PO_4)_2(s) + \underline{6}SiO_2(s) + \_\_C(s) \rightarrow \_\_P_4(g) + \underline{6}CaSiO_3(l) + \_\_CO(g)$

There are 28 O atoms on the left (16 in $2Ca_3(PO_4)_2$ and 12 in $6SiO_2$); there are 18 O atoms on the right in $6CaSiO_3$ so a coefficient of 10 in front of CO on the right will bring the total O atoms to 18 on the right:

$\underline{2}Ca_3(PO_4)_2(s) + \underline{6}SiO_2(s) + \_\_C(s) \rightarrow \_\_P_4(g) + \underline{6}CaSiO_3(l) + \underline{10}CO(g)$

The 10 C atoms in 10CO on the right require a coefficient of 10 in front of C on the left:

$$2Ca_3(PO_4)_2(s) + 6SiO_2(s) + 10C(s) \rightarrow P_4(g) + 6CaSiO_3(l) + 10CO(g)$$

c) $\_\_Fe(s) + \_\_H_2O(g) \rightarrow \_\_Fe_3O_4(s) + \_\_H_2(g)$

The 3 Fe atoms in Fe_3O_4 on the right require a coefficient of 3 in front of Fe on the left:

$\underline{3}Fe(s) + \_\_H_2O(g) \rightarrow \_\_Fe_3O_4(s) + \_\_H_2(g)$

The 4 O atoms in Fe_3O_4 on the right require a coefficient of 4 in front of H_2O on the left:

$\underline{3}Fe(s) + \underline{4}H_2O(g) \rightarrow \_\_Fe_3O_4(s) + \_\_H_2(g)$

The 8 H atoms on the left in $4H_2O$ require a coefficient of 4 in front of H_2 on the right:

$$3Fe(s) + 4H_2O(g) \rightarrow Fe_3O_4(s) + 4H_2(g)$$

d) $\_\_S_2Cl_2(l) + \_\_NH_3(g) \rightarrow \_\_S_4N_4(s) + \_\_S_8(s) + \_\_NH_4Cl(s)$

The 12 S atoms on the right (4 in S_4N_4 and 8 in S_8) require a coefficient of 6 in front of S_2Cl_2 on the left:

$\underline{6}S_2Cl_2(l) + \_\_NH_3(g) \rightarrow \_\_S_4N_4(s) + \_\_S_8(s) + \_\_NH_4Cl(s)$

The 12 Cl atoms in $6S_2Cl_2$ on the left require a coefficient of 12 in front of NH_4Cl on the right:

$\underline{6}S_2Cl_2(l) + \_\_NH_3(g) \rightarrow \_\_S_4N_4(s) + \_\_S_8(s) + \underline{12}NH_4Cl(s)$

The 16 N atoms on the right (4 in S_4N_4 and 12 in $12NH_4Cl$) require a coefficient of 16 in front of NH_3 on the left:

$$6S_2Cl_2(l) + 16NH_3(g) \rightarrow S_4N_4(s) + S_8(s) + 12NH_4Cl(s)$$

Note there are 48 H atoms on both sides, so the equation is balanced.

3.58   Plan: The names must first be converted to chemical formulas. Balancing is a trial-and-error procedure. Balance one element at a time, placing coefficients where needed to have the same number of atoms of a particular element on each side of the equation. The smallest whole-number coefficients should be used. Remember that oxygen is diatomic.

Solution:

a) Gallium (a solid) and oxygen (a gas) are reactants and solid gallium(III) oxide is the only product:

$\_\_Ga(s) + \_\_O_2(g) \rightarrow \_\_Ga_2O_3(s)$

A coefficient of 2 in front of Ga on the left is needed to balance the 2 Ga atoms in Ga_2O_3:

$\underline{2}Ga(s) + \_\_O_2(g) \rightarrow \_\_Ga_2O_3(s)$

The 3 O atoms in Ga_2O_3 on the right require a coefficient of 3/2 in front of O_2 on the left:

$\underline{2}Ga(s) + \underline{3/2}O_2(g) \rightarrow \_\_Ga_2O_3(s)$

Multiply all coefficients by 2 to obtain whole numbers:

$4Ga(s) + 3O_2(g) \rightarrow 2Ga_2O_3(s)$

b) Liquid hexane and oxygen gas are the reactants while carbon dioxide gas and gaseous water are the products:

$\_\_C_6H_{14}(l) + \_\_O_2(g) \rightarrow \_\_CO_2(g) + \_\_H_2O(g)$

The 6 C atoms in C_6H_{14} on the left require a coefficient of 6 in front of CO_2 on the right:

$\_\_C_6H_{14}(l) + \_\_O_2(g) \rightarrow \underline{6}CO_2(g) + \_\_H_2O(g)$

The 14 H atoms in C_6H_{14} on the left require a coefficient of 7 in front of H_2O on the right:

$\_\_C_6H_{14}(l) + \_\_O_2(g) \rightarrow \underline{6}CO_2(g) + \underline{7}H_2O(g)$

The 19 O atoms on the right (12 in $6CO_2$ and 7 in $7H_2O$) require a coefficient of 19/2 in front of O_2 on the left:

Multiply all coefficients by 2 to obtain whole numbers:

$2C_6H_{14}(l) + 19O_2(g) \rightarrow 12CO_2(g) + 14H_2O(g)$

c) Aqueous solutions of calcium chloride and sodium phosphate are the reactants; solid calcium phosphate and an aqueous solution of sodium chloride are the products:

$\_\_CaCl_2(aq) + \_\_Na_3PO_4(aq) \rightarrow \_\_Ca_3(PO_4)_2(s) + \_\_NaCl(aq)$

The 3 Ca atoms in $Ca_3(PO_4)_2$ on the right require a coefficient of 3 in front of $CaCl_2$ on the left:

$\underline{3}CaCl_2(aq) + \_\_Na_3PO_4(aq) \rightarrow \_\_Ca_3(PO_4)_2(s) + \_\_NaCl(aq)$

The 6 Cl atoms in $3CaCl_2$ on the left require a coefficient of 6 in front of NaCl on the right:

$\underline{3}CaCl_2(aq) + \_\_Na_3PO_4(aq) \rightarrow \_\_Ca_3(PO_4)_2(s) + \underline{6}NaCl(aq)$

The 6 Na atoms in 6NaCl on the right require a coefficient of 2 in front of Na_3PO_4 on the left:

$\underline{3}CaCl_2(aq) + \underline{2}Na_3PO_4(aq) \rightarrow \_\_Ca_3(PO_4)_2(s) + \underline{6}NaCl(aq)$

There are now 2 P atoms on each side:

$3CaCl_2(aq) + 2Na_3PO_4(aq) \rightarrow Ca_3(PO_4)_2(s) + 6NaCl(aq)$

3.64   Plan: First, write a balanced chemical equation. Since A is the limiting reagent (B is in excess), A is used to determine the amount of C formed, using the mole ratio between reactant A and product C.
Solution:
Plan: The balanced equation is aA + bB → cC. Divide the mass of A by its molar mass to obtain amount (mol) of A. Use the molar ratio from the balanced equation to find the amount (mol) of C. Multiply amount (mol) of C by its molar mass to obtain mass of C.

Road Map

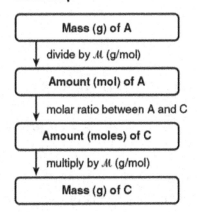

3.66   Plan: Always check to see if the initial equation is balanced. If the equation is not balanced, it should be balanced before proceeding. Use the mole ratio from the balanced chemical equation to determine the amount (mol) of Cl_2 produced. The equation shows that 1 mole of Cl_2 is produced for every 4 moles of HCl that react. Multiply the amount (mol) of Cl_2 produced by the molar mass to convert to mass in grams.
Solution:
$4HCl(aq) + MnO_2(s) \rightarrow MnCl_2(aq) + 2H_2O(g) + Cl_2(g)$

a) Amount (mol) of Cl_2 = $(1.82 \text{ mol HCl})\left(\dfrac{1 \text{ mol } Cl_2}{4 \text{ mol HCl}}\right)$ = **0.455 mol Cl_2**

b) Mass (g) of Cl_2 = $(0.455 \text{ mol } Cl_2)\left(\dfrac{70.90 \text{ g } Cl_2}{1 \text{ mol } Cl_2}\right)$ = 32.2595 g= **32.3 g Cl_2**

3.68   Plan: Convert the mass of oxygen from kilograms to grams and then convert mass (g) to amount (mol) of oxygen by dividing by its molar
mass. Use the amount (mol) of oxygen and the mole ratio from the balanced chemical equation to determine the amount (mol) of KNO_3 required. Multiply the amount (mol) of KNO_3 by its molar mass to obtain the mass in grams.
Solution:

a) Mass (g) of O_2 = $(56.6 \text{ kg } O_2)\left(\dfrac{10^3 \text{ g}}{1 \text{ kg}}\right)$ = 5.66×10^4 g O_2

Amount (mol) of O_2 = $(5.66\times10^4 \text{ g } O_2)\left(\dfrac{1 \text{ mol } O_2}{32.00 \text{ g } O_2}\right)$ = 1.76875×10^3 mol O_2

Amount (mol) of KNO_3 = $(1.76875 \text{ mol } O_2)\left(\dfrac{4 \text{ mol } KNO_3}{5 \text{ mol } O_2}\right)$ = 1415 mol= **1.42×10^3 mol KNO_3**

b) Mass (g) of KNO_3 = $(1415 \text{ mol } KNO_3)\left(\dfrac{101.11 \text{ g } KNO_3}{1 \text{ mol } KNO_3}\right)$ = 143070.65 g= **1.43×10^5 g KNO_3**

Combining all steps gives:

Mass (g) of KNO_3 = $(56.6 \text{ kg } O_2)\left(\dfrac{10^3 \text{ g}}{1 \text{ kg}}\right)\left(\dfrac{1 \text{ mol } O_2}{32.00 \text{ g } O_2}\right)\left(\dfrac{4 \text{ mol } KNO_3}{5 \text{ mol } O_2}\right)\left(\dfrac{101.11 \text{ g } KNO_3}{1 \text{ mol } KNO_3}\right)$

= 143070.65 g = **1.43×10^5 g KNO_3**

3.70   Plan: First, balance the equation. Convert the mass (g) of diborane to amount (mol) of diborane by dividing by its molar mass. Use mole ratios from the balanced chemical equation to determine the amount (mol) of the products. Multiply the mole amount of each product by its molar mass to obtain mass in grams.
Solution:
The balanced equation is: $B_2H_6(g) + 6H_2O(l) \rightarrow 2H_3BO_3(s) + 6H_2(g)$.

Amount (mol) of B_2H_6 = $(43.82 \text{ g } B_2H_6)\left(\dfrac{1 \text{ mol } B_2H_6}{27.67 \text{ g } B_2H_6}\right)$ = 1.583665 mol B_2H_6

Amount (mol) of H_3BO_3 = $(1.583665 \text{ mol } B_2H_6)\left(\dfrac{2 \text{ mol } H_3BO_3}{1 \text{ mol } B_2H_6}\right)$ = 3.16733 mol H_3BO_3

Mass (g) of H_3BO_3 = $(3.16733 \text{ mol } H_3BO_3)\left(\dfrac{61.83 \text{ g } H_3BO_3}{1 \text{ mol } H_3BO_3}\right)$ = 195.83597 g= **195.8 g H_3BO_3**

Combining all steps gives:

Mass (g) of H_3BO_3 = $(43.82 \text{ g } B_2H_6)\left(\dfrac{1 \text{ mol } B_2H_6}{27.67 \text{ g } B_2H_6}\right)\left(\dfrac{2 \text{ mol } H_3BO_3}{1 \text{ mol } B_2H_6}\right)\left(\dfrac{61.83 \text{ g } H_3BO_3}{1 \text{ mol } H_3BO_3}\right)$

= 195.83597 g= **195.8 g H_3BO_3**

Amount (mol) of H_2 = $(1.583665 \text{ mol } B_2H_6)\left(\dfrac{6 \text{ mol } H_2}{1 \text{ mol } B_2H_6}\right)$ = 9.50199 mol H_2

Mass (g) of H_2 = $(9.50199 \text{ mol } H_2)\left(\dfrac{2.016 \text{ g } H_2}{1 \text{ mol } H_2}\right)$ = 19.15901 g H_2 = **19.16 g H_2**

Combining all steps gives:

$$\text{Mass (g) of } H_2 = (43.82 \text{ g } B_2H_6)\left(\frac{1 \text{ mol } B_2H_6}{27.67 \text{ g } B_2H_6}\right)\left(\frac{6 \text{ mol } H_2}{1 \text{ mol } B_2H_6}\right)\left(\frac{2.016 \text{ g } H_2}{1 \text{ mol } H_2}\right) = 19.15601 \text{ g} = \mathbf{19.16 \text{ g } H_2}$$

3.72   Plan: Write the balanced equation by first writing the formulas for the reactants and products. Convert the mass of phosphorus to amount (mol) by dividing by the molar mass, use the mole ratio between phosphorus and chlorine from the balanced chemical equation to obtain amount (mol) of chlorine, and finally divide the amount (mol) of chlorine by its molar mass to obtain amount in grams.
Solution:
Reactants: formula for phosphorus is given as P_4 and formula for chlorine gas is Cl_2 (chlorine occurs as a diatomic molecule). Product: formula for phosphorus pentachloride (the name indicates one phosphorus atom and five chlorine atoms) is PCl_5.
Equation: $P_4 + Cl_2 \rightarrow PCl_5$
Balancing the equation: $P_4 + 10Cl_2 \rightarrow 4PCl_5$

$$\text{Amount (mol) of } P_4 = (455 \text{ g } P_4)\left(\frac{1 \text{ mol } P_4}{123.88 \text{ g } P_4}\right) = 3.67291 \text{ mol } P_4$$

$$\text{Amount (mol) of } Cl_2 = (3.67291 \text{ mol } P_4)\left(\frac{10 \text{ mol } Cl_2}{1 \text{ mol } P_4}\right) = 36.7291 \text{ mol } Cl_2$$

$$\text{Mass (g) of } Cl_2 = (36.7291 \text{ mol } Cl_2)\left(\frac{70.90 \text{ g } Cl_2}{1 \text{ mol } Cl_2}\right) = 2604.09 \text{ g} = \mathbf{2.60 \times 10^3 \text{ g } Cl_2}$$

Combining all steps gives:

$$\text{Mass (g) of } Cl_2 = (455 \text{ g } P_4)\left(\frac{1 \text{ mol } P_4}{123.88 \text{ g } P_4}\right)\left(\frac{10 \text{ mol } Cl_2}{1 \text{ mol } P_4}\right)\left(\frac{70.90 \text{ g } Cl_2}{1 \text{ mol } Cl_2}\right) = 2604.09267 \text{ g} = \mathbf{2.60 \times 10^3 \text{ g } Cl_2}$$

3.74   Plan: Begin by writing the chemical formulas of the reactants and products in each step. Next, balance each of the equations. Combine the equations for the separate steps by adjusting the equations so the intermediate (iodine monochloride) cancels. Finally, change the mass of product from kg to grams to amount (mol) by dividing by the molar mass and use the mole ratio between iodine and product to find the amount (mol) of iodine. Multiply amount (mol) by the molar mass of iodine to obtain mass of iodine.
Solution:
a) Step 1 $I_2(s) + Cl_2(g) \rightarrow 2ICl(s)$
    Step 2 $ICl(s) + Cl_2(g) \rightarrow ICl_3(s)$
b) Multiply the coefficients of the second equation by 2, so that $ICl(s)$, an intermediate product, can be eliminated from the overall equation.

$$I_2(s) + Cl_2(g) \longrightarrow 2ICl(s)$$

$$2ICl(s) + 2Cl_2(g) \longrightarrow 2ICl_3(s)$$

$I_2(s) + Cl_2(g) + \cancel{2ICl(s)} + 2Cl_2(g) \rightarrow \cancel{2ICl(s)} + 2ICl_3(s)$
Overall equation: $\mathbf{I_2(s) + 3Cl_2(g) \rightarrow 2ICl_3(s)}$

$$\text{c) Mass (g) of } ICl_3 = (2.45 \text{ kg } ICl_3)\left(\frac{10^3 \text{ g}}{1 \text{ kg}}\right) = 2450 \text{ g } ICl_3$$

$$\text{Amount (mol) of } ICl_3 = (2450 \text{ g } ICl_3)\left(\frac{1 \text{ mol } ICl_3}{233.2 \text{ g } ICl_3}\right) = 10.506 \text{ mol } ICl_3$$

$$\text{Amount (mol) of } I_2 = (10.506 \text{ mol } ICl_3)\left(\frac{1 \text{ mol } I_2}{2 \text{ mol } ICl_3}\right) = 5.253 \text{ mol } I_2$$

$$\text{Mass (g) of } I_2 = (5.253 \text{ mol } I_2)\left(\frac{253.8 \text{ g } I_2}{1 \text{ mol } I_2}\right) = 1333.211 \text{ g} = \mathbf{1.33 \times 10^3 \text{ g } I_2}$$

Combining all steps gives:

Mass (g) of $I_2 = (2.45 \text{ kg ICl}_3) \left(\dfrac{10^3 \text{ g}}{1 \text{ kg}} \right) \left(\dfrac{1 \text{ mol ICl}_3}{233.2 \text{ g ICl}_3} \right) \left(\dfrac{1 \text{ mol } I_2}{2 \text{ mol ICl}_3} \right) \left(\dfrac{253.8 \text{ g } I_2}{1 \text{ mol } I_2} \right) = 1333.211 \text{ g} = \mathbf{1.33 \times 10^3 \text{ g } I_2}$

3.76 <u>Plan:</u> Convert the given mass of each reactant to amount (mol) by dividing by the molar mass of that reactant. Use the mole ratio from the balanced chemical equation to find the amount (mol) of CaO formed from each reactant, assuming an excess of the other reactant. The reactant that produces fewer moles of CaO is the limiting reactant. Convert the amount (mol) of CaO obtained from the limiting reactant to grams using the molar mass.
<u>Solution:</u>
$2Ca(s) + O_2(g) \rightarrow 2CaO(s)$

a) Amount (mol) of Ca $= (4.20 \text{ g Ca}) \left(\dfrac{1 \text{ mol Ca}}{40.08 \text{ g Ca}} \right) = 0.104790 \text{ mol Ca}$

Amount (mol) of CaO from Ca $= (0.104790 \text{ mol Ca}) \left(\dfrac{2 \text{ mol CaO}}{2 \text{ mol Ca}} \right) = 0.104790 \text{ mol} = \mathbf{0.105 \text{ mol CaO}}$

b) Amount (mol) of $O_2 = (2.80 \text{ g } O_2) \left(\dfrac{1 \text{ mol } O_2}{32.00 \text{ g } O_2} \right) = 0.0875 \text{ mol } O_2$

Amount (mol) of CaO from $O_2 = (0.0875 \text{ mol } O_2) \left(\dfrac{2 \text{ mol CaO}}{1 \text{ mol } O_2} \right) = 0.17500 \text{ mol} = \mathbf{0.175 \text{ mol CaO}}$

c) **Calcium** is the limiting reactant since it will form less calcium oxide.
d) The mass of CaO formed is determined by the limiting reactant, Ca.

Mass (g) of CaO $= (0.104790 \text{ mol CaO}) \left(\dfrac{56.08 \text{ g CaO}}{1 \text{ mol CaO}} \right) = 5.8766 \text{ g} = \mathbf{5.88 \text{ g CaO}}$

Combining all steps gives:

Mass (g) of CaO $= (4.20 \text{ g Ca}) \left(\dfrac{1 \text{ mol Ca}}{40.08 \text{ g Ca}} \right) \left(\dfrac{2 \text{ mol CaO}}{2 \text{ mol Ca}} \right) \left(\dfrac{56.08 \text{ g CaO}}{1 \text{ mol CaO}} \right) = 5.8766 \text{ g} = \mathbf{5.88 \text{ g CaO}}$

3.78 <u>Plan:</u> First, balance the chemical equation. To determine which reactant is limiting, calculate the amount of HIO_3 formed from each reactant, assuming an excess of the other reactant. The reactant that produces less product is the limiting reagent. Use the limiting reagent and the mole ratio from the balanced chemical equation to determine the amount of HIO_3 formed and the amount of the excess reactant that reacts. The difference between the amount of excess reactant that reacts and the initial amount of reactant supplied gives the amount of excess reactant remaining.
<u>Solution:</u>
The balanced chemical equation for this reaction is:
   $2ICl_3(s) + 3H_2O\ (l) \rightarrow ICl(g) + HIO_3(aq) + 5HCl(g)$
Hint: Balance the equation by starting with oxygen. The other elements are in multiple reactants and/or products and are harder to balance initially.
Finding the amount (mol) of HIO_3 from the amount (mol) of ICl_3 (if H_2O is limiting):

Amount (mol) of $ICl_3 = (635 \text{ g ICl}_3) \left(\dfrac{1 \text{ mol ICl}_3}{233.2 \text{ g ICl}_3} \right) = 2.722985 \text{ mol ICl}_3$

Amount (mol) of HIO_3 from $ICl_3 = (2.722985 \text{ mol ICl}_3) \left(\dfrac{1 \text{ mol HIO}_3}{2 \text{ mol ICl}_3} \right) = 1.361492 \text{ mol} = 1.36 \text{ mol HIO}_3$

Finding the amount (mol) of HIO_3 from the amount (mol) of H_2O (if ICl_3 is limiting):

Amount (mol) of $H_2O = (118.5 \text{ g } H_2O) \left(\dfrac{1 \text{ mol } H_2O}{18.02 \text{ g } H_2O} \right) = 6.57603 \text{ mol } H_2O$

Amount (mol) HIO_3 from $H_2O = (6.57603 \text{ mol } H_2O) \left(\dfrac{1 \text{ mol HIO}_3}{3 \text{ mol } H_2O} \right) = 2.19201 \text{ mol} = 2.19 \text{ mol HIO}_3$

ICl_3 is the limiting reagent and will produce **1.36 mol HIO_3**.

$$\text{Mass (g) of } HIO_3 = \left(1.361492 \text{ mol } HIO_3\right)\left(\frac{175.9 \text{ g } HIO_3}{1 \text{ mol } HIO_3}\right) = 239.486 \text{ g} = \textbf{239 g } HIO_3$$

Combining all steps gives:

$$\text{Mass (g) of } HIO_3 = \left(635 \text{ g } ICl_3\right)\left(\frac{1 \text{ mol } ICl_3}{233.2 \text{ g } ICl_3}\right)\left(\frac{1 \text{ mol } HIO_3}{2 \text{ mol } ICl_3}\right)\left(\frac{175.9 \text{ g } HIO_3}{1 \text{ mol } HIO_3}\right) = 239.486 \text{ g} = \textbf{239 g } HIO_3$$

The remaining mass of the excess reagent can be calculated from the amount of H_2O combining with the limiting reagent.

$$\text{Amount (mol) of } H_2O \text{ required to react with 635 g } ICl_3 = \left(2.722985 \text{ mol } ICl_3\right)\left(\frac{3 \text{ mol } H_2O}{2 \text{ mol } ICl_3}\right)$$

$$= 4.0844775 \text{ mol } H_2O$$

$$\text{Mass (g) of } H_2O \text{ required to react with 635 g } ICl_3 = \left(4.0844775 \text{ mol } H_2O\right)\left(\frac{18.02 \text{ g } H_2O}{1 \text{ mol } H_2O}\right)$$

$$= 73.6023 \text{ g} = 73.6 \text{ g } H_2O \text{ reacted}$$

Mass (g) of remaining H_2O = 118.5 g – 73.6 g = **44.9 g H_2O**

3.80 Plan: Write the balanced equation; the formula for carbon is C, the formula for oxygen is O_2, and the formula for carbon dioxide is CO_2. To determine which reactant is limiting, calculate the amount of CO_2 formed from each reactant, assuming an excess of the other reactant. The reactant that produces less product is the limiting reagent. Use the limiting reagent and the mole ratio from the balanced chemical equation to determine the amount of CO_2 formed and the amount of the excess reactant that reacts. The difference between the amount of excess reactant that reacts and the initial amount of reactant supplied gives the amount of excess reactant remaining.
Solution:
The balanced equation is: $C(s) + O_2(g) \rightarrow CO_2(g)$
Finding the amount (mol) of CO_2 from the amount (mol) of carbon (if O_2 is limiting):

$$\text{Amount (mol) of } CO_2 \text{ from C} = \left(0.100 \text{ mol C}\right)\left(\frac{1 \text{ mol } CO_2}{1 \text{ mol C}}\right) = 0.100 \text{ mol } CO_2$$

Finding the amount (mol) of CO_2 from the amount (mol) of oxygen (if C is limiting):

$$\text{Amount (mol) of } O_2 = \left(8.00 \text{ g } O_2\right)\left(\frac{1 \text{ mol } O_2}{32.00 \text{ g } O_2}\right) = 0.250 \text{ mol } O_2$$

$$\text{Amount (mol) of } CO_2 \text{ from } O_2 = \left(0.250 \text{ mol } O_2\right)\left(\frac{1 \text{ mol } CO_2}{1 \text{ mol } O_2}\right) = 0.25000 \text{ mol} = 0.250 \text{ mol } CO_2$$

Carbon is the limiting reactant and will be used to determine the amount of CO_2 that will form.

$$\text{Mass (g) of } CO_2 = \left(0.100 \text{ mol } CO_2\right)\left(\frac{44.01 \text{ g } CO_2}{1 \text{ mol } CO_2}\right) = 4.401 \text{ g} = \textbf{4.40 g } CO_2$$

Since carbon is limiting, the **O_2 is in excess**. The amount remaining depends on how much combines with the limiting reagent.

$$\text{Amount (mol) of } O_2 \text{ required to react with 0.100 mol of C} = \left(0.100 \text{ mol C}\right)\left(\frac{1 \text{ mol } O_2}{1 \text{ mol C}}\right) = 0.100 \text{ mol } O_2$$

$$\text{Mass (g) of } O_2 \text{ required to react with 0.100 mol of C} = \left(0.100 \text{ mol } O_2\right)\left(\frac{32.00 \text{ mol } O_2}{1 \text{ mol } O_2}\right) = 3.20 \text{ g } O_2$$

Mass (g) of remaining O_2 = 8.00 g – 3.20 g = **4.80 g O_2**

3.82   Plan: The question asks for the mass of each substance present at the end of the reaction. "Substance" refers to both reactants and products. Solve this problem using multiple steps. Recognizing that this is a limiting reactant problem, first write a balanced chemical equation. To determine which reactant is limiting, calculate the amount of any product formed from each reactant, assuming an excess of the other reactant. The reactant that produces less product is the limiting reagent. Any product can be used to predict the limiting reactant; in this case, $AlCl_3$ is used. Use the limiting reagent and the mole ratio from the balanced chemical equation to determine the amount of both products formed and the amount of the excess reactant that reacts. The difference between the amount of excess reactant that reacts and the initial amount of reactant supplied gives the amount of excess reactant remaining.

Solution:

The balanced chemical equation is:

$$Al(NO_2)_3(aq) + 3NH_4Cl(aq) \rightarrow AlCl_3(aq) + 3N_2(g) + 6H_2O(l)$$

Now determine the limiting reagent. We will use the amount (mol) of $AlCl_3$ produced to determine which is limiting.

Finding the amount (mol) of $AlCl_3$ from the amount (mol) of $Al(NO_2)_3$ (if NH_4Cl is limiting):

$$\text{Amount (mol) of } Al(NO_2)_3 = \left(72.5 \text{ g } Al(NO_2)_3\right)\left(\frac{1 \text{ mol } Al(NO_2)_3}{165.01 \text{ g } Al(NO_2)_3}\right) = 0.439367 \text{ mol } Al(NO_2)_3$$

$$\text{Amount (mol) of } AlCl_3 \text{ from } Al(NO_2)_3 = \left(0.439367 \text{ mol } Al(NO_2)_3\right)\left(\frac{1 \text{ mol } AlCl_3}{1 \text{ mol } Al(NO_2)_3}\right) = 0.439367 \text{ mol} = 0.439 \text{ mol } AlCl_3$$

Finding the amount (mol) of $AlCl_3$ from the amount (mol) of NH_4Cl (if $Al(NO_2)_3$ is limiting):

$$\text{Amount (mol) of } NH_4Cl = \left(58.6 \text{ g } NH_4Cl\right)\left(\frac{1 \text{ mol } NH_4Cl}{53.49 \text{ g } NH_4Cl}\right) = 1.09553 \text{ mol } NH_4Cl$$

$$\text{Amount (mol) of } AlCl_3 \text{ from } NH_4Cl = \left(1.09553 \text{ mol } NH_4Cl\right)\left(\frac{1 \text{ mol } AlCl_3}{3 \text{ mol } NH_4Cl}\right) = 0.365177 \text{ mol} = 0.365 \text{ mol } AlCl_3$$

Ammonium chloride is the limiting reactant, and it is used for all subsequent calculations.

Mass of substances after the reaction:

$Al(NO_2)_3$:

Mass (g) of $Al(NO_2)_3$ (the excess reactant) required to react with 58.6 g of NH_4Cl =

$$\left(1.09553 \text{ mol } NH_4Cl\right)\left(\frac{1 \text{ mol } Al(NO_2)_3}{3 \text{ mol } NH_4Cl}\right)\left(\frac{165.01 \text{ g } Al(NO_2)_3}{1 \text{ mol } Al(NO_2)_3}\right) = 60.2579 \text{ g} = 60.3 \text{ g } Al(NO_2)_3$$

$Al(NO_2)_3$ remaining: 72.5 g – 60.3 g = **12.2 g Al(NO₂)₃**

NH_4Cl: **None left** since it is the limiting reagent.

$AlCl_3$:

$$\text{Mass (g) of } AlCl_3 = \left(0.365177 \text{ mol } AlCl_3\right)\left(\frac{133.33 \text{ g } AlCl_3}{1 \text{ mol } AlCl_3}\right) = 48.689 \text{ g} = \mathbf{48.7 \text{ g } AlCl_3}$$

N_2:

$$\text{Mass (g) of } N_2 = \left(1.09553 \text{ mol } NH_4Cl\right)\left(\frac{3 \text{ mol } N_2}{3 \text{ mol } NH_4Cl}\right)\left(\frac{28.02 \text{ g } N_2}{1 \text{ mol } N_2}\right) = 30.697 \text{ g} = \mathbf{30.7 \text{ g } N_2}$$

H_2O:

$$\text{Mass (g) of } H_2O = \left(1.09553 \text{ mol } NH_4Cl\right)\left(\frac{6 \text{ mol } H_2O}{3 \text{ mol } NH_4Cl}\right)\left(\frac{18.02 \text{ g } H_2O}{1 \text{ mol } H_2O}\right) = 39.483 \text{ g} = \mathbf{39.5 \text{ g } H_2O}$$

3.84   Plan: Express the yield of each step as a fraction of 1.00; multiply the fraction of the first step by that of the second step and then multiply by 100 to get the overall percent yield.

Solution:

73% = 0.73; 68% = 0.68

(0.73 x 0.68) x 100% = 49.64% = **50.%**

3.86   Plan: Write and balance the chemical equation using the formulas of the substances. Determine the theoretical yield of the reaction from the mass of tungsten(VI) oxide. To do that, convert the mass of tungsten(VI) oxide to amount (mol) by dividing by its molar mass and then use the mole ratio between tungsten(VI) oxide and water to determine the amount (mol) and then mass of water that should be produced. Use the density of water to determine the actual yield of water in grams. The actual yield divided by the theoretical yield just calculated (with the result multiplied by 100%) gives the percent yield.
Solution:
The balanced chemical equation is:
$WO_3(s) + 3H_2(g) \rightarrow W(s) + 3H_2O(l)$
Determining the theoretical yield of H_2O:

Amount (mol) of $WO_3 = \left(45.5 \text{ g } WO_3\right)\left(\dfrac{1 \text{ mol } WO_3}{231.9 \text{ g } WO_3}\right) = 0.1962053 \text{ mol } WO_3$

Mass (g) of H_2O (theoretical yield) $= \left(0.1962053 \text{ mol } WO_3\right)\left(\dfrac{3 \text{ mol } H_2O}{1 \text{ mol } WO_3}\right)\left(\dfrac{18.02 \text{ g } H_2O}{1 \text{ mol } H_2O}\right) = 10.60686 \text{ g } H_2O$

Determining the actual yield of H_2O:

Mass (g) of H_2O (actual yield) $= \left(9.60 \text{ mL } H_2O\right)\left(\dfrac{1.00 \text{ g } H_2O}{1 \text{ mL } H_2O}\right) = 9.60 \text{ g } H_2O$

% yield $= \left(\dfrac{\text{actual Yield}}{\text{theoretical Yield}}\right) \times 100\% = \left(\dfrac{9.60 \text{ g } H_2O}{10.60686 \text{ g } H_2O}\right) \times 100\% = 90.5075\% = \mathbf{90.5\%}$

3.88   Plan: Write the balanced chemical equation. Since quantities of two reactants are given, we must determine which is the limiting reactant. To determine which reactant is limiting, calculate the amount of any product formed from each reactant, assuming an excess of the other reactant. The reactant that produces less product is the limiting reagent. Any product can be used to predict the limiting reactant; in this case, CH_3Cl is used. Only 75.0% of the calculated amounts of products actually form, so the actual yield is 75% of the theoretical yield.
Solution:
The balanced equation is: $CH_4(g) + Cl_2(g) \rightarrow CH_3Cl(g) + HCl(g)$
Determining the limiting reactant:
Finding the amount (mol) of CH_3Cl from the amount (mol) of CH_4 (if Cl_2 is limiting):

Amount (mol) of $CH_4 = \left(20.5 \text{ g } CH_4\right)\left(\dfrac{1 \text{ mol } CH_4}{16.04 \text{ g } CH_4}\right) = 1.278055 \text{ mol } CH_4$

Amount (mol) of CH_3Cl from $CH_4 = \left(1.278055 \text{ mol } CH_4\right)\left(\dfrac{1 \text{ mol } CH_3Cl}{1 \text{ mol } CH_4}\right) = 1.278055 \text{ mol } CH_3Cl$

Finding the amount (mol) of CH_3Cl from the amount (mol) of Cl_2 (if CH_4 is limiting):

Amount (mol) of $Cl_2 = \left(45.0 \text{ g } Cl_2\right)\left(\dfrac{1 \text{ mol } Cl_2}{70.90 \text{ g } Cl_2}\right) = 0.634697 \text{ mol } Cl_2$

Amount (mol) of CH_3Cl from $Cl_2 = \left(0.634697 \text{ mol } Cl_2\right)\left(\dfrac{1 \text{ mol } CH_3Cl}{1 \text{ mol } Cl_2}\right) = 0.634697 \text{ mol } CH_3Cl$

Chlorine is the limiting reactant and is used to determine the theoretical yield of CH_3Cl:

Mass (g) of CH_3Cl (theoretical yield) $= \left(0.634697 \text{ mol } CH_3Cl\right)\left(\dfrac{50.48 \text{ g } CH_3Cl}{1 \text{ mol } CH_3Cl}\right) = 32.0395 \text{ g } CH_3Cl$

% yield $= \left(\dfrac{\text{actual yield}}{\text{theoretical yield}}\right) \times 100\%$

Actual yield (g) of $CH_3Cl = \dfrac{\% \text{ yield}}{100\%}(\text{theoretical yield}) = \dfrac{75\%}{100\%}\left(32.0395 \text{ g } CH_3Cl\right)$
$= 24.02962 \text{ g} = \mathbf{24.0 \text{ g } CH_3Cl}$

3.90   <u>Plan:</u> Write the balanced equation; the formula for fluorine is F_2, the formula for carbon tetrafluoride is CF_4, and the formula for nitrogen trifluoride is NF_3. To determine which reactant is limiting, calculate the amount of CF_4 formed from each reactant, assuming an excess of the other reactant. The reactant that produces less product is the limiting reagent. Use the limiting reagent and the mole ratio from the balanced chemical equation to determine the mass of CF_4 formed.
<u>Solution:</u>
The balanced chemical equation is:
$(CN)_2(g) + 7F_2(g) \rightarrow 2CF_4(g) + 2NF_3(g)$
Determining the limiting reactant:
Finding the amount (mol) of CF_4 from the amount (mol) of $(CN)_2$ (if F_2 is limiting):

$$\text{Amount (mol) of } CF_4 \text{ from } (CN)_2 = \left(60.0 \text{ g } (CN)_2\right)\left(\frac{1 \text{ mol } (CN)_2}{52.04 \text{ g } (CN)_2}\right)\left(\frac{2 \text{ mol } CF_4}{1 \text{ mol } (CN)_2}\right) = 2.30592 \text{ mol } CF_4$$

Finding the amount (mol) of CF_4 from the amount (mol) of F_2 (if $(CN)_2$ is limiting):

$$\text{Amount (mol) of } CF_4 \text{ from } F_2 = \left(60.0 \text{ g } F_2\right)\left(\frac{1 \text{ mol } F_2}{38.00 \text{ g } F_2}\right)\left(\frac{2 \text{ mol } CF_4}{7 \text{ mol } F_2}\right) = 0.4511278 \text{ mol } CF_4$$

F_2 is the limiting reactant, and will be used to calculate the amount of CF_4 produced.

$$\text{Mass (g) of } CF_4 = \left(60.0 \text{ g } F_2\right)\left(\frac{1 \text{ mol } F_2}{38.00 \text{ g } F_2}\right)\left(\frac{2 \text{ mol } CF_4}{7 \text{ mol } F_2}\right)\left(\frac{88.01 \text{ g } CF_4}{1 \text{ mol } CF_4}\right) = 39.70376 \text{ g} = \mathbf{39.7 \text{ g } CF_4}$$

3.91   <u>Plan:</u> Write and balance the chemical reaction. Remember that both chlorine and oxygen exist as diatomic molecules. Use the mole ratio between oxygen and dichlorine monoxide to find the amount (mol) of dichlorine monoxide that reacted. Multiply the amount in moles by Avogadro's number to convert to number of molecules.
<u>Solution:</u>
a) Both oxygen and chlorine are diatomic. **Scene A** best represents the product mixture as there are O_2 and Cl_2 molecules in Scene A. Scene B shows oxygen and chlorine atoms and Scene C shows atoms and molecules. Oxygen and chlorine atoms are NOT products of this reaction.
b) The balanced reaction is $\mathbf{2Cl_2O(g) \rightarrow 2Cl_2(g) + O_2(g)}$.
c) There is a 2:1 mole ratio between Cl_2 and O_2. In Scene A, there are 6 green molecules and 3 red molecules. Since twice as many Cl_2 molecules are produced as there are O_2 molecules produced, the red molecules are the O_2 molecules.
Amount (mol) of Cl_2O =

$$\left(3 \text{ } O_2 \text{ molecules}\right)\left(\frac{2 \text{ O atoms}}{1 \text{ } O_2 \text{ molecule}}\right)\left(\frac{0.050 \text{ mol O atoms}}{1 \text{ O atom}}\right)\left(\frac{1 \text{ mol } O_2 \text{ molecules}}{2 \text{ mol O atoms}}\right)\left(\frac{2 \text{ mol } Cl_2O}{1 \text{ mol } O_2}\right)$$
$$= 0.30 \text{ mol } Cl_2O$$

$$\text{Molecules of } Cl_2O = \left(0.30 \text{ mol } Cl_2O\right)\left(\frac{6.022 \times 10^{23} \text{ } Cl_2O \text{ molecules}}{1 \text{ mol } Cl_2O}\right)$$
$$= 1.8066 \times 10^{23} \text{ molecules} = \mathbf{1.8 \times 10^{23} \text{ } Cl_2O \text{ molecules}}$$

3.95   <u>Plan:</u> The spheres represent particles of solute and the amount of *solute* per given volume of *solution* determines its concentration. Concentration(mol/L) = amount (mol) of solute/volume (L) of solution.
<u>Solution:</u>
a) **Box C** has more solute added because it contains 2 more spheres than Box A contains.
b) **Box B** has more solvent because solvent molecules have displaced two solute molecules.
c) **Box C** has a higher concentration, because it has a greater amount (mol) of solute per volume of solution.
d) **Box B** has a lower concentration, because it has a smaller amount (mol) of solute per volume of solution.

3.98   <u>Plan:</u> Remember that concentration (mol/L)is amount (mol) of solute/volume of solution.
<u>Solution:</u>
Volumes may **not** be additive when two different solutions are mixed, so the final volume may be slightly different from 1000.0 mL. The correct method would state, "Take 100.0 mL of the 10.0 mol/L solution and add water until the total volume is 1000. mL."

3.99   Plan: In all cases, use the known quantities and the definition of concentration (mol/L) $\left(c = \dfrac{\text{moles solute}}{\text{V of solution (L)}} \right)$ to find the unknown quantity. Volume must be expressed in litres. The molar mass is used to convert amount (mol) to mass (g). The chemical formulas must be written to determine the molar mass. (a) You will need to convert volume from millilitres to litres, multiply by the concentration (mol/L) to find amount (mol), and convert amount (mol) to mass in grams. (b) Convert mass of solute to amount (mol) and volume from mL to litres. Divide the amount (mol) by the volume. (c) Multiply the concentration (mol/L) by the volume.

Solution:

a) Calculating amount (mol) of solute in solution:

$$\text{Amount (mol) of Ca(C}_2\text{H}_3\text{O}_2)_2 = \left(185.8 \text{ mL} \right)\left(\frac{10^{-3} \text{ L}}{1 \text{ mL}} \right)\left(\frac{0.267 \text{ mol Ca(C}_2\text{H}_3\text{O}_2)_2}{1 \text{ L}} \right)$$

$$= 0.0496086 \text{ mol Ca(C}_2\text{H}_3\text{O}_2)_2$$

Converting from amount (mol) of solute to mass:

$$\text{Mass (g) of Ca(C}_2\text{H}_3\text{O}_2)_2 = \left(0.0496086 \text{ mol Ca(C}_2\text{H}_3\text{O}_2)_2 \right)\left(\frac{158.17 \text{ g Ca(C}_2\text{H}_3\text{O}_2)_2}{1 \text{ mol Ca(C}_2\text{H}_3\text{O}_2)_2} \right)$$

$$= 7.84659 \text{ g} = \textbf{7.85 g Ca(C}_2\textbf{H}_3\textbf{O}_2\textbf{)}_2$$

b) Converting mass of solute to amount (mol):

$$\text{Amount (mol) of KI} = \left(21.1 \text{ g KI} \right)\left(\frac{1 \text{ mol KI}}{166.0 \text{ g KI}} \right) = 0.127108 \text{ moles KI}$$

$$\text{Volume (L)} = \left(500. \text{ mL} \right)\left(\frac{10^{-3} \text{ L}}{1 \text{ mL}} \right) = 0.500 \text{ L}$$

$$\text{concentration (mol/L) of KI} = \frac{0.127108 \text{ mol KI}}{0.500 \text{ L}} = 0.254216 \text{ mol/L} = \textbf{0.254 mol/L KI}$$

c) $\text{Amount (mol) of NaCN} = \left(145.6 \text{ L} \right)\left(\dfrac{0.850 \text{ mol NaCN}}{1 \text{ L}} \right) = 123.76 \text{ mol} = \textbf{124 mol NaCN}$

3.101   Plan: In all cases, use the known quantities and the definition of concentration (mol/L) $\left(c = \dfrac{\text{moles solute}}{\text{V of solution (L)}} \right)$ to find the unknown quantity. Volume must be expressed in litres. The molar mass is used to convert amount (mol) to mass (g). The chemical formulas must be written to determine the molar mass. (a) Convert volume in millilitres to litres, multiply the volume by the concentration (mol/L) to obtain amount (mol) of solute, and convert amount (mol) to mass in grams. (b) The simplest way will be to convert the mass (milligrams) to amount (millimoles). concentration (mol/L) may not only be expressed as moles/L, but also as mmoles/mL. (c) Convert the volume from millilitres to litres and find the amount (mol) of solute and amount (mol) of ions by multiplying the volume and concentration (mol/L). Use Avogadro's number to determine the number of ions present.

Solution:

a) Calculating amount (mol) of solute in solution:

$$\text{Amount (mol) of K}_2\text{SO}_4 = \left(475 \text{ mL} \right)\left(\frac{10^{-3} \text{ L}}{1 \text{ mL}} \right)\left(\frac{5.62 \times 10^{-2} \text{ mol K}_2\text{SO}_4}{\text{L}} \right) = 0.026695 \text{ mol K}_2\text{SO}_4$$

Converting amount (mol) of solute to mass:

$$\text{Mass (g) of K}_2\text{SO}_4 = \left(0.026695 \text{ mol K}_2\text{SO}_4 \right)\left(\frac{174.27 \text{ g K}_2\text{SO}_4}{1 \text{ mol K}_2\text{SO}_4} \right) = 4.6521 \text{ g} = \textbf{4.65 g K}_2\textbf{SO}_4$$

b) Calculating amount (mmol) of solute:

$$\text{amount (mmol) of CaCl}_2 = \left(\frac{7.25 \text{ mg CaCl}_2}{1 \text{ mL}} \right)\left(\frac{1 \text{ mmol CaCl}_2}{110.98 \text{ mg CaCl}_2} \right) = 0.065327 \text{ mmol CaCl}_2$$

Calculating concentration (mol/L):

$$\text{concentration (mol/L) of CaCl}_2 = \left(\frac{0.065327 \text{ mmol CaCl}_2}{1 \text{ mL}}\right) = 0.065327 \text{ mol/L} = \textbf{0.0653 mol/L CaCl}_2$$

If you believe that concentration (mol/L) must be moles/litres then the calculation becomes:

$$\text{concentration (mol/L) of CaCl}_2 = \left(\frac{7.25 \text{ mg CaCl}_2}{1 \text{ mL}}\right)\left(\frac{10^{-3} \text{ g}}{1 \text{ mg}}\right)\left(\frac{1 \text{ mL}}{10^{-3} \text{ L}}\right)\left(\frac{1 \text{ mol CaCl}_2}{110.98 \text{ g CaCl}_2}\right)$$

$$= 0.065327 \text{ mol/L} = \textbf{0.0653 mol/L CaCl}_2$$

Notice that the two central terms cancel each other.

c) Converting volume in L to mL:

$$\text{Volume (L)} = \left(1 \text{ mL}\right)\left(\frac{10^{-3} \text{ L}}{1 \text{ mL}}\right) = 0.001 \text{ L}$$

Calculating amount (mol) of solute and amount (mol) of ions:

$$\text{Amount (mol) of MgBr}_2 = \left(0.001 \text{ L}\right)\left(\frac{0.184 \text{ mol MgBr}_2}{1 \text{ L}}\right) = 1.84 \times 10^{-4} \text{ mol MgBr}_2$$

$$\text{Amount (mol) of Mg}^{2+} \text{ ions} = \left(1.84 \times 10^{-4} \text{ mol MgBr}_2\right)\left(\frac{1 \text{ mol Mg}^{2+}}{1 \text{ mol MgBr}_2}\right) = 1.84 \times 10^{-4} \text{ mol Mg}^{2+} \text{ ions}$$

$$\text{Number of Mg}^{2+} \text{ ions} = \left(1.84 \times 10^{-4} \text{ Mg}^{2+} \text{ ions}\right)\left(\frac{6.022 \times 10^{23} \text{ Mg}^{2+} \text{ ions}}{1 \text{ mol Mg}^{2+} \text{ ions}}\right)$$

$$= 1.1080 \times 10^{20} \text{ ions} = \textbf{1.11} \times \textbf{10}^{\textbf{20}} \textbf{ Mg}^{\textbf{2+}} \textbf{ ions}$$

3.103   Plan: These are dilution problems. Dilution problems can be solved by converting to amount (mol) and using the new volume; however, it is much easier to use $c_1V_1 = c_2V_2$. The dilution equation does not require a volume in litres; it only requires that the volume units match. In part c), it is necessary to find the amount (mol) of sodium ions in each separate solution, add these two mole amounts, and divide by the total volume of the two solutions.
Solution:
a) $c_1 = 0.250$ mol/LKCl $V_1 = 37.00$ mL $c_2 = ?$ $V_2 = 150.00$ mL
$c_1V_1 = c_2V_2$

$$c_2 = \frac{c_1 \times V_1}{V_2} = \frac{(0.250 \text{ mol/L})(37.00 \text{ mL})}{150.0 \text{ mL}} = 0.061667 \text{ mol/L} = \textbf{0.0617 mol/L KCl}$$

b) $c_1 = 0.0706$ mol/L $(NH_4)_2SO_4$ $V_1 = 25.71$ mL $c_2 = ?$ $V_2 = 500.00$ mL
$c_1V_1 = c_2V_2$

$$c_2 = \frac{c_1 \times V_1}{V_2} = \frac{(0.0706 \text{ mol/L})(25.71 \text{ mL})}{500.0 \text{ mL}} = 0.003630 \text{ mol/L} = \textbf{0.00363 mol/L (NH}_4\textbf{)}_2\textbf{SO}_4$$

c) Amount (mol) of Na^+ from NaCl solution $= \left(3.58 \text{ mL}\right)\left(\dfrac{10^{-3} \text{ L}}{1 \text{ mL}}\right)\left(\dfrac{0.348 \text{ mol NaCl}}{1 \text{ L}}\right)\left(\dfrac{1 \text{ mol Na}^+}{1 \text{ mol NaCl}}\right)$

$$= 0.00124584 \text{ mol Na}^+$$

Amount (mol) of Na^+ from Na_2SO_4 solution $= \left(500. \text{ mL}\right)\left(\dfrac{10^{-3} \text{ L}}{1 \text{ mL}}\right)\left(\dfrac{6.81 \times 10^{-2} \text{ mol Na}_2SO_4}{1 \text{ L}}\right)\left(\dfrac{2 \text{ mol Na}^+}{1 \text{ mol Na}_2SO_4}\right)$

$$= 0.0681 \text{ mol Na}^+$$

Total amount (mol) of Na^+ ions $= 0.00124584$ mol Na^+ ions $+ 0.0681$ mol Na^+ ions $= 0.06934584$ mol Na^+ ions
Total volume $= 3.58$ mL $+ 500.$ mL $= 503.58$ mL $= 0.50358$ L

$$\text{concentration (mol/L) of Na}^+ = \frac{\text{total moles Na}^+ \text{ ions}}{\text{total volume}} = \frac{0.06934584 \text{ mol Na}^+ \text{ ions}}{0.50358 \text{ L}}$$

$$= 0.1377057 \text{ mol/L} = \textbf{0.138 mol/L Na}^+ \textbf{ ions}$$

3.105 Plan: Use the density of the solution to find the mass of 1 L of solution. Volume in litres must be converted to volume in mL. The 70.0% by mass translates to 70.0 g solute/100 g solution and is used to find the mass of HNO_3 in 1 L of solution. Convert mass of HNO_3 to amount (mol) to obtain amount (mol)/L, concentration (mol/L).

Solution:

a) Mass (g) of 1 L of solution = $\left(1 \text{ L solution}\right)\left(\dfrac{1 \text{ mL}}{10^{-3} \text{ L}}\right)\left(\dfrac{1.41 \text{ g solution}}{1 \text{ mL}}\right)$ = 1410 g solution

Mass (g) of HNO_3 in 1 L of solution = $\left(1410 \text{ g solution}\right)\left(\dfrac{70.0 \text{ g } HNO_3}{100 \text{ g solution}}\right)$ = **987 g HNO_3/L**

b) Amount (mol) of HNO_3 = $\left(987 \text{ g } HNO_3\right)\left(\dfrac{1 \text{ mol } HNO_3}{63.02 \text{ g } HNO_3}\right)$ = 15.6617 mol HNO_3

concentration (mol/L) of HNO_3 = $\left(\dfrac{15.6617 \text{ mol } HNO_3}{1 \text{ L solution}}\right)$ = 15.6617 mol/L= **15.7 mol/L HNO_3**

3.107 Plan: Convert the mass of calcium carbonate to amount (mol), and use the mole ratio in the balanced chemical equation to find the amount (mol) of hydrochloric acid required to react with this amount (mol) of calcium carbonate. Use the concentration (mol/L) of HCl to find the volume that contains this amount (mol).

Solution:

$2HCl(aq) + CaCO_3(s) \rightarrow CaCl_2(aq) + CO_2(g) + H_2O(l)$

Converting from mass of $CaCO_3$ to amount (mol):

Amount (mol) of $CaCO_3$ = $\left(16.2 \text{ g } CaCO_3\right)\left(\dfrac{1 \text{ mol } CaCO_3}{100.09 \text{ g } CaCO_3}\right)$ = 0.161854 mol $CaCO_3$

Converting from amount (mol) of $CaCO_3$ to amount (mol) of HCl:

Amount (mol) of HCl = $\left(0.161854 \text{ mol } CaCO_3\right)\left(\dfrac{2 \text{ mol HCl}}{1 \text{ mol } CaCO_3}\right)$ = 0.323708 mol HCl

Converting from amount (mol) of HCl to volume:

Volume (mL) of HCl = $\left(0.323708 \text{ mol HCl}\right)\left(\dfrac{1 \text{ L}}{0.383 \text{ mol HCl}}\right)\left(\dfrac{1 \text{ mL}}{10^{-3} \text{ L}}\right)$ = 845.1906 mL= **845 mL HCl solution**

3.109 Plan: The first step is to write and balance the chemical equation for the reaction. Multiply the concentration (mol/L) and volume of each of the reactants to determine the amount (mol) of each. To determine which reactant is limiting, calculate the amount of barium sulfate formed from each reactant, assuming an excess of the other reactant. The reactant that produces less product is the limiting reagent. Use the limiting reagent and the mole ratio from the balanced chemical equation to determine the mass of barium sulfate formed.

Solution:

The balanced chemical equation is:

$BaCl_2(aq) + Na_2SO_4(aq) \rightarrow BaSO_4(s) + 2NaCl(aq)$

Amount (mol) of $BaCl_2$ = $\left(35.0 \text{ mL}\right)\left(\dfrac{10^{-3} \text{ L}}{1 \text{ mL}}\right)\left(\dfrac{0.160 \text{ mol } BaCl_2}{1 \text{ L}}\right)$ = 0.00560 mol $BaCl_2$

Finding the amount (mol) of $BaSO_4$ from the amount (mol) of $BaCl_2$ (if Na_2SO_4 is limiting):

Amount (mol) of $BaSO_4$ from $BaCl_2$ = $\left(0.00560 \text{ moL } BaCl_2\right)\left(\dfrac{1 \text{ mol } BaSO_4}{1 \text{ mol } BaCl_2}\right)$ = 0.00560 mol $BaSO_4$

Amount (mol) of Na_2SO_4 = $\left(58.0 \text{ mL}\right)\left(\dfrac{10^{-3} \text{ L}}{1 \text{ mL}}\right)\left(\dfrac{0.065 \text{ mol } Na_2SO_4}{1 \text{ L}}\right)$ = 0.00377 mol Na_2SO_4

Finding the amount (mol) of $BaSO_4$ from the amount (mol) of Na_2SO_4 (if $BaCl_2$ is limiting):

Amount (mol) $BaSO_4$ from Na_2SO_4 = $(0.00377 \text{ moL } Na_2SO_4)\left(\dfrac{1 \text{ mol } BaSO_4}{1 \text{ mol } Na_2SO_4}\right)$ = 0.00377 mol $BaSO_4$

Sodium sulfate is the limiting reactant.
Converting from amount (mol) of $BaSO_4$ to mass:

Mass (g) of $BaSO_4$ = $(0.0377 \text{ moL } BaSO_4)\left(\dfrac{233.4 \text{ g } BaSO_4}{1 \text{ mol } BaSO_4}\right)$ = 0.879918 g= **0.88 g BaSO₄**

3.112   <u>Plan:</u> The first part of the problem is a simple dilution problem ($c_1V_1 = c_2V_2$). The volume in units of litres can be used. In part b), convert mass of HCl to amount (mol) and use the concentration (mol/L) to find the volume that contains that amount (mol).
<u>Solution:</u>
a) c_1 = 11.7 mol/L V_1 = ? c_2 = 3.5 mol/L V_2 = 3.0 L

$V_1 = \dfrac{c_2 \times V_2}{c_1} = \dfrac{(3.5 \text{ mol/L})(3.0 \text{ L})}{11.7 \text{ mol/L}}$ = 0.897436 L

Instructions: Be sure to wear goggles to protect your eyes! Pour approximately 2.0 L of water into the container. Add slowly and with mixing 0.90 L of 11.7 mol/L HCl into the water. Dilute to 3.0 L with water.
b) Converting from mass of HCl to amount (mol) of HCl:

Amount (mol) of HCl = $(9.66 \text{ g HCl})\left(\dfrac{1 \text{ mol HCl}}{36.46 \text{ g HCl}}\right)$ = 0.264948 mol HCl

Converting from amount (mol) of HCl to volume:

Volume (mL) of solution = $(0.264948 \text{ mol HCl})\left(\dfrac{1 \text{ L}}{11.7 \text{ mol HCl}}\right)\left(\dfrac{1 \text{ mL}}{10^{-3} \text{ L}}\right)$

= 22.64513 mL= **22.6 mL muriatic acid solution**

3.115   <u>Plan:</u> Review the discussion on water soluble compounds.
<u>Solution:</u>
Ionic and polar covalent compounds are most likely to be soluble in water. Because water is polar, the partial charges in its molecules are able to interact with the charges, either ionic or dipole-induced, in other substances.

3.116   <u>Plan:</u> Solutions that conduct an electric current contain electrolytes.
<u>Solution:</u>
Ions must be present in an aqueous solution for it to conduct an electric current. Ions come from ionic compounds or from other electrolytes such as acids and bases.

3.119   <u>Plan:</u> Write the formula for magnesium nitrate and note the ratio of magnesium ions to nitrate ions.
<u>Solution:</u>
Upon dissolving the salt in water, magnesium nitrate, $Mg(NO_3)_2$, would dissociate to form one Mg^{2+} ion for every two NO_3^{-} ions, thus forming twice as many nitrate ions. **Scene B** best represents a volume of magnesium nitrate solution. Only **Scene B** has twice as many nitrate ions (red circles) as magnesium ions (blue circles).

3.123   <u>Plan:</u> Compounds that are soluble in water tend to be ionic compounds or covalent compounds that have polar bonds. Many ionic compounds are soluble in water because the attractive force between the oppositely charged ions in an ionic compound are replaced with an attractive force between the polar water molecule and the ions when the compound is dissolved in water. Covalent compounds with polar bonds are often soluble in water since the polar bonds of the covalent compound interact with those in water.
<u>Solution:</u>
a) Benzene, a covalent compound, is likely to be **insoluble** in water because it is nonpolar and water is polar.
b) Sodium hydroxide (NaOH) is an ionic compound and is therefore likely to be **soluble** in water.
c) Ethanol (CH_3CH_2OH) will likely be **soluble** in water because it contains a polar –OH bond like water.
d) Potassium acetate ($KC_2H_3O_2$) is an ionic compound and will likely be **soluble** in water.

3.125   Plan: Substances whose aqueous solutions conduct an electric current are electrolytes such as ionic compounds, acids, and bases.
Solution:
a) Cesium bromide, CsBr, is a soluble ionic compound, and a solution of this salt in water contains Cs^+ and Br^- ions. Its solution **conducts** an electric current.
b) HI is a strong acid that dissociates completely in water. Its aqueous solution contains H^+ and I^- ions, so it **conducts** an electric current.

3.127   Plan: To determine the total amount (mol) of ions released, write an equation that shows the compound dissociating into ions with the correct molar ratios. Convert mass and formula units to amount (mol) of compound and use the molar ratio to convert amount (mol) of compound to amount (mol) of ions.
Solution:
a) Each mole of NH_4Cl dissolves in water to form 1 mole of NH^{4+} ions and 1 mole of Cl^- ions, or a total of 2 moles of ions: $NH_4Cl(s) \rightarrow NH_4^+(aq) + Cl^-(aq)$.

$$\text{Amount (mol) of ions} = (0.32 \text{ mol } NH_4Cl)\left(\frac{2 \text{ mol ions}}{1 \text{ mol } NH_4Cl}\right) = \textbf{0.64 mol of ions}$$

b) Each mole of $Ba(OH)_2 \cdot 8H_2O$ forms 1 mole of Ba^{2+} ions and 2 moles of OH^- ions, or a total of 3 moles of ions: $Ba(OH)_2 \cdot 8H_2O(s) \rightarrow Ba^{2+}(aq) + 2OH^-(aq)$. The waters of hydration become part of the larger bulk of water. Convert mass to amount (mol) using the molar mass.

$$\text{Amount (mol) of ions} = (25.4 \text{ g } Ba(OH)_2 \cdot 8H_2O)\left(\frac{1 \text{ mol } Ba(OH)_2 \cdot 8H_2O}{315.4 \text{ g } Ba(OH)_2 \cdot 8H_2O}\right)\left(\frac{3 \text{ mol ions}}{1 \text{ mol } Ba(OH)_2 \cdot 8H_2O}\right)$$

$$= 0.2415980 \text{ mol} = \textbf{0.242 mol of ions}$$

c) Each mole of LiCl produces 2 moles of ions (1 mole of Li^+ ions and 1 mole of Cl^- ions): $LiCl(s) \rightarrow Li^+(aq) + Cl^-(aq)$. Recall that a mole contains 6.022×10^{23} entities, so a mole of LiCl contains 6.022×10^{23} units of LiCl, more easily expressed as formula units.

$$\text{Amount (mol) of ions} = (3.55 \times 10^{19} \text{ FU LiCl})\left(\frac{1 \text{ mol LiCl}}{6.022 \times 10^{23} \text{ FU LiCl}}\right)\left(\frac{2 \text{ mol ions}}{1 \text{ mol LiCl}}\right)$$

$$= 1.17901 \times 10^{-4} \text{ mol} = \textbf{1.18} \times \textbf{10}^{-4} \textbf{ mol of ions}$$

3.129   Plan: To determine the total amount (mol) of ions released, write an equation that shows the compound dissociating into ions with the correct molar ratios. Convert mass and formula units to amount (mol) of compound and use the molar ratio to convert amount (mol) of compound to amount (mol) of ions.
Solution:
a) Each mole of K_3PO_4 forms 3 moles of K^+ ions and 1 mole of PO_4^{3-} ions, or a total of 4 moles of ions: $K_3PO_4(s) \rightarrow 3K^+(aq) + PO_4^{3-}(aq)$

$$\text{Amount (mol) of ions} = (0.75 \text{ mol } K_3PO_4)\left(\frac{4 \text{ mol ions}}{1 \text{ mol } K_3PO_4}\right) = \textbf{3.0 mol of ions.}$$

b) Each mole of $NiBr_2 \cdot 3H_2O$ forms 1 mole of Ni^{2+} ions and 2 moles of Br^- ions, or a total of 3 moles of ions: $NiBr_2 \cdot 3H_2O(s) \rightarrow Ni^{2+}(aq) + 2Br^-(aq)$. The waters of hydration become part of the larger bulk of water. Convert mass to amount (mol) using the molar mass.

$$\text{Amount (mol) of ions} = (6.88 \times 10^{-3} \text{ g } NiBr_2 \cdot 3H_2O)\left(\frac{1 \text{ mol } NiBr_2 \cdot 3H_2O}{272.54 \text{ g } NiBr_2 \cdot 3H_2O}\right)\left(\frac{3 \text{ mol ions}}{1 \text{ mol } NiBr_2 \cdot 3H_2O}\right)$$

$$= 7.5732 \times 10^{-5} \text{ mol} = \textbf{7.57} \times \textbf{10}^{-5} \textbf{ mol of ions}$$

c) Each mole of $FeCl_3$ forms 1 mole of Fe^{3+} ions and 3 moles of Cl^- ions, or a total of 4 moles of ions: $FeCl_3(s) \rightarrow Fe^{3+}(aq) + 3Cl^-(aq)$. Recall that a mole contains 6.022×10^{23} entities, so a mole of $FeCl_3$ contains 6.022×10^{23} units of $FeCl_3$, more easily expressed as formula units.

$$\text{Amount (mol) of ions} = (2.23 \times 10^{22} \text{ FU } FeCl_3)\left(\frac{1 \text{ mol } FeCl_3}{6.022 \times 10^{23} \text{ FU } FeCl_3}\right)\left(\frac{4 \text{ mol ions}}{1 \text{ mol } FeCl_3}\right)$$

$$= 0.148124 \text{ mol} = \textbf{0.148 mol of ions}$$

3.131 <u>Plan:</u> To determine the total amount (mol) of ions released, write an equation that shows the compound dissociating into ions with the correct molar ratios. Convert the information given to amount (mol) of compound and use the molar ratio to convert amount (mol) of compound to amount (mol) of ions. Avogadro's number is used to convert amount (mol) of ions to numbers of ions.
<u>Solution:</u>
a) Each mole of $AlCl_3$ forms 1mole of Al^{3+} ions and 3 moles of Cl^- ions: $AlCl_3(s) \rightarrow Al^{3+}(aq) + 3Cl^-(aq)$.
Concentration (mol/L) and volume must be converted to amount (mol) of $AlCl_3$.

$$\text{Amount (mol) of } AlCl_3 = (130.\text{ mL})\left(\frac{10^{-3}\text{ L}}{1\text{ mL}}\right)\left(\frac{0.45\text{ mol } AlCl_3}{L}\right) = \textbf{0.0585 mol AlCl3}$$

$$\text{Amount (mol) of } Al^{3+} = (0.0585\text{ mol } AlCl_3)\left(\frac{1\text{ mol } Al^{3+}}{1\text{ mol } AlCl_3}\right) = 0.0585\text{ mol} = \textbf{0.058 mol } Al^{3+}$$

$$\text{Number of } Al^{3+}\text{ ions} = (0.0585\text{ mol } Al^{3+})\left(\frac{6.022\text{x}10^{23}\text{ } Al^{3+}}{1\text{ mol } Al^{3+}}\right) = 3.52287\text{x }10^{22}\text{ ions} = \textbf{3.5x}10^{22}\textbf{ } Al^{3+}\textbf{ ions}$$

$$\text{Amount (mol) of } Cl^- = (0.0585\text{ mol } AlCl_3)\left(\frac{3\text{ mol } Cl^-}{1\text{ mol } AlCl_3}\right) = 0.1755\text{ mol} = \textbf{0.18 mol } Cl^-$$

$$\text{Number of } Cl^-\text{ ions} = (0.1755\text{ mol } Cl^-)\left(\frac{6.022\text{x}10^{23}\text{ } Cl^-}{1\text{ mol } Cl^-}\right) = 1.05686\text{x}10^{23}\text{ ions} = \textbf{1.1x}10^{23}\textbf{ } Cl^-\textbf{ ions}$$

b) Each mole of Li_2SO_4 forms 2 moles of Li^+ ions and 1 mole of SO_4^{2-} ions: $Li_2SO_4(s) \rightarrow 2Li^+(aq) + SO_4^{2-}(aq)$.

$$\text{Amount (mol) of } Li_2SO_4 = (9.80\text{ mL})\left(\frac{10^{-3}\text{ L}}{1\text{ mL}}\right)\left(\frac{2.59\text{ g } Li_2SO_4}{1\text{ L}}\right)\left(\frac{1\text{ mol } Li_2SO_4}{109.95\text{ g } Li_2SO_4}\right)$$
$$= \textbf{2.3085x}10^{-4}\textbf{ mol } Li_2SO_4$$

$$\text{Amount (mol) of } Li^+ = (2.3085\text{x}10^{-4}\text{ mol } Li_2SO_4)\left(\frac{2\text{ mol } Li^+}{1\text{ mol } Li_2SO_4}\right) = 4.6170\text{x}10^{-4}\text{ mol} = \textbf{4.62x}10^{-4}\textbf{ mol } Li^+$$

$$\text{Number of } Li^+\text{ ions} = (4.6170\text{x}10^{-4}\text{ mol } Li^+)\left(\frac{6.022\text{ x }10^{23}\text{ } Li^+}{1\text{ mol } Li^+}\right) = 2.7804\text{x}10^{20}\text{ ions} = \textbf{2.78x}10^{20}\textbf{ } Li^+\textbf{ ions}$$

$$\text{Amount (mol) of } SO_4^{2-} = (2.3085\text{x}10^{-4}\text{ mol } Li_2SO_4)\left(\frac{1\text{ mol } SO_4^{2-}}{1\text{ mol } Li_2SO_4}\right) = 2.3085\text{x}10^{-4}\text{ mol} = \textbf{2.31x}10^{-4}\textbf{ mol } SO_4^{2-}$$

$$\text{Number of } SO_4^{2-}\text{ ions} = (2.3085\text{x}10^{-4}\text{ mol } SO_4^{2-})\left(\frac{6.022\text{ x }10^{23}\text{ } SO_4^{2-}}{1\text{ mol } SO_4^{2-}}\right)$$
$$= 1.39018\text{x}10^{20} = \textbf{1.39x}10^{20}\textbf{ } SO_4^{2-}\textbf{ ions}$$

c) Each mole of KBr forms 1 mole of K^+ ions and 1 mole of Br^- ions: $KBr(s) \rightarrow K^+(aq) + Br^-(aq)$.

$$\text{Amount (mol) of KBr} = (245\text{ mL})\left(\frac{10^{-3}\text{ L}}{1\text{ mL}}\right)\left(\frac{3.68\text{x}10^{22}\text{ FU KBr}}{L}\right)\left(\frac{1\text{ mol KBr}}{6.022\text{x}10^{23}\text{ FU KBr}}\right) = \textbf{0.01497 mol KBr}$$

$$\text{Amount (mol) of } K^+ = (0.01497\text{ mol KBr})\left(\frac{1\text{ mol } K^+}{1\text{ mol KBr}}\right) = 0.01497\text{ mol} = \textbf{1.50x}10^{-2}\textbf{ mol } K^+$$

$$\text{Number of } K^+\text{ ions} = (0.01497\text{ mol } K^+)\left(\frac{6.022\text{ x}10^{23}\text{ } K^+}{1\text{ mol } K^+}\right) = 9.016\text{x}10^{21}\text{ ions} = \textbf{9.02x}10^{21}\textbf{ } K^+\textbf{ ions}$$

$$\text{Amount (mol) of } Br^- = (0.01497\text{ mol KBr})\left(\frac{1\text{ mol } Br^-}{1\text{ mol KBr}}\right) = 0.01497\text{ mol} = \textbf{1.50x}10^{-2}\textbf{ mol } Br^-$$

Number of Br⁻ ions = $\left(0.01497 \text{ mol Br}^-\right)\left(\dfrac{6.022 \times 10^{23} \text{ Br}^-}{1 \text{ mol Br}^-}\right) = 9.016 \times 10^{21}$ ions= $\mathbf{9.02 \times 10^{21}}$ **Br⁻ ions**

3.133   Plan: The acids in this problem are all strong acids, so you can assume that all acid molecules dissociate completely to yield H⁺ ions and associated anions. One mole of $HClO_4$, HNO_3, and HCl each produce one mole of H⁺ upon dissociation, so amount (mol) H⁺ = amount (mol) acid. Calculate the amount (mol) of acid by multiplying the concentration (mol/L) by the volume in litres.
Solution:
a) $HClO_4(aq) \rightarrow H^+(aq) + ClO_4^-(aq)$

Amount (mol) H⁺ = mol $HClO_4$ = $\left(1.40 \text{ L}\right)\left(\dfrac{0.25 \text{ mol}}{1 \text{ L}}\right) = \mathbf{0.35 \text{ mol H}^+}$

b) $HNO_3(aq) \rightarrow H^+(aq) + NO_3^-(aq)$

Amount (mol) H⁺ = mol HNO_3 = $\left(6.8 \text{ mL}\right)\left(\dfrac{10^{-3} \text{ L}}{1 \text{ mL}}\right)\left(\dfrac{0.92 \text{ mol}}{1 \text{ L}}\right) = 6.256 \times 10^{-3}$ mol= $\mathbf{6.3 \times 10^{-3} \text{ mol H}^+}$

c) $HCl(aq) \rightarrow H^+(aq) + Cl^-(aq)$

Amount (mol) H⁺ = mol HCl = $\left(2.6 \text{ L}\right)\left(\dfrac{0.085 \text{ mol}}{1 \text{ L}}\right) = 0.221$ mol= $\mathbf{0.22 \text{ mol H}^+}$

3.137   Plan: Review the definition of spectator ions.
Solution:
Ions in solution that do not participate in the reaction do not appear in a net ionic equation. These spectator ions remain as dissolved ions throughout the reaction. These ions are only present to balance charge.

3.142   Plan: The amount (mol) of narceine and the amount (mol) of water are required. We can assume any mass of narceine hydrate (we will use 100 g), and use this mass to determine the amount (mol) of hydrate. The amount (mol) of water in the hydrate is obtained by taking 10.8% of the 100 g mass of hydrate and converting the mass to amount (mol) of water. Divide the amount (mol) of water by the amount (mol) of hydrate to find the value of x.
Solution:
Assuming a 100 g sample of narceine hydrate:

Amount (mol) of narceine hydrate = $\left(100 \text{ g narceine hydrate}\right)\left(\dfrac{1 \text{ mol narceine hydrate}}{499.52 \text{ g narceine hydrate}}\right)$

= 0.20019 mol narceine hydrate

Mass (g) of H_2O = $\left(100 \text{ g narceine hydrate}\right)\left(\dfrac{10.8\% \text{ } H_2O}{100\% \text{ narceine hydrate}}\right) = 10.8 \text{ g } H_2O$

Amount (mol) of H_2O = $\left(10.8 \text{ g } H_2O\right)\left(\dfrac{1 \text{ mol } H_2O}{18.02 \text{ g } H_2O}\right) = 0.59933 \text{ mol } H_2O$

$x = \dfrac{\text{moles of } H_2O}{\text{moles of hydrate}} = \dfrac{0.59933 \text{ mol}}{0.20019 \text{ mol}} = 3$

Thus, there are three water molecules per mole of hydrate. The formula for narceine hydrate is **narceine•3H₂O**.

3.143   Plan: Determine the formula and the molar mass of each compound. The formula gives the relative amount (mol) of each element present. Multiply the amount (mol) of each element by its molar mass to find the total mass of element in 1 mole of compound. Mass percent = $\dfrac{\text{total mass of element}}{\text{molar mass of compound}}(100)$. List the compounds from the highest %H to the lowest.

Solution:

Name	Chemical formula	Molar mass (g/mol)	Mass percent H $= \dfrac{\text{moles of H x molar mass}}{\text{molar mass of compound}}(100)$
Ethane	C_2H_6	30.07	$\dfrac{6 \text{ mol}(1.008 \text{ g/mol})}{30.07 \text{ g}}(100\%) = 20.11\% \text{ H}$
Propane	C_3H_8	44.09	$\dfrac{8 \text{ mol}(1.008 \text{ g/mol})}{44.09 \text{ g}}(100\%) = 18.29\% \text{ H}$
Benzene	C_6H_6	78.11	$\dfrac{6 \text{ mol}(1.008 \text{ g/mol})}{78.11 \text{ g}}(100\%) = 7.743\% \text{ H}$
Ethanol	C_2H_5OH	46.07	$\dfrac{6 \text{ mol}(1.008 \text{ g/mol})}{46.07 \text{ g}}(100\%) = 13.13\% \text{ H}$
Cetyl palmitate	$C_{32}H_{64}O_2$	480.83	$\dfrac{64 \text{ mol}(1.008 \text{ g/mol})}{480.83 \text{ g}}(100\%) = 13.42\% \text{ H}$

The hydrogen percentage decreases in the following order:
Ethane > Propane > Cetyl palmitate > Ethanol > Benzene

3.148   Plan: The key to solving this problem is determining the overall balanced equation. Each individual step must be set up and balanced first. The separate equations can then be combined to get the overall equation. The mass of iron is converted to amount (mol) of iron by dividing by the molar mass, and the mole ratio from the balanced equation is used to find the amount (mol) and then the mass of CO required to produce that amount (mol) of iron.
Solution:
a) In the first step, ferric oxide (ferric denotes Fe^{3+}) reacts with carbon monoxide to form Fe_3O_4 and carbon dioxide:
$$3Fe_2O_3(s) + CO(g) \rightarrow 2Fe_3O_4(s) + CO_2(g) \quad (1)$$
In the second step, Fe_3O_4 reacts with more carbon monoxide to form ferrous oxide:
$$Fe_3O_4(s) + CO(g) \rightarrow 3FeO(s) + CO_2(g) \quad (2)$$
In the third step, ferrous oxide reacts with more carbon monoxide to form molten iron:
$$FeO(s) + CO(g) \rightarrow Fe(l) + CO_2(g) \quad (3)$$
Common factors are needed to allow these equations to be combined. The intermediate products are Fe_3O_4 and FeO, so multiply equation (2) by 2 to cancel Fe_3O_4 and equation (3) by 6 to cancel FeO:
$$3Fe_2O_3(s) + CO(g) \rightarrow \cancel{2Fe_3O_4(s)} + CO_2(g)$$
$$\cancel{2Fe_3O_4(s)} + 2CO(g) \rightarrow \cancel{6FeO(s)} + 2CO_2(g)$$
$$\cancel{6FeO(s)} + 6CO(g) \rightarrow 6Fe(l) + 6CO_2(g)$$
$$\overline{3Fe_2O_3(s) + 9CO(g) \rightarrow 6Fe(l) + 9CO_2(g)}$$
Then divide by 3 to obtain the smallest integer coefficients:
$$\textbf{Fe}_2\textbf{O}_3\textbf{(s)} + 3\textbf{CO(g)} \rightarrow 2\textbf{Fe(s)} + 3\textbf{CO}_2\textbf{(g)}$$
b) A metric tonne is equal to 1000 kg.
Converting 45.0 metric tons of Fe to mass in grams:
$$\text{Mass (g) of Fe} = (45.0 \text{ ton Fe})\left(\frac{10^3 \text{ kg}}{1 \text{ ton}}\right)\left(\frac{10^3 \text{ g}}{1 \text{ kg}}\right) = 4.50\text{x}10^7 \text{ g Fe}$$

$$\text{Amount (mol) of Fe} = \left(4.50\text{x}10^7 \text{ g Fe}\right)\left(\frac{1 \text{ mol Fe}}{55.85 \text{ g Fe}}\right) = 8.05730\text{x}10^5 \text{ mol Fe}$$

$$\text{Mass (g) of CO} = \left(8.05730\text{x}10^5 \text{ mol Fe}\right)\left(\frac{3 \text{ mol CO}}{2 \text{ mol Fe}}\right)\left(\frac{28.01 \text{ g CO}}{1 \text{ mol CO}}\right) = 3.38527\text{x}10^7 \text{ g} = \textbf{3.39x10}^7 \textbf{ g CO}$$

3.150   Plan: If 100.0 g of dinitrogen tetroxide reacts with 100.0 g of hydrazine (N_2H_4), what is the theoretical yield of nitrogen if no side reaction takes place? First, we need to identify the limiting reactant. To determine which reactant is limiting, calculate the amount of nitrogen formed from each reactant, assuming an excess of the other reactant. The reactant that produces less product is the limiting reagent. Use the limiting reagent and the mole ratio from the balanced chemical equation to determine the theoretical yield of nitrogen. Then determine the amount of limiting reactant required to produce 10.0 grams of NO. Reduce the amount of limiting reactant by the amount used to produce NO. The reduced amount of limiting reactant is then used to calculate an "actual yield." The "actual" and theoretical yields will give the maximum percent yield.

Solution:

The balanced reaction is $2N_2H_4(l) + N_2O_4(l) \rightarrow 3N_2(g) + 4H_2O(g)$

Determining the limiting reactant:

Finding the amount (mol) of N_2 from the amount of N_2O_4 (if N_2H_4 is limiting):

$$\text{Amount (mol) of } N_2 \text{ from } N_2O_4 = \left(100.0 \text{ g } N_2O_4\right)\left(\frac{1 \text{ mol } N_2O_4}{92.02 \text{ g } N_2O_4}\right)\left(\frac{3 \text{ mol } N_2}{1 \text{ mol } N_2O_4}\right) = 3.26016 \text{ mol } N_2$$

Finding the amount (mol) of N_2 from the amount of N_2H_4 (if N_2O_4 is limiting):

$$N_2 \text{ from } N_2H_4 = \left(100.0 \text{ g } N_2H_4\right)\left(\frac{1 \text{ mol } N_2H_4}{32.05 \text{ g } N_2H_4}\right)\left(\frac{3 \text{ mol } N_2}{2 \text{ mol } N_2H_4}\right) = 4.68019 \text{ mol } N_2$$

N_2O_4 is the limiting reactant.

$$\text{Theoretical yield of } N_2 = \left(100.0 \text{ g } N_2O_4\right)\left(\frac{1 \text{ mol } N_2O_4}{92.02 \text{ g } N_2O_4}\right)\left(\frac{3 \text{ mol } N_2}{1 \text{ mol } N_2O_4}\right)\left(\frac{28.02 \text{ g } N_2}{1 \text{ mol } N_2}\right) = 91.3497 \text{ g } N_2$$

How much of the limiting reactant is used to produce 10.0 g NO?

$N_2H_4(l) + 2N_2O_4(l) \rightarrow 6NO(g) + 2H_2O(g)$

$$\text{Mass (g) of } N_2O_4 \text{ used} = \left(10.0 \text{ g } NO\right)\left(\frac{1 \text{ mol } NO}{30.01 \text{ g } NO}\right)\left(\frac{2 \text{ mol } N_2O_4}{6 \text{ mol } NO}\right)\left(\frac{92.02 \text{ g } N_2O_4}{1 \text{ mol } N_2O_4}\right)$$

$$= 10.221 \text{ g } N_2O_4$$

Amount of N_2O_4 available to produce N_2 = 100.0 g N_2O_4 – mass of N_2O_4 required to produce 10.0 g NO

$$= 100.0 \text{ g} - 10.221 \text{ g} = 89.779 \text{ g } N_2O_4$$

Determine the "actual yield" of N_2 from 89.779 g N_2O_4:

$$\text{"Actual yield" of } N_2 = \left(89.779 \text{ g } N_2O_4\right)\left(\frac{1 \text{ mol } N_2O_4}{92.02 \text{ g } N_2O_4}\right)\left(\frac{3 \text{ mol } N_2}{1 \text{ mol } N_2O_4}\right)\left(\frac{28.02 \text{ g } N_2}{1 \text{ mol } N_2}\right)$$

$$= 82.01285 \text{ g } N_2$$

$$\text{Theoretical yield} = \left(\frac{\text{actual yield}}{\text{theoretical yield}}\right)(100\%) = \left(\frac{82.01285}{91.3497}\right)(100\%) = 89.7790 \% = \textbf{89.8\%}$$

3.152   **Plan:** Identify the product molecules and write the balanced equation. To determine the limiting reactant for part b), examine the product circle to see which reactant remains in excess and which reactant was totally consumed. For part c), use the mole ratios in the balanced equation to determine the number of moles of product formed by each reactant, assuming the other reactant is in excess. The reactant that produces fewer moles of product is the limiting reactant. Use the mole ratio between the two reactants to determine the amount (mol) of excess reactant required to react with the limiting reactant. The difference between the initial amount (mol) of excess reactant and the amount (mol) required for reaction is the amount (mol) of excess reactant that remain.

Solution:

a) The contents of the boxes give: $AB_2 + B_2 \rightarrow AB_3$

Balancing the reaction gives: $\mathbf{2AB_2 + B_2 \rightarrow 2AB_3}$

b) Two B_2 molecules remain after reaction so B_2 is in excess. All of the AB_2 molecules have reacted so $\mathbf{AB_2}$ is the limiting reactant.

c) Finding the amount (mol) of AB_3 from the amount (mol) of AB_2 (if B_2 is limiting):

$$\text{Amount (mol) of } AB_3 \text{ from } AB_2 = \left(5.0 \text{ mol } AB_2\right)\left(\frac{2 \text{ mol } AB_3}{2 \text{ mol } AB_2}\right) = 5.0 \text{ mol } AB_3$$

Finding the amount (mol) of AB_3 from the amount (mol) of B_2 (if AB_2 is limiting):

$$\text{Amount (mol) of } AB_3 \text{ from } B_2 = \left(3.0 \text{ mol } B_2\right)\left(\frac{2 \text{ mol } AB_3}{1 \text{ mol } B_2}\right) = 6.0 \text{ mol } AB_3$$

AB_2 is the limiting reagent and **5.0 mol of AB_3** is formed.

d) Amount (mol) of B_2 that react with 5.0 mol AB_2 = $(5.0 \text{ mol } AB_2)\left(\dfrac{1 \text{ mol } B_2}{2 \text{ mol } AB_2}\right)$ = 2.5 mol B_2

The unreacted B_2 is 3.0 mol – 2.5 mol = **0.5 mol B_2**.

3.154 Plan: Write the formulas in the form $C_xH_yO_z$. Reduce the formulas to obtain the empirical formulas. Add the atomic masses in that empirical formula to obtain the molecular mass.
Solution:
Compound A: $C_4H_{10}O_2 = C_2H_5O$ Compound B: C_2H_4O
Compound C: $C_4H_8O_2 = C_2H_4O$ Compound D: $C_6H_{12}O_3 = C_2H_4O$
Compound E: $C_5H_8O_2$
Compounds **B, C and D** all have the same empirical formula, C_2H_4O. The molecular mass of this formula is (2 x 12.01 g/mol C) + (4 x 1.008 g/mol H) + (1 x 16.00 g/mol O) = **44.05 g/mol**.

3.155 Plan: Write the balanced chemical equation. Since quantities of two reactants are given, we must determine which is the limiting reactant. To determine which reactant is limiting, calculate the amount of product formed from each reactant, assuming an excess of the other reactant. The reactant that produces less product is the limiting reagent. Use the limiting reactant to determine the theoretical yield of product. The actual yield is given. The actual yield divided by the theoretical yield just calculated (with the result multiplied by 100%) gives the percent yield.
Solution:
Determine the balanced chemical equation:
$ZrOCl_2 \cdot 8H_2O(s) + 4H_2C_2O_4 \cdot 2H_2O(s) + 4KOH(aq) \rightarrow K_2Zr(C_2O_4)_3(H_2C_2O_4) \cdot H_2O(s) + 2KCl(aq) + 20H_2O(l)$
Determining the limiting reactant:
Finding the amount (mol) of product from the amount of $ZrOCl_2 \cdot 8H_2O$ (if $H_2C_2O_4 \cdot 2H_2O$ is limiting):
Amount (mol) of product from $ZrOCl_2 \cdot 8H_2O$ =

$(1.68 \text{ g } ZrOCl_2 \cdot 8H_2O)\left(\dfrac{1 \text{ mol } ZrOCl_2 \cdot 8H_2O}{322.25 \text{ g } ZrOCl_2 \cdot 8H_2O}\right)\left(\dfrac{1 \text{ mol product}}{1 \text{ mol } ZrOCl_2 \cdot 8H_2O}\right)$ = 0.00521334 mol product

Finding the amount (mol) of product from the amount of $H_2C_2O_4 \cdot 2H_2O$ (if $ZrOCl_2 \cdot 8H_2O$ is limiting):
Amount (mol) of product from $H_2C_2O_4 \cdot 2H_2O$ =

$(5.20 \text{ g } H_2C_2O_4 \cdot 2H_2O)\left(\dfrac{1 \text{ mol } H_2C_2O_4 \cdot H_2O}{126.07 \text{ g } H_2C_2O_4 \cdot 2H_2O}\right)\left(\dfrac{1 \text{ mol product}}{4 \text{ mol } H_2C_2O_4 \cdot 2H_2O}\right)$ = 0.0103117 mol product

It is not necessary to find the amount (mol) of product from KOH because KOH is stated to be in excess. The $ZrOCl_2 \cdot 8H_2O$ is the limiting reactant, and will be used to calculate the theoretical yield:

Mass (g) of product = $(0.00521334 \text{ mol product})\left(\dfrac{541.53 \text{ g product}}{1 \text{ mol product}}\right)$ = 2.82318 g product

Calculating the percent yield:

Percent yield = $\left(\dfrac{\text{actual Yield}}{\text{theoretical Yield}}\right)$ x 100% = $\left(\dfrac{1.25 \text{ g}}{2.82318 \text{ g}}\right)$ x 100% = 44.276 % = **44.3% yield**

3.158 Plan: Count the total number of spheres in each box. The number in box A divided by the volume change in each part will give the number we are looking for and allow us to match boxes.
Solution:
The number in each box is: A = 12, B = 6, C = 4, and D = 3.
a) When the volume is tripled, there should be 12/3 = 4 spheres in a box. This is box **C**.
b) When the volume is doubled, there should be 12/2 = 6 spheres in a box. This is box **B**.
c) When the volume is quadrupled, there should be 12/4 = 3 spheres in a box. This is box **D**.

3.165 Plan: Deal with the methane and propane separately, and combine the results. Balanced equations are needed for each hydrocarbon. The total mass and the percentages will give the mass of each hydrocarbon. The mass of each hydrocarbon is changed to amount (mol), and through the balanced chemical equation the amount of CO_2 produced by each gas may be found. Summing the amounts of CO_2 gives the total from the mixture. For part b), let x and 252 – x represent the masses of CH_4 and C_3H_8, respectively.

Solution:

a) The balanced chemical equations are:

Methane: $CH_4(g) + 2O_2(g) \rightarrow CO_2(g) + 2H_2O(l)$

Propane: $C_3H_8(g) + 5O_2(g) \rightarrow 3CO_2(g) + 4H_2O(l)$

Mass (g) of CO_2 from each:

Methane: $(200.\text{g Mixture})\left(\dfrac{25.0\%}{100\%}\right)\left(\dfrac{1 \text{ mol } CH_4}{16.04 \text{ g } CH_4}\right)\left(\dfrac{1 \text{ mol } CO_2}{1 \text{ mol } CH_4}\right)\left(\dfrac{44.01 \text{ g } CO_2}{1 \text{ mol } CO_2}\right) = 137.188 \text{ g } CO_2$

Propane: $(200.\text{g Mixture})\left(\dfrac{75.0\%}{100\%}\right)\left(\dfrac{1 \text{ mol } C_3H_8}{44.09 \text{ g } C_3H_8}\right)\left(\dfrac{3 \text{ mol } CO_2}{1 \text{ mol } C_3H_8}\right)\left(\dfrac{44.01 \text{ g } CO_2}{1 \text{ mol } CO_2}\right) = 449.183 \text{ g } CO_2$

Total $CO_2 = 137.188 \text{ g} + 449.183 \text{ g} = 586.371 = \textbf{586 g } CO_2$

b) Since the mass of CH_4 + the mass of $C_3H_8 = 252$ g, let x = mass of CH_4 in the mixture and $252 - x$ = mass of C_3H_8 in the mixture. Use mole ratios to calculate the amount of CO_2 formed from x amount of CH_4 and the amount of CO_2 formed from $252 - x$ amount of C_3H_8.

The total mass of CO_2 produced = 748 g.

The total amount (mol) of CO_2 produced $= (748 \text{ g } CO_2)\left(\dfrac{1 \text{ mol } CO_2}{44.01 \text{ g } CO_2}\right) = 16.996 \text{ mol } CO_2$

$16.996 \text{ mol } CO_2 =$

$(x \text{ g } CH_4)\left(\dfrac{1 \text{ mol } CH_4}{16.04 \text{ g } CH_4}\right)\left(\dfrac{1 \text{ mol } CO_2}{1 \text{ mol } CH_4}\right) + (252 - x \text{ g } C_3H_8)\left(\dfrac{1 \text{ mol } C_3H_8}{44.09 \text{ g } C_3H_8}\right)\left(\dfrac{3 \text{ mol } CO_2}{1 \text{ mol } C_3H_8}\right)$

$16.996 \text{ mol } CO_2 = \dfrac{x}{16.04} \text{ mol } CO_2 + \dfrac{3(252 - x)}{44.09} \text{ mol } CO_2$

$16.996 \text{ mol } CO_2 = \dfrac{x}{16.04} \text{ mol } CO_2 + \dfrac{756 - 3x}{44.09} \text{ mol } CO_2$

$16.996 \text{ mol } CO_2 = 0.06234x \text{ mol } CO_2 + (17.147 - 0.06804x \text{ mol } CO_2)$

$16.996 = 17.147 - 0.0057x$

$x = 26.49 \text{ g } CH_4$ $\qquad 252 - x = 252 \text{ g} - 26.49 \text{ g} = 225.51 \text{ g } C_3H_8$

Mass % $CH_4 = \dfrac{\text{mass of } CH_4}{\text{mass of mixture}}(100\%) = \dfrac{26.49 \text{ g } CH_4}{252 \text{ g mixture}}(100\%) = \textbf{10.5\% } CH_4$

Mass % $C_3H_8 = \dfrac{\text{mass of } C_3H_8}{\text{mass of mixture}}(100\%) = \dfrac{225.51 \text{ g } C_3H_8}{252 \text{ g mixture}}(100\%) = \textbf{89.5\% } C_3H_8$

3.167 Plan: If we assume a 100-gram sample of fertilizer, then the 30:10:10 percentages become the masses, in grams, of N, P_2O_5, and K_2O. These masses may be changed to amount (mol) of substance, and then to amount (mol) of each element. To get the desired x:y:1.0 ratio, divide the amount (mol) of each element by the amount (mol) of potassium.

Solution:

A 100-gram sample of 30:10:10 fertilizer contains 30 g N, 10 g P_2O_5, and 10 g K_2O.

Amount (mol) of N $= (30 \text{ g N})\left(\dfrac{1 \text{ mol N}}{14.01 \text{ g N}}\right) = 2.1413 \text{ mol N}$

Amount (mol) of P $= (10 \text{ g } P_2O_5)\left(\dfrac{1 \text{ mol } P_2O_5}{141.94 \text{ g } P_2O_5}\right)\left(\dfrac{2 \text{ mol P}}{1 \text{ mol } P_2O_5}\right) = 0.14090 \text{ mol P}$

Amount (mol) of K $= (10 \text{ g } K_2O)\left(\dfrac{1 \text{ mol } K_2O}{94.20 \text{ g } K_2O}\right)\left(\dfrac{2 \text{ mol K}}{1 \text{ mol } K_2O}\right) = 0.21231 \text{ mol K}$

This gives a N:P:K ratio of 2.1413:0.14090:0.21231

The ratio must be divided by the amount (mol) of K and rounded.

$$\frac{2.1413 \text{ mol N}}{0.21231} = 10.086 \qquad \frac{0.14090 \text{ mol P}}{0.21231} = 0.66365 \qquad \frac{0.21231 \text{ mol K}}{0.21231} = 1$$

$$10.086 : 0.66365 : 1.000 \qquad \text{or} \qquad \textbf{10 : 0.66 : 1.0}$$

3.172   <u>Plan:</u> Determine the molecular formula from the figure. Once the molecular formula is known, use the periodic table to determine the molar mass. Convert the volume of lemon juice in part b) from L to mL and use the density to convert from mL to mass in g. Take 6.82% of that mass to find the mass of citric acid and use the molar mass to convert to amount (mol).

<u>Solution:</u>

a) The formula of citric acid obtained by counting the number of carbon atoms, oxygen atoms, and hydrogen atoms is $\textbf{C}_6\textbf{H}_8\textbf{O}_7$.

     Molar mass = (6 x 12.01 g/mol C) + (8 x 1.008 g/mol H) + (7 x 16.00 g/mol O) = **192.12 g/mol**

b) Converting volume of lemon juice in L to mL:

$$\text{Volume (mL) of lemon juice} = (1.50 \text{ L})\left(\frac{1 \text{ mL}}{10^{-3} \text{ L}}\right) = 1.50 \times 10^3 \text{ mL}$$

Converting volume to mass in grams:

$$\text{Mass (g) of lemon juice} = (1.50 \times 10^3 \text{ mL})\left(\frac{1.09 \text{ g}}{\text{mL}}\right) = 1635 \text{ g lemon juice}$$

$$\text{Mass (g) of } C_6H_8O_7 = (1635 \text{ g lemon juice})\left(\frac{6.82\% \ C_6H_8O_7}{100\% \text{ lemon juice}}\right) = 111.507 \text{ g } C_6H_8O_7$$

$$\text{Amount (mol) of } C_6H_8O_7 = (111.507 \text{ g } C_6H_8O_7)\left(\frac{1 \text{ mol } C_6H_8O_7}{192.12 \text{ g } C_6H_8O_7}\right) = 0.580403 \text{ mol} = \textbf{0.580 mol } \textbf{C}_6\textbf{H}_8\textbf{O}_7$$

3.173   <u>Plan:</u> Determine the formulas of each reactant and product, then balance the individual equations. Remember that nitrogen and oxygen are diatomic. Combine the three smaller equations to give the overall equation, where some substances serve as intermediates and will cancel. Use the mole ratio between nitrogen and nitric acid in the overall equation to find the amount (mol) and then mass of nitric acid produced. The amount of nitrogen in metric tons must be converted to mass in grams to convert the mass of nitrogen to moles.

<u>Solution:</u>

a) Nitrogen and oxygen combine to form nitrogen monoxide:

     $\textbf{N}_2\textbf{(g)} + \textbf{O}_2\textbf{(g)} \rightarrow \textbf{2NO(g)}$

Nitrogen monoxide reacts with oxygen to form nitrogen dioxide:

     $\textbf{2NO(g)} + \textbf{O}_2\textbf{(g)} \rightarrow \textbf{2NO}_2\textbf{(g)}$

Nitrogen dioxide combines with water to form nitric acid and nitrogen monoxide:

     $\textbf{3NO}_2\textbf{(g)} + \textbf{H}_2\textbf{O(g)} \rightarrow \textbf{2HNO}_3\textbf{(aq)} + \textbf{NO(g)}$

b) Combining the reactions may involve adjusting the equations in various ways to cancel out as many materials as possible other than the reactants added and the desired products.

     $2 \times (N_2(g) + O_2(g) \rightarrow 2NO(g)) =$ $2N_2(g) + 2O_2(g) \rightarrow \cancel{4NO(g)}$

     $3 \times (2NO(g) + O_2(g) \rightarrow 2NO_2(g)) =$ $\cancel{6NO(g)} + 3O_2(g) \rightarrow \cancel{6NO_2(g)}$

     $2 \times (3NO_2(g) + H_2O(g) \rightarrow 2HNO_3(aq) + NO(g)) = \cancel{6NO_2(g)} + 2H_2O(g) \rightarrow 4HNO_3(aq) + \cancel{2NO(g)}$

Multiplying the above equations as shown results in the 6 moles of NO on each side and the 6 moles of NO₂ on each side canceling. Adding the equations gives:

     $\textbf{2N}_2\textbf{(g)} + \textbf{5O}_2\textbf{(g)} + \textbf{2H}_2\textbf{O(g)} \rightarrow \textbf{4HNO}_3\textbf{(aq)}$

c) $\text{Mass (g) of } N_2 = (1350 \text{ t } N_2)\left(\dfrac{10^3 \text{ kg}}{1 \text{t}}\right)\left(\dfrac{10^3 \text{ g}}{1 \text{ kg}}\right) = 1.35 \times 10^9 \text{ g } N_2$

$\text{Moles of } N_2 = (1.35 \times 10^9 \text{ g } N_2)\left(\dfrac{1 \text{ mol } N_2}{28.02 \text{ g } N_2}\right) = 4.817987 \times 10^7 \text{ mol } N_2$

$\text{Mass (g) of } HNO_3 = (4.817987 \times 10^7 \text{ mol } N_2)\left(\dfrac{4 \text{ mol } HNO_3}{2 \text{ mol } N_2}\right)\left(\dfrac{63.02 \text{ g } HNO_3}{1 \text{ mol } HNO_3}\right) = 6.072591 \times 10^9 \text{ g } HNO_3$

Mass (metric tons) HNO_3 =

$$\left(6.072591\times10^9 \text{ g } HNO_3\right)\left(\frac{1 \text{ kg}}{10^3 \text{ g}}\right)\left(\frac{1 \text{ t}}{10^3 \text{ kg}}\right) = 6.072591\times10^3 \text{ t} = \textbf{6.07x10}^3 \textbf{ t } \textbf{HNO}_3$$

3.174   Plan: Write and balance the chemical reaction. Use the mole ratio to find the amount of product that should be produced and take 66% of that amount to obtain the actual yield.
Solution:
$2NO(g) + O_2(g) \rightarrow 2NO_2(g)$
With 6 molecules of NO and 3 molecules of O_2 reacting, 6 molecules of NO_2 can be produced.
If the reaction only has a 66% yield, then $(0.66)(6) = 4$ molecules of NO_2 will be produced. **Circle A** shows the formation of 4 molecules of NO_2. Circle B also shows the formation of 4 molecules of NO_2 but also has 2 unreacted molecules of NO and 1 unreacted molecule of O_2. Since neither reactant is limiting, there will be no unreacted reactant remaining after the reaction is over.

3.176   Plan: Use the mass percent to find the mass of heme in the sample; use the molar mass to convert the mass of heme to amount (mol). Then find the mass of Fe in the sample by using the mole ratio between heme and iron. The mass of hemin is found by using the mole ratio between heme and hemoglobin.
Solution:

a) Mass (g) of heme = $\left(0.65 \text{ g hemoglobin}\right)\left(\dfrac{6.0\% \text{ heme}}{100\% \text{ hemoglobin}}\right)$ = **0.039 g heme**

b) Amount (mol) of heme = $\left(0.039 \text{ g heme}\right)\left(\dfrac{1 \text{ mol heme}}{616.49 \text{ g heme}}\right) = 6.32614\times10^{-5} \text{ mol} = \textbf{6.3x10}^{-5} \textbf{ mol heme}$

c) Mass (g) of Fe = $\left(6.32614\times10^{-5} \text{ mol heme}\right)\left(\dfrac{1 \text{ mol Fe}}{1 \text{ mol heme}}\right)\left(\dfrac{55.85 \text{ g Fe}}{1 \text{ mol Fe}}\right)$

$= 3.5331\times10^{-3} \text{ g} = \textbf{3.5x10}^{-3} \textbf{ g Fe}$

d) Mass (g) of hemin = $\left(6.32614\times10^{-5} \text{ mol heme}\right)\left(\dfrac{1 \text{ mol hemin}}{1 \text{ mol heme}}\right)\left(\dfrac{651.94 \text{ g hemin}}{1 \text{ mol hemin}}\right)$

$= 4.1243\times10^{-2} \text{ g} = \textbf{4.1x10}^{-2} \textbf{ g hemin}$

3.178   Plan: Determine the formula and the molar mass of each compound. The formula gives the relative number of amount (mol) of nitrogen present. Multiply the amount (mol) of nitrogen by its molar mass to find the total mass of nitrogen in 1 mole of compound. Mass percent = $\dfrac{\text{total mass of element}}{\text{molar mass of compound}}(100\%)$. For part b), convert mass of ornithine to amount (mol), use the mole ratio between ornithine and urea to find the moles of urea, and then use the ratio between amount (mol) of urea and nitrogen to find the amount (mol) and mass of nitrogen produced.

Solution:
a) Urea: CH_4N_2O, $\mathcal{M} = 60.06$ g/mol
There are 2 moles of N in 1 mole of CH_4N_2O.

Mass (g) of N = $\left(2 \text{ mol N}\right)\left(\dfrac{14.01 \text{ g N}}{1 \text{ mol N}}\right) = 28.02 \text{ g N}$

Mass percent = $\dfrac{\text{total mass N}}{\text{molar mass of compound}}(100\%) = \dfrac{28.02 \text{ g N}}{60.06 \text{ g } CH_4N_2O}(100\%) = 46.6533 \%$

$= \textbf{46.65\% N in urea}$

Arginine: $C_6H_{15}N_4O_2$, $\mathcal{M} = 175.22$ g/mol
There are 4 moles of N in 1 mole of $C_6H_{15}N_4O_2$.

Mass (g) of N = $\left(4 \text{ mol N}\right)\left(\dfrac{14.01 \text{ g N}}{1 \text{ mol N}}\right) = 56.04 \text{ g N}$

$$\text{Mass percent } = \frac{\text{total mass N}}{\text{molar mass of compound}}(100\%) = \frac{56.04 \text{ g N}}{175.22 \text{ g C}_6\text{H}_{15}\text{N}_4\text{O}_2}(100\%)$$

$$= 31.98265 \% = \textbf{31.98\% N in arginine}$$

Ornithine: $C_5H_{13}N_2O_2$, $\mathcal{M}$ = 133.17 g/mol

There are 2 moles of N in 1 mole of $C_5H_{13}N_2O_2$.

$$\text{Mass (g) of N} = \left(2 \text{ mol N}\right)\left(\frac{14.01 \text{ g N}}{1 \text{ mol N}}\right) = 28.02 \text{ g N}$$

$$\text{Mass percent } = \frac{\text{total mass N}}{\text{molar mass of compound}}(100\%) = \frac{28.02 \text{ g N}}{133.17 \text{ g C}_5\text{H}_{13}\text{N}_2\text{O}_2}(100\%)$$

$$= 21.04077 \% = \textbf{21.04\% N in ornithine}$$

b) Amount (mol) of urea $= \left(135.2 \text{ g C}_5\text{H}_{13}\text{N}_2\text{O}_2\right)\left(\frac{1 \text{ mol C}_5\text{H}_{13}\text{N}_2\text{O}_2}{133.17 \text{ g C}_5\text{H}_{13}\text{N}_2\text{O}_2}\right)\left(\frac{1 \text{ mol CH}_4\text{N}_2\text{O}}{1 \text{ mol C}_5\text{H}_{13}\text{N}_2\text{O}_2}\right)$

$$= 1.015244 \text{ mol urea}$$

Mass (g) of nitrogen $= \left(1.015244 \text{ mol CH}_4\text{N}_2\text{O}\right)\left(\frac{2 \text{ mol N}}{1 \text{ mol CH}_4\text{N}_2\text{O}}\right)\left(\frac{14.01 \text{ g N}}{1 \text{ mol N}}\right) = 28.447 \text{ g} = \textbf{28.45 g N}$

3.180 Plan: Determine the molar mass of each product and use the equation for percent atom economy.
Solution:
Molar masses of product: N_2H_4: 32.05 g/mol   NaCl: 58.44 g/mol H_2O: 18.02 g/mol

$$\% \text{ atom economy} = \frac{\text{no. of moles x molar mass of desired products}}{\text{sum of }\left(\text{no. of moles x molar mass}\right) \text{ for all products}} \text{ x } 100\%$$

$$= \frac{\left(1 \text{ mol}\right)\left(\text{molar mass of N}_2\text{H}_4\right)}{\left(1 \text{ mol}\right)\left(\text{molar mass of N}_2\text{H}_4\right) + \left(1 \text{ mol}\right)\left(\text{molar mass of NaCl}\right) + \left(1 \text{ mol}\right)\left(\text{molar mass of H}_2\text{O}\right)} \text{ x } 100\%$$

$$= \frac{\left(1 \text{ mol}\right)\left(32.05 \text{ g/mol}\right)}{\left(1 \text{ mol}\right)\left(32.05 \text{ g/mol}\right) + \left(1 \text{ mol}\right)\left(58.44 \text{ g/mol}\right) + \left(1 \text{ mol}\right)\left(18.02 \text{ g/mol}\right)} \text{ x } 100\%$$

$$= 29.5364 \% = \textbf{29.54\% atom economy}$$

3.182 Plan: Convert the mass of ethanol to amount (mol), and use the mole ratio between ethanol and diethyl ether to determine the theoretical yield of diethyl ether. The actual yield divided by the theoretical yield just calculated (with the result multiplied by 100%) gives the percent yield. The difference between the actual and theoretical yields is related to the quantity of ethanol that did not produce diethyl ether, forty-five percent of which produces ethylene instead. Use the mole ratio between ethanol and ethylene to find the mass of ethylene produced by the forty-five percent of ethanol that did not produce diethyl ether.
Solution:
a) The determination of the theoretical yield:
Mass (g) of diethyl ether =

$$\left(50.0 \text{ g CH}_3\text{CH}_2\text{OH}\right)\left(\frac{1 \text{ mol CH}_3\text{CH}_2\text{OH}}{46.07 \text{ g CH}_3\text{CH}_2\text{OH}}\right)\left(\frac{1 \text{ mol CH}_3\text{CH}_2\text{OCH}_2\text{CH}_3}{2 \text{ mol CH}_3\text{CH}_2\text{OH}}\right)\left(\frac{74.12 \text{ g CH}_3\text{CH}_2\text{OCH}_2\text{CH}_3}{1 \text{ mol CH}_3\text{CH}_2\text{OCH}_2\text{CH}_3}\right)$$

$$= 40.2214 \text{ g diethyl ether}$$

Determining the percent yield:

$$\text{Percent yield} = \left(\frac{\text{actual yield}}{\text{theoretical yield}}\right) \text{ x } 100\% = \left(\frac{35.9 \text{ g}}{40.2214 \text{ g}}\right) \text{ x } 100\% = 89.2560 \% = \textbf{89.3\% yield}$$

b) To determine the amount of ethanol not producing diethyl ether, we will use the difference between the theoretical yield and actual yield to determine the amount of diethyl ether that did not form and hence, the amount of ethanol that did not produce the desired product. Forty-five percent of this amount will be used to determine the amount of ethylene formed.

Mass difference = theoretical yield – actual yield = 40.2214 g – 35.9 g = 4.3214 g diethyl ether that did not form

Mass (g) of ethanol not producing diethyl ether =

$$\left(4.3214 \text{ g CH}_3\text{CH}_2\text{OCH}_2\text{CH}_3\right)\left(\frac{1 \text{ mol CH}_3\text{CH}_2\text{OCH}_2\text{CH}_3}{74.12 \text{ g CH}_3\text{CH}_2\text{OCH}_2\text{CH}_3}\right)\left(\frac{2 \text{ mol CH}_3\text{CH}_2\text{OH}}{1 \text{ mol CH}_3\text{CH}_2\text{OCH}_2\text{CH}_3}\right)\left(\frac{46.07 \text{ g CH}_3\text{CH}_2\text{OH}}{1 \text{ mol CH}_3\text{CH}_2\text{OH}}\right)$$

$$= 5.37202 \text{ g ethanol}$$

Mass of ethanol producing ethylene = $\left(5.37202 \text{ g CH}_3\text{CH}_2\text{OH}\right)\left(\frac{45.0\%}{100\%}\right) = 2.417409 \text{ g ethanol}$

Mass (g) of ethylene = $\left(2.417409 \text{ g CH}_3\text{CH}_2\text{OH}\right)\left(\frac{1 \text{ mol CH}_3\text{CH}_2\text{OH}}{46.07 \text{ g CH}_3\text{CH}_2\text{OH}}\right)\left(\frac{1 \text{ mol C}_2\text{H}_4}{1 \text{ mol CH}_3\text{CH}_2\text{OH}}\right)\left(\frac{28.05 \text{ g C}_2\text{H}_4}{1 \text{ mol C}_2\text{H}_4}\right)$

$$= 1.47185 \text{ g} = \textbf{1.47 g ethylene}$$

3.184   Plan: For part a), use the given solubility of the salt to find the mass that is soluble in the given volume of water. For part b), convert the mass of dissolved salt in part a) to amount (mol) of salt and then to amount (mol) of cocaine and then to mass of cocaine. Use the solubility of cocaine to find the volume of water needed to dissolve this mass of cocaine.

Solution:

a) Mass (g) of dissolved salt = $\left(50.0 \text{ mL H}_2\text{O}\right)\left(\frac{10^{-3} \text{ L H}_2\text{O}}{1 \text{ mL H}_2\text{O}}\right)\left(\frac{2.50 \text{ kg salt}}{1 \text{ L H}_2\text{O}}\right)\left(\frac{10^3 \text{ g}}{1 \text{ kg}}\right) = \textbf{125 g salt}$

b) Amount (mol) of dissolved salt = $\left(125 \text{ g salt}\right)\left(\frac{1 \text{ mol salt}}{339.81 \text{ g salt}}\right) = 0.367853 \text{ mol salt}$

Mass (g) cocaine = $\left(0.367853 \text{ mol salt}\right)\left(\frac{1 \text{ mol cocaine}}{1 \text{ mol salt}}\right)\left(\frac{303.35 \text{ g cocaine}}{1 \text{ mol cocaine}}\right) = 111.588 \text{ g cocaine}$

Volume (L) of water needed to dissolve the cocaine = $\left(111.588 \text{ g cocaine}\right)\left(\frac{1 \text{ L}}{1.70 \text{ g cocaine}}\right) = 65.64 \text{ L}$

Additional water needed = total volume needed – original volume of water

$$= 65.64 \text{ L} – 0.0500 \text{ L} = 65.59 \text{ L} = \textbf{65.6 L H}_2\textbf{O}$$

CHAPTER 4 GASES AND THE KINETIC-MOLECULAR THEORY

CHEMICAL CONNECTIONS BOXED READING PROBLEMS

B4.1   Plan: Examine the change in density of the atmosphere as altitude changes.
Solution:
The density of the atmosphere decreases with increasing altitude. High density causes more drag
on the aircraft. At high altitudes, low density means that there are relatively few gas particles
present to collide with the aircraft.

B4.3   Plan: To find the volume percent of argon, multiply its mole fraction by 100. The partial pressure of argon gas can
be found by using the relationship $p_{Ar} = X_{Ar} \times p_{total}$. The mole fraction of argon is given in Table B4.1.
Solution:
Volume percent = mole fraction x 100 = 0.00934 x 100% = **0.934 %**
The total pressure at sea level is 101.3 kPa
$p_{Ar} = X_{Ar} \times p_{total}$ = 0.00934 x 101.3 kPa = 0.946142 .kPa = 946 Pa

END–OF–CHAPTER PROBLEMS

4.1   Plan: Review the behaviour of the gas phase vs. the liquid phase.
Solution:
a) The volume of the liquid remains constant, but the volume of the gas increases to the volume of the larger
container.
b) The volume of the container holding the gas sample increases when heated, but the volume of the container
holding the liquid sample remains essentially constant when heated.
c) The volume of the liquid remains essentially constant, but the volume of the gas is reduced.

4.6   Plan: The ratio of the heights of columns of mercury and water are inversely proportional to the ratio of the
densities of the two liquids. Convert the height in mm to height in cm.
Solution:

$$\frac{h_{H_2O}}{h_{Hg}} = \frac{d_{Hg}}{d_{H_2O}}$$

$$h_{H_2O} = \frac{d_{Hg}}{d_{H_2O}} \times h_{Hg} = \left(\frac{13.5\ g/mL}{1.00\ g/mL}\right)(730\ mmHg)\left(\frac{10^{-3}\ m}{1\ mm}\right)\left(\frac{1\ cm}{10^{-2}\ m}\right) = 985.5\ cm = \textbf{990 cm } \textbf{H}_2\textbf{O}$$

4.8   Plan: Use the conversion factors between pressure units:
1 atm = 760 mmHg = 760 Torr = 101.325 kPa = 1.01325 bar = 1.01325×10^5 Pa
Solution:

a) Converting from atm to kPa: $p(kPa) = (0.745\ atm)\left(\dfrac{101.325\ kPa}{1\ atm}\right) = 75.4871\ kPa = \textbf{75.5 kPa}$

b) Converting from Torr to bar: $p(bar) = (992\ Torr)\left(\dfrac{1.01325\ bar}{760\ Torr}\right) = 1.32256\ bar = \textbf{1.32 bar}$

c) Converting from kPa to Pa: $p(Pa) = (36.5\ kPa)\left(\dfrac{1000\ Pa}{1\ kPa}\right) = 3.6500\ \times 10^4\ Pa = \textbf{3.65} \times \textbf{10}^4\textbf{ Pa}$

d) Converting from mmHg to kPa: $p(kPa) = (804\ mmHg)\left(\dfrac{101.325\ kPa}{760\ mmHg}\right) = 107.191\ kPa = \textbf{107 kPa}$

4.10   Plan: This is an open-end manometer. Since the height of the mercury column in contact with the gas is higher than the column in contact with the air, the gas is exerting less pressure on the mercury than the air. Therefore the pressure corresponding to the height difference (Δh) between the two arms is subtracted from the atmospheric pressure. Since the height difference is in units of cm and the barometric pressure is given in units of Torr, cm must be converted to mm and then Torr before the subtraction is performed. The overall pressure is then given in units of bar.
Solution:

$$\left(2.35 \text{ cm}\right)\left(\frac{10 \text{ mm}}{1 \text{ cm}}\right)\left(\frac{1 \text{ Torr}}{1 \text{ mmHg}}\right) = 23.5 \text{ Torr}$$

738.5 Torr – 23.5 Torr = 715.0 Torr

$$p(\text{bar}) = \left(715.0 \text{ torr}\right)\left(\frac{1.01325 \text{ bar}}{760 \text{ torr}}\right) = 0.9532540789 \text{ bar} = \textbf{0.953 bar}$$

4.12   Plan: This is a closed-end manometer. The difference in the height of the Hg (Δh) equals the gas pressure. The height difference is given in units of m and must be converted to mmHg and then to bar.
Solution:

$$p(\text{bar}) = \left(0.734 \text{ mHg}\right)\left(\frac{1 \text{ mmHg}}{10^{-3} \text{ mHg}}\right)\left(\frac{1.01325 \text{ bar}}{760 \text{ mmHg}}\right) = 0.97859 \text{ bar} = \textbf{0.979 bar}$$

4.18   Plan: Examine the ideal gas law; volume and temperature are constant and pressure and amount in moles are variable.
Solution:

$$pV = nRT \qquad p = n\frac{RT}{V} \qquad R, T, \text{ and } V \text{ are constant}$$

$p = n$ x constant
At constant temperature and volume, the pressure of the gas is directly proportional to the amount of gas in moles.

4.20   Plan: Use the relationship $\dfrac{p_1 V_1}{n_1 T_1} = \dfrac{p_2 V_2}{n_2 T_2}$ or $V_2 = \dfrac{p_1 V_1 n_2 T_2}{p_2 n_1 T_1}$.

Solution:
a) As the pressure on a fixed amount of gas (n is fixed) increases at constant temperature (T is fixed), the molecules move closer together, decreasing the volume. When the pressure is tripled, the **volume decreases to one-third of the original volume** at constant temperature (Boyle's law).

$$V_2 = \frac{p_1 V_1 n_2 T_2}{p_2 n_1 T_1} = \frac{(p_1)(V_1)(1)(1)}{(3P_1)(1)(1)} \qquad V_2 = \tfrac{1}{3}V_1$$

b) As the temperature of a fixed amount of gas (n is fixed) increases at constant pressure (p is fixed), the gas molecules gain kinetic energy. With higher energy, the gas molecules collide with the walls of the container with greater force, which increases the size (volume) of the container. If the temperature is increased by a factor of 3.0 (at constant pressure) then the **volume will increase by a factor of 3.0** (Charles's law).

$$V_2 = \frac{p_1 V_1 n_2 T_2}{p_2 n_1 T_1} = \frac{(1)(V_1)(1)(3T_1)}{(1)(1)(T_1)} \qquad V_2 = 3V_1$$

c) As the number of molecules of gas increases at constant pressure and temperature (p and T are fixed), the force they exert on the container increases. This results in an increase in the volume of the container. Adding 3 moles of gas to 1 mole increases the amount in moles by a factor of 4, thus the **volume increases by a factor of 4** (Avogadro's law).

$$V_2 = \frac{p_1 V_1 n_2 T_2}{p_2 n_1 T_1} = \frac{(1)(V_1)(4n_1)(1)}{(1)(n_1)(1)} \qquad V_2 = 4V_1$$

4.22   <u>Plan:</u> Use the relationship $\dfrac{p_1V_1}{T_1} = \dfrac{p_2V_2}{T_2}$ or $V_2 = \dfrac{p_1V_1T_2}{p_2T_1}$. R and n are fixed.

<u>Solution:</u>
a) The temperature is decreased by a factor of 2, so **the volume is decreased by a factor of 2** (Charles's law).

$$V_2 = \frac{p_1V_1T_2}{p_2T_1} = \frac{(1)(V_1)(400\ K)}{(1)(800\ K)} \qquad V_2 = \tfrac{1}{2}\,V_1$$

b) $T_1 = 250°C + 273 = 523\ K$ $\qquad\qquad\qquad\qquad T_2 = 500°C + 273 = 773\ K$
The temperature increases by a factor of $773/523 = 1.48$, so **the volume is increased by a factor of 1.48**

(Charles's law). $\qquad V_2 = \dfrac{p_1V_1T_2}{p_2T_1} = \dfrac{(1)(V_1)(773\ K)}{(1)(523\ K)} \qquad V_2 = 1.48V_1$

c) The pressure is increased by a factor of 3, so **the volume decreases by a factor of 3** (Boyle's law).

$$V_2 = \frac{p_1V_1T_2}{p_2T_1} = \frac{(2\ bar)(V_1)(1)}{(6\ bar)(1)} \qquad\qquad V_2 = \tfrac{1}{3}V_1$$

4.24   <u>Plan:</u> This is Charles's law: at constant pressure and with a fixed amount of gas, the volume of a gas is directly proportional to the absolute temperature of the gas. The temperature must be lowered to reduce the volume of a gas. Arrange the ideal gas law, solving for T_2 at fixed n and p. Temperature must be converted to kelvin.
<u>Solution:</u>
$V_1 = 9.10\ L$ $\qquad\qquad\qquad\qquad\qquad V_2 = 2.50\ L$
$T_1 = 198°C$ (convert to K) $\qquad\qquad T_2 = $ unknown
n and p remain constant
Converting T from °C to K: $T_1 = 198°C + 273 = 471K$
Arranging the ideal gas law and solving for T_2:

$$\frac{\not{p}_1V_1}{\not{n}_1T_1} = \frac{\not{p}_2V_2}{\not{n}_2T_2} \quad \text{or} \quad \frac{V_1}{T_1} = \frac{V_2}{T_2}$$

$$T_2 = T_1\frac{V_2}{V_1} = 471\ K\left(\frac{2.50\ L}{9.10\ L}\right) = 129.396\ K - 273 = -143.604\ °C = \mathbf{-144°C}$$

4.26   <u>Plan:</u> Since the volume, temperature, and pressure of the gas are changing, use the combined gas law. Arrange the ideal gas law, solving for V_2 at fixed n. STP is 0°C (273 K) and 1 bar
<u>Solution:</u>
$p_1 = 153.3\ kPa$ $\qquad\qquad\qquad\qquad p_2 = 1\ bar = 1bar\ (100\ kPa/1\ bar) = 100\ kPa$
$V_1 = 25.5\ L$ $\qquad\qquad\qquad\qquad\qquad V_2 = $ unknown
$T_1 = 298\ K$ $\qquad\qquad\qquad\qquad\qquad T_2 = 273\ K$
n remains constant
Arranging the ideal gas law and solving for V_2:

$$\frac{p_1V_1}{\not{n}_1T_1} = \frac{p_2V_2}{\not{n}_2T_2} \quad \text{or} \quad \frac{p_1V_1}{T_1} = \frac{p_2V_2}{T_2}$$

$$V_2 = V_1\left(\frac{T_2}{T_1}\right)\left(\frac{p_1}{p_2}\right) = (25.5\ L)\left(\frac{273\ K}{298\ K}\right)\left(\frac{153.3\ kPa}{100\ kPa}\right) = 35.81201\ L = \mathbf{35.8\ L}$$

4.28   <u>Plan:</u> Given the volume, pressure, and temperature of a gas, the amount in moles of the gas can be calculated using the ideal gas law, solving for n. The gas constant, $R = 8.31446\ L{\cdot}kPa/mol{\cdot}K$, gives pressure in kPa and temperature in kelvin. The given temperature must be converted to kelvin.
<u>Solution:</u>
$p = 32.8\ kPa$ $\qquad V = 5.0\ L$
$T = 37°C$ $\qquad\qquad\qquad\qquad\qquad n = $ unknown

Converting T from °C to K: $\qquad T = 37°C + 273 = 310\ K$
$pV = nRT$

Solving for n:

$$n = \frac{pV}{RT} = \frac{(74.5\ \text{kPa})(5.0\ \text{L})}{\left(8.31446\ \dfrac{\text{L}\cdot\text{kPa}}{\text{mol}\cdot\text{K}}\right)(310\ \text{K})} = 0.144521\ \text{mol} = \mathbf{0.14\ mol\ chlorine}$$

4.30   Plan: Solve the ideal gas law for amount (mol) and convert to mass using the molar mass of ClF_3.
The gas constant, $R = 8.31446$ L•kPa/mol•K, gives volume in litres, pressure in kPa, and temperature in kelvin so volume must be converted to L and temperature to K.
Solution:
$V = 357$ mL $T = 45°C$
$p = 69.9$ kPa $n =$ unknown

Converting V from mL to L: $V = \left(357\ \text{mL}\right)\left(\dfrac{10^{-3}\ \text{L}}{1\ \text{mL}}\right) = 0.357\ \text{L}$

Converting T from °C to K: $T = 45°C + 273 = 318\ \text{K}$
$pV = nRT$
Solving for n:

$$n = \frac{pV}{RT} = \frac{(69.9\ \text{kPa})(0.357\ \text{L})}{\left(8.31446\ \dfrac{\text{L}\cdot\text{kPa}}{\text{mol}\cdot\text{K}}\right)(318\ \text{K})} = 0.009438\ \text{mol}\ ClF_3$$

$$\text{Mass}\ ClF_3 = \left(0.009438\ \text{mol}\ ClF_3\right)\left(\frac{92.45\ \text{g}\ ClF_3}{1\ \text{mol}\ ClF_3}\right) = 0.87255\ \text{g} = \mathbf{0.873\ g\ ClF_3}$$

4.33   Plan: Assuming that while rising in the atmosphere the balloon will neither gain nor lose gas molecules, the amount in moles of gas calculated at sea level will be the same as the amount in moles of gas at the higher altitude (n is fixed). Volume, temperature, and pressure of the gas are changing. Arrange the ideal gas law, solving for V_2 at fixed n. Given the sea-level conditions of volume, pressure, and temperature, and the temperature and pressure at the higher altitude for the gas in the balloon, we can set up an equation to solve for the volume at the higher altitude. Comparing the calculated volume to the given maximum volume of 835 L will tell us if the balloon has reached its maximum volume at this altitude. Temperature must be converted to kelvin and pressure in bar must be converted to kPa for unit agreement.
Solution:
$p_1 = 0.993$ barr $p_2 = 6.9$ kPa
$V_1 = 65$ L $V_2 =$ unknown
$T_1 = 25°C + 273 = 298\ \text{K}$ $T_2 = -5°C + 273 = 268\ \text{K}$
n remains constant

Converting p from bar to kPa: $p = \left(0.993\ \text{bar}\right)\left(\dfrac{101.3\ \text{kPa}}{1.1013\ \text{bar}}\right) = 99.3\ \text{kPa}$

Arranging the ideal gas law and solving for V_2:

$$\frac{p_1 V_1}{\cancel{n}_1 T_1} = \frac{p_2 V_2}{\cancel{n}_2 T_2} \quad \text{or} \quad \frac{p_1 V_1}{T_1} = \frac{p_2 V_2}{T_2}$$

$$V_2 = V_1 \left(\frac{T_2}{T_1}\right)\left(\frac{p_1}{p_2}\right) = \left(65\ \text{L}\right)\left(\frac{268\ \text{K}}{298\ \text{K}}\right)\left(\frac{99.3\ \text{kPa}}{6.9\ \text{kPa}}\right) = 841.26\ \text{L} = \mathbf{840\ L}$$

The calculated volume of the gas at the higher altitude is more than the maximum volume of the balloon. **Yes**, the balloon will reach its maximum volume.
Check: Should we expect that the volume of the gas in the balloon should increase? At the higher altitude, the pressure decreases; this increases the volume of the gas. At the higher altitude, the temperature decreases, this decreases the volume of the gas. Which of these will dominate? The pressure decreases by a factor of 99.3/6.9 = 14.4. If we label the initial volume V_1, then the resulting volume is $14.4V_1$. The temperature decreases by a factor of 298/268 = 1.1, so the resulting volume is $V_1/1.1$ or $0.91V_1$. The increase in volume due to the change

in pressure is greater than the decrease in volume due to change in temperature, so the volume of gas at the higher altitude should be greater than the volume at sea level.

4.35   The molar mass of H_2 is less than the average molar mass of air (mostly N_2, O_2, and Ar), so air is denser. To collect a beaker of $H_2(g)$, **invert** the beaker so that the air will be replaced by the lighter H_2. The molar mass of CO_2 is greater than the average molar mass of air, so $CO_2(g)$ is more dense. Collect the CO_2 holding the beaker **upright**, so the lighter air will be displaced out the top of the beaker.

4.39   <u>Plan:</u> Rearrange the ideal gas law to calculate the density of xenon from its molar mass at STP. Standard temperature is 0°C (273 K) and standard pressure is 100 kPa. Do not forget that the pressure at STP is exact and will not affect the significant figures.
<u>Solution:</u>
$p = 100$ kPa $T = 273$ K
$\mathcal{M}$ of Xe $= 131.3$ g/mol $d =$ unknown
$pV = nRT$
Rearranging to solve for density:
$$d = \frac{p\mathcal{M}}{RT} = \frac{(100 \text{ kPa})(131.3 \text{ g/mol})}{\left(8.31446 \dfrac{\text{L} \cdot \text{kPa}}{\text{mol} \cdot \text{K}}\right)(273 \text{ K})} = 5.7845 \text{ g/L} = \mathbf{5.78 \text{ g/L}}$$

4.41   <u>Plan:</u> Solve the ideal gas law for amount in moles. Convert amount in moles to mass using the molar mass of AsH_3 and divide this mass by the volume to obtain density in g/L. Standard temperature is 0°C (273 K) and standard pressure is 100 kPa. Do not forget that the pressure at STP is exact and will not affect the significant figures.
<u>Solution:</u>
$V = 0.0400$ L $T = 0°C + 273 = 273$ K
$p = 100$ kPa $n =$ unknown
$\mathcal{M}$ of $AsH_3 = 77.94$ g/mol
$pV = nRT$
Solving for n:
$$n = \frac{pV}{RT} = \frac{(100 \text{ kPa})(0.0400 \text{ L})}{\left(8.31446 \dfrac{\text{L} \cdot \text{kPa}}{\text{mol} \cdot \text{K}}\right)(273 \text{ K})} = 1.76223 \times 10^{-3} \text{ mol} = \mathbf{1.76 \times 10^{-3} \text{ mol } AsH_3}$$

Converting amount in moles of AsH_3 to mass of AsH_3:
$$\text{Mass (g) of } AsH_3 = \left(1.76223 \times 10^{-3} \text{ mol } AsH_3\right)\left(\frac{77.94 \text{ g } AsH_3}{1 \text{ mol } AsH_3}\right) = 0.1373 \text{ g } AsH_3$$

$$d = \frac{\text{mass}}{\text{volume}} = \frac{(0.1373 \text{ g})}{(0.0400 \text{ L})} = 3.4337 \text{ g} = \mathbf{3.43 \text{ g/L}}$$

4.43   <u>Plan:</u> Rearrange the formula $pV = (m/\mathcal{M})RT$ to solve for molar mass. Convert the mass in ng to g and volume in µL to L. Temperature must be in kelvin.
<u>Solution:</u>
$V = 0.206$ µL $T = 45°C + 273 = 318$ K
$p = 0.517$ bar $m = 206$ ng
$\mathcal{M} =$ unknown
kPa

Converting V from µL to L: $V = (0.206 \text{ µL})\left(\dfrac{10^{-6} \text{ L}}{1 \text{ µL}}\right) = 2.06 \times 10^{-7} \text{ L}$

Converting m from ng to g: $m = (206 \text{ ng})\left(\dfrac{10^{-9} \text{ g}}{1 \text{ ng}}\right) = 2.06 \times 10^{-7} \text{ g}$

$$pV = \left(\frac{m}{\mathcal{M}}\right)RT$$

Solving for molar mass, $\mathcal{M}$:

$$\mathcal{M} = \frac{mRT}{pV} = \frac{\left(2.06 \times 10^{-7} \text{ g}\right)\left(0.08314\,\frac{\text{L·bar}}{\text{mol·K}}\right)\left(318 \text{ K}\right)}{\left(0.517 \text{ bar}\right)\left(2.06 \times 10^{-7} \text{ L}\right)} = 51.1383 \text{ g/mol} = \textbf{51.1 g/mol}$$

4.45   Plan: Use the ideal gas law to determine the amount in moles of Ar and of O_2. The gases are combined
($n_{total} = n_{Ar} + n_{O_2}$) into a 400 mL flask ($V$) at 27°C ($T$). Use the ideal gas law again to determine the total pressure
from n_{total}, V, and T. Volume must be in units of L and temperature in K.
Solution:
For Ar:
V = 0.600 L T = 227°C + 273 = 500. K
p = 1.22 bar n = unknown
$pV = nRT$
Solving for n:

$$n = \frac{pV}{RT} = \frac{\left(1.22 \text{ bar}\right)\left(0.600 \text{ L}\right)}{\left(0.08314\,\dfrac{\text{L·bar}}{\text{mol·K}}\right)\left(500.\text{ K}\right)} = 0.017608852 \text{ mol Ar}$$

For O_2:
V = 0.200 L T = 127°C + 273 = 400. K
p = 66.8 kPa n = unknown
$pV = nRT$
Solving for n:

$$n = \frac{pV}{RT} = \frac{\left(66.8 \text{ kPa}\right)\left(0.200 \text{ L}\right)}{\left(8.31446\,\dfrac{\text{L·kPa}}{\text{mol·K}}\right)\left(400.\text{ K}\right)} = 0.004017097 \text{ mol } O_2$$

$n_{total} = n_{Ar} + n_{O_2}$ = 0.017608852 mol + 0.004017097 mol = 0.021625931 mol
For the mixture of Ar and O_2:
V = 400 mL T = 27°C + 273 = 300. K
p = unknownn n = 0.021554265 mol

Converting V from mL to L: $V = \left(400 \text{ mL}\right)\left(\dfrac{10^{-3} \text{ L}}{1 \text{ mL}}\right) = 0.400$ L

$pV = nRT$
Solving for p:

$$p_{mixture} = \frac{nRT}{V} = \frac{\left(0.021624651 \text{ mol}\right)\left(8.31446\,\dfrac{\text{L·kPa}}{\text{mol·K}}\right)\left(300 \text{ K}\right)}{\left(0.400 \text{ L}\right)} = 134.848 \text{ kPa} = \textbf{135 kPa} = \textbf{1.35 bar}$$

4.47   Plan: Use the ideal gas law, solving for n to find the amount (mol) of O_2. Use the molar ratio from the balanced
equation to determine the amount in moles (and then mass) of phosphorus that will react with the oxygen.
Standard temperature is 0°C (273 K) and standard pressure is 100 kPa.
Solution:
V = 35.5 L T = 0°C + 273 = 273 K
p = 100 kPa n = unknown
$pV = nRT$
Solving for n:

$$n = \frac{pV}{RT} = \frac{(100 \text{ kPa})(35.5 \text{ L})}{\left(8.31446 \frac{\text{L} \cdot \text{kPa}}{\text{mol} \cdot \text{K}}\right)(273 \text{ K})} = 1.563982 \text{ mol O}_2$$

$$P_4(s) + 5O_2(g) \rightarrow P_4O_{10}(s)$$

$$\text{Mass P}_4 = (1.563982 \text{ mol O}_2)\left(\frac{1 \text{ mol P}_4}{5 \text{ mol O}_2}\right)\left(\frac{123.88 \text{ g P}_4}{1 \text{ mol P}_4}\right) = 38.7492 \text{ g} = \mathbf{38.7 \text{ g P}_4}$$

4.49   Plan: Since the amounts of two reactants are given, this is a limiting reactant problem. To find the mass of PH_3, write the balanced equation and use molar ratios to find the amount in moles of PH_3 produced by each reactant. The smaller amount in moles of product indicates the limiting reagent. Solve for amount in moles of H_2 using the ideal gas law.
Solution:
Amount (mol) of hydrogen:
$V = 83.0 \text{ L}$ 　　　　　　　　　　$T = 0°C + 273 = 273 \text{ K}$
$p = 100 \text{ kPa}$ 　　　　　　　　　　$n = \text{unknown}$
$pV = nRT$
Solving for n:

$$n = \frac{pV}{RT} = \frac{(100 \text{ kPa})(83.0 \text{ L})}{\left(8.31446 \frac{\text{L} \cdot \text{kPa}}{\text{mol} \cdot \text{K}}\right)(273 \text{ K})} = 3.656633 \text{ mol H}_2$$

$$P_4(s) + 6H_2(g) \rightarrow 4PH_3(g)$$

$$\text{PH}_3 \text{ from H}_2 = (3.656633 \text{ mol H}_2)\left(\frac{4 \text{ mol PH}_3}{6 \text{ mol H}_2}\right) = 2.43775546 \text{ mol PH}_3$$

$$\text{PH}_3 \text{ from P}_4 = (37.5 \text{ g P}_4)\left(\frac{1 \text{ mol P}_4}{123.88 \text{ g P}_4}\right)\left(\frac{4 \text{ mol PH}_3}{1 \text{ mol P}_4}\right) = 1.21085 \text{ mol PH}_3$$

P_4 is the limiting reactant because it forms less PH_3.

$$\text{Mass PH}_3 = (37.5 \text{ g P}_4)\left(\frac{1 \text{ mol P}_4}{123.88 \text{ g P}_4}\right)\left(\frac{4 \text{ mol PH}_3}{1 \text{ mol P}_4}\right)\left(\frac{33.99 \text{ g PH}_3}{1 \text{ mol PH}_3}\right) = 41.15676 \text{ g} = \mathbf{41.2 \text{ g PH}_3}$$

4.51   Plan: First, write the balanced equation. The amount (mol) of hydrogen produced can be calculated from the ideal gas law. The problem specifies that the hydrogen gas is collected over water, so the partial pressure of water vapour must be subtracted from the overall pressure given. Table 4.2 reports the pressure at 27°C as 3.5681 kPa. Volume must be in units of litres, pressure in kPa, and temperature in kelvin. Once the amount in moles of hydrogen produced are known, the molar ratio from the balanced equation is used to determine the amount in moles of aluminum that reacted.
Solution:
$$2Al(s) + 6HCl(aq) \rightarrow 2AlCl_3(aq) + 3H_2(g)$$

$V = 35.8 \text{ mL} = 0.0358 \text{ L}$ 　　　　　　　　$T = 27°C + 273 = 300 \text{ K}$
$p_{\text{total}} = 1.00 \text{ bar}$ 　　$= 100 \text{ kPa}$ 　　　　$n = \text{unknown}$
$p_{\text{water vapour}} = 3.5681 \text{ kPa}$
$p_{\text{hydrogen}} = p_{\text{total}} - p_{\text{water vapour}} = 100 \text{ kPa} - 3.5681 \text{ kPa} = 96.4319 \text{ kPa}$

Converting V from mL to L: 　　　　　$V = (35.8 \text{ mL})\left(\frac{10^{-3} \text{ L}}{1 \text{ mL}}\right) = 0.0358 \text{ L}$

$pV = nRT$
Solving for n:

$$n = \frac{pV}{RT} = \frac{(96.4319 \text{ kPa})(0.0358 \text{ L})}{\left(8.31446 \dfrac{\text{L} \cdot \text{kPa}}{\text{mol} \cdot \text{K}}\right)(300. \text{ K})} = 0.00138404 \text{ mol } H_2$$

$$\text{Mass (g) of Al} = (0.00138404 \text{ mol } H_2)\left(\frac{2 \text{ mol Al}}{3 \text{ mol } H_2}\right)\left(\frac{26.98 \text{ g Al}}{1 \text{ mol Al}}\right) = 0.0248943 \text{ g} = \textbf{0.0249 g Al}$$

4.55   Plan: The problem gives the mass, volume, temperature, and pressure of a gas; rearrange the formula
$PV = (m/\mathcal{M})RT$ to solve for the molar mass of the gas. Temperature must be in kelvin and pressure in bar. The
problem also states that the gas is a hydrocarbon, which by, definition, contains only carbon and hydrogen atoms.
We are also told that each molecule of the gas contains five carbon atoms so we can use this information and the
calculated molar mass to find out how many hydrogen atoms are present and the formula of the compound.
Solution:
$V = 0.204$ L $T = 101°C + 273 = 374$ K
$p = 1.02$ bar $m = 0.482$ g
$\mathcal{M} = $ unknown

$$pV = \left(\frac{m}{\mathcal{M}}\right)RT$$

Solving for molar mass, $\mathcal{M}$:

$$\mathcal{M} = \frac{mRT}{pV} = \frac{(0.482 \text{ g})\left(0.08314 \dfrac{\text{L} \cdot \text{bar}}{\text{mol} \cdot \text{K}}\right)(374 \text{ K})}{(1.02 \text{ bar})(0.204 \text{ L})} = 72.0275 \text{ g/mol (unrounded)}$$

The mass of the five carbon atoms accounts for [5(12 g/mol)] = 60 g/mol; thus, the hydrogen atoms must make up
the difference (72 – 60) = 12 g/mol. A value of 12 g/mol corresponds to 12 H atoms. (Since fractional atoms are
not possible, rounding is acceptable.) Therefore, the molecular formula is $\textbf{C}_5\textbf{H}_{12}$.

4.57   Plan: Since you have the pressure, volume, and temperature, use the ideal gas law to solve for n, the total
amount (mol) of gas. Pressure must be in units of bar and temperature in units of kelvin. The partial pressure
of SO_2 can be found by multiplying the total pressure by the volume fraction of SO_2.
Solution:
a) $V = 21$ L $T = 45°C + 273 = 318$ K
  $p = 1.13$ bar $n = $ unknown
$pV = nRT$

$$\text{Amount (mol) of gas} = n = \frac{pV}{RT} = \frac{(1.13 \text{ bar})(21 \text{ L})}{\left(0.08314 \dfrac{\text{L} \cdot \text{bar}}{\text{mol} \cdot \text{K}}\right)(318 \text{ K})} = 0.89755 \text{ mol} = \textbf{0.90 mol gas}$$

b) The equation $p_{SO_2} = X_{SO_2} \times p_{\text{total}}$ can be used to find partial pressure. The information given in ppm is a way
of expressing the proportion, or fraction, of SO_2 present in the mixture. Since n is directly proportional to V, the
volume fraction can be used in place of the *mole* fraction, X_{SO_2}. There are 7.95×10^3 parts SO_2 in a million parts
of mixture, so volume fraction = $(7.95 \times 10^3 / 1 \times 10^6) = 7.95 \times 10^{-3}$.
$p_{SO_2} = $ volume fraction x $p_{\text{total}} = (7.95 \times 10^{-3})(1.13 \text{ bar}) = 0.0089835 \text{ bar} = \textbf{0.00898 bar}$

4.58   Plan: First, write the balanced equation. Convert mass of P_4S_3 to amount (mol) and use the molar ratio from the
balanced equation to find the amount in moles of SO_2 gas produced. Use the ideal gas law to find the volume of
that amount of SO_2. Temperature must be in units of kelvin.
Solution:
$$P_4S_3(s) + 8O_2(g) \rightarrow P_4O_{10}(s) + 3SO_2(g)$$

$$\text{amount in moles } SO_2 = (0.800 \text{ g } P_4S_3)\left(\frac{1 \text{ mol } P_4S_3}{220.09 \text{ g } P_4S_3}\right)\left(\frac{3 \text{ mol } SO_2}{1 \text{ mol } P_4S_3}\right) = 0.010905 \text{ mol } SO_2$$

Finding the volume of SO_2:
V = unknown $\qquad\qquad\qquad\qquad T = 32°C + 273 = 305$ K
$p = 96.7$ kPa $\qquad\qquad\qquad\qquad n = 0.010905$ mol
$pV = nRT$
Solving for V:

$$V = \frac{nRT}{p} = \frac{(0.010905 \text{ mol})\left(8.31446\frac{\text{L•atm}}{\text{mol•K}}\right)(305 \text{ K})}{(96.7 \text{ kPa})} = 0.285978 \text{ L}$$

Converting V from L to mL:

$$V = (0.285978 \text{ L})\left(\frac{1 \text{ mL}}{10^{-3} \text{ L}}\right) = 285.99 = \textbf{286 mL } SO_2$$

4.60   Plan: First, write the balanced equation. Given the amount of xenon hexafluoride that reacts, we can find the amount in moles of silicon tetrafluoride gas formed by using the molar ratio in the balanced equation. Then, using the ideal gas law with the amount in moles of gas, the temperature, and the volume, we can calculate the pressure of the silicon tetrafluoride gas.   Temperature must be in units of kelvin.
Solution:

$$2XeF_6(s) + SiO_2(s) \rightarrow 2XeOF_4(l) + SiF_4(g)$$

$$\text{amount in moles } SiF_4 = n = (2.00 \text{ g } XeF_6)\left(\frac{1 \text{ mol } XeF_6}{245.3 \text{ g } XeF_6}\right)\left(\frac{1 \text{ mol } SiF_4}{2 \text{ mol } XeF_6}\right) = 0.0040766 \text{ mol } SiF_4$$

Finding the pressure of SiF_4:
$V = 1.00$ L $\qquad\qquad\qquad\qquad T = 25°C + 273 = 298$ K
p = unknown $\qquad\qquad\qquad\qquad n = 0.0040766$ mol
$pV = nRT$
Solving for p:

$$\text{Pressure } SiF_4 = p = \frac{nRT}{V} = \frac{(0.0040766 \text{ mol } SiF_4)\left(8.31446\frac{\text{L•kPa}}{\text{mol•K}}\right)(298 \text{ K})}{1.00 \text{ L}} = 10.1006 \text{ kPa} = \textbf{10.1 kPa } SiF_4$$

4.65   At STP (or any identical temperature and pressure), the volume occupied by a mole of any gas will be identical. One mole of krypton has the same number of particles as one mole of helium and, at the same temperature, all of the gas particles have the same average kinetic energy, resulting in the same pressure and volume.

4.68   Plan: The molar masses of the three gases are 2.016 for H_2 (Flask A), 4.003 for He (Flask B), and 16.04 for CH_4 (Flask C). Since hydrogen has the smallest molar mass of the three gases, 4 g of H_2 will contain more gas molecules (about 2 mole's worth) than 4 g of He or 4 g of CH_4. Since helium has a smaller molar mass than methane, 4 g of He will contain more gas molecules (about 1 mole's worth) than 4 g of CH_4 (about 0.25 mole's worth).
Solution:
a) $\textbf{p}_A > \textbf{p}_B > \textbf{p}_C$ The pressure of a gas is proportional to the number of gas molecules ($pV = nRT$). So, the gas sample with more gas molecules will have a greater pressure.
b) $E_A = E_B = E_C$ Average kinetic energy depends only on temperature. The temperature of each gas sample is 273 K, so they all have the same average kinetic energy.
c) $\textbf{rate}_A > \textbf{rate}_B > \textbf{rate}_C$ When comparing the speed of two gas molecules, the one with the lower mass travels faster.
d) $\textbf{total } E_A > \textbf{total } E_B > \textbf{total } E_C$ Since the average kinetic energy for each gas is the same (part b) of this problem), the total kinetic energy would equal the average times the number of molecules. Since the hydrogen flask contains the most molecules, its total kinetic energy will be the greatest.
e) $d_A = d_B = d_C$ Under the conditions stated in this problem, each sample has the same volume, 5 L, and the same mass, 4 g. Thus, the density of each is 4 g/5 L = 0.8 g/L.

f) Collision frequency (A) > collision frequency (B) > collision frequency (C) The number of collisions depends on both the speed and the distance between gas molecules. Since hydrogen is the lightest molecule it has the greatest speed and the 5 L flask of hydrogen also contains the most molecules, so collisions will occur more frequently between hydrogen molecules than between helium molecules. By the same reasoning, collisions will occur more frequently between helium molecules than between methane molecules.

4.69 Plan: To find the ratio of effusion rates, calculate the inverse of the ratio of the square roots of the molar masses (Graham's law).
Solution:

$$\frac{\text{Rate H}_2}{\text{Rate UF}_6} = \sqrt{\frac{\mathcal{M} \text{ of UF}_6}{\mathcal{M} \text{ of H}_2}} = \sqrt{\frac{352.0 \text{ g/mol}}{2.016 \text{ g/mol}}} = 13.2137 = \mathbf{13.21}$$

4.71 Plan: Recall that the heavier the gas, the slower the molecular speed. The molar mass of Ar is 39.95 g/mol while the molar mass of He is 4.003 g/mol.
Solution:
a) The gases have the same average kinetic energy because they are at the same temperature. The heavier Ar atoms are moving more slowly than the lighter He atoms to maintain the same average kinetic energy. Therefore, **Curve 1** with the lower average molecular speed, better represents the behaviour of Ar.
b) A gas that has a slower molecular speed would effuse more slowly, so **Curve 1** is the better choice.
c) Fluorine gas exists as a diatomic molecule, F_2, with $\mathcal{M}$ = 38.00 g/mol. Therefore, F_2 is much closer in mass to Ar (39.95 g/mol) than He (4.003 g/mol), so **Curve 1** more closely represents the behaviour of F_2.

4.73 Plan: To find the ratio of effusion rates, calculate the inverse of the ratio of the square roots of the molar masses (Graham's law). Then use the ratio of effusion rates to find the time for the F_2 effusion. Effusion rate and time required for the effusion are inversely proportional.
Solution:
$\mathcal{M}$ of He = 4.003 g/mol $\mathcal{M}$ of F_2 = 38.00 g/mol

$$\frac{\text{Rate He}}{\text{Rate F}_2} = \sqrt{\frac{\mathcal{M} \text{ of F}_2}{\mathcal{M} \text{ of He}}} = \sqrt{\frac{38.00 \text{ g/mol}}{4.003 \text{ g/mol}}} = 3.08105 \text{ (unrounded)}$$

$$\frac{\text{Rate He}}{\text{Rate F}_2} = \frac{\text{time F}_2}{\text{time He}} \qquad \frac{3.08105}{1.00} = \frac{\text{time F}_2}{4.85 \text{ min He}} \qquad \text{Time F}_2 = 14.9431 \text{ min} = \mathbf{14.9 \text{ min}}$$

4.75 Plan: White phosphorus is a molecular form of the element phosphorus consisting of some number, x, of phosphorus atoms; the number of atoms in a molecule determines the molar mass of the phosphorus molecule. Use the relative rates of effusion of white phosphorus and neon (Graham's law) to determine the molar mass of white phosphorus. From the molar mass of white phosphorus, determine the number of phosphorus atoms, x, in one molecule of white phosphorus.
Solution:
$\mathcal{M}$ of Ne = 20.18 g/mol

$$\frac{\text{Rate P}_x}{\text{Rate Ne}} = 0.404 = \sqrt{\frac{\mathcal{M} \text{ of Ne}}{\mathcal{M} \text{ of P}_x}}$$

$$0.404 = \sqrt{\frac{20.18 \text{ g/mol}}{\mathcal{M} \text{ of P}_x}}$$

$$(0.404)^2 = \frac{20.18 \text{ g/mol}}{\mathcal{M} \text{ of P}_x}$$

$$0.163216 = \frac{20.18 \text{ g/mol}}{\mathcal{M} \text{ of P}_x}$$

$\mathcal{M}(P_x) = 123.6398$ g/mol

$$\left(\frac{123.6398 \text{ g}}{\text{mol } P_x}\right)\left(\frac{1 \text{ mol P}}{30.97 \text{ g P}}\right) = 3.992244 = 4 \text{ mol P/mol } P_x \quad \text{or 4 atoms P/molecule } P_x$$

Thus, **4 atoms per molecule**, so $P_x = P_4$.

4.78   Interparticle attractions cause the real pressure to be *less than* ideal pressure, so it causes a **negative** deviation. The size of the interparticle attraction is related to the constant a. According to Table 4.3, $a_{N_2} = 1.39$, $a_{Kr} = 2.32$, and $a_{CO_2} = 3.59$. Therefore, CO_2 experiences a greater negative deviation in pressure than the other two gases: $\mathbf{N_2 < Kr < CO_2.}$

4.80   Nitrogen gas behaves more ideally at **1 bar** than at 500 bar because at lower pressures the gas molecules are farther apart. An ideal gas is defined as consisting of gas molecules that act independently of the other gas molecules. When gas molecules are far apart they act more ideally, because intermolecular attractions are less important and the volume of the molecules is a smaller fraction of the container volume.

4.83   Plan: Use the ideal gas law to find the amount in moles of O_2. amount in moles of O_2 is divided by 4 to find amount in moles of Hb since O_2 combines with Hb in a 4:1 ratio. Divide the given mass of Hb by the amount in moles of Hb to obtain molar mass, g/mol. Temperature must be in units of kelvin, , and volume in L.
Solution:
$V = 1.53 \text{ mL}$ $T = 37°C + 273 = 310 \text{ K}$
$p = 97.8 \text{ kPa}$ $n = \text{unknown}$

Converting V from mL to L: $V = (1.53 \text{ mL})\left(\frac{10^{-3} \text{ L}}{1 \text{ mL}}\right) = 1.53 \times 10^{-3} \text{ L}$

$pV = nRT$

Solving for n:

amount in moles of $O_2 = n = \dfrac{pV}{RT} = \dfrac{(97.8 \text{ kPa})(1.53 \times 10^{-3} \text{ L})}{\left(8.31446 \frac{\text{L} \cdot \text{kPa}}{\text{mol} \cdot \text{K}}\right)(310 \text{ K})} = 5.80543 \times 10^{-5} \text{ mol } O_2$

amount in moles Hb $= \left(5.80543 \times 10^{-5} \text{ mol } O_2\right)\left(\dfrac{1 \text{ mol Hb}}{4 \text{ mol } O_2}\right) = 1.45136 \times 10^{-5} \text{ mol Hb (unrounded)}$

Molar mass hemoglobin $= \dfrac{1.00 \text{ g Hb}}{1.45136 \times 10^{-5} \text{ Hb}} = 6.890099 \times 10^4 \text{ g/mol} = \mathbf{6.89 \times 10^4 \text{ g/mol}}$

4.86   Plan: Convert the mass of Cl_2 to amount in moles and use the ideal gas law and van der Waals equation to find the pressure of the gas.
Solution:

a) amount in moles Cl_2: $(0.5950 \text{ kg } Cl_2)\left(\dfrac{10^3 \text{ g}}{1 \text{ kg}}\right)\left(\dfrac{1 \text{ mol } Cl_2}{70.90 \text{ g } Cl_2}\right) = 8.3921016 \text{ mol}$

$V = 15.50 \text{ L}$ $T = 225°C + 273 = 498 \text{ K}$
$n = 8.3921016 \text{ mol}$ $P = \text{unknown}$
Ideal gas law: $PV = nRT$
Solving for P:

$$p_{IGL} = \frac{nRT}{V} = \frac{(8.3921016 \text{ mol})\left(8.31446 \frac{\text{L} \cdot \text{kPa}}{\text{mol} \cdot \text{K}}\right)(498 \text{ K})}{15.50 \text{ L}} = 2241.829 \text{ kPa} = \mathbf{2.24 \times 10^3 \text{ kPa}}$$

b) van der Waals equation: $\left(p + \dfrac{n^2 a}{V^2}\right)(V - nb) = nRT$

Solving for p:

$p_{VDW} = \dfrac{nRT}{V - nb} - \dfrac{n^2 a}{V^2}$ From Table 4.4: $a = 6.343\,\dfrac{bar \cdot L^2}{mol^2}$; $b = 0.05422\,\dfrac{L}{mol}$

$n = 8.3921016$ mol from part a)

$$p_{VDW} = \dfrac{(8.3921016 \text{ mol } Cl_2)\left(8.31446\,\dfrac{L \cdot kPa}{mol \cdot K}\right)(498 \text{ K})}{15.50 \text{ L} - (8.3921016 \text{ mol } Cl_2)\left(0.05422\,\dfrac{L}{mol}\right)} - \dfrac{(8.3921016 \text{ mol } Cl_2)^2\left(6.343\,\dfrac{bar \cdot L^2}{mol^2}\right)\left(\dfrac{100\,kPa}{1\,bar}\right)}{(15.50 \text{ L})^2}$$

$= 2123.69$ kPa $= \mathbf{2124\ kPa}$

4.90   Plan: Partial pressures and mole fractions are calculated from Dalton's law of partial pressures: $P_A = X_A \times P_{total}$. Solve the ideal gas law for amount (mol) and then convert to molecules using Avogadro's number to calculate the number of O_2 molecules in the volume of an average breath.
Solution:
a) Convert each mole percent to a mole fraction by dividing by 100%. $P_{total} = 1.01$ bar $= 101$ kPa
    $p_{Nitrogen} = X_{Nitrogen} \times p_{total} = 0.786 \times 101$ kpa $= 79.39$ kpa $= \mathbf{79.4\ kpa\ N_2}$
    $p_{Oxygen} = X_{Oxygen} \times p_{total} = 0.209 \times 101$ kpa $= 21.11$ kpa $= \mathbf{21.1\ kpa\ O_2}$
    $p_{Carbon\ Dioxide} = X_{Carbon\ Dioxide} \times p_{total} = 0.0004 \times 101$ kpa $= 0.0404$ kpa $= \mathbf{0.04\ kpa\ CO_2}$
    $p_{Water} = X_{Water} \times p_{total} = 0.0046 \times 101$ kPa $= 0.4646$ kPa $= \mathbf{0.46\ kPa\ H_2O}$
b) Mole fractions can be calculated by rearranging Dalton's law of partial pressures:

$X_A = \dfrac{p_A}{p_{total}}$ and multiply by 100 to express mole fraction as percent

$p_{total} = 1.01$ bar $= 101$ kPa

$X_{Nitrogen} = \dfrac{74.9 \text{ kPa}}{101 \text{ kPa}} \times 100\% = 74.1584\% = \mathbf{74.2\ mol\%\ N_2}$

$X_{Oxygen} = \dfrac{13.7 \text{ kPa}}{101 \text{ kPa}} \times 100\% = 13.5644\% = \mathbf{13.6\ mol\%\ O_2}$

$X_{Carbon\ Dioxide} = \dfrac{5.3 \text{ kPa}}{101 \text{ kPa}} \times 100\% = 5.2475\% = \mathbf{5.2\ mol\%\ CO_2}$

$X_{Water} = \dfrac{6.2 \text{ kPa}}{101 \text{ kPa}} \times 100\% = 6.1386\% = \mathbf{6.1\ mol\%\ H_2O}$

c) $V = 0.50$ L $T = 37°C + 273 = 310$ K
   $p = 13.7$ kPa (from table) $n =$ unknown
$pV = nRT$
Solving for n:

$n = \dfrac{PV}{RT} = \dfrac{(13.7 \text{ kPa})(0.50 \text{ L})}{\left(8.31446\,\dfrac{L \cdot kPa}{mol \cdot K}\right)(310 \text{ K})} = 0.0026576$ mol O_2

Molecules of $O_2 = (0.0026576 \text{ mol } O_2)\left(\dfrac{6.022 \times 10^{23} \text{ molecules } O_2}{1 \text{ mol } O_2}\right) = 1.6004 \times 10^{21} = \mathbf{1.6 \times 10^{21}}$

molecules O_2

4.92   Plan: For part a), since the volume, temperature, and pressure of the gas are changing, use the combined gas law. For part b), use the ideal gas law to solve for amount in moles of air and then amount in moles of N_2.
Solution:
a) p_1 = 1.933 bar p_2 = 1 bar
V_1 = 208 mL V_2 = unknown
T_1 = 286 K T_2 = 298 K
Arranging the ideal gas law and solving for V_2:

$$\frac{p_1 V_1}{T_1} = \frac{p_2 V_2}{T_2}$$

$$V_2 = V_1 \left(\frac{T_2}{T_1}\right)\left(\frac{p_1}{p_2}\right) = (208\ L)\left(\frac{298\ K}{286\ K}\right)\left(\frac{1.933\ bar}{1\ bar}\right) = 418.934\ mL = \textbf{4x10}^2\ \textbf{mL}$$

b) V = 208 mL T = 286 K
   p = 1.933 bar n = unknown

Converting V from mL to L: $V = (208\ mL)\left(\frac{10^{-3}\ L}{1\ mL}\right) = 0.208\ L$

$pV = nRT$
Solving for n:

amount in moles of air = $n = \dfrac{pV}{RT} = \dfrac{(1.933\ bar)(0.208\ L)}{\left(0.08314\dfrac{L\bullet bar}{mol\bullet K}\right)(286\ K)} = 0.016909$ mol air

amount in mole of N_2 = $(0.016909\ mol)\left(\dfrac{77\%\ N_2}{100\%}\right) = 0.01302 = \textbf{0.013 mol } \textbf{N}_2$

4.93   Plan: The amounts of both reactants are given, so the first step is to identify the limiting reactant.
Write the balanced equation and use molar ratios to find the amount in moles of NO_2 produced by each reactant. The smaller amount in moles of product indicates the limiting reagent. Solve for volume of NO_2 using the ideal gas law.
Solution:
$Cu(s) + 4HNO_3(aq) \rightarrow Cu(NO_3)_2(aq) + 2NO_2(g) + 2H_2O(l)$

amount in moles NO_2 from Cu = $\left(4.95\ cm^3\right)\left(\dfrac{8.95\ g\ Cu}{cm^3}\right)\left(\dfrac{1\ mol\ Cu}{63.55\ g\ Cu}\right)\left(\dfrac{2\ mol\ NO_2}{1\ mol\ Cu}\right) = 1.394256$ mol NO_2

amount in moles NO_2 from HNO_3 = $(230.0\ mL)\left(\dfrac{68.0\%\ HNO_3}{100\%}\right)\left(\dfrac{1\ cm^3}{1\ mL}\right)\left(\dfrac{1.42\ g}{cm^3}\right)\left(\dfrac{1\ mol\ HNO_3}{63.02\ g}\right)\left(\dfrac{2\ mol\ NO_2}{4\ mol\ HNO_3}\right)$

$= 1.7620$ mol NO_2

Since less product can be made from the copper, it is the limiting reactant and excess nitric acid will be left after the reaction goes to completion. Use the calculated amount in moles of NO_2 and the given temperature and pressure in the ideal gas law to find the volume of nitrogen dioxide produced. Note that nitrogen dioxide is the only gas involved in the reaction.
V = unknown T = 28.2°C + 273.2 = 301.4 K
p = 0.980 bar n = 1.394256 mol NO_2
$pV = nRT$
Solving for V:

$$V = \frac{nRT}{p} = \frac{(1.394256\ mol)\left(0.08314\dfrac{L\bullet bar}{mol\bullet K}\right)(301.4\ K)}{(0.980\ bar)} = 36.71539\ L = \textbf{36.7 L } \textbf{NO}_2$$

4.98   <u>Plan:</u> The empirical formula for aluminum chloride is $AlCl_3$ (Al^{3+} and Cl^-). The empirical formula mass is (133.33 g/mol). Calculate the molar mass of the gaseous species from the ratio of effusion rates (Graham's law). This molar mass, divided by the empirical weight, should give a whole-number multiple that will yield the molecular formula.
<u>Solution:</u>

$$\frac{\text{Rate unknown}}{\text{Rate He}} = 0.122 = \sqrt{\frac{\mathcal{M}\,\text{of He}}{\mathcal{M}\,\text{of unknown}}}$$

$$0.122 = \sqrt{\frac{4.003 \text{ g/mol}}{\mathcal{M}\,\text{of unknown}}}$$

$$0.014884 = \frac{4.003 \text{ g/mol}}{\mathcal{M}\,\text{of unknown}}$$

$\mathcal{M}$ of unknown = 268.9465 g/mol
The whole-number multiple is 268.9465/133.33, which is about 2. Therefore, the molecular formula of the gaseous species is 2 x ($AlCl_3$) = **Al_2Cl_6**.

4.100   <u>Plan:</u> First, write the balanced equation for the reaction: $2SO_2 + O_2 \rightarrow 2SO_3$. The total amount in moles of gas will change as the reaction occurs since 3 moles of reactant gas forms 2 moles of product gas. From the volume, temperature, and pressures given, we can calculate the amount in moles of gas before and after the reaction using the ideal gas law. For each mole of SO_3 formed, the total amount in moles of gas decreases by 1/2 mole. Thus, twice the decrease in amount in moles of gas equals the amount in moles of SO_3 formed.
<u>Solution:</u>
amount in moles of gas before and after reaction:

$V = 2.00$ L $T = 800.$ K
$p_{total} = 192.5$ kPa $n =$ unknown
$pV = nRT$

$$\text{Initial amount in moles} = n = \frac{pV}{RT} = \frac{(192.5 \text{ kPa})(2.00 \text{ L})}{\left(8.31446\dfrac{\text{L}\bullet\text{kPa}}{\text{mol}\bullet\text{K}}\right)(800. \text{ K})} = 0.05788109 \text{ mol}$$

$$\text{Final amount in moles} = n = \frac{pV}{RT} = \frac{(167.2 \text{ kPa})(2.00 \text{ L})}{\left(8.31446\dfrac{\text{L}\bullet\text{kPa}}{\text{mol}\bullet\text{K}}\right)(800. \text{ K})} = 0.05027356 \text{ mol}$$

amount in moles of SO_3 produced = 2 x decrease in the total amount in moles
        = 2 x (0.05788109 mol – 0.05027356 mol)
        = 0.01521506 mol = **1.52×10^{-2} mol**

<u>Check:</u> If the starting amount is 0.0578 total moles of SO_2 and O_2, then x + y = 0.0578 mol,
where x = mol of SO_2 and y = mol of O_2. After the reaction:
(x – z) + (y – 0.5z) + z = 0.0502 mol
Where z = mol of SO_3 formed = mol of SO_2 reacted = 2(mol of O_2 reacted).
Subtracting the two equations gives:
        x – (x – z) + y – (y – 0.5z) – z = 0.0578 – 0.0502
        z = 0.0152 mol SO_3
The approach of setting up two equations and solving them gives the same result as above.

4.104   <u>Plan:</u> First, write the balanced equation. The amount in moles of CO that react in part a) can be calculated from the ideal gas law. Volume must be in units of L, pressure in kPa, and temperature in kelvin. Once the amount in moles of CO that react are known, the molar ratio from the balanced equation is used to determine the mass of nickel that will react with the CO. For part b), assume the volume is 1 m^3. Use the ideal gas law to solve for amount in moles of $Ni(CO)_4$, which equals the amount in moles of Ni, and convert amount in moles to mass using the molar mass. For part c), the mass of Ni obtained from 1 m^3 (part b)) can be used to calculate the amount of CO released. Use the ideal gas law to calculate the volume of CO. The vapour pressure of water at 35°C (5.629 kPa) must be subtracted from the overall pressure (see Table 4.2).

Solution:

a) $Ni(s) + 4CO(g) \rightarrow Ni(CO)_4(g)$

$V = 3.55 \text{ m}^3$ $T = 50°C + 273 = 323 \text{ K}$

$p = 100.7 \text{ kPa}$ $n = \text{unknown}$

Converting V from m^3 to L: $V = \left(3.55 \text{ m}^3\right)\left(\dfrac{1 \text{ L}}{10^{-3} \text{ m}^3}\right) = 3550 \text{ L}$

$pV = nRT$

Solving for n:

amount in moles of CO $= n = \dfrac{pV}{RT} = \dfrac{\left(100.7 \text{ kPa}\right)\left(3550 \text{ L}\right)}{\left(8.31446 \dfrac{\text{L·kPa}}{\text{mol·K}}\right)\left(323 \text{ K}\right)} = 133.1132 \text{ mol CO}$

Mass Ni $= \left(133.1132 \text{ mol CO}\right)\left(\dfrac{1 \text{ mol Ni}}{4 \text{ mol CO}}\right)\left(\dfrac{58.69 \text{ g Ni}}{1 \text{ mol Ni}}\right) = 1953.10 \text{ g} = \mathbf{1.95 \times 10^3 \text{ g Ni}}$

b) $Ni(s) + 4 CO(g) \rightarrow Ni(CO)_4(g)$

$V = 1 \text{ m}^3$ $T = 155°C + 273 = 428 \text{ K}$

$p = 21 \text{ bar}$ $n = \text{unknown}$

Converting V from m^3 to L: $V = \left(1 \text{ m}^3\right)\left(\dfrac{1 \text{ L}}{10^{-3} \text{ m}^3}\right) = 1000 \text{ L}$

$pV = nRT$

Solving for n:

amount in moles of $Ni(CO)_4 = n = \dfrac{pV}{RT} = \dfrac{\left(21 \text{ bar}\right)\left(1000 \text{ L}\right)}{\left(0.08314 \dfrac{\text{L·bar}}{\text{mol·K}}\right)\left(428 \text{ K}\right)} = 590.1542 \text{ mol Ni(CO)}_4$

Mass Ni $= \left(590.1542 \text{ mol Ni(CO)}_4\right)\left(\dfrac{1 \text{ mol Ni}}{1 \text{ mol Ni(CO)}_4}\right)\left(\dfrac{58.69 \text{ g Ni}}{1 \text{ mol Ni}}\right)$

$= 3.4636 \times 10^4 = \mathbf{3.5 \times 10^4 \text{ g Ni}}$

The pressure limits the significant figures.

c) amount in moles CO $= \left(3.4636 \times 10^4 \text{ g Ni}\right)\left(\dfrac{1 \text{ mol Ni}}{58.69 \text{ g Ni}}\right)\left(\dfrac{4 \text{ mol CO}}{1 \text{ mol Ni}}\right) = 2360.60658 \text{ mol CO}$

Finding the volume of CO:

$V = \text{unknown}$ $T = 35°C + 273 = 308 \text{ K}$

$p_{\text{total}} = 1.03 \text{ bar} = 103 \text{ kPa}$ $n = 2390.51968 \text{ mol}$

$p_{\text{water vapour}} = 5.629 \text{ kPa}$

$p_{CO} = p_{\text{total}} - p_{\text{water vapour}} = 103 \text{ kPa} - 5.629 \text{ kPa} = 97.371 \text{ kPa}$

$pV = nRT$

Solving for V:

$V = \dfrac{nRT}{p} = \dfrac{\left(2360.60658 \text{ mol}\right)\left(8.31446 \dfrac{\text{L·kPa}}{\text{mol·K}}\right)\left(308 \text{ K}\right)}{\left(97.371 \text{ kPa}\right)} = 62083.87 \text{ L CO}$

Converting V from L to m^3: $V = \left(62083.87 \text{ L}\right)\left(\dfrac{10^{-3} \text{ m}^3}{1 \text{ L}}\right) = 62.08387 \text{ m}^3 = \mathbf{62 \text{ m}^3 \text{ CO}}$

The answer is limited to two significant figures because the mass of Ni comes from part b).

4.106   a) A preliminary equation for this reaction is $4C_xH_yN_z + nO_2 \rightarrow 4CO_2 + 2N_2 + 10H_2O$.
Since the organic compound does not contain oxygen, the only source of oxygen as a reactant is oxygen gas. To form 4 volumes of CO_2 would require 4 volumes of O_2 and to form 10 volumes of H_2O would require 5 volumes of O_2. Thus, 9 **volumes of O_2** was required.

b) Since the volume of a gas is proportional to the amount in moles of the gas we can equate volume and amount in moles. From a volume ratio of $4CO_2:2N_2:10H_2O$ we deduce a mole ratio of 4C:4N:20H or 1C:1N:5H for an empirical formula of **CH_5N**.

4.109   <u>Plan:</u> To find the factor by which a diver's lungs would expand, find the factor by which P changes from 38.1 m to the surface, and apply Boyle's law. To find that factor, calculate $P_{seawater}$ at 38.1 m by converting the given depth from m-seawater to mmHg to kPa and adding the surface pressure (101.3 kPa).
<u>Solution:</u>

$$p(H_2O) = (38.1\,m)\left(\frac{1\ mm}{10^{-3}\ m}\right) = 3.81 \times 10^4\ mmH_2O$$

$p(Hg)$: $\dfrac{h_{H_2O}}{h_{Hg}} = \dfrac{d_{Hg}}{d_{H_2O}}$ $\dfrac{3.81 \times 10^4\ mmH_2O}{h_{Hg}} = \dfrac{13.5\ g/mL}{1.04\ g/mL}$ $h_{Hg} = 2935.1111\ mmHg$

$$p(Hg) = (2935.11111\ mmHg)\left(\frac{101.3\ kPa}{760\ mm\ Hg}\right) = 391.2194\ kPa\ \text{(unrounded)}$$

$p_{total} = (101.3\ kPa) + (391.2194\ kPa) = 492.5194\ kPa$ (unrounded)
Use Boyle's law to find the volume change of the diver's lungs:
$p_1V_1 = p_2V_2$

$\dfrac{V_2}{V_1} = \dfrac{p_1}{p_2}$ $\dfrac{V_2}{V_1} = \dfrac{492.5194\ kPa}{101.3\ kPa} = \mathbf{4.86}$

To find the depth to which the diver could ascend safely, use the given safe expansion factor (1.5) and the pressure at 38.1 m, $P_{38.1}$, to find the safest ascended pressure, P_{safe}.
    $p_{38.1}/p_{safe} = 1.5$
    $p_{safe} = p_{38.1}/1.5 = (492.5194\ kPa)/1.5 = 328.3463\ kPa$ (unrounded)
Convert the pressure in kPa to pressure in m of seawater using the conversion factors above. Subtract this distance from the initial depth to find how far the diver could ascend.

$$h(Hg):\quad (492.5194 - 328.3463\ )kPa\left(\frac{760\ mmHg}{101.3\ kPa}\right) = 1231.7034\ mmHg$$

$\dfrac{h_{H_2O}}{h_{Hg}} = \dfrac{d_{Hg}}{d_{H_2O}}$ $\dfrac{h_{H_2O}}{1231.7034\ mmHg} = \dfrac{13.5\ g/mL}{1.04\ g/mL}$ $h_{H_2O} = 15988.458\ mmH_2O$

$$\left(15988.458\ mmH_2O\right)\left(\frac{10^{-3}\ m}{1\ mm}\right) = 15.9885\ m$$

Therefore, the diver can safely ascend 16.0 m to a depth of (38.1- 15.9885)m = 22.1015 m = **22 m**.

4.111   <u>Plan:</u> First, write the balanced equation. According to the description in the problem, a given volume of peroxide solution (0.100 L) will release a certain number of "volumes of oxygen gas" (20). Assume that 20 is exact. A 0.100 L solution will produce (20 x 0.100 L) = 2.00 L O_2 gas. Use the ideal gas law to convert this volume of O_2 gas to amount in moles of O_2 gas and convert to amount in moles and then mass of H_2O_2 using the molar ratio in the balanced equation.
<u>Solution:</u>
      $2H_2O_2(aq) \rightarrow 2H_2O(l) + O_2(g)$
$V = 2.00$ L $T = 0°C + 273 = 273$ K
$p = 100$ kPa $n =$ unknown
$pV = nRT$
Solving for n:

$$\text{amount in moles of } O_2 = n = \frac{pV}{RT} = \frac{(100\ kPa)(2.00\ L)}{\left(8.31446\ \dfrac{L \cdot kPa}{mol \cdot K}\right)(273\ K)} = 8.81116 \times 10^{-2}\ mol\ O_2$$

$$\text{Mass } H_2O_2 = \left(8.81116 \times 10^{-2} \text{ mol } O_2\right)\left(\frac{2 \text{ mol } H_2O_2}{1 \text{ mol } O_2}\right)\left(\frac{34.02 \text{ g } H_2O_2}{1 \text{ mol } H_2O_2}\right) = 5.995116 \text{ g} = \mathbf{6.00 \text{ g } H_2O_2}$$

4.116   Plan: The diagram below describes the two Hg height levels within the barometer. First, find the pressure of the N_2. The P_{N_2} is directly related to the change in column height of Hg. Then find the volume occupied by the N_2.

The volume of the space occupied by the $N_2(g)$ is calculated from the length and cross-sectional area of the barometer. To find the mass of N_2, use these values of p and V (T is given) in the ideal gas law to find amount in moles which is converted to mass using the molar mass of nitrogen.

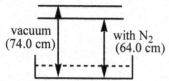

Solution:

$$\text{Pressure of the nitrogen} = \left(74.0 \text{ cm} - 64.0 \text{ cm}\right)\left(\frac{10^{-2} \text{ m}}{1 \text{ cm}}\right)\left(\frac{1 \text{ mm}}{10^{-3} \text{ m}}\right)\left(\frac{1 \text{ atm}}{760 \text{ mmHg}}\right)\left(\frac{101.3 \text{ kPa}}{1 \text{ atm}}\right) = 13.3289 \text{ kPa}$$

$$\text{Volume of the nitrogen} = \left(1.00 \times 10^2 \text{ cm} - 64.0 \text{ cm}\right)\left(1.20 \text{ cm}^2\right)\left(\frac{1 \text{ mL}}{1 \text{ cm}^3}\right)\left(\frac{10^{-3} \text{ L}}{1 \text{ mL}}\right) = 0.0432 \text{ L}$$

$V = 0.0432 \text{ L}$ $T = 24°C + 273 = 297 \text{ K}$
$p = 13.3289 \text{ kPa}$ $n = \text{unknown}$
$pV = nRT$
Solving for n:

$$\text{amount in moles of } N_2 = n = \frac{pV}{RT} = \frac{\left(13.3289 \text{ kPa}\right)\left(0.0432 \text{ L}\right)}{\left(8.31446 \frac{\text{L} \cdot \text{kPa}}{\text{mol} \cdot \text{K}}\right)\left(297 \text{ K}\right)} = 2.3317799 \times 10^{-4} \text{ mol } N_2$$

$$\text{Mass of } N_2 = \left(2.3317799 \times 10^{-4} \text{ mol } N_2\right)\left(\frac{28.02 \text{ g } N_2}{1 \text{ mol } N_2}\right) = 6.5336 \times 10^{-3} = \mathbf{6.53 \times 10^{-3} \text{ g } N_2}$$

4.120   Plan: Deviations from ideal gas behaviour are due to attractive forces between particles which reduce the pressure of the real gas and due to the size of the particle which affects the volume. Compare the size and/or attractive forces between the substances. The greater the size and/or the stronger the attractive forces, the greater the deviation from ideal gas behaviour.
Solution:
a) **Xenon** would show greater deviation from ideal behaviour than argon since xenon is a larger atom than argon. The electron cloud of Xe is more easily distorted so intermolecular attractions are greater. Xe's larger size also means that the volume the gas occupies becomes a greater proportion of the container's volume at high pressures.
b) **Water vapour** would show greater deviation from ideal behaviour than neon gas since the attractive forces between water molecules are greater than the attractive forces between neon atoms. We know the attractive forces are greater for water molecules because it remains a liquid at a higher temperature than neon (water is a liquid at room temperature while neon is a gas at room temperature).
c) **Mercury vapour** would show greater deviation from ideal behaviour than radon gas since the attractive forces between mercury atoms is greater than that between radon atoms. We know that the attractive forces for mercury are greater because it is a liquid at room temperature while radon is a gas.
d) **Water** is a liquid at room temperature; methane is a gas at room temperature. Therefore, water molecules have stronger attractive forces than methane molecules and should deviate from ideal behaviour to a greater extent than methane molecules.

4.124 Plan: V and T are not given, so the ideal gas law cannot be used. The total pressure of the mixture is given. Use $p_A = X_A \times p_{total}$ to find the mole fraction of each gas and then the mass fraction. The total mass of the two gases is 35.0 g.
Solution:

$$p_{total} = p_{krypton} + p_{carbon\ dioxide} = 0.717 \text{ bar}$$

The NaOH absorbed the CO_2 leaving the Kr, thus $P_{krypton} = 0.256$ bar.

$$p_{carbon\ dioxide} = p_{total} - p_{krypton} = 0.717 \text{ bar} - 0.256 \text{ bar} = 0.461 \text{ bar}$$

Determining mole fractions: $p_A = X_A \times p_{total}$

Carbon dioxide: $X = \dfrac{p_{CO_2}}{p_{total}} = \dfrac{0.461 \text{ bar}}{0.717 \text{ bar}} = 0.64296$

Krypton: $X = \dfrac{p_{Kr}}{p_{total}} = \dfrac{0.256 \text{ bar}}{0.717 \text{ bar}} = 0.35704$

$$\text{Relative mass fraction} = \left| \dfrac{(0.35704)\left(\dfrac{83.80 \text{ g Kr}}{\text{mol}}\right)}{(0.64296)\left(\dfrac{44.01 \text{ g } CO_2}{\text{mol}}\right)} \right| = 1.05737$$

35.0 g = x g CO_2 + (1.05737 x) g Kr
35.0 g = 2.05737 x
mass of CO_2 = x = (35.0 g)/(2.057378) = 17.01201 g = **17.0 g CO_2**
mass of Kr = 35.0 g – 17.01201 g CO_2 = 17.98799 g = **18.0 g Kr**

4.130 Plan: Use the equation for root mean speed (u_{rms}). Molar mass values must be in units of kg/mol and temperature in kelvin.
Solution:

$$u_{rms} = \sqrt{\dfrac{3\,RT}{\mathcal{M}}}$$

$$u_{rms}\ Ne = \sqrt{\dfrac{3(8.314\ J/mol\cdot K)(370\ K)}{(20.18\ g/mol)}\left(\dfrac{10^3\ g}{kg}\right)\left(\dfrac{kg\cdot m^2/s^2}{J}\right)} = 676.24788 \text{ m/s} = \textbf{676 m/s Ne}$$

$$u_{rms}\ Ar = \sqrt{\dfrac{3(8.314\ J/mol\cdot K)(370\ K)}{(39.95\ g/mol)}\left(\dfrac{10^3\ g}{kg}\right)\left(\dfrac{kg\cdot m^2/s^2}{J}\right)} = 480.6269 \text{ m/s} = \textbf{481 m/s Ar}$$

$$u_{rms}\ He = \sqrt{\dfrac{3(8.314\ J/mol\cdot K)(370\ K)}{(4.003\ g/mol)}\left(\dfrac{10^3\ g}{kg}\right)\left(\dfrac{kg\cdot m^2/s^2}{J}\right)} = 1518.356 \text{ m/s} = \textbf{1.52x10}^3 \textbf{ m/s He}$$

4.132 Plan: For part a), the amount in moles of water vapour can be found using the ideal gas law. Convert amount in moles of water to mass using the molar mass and adjust to the 1.6% water content of the kernel. For part b), use the ideal gas law to find the volume of water vapour at the stated set of condition.
Solution:

a) Volume of water in kernel = $(0.25 \text{ mL kernel})\left(\dfrac{75\% \ H_2O}{100 \% \text{ kernel}}\right) = 0.1875 \text{ mL} = 1.875\text{x}10^{-4} \text{ L}$

$V = 1.875\text{x}10^{-4}$ L $T = 170°C + 273.2 = 443$ K
$p = 9.1$ bar n = unknown
$pV = nRT$
Solving for n:

$$\text{Amount (mol) of } H_2O = n = \dfrac{pV}{RT} = \dfrac{(9.1\,bar)(1.875\ 10^{-4}\ L)}{\left(0.08314\dfrac{L\cdot bar}{mol\cdot K}\right)(443\ K)} = 4.632644\text{x}10^{-5} \text{ mol}$$

$$\text{Mass (g) of} = \left(4.632644 \times 10^{-5} \text{ mol } H_2O\right)\left(\frac{18.02 \text{ g } H_2O}{1 \text{ mol } H_2O}\right)\left(\frac{100\%}{1.6\%}\right) = 0.052175 \text{ g} = \textbf{0.052 g}$$

b) V = unknown $T = 25°C + 273 = 298$ K
$p = 1.01$ bar $n = 4.632644 \times 10^{-5}$ mol
$pV = nRT$
Solving for V:

$$V = \frac{nRT}{p} = \frac{\left(4.632644 \times 10^{-5} \text{ mol}\right)\left(0.08314 \frac{L \cdot bar}{mol \cdot K}\right)(298 \text{ K})}{(1.01 \text{ bar})} = 0.0011364 \text{ L} = 1.1364 \text{ mL} = \textbf{1.1 mL}$$

4.139   Plan: For part a), convert mass of glucose to amount in moles and use the molar ratio from the balanced equation to find the amount in moles of CO_2 gas produced. Use the ideal gas law to find the volume of that amount of CO_2. Pressure must be in units of atm and temperature in kelvin. For part b), use the molar ratios in the balanced equation to calculate the amount in moles of each gas and then use Dalton's law of partial pressures to determine the pressure of each gas.
Solution:
a) $C_6H_{12}O_6(s) + 6O_2(g) \rightarrow 6CO_2(g) + 6H_2O(g)$

amount in moles CO_2: $\left(20.0 \text{ g } C_6H_{12}O_6\right)\left(\frac{1 \text{ mol } C_6H_{12}O_6}{180.16 \text{ g } C_6H_{12}O_6}\right)\left(\frac{6 \text{ mol } CO_2}{1 \text{ mol } C_6H_{12}O_6}\right) = 0.666075 \text{ mol } CO_2$

Finding the volume of CO_2:
V = unknown $T = 37°C + 273 = 310$ K
$p = 104$ kPa $n = 0.666075$ mol
$pV = nRT$
Solving for V:

$$V = \frac{nRT}{p} = \frac{(0.666075 \text{ mol})\left(8.31446 \frac{L \cdot kPa}{mol \cdot K}\right)(310 \text{ K})}{(104 \text{ kPa})} = 16.5077 \text{ L} = \textbf{16.5 L } CO_2$$

This solution assumes that partial pressure of O_2 does not interfere with the reaction conditions.

b) amount in moles CO_2 = amount (mol) $O_2 = \left(10.0 \text{ g } C_6H_{12}O_6\right)\left(\frac{1 \text{ mol } C_6H_{12}O_6}{180.16 \text{ g } C_6H_{12}O_6}\right)\left(\frac{6 \text{ mol}}{1 \text{ mol } C_6H_{12}O_6}\right)$

                        $= 0.333037 \text{ mol } CO_2 = 0.333037 \text{ mol } O_2$
At 37°C, the vapour pressure of water is 6.51 kPa. No matter how much water is produced, the partial pressure of H_2O will still be 6.51 kPa. The remaining pressure, 104 kPa – 6.51 kPa = 97.49 kPa is the sum of partial pressures for O_2 and CO_2. Since the mole fractions of O_2 and CO_2 are equal, their pressures must be equal, and must be one-half of 97.49 kPa.
$p_{water} = \textbf{6.51 kPa}$
(97.49 kPa)/2 = 48.75 kPa = $\textbf{49 kPa}$ = p_{oxygen} = $p_{carbon\ dioxide}$

4.144   Plan: To find the number of steps through the membrane, calculate the molar masses to find the ratio of effusion rates. This ratio is the enrichment factor for each step.
Solution:

$$\frac{\text{Rate}_{235\text{ UF}_6}}{\text{Rate}_{238\text{ UF}_6}} = \sqrt{\frac{\mathcal{M} \text{ of } {}^{238}UF_6}{\mathcal{M} \text{ of } {}^{235}UF_6}} = \sqrt{\frac{352.04 \text{ g/mol}}{349.03 \text{ g/mol}}}$$

                        = 1.004302694 enrichment factor
Therefore, the abundance of ${}^{235}UF_6$ after one membrane is 0.72% x 1.004302694
Abundance of ${}^{235}UF_6$ after "N" membranes = 0.72% x $(1.004302694)^N$
Desired abundance of ${}^{235}UF_6$ = 3.0% = 0.72% x $(1.004302694)^N$
Solving for N:
3.0% = 0.72% x $(1.004302694)^N$
4.16667 = $(1.004302694)^N$

ln 4.16667 = ln (1.004302694)^N
ln 4.16667 = N x ln (1.004302694)
N = (ln 4.16667)/(ln 1.004302694)
N = 1.4271164/0.004293464 = 332.39277 = **332 steps**

4.146   Plan: The amount of each gas that leaks from the balloon is proportional to its effusion rate. Using 35% as the rate for H_2, the rate for O_2 can be determined from Graham's law.
Solution:
$$\frac{\text{Rate } O_2}{\text{Rate } H_2} = \sqrt{\frac{\mathcal{M} \text{ of } H_2}{\mathcal{M} \text{ of } O_2}} = \sqrt{\frac{2.016 \text{ g/mol}}{32.00 \text{ g/mol}}} = \frac{\text{rate } O_2}{35}$$

$$0.250998008 = \frac{\text{rate } O_2}{35}$$

Rate O_2 = 8.78493
Amount of H_2 that leaks = 35%; 100%–35% = 65% H_2 remains
Amount of O_2 that leaks = 8.78493%; 100%–8.78493% = 91.21507% O_2 remains
$$\frac{O_2}{H_2} = \frac{91.21507}{65} = 1.40331 = \mathbf{1.4}$$

4.150   Plan: Since the amounts of two reactants are given, this is a limiting reactant problem. Write the balanced equation and use molar ratios to find the amount in moles of IF_7 produced by each reactant. The mass of I_2 is converted to amount in moles using its molar mass and the amount in moles of F_2 is found using the ideal gas law. The smaller amount in moles of product indicates the limiting reagent. Determine the amount in moles of excess reactant gas and the amount in moles of product gas and use the ideal gas law to solve for the total pressure.
Solution:
amount in moles of F_2:
V = 2.50 L T = 250. K
p = 46.7 kPa n = unknown
$pV = nRT$
Solving for n:
$$n = \frac{pV}{RT} = \frac{(46.7 \text{ kPa})(2.50 \text{ L})}{\left(8.31446 \dfrac{\text{L} \cdot \text{kPa}}{\text{mol} \cdot \text{K}}\right)(250. \text{ K})} = 0.0561672 \text{ mol } F_2$$

$$7F_2(g) + I_2(s) \rightarrow 2IF_7(g$$

amount in moles IF_7 from F_2 = $(0.0561672 \text{ mol } F_2)\left(\dfrac{2 \text{ mol } IF_7}{7 \text{ mol } F_2}\right)$ = 0.01604777 mol IF_7 (unrounded)

amount in moles IF_7 from I_2 = $(2.50 \text{ g } I_2)\left(\dfrac{1 \text{ mol } I_2}{253.8 \text{ g } I_2}\right)\left(\dfrac{2 \text{ mol } IF_7}{1 \text{ mol } I_2}\right)$ = 0.019700551 mol IF_7 (unrounded)

F_2 is limiting. All of the F_2 is consumed.
amount in mole I_2 remaining = original amount of moles of I_2 – amount of I_2 (mol) reacting with F_2

amount in mole I_2 remaining = $(2.50 \text{ g } I_2)\left(\dfrac{1 \text{ mol } I_2}{253.8 \text{ g } I_2}\right) - (0.0561672 \text{ mol } F_2)\left(\dfrac{1 \text{ mol } I_2}{7 \text{ mol } F_2}\right)$ = 1.82639x10^{-3} mol I_2

Total amount in moles of gas = (0 mol F_2) + (0.01604777 mol IF_7) + (1.82639x10^{-3} mol I_2)
        = 0.01787416 mol gas
V = 2.50 L T = 550. K
p = unknown n = 0.01787416 mol
$pV = nRT$
Solving for P:

$$p \text{ (kpa)} = \frac{nRT}{V} = \frac{(0.01787416 \text{ mol})\left(8.31446 \dfrac{\text{L} \cdot \text{kPa}}{\text{mol} \cdot \text{K}}\right)(550. \text{ K})}{2.50 \text{ L}} = 32.6950 \text{ kPa}$$

$$p \text{ (bar)} = \left(32.6950 \text{ kPa}\right)\left(\frac{1 \text{ bar}}{100 \text{ kPa}}\right) = 0.32695 \text{ bar} = \textbf{0.327 bar}$$

$$p_{\text{iodine}} \text{ (bar)} = X_{\text{iodine}} \, p_{\text{total}} = [(1.82639 \times 10^{-3} \text{ mol I}_2)/(0.01787416 \text{ mol})] \, (0.32695 \text{ bar})$$
$$= 0.033408 \text{ bar} = \textbf{33.4} \times \textbf{10}^{-\textbf{3}} \textbf{ bar}$$

CHAPTER 5 THERMOCHEMISTRY: ENERGY FLOW AND CHEMICAL CHANGE

CHEMICAL CONNECTIONS BOXED READING PROBLEMS

B5.2   Plan: Three reactions are given. Equation 1) must be multiplied by 2, and then the reactions can be added, canceling substances that appear on both sides of the arrow. Add the $\Delta_r H°$ values for the three reactions to get the $\Delta_r H°$ for the overall gasification reaction of 2 moles of coal. Use the relationship $\Delta_r H° = \sum m \Delta_{f \, (products)} H°$ $- \sum n \Delta_{f \, (reactants)} H°$ to find the heat of combustion of 1 mole of methane. Then find the $\Delta_r H°$ for the gasification of 1.00 kg of coal and $\Delta_r H°$ for the combustion of the methane produced from 1.00 kg of coal and sum these values.

Solution:
a) 1) $2C(s, coal) + 2H_2O(g) \rightarrow \cancel{2CO(g)} + \cancel{2H_2(g)}$ $\Delta_r H° = 2(129.7 \text{ kJ/mol})$

   2) $\cancel{CO(g)} + \cancel{H_2O(g)} \rightarrow CO_2(g) + \cancel{H_2(g)}$ $\Delta_r H° = -41 \text{ kJ/mol}$

   3) $\cancel{CO(g)} + \cancel{3H_2(g)} \rightarrow CH_4(g) + \cancel{H_2O(g)}$ $\Delta_r H° = -206 \text{ kJ/mol}$

   $2C(s, coal) + 2H_2O(g) \rightarrow CH_4(g) + CO_2(g)$

b) The total may be determined by doubling the value for equation 1) and adding to the other two values.

   $\Delta_r H° = 2(129.7 \text{ kJ/mol}) + (-41 \text{ kJ/mol}) + (-206 \text{ kJ/mol}) = 12.4 \text{ kJ/mol} = \textbf{12 kJ/mol}$

c) Calculating the heat of combustion of CH_4:

   $CH_4(g) + 2O_2(g) \rightarrow CO_2(g) + 2H_2O(g)$

$\Delta_r H° = \sum m \Delta_{f \, (products)} H° - \sum n \Delta_{f \, (reactants)} H°$

$\Delta_r H° = [(\Delta_f H° \text{ of } CO_2) + 2(\Delta_f H° \text{ of } H_2O)]$

$\qquad\qquad\qquad\qquad\qquad - [(\Delta_f H° \text{ of } CH_4) + 2(\Delta_f H° \text{ of } O_2)]$

$\Delta_r H° = [1(-393.5 \text{ kJ/mol}) + 2(-241.826 \text{ kJ/mol})]$

$\qquad\qquad\qquad\qquad - [1(-74.87 \text{ kJ/mol}) + 2(0.0 \text{ kJ/mol})]$

$\Delta_r H° = -802.282 \text{ kJ/mol}$

Total heat for gasification of 1.00 kg coal:

$q_{tot} = \left(1.00 \text{ kg coal}\right)\left(\dfrac{10^3 \text{ g}}{1 \text{ kg}}\right)\left(\dfrac{1 \text{ mol coal}}{12.00 \text{ g coal}}\right)\left(\dfrac{12.4 \text{ kJ}}{2 \text{ mol coal}}\right) = 516.667 \text{ kJ}$

Total heat from burning the methane formed from 1.00 kg of coal:

$q_{tot} = (1.00 \text{ kg of coal})\left(\dfrac{10^3 \text{ g}}{1 \text{ kg}}\right)\left(\dfrac{1 \text{ mol coal}}{12.00 \text{ g coal}}\right)\left(\dfrac{1 \text{ mol } CH_4}{2 \text{ mol coal}}\right)\left(\dfrac{-802.282 \text{ kJ}}{1 \text{ mol } CH_4}\right) = -33428.42 \text{ kJ}$

Total heat = q_{tot} = 516.667 kJ + (−33511.75 kJ) = −32995.083 kJ = **−3.30x10⁴ kJ**

END–OF–CHAPTER PROBLEMS

5.4   Plan: Remember that an increase in internal energy is a result of the system (body) gaining heat or having work done on it and a decrease in internal energy is a result of the system (body) losing heat or doing work.
Solution:
The internal energy of the body is the sum of the cellular and molecular activities occurring from skin level inward. The body's internal energy can be increased by adding food, which adds energy to the body through the

breaking of bonds in the food. The body's internal energy can also be increased through addition of work and heat, like the rubbing of one person's warm hands on the cold hands of another. The body can lose energy if it performs work, like pushing a lawnmower, and can lose energy by losing heat to a cold room.

5.6   Plan: Use the law of conservation of energy.
Solution:
The amount of the change in internal energy in the two cases is the same. By the law of energy conservation, the change in energy of the universe is zero. This requires that the change in energy of the system (heater or air conditioner) equals an opposite change in energy of the surroundings (room air). Since both systems consume the same amount of electrical energy, the change in energy of the heater equals that of the air conditioner.

5.8   Plan: The change in a system's energy is $\Delta U = q + w$. If the system <u>receives</u> heat, then its q_{final} is greater than $q_{initial}$ so q is positive. Since the system <u>performs</u> work, its $w_{final} < w_{initial}$ so w is negative.
Solution:
$\Delta U = q + w$
$\Delta U = (+425 \text{ J/mol}) + (-425 \text{ J/mol}) = \textbf{0 J/mol}$

5.10   Plan: The change in a system's energy is $\Delta U = q + w$. A system that releases thermal energy has a negative value for q and a system that has work done on it has a positive value for work. Convert work in calories to work in joules.
Solution:

$$\text{Work (J/mol)} = (530 \text{ cal/mol})\left(\frac{4.184 \text{ J}}{1 \text{ cal}}\right) = 2217.52 \text{ J/mol}$$

$$\Delta U = q + w = -675 \text{ J/mol} + 2217.52 \text{ J/mol} = 1542.52 \text{ J/mol} = \textbf{1.54x10}^3 \textbf{ J/mol}$$

5.12   Plan: Convert $6.6\text{x}10^{10}$ J to the other units using conversion factors.
Solution:
$C(s) + O_2(g) \rightarrow CO_2(g) + 6.6\text{x}10^{10}$ J
(2.0 tonnes)

a) $\Delta U \text{ (kJ)} = (6.6 \text{ x } 10^{10} \text{ J})\left(\frac{1 \text{ kJ}}{10^3 \text{ J}}\right) = \textbf{6.6x10}^7 \textbf{ kJ}$

b) $\Delta U \text{ (kcal)} = (6.6 \text{ x } 10^{10} \text{ J})\left(\frac{1 \text{ cal}}{4.184 \text{ J}}\right)\left(\frac{1 \text{ kcal}}{10^3 \text{ cal}}\right) = 1.577\text{x}10^7 \text{ kcal} = \textbf{1.6x10}^7 \textbf{ kcal}$

5.15   Plan: 454 g of body fat is equivalent to about $4.1\text{x}10^3$ Calories. Convert Calories to kJ with the appropriate conversion factors.
Solution:

$$\text{Time} = (454\,\text{g})\left(\frac{4.1\text{x}10^3 \text{ Cal}}{454 \text{ g}}\right)\left(\frac{10^3 \text{ cal}}{1 \text{ Cal}}\right)\left(\frac{4.184 \text{ J}}{1 \text{ cal}}\right)\left(\frac{1 \text{ kJ}}{10^3 \text{ J}}\right)\left(\frac{h}{1950 \text{ kJ}}\right) = 8.79713 \text{ h} = \textbf{8.8 h}$$

5.17   Since many reactions are performed in an open flask, the reaction proceeds at constant pressure. The determination of ΔH (constant pressure conditions) requires a measurement of heat only, whereas ΔU requires measurement of heat and PV work.

5.19   Plan: An exothermic process releases heat and an endothermic process absorbs heat.
Solution:
a) **Exothermic**, the system (water) is releasing heat in changing from liquid to solid.
b) **Endothermic**, the system (water) is absorbing heat in changing from liquid to gas.
c) **Exothermic**, the process of digestion breaks down food and releases energy.
d) **Exothermic**, heat is released as a person runs and muscles perform work.
e) **Endothermic**, heat is absorbed as food calories are converted to body tissue.
f) **Endothermic**, the wood being chopped absorbs heat (and work).

g) **Exothermic**, the furnace releases heat from fuel combustion. Alternatively, if the system is defined as the air in the house, the change is endothermic since the air's temperature is increasing by the input of heat energy from the furnace.

5.22   Plan: An exothermic reaction releases heat, so the reactants have greater H ($H_{initial}$) than the products (H_{final}). $\Delta H = H_{final} - H_{initial} < 0$.
Solution:

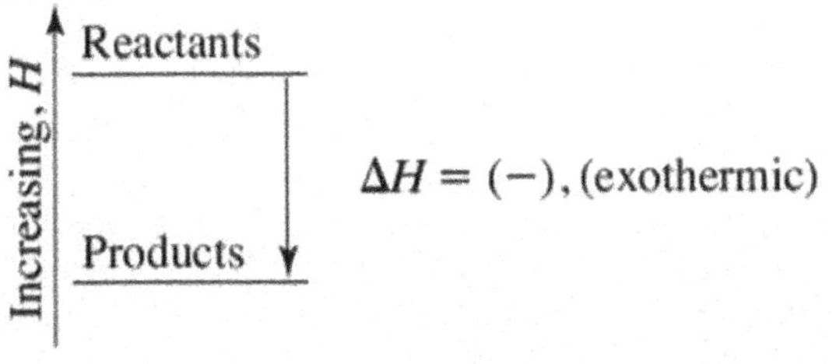

Reactants

Products

$\Delta H = (-), (\text{exothermic})$

Increasing, H

5.24   Plan: Combustion of hydrocarbons and related compounds require oxygen (and a heat catalyst) to yield carbon dioxide gas, water vapour, and heat. Combustion reactions are exothermic. The freezing of liquid water is an exothermic process as heat is removed from the water in the conversion from liquid to solid. An exothermic reaction or process releases heat, so the reactants have greater H ($H_{initial}$) than the products (H_{final}).

Solution:
a) Combustion of ethane: $2C_2H_6(g) + 7O_2(g) \rightarrow 4CO_2(g) + 6H_2O(g) + \text{heat}$

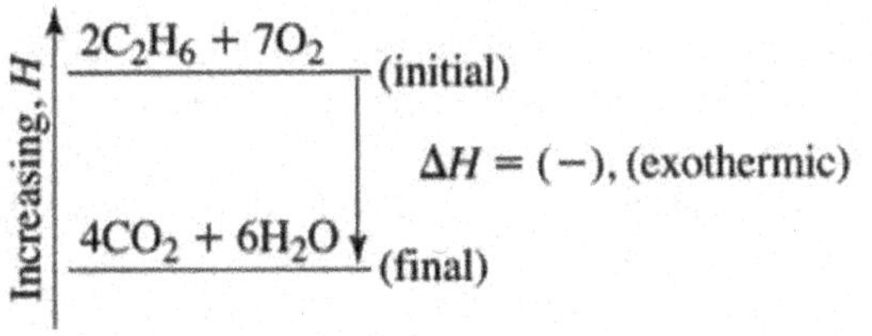

$2C_2H_6 + 7O_2$ (initial)

$4CO_2 + 6H_2O$ (final)

$\Delta H = (-), (\text{exothermic})$

Increasing, H

b) Freezing of water: $H_2O(l) \rightarrow H_2O(s) + \text{heat}$

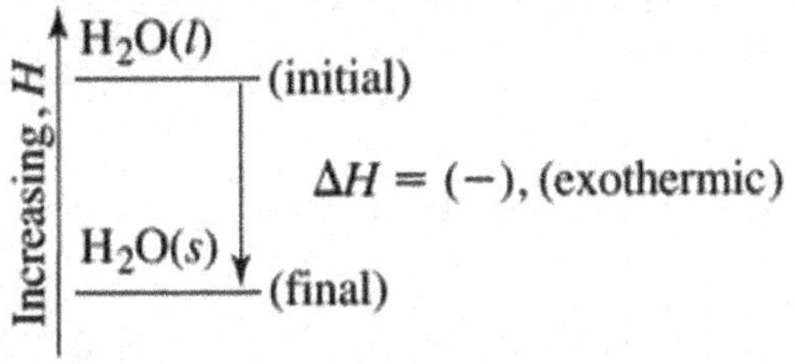

$H_2O(l)$ (initial)

$H_2O(s)$ (final)

$\Delta H = (-), (\text{exothermic})$

Increasing, H

5.26   Plan: Combustion of hydrocarbons and related compounds require oxygen (and a heat catalyst) to yield carbon dioxide gas, water vapour, and heat. Combustion reactions are exothermic. An exothermic reaction releases heat, so the reactants have greater H ($H_{initial}$) than the products (H_{final}). If heat is absorbed, the reaction is endothermic and the products have greater H (H_{final}) than the reactants ($H_{initial}$).
Solution:
a) $2CH_3OH(l) + 3O_2(g) \rightarrow 2CO_2(g) + 4H_2O(g) + \text{heat}$

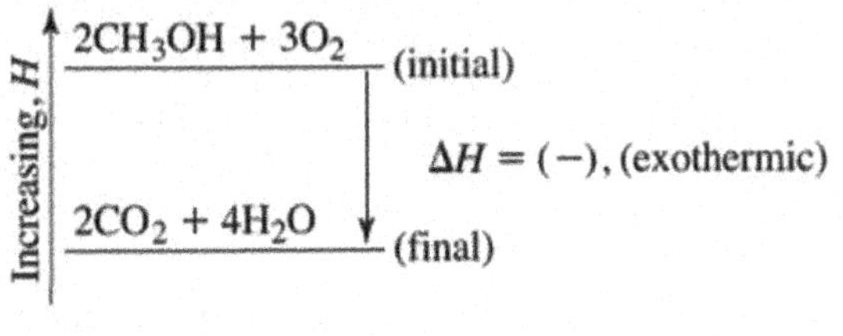

$2CH_3OH + 3O_2$ (initial)

$2CO_2 + 4H_2O$ (final)

$\Delta H = (-), (\text{exothermic})$

Increasing, H

b) Nitrogen dioxide, NO_2, forms from N_2 and O_2.

$1/2N_2(g) + O_2(g) + heat \rightarrow NO_2(g)$

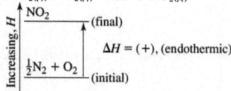

$\Delta H = (+)$, (endothermic)

5.28   <u>Plan:</u> Recall that q_{sys} is positive if heat is absorbed by the system (endothermic) and negative if heat is released by the system (exothermic). Since $\Delta U = q + w$, the work must be considered in addition to q_{sys} to find ΔU_{sys}.
<u>Solution:</u>
a) This is a phase change from the solid phase to the gas phase. Heat is absorbed by the system so q_{sys} is **positive (+)**.
b) The system is expanding in volume as more moles of gas exist after the phase change than were present before the phase change. So the system has done work of expansion and w is negative. $\Delta U_{sys} = q + w$. Since q is positive and w is negative, the sign of ΔU_{sys} **cannot be predicted**. It will be positive if $q > w$ and negative if $q < w$.
c) $\Delta U_{univ} = \mathbf{0}$. If the system loses energy, the surroundings gain an equal amount of energy. The sum of the energy of the system and the energy of the surroundings remains constant.

5.31   To determine the specific heat capacity of a substance, you need its mass, the heat added (or lost), and the change in temperature.

5.33   Specific heat capacity is the quantity of heat required to raise 1g of a substance by 1 K. Molar heat capacity is the quantity of heat required to raise 1 mole of substance by 1 K. Heat capacity is also the quantity of heat required for a 1 K temperature change, but it applies to an object instead of a specified amount of a substance. Thus, specific heat capacity and molar heat capacity are used when talking about an element or compound while heat capacity is used for a calorimeter or other object.

5.35   <u>Plan:</u> The heat required to raise the temperature of water is found by using the equation
$q = c$ x mass x ΔT. The specific heat capacity, c_{water}, is found in Table 5.2. Because $1°C=1K$,
$\Delta T = 100°C - 25°C = 75°C = 75$ K.
<u>Solution:</u>

$$q \text{ (J)} = c \text{ x mass x } \Delta T = \left(4.184\frac{J}{g\bullet K}\right)(22.0 \text{ g})(75 \text{ K}) = 6903.6 \text{ J} = \mathbf{6.9x10^3 \text{ J}}$$

5.37   <u>Plan:</u> Use the relationship $q = c$ x mass x ΔT. We know the heat (change kJ to J), the specific heat capacity, and the mass, so ΔT can be calculated. Once ΔT is known, that value is added to the initial temperature to find the final temperature.
<u>Solution:</u>
$q \text{ (J)} = c$ x mass x ΔT $T_{initial} = 13.00°C$ $T_{final} = ?$ mass $= 295$ g $c = 0.900$ J/g•K

$$q = (75.0 \text{ kJ})\left(\frac{10^3 \text{ J}}{1 \text{ kJ}}\right) = 7.50x10^4 \text{ J}$$

$7.50x10^4 \text{ J} = (0.900 \text{ J/g}\bullet K)(295 \text{ g})(\Delta T)$

$$\Delta T = \frac{\left(7.50x10^4 \text{ J}\right)}{(295 \text{ g})\left(\dfrac{0.900 \text{ J}}{g\bullet K}\right)}$$

$\Delta T = 282.4859$ K $= 282.4859°C$ (Because $1°C=1K$, ΔT is the same in either temperature unit.)
$\Delta T = T_{final} - T_{initial}$
$T_{final} = \Delta T + T_{initial}$
$T_{final} = 282.4859°C + 13.00°C = 295.49$ **°C= 295°C**

5.39   <u>Plan:</u> Since the bolts have the same mass and same specific heat capacity, and one must cool as the other heats (the heat lost by the "hot" bolt equals the heat gained by the "cold" bolt), the final temperature is an average of the two initial temperatures.
<u>Solution:</u>

$$\left[\frac{(T_1 + T_2)}{2}\right] = \left[\frac{(100.°C + 55°C)}{2}\right] = \mathbf{77.5°C}$$

5.41   <u>Plan:</u> The heat lost by the water originally at 85°C is gained by the water that is originally at 26°C. Therefore $-q_{lost} = q_{gained}$. Both volumes are converted to mass using the density.
<u>Solution:</u>

Mass (g) of 75 mL = $(75 \text{ mL})\left(\dfrac{1.00 \text{ g}}{1 \text{ mL}}\right) = 75$ g   Mass (g) of 155 mL = $(155 \text{ mL})\left(\dfrac{1.00 \text{ g}}{1 \text{ mL}}\right) = 155$ g

$-q_{lost} = q_{gained}$
c x mass x ΔT (85°C water)= c x mass x ΔT (26°C water)
$-$ (4.184 J/g°C)(75 g)($T_{final} - 85$)°C =(4.184 J/g°C)(155 g)($T_{final} - 26$)°C
$-$ (75 g)($T_{final} - 85$)°C = (155 g) ($T_{final} - 26$)°C
$6375 - 75T_{final} = 155T_{final} - 4030$
$6375 + 4030 = 155T_{final} + 75T_{final}$
$10405 = 230.T_{final}$
$T_{final} = (10405/230.) = 45.24$°C = **45°C**

5.43   <u>Plan:</u> Heat gained by water and the container equals the heat lost by the copper tubing so
$q_{water} + q_{calorimeter} = -q_{copper}$.
<u>Solution:</u>
$\Delta T = T_{final} - T_{initial}$
Specific heat capacity in units of J/g•K has the same value in units of J/g°C since the Celsius and Kelvin unit are the same size.
$-q_{lost} = q_{gained} = q_{water} + q_{calorimeter}$
$-$ (455 g Cu)(0.387 J/g)($T_{final} - 89.5$)°C
          = (159 g H$_2$O)(4.184 J/g°C)($T_{final} - 22.8$)°C + (10.0 J/°C)($T_{final} - 22.8$)°C
$-$ (176.085)($T_{final} - 89.5$) = (665.256)($T_{final} - 22.8$) + (10.0)($T_{final} - 22.8$)
$15759.6075 - 176.085T_{final} = 665.256T_{final} - 15167.8368 + 10.0T_{final} - 228$
$15759.6075 + 15167.8368 + 228 = 176.085T_{final} + 665.256T_{final} + 10.0T_{final}$
$31155.4443 = 851.341T_{final}$
$T_{final} = 31155.4443/(851.341) = 36.59573 = \mathbf{36.6°C}$

5.50   <u>Plan:</u> Recall that ΔH is positive for an endothermic reaction in which heat is absorbed, while ΔH is negative for an exothermic reaction in which heat is released.
<u>Solution:</u>
The reaction has a **positive $\Delta_r H$**, because this reaction requires the input of energy to break the oxygen-oxygen bond in O$_2$:
          $O_2(g) + \text{energy} \rightarrow 2O(g)$

5.51   <u>Plan:</u> Recall that ΔH is positive for an endothermic reaction in which heat is absorbed, while ΔH is negative for an exothermic reaction in which heat is released.
<u>Solution:</u>
As a substance changes from the gaseous state to the liquid state, energy is released so ΔH would be negative for the condensation of 1 mol of water. The value of ΔH for the vapourization of 2 mol of water would be twice the value of ΔH for the condensation of 1 mol of water vapour but would have an opposite sign ($+\Delta H$).
          $H_2O(g) \rightarrow H_2O(l) + \text{Energy}$ $2H_2O(l) + \text{Energy} \rightarrow 2H_2O(g)$
          $\Delta_{condensation}H = (-)$ $\Delta_{vapourization}H = (+)2[\Delta_{condensation}H]$
The enthalpy for 1 mole of water condensing would be opposite in sign to and one-half the value for the conversion of 2 moles of liquid H$_2$O to H$_2$O vapour.

5.52   Plan: Recall that ΔH is positive for an endothermic reaction in which heat is absorbed, while ΔH is negative for an exothermic reaction in which heat is released. The $\Delta_r H$ is specific for the reaction as written, meaning that 20.2 kJ is released when one-eighth of a mole of sulfur reacts. Use the ratio between moles of sulfur and ΔH to convert between amount of sulfur and heat released.
Solution:
a) This reaction is **exothermic** because ΔH is negative.
b) Because ΔH is a state function, the total energy required for the reverse reaction, regardless of how the change occurs, is the same magnitude but different sign of the forward reaction. Therefore, $\Delta H = $ **+20.2 kJ per 1/8 mol of S_8 produced**.

$$c)\ q = \left(2.6\ \text{mol}\ S_8\right)\left(\frac{-20.2\ \text{kJ}}{(1/8)\ \text{mol}\ S_8}\right) = -420.16\ \text{kJ} = \mathbf{-4.2 \times 10^2\ kJ}$$

d) The mass of S_8 requires conversion to moles and then a calculation identical to part c) can be performed.

$$q = \left(25.0\ \text{g}\ S_8\right)\left(\frac{1\ \text{mol}\ S_8}{256.56\ \text{g}\ S_8}\right)\left(\frac{-20.2\ \text{kJ}}{(1/8)\ \text{mol}\ S_8}\right) = -15.7468\ \text{kJ} = \mathbf{-15.7\ kJ}$$

5.54   Plan: A thermochemical equation is a balanced equation that includes the heat of reaction. Since heat is absorbed in this reaction, ΔH will be positive. Convert the mass of NO to moles and use the ratio between NO and ΔH to find the heat involved for this amount of NO.
Solution:
a) $1/2 N_2(g) + 1/2 O_2(g) \rightarrow NO(g)$ $\Delta H = 90.29$ kJ/mol

$$b)\ q = \left(3.50\ \text{g}\ NO\right)\left(\frac{1\ \text{mol}\ NO}{30.01\ \text{g}\ NO}\right)\left(\frac{-90.29\ \text{kJ}}{1\ \text{mol}\ NO}\right) = -10.5303\ \text{kJ} = \mathbf{-10.5\ kJ}$$

5.56   Plan: For the reaction written, 2 moles of H_2O_2 release 196.1 kJ of energy upon decomposition. Use this ratio to convert between the given amount of reactant and the amount of heat released. The amount of H_2O_2 must be converted from kg to g to moles.
Solution:
$$2 H_2O_2(l) \rightarrow 2 H_2O(l) + O_2(g)\qquad\qquad \Delta_r H = -196.1\ \text{kJ/mol}$$

$$\text{Heat (kJ)} = q = \left(652\ \text{kg}\ H_2O_2\right)\left(\frac{10^3\ \text{g}}{1\ \text{kg}}\right)\left(\frac{1\ \text{mol}\ H_2O_2}{34.02\ \text{g}\ H_2O_2}\right)\left(\frac{-196.1\ \text{kJ}}{2\ \text{mol}\ H_2O_2}\right) = -1.87915 \times 10^6\ \text{kJ} = \mathbf{-1.88 \times 10^6\ kJ}$$

5.60   Plan: A thermochemical equation is a balanced equation that includes the heat of reaction. Heat is released in this reaction so ΔH is negative. Use the ratio between ΔH and moles of C_2H_4 to find the amount of C_2H_4 that must react to produce the given quantity of heat.
Solution:
a) $C_2H_4(g) + 3 O_2(g) \rightarrow 2 CO_2(g) + 2 H_2O(g)$ $\Delta_r H = -1411$ kJ/mol

$$b)\ \text{Mass (g) of}\ C_2H_4 = \left(-70.0\ \text{kJ}\right)\left(\frac{1\ \text{mol}\ C_2H_4}{-1411\ \text{kJ}}\right)\left(\frac{28.05\ \text{g}\ C_2H_4}{1\ \text{mol}\ C_2H_4}\right) = 1.39157\ \text{g} = \mathbf{1.39\ g\ C_2H_4}$$

5.64   Plan: Two chemical equations can be written based on the description given:
$$\begin{array}{lll} C(s,\ graphite) + O_2(g) \rightarrow CO_2(g) & \Delta_1 H & (1) \\ CO(g) + 1/2 O_2(g) \rightarrow CO_2(g) & \Delta_2 H & (2) \end{array}$$
The second reaction can be reversed and its ΔH sign changed. In this case, no change in the coefficients is necessary since the CO_2 cancels. Add the two ΔH values together to obtain the ΔH of the desired reaction.
Solution:

$$\begin{array}{lll} C(s,\ graphite) + O_2(g) \rightarrow \cancel{CO_2(g)} & \Delta_1 H & \\ \cancel{CO_2(g)} \rightarrow CO(g) + 1/2 O_2(g) & -\Delta_2 H & \text{(reaction is reversed)} \\ \hline \end{array}$$

Total $C(s,\ graphite) + 1/2 O_2(g) \rightarrow CO(g)$ $\Delta_r H = \Delta_1 H + -(\Delta_2 H)$

How are the ΔH values for each reaction determined? The ΔH_1 can be found by using the heats of formation in Appendix B:

$\Delta_1 H = [\Delta_f H(CO_2)] - [\Delta_f H(C) + \Delta_f H(O_2)] = [-393.5 \text{ kJ/mol}] - [0 + 0] = -393.5 \text{ kJ/mol}$.

The ΔH_2 can be found by using the heats of formation in Appendix B:

$\Delta_2 H = [\Delta_f H(CO_2)] - [\Delta_f H(CO) + 1/2\Delta_f H(O_2)] = [-393.5 \text{ kJ/mol}] - [-110.5 \text{ kJ/mol} + 0)] = -283 \text{ kJ/mol}$.

$\Delta_r H = \Delta_1 H + - (\Delta_2 H) = -393.5 \text{ kJ/mol} + - (-283.0 \text{ kJ/mol}) = \textbf{-110.5 kJ/mol}$

5.65   Plan: To obtain the overall reaction, add the first reaction to the reverse of the second. When the second reaction is reversed, the sign of its enthalpy change is reversed from positive to negative.
Solution:

$Ca(s) + 1/2O_2(g) \rightarrow \text{CaO}(s)$	$\Delta H = -635.1 \text{ kJ/mol}$
$\text{CaO}(s) + CO_2(g) \rightarrow CaCO_3(s)$	$\Delta H = -178.3 \text{ kJ/mol}$ (reaction is reversed)
$Ca(s) + 1/2O_2(g) + CO_2(g) \rightarrow CaCO_3(s)$	$\Delta H = \textbf{-813.4 kJ/mol}$

5.67   Plan: Add the two equations, canceling substances that appear on both sides of the arrow. When matching the equations with the arrows in the Figure, remember that a positive ΔH corresponds to an arrow pointing up while a negative ΔH corresponds to an arrow pointing down.
Solution:

1)	$N_2(g) + O_2(g) \rightarrow \text{2NO}(g)$	$\Delta H = 180.6 \text{ kJ/mol}$
2)	$\text{2NO}(g) + O_2(g) \rightarrow 2NO_2(g)$	$\Delta H = -114.2 \text{ kJ/mol}$
3)	$\textbf{N}_2\textbf{(g) + 2O}_2\textbf{(g)} \rightarrow \textbf{2NO}_2\textbf{(g)}$	$\Delta_r H = \textbf{+66.4 kJ/mol}$

In Figure P5.67, **A represents reaction 1** with a larger amount of energy absorbed, **B represents reaction 2** with a smaller amount of energy released, and **C represents reaction 3** as the sum of A and B.

5.69   Plan: Vapourization is the change in state from a liquid to a gas: $H_2O(l) \rightarrow H_2O(g)$. The two equations describing the chemical reactions for the formation of gaseous and liquid water can be combined to yield the equation for vapourization.
Solution:

1) Formation of $H_2O(g)$:	$H_2(g) + 1/2O_2(g) \rightarrow H_2O(g)$	ΔH	$= -241.8 \text{ kJ/mol}$
2) Formation of $H_2O(l)$:	$H_2(g) + 1/2O_2(g) \rightarrow H_2O(l)$	ΔH	$= -285.8 \text{ kJ/mol}$

Reverse reaction 2 (change the sign of ΔH) and add the two reactions:

$\text{H}_2\text{(g)} + \text{1/2O}_2\text{(g)} \rightarrow H_2O(g)$	$\Delta H = -241.8 \text{ kJ/mol}$
$H_2O(l) \rightarrow \text{H}_2\text{(g)} + \text{1/2O}_2\text{(g)}$	$\Delta H = +285.8 \text{ kJ/mol}$
$H_2O(l) \rightarrow H_2O(g)$	$\Delta_{vap}H = \textbf{44.0 kJ/mol}$

5.72   The standard heat of reaction, $\Delta_r H°$, is the enthalpy change for any reaction where all substances are in their standard states. The standard heat of formation, $\Delta_f H°$, is the enthalpy change that accompanies the formation of one mole of a compound in its standard state from elements in their standard states. Standard state 1 bar for gases, 1 mol/L for solutes, and the most stable form for liquids and solids. Standard state does not include a specific temperature, but a temperature must be specified in a table of standard values.

5.74   Plan: $\Delta_f H°$ is for the reaction that shows the formation of <u>one</u> mole of compound from its elements in their standard states.
Solution:
a) $1/2Cl_2(g) + Na(s) \rightarrow NaCl(s)$ The element chlorine occurs as Cl_2, not Cl.
b) $H_2(g) + 1/2O_2(g) \rightarrow H_2O(g)$ The element hydrogen exists as H_2, not H, and the formation of water is written with water as the product.
c) No changes

5.75   Plan: Formation equations show the formation of one mole of compound from its elements. The elements must be in their most stable states ($\Delta_f H° = 0$).
Solution:
a) $Ca(s) + Cl_2(g) \rightarrow CaCl_2(s)$
b) $Na(s) + 1/2H_2(g) + C(graphite) + 3/2O_2(g) \rightarrow NaHCO_3(s)$
c) $C(graphite) + 2Cl_2(g) \rightarrow CCl_4(l)$
d) $1/2H_2(g) + 1/2N_2(g) + 3/2O_2(g) \rightarrow HNO_3(l)$

5.77   Plan: The enthalpy change of a reaction is the sum of the heats of formation of the products minus the sum of the heats of formation of the reactants. Since the $\Delta_f H°$ values (Appendix B) are reported as energy per one mole, use the appropriate stoichiometric coefficient to reflect the higher number of moles.
Solution:

$$\Delta_r H° = \sum m\, \Delta_{f\,(products)} H° - \sum n\, \Delta_{f\,(reactants)} H°$$

a) $\Delta_r H° = \{2\, \Delta_f H°\ [SO_2(g)] + 2\, \Delta_f H°\ [H_2O(g)]\} - \{2\, \Delta_f H°\ [H_2S(g)] + 3\, \Delta_f H°\ [O_2(g)]\}$
        $= [2(-296.8\ kJ/mol) + 2(-241.826\ kJ/mol)] - [2(-20.2\ kJ/mol) + 3(0.0\ kJ/mol)]$
        $= \mathbf{-1036.9\ kJ/mol}$
b) The balanced equation is $CH_4(g) + 4Cl_2(g) \rightarrow CCl_4(l) + 4HCl(g)$

$\Delta_r H° = \{1\, \Delta_f H°\ [CCl_4(l)] + 4\, \Delta_f H°\ [HCl(g)]\} - \{1\, \Delta_f H°\ [CH_4(g)] + 4\, \Delta_f H°\ [Cl_2(g)]\}$

$\Delta_r H° = [(-139\ kJ/mol) + 4(-92.31\ kJ/mol)] - [(-74.87\ kJ/mol) + 4(0\ kJ/mol)]$
        $= \mathbf{-433\ kJ/mol}$

5.79   Plan: The enthalpy change of a reaction is the sum of the heats of formation of the products minus the sum of the heats of formation of the reactants. Since the $\Delta_f H°$ values (Appendix B) are reported as energy per one mole, use the appropriate stoichiometric coefficient to reflect the higher number of moles. In this case, $\Delta_r H°$ is known and $\Delta_f H°$ of CuO must be calculated.
Solution:

$$\Delta_r H° = \sum m\, \Delta_{f\,(products)} H° - \sum n\, \Delta_{f\,(reactants)} H°$$

$Cu_2O(s) + 1/2O_2(g) \rightarrow 2CuO(s)$ $\Delta_{rxn} H° = -146.0\ kJ/mol$

$\Delta_r H° = \{2\, \Delta_f H°\ [CuO(s)]\} - \{1\, \Delta_f H°\ [Cu_2O(s)] + 1/2\, \Delta_f H°\ [O_2(g)]\}$

$-146.0\ kJ/mol = \{2\, \Delta_f H°\ [CuO(s)]\} - \{(-168.6\ kJ/mol) + 1/2(0\ kJ/mol)\}$

$-146.0\ kJ/mol = 2\, \Delta_f H°\ [CuO(s)] + 168.6\ kJ/mol$

$\Delta_f H°\ [CuO(s)] = -\dfrac{314.6\ kJ/mol}{2} = \mathbf{-157.3\ kJ/mol}$

5.81   Plan: The enthalpy change of a reaction is the sum of the heats of formation of the products minus the sum of the heats of formation of the reactants. Since the $\Delta_f H°$ values (Appendix B) are reported as energy per one mole, use the appropriate stoichiometric coefficient to reflect the higher number of moles. Hess's law can also be used to calculate the enthalpy of reaction. In part b), rearrange equations 1) and 2) to give the equation wanted.
Reverse the first equation (changing the sign of $\Delta_r H°$) and multiply the coefficients (and $\Delta_r H°$) of the second reaction by 2.
Solution:
$2PbSO_4(s) + 2H_2O(l) \rightarrow Pb(s) + PbO_2(s) + 2H_2SO_4(l)$

$$\Delta_r H° = \sum m\, \Delta_{f\,(products)} H° - \sum n\, \Delta_{f\,(reactants)} H°$$

a) $\Delta_r H^\circ = \{1\,\Delta_f H^\circ\ [Pb(s)] + 1\,\Delta_f H^\circ\ [PbO_2(s)] + 2\,\Delta_f H^\circ\ [H_2SO_4(l)]\}$

$\qquad\qquad\qquad\qquad - \{2\,\Delta_f H^\circ\ [PbSO_4(s)] + 2\,\Delta_f H^\circ\ [H_2O(l)]\}$

$\qquad = [(0\ kJ/mol) + (-276.6\ kJmol) + 2(-813.989\ kJ/mol)]$

$\qquad\qquad\qquad\qquad - [2(-918.39\ kJ/mol) + 2(-285.840\ kJ/mol)]$

$\qquad = \textbf{503.9 kJ/mol}$

b) Use Hess's law:

$PbSO_4(s) \rightarrow Pb(s) + PbO_2(s) + \cancel{2SO_3(g)}$	$\Delta_r H^\circ = -(-768\ kJ/mol)$ Equation has been reversed.
$\cancel{2SO_3(g)} + 2H_2O\ (l) \rightarrow 2H_2SO_4(l)$	$\Delta_r H^\circ = 2(-132\ kJ/mol)$
$2PbSO_4(s) + 2H_2O(l) \rightarrow Pb(s) + PbO_2(s) + 2H_2SO_4(l)$	$\Delta_r H^\circ = \textbf{504 kJ/mol}$

5.82   Plan: The enthalpy change of a reaction is the sum of the heats of formation of the products minus the sum of the heats of formation of the reactants. Since the $\Delta_f H^\circ$ values (Appendix B) are reported as energy per one mole, use the appropriate stoichiometric coefficient to reflect the higher number of moles. Convert the mass of stearic acid to moles and use the ratio between stearic acid and $\Delta_r H^\circ$ to find the heat involved for this amount of acid. For part d), use the kcal/g of fat relationship calculated in part c) to convert 11.0 g of fat to total kcal and compare to the 100. Cal amount.

Solution:

a) $C_{18}H_{36}O_2(s) + 26O_2(g) \rightarrow 18CO_2(g) + 18H_2O(g)$

b) $\Delta_r H^\circ = \Sigma m\,\Delta_{f\ (products)}H^\circ - \Sigma n\,\Delta_{f\ (reactants)}H^\circ$

$\Delta_r H^\circ = \{18\,\Delta_f H^\circ\ [CO_2(g)] + 18\,\Delta_f H^\circ\ [H_2O(g)]\} - \{1\,\Delta_f H^\circ\ [C_{18}H_{36}O_2(s)] + 26\,\Delta_f H^\circ\ [O_2(g)]\}$

$\qquad = [18(-393.5\ kJ/mol) + 18(-241.826\ kJ/mol)] - [(-948\ kJ/mol) + 26(0\ kJ/mol)]$

$\qquad = -10{,}487.868\ kJ/mol = \textbf{--10,488 kJ/mol}$

c) $q\ (kJ) = \left(1.00\ g\ C_{18}H_{36}O_2\right)\left(\dfrac{1\ mol\ C_{18}H_{36}O_2}{284.47\ C_{18}H_{36}O_2}\right)\left(\dfrac{-10{,}487.868\ kJ}{1\ mol\ C_{18}H_{36}O_2}\right) = -36.8681\ kJ = \textbf{--36.9 kJ}$

$q\ (kcal) = \left(-36.8681\ kJ\right)\left(\dfrac{1\ kcal}{4.184\ kJ}\right) = -8.811688\ kcal = \textbf{--8.81 kcal}$

d) $q\ (kcal) = \left(11.0\ g\ fat\right)\left[\dfrac{-8.811688\ kcal}{1.0\ g\ fat}\right] = 96.9286\ kcal = \textbf{96.9 kcal}$

Since 1 kcal = 1 Cal, 96.9 kcal = 96.9 Cal. The calculated calorie content is consistent with the package information.

5.84   Plan: Use the ideal gas law, $PV = nRT$, to calculate the volume of one mole of helium at each temperature. Then use the given equation for ΔE to find the change in internal energy. The equation for work, $w = -P\Delta V$, is needed for part c), and $q_P = \Delta U + P\Delta V$ is used for part d). For part e), recall that $\Delta H = q_P$.

Solution:

a) $PV = nRT$ or $V = \dfrac{nRT}{P}$

$T = 273 + 15 = 288\ K$ and $T = 273 + 30 = 303\ K$

Initial volume (L) $= V = \dfrac{nRT}{P} = \dfrac{\left(0.08314\dfrac{L\cdot bar}{mol\cdot K}\right)(288\ K)}{(1.01\ bar)} = 23.7072\ L/mol = \textbf{23.7 L/mol}$

Final volume (L) $= V = \dfrac{nRT}{P} = \dfrac{\left(0.08314\dfrac{L\cdot bar}{mol\cdot K}\right)(303\ K)}{(1.01\ bar)} = 24.9420\ L/mol = \textbf{24.9 L/mol}$

b) Internal energy is the sum of the potential and kinetic energies of each He atom in the system (the balloon). The energy of one mole of helium atoms can be described as a function of temperature, $U = 3/2nRT$, where $n = 1$ mole. Therefore, the internal energy at 15°C and 30°C can be calculated. The inside back cover lists values of R with different units.

$\Delta U = 3/2nR\Delta T = (3/2)(1.00 \text{ mol})(8.314 \text{ J/mol·K})(303 - 288)\text{K} = 187.065 \text{ J} = \textbf{187 J}$

c) When the balloon expands as temperature rises, the balloon performs PV work. However, the problem specifies that pressure remains constant, so work done <u>on</u> the surroundings by the balloon is defined by the equation: $w = -P\Delta V$. When pressure and volume are multiplied together, the unit is L·bar, so a conversion factor is needed to convert work in units of L·bar to joules.

$$w = -P\Delta V = -(1.01 \text{ bar})\left((24.9434 - 23.7085) \text{ L}\right)\left(\frac{100 \text{ J}}{1 \text{ L·bar}}\right) = -124.72 \text{ J} = \textbf{-1.2x10}^2 \textbf{ J}$$

d) $q_P = \Delta U + P\Delta V = (187.065 \text{ J}) + (124.72 \text{ J}) = 311.785 \text{ J} = \textbf{3.1x10}^2 \textbf{ J}$

e) $\Delta H = q_P = \textbf{310 J}$.

f) When a process occurs at constant pressure, the change in heat energy of the system can be described by a state function called enthalpy. The change in enthalpy equals the heat (q) lost at constant pressure: $\Delta H = \Delta U + P\Delta V = \Delta U - w = (q + w) - w = q_P$

5.93   Plan: For part a), first find the heat of reaction for the combustion of methane by using the heats of formation of the reactants and products. The enthalpy change of a reaction is the sum of the heats of formation of the products minus the sum of the heats of formation of the reactants. Since the $\Delta_f H°$ values (Appendix B) are reported as energy per one mole, use the appropriate stoichiometric coefficient to reflect the higher Amount in moles. For part c), convert the amount of water in L to mass in g and use the relationship $q = c$ x mass x ΔT to find the heat needed; then determine the total cost of heating the water.
Solution:
a) $CH_4(g) + 2O_2(g) \rightarrow CO_2(g) + 2H_2O(g)$

$\Delta_r H° = \{1 \Delta_f H° [CO_2(g)] + 2 \Delta_f H° [H_2O(g)]\} - \{1 \Delta_f H° [CH_4(g)] + 2 \Delta_f H° [O_2(g)]\}$
     $= [(-393.5 \text{ kJ/mol}) + 2(-241.826 \text{ kJ/mol})] - [(-74.87 \text{ kJ/mol}) + 2(0.0 \text{ kJ/mol})]$
     $= -802.282 \text{ kJ/mol} = -802.3 \text{ kJ/mol}$

$$\text{Amount in moles of } CH_4 = \left(1x10^8 \text{ J}\right)\left(\frac{1 \text{ kJ}}{10^3 \text{ J}}\right)\left(\frac{1 \text{ mol } CH_4}{802.282 \text{ kJ}}\right)$$

$$= 124.644 \text{ mol} = \textbf{1.2x10}^2 \textbf{ mol } CH_4$$

b) $\text{Cost} = \left(\dfrac{\$0.66}{10^8 \text{ J}}\right)\left(\dfrac{1x10^8 \text{ J}}{124.644 \text{ mol}}\right) = \$0.005295/\text{mol} = \textbf{\$0.0053/mol}$

c) $\text{Mass (g) of} = \left(1202 \text{ L}\right)\left(\dfrac{1 \text{ mL}}{10^{-3} \text{ L}}\right)\left(\dfrac{1.0 \text{ g}}{\text{mL}}\right) = 1.202x10^6 \text{ g}$

$$q = c \text{ x mass x } \Delta T = \left(\frac{4.184 \text{ J}}{\text{g °C}}\right)\left(1.202x10^6 \text{ g}\right)\left((42.0 - 15.0)\text{°C}\right) = 1.357875x10^8 \text{ J}$$

$$\text{Cost} = \left(1.357875x10^8 \text{ J}\right)\left(\frac{\$0.66}{1x10^8 \text{ J}}\right) = \$0.8962 = \textbf{\$0.90}$$

5.98   Plan: Heat of reaction is calculated using the relationship $\Delta_r H° = \Sigma m \Delta_{f \text{ (products)}} H° - \Sigma n \Delta_{f \text{ (reactants)}} H°$.
The heats of formation for all of the species, except $SiCl_4$, are found in Appendix B. Use reaction 3, with its given $\Delta_r H°$, to find the heat of formation of $SiCl_4(g)$. Once the heat of formation of $SiCl_4$ is known, the heat of reaction of the other two reactions can be calculated. When reactions 2 and 3 are added to obtain a fourth reaction, the heats of reaction of reactions 2 and 3 are also added to obtain the heat of reaction for the fourth reaction.

Solution:

a) (3) $SiCl_4(g) + 2H_2O(g) \rightarrow SiO_2(s) + 4HCl(g)$

$\Delta_r H^\circ = \{1 \Delta_f H^\circ \ [SiO_2(s)] + 4 \Delta_f H^\circ \ [HCl(g)]\} - \{1 \Delta_f H^\circ \ [SiCl_4(g)] + 2 \Delta_f H^\circ \ [H_2O(g)]\}$

$-139.5 \ kJ = [(-910.9 \ kJ/mol) + 4(-92.31 \ kJ/mol)] - [\Delta_f H^\circ \ [SiCl_4(g)] + 2(-241.826 \ kJ/mol)]$

$-139.5 \ kJ/mol = -1280.14 kJ/mol - [\Delta_f H^\circ \ [SiCl_4(g)] + (-483.652 \ kJ/mol)]$

$1140.64 \ kJ/mol = - \Delta_f H^\circ \ [SiCl_4(g)] + 483.652 \ kJ/mol$

$\Delta_f H^\circ \ [SiCl_4(g)] = -656.988 \ kJ/mol$

The heats of reaction for the first two steps can now be calculated.

1) $Si(s) + 2Cl_2(g) \rightarrow SiCl_4(g)$

$\Delta_r H^\circ = \{1 \Delta_f H^\circ \ [SiCl_4(g)]\} - \{1 \Delta_f H^\circ \ [Si(s)] + 2 \Delta_f H^\circ \ [Cl_2(g)]\}$

$\quad = [(-656.988 \ kJ/mol)] - [(0 \ kJ/mol) + 2(0 \ kJ/mol)] = -656.988 \ kJ/mol = \mathbf{-657.0 \ kJ/mol}$

2) $SiO_2(s) + 2C(graphite) + 2Cl_2(g) \rightarrow SiCl_4(g) + 2CO(g)$

$\Delta_r H^\circ = \{1 \Delta_f H^\circ \ [SiCl_4(g)] + 2 \Delta_f H^\circ \ [CO(g)]\}$

$\qquad\qquad - \{1 \Delta_f H^\circ \ [SiO_2(g)] + 2 \Delta_f H^\circ \ [C(graphite)] + 2 \Delta_f H^\circ \ [Cl_2(g)]\}$

$\quad = [(-656.988 \ kJ/mol) + 2(-110.5 \ kJ/mol)]$

$\qquad\qquad - [(-910.9 \ kJ/mol) + 2(0 \ kJ/mol) + 2(0 \ kJ/mol)]$

$\quad = 32.912 \ kJ/mol = \mathbf{32.9 \ kJ/mol}$

b) Adding reactions 2 and 3 yields:

(2) $\text{SiO}_2(s) + 2C(graphite) + 2Cl_2(g) \rightarrow \text{SiCl}_4(g) + 2CO(g) \qquad \Delta_{rxn} H^\circ = \quad 32.912 \ kJ/mol$

(3) $\text{SiCl}_4(g) + 2H_2O(g) \rightarrow \text{SiO}_2(s) + 4HCl(g) \qquad\qquad \Delta_{rxn} H^\circ = -139.5 \ kJ/mol$

$2C(graphite) + 2Cl_2(g) + 2H_2O(g) \rightarrow 2CO(g) + 4HCl(g) \qquad \Delta_{rxn} H^\circ = -106.588 \ kJ/mol = \mathbf{-106.6 \ kJ/mol}$

Confirm this result by calculating $\Delta_r H^\circ$ using Appendix B values.

$2C(graphite) + 2Cl_2(g) + 2H_2O(g) \rightarrow 2CO(g) + 4HCl(g)$

$\Delta_r H^\circ = \{2 \Delta_f H^\circ \ [CO(g)] + 4 \Delta_f H^\circ \ [HCl(g)]\} - \{2 \Delta_f H^\circ \ [C(graphite)] + 2 \Delta_f H^\circ \ [Cl_2(g)] + 2 \Delta_f H^\circ \ [H_2O(g)]\}$

$\quad = [2(-110.5 \ kJ/mol) + 4(-92.31 \ kJ)$

$\qquad\qquad - [2(0 \ kJ/mol) + 2(0 \ kJ/mol) + 2(-241.826 \ kJ/mol)]$

$\quad = -106.588 \ kJ/mol = \mathbf{-106.6 \ kJ/mol}$

5.99   Plan: Use $PV = nRT$ to find the initial volume of nitrogen gas at $0°C$ and then the final volume at $819°C$. Then the relationship $w = -P\Delta V$ can be used to calculate the work of expansion.

Solution:

a) $PV = nRT$

P=1.01 bar

Initial volume at $0°C + 273 = 273 \ K = V = \dfrac{nRT}{P} = \dfrac{(1 \ mol)\left(0.08314\dfrac{L \cdot bar}{mol \cdot K}\right)(273 \ K)}{(1.01 \ bar)} = 22.4725 \ L$

Final volume at $819°C + 273 = 1092 \ K = V = \dfrac{nRT}{P} = \dfrac{(1 \ mol)\left(0.08314\dfrac{L \cdot bar}{mol \cdot K}\right)(1092 \ K)}{(1.01 \ bar)} = 89.8900 L$

$\Delta V = V_{final} - V_{initial} = 89.8900 \ L - 22.4725 \ L = 67.4175 \ L$

$w = -P\Delta V = -(1.01 \ bar) \times 67.4275 \ L = -68.0917 \ bar \cdot L$

$w \ (J) = (-68.0917 \ bar \cdot L)\left(\dfrac{100 \ J}{1 \ bar \cdot L}\right) = -6809.17 \ J = \mathbf{-6.81 \times 10^3 \ J}$

b) $q = c$ x mass x ΔT

Mass (g) of $N_2 = (1\ mol\ N_2)\left(\dfrac{28.02\ g}{1\ mol\ N_2}\right) = 28.02\ g$

$\Delta T = \dfrac{q}{(c)(mass)} = \dfrac{6.80917 \times 10^3\ J}{(28.02\ g)(1.00\ J/g \cdot K)} = 243.011\ K = 243\ K = \mathbf{243°C}$

5.100   Plan: Note the numbers of moles of the reactants and products in the target equation and manipulate equations 1-5 and their $\Delta_r H°$ values so that these equations sum to give the target equation. Then the manipulated $\Delta_r H°$ values will add to give the $\Delta_r H°$ value of the target equation.

Solution:
Only reaction 3 contains $N_2O_4(g)$, and only reaction 1 contains $N_2O_3(g)$, so we can use those reactions as a starting point. N_2O_5 appears in both reactions 2 and 5, but note the physical states present: solid and gas. As a rough start, adding reactions 1, 3, and 5 yields the desired reactants and products, with some undesired intermediates:

Reverse (1)	$N_2O_3(g) \rightarrow NO(g) + NO_2(g)$	$\Delta_r H° = -(-39.8\ kJ/mol) = 39.8\ kJ/mol$
Multiply (3) by 2	$4NO_2(g) \rightarrow 2N_2O_4(g)$	$\Delta_r H° = 2(-57.2\ kJ/mol) = -114.4\ kJ/mol$
(5)	$N_2O_5(s) \rightarrow N_2O_5(g)$	$\Delta_r H° = (54.1\ kJ/mol) = 54.1\ kJ/mol$

$N_2O_3(g) + 4NO_2(g) + N_2O_5(s) \rightarrow NO(g) + NO_2(g) + 2N_2O_4(g) + N_2O_5(g)$

To cancel out the $N_2O_5(g)$ intermediate, reverse equation 2. This also cancels out some of the undesired $NO_2(g)$ but adds $NO(g)$ and $O_2(g)$. Finally, add equation 4 to remove those intermediates:

Reverse (1)	$N_2O_3(g) \rightarrow \cancel{NO(g)} + \cancel{NO_2(g)}$	$\Delta_r H° = -(-39.8\ kJ/mol) = 39.8\ kJ/mol$
Multiply (3) by 2	$\cancel{4NO_2(g)} \rightarrow 2N_2O_4(g)$	$\Delta_r H° = 2(-57.2\ kJ/mol) = -114.4\ kJ/mol$
(5)	$N_2O_5(s) \rightarrow \cancel{N_2O_5(g)}$	$\Delta_r H° = 54.1\ kJ/mol$
Reverse (2)	$\cancel{N_2O_5(g)} \rightarrow \cancel{NO(g)} + \cancel{NO_2(g)} + \cancel{O_2(g)}$	$\Delta_r H° = -(-112.5\ kJ/mol) = 112.5\ kJ/mol$
(4)	$\cancel{2NO(g)} + \cancel{O_2(g)} \rightarrow \cancel{2NO_2(g)}$	$\Delta_r H° = -114.2\ kJ/mol$
Total:	$N_2O_3(g) + N_2O_5(s) \rightarrow 2N_2O_4(g)$	$\Delta_r H° = \mathbf{-22.2\ kJ/mol}$

5.101   Plan: The enthalpy change of a reaction is the sum of the heats of formation of the products minus the sum of the heats of formation of the reactants. Since the $\Delta_f H°$ values (Appendix B) are reported as energy per one mole, use the appropriate stoichiometric coefficient to reflect the higher amount in moles. In this case, $\Delta_r H°$ of the second reaction is known and $\Delta_f H°$ of $N_2H_4(aq)$ must be calculated. For part b), calculate $\Delta_r H°$ for the reaction between $N_2H_4(aq)$ and O_2, using the value of $\Delta_f H°$ for $N_2H_4(aq)$ found in part a); then determine the amount in moles of O_2 present by multiplying volume and concentration (mol/L) and multiply by the $\Delta_r H°$ for the reaction.

Solution:
a) $2NH_3(aq) + NaOCl(aq) \rightarrow N_2H_4(aq) + NaCl(aq) + H_2O(l)$

$\Delta_r H° = \{1\ \Delta_f H°\ [N_2H_4(aq)] + 1\ \Delta_f H°\ [NaCl(aq)] + 1\ \Delta_f H°\ [H_2O(l)]\}$

$\qquad\qquad\qquad\qquad\qquad - \{2\ \Delta_f H°\ [NH_3(aq)] + 1\ \Delta_f H°\ [NaOCl(aq)]\}$

Note that the Appendix B value for N_2H_4 is for $N_2H_4(l)$, not for $N_2H_4(aq)$, so this term must be calculated. In addition, Appendix B does not list a value for $NaCl(aq)$, so this term must be broken down into $\Delta_f H°\ [Na^+(aq)]$ and $\Delta_f H°\ [Cl^-(aq)]$.

$-151\ kJ/mol = [\ \Delta_f H°\ [N_2H_4(aq)] + (-239.66\ kJ/mol) + (-167.46\ kJ/mol) + (-285.840\ kJ/mol)]$

$\qquad\qquad\qquad\qquad\qquad - [2(-80.83\ kJ/mol) + (-346\ kJ/mol)]$

$-151\ kJ/mol = [\ \Delta_f H°\ [N_2H_4(aq)] + (-692.96\ kJ/mol)] - [-507.66\ kJ/mol]$

$-151 \text{ kJ/mol} = [\Delta_f H^\circ \ [N_2H_4(aq)] + (-185.3 \text{ kJ/mol})$

$\Delta_f H^\circ \ [N_2H_4(aq)] = 34.3 \text{ kJ/mol} = \mathbf{34 \ kJ/mol}$

b) Amount in moles of $O_2 = \left(5.00 \times 10^3 \ L\right)\left(\dfrac{2.50 \times 10^{-4} \ \text{mol}}{1 \ L}\right) = 1.25 \text{ mol } O_2$

$N_2H_4(aq) \ + \ O_2(g) \rightarrow \ N_2(g) \ + \ 2H_2O(l)$

$\Delta_r H^\circ = \{1\,\Delta_f H^\circ \ [N_2(g)] + 2\,\Delta_f H^\circ \ [H_2O(l)]\} - \{1\,\Delta_f H^\circ \ [N_2H_4(aq)] + 1\,\Delta_f H^\circ \ [O_2(g)]\}$

$\quad = [(0 \text{ kJ/mol}) + 2(-285.840 \text{ kJ/mol})] - [(34.3 \text{ kJ/mol}) + (0 \text{ kJ/mol}]$

$\quad = -605.98 \text{ kJ}$

Heat (kJ) $= q = \left(1.25 \text{ mol } O_2\right)\left(\dfrac{-605.98 \text{ kJ}}{1 \text{ mol } O_2}\right) = -757.475 \text{ kJ} = \mathbf{-757 \ kJ}$

5.103 Plan: First find the heat of reaction for the combustion of methane. The enthalpy change of a reaction is the sum of the heats of formation of the products minus the sum of the heats of formation of the reactants. Since the $\Delta_f H^\circ$ values (Appendix B) are reported as energy per one mole, use the appropriate stoichiometric coefficient to reflect the higher amount in moles. Convert the mass of methane to amount in moles and multiply that Amount in molesby the heat of combustion.
Solution:
a) The balanced chemical equation for this reaction is:

$CH_4(g) + 2O_2(g) \rightarrow CO_2(g) + 2H_2O(g)$

$\Delta_r H^\circ = \{1\,\Delta_f H^\circ \ [CO_2(g)] + 2\,\Delta_f H^\circ \ [H_2O(g)]\} - \{1\,\Delta_f H^\circ \ [CH_4(g)] + 2\,\Delta_f H^\circ \ [O_2(g)]\}$

$\quad = [(-393.5 \text{ kJ/mol}) + 2(-241.826 \text{ kJ/mol})] - [(-74.87 \text{ kJ/mol}) + 2(0.0 \text{ kJ/mol})]$

$\quad = -802.282 \text{ kJ/mol}$

Amount in moles of $CH_4 = \left(25.0 \text{ g } CH_4\right)\left(\dfrac{1 \text{ mol}}{16.04 \text{ g } CH_4}\right) = 1.5586 \text{ mol } CH_4$

Heat (kJ) $= q = \left(1.5586 \text{ mol } CH_4\right)\left(\dfrac{-802.282 \text{ kJ}}{1 \text{ mol } CH_4}\right) = -1250.4 = \mathbf{-1.25 \times 10^3 \ kJ}$

b) The heat released by the reaction is "stored" in the gaseous molecules by virtue of their specific heat capacities, c, using the equation $q = c \times \text{mass} \times \Delta T$. The problem specifies heat capacities on a molar basis, so we modify the equation to use amount in moles, instead of mass. The gases that remain at the end of the reaction are CO_2 and H_2O. All of the methane and oxygen molecules were consumed. However, the oxygen was added as a component of air, which is 78% N_2 and 21% O_2, and there is leftover N_2.

Amount in moles of $CO_2(g) = \left(1.5586 \text{ mol } CH_4\right)\left(\dfrac{1 \text{ mol } CO_2}{1 \text{ mol } CH_4}\right) = 1.5586 \text{ mol } CO_2(g)$

Amount in moles of $H_2O(g) = \left(1.5586 \text{ mol } CH_4\right)\left(\dfrac{2 \text{ mol } H_2O}{1 \text{ mol } CH_4}\right) = 3.1172 \text{ mol } H_2O(g)$

Amount in moles of $O_2(g)$ reacted $= \left(1.5586 \text{ mol } CH_4\right)\left(\dfrac{2 \text{ mol } O_2}{1 \text{ mol } CH_4}\right) = 3.1172 \text{ mol } O_2(g)$

Amount in mole fraction $N_2 = (79\%/100\%) = 0.79$
Amount in mole fraction $O_2 = (21\%/100\%) = 0.21$

Amount in moles of $N_2(g) = \left(3.1172 \text{ mol } O_2 \text{ reacted}\right)\left(\dfrac{0.79 \text{ mol } N_2}{0.21 \text{ mol } O_2}\right) = 11.72661 \text{ mol } N_2$

$q = (\text{molar heat capacity})(\text{amount, mol})(\Delta T)$

$q = \left(1250.4 \text{ kJ}\right)\left(\dfrac{10^3 \ J}{1 \text{ kJ}}\right) = 1.2504 \times 10^6 \text{ J}$

1.2504×10^6 J = (1.5586 mol CO_2)(57.2 J/mol°C)(T_{final} − 0.0)°C
$$+ (3.1172 \text{ mol } H_2O)(36.0 \text{ J/mol°C})(T_{final} - 0.0)°C$$
$$+ (11.72661 \text{ mol } N_2)(30.5 \text{ J/mol°C})(T_{final} - 0.0)°C$$
1.2504×10^6 J = 89.15192 J/°C(T_{final}) + 112.2192 J/°C(T_{final}) + 357.6616 J/°C(T_{final})
1.2504×10^6 J = (559.03272 J/°C)T_{final}
T_{final} = (1.2504×10^6 J)/(559.0324 J/°C) = 2236.72°C = **2.24×10^3°C**

CHAPTER 6 QUANTUM THEORY AND ATOMIC STRUCTURE

The value for the speed of light will be 3.00×10^8 m/s except when more significant figures are necessary, in which cases, 2.9979×10^8 m/s will be used.

TOOLS OF THE LABORATORY BOXED READING PROBLEMS

B6.1 Plan: Plot absorbance on the y-axis and concentration on the x-axis. Since this is a linear plot, the graph is of the type $y = mx + b$, with m = slope and b = intercept. Any two points may be used to find the slope, and the slope is used to find the intercept. Once the equation for the line is known, the absorbance of the solution in part b) is used to find the concentration of the diluted solution, after which the dilution equation is used to find the concentration (mol/L) of the original solution.
Solution:
a) Absorbance vs. Concentration:

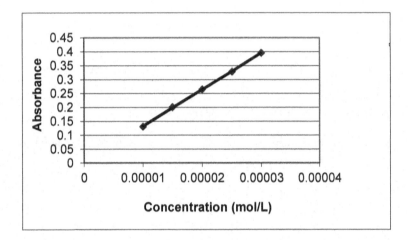

This is a linear plot, thus, using the first and last points given:

$$m = \frac{y_2 - y_1}{x_2 - x_1} = \frac{(0.396 - 0.131)}{(3.0 \times 10^{-5} - 1.0 \times 10^{-5}) \text{mol / L}} = 13,250 \text{ /mol/L} = \mathbf{1.3 \times 10^4 / mol/L}$$

Using the slope just calculated and any of the data points, the value of the intercept may be found.
$b = y - mx = 0.396 - (13,250/\text{mol/L})(3.0 \times 10^{-5} \text{ mol/L}) = -0.0015 = \mathbf{0.00}$ (absorbance has no units)
b) Use the equation just determined: $y = (1.3 \times 10^4/\text{mol/L}) \, x + 0.00$.
$x = (y - 0.00)/(1.3 \times 10^4/\text{mol/L}) = (0.236/1.3 \times 10^4) \text{ mol/L} = 1.81538 \times 10^{-5} \text{ mol/L} = \mathbf{1.8 \times 10^{-5} \ mol/L}$
This value is c_f in a dilution problem $(c_i V_i) = (c_f V_f)$ with $V_i = 20.0$ mL and $V_f = 150.$ mL.

$$M_i = \frac{(c_f)(V_f)}{(V_i)} = \frac{(1.81538 \times 10^{-5} \text{ mol / L})(150. \text{ mL})}{(20.0 \text{ mL})} = 1.361538 \times 10^{-4} \text{ mol/L} = \mathbf{1.4 \times 10^{-4} \ mol/L}$$

END–OF–CHAPTER PROBLEMS

6.2 Plan: Recall that the shorter the wavelength, the higher the frequency and the greater the energy. Figure 6.3 describes the electromagnetic spectrum by wavelength and frequency.
Solution:
a) Wavelength increases from left (10^{-2} nm) to right (10^{12} nm) in Figure 6.3. The trend in increasing wavelength is: **x-ray < ultraviolet < visible < infrared < microwave < radio wave.**

b) Frequency is inversely proportional to wavelength according to the equation $c = \lambda v$, so frequency has the opposite trend: **radio wave < microwave < infrared < visible < ultraviolet < x-ray**.

c) Energy is directly proportional to frequency according to the equation $E = hv$. Therefore, the trend in increasing energy matches the trend in increasing frequency: **radio wave < microwave < infrared < visible < ultraviolet < x-ray**.

6.7   Plan: Wavelength is related to frequency through the equation $c = \lambda v$. Recall that a Hz is a reciprocal second, or $1/s = s^{-1}$. Assume that the number "950" has three significant figures.

Solution:

$c = \lambda v$

$$\lambda \, (m) = \frac{c}{v} = \frac{3.00 \times 10^8 \text{ m/s}}{(950. \text{ kHz})\left(\dfrac{10^3 \text{ Hz}}{1 \text{ kHz}}\right)\left(\dfrac{s^{-1}}{Hz}\right)} = 315.789 \text{ m} = \textbf{316 m}$$

$$\lambda \, (nm) = \frac{c}{v} = (315.789 \text{ m})\left(\frac{1 \text{ nm}}{10^{-9} \text{ m}}\right) = 3.15789 \times 10^{11} \text{ m} = \textbf{3.16} \times \textbf{10}^{\textbf{11}} \textbf{ nm}$$

6.9   Plan: Frequency is related to energy through the equation $E = hv$. Note that $1 \text{ Hz} = 1 \text{ s}^{-1}$.

Solution:

$E = hv$

$E = (6.626 \times 10^{-34} \text{ J} \cdot \text{s})(3.8 \times 10^{10} \text{ s}^{-1}) = 2.51788 \times 10^{-23} \text{ J} = \textbf{2.5} \times \textbf{10}^{-\textbf{23}} \textbf{ J}$

6.11   Plan: Energy is inversely proportional to wavelength ($E = \dfrac{hc}{\lambda}$). As wavelength decreases, energy increases.

Solution:

In terms of increasing energy the order is **red < yellow < blue**.

6.13   Plan: Wavelength is related to frequency through the equation $c = \lambda v$. Recall that a Hz is a reciprocal second, or $1/s = s^{-1}$.

Solution:

$$v = (s^{-1}) = (22.235 \text{ GHz})\left(\frac{10^9 \text{ Hz}}{1 \text{ GHz}}\right)\left(\frac{s^{-1}}{Hz}\right) = 2.2235 \times 10^{10} \text{ s}^{-1}$$

$$\lambda \, (nm) = \frac{c}{v} = \frac{2.9979 \times 10^8 \text{ m/s}}{2.2235 \times 10^{10} \text{ s}^{-1}}\left(\frac{1 \text{ nm}}{10^{-9} \text{ m}}\right) = 1.3482797 \times 10^7 \text{ nm} = \textbf{1.3483} \times \textbf{10}^{\textbf{7}} \textbf{ nm}$$

6.16   Plan: The least energetic photon in part a) has the longest wavelength (242 nm). The most energetic photon in part b) has the shortest wavelength (220 nm). Use the relationship $c = \lambda v$ to find the frequency of the photons and relationship $E = \dfrac{hc}{\lambda}$ to find the energy.

Solution:

a) $c = \lambda v$

$$v = \frac{c}{\lambda} = \frac{3.00 \times 10^8 \text{ m/s}}{242 \text{ nm}}\left(\frac{1 \text{ nm}}{10^{-9} \text{ m}}\right) = 1.239669 \times 10^{15} \text{ s}^{-1} = \textbf{1.24} \times \textbf{10}^{\textbf{15}} \textbf{ s}^{-1}$$

$$E = \frac{hc}{\lambda} = \frac{\left(6.626 \times 10^{-34} \text{ J} \cdot \text{s}\right)\left(3.00 \times 10^8 \text{ m/s}\right)}{242 \text{ nm}}\left(\frac{1 \text{ nm}}{10^{-9} \text{ m}}\right) = 8.2140 \times 10^{-19} \text{ J} = \textbf{8.21} \times \textbf{10}^{-\textbf{19}} \textbf{ J}$$

b) $v = \dfrac{c}{\lambda} = \dfrac{3.00\text{x}10^8 \text{ m/s}}{220 \text{ nm}}\left(\dfrac{1 \text{ nm}}{10^{-9} \text{ m}}\right) = 1.3636\text{x}10^{15} \text{ s}^{-1} = \mathbf{1.4\text{x}10^{15} \text{ s}^{-1}}$

$E = \dfrac{hc}{\lambda} = \dfrac{\left(6.626\text{x}10^{-34} \text{ J}\bullet\text{s}\right)\left(3.00\text{x}10^8 \text{ m/s}\right)}{220 \text{ nm}}\left(\dfrac{1 \text{ nm}}{10^{-9} \text{ m}}\right) = 9.03545\text{x}10^{-19} \text{ J} = \mathbf{9.0\text{x}10^{-19} \text{ J}}$

6.18   Bohr's key assumption was that the electron in an atom does not radiate energy while in a stationary state, and the electron can move to a different orbit by absorbing or emitting a photon whose energy is equal to the difference in energy between two states. These differences in energy correspond to the wavelengths in the known spectra for the hydrogen atoms. A Solar System model does not allow for the movement of electrons between levels.

6.20   Plan: The quantum number n is related to the energy level of the electron. An electron *absorbs* energy to change from lower energy (lower n) to higher energy (higher n), giving an absorption spectrum. An electron *emits* energy as it drops from a higher energy level (higher n) to a lower one (lower n), giving an emission spectrum.
Solution:
a) The electron is moving from a lower value of n (2) to a higher value of n (4): **absorption**
b) The electron is moving from a higher value of n (3) to a lower value of n (1): **emission**
c) The electron is moving from a higher value of n (5) to a lower value of n (2): **emission**
d) The electron is moving from a lower value of n (3) to a higher value of n (4): **absorption**

6.22   The Bohr model has successfully predicted the line spectra for the H atom and Be^{3+} ion since both are one-electron species. The energies could be predicted from $E_n = \dfrac{-\left(Z^2\right)\left(2.18\text{x}10^{-18} \text{ J}\right)}{n^2}$ where Z is the atomic number for the atom or ion. The line spectra for H would not match the line spectra for Be^{3+} since the H nucleus contains one proton while the Be^{3+} nucleus contains 4 protons (the Z values in the equation do not match); the force of attraction of the nucleus for the electron would be greater in the beryllium ion than in the hydrogen atom. This means that the pattern of lines would be similar, but at different wavelengths.

6.23   Plan: Calculate wavelength by substituting the given values into Equation 7.3, where $n_1 = 2$ and $n_2 = 5$ because $n_2 > n_1$. Although more significant figures could be used, five significant figures are adequate for this calculation.
Solution:

$\dfrac{1}{\lambda} = R\left(\dfrac{1}{n_1^2} - \dfrac{1}{n_2^2}\right)$ $R = 1.096776\text{x}10^7 \text{ m}^{-1}$

$n_1 = 2$ $n_2 = 5$

$\dfrac{1}{\lambda} = R\left(\dfrac{1}{n_1^2} - \dfrac{1}{n_2^2}\right) = \left(1.096776\text{x}10^7 \text{ m}^{-1}\right)\left(\dfrac{1}{2^2} - \dfrac{1}{5^2}\right) = 2{,}303{,}229.6 \text{ m}^{-1}$

$\lambda \text{ (nm)} = \left(\dfrac{1}{2{,}303{,}229.6 \text{ m}^{-1}}\right)\left(\dfrac{1 \text{ nm}}{10^{-9} \text{ m}}\right) = 434.1729544 \text{ nm} = \mathbf{434.17 \text{ nm}}$

6.25   Plan: The Rydberg equation is needed. For the infrared series of the H atom, n_1 equals 3. The least energetic spectral line in this series would represent an electron moving from the next highest energy level, $n_2 = 4$. Although more significant figures could be used, five significant figures are adequate for this calculation.
Solution:

$\dfrac{1}{\lambda} = R\left(\dfrac{1}{n_1^2} - \dfrac{1}{n_2^2}\right) = \left(1.096776\text{x}10^7 \text{ m}^{-1}\right)\left(\dfrac{1}{3^2} - \dfrac{1}{4^2}\right) = 533{,}155 \text{ m}^{-1}$

$\lambda \text{ (nm)} = \left(\dfrac{1}{533{,}155 \text{ m}^{-1}}\right)\left(\dfrac{1 \text{ nm}}{10^{-9} \text{ m}}\right) = 1875.627 \text{ nm} = \mathbf{1875.6 \text{ nm}}$

6.27   <u>Plan:</u> To find the transition energy, use the equation for the energy of an electron transition and multiply by Avogadro's number to convert to energy per mole.
<u>Solution:</u>

$$\Delta E = \left(-2.18\text{x}10^{-18}\ \text{J}\right)\left(\frac{1}{n_{\text{final}}^2} - \frac{1}{n_{\text{initial}}^2}\right)$$

$$\Delta E = \left(-2.18\text{x}10^{-18}\ \text{J}\right)\left(\frac{1}{2^2} - \frac{1}{5^2}\right) = -4.578\text{x}10^{-19}\ \text{J/photon}$$

$$\Delta E = \left(\frac{-4.578\text{x}10^{-19}\ \text{J}}{\text{photon}}\right)\left(\frac{6.022\text{x}10^{23}\ \text{photons}}{1\ \text{mol}}\right) = -2.75687\text{x}10^5\ \text{J/mol} = \mathbf{-2.76\text{x}10^5\ \text{J/mol}}$$

The energy has a negative value since this electron transition to a lower n value is an emission of energy.

6.29   <u>Plan:</u> Determine the relative energy of the electron transitions. Remember that energy is directly proportional to frequency ($E = h\nu$).
<u>Solution:</u>
Looking at an energy chart will help answer this question.

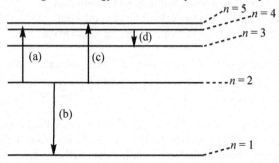

Frequency is proportional to energy so the smallest frequency will be d) $n = 4$ to $n = 3$; levels 3 and 4 have a smaller ΔE than the levels in the other transitions. The largest frequency is b) $n = 2$ to $n = 1$ since levels 1 and 2 have a larger ΔE than the levels in the other transitions. Transition a) $n = 2$ to $n = 4$ will be smaller than transition c) $n = 2$ to $n = 5$ since level 5 is a higher energy than level 4. In order of increasing frequency the transitions are **d < a < c < b**.

6.31   <u>Plan:</u> Use the Rydberg equation. Since the electron is in the ground state (lowest energy level), $n_1 = 1$. Convert the wavelength from nm to units of meters.
<u>Solution:</u>

$$\lambda = \left(97.20\ \text{nm}\right)\left(\frac{10^{-9}\ \text{m}}{1\ \text{nm}}\right) = 9.720\text{x}10^{-8}\ \text{m} \qquad \text{ground state: } n_1 = 1;\quad n_2 = ?$$

$$\frac{1}{\lambda} = \left(1.096776\text{x}10^7\ \text{m}^{-1}\right)\left(\frac{1}{n_1^2} - \frac{1}{n_2^2}\right)$$

$$\frac{1}{9.72\text{x}10^{-8}\ \text{m}} = \left(1.096776\text{x}10^7\ \text{m}^{-1}\right)\left(\frac{1}{1^2} - \frac{1}{n_2^2}\right)$$

$$0.93803 = \left(\frac{1}{1^2} - \frac{1}{n_2^2}\right)$$

$$\frac{1}{n_2^2} = 1 - 0.93803 = 0.06197$$

$$n_2^2 = 16.14$$

$$n_2 = \mathbf{4}$$

6.37   Macroscopic objects have significant mass. A large m in the denominator of $\lambda = h/mu$ will result in a very small wavelength. Macroscopic objects do exhibit a wavelike motion, but the wavelength is too small for humans to see it.

6.39   Plan: Use the de Broglie equation. Velocity in km/h must be converted to m/s because a joule is equivalent to $kg \cdot m^2/s^2$.
Solution:
a)

$$\text{Velocity (m/s)} = \left(\frac{19.8 \text{ km}}{h}\right)\left(\frac{10^3 \text{ m}}{1 \text{ km}}\right)\left(\frac{1 \text{ h}}{3600 \text{ s}}\right) = 5.50 \text{ m/s}$$

$$\lambda = \frac{h}{mu} = \frac{\left(6.626 \times 10^{-34} \text{ J} \cdot \text{s}\right)}{(105 \text{ kg})\left(5.50 \frac{m}{s}\right)}\left(\frac{kg \cdot m^2/s^2}{J}\right) = 1.147359 \times 10^{-36} \text{ m} = \mathbf{1.15 \times 10^{-36} \text{ m}}$$

b) Uncertainty in velocity (m/s) = $\left(\dfrac{0.1 \text{ km}}{h}\right)\left(\dfrac{10^3 \text{ m}}{1 \text{ km}}\right)\left(\dfrac{1 \text{ h}}{3600 \text{ s}}\right) = 0.02778 \text{ m/s}$

$$\Delta x \bullet m \Delta v \geq \frac{h}{4\pi}$$

$$\Delta x \geq \frac{h}{4\pi m \Delta v} \geq \frac{\left(6.626 \times 10^{-34} \text{ J} \cdot \text{s}\right)}{4\pi(105 \text{ kg})\left(\frac{0.02778 \text{ m}}{s}\right)}\left(\frac{kg \cdot m^2/s^2}{J}\right) \geq 1.807674 \times 10^{-33} \text{ m} \geq \mathbf{2 \times 10^{-33} \text{ m}}$$

6.41   Plan: Use the de Broglie equation. Mass in g must be converted to kg and wavelength in nm must be converted to m because a joule is equivalent to $kg \cdot m^2/s^2$.
Solution:

$$\text{Mass (kg)} = (56.5 \text{ g})\left(\frac{1 \text{ kg}}{10^3 \text{ g}}\right) = 0.0565 \text{ kg}$$

$$\text{Wavelength (m)} = (5400 \text{ nm})\left(\frac{10^{-9} \text{ m}}{1 \text{ nm}}\right) = 5.4 \times 10^{-7} \text{ m}$$

$$\lambda = \frac{h}{mu}$$

$$u = \frac{h}{m\lambda} = \frac{\left(6.626 \times 10^{-34} \text{ J} \cdot \text{s}\right)}{(0.0565 \text{ kg})\left(5.4 \times 10^{-7} \text{ m}\right)}\left(\frac{kg \cdot m^2/s^2}{J}\right) = 2.1717 \times 10^{-26} \text{ m/s} = \mathbf{2.2 \times 10^{-26} \text{ m/s}}$$

6.43   Plan: The de Broglie wavelength equation will give the mass equivalent of a photon with known wavelength and velocity. The term "mass equivalent" is used instead of "mass of photon" because photons are quanta of electromagnetic energy that have no mass. A light photon's velocity is the speed of light, 3.00×10^8 m/s. Wavelength in nm must be converted to m.
Solution:

$$\text{Wavelength (m)} = (589 \text{ nm})\left(\frac{10^{-9} \text{ m}}{1 \text{ nm}}\right) = 5.89 \times 10^{-7} \text{ m}$$

$$\lambda = \frac{h}{mu}$$

$$m = \frac{h}{\lambda u} = \frac{\left(6.626 \times 10^{-34} \text{ J} \cdot \text{s}\right)}{\left(5.89 \times 10^{-7} \text{ m}\right)\left(3.00 \times 10^8 \text{ m/s}\right)}\left(\frac{kg \cdot m^2/s^2}{J}\right) = 3.7499 \times 10^{-36} \text{ kg/photon} = \mathbf{3.75 \times 10^{-36} \text{ kg/photon}}$$

6.47   A peak in the radial probability distribution at a certain distance means that the total probability of finding the electron is greatest within a thin spherical volume having a radius very close to that distance. Since principal quantum number (n) correlates with distance from the nucleus, the peak for $n = 2$ would occur at a greater distance from the nucleus than 52.9 pm. Thus, the probability of finding an electron at 52.9 pm is much greater for the 1s orbital than for the 2s.

6.48   a) Principal quantum number, n, relates to the size of the orbital. More specifically, it relates to the distance from the nucleus at which the probability of finding an electron is greatest. This distance is determined by the energy of the electron.
b) Angular momentum quantum number, l, relates to the shape of the orbital. It is also called the azimuthal quantum number.
c) Magnetic quantum number, m_l, relates to the orientation of the orbital in space in three-dimensional space.

6.49   Plan: The following letter designations correlate with the following l quantum numbers:
$l = 0 = s$ orbital; $l = 1 = p$ orbital; $l = 2 = d$ orbital; $l = 3 = f$ orbital. Remember that allowed m_l values are $-l$ to $+l$. The number of orbitals of a particular type is given by the number of possible m_l values.
Solution:
a) There is only a single s orbital in any shell. $l = 1$ and $m_l = 0$: one value of $m_l = $ **one** s orbital.
b) There are five d orbitals in any shell. $l = 2$ and $m_l = -2, -1, 0, +1, +2$. Five values of $m_l = $ **five** d orbitals.
c) There are three p orbitals in any shell. $l = 1$ and $m_l = -1, 0, +1$. Three values of $m_l = $ **three** p orbitals.
d) If $n = 3$, $l = 0(s)$, $1(p)$, and $2(d)$. There is a 3s (1 orbital), a 3p set (3 orbitals), and a 3d set (5 orbitals) for a total of **nine** orbitals ($1 + 3 + 5 = 9$).

6.51   Plan: Magnetic quantum numbers (m_l) can have integer values from $-l$ to $+l$. The l quantum number can have integer values from 0 to $n - 1$.
Solution:
a) $l = 2$ so $m_l = $ **$-2, -1, 0, +1, +2$**
b) $n = 1$ so $l = 1 - 1 = 0$ and $m_l = $ **0**
c) $l = 3$ so $m_l = $ **$-3, -2, -1, 0, +1, +2, +3$**

6.53   Plan: The s orbital is spherical; p orbitals have two lobes; the subscript x indicates that this orbital lies along the x-axis.
Solution:
a) s: spherical   b) p_x: 2 lobes along the x-axis

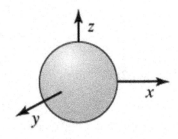   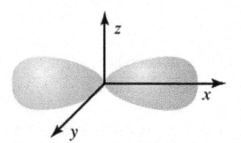

The variations in colouring of the p orbital are a consequence of the quantum mechanical derivation of atomic orbitals that are beyond the scope of this course.

6.55   Plan: The following letter designations for the various subshell (orbitals) correlate with the following l quantum numbers: $l = 0 = s$ orbital; $l = 1 = p$ orbital; $l = 2 = d$ orbital; $l = 3 = f$ orbital. Remember that allowed m_l values are $-l$ to $+l$. The number of orbitals of a particular type is given by the number of possible m_l values.
Solution:

subshell	allowable m_l	# of possible orbitals
a) d ($l = 2$)	$-2, -1, 0, +1, +2$	5
b) p ($l = 1$)	$-1, 0, +1$	3
c) f ($l = 3$)	$-3, -2, -1, 0, +1, +2, +3$	7

6.57   Plan: The integer in front of the letter represents the n value. The letter designates the l value:
$l = 0 = s$ orbital; $l = 1 = p$ orbital; $l = 2 = d$ orbital; $l = 3 = f$ orbital. Remember that allowed m_l values are $-l$ to $+l$.
Solution:
a) For the 5s subshell, $\boldsymbol{n = 5}$ and $\boldsymbol{l = 0}$. Since $m_l = 0$, there is **one** orbital.
b) For the 3p subshell, $\boldsymbol{n = 3}$ and $\boldsymbol{l = 1}$. Since $m_l = -1, 0, +1$, there are **three** orbitals.
c) For the 4f subshell, $\boldsymbol{n = 4}$ and $\boldsymbol{l = 3}$. Since $m_l = -3, -2, -1, 0, +1, +2, +3$, there are **seven** orbitals.

6.59   Plan: Allowed values of quantum numbers: $n =$ positive integers; $l =$ integers from 0 to $n - 1$;
$m_l =$ integers from $-l$ through 0 to $+l$.
Solution:
a) $n = 2$; $l = 0$; $m_l = -1$: With $n = 2$, l can be 0 or 1; with $l = 0$, the only allowable m_l value is 0. This combination is not allowed. To correct, either change the l or m_l value.
Correct: $n = 2$; $l = 1$; $m_l = -1$ or $n = 2$; $l = 0$; $m_l = 0$.
b) $n = 4$; $l = 3$; $m_l = -1$: With $n = 4$, l can be 0, 1, 2, or 3; with $l = 3$, the allowable m_l values are $-3, -2, -1, 0, +1, +2, +3$. Combination is allowed.
c) $n = 3$; $l = 1$; $m_l = 0$: With $n = 3$, l can be 0, 1, or 2; with $l = 1$, the allowable m_l values are $-1, 0, +1$. Combination is allowed.
d) $n = 5$; $l = 2$; $m_l = +3$: With $n = 5$, l can be 0, 1, 2, 3, or 4; with $l = 2$, the allowable m_l values are $-2, -1, 0, +1, +2$. +3 is not an allowable m_l value. To correct, either change l or m_l value.
Correct: $n = 5$; $l = 3$; $m_l = +3$ or $n = 5$; $l = 2$; $m_l = 0$.

6.62   Plan: For Part a, use the values of the constants h, π, m_e, and a_0 to find the overall constant in the equation. Use the resulting equation to calculate ΔE in part b). Use the relationship $E = \dfrac{hc}{\lambda}$ to calculate the wavelength in part c).
Remember that a joule is equivalent to kg•m²/s².
Solution:
a) $h = 6.626 \times 10^{-34}$ J•s; $m_e = 9.1094 \times 10^{-31}$ kg; $a_0 = 52.92 \times 10^{-12}$ m

$$E = -\frac{h^2}{8\pi^2 m_e a_0^2 n^2} = -\frac{h^2}{8\pi^2 m_e a_0^2}\left(\frac{1}{n^2}\right)$$

$$E = -\frac{\left(6.626 \times 10^{-34}\ \text{J•s}\right)^2}{8\pi^2\left(9.1094 \times 10^{-31}\ \text{kg}\right)\left(52.92 \times 10^{-12}\ \text{m}\right)^2}\left(\frac{\text{kg•m}^2/\text{s}^2}{\text{J}}\right)\left(\frac{1}{n^2}\right)$$

$$= -(2.17963 \times 10^{-18}\ \text{J})\left(\frac{1}{n^2}\right) = -(2.180 \times 10^{-18}\ \text{J})\left(\frac{1}{n^2}\right)$$

This is identical with the result from Bohr's theory. For the H atom, $Z = 1$ and Bohr's constant $= -2.18 \times 10^{-18}$ J. For the hydrogen atom, derivation using classical principles or quantum-mechanical principles yields the same constant.
b) The $n = 3$ energy level is higher in energy than the $n = 2$ level. Because the zero point of the atom's energy is defined as an electron's infinite distance from the nucleus, a larger negative number describes a lower energy level. Although this may be confusing, it makes sense that an energy *change* would be a positive number.

$$\Delta E = -(2.180 \times 10^{-18}\ \text{J})\left(\frac{1}{3^2} - \frac{1}{2^2}\right) = 3.027778 \times 10^{-19}\ \text{J} = \mathbf{3.028 \times 10^{-19}\ J}$$

c) $E = \dfrac{hc}{\lambda}$

$$\lambda\ (\text{m}) = \frac{hc}{E} = \frac{\left(6.626 \times 10^{-34}\ \text{J•s}\right)\left(2.9979 \times 10^8\ \text{m/s}\right)}{\left(3.027778 \times 10^{-19}\ \text{J}\right)} = 6.56061 \times 10^{-7}\ \text{m} = \mathbf{6.561 \times 10^{-7}\ m}$$

$$\lambda\ (\text{nm}) = \left(6.56061 \times 10^{-7}\ \text{m}\right)\left(\frac{1\ \text{nm}}{10^{-9}\ \text{m}}\right) = 656.061\ \text{nm} = \mathbf{656.1\ nm}$$

This is the wavelength for the observed red line in the hydrogen spectrum.

6.63   Plan: When light of sufficient frequency (energy) shines on metal, electrons in the metal break free and a current flows.
Solution:
a) The lines do not begin at the origin because an electron must absorb a minimum amount of energy before it has enough energy to overcome the attraction of the nucleus and leave the atom. This minimum energy is the energy of photons of light at the threshold frequency.
b) The lines for K and Ag do not begin at the same point. The amount of energy that an electron must absorb to leave the K atom is less than the amount of energy that an electron must absorb to leave the Ag atom, where the attraction between the nucleus and outer electron is stronger than in a K atom.
c) Wavelength is inversely proportional to energy. Thus, the metal that requires a larger amount of energy to be absorbed before electrons are emitted will require a shorter wavelength of light. Electrons in Ag atoms require more energy to leave, so Ag requires a shorter wavelength of light than K to eject an electron.
d) The slopes of the line show an increase in kinetic energy as the frequency (or energy) of light is increased. Since the slopes are the same, this means that for an increase of one unit of frequency (or energy) of light, the increase in kinetic energy of an electron ejected from K is the same as the increase in the kinetic energy of an electron ejected from Ag. After an electron is ejected, the energy that it absorbs above the threshold energy becomes the kinetic energy of the electron. For the same increase in energy above the threshold energy, for either K or Ag, the kinetic energy of the ejected electron will be the same.

6.66   Plan: The Bohr model has been successfully applied to predict the spectral lines for one-electron species other than H. Common one-electron species are small cations with all but one electron removed. Since the problem specifies a metal ion, assume that the possible choices are Li^{2+} or Be^{3+}. Use the relationship $E = h\nu$ to convert the frequency to energy and then solve Bohr's equation $E = \left(2.18\times10^{-18} \text{ J}\right)\left(\dfrac{Z^2}{n^2}\right)$ to verify if a whole number for Z can be calculated. Recall that the negative sign is a convention based on the zero point of the atom's energy; it is deleted in this calculation to avoid taking the square root of a negative number.
Solution:
The highest energy line corresponds to the transition from $n = 1$ to $n = \infty$.
$E = h\nu = (6.626\times10^{-34} \text{ J}\cdot\text{s}) (2.961\times10^{16} \text{ Hz}) (\text{s}^{-1}/\text{Hz}) = 1.9619586\times10^{-17} \text{ J}$

$$E = \left(2.18\times10^{-18} \text{ J}\right)\left(\frac{Z^2}{n^2}\right) \qquad\qquad Z = \text{charge of the nucleus}$$

$$Z^2 = \frac{En^2}{2.18\times10^{-18}\text{J}} = \frac{1.9619586\times10^{-17}(1^2)}{2.18\times10^{-18} \text{ J}} = 8.99998$$

Then $Z^2 = 9$ and $Z = 3$.
Therefore, the ion is $\mathbf{Li^{2+}}$ with an atomic number of 3.

6.68   Plan: The electromagnetic spectrum shows that the visible region goes from 400 to 750 nm. Thus, wavelengths b, c, and d are for the three transitions in the visible series with $n_{final} = 2$. Wavelength a is in the ultraviolet region of the spectrum and the ultraviolet series has $n_{final} = 1$. Wavelength e is in the infrared region of the spectrum and the infrared series has $n_{final} = 3$. Use the Rydberg equation to find the $n_{initial}$ for each line. Convert the wavelengths from nm to units of m.
Solution:
$n = ? \rightarrow n = 1$; $\lambda = 121$ nm (shortest λ corresponds to the largest ΔE)

$$\lambda \text{ (m)} = \left(121 \text{ nm}\right)\left(\frac{10^{-9} \text{ m}}{1 \text{ nm}}\right) = 1.21\times10^{-7} \text{ m}$$

$$\frac{1}{\lambda} = \left(1.096776\times10^7 \text{ m}^{-1}\right)\left(\frac{1}{n_1^2} - \frac{1}{n_2^2}\right)$$

$$\left(\frac{1}{1.21\times10^{-7}\text{m}}\right) = \left(1.096776\times10^7\text{m}^{-1}\right)\left(\frac{1}{1^2} - \frac{1}{n_2^2}\right)$$

$$0.7535233 = \left(\frac{1}{1^2} - \frac{1}{n_2^2}\right)$$

$$\left(\frac{1}{n_2^2}\right) = 1 - 0.7535233$$

$$\left(\frac{1}{n_2^2}\right) = 0.2464767$$

$n_2 = 2$ for line (a) ($n = 2 \rightarrow n = 1$)

$n = ? \rightarrow n = 3$; $\lambda = 1094$ nm (longest λ corresponds to the smallest ΔE)

$$\lambda \,(\text{m}) = (1094 \text{ nm})\left(\frac{10^{-9} \text{ m}}{1 \text{ nm}}\right) = 1.094\text{x}10^{-6} \text{ m}$$

$$\frac{1}{\lambda} = \left(1.096776\text{x}10^7 \text{ m}^{-1}\right)\left(\frac{1}{n_1^2} - \frac{1}{n_2^2}\right)$$

$$\left(\frac{1}{1.094\text{x}10^{-6}\text{m}}\right) = \left(1.096776\text{x}10^7 \text{ m}^{-1}\right)\left(\frac{1}{3^2} - \frac{1}{n_2^2}\right)$$

$$0.083342158 = \left(\frac{1}{3^2} - \frac{1}{n_2^2}\right)$$

$$0.083342158 = 0.111111111 - \frac{1}{n_2^2}$$

$$\left(\frac{1}{n_2^2}\right) = 0.11111111 - 0.083342158$$

$$\left(\frac{1}{n_2^2}\right) = 0.0277689535$$

$n_2^2 = 36.01143$

$n_2 = 6$ for line (e) ($n = 6 \rightarrow n = 3$)

For the other three lines, $n_1 = 2$.

For line (d), $n_2 = 3$ (largest $\lambda \rightarrow$ smallest ΔE).

For line (b), $n_2 = 5$ (smallest $\lambda \rightarrow$ largest ΔE).

For line (c), $n_2 = 4$.

6.72   <u>Plan:</u> Allowed values of quantum numbers: n = positive integers; l = integers from 0 to $n - 1$; m_l = integers from $- l$ through 0 to $+ l$.

<u>Solution:</u>

a) The l value must be at least 1 for m_l to be $- 1$, but cannot be greater than $n - 1 = 3 - 1 = 2$. Increase the l value to 1 or 2 to create an allowable combination.

b) The l value must be at least 1 for m_l to be $+1$, but cannot be greater than $n - 1 = 3 - 1 = 2$. Decrease the l value to 1 or 2 to create an allowable combination.

c) The l value must be at least 3 for m_l to be $+3$, but cannot be greater than $n - 1 = 7 - 1 = 6$. Increase the l value to 3, 4, 5, or 6 to create an allowable combination.

d) The l value must be at least 2 for m_l to be -2, but cannot be greater than $n - 1 = 4 - 1 = 3$. Increase the l value to 2 or 3 to create an allowable combination.

6.74 <u>Plan:</u> Ionization occurs when the electron is completely removed from the atom, or when $n_{final} = \infty$. We can use the equation for the energy of an electron transition to find the quantity of energy needed to remove completely the electron, called the ionization energy (IE). To obtain the ionization energy per mole of species, multiply by Avogadro's number. The charge on the nucleus must affect the IE because a larger nucleus would exert a greater pull on the escaping electron. The Bohr equation applies to H and other one-electron species. Use the expression to determine the ionization energy of B^{4+} and to find the energies of the transitions listed. Use $E = \dfrac{hc}{\lambda}$ to convert energy to wavelength.

<u>Solution:</u>

a) $E = \left(-2.18 \times 10^{-18}\,\text{J}\right)\left(\dfrac{Z^2}{n^2}\right)$ Z = atomic number

$\Delta E = \left(-2.18 \times 10^{-18}\,\text{J}\right)\left(\dfrac{1}{n_{final}^2} - \dfrac{1}{n_{initial}^2}\right)Z^2$

$\Delta E = \left(-2.18 \times 10^{-18}\,\text{J}\right)\left(\dfrac{1}{\infty^2} - \dfrac{1}{n_{initial}^2}\right)Z^2\left(\dfrac{6.022 \times 10^{23}}{1\,\text{mol}}\right)$

$= (1.312796 \times 10^6)\,Z^2$ for $n = 1$

b) In the ground state $n = 1$, the initial energy level for the single electron in B^{4+}. Once ionized, $n = \infty$ is the final energy level.

$Z = 5$ for B^{4+}.

$\Delta E = \text{IE} = (1.312796 \times 10^6)\,Z^2 = (1.312796 \times 10^6\,\text{J/mol})(5^2) = 3.28199 \times 10^7\,\text{J/mol} = \mathbf{3.28 \times 10^7\ J/mol}$

c) $n_{final} = \infty$, $n_{initial} = 3$, and $Z = 2$ for He^+.

$\Delta E = \left(-2.18 \times 10^{-18}\,\text{J}\right)\left(\dfrac{1}{n_{final}^2} - \dfrac{1}{n_{initial}^2}\right)Z^2 = \left(-2.18 \times 10^{-18}\,\text{J}\right)\left(\dfrac{1}{\infty^2} - \dfrac{1}{3^2}\right)2^2 = 9.68889 \times 10^{-19}\,\text{J}$

$E = \dfrac{hc}{\lambda}$

$\lambda\,(\text{m}) = \dfrac{hc}{E} = \dfrac{\left(6.626 \times 10^{-34}\,\text{J} \cdot \text{s}\right)\left(3.00 \times 10^8\,\text{m/s}\right)}{9.68889 \times 10^{-19}\,\text{J}} = 2.051628 \times 10^{-7}\,\text{m}$

$\lambda\,(\text{nm}) = \left(2.051628 \times 10^{-7}\,\text{m}\right)\left(\dfrac{1\,\text{nm}}{10^{-9}\,\text{m}}\right) = 205.1628\,\text{nm} = \mathbf{205\ nm}$

d) $n_{final} = \infty$, $n_{initial} = 2$, and $Z = 4$ for Be^{3+}.

$\Delta E = \left(-2.18 \times 10^{-18}\,\text{J}\right)\left(\dfrac{1}{\infty^2} - \dfrac{1}{n_{initial}^2}\right)Z^2 = \left(-2.18 \times 10^{-18}\,\text{J}\right)\left(\dfrac{1}{\infty^2} - \dfrac{1}{2^2}\right)4^2 = 8.72 \times 10^{-18}\,\text{J}$

$\lambda\,(\text{m}) = \dfrac{hc}{E} = \dfrac{\left(6.626 \times 10^{-34}\,\text{J} \cdot \text{s}\right)\left(3.00 \times 10^8\,\text{m/s}\right)}{8.72 \times 10^{-18}\,\text{J}} = 2.279587 \times 10^{-8}\,\text{m}$

$\lambda\,(\text{nm}) = \left(2.279587 \times 10^{-8}\,\text{m}\right)\left(\dfrac{1\,\text{nm}}{10^{-9}\,\text{m}}\right) = 22.79587\,\text{nm} = \mathbf{22.8\ nm}$

6.76   Plan: Use the values and the equation given in the problem to calculate the appropriate values.
Solution:

a) $r_n = \dfrac{n^2 h^2 \varepsilon_0}{\pi m_e e^2}$

$$r_1 = \dfrac{1^2 \left(6.626\times10^{-34}\ \text{J}\cdot\text{s}\right)^2 \left(8.854\times10^{-12}\ \dfrac{\text{C}^2}{\text{J}\cdot\text{m}}\right)}{\pi\left(9.109\times10^{-31}\ \text{kg}\right)\left(1.602\times10^{-19}\ \text{C}\right)^2}\left(\dfrac{\text{kg}\cdot\text{m}^2/\text{s}^2}{\text{J}}\right) = 5.2929377\times10^{-11}\ \text{m} = \mathbf{5.293\times10^{-11}\ m}$$

b) $$r_{10} = \dfrac{10^2 \left(6.626\times10^{-34}\ \text{J}\cdot\text{s}\right)^2 \left(8.854\times10^{-12}\ \dfrac{\text{C}^2}{\text{J}\cdot\text{m}}\right)}{\pi\left(9.109\times10^{-31}\ \text{kg}\right)\left(1.602\times10^{-19}\ \text{C}\right)^2}\left(\dfrac{\text{kg}\cdot\text{m}^2/\text{s}^2}{\text{J}}\right) = 5.2929377\times10^{-9}\ \text{m} = \mathbf{5.293\times10^{-9}\ m}$$

6.78   Plan: Refer to Chapter 5 for the calculation of the amount of heat energy absorbed by a substance from its specific heat capacity and temperature change ($q = c$ x mass x ΔT). Using this equation, calculate the energy absorbed by the water. This energy equals the energy from the microwave photons. The energy of each photon can be calculated from its wavelength: $E = hc/\lambda$. Dividing the total energy by the energy of each photon gives the number of photons absorbed by the water.
Solution:
$q = c$ x mass x ΔT
$q = (4.184\ \text{J/g}^\circ\text{C})(252\ \text{g})(98 - 20.)^\circ\text{C} = 8.22407\times10^4\ \text{J}$

$$E = \dfrac{hc}{\lambda} = \dfrac{\left(6.626\times10^{-34}\ \text{J}\cdot\text{s}\right)\left(3.00\times10^8\ \text{m/s}\right)}{1.55\times10^{-2}\ \text{m}} = 1.28245\times10^{-23}\ \text{J/photon}$$

Number of photons $= \left(8.22407\times10^4\ \text{J}\right)\left(\dfrac{1\ \text{photon}}{1.28245\times10^{-23}\ \text{J}}\right) = 6.41278\times10^{27}\ \text{photons} = \mathbf{6.4\times10^{27}\ photons}$

6.80   Plan: In general, to test for overlap of the two series, compare the longest wavelength in the "n" series with the shortest wavelength in the "$n+1$" series. The longest wavelength in any series corresponds to the transition between the n_1 level and the next level above it; the shortest wavelength corresponds to the transition between the n_1 level and the $n = \infty$ level. Use the relationship $\dfrac{1}{\lambda} = R\left(\dfrac{1}{n_1^2} - \dfrac{1}{n_2^2}\right)$ to calculate the wavelengths.

Solution:

$$\dfrac{1}{\lambda} = R\left(\dfrac{1}{n_1^2} - \dfrac{1}{n_2^2}\right) = \left(1.096776\times10^7\ \text{m}^{-1}\right)\left(\dfrac{1}{n_1^2} - \dfrac{1}{n_2^2}\right)$$

a) The overlap between the $n_1 = 1$ series and the $n_1 = 2$ series would occur between the longest wavelengths for $n_1 = 1$ and the shortest wavelengths for $n_1 = 2$.
Longest wavelength in $n_1 = 1$ series has n_2 equal to 2.

$$\dfrac{1}{\lambda} = \left(1.096776\times10^7\ \text{m}^{-1}\right)\left(\dfrac{1}{1^2} - \dfrac{1}{2^2}\right) = 8{,}225{,}820\ \text{m}^{-1}$$

$$\lambda = \dfrac{1}{8{,}225{,}820\ \text{m}^{-1}} = 1.215684272\times10^{-7}\ \text{m} = \mathbf{1.215684\times10^{-7}\ m}$$

Shortest wavelength in the $n_1 = 2$ series:

$$\dfrac{1}{\lambda} = \left(1.096776\times10^7\ \text{m}^{-1}\right)\left(\dfrac{1}{2^2} - \dfrac{1}{\infty^2}\right) = 2{,}741{,}940\ \text{m}^{-1}$$

$$\lambda = \dfrac{1}{2{,}741{,}940\ \text{m}^{-1}} = 3.647052817\times10^{-7}\ \text{m} = \mathbf{3.647053\times10^{-7}\ m}$$

Since the longest wavelength for $n_1 = 1$ series is shorter than shortest wavelength for $n_1 = 2$ series, there is **no overlap** between the two series.

b) The overlap between the $n_1 = 3$ series and the $n_1 = 4$ series would occur between the longest wavelengths for $n_1 = 3$ and the shortest wavelengths for $n_1 = 4$.

Longest wavelength in $n_1 = 3$ series has n_2 equal to 4.

$$\frac{1}{\lambda} = \left(1.096776 \times 10^7 \ \text{m}^{-1}\right)\left(\frac{1}{3^2} - \frac{1}{4^2}\right) = 533{,}155 \ \text{m}^{-1}$$

$$\lambda = \frac{1}{533{,}155 \ \text{m}^{-1}} = 1.875627163 \times 10^{-6} \ \text{m} = \textbf{1.875627} \boldsymbol{\times} \textbf{10}^{\textbf{-6}} \ \textbf{m}$$

Shortest wavelength in $n_1 = 4$ series has $n_2 = \infty$.

$$\frac{1}{\lambda} = \left(1.096776 \times 10^7 \ \text{m}^{-1}\right)\left(\frac{1}{4^2} - \frac{1}{\infty^2}\right) = 685{,}485 \ \text{m}^{-1}$$

$$\lambda = \frac{1}{685{,}485 \ \text{m}^{-1}} = 1.458821127 \times 10^{-6} \ \text{m} = \textbf{1.458821} \boldsymbol{\times} \textbf{10}^{\textbf{-6}} \ \textbf{m}$$

Since the $n_1 = 4$ series shortest wavelength is shorter than the $n_1 = 3$ series longest wavelength, the **series do overlap**.

c) Shortest wavelength in $n_1 = 5$ series has $n_2 = \infty$.

$$\frac{1}{\lambda} = \left(1.096776 \times 10^7 \ \text{m}^{-1}\right)\left(\frac{1}{5^2} - \frac{1}{\infty^2}\right) = 438{,}710.4 \ \text{m}^{-1}$$

$$\lambda = \frac{1}{438{,}710.4 \ \text{m}^{-1}} = 2.27940801 \times 10^{-6} \ \text{m} = \textbf{2.279408} \boldsymbol{\times} \textbf{10}^{\textbf{-6}} \ \textbf{m}$$

Calculate the first few longest lines in the $n_1 = 4$ series to determine if any overlap with the shortest wavelength in the $n_1 = 5$ series:

For $n_1 = 4$, $n_2 = 5$:

$$\frac{1}{\lambda} = \left(1.096776 \times 10^7 \ \text{m}^{-1}\right)\left(\frac{1}{4^2} - \frac{1}{5^2}\right) = 246{,}774.6 \ \text{m}^{-1}$$

$$\lambda = \frac{1}{246{,}774.6 \ \text{m}^{-1}} = \textbf{4.052281} \boldsymbol{\times} \textbf{10}^{\textbf{-6}} \ \textbf{m}$$

For $n_1 = 4$, $n_2 = 6$:

$$\frac{1}{\lambda} = \left(1.096776 \times 10^7 \ \text{m}^{-1}\right)\left(\frac{1}{4^2} - \frac{1}{6^2}\right) = 380{,}825 \ \text{m}^{-1}$$

$$\lambda = \frac{1}{380{,}825 \ \text{m}^{-1}} = = \textbf{2.625878} \boldsymbol{\times} \textbf{10}^{\textbf{-6}} \ \textbf{m}$$

For $n_1 = 4$, $n_2 = 7$:

$$\frac{1}{\lambda} = \left(1.096776 \times 10^7 \ \text{m}^{-1}\right)\left(\frac{1}{4^2} - \frac{1}{7^2}\right) = 461{,}653.2 \ \text{m}^{-1}$$

$$\lambda = \frac{1}{461{,}653.2 \ \text{m}^{-1}} = \textbf{2.166128} \boldsymbol{\times} \textbf{10}^{\textbf{-6}} \ \textbf{m}$$

The wavelengths of the first **two lines** of the $n_1 = 4$ series are longer than the shortest wavelength in the $n_1 = 5$ series. Therefore, only the first **two lines** of the $n_1 = 4$ series overlap the $n_1 = 5$ series.

d) At longer wavelengths (i.e., lower energies), there is increasing overlap between the lines from different series (i.e., with different n_1 values). The hydrogen spectrum becomes more complex, since the lines begin to merge into a more-or-less continuous band, and much more care is needed to interpret the information.

6.82   Plan: The energy differences sought may be determined by looking at the energy changes in steps. The wavelength is calculated from the relationship $\lambda = \dfrac{hc}{E}$.

Solution:
a) The difference between levels 3 and 2 (E_{32}) may be found by taking the difference in the energies for the $3 \rightarrow 1$ transition (E_{31}) and the $2 \rightarrow 1$ transition (E_{21}).
$E_{32} = E_{31} - E_{21} = (4.854 \times 10^{-17}\ \text{J}) - (4.098 \times 10^{-17}\ \text{J}) = \textbf{7.56} \times \textbf{10}^{\textbf{-18}}\ \textbf{J}$

$$\lambda = \frac{hc}{E} = \frac{\left(6.626 \times 10^{-34}\ \text{J} \bullet \text{s}\right)\left(3.00 \times 10^{8}\ \text{m/s}\right)}{\left(7.56 \times 10^{-18}\ \text{J}\right)} = 2.629365 \times 10^{-8}\ \text{m} = \textbf{2.63} \times \textbf{10}^{\textbf{-8}}\ \textbf{m}$$

b) The difference between levels 4 and 1 (E_{41}) may be found by adding the energies for the $4 \rightarrow 2$ transition (E_{42}) and the $2 \rightarrow 1$ transition (E_{21}).
$E_{41} = E_{42} + E_{21} = (1.024 \times 10^{-17}\ \text{J}) + (4.098 \times 10^{-17}\ \text{J}) = \textbf{5.122} \times \textbf{10}^{\textbf{-17}}\ \textbf{J}$

$$\lambda = \frac{hc}{E} = \frac{\left(6.626 \times 10^{-34}\ \text{J} \bullet \text{s}\right)\left(3.00 \times 10^{8}\ \text{m/s}\right)}{\left(5.122 \times 10^{-17}\ \text{J}\right)} = 3.88091 \times 10^{-9}\ \text{m} = \textbf{3.881} \times \textbf{10}^{\textbf{-9}}\ \textbf{m}$$

c) The difference between levels 5 and 4 (E_{54}) may be found by taking the difference in the energies for the $5 \rightarrow 1$ transition (E_{51}) and the $4 \rightarrow 1$ transition (see part b)).
$E_{54} = E_{51} - E_{41} = (5.242 \times 10^{-17}\ \text{J}) - (5.122 \times 10^{-17}\ \text{J}) = \textbf{1.2} \times \textbf{10}^{\textbf{-18}}\ \textbf{J}$

$$\lambda = \frac{hc}{E} = \frac{\left(6.626 \times 10^{-34}\ \text{J} \bullet \text{s}\right)\left(3.00 \times 10^{8}\ \text{m/s}\right)}{\left(1.2 \times 10^{-18}\ \text{J}\right)} = 1.6565 \times 10^{-7}\ \text{m} = \textbf{1.66} \times \textbf{10}^{\textbf{-7}}\ \textbf{m}$$

6.84   Plan: For part a), use the equation for kinetic energy, $E_k = \frac{1}{2}mu^2$. For part b), use the relationship $E = hc/\lambda$ to find the energy of the photon absorbed. From that energy subtract the kinetic energy of the dislodged electron to obtain the work function.

Solution:
a) The energy of the electron is a function of its speed leaving the surface of the metal. The mass of the electron is 9.109×10^{-31} kg.

$$E_k = \frac{1}{2}mu^2 = \frac{1}{2}\left(9.109 \times 10^{-31}\ \text{kg}\right)\left(6.40 \times 10^{5}\ \text{m/s}\right)^2 \left(\frac{\text{J}}{\text{kg} \bullet \text{m}^2/\text{s}^2}\right) = 1.86552 \times 10^{-19}\ \text{J} = \textbf{1.87} \times \textbf{10}^{\textbf{-19}}\ \textbf{J}$$

b) The minimum energy required to dislodge the electron (ϕ) is a function of the incident light. In this example, the incident light is higher than the threshold frequency, so the kinetic energy of the electron, E_k, must be subtracted from the total energy of the incident light, $h\nu$, to yield the work function, ϕ. (The number of significant figures given in the wavelength requires more significant figures in the speed of light.)

$$\lambda\ (\text{m}) = \left(358.1\ \text{nm}\right)\left(\frac{10^{-9}\ \text{m}}{1\ \text{nm}}\right) = 3.581 \times 10^{-7}\ \text{m}$$

$$E = hc/\lambda = \frac{\left(6.626 \times 10^{-34}\ \text{J} \bullet \text{s}\right)\left(2.9979 \times 10^{8}\ \text{m/s}\right)}{\left(3.581 \times 10^{-7}\ \text{m}\right)} = 5.447078 \times 10^{-19}\ \text{J}$$

$\Phi = h\nu - E_k = (5.447078 \times 10^{-19}\ \text{J}) - (1.86552 \times 10^{-19}\ \text{J}) = 3.581558 \times 10^{-19}\ \text{J} = \textbf{3.58} \times \textbf{10}^{\textbf{-19}}\ \textbf{J}$

6.86   Plan: Examine Figure 7.3 and match the given wavelengths to their colours. For each salt, convert the mass of salt to moles and multiply by Avogadro's number to find the number of photons emitted by that amount of salt (assuming that each atom undergoes one-electron transition). Use the relationship $E = \dfrac{hc}{\lambda}$ to find the energy of one photon and multiply by the total number of photons for the total energy of emission.

Solution:
a) Figure 7.3 indicates that the 641 nm wavelength of Sr falls in the **red** region and the 493 nm wavelength of Ba falls in the **green** region.
b) $SrCl_2$

Number of photons $= \left(5.00 \text{ g SrCl}_2\right)\left(\dfrac{1 \text{ mol SrCl}_2}{158.52 \text{ g SrCl}_2}\right)\left(\dfrac{6.022 \times 10^{23} \text{ photons}}{1 \text{ mol SrCl}_2}\right) = 1.8994449 \times 10^{22}$ photons

$\lambda \text{ (m)} = \left(641 \text{ nm}\right)\left(\dfrac{10^{-9} \text{ m}}{1 \text{ nm}}\right) = 6.41 \times 10^{-7}$ m

$E_{\text{photon}} = \dfrac{hc}{\lambda} = \dfrac{\left(6.626 \times 10^{-34} \text{ J} \cdot \text{s}\right)\left(3.00 \times 10^{8} \text{ m/s}\right)}{6.41 \times 10^{-7} \text{ m}}\left(\dfrac{1 \text{ kJ}}{10^{3} \text{ J}}\right) = 3.10109 \times 10^{-22}$ kJ/photon

$E_{\text{total}} = \left(1.8994449 \times 10^{22} \text{ photons}\right)\left(\dfrac{3.10109 \times 10^{-22} \text{ kJ}}{1 \text{ photon}}\right) = 5.89035 \text{ kJ} = \textbf{5.89 kJ}$

$BaCl_2$

Number of photons $= \left(5.00 \text{ g BaCl}_2\right)\left(\dfrac{1 \text{ mol BaCl}_2}{208.2 \text{ g BaCl}_2}\right)\left(\dfrac{6.022 \times 10^{23} \text{ photons}}{1 \text{ mol BaCl}_2}\right) = 1.44620557 \times 10^{22}$ photons

$\lambda \text{ (m)} = \left(493 \text{ nm}\right)\left(\dfrac{10^{-9} \text{ m}}{1 \text{ nm}}\right) = 4.93 \times 10^{-7}$ m

$E_{\text{photon}} = \dfrac{hc}{\lambda} = \dfrac{\left(6.626 \times 10^{-34} \text{ J} \cdot \text{s}\right)\left(3.00 \times 10^{8} \text{ m/s}\right)}{4.93 \times 10^{-7} \text{ m}}\left(\dfrac{1 \text{ kJ}}{10^{3} \text{ J}}\right) = 4.0320487 \times 10^{-22}$ kJ/photon

$E_{\text{total}} = \left(1.44620557 \times 10^{22} \text{ photons}\right)\left(\dfrac{4.0320487 \times 10^{-22} \text{ kJ}}{1 \text{ photon}}\right) = 5.83117 \text{ kJ} = \textbf{5.83 kJ}$

6.88   <u>Plan:</u> Examine Figure 7.3 to find the region of the electromagnetic spectrum in which the wavelength lies. Compare the absorbance of the given concentration of Vitamin A to the absorbance of the given amount of fish-liver oil to find the concentration of Vitamin A in the oil.
<u>Solution:</u>
a) At this wavelength the sensitivity to absorbance of light by Vitamin A is maximized while minimizing interference due to the absorbance of light by other substances in the fish-liver oil.
b) The wavelength 329 nm lies in the **ultraviolet region** of the electromagnetic spectrum.
c) A <u>known</u> quantity of vitamin A (1.67×10^{-3} g) is dissolved in a <u>known</u> volume of solvent (250. mL) to give a <u>standard</u> concentration with a <u>known</u> response (1.018 units). This can be used to find the <u>unknown</u> quantity of Vitamin A that gives a response of 0.724 units. An equality can be made between the two concentration-to-absorbance ratios.

Concentration (C_1, g/mL) of Vitamin A $= \left(\dfrac{1.67 \times 10^{-3} \text{ g}}{250. \text{ mL}}\right) = 6.68 \times 10^{-6}$ g/mL Vitamin A

Absorbance (A_1) of Vitamin A $= 1.018$ units.
Absorbance (A_2) of fish-liver oil $= 0.724$ units
Concentration (g/mL) of Vitamin A in fish-liver oil sample $= C_2$

$$\dfrac{A_1}{C_1} = \dfrac{A_2}{C_2}$$

$$C_2 = \dfrac{A_2 C_1}{A_1} = \dfrac{(0.724)\left(6.68 \times 10^{-6} \text{ g/mL}\right)}{(1.018)} = 4.7508 \times 10^{-6} \text{ g/mL Vitamin A}$$

Mass (g) of Vitamin A in oil sample $= (500. \text{ mL oil}) \left(\dfrac{4.7508 \times 10^{-6} \text{ g Vitamin A}}{1 \text{ mL oil}} \right) = 2.3754 \times 10^{-3}$ g Vitamin A

Concentration of Vitamin A in oil sample $= \dfrac{\left(2.3754 \times 10^{-3} \text{ g} \right)}{\left(0.1232 \text{ g Oil} \right)} = 1.92808 \times 10^{-2}$ g$= \mathbf{1.93 \times 10^{-2}}$ **g Vitamin A/g oil**

6.92   Plan: First find the energy in joules from the light that shines on the text. Each watt is one joule/s for a total of 75 J; take 5% of that amount of joules and then 10% of that amount. Use $E = \dfrac{hc}{\lambda}$ to find the energy of one photon of light with a wavelength of 550 nm. Divide the energy that shines on the text by the energy of one photon to obtain the number of photons.
Solution:
The amount of energy is calculated from the wavelength of light:

$$\lambda \text{ (m)} = (550 \text{ nm}) \left(\dfrac{10^{-9} \text{ m}}{1 \text{ nm}} \right) = 5.50 \times 10^{-7} \text{ m}$$

$$E = \dfrac{hc}{\lambda} = \dfrac{\left(6.626 \times 10^{-34} \text{ J} \cdot \text{s} \right) \left(3.00 \times 10^{8} \text{ m/s} \right)}{5.50 \times 10^{-7} \text{ m}} = 3.614182 \times 10^{-19} \text{ J/photon}$$

Amount of power from the bulb $= (75 \text{ W}) \left(\dfrac{1 \text{ J/s}}{1 \text{ W}} \right) = 75 \text{ J/s}$

Amount of power converted to light $= (75 \text{ J/s}) \left(\dfrac{5\%}{100\%} \right) = 3.75 \text{ Js}$

Amount of light shining on book $= (3.75 \text{ J/s}) \left(\dfrac{10\%}{100\%} \right) = 0.375 \text{ J/s}$

Number of photons: $\left(\dfrac{0.375 \text{ J}}{\text{s}} \right) \left(\dfrac{1 \text{ photon}}{3.614182 \times 10^{-19} \text{ J}} \right) = 1.0376 \times 10^{18}$ photons/s$= \mathbf{1.0 \times 10^{18}}$ **photons/s**

6.95   Plan: In the visible series with $n_{final} = 2$, the transitions will end in either the 2s or 2p orbitals since those are the only two types of orbitals in the second main energy level. With the restriction that the angular momentum quantum number can change by only ± 1, the allowable transitions are from a p orbital to 2s ($l = 1$ to $l = 0$), from an s orbital to 2p ($l = 0$ to $l = 1$), and from a d orbital to 2p ($l = 2$ to $l = 1$). The problem specifies a change in energy level, so n_{init} must be 3, 4, 5, etc. (Although a change from 2p to 2s would result in a +1 change in l, this is not a change in energy level.)
Solution:
The first four transitions are as follows:
3s → 2p
3d → 2p
4s → 2p
3p → 2s

CHAPTER 7 ELECTRON CONFIGURATION AND CHEMICAL PERIODICITY

END–OF–CHAPTER PROBLEMS

7.1   Elements are listed in the periodic table in an ordered, systematic way that correlates with a periodicity of their chemical and physical properties. The theoretical basis for the table in terms of atomic number and electron configuration does not allow for an "unknown element" between Sn and Sb.

7.3   <u>Plan:</u> The value should be the average of the elements above and below the one of interest.
       <u>Solution:</u>
       a) Predicted atomic mass (K) =
       $$\frac{Na + Rb}{2} = \frac{22.99\,u + 85.47\,u}{2} = \textbf{54.23 u} \qquad \text{(actual value} = 39.10 \text{ u)}$$
       b) Predicted melting point (Br_2) =
       $$\frac{Cl_2 + I_2}{2} = \frac{-101.0°C + 113.6°C}{2} = \textbf{6.3°C} \qquad \text{(actual value} = -7.2°C)$$

7.6   The quantum number m_s relates to just the electron; all the others describe the orbital.

7.9   Shielding occurs when core electrons protect or shield valence electrons from the full nuclear attractive force. The effective nuclear charge is the nuclear charge an electron actually experiences. As the number of core electrons increases, shielding increases and the effective nuclear charge decreases.

7.11   <u>Plan:</u> The integer in front of the letter represents the n value. The l value designates the orbital type: $l = 0 = s$ orbital; $l = 1 = p$ orbital; $l = 2 = d$ orbital; $l = 3 = f$ orbital. Remember that a p orbital set contains 3 orbitals, a d orbital set has 5 orbitals, and an f orbital set has 7 orbitals. Any one orbital can hold a maximum of 2 electrons.
       <u>Solution:</u>
       a) The $l = 1$ quantum number can only refer to a p orbital. These quantum numbers designate the $2p$ orbital set ($n = 2$), which hold a maximum of **6** electrons, 2 electrons in each of the three $2p$ orbitals.
       b) There are five $3d$ orbitals, therefore a maximum of **10** electrons can have the $3d$ designation, 2 electrons in each of the five $3d$ orbitals.
       c) There is one $4s$ orbital which holds a maximum of **2** electrons.

7.13   <u>Plan:</u> The integer in front of the letter represents the n value. The l value designates the orbital type: $l = 0 = s$ orbital; $l = 1 = p$ orbital; $l = 2 = d$ orbital; $l = 3 = f$ orbital. Remember that a p orbital set contains 3 orbitals, a d orbital set has 5 orbitals, and an f orbital set has 7 orbitals. Any one orbital can hold a maximum of 2 electrons.
       <u>Solution:</u>
       a) **6** electrons can be found in the three $4p$ orbitals, 2 in each orbital.

       b) The $l = 1$ quantum number can only refer to a p orbital, and the m_l value of $+1$ specifies one particular p orbital, which holds a maximum of **2** electrons with the difference between the two electrons being in the m_s quantum number.

       c) **14** electrons can be found in the $5f$ orbitals ($l = 3$ designates f orbitals; there are $7f$ orbitals in a set).

7.16   Hund's rule states that electrons will fill empty orbitals in the same subshell before filling half-filled orbitals. This lowest-energy arrangement has the maximum number of unpaired electrons with parallel spins. In the correct electron configuration for nitrogen shown in (a), the $2p$ orbitals each have one unpaired electron; in the incorrect configuration shown in (b), electrons were paired in one of the $2p$ orbitals while leaving one $2p$ orbital empty. The arrows in the $2p$ orbitals of configuration (a) could alternatively all point down.

(a) – correct   (b) – incorrect

  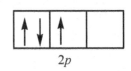

7.18   For elements in the same group (vertical column in periodic table), the electron configuration of the valence electrons is identical except for the n value. For elements in the same period (horizontal row in periodic table), their configurations vary because each succeeding element has one additional electron. The electron configurations are similar only in the fact that the same level (principal quantum number) is the valence level.

7.20   The total electron capacity for an energy level is $2n^2$, so the $n = 4$ energy level holds a maximum of $2(4^2) = $ **32 electrons**. A filled $n = 4$ energy level would have the following configuration: $4s^2 4p^6 4d^{10} 4f^{14}$.

7.21   Plan: Write the electron configuration for the atom or ion and find the electron for which you are writing the quantum numbers. Assume that the electron is in the ground-state configuration. By convention, $m_l = -1$ for the p_x orbital, $m_l = 0$ for the p_y orbital, and $m_l = +1$ for the p_z orbital. Also, keep in mind the following letter orbital designation for each l value: $l = 0 = s$ orbital, $l = 1 = p$ orbital, $l = 2 = d$ orbital, and $l = 3 = f$ orbital.
Solution:
a) Rb: $[Kr]5s^1$. The outermost electron in a rubidium atom would be in a $5s$ orbital (rubidium is in Row 5, Group 1). The quantum numbers for this electron could be $n = 5, l = 0, m_l = 0$, and $m_s = +1/2$ or $-1/2$.
b) The S^- ion would have the configuration $[Ne]3s^2 3p^5$. The electron added would go into a different orbital than the first electron paired electron and would be the second electron in the orbital it enters. Quantum numbers could be $n = 3, l = 1, m_l = +1, 0$ or -1 **(depending on where the 4th electron has been placed), and $m_s = -1/2$ or $+1/2$ depending on the spin of the electron already in the orbital that the added electron enters.**
c) Ag atoms have the configuration $[Kr]5s^1 4d^{10}$. The electron lost would be from the $5s$ orbital with quantum numbers $n = 5, l = 0, m_l = 0$, and $m_s = +1/2$ or $-1/2$, **depending on which electron was lost.**
d) The F atom has the configuration $[He]2s^2 2p^5$. The electron gained would go into the only 2p orbital with a single electron and would be the second electron in that orbital. Quantum numbers could be $n = 2, l = 1, m_l = +1$, and $m_s = -1/2$ or $+1/2$ **depending on the spin of the electron already in that orbital.**

7.23   Plan: The atomic number gives the number of electrons and the periodic table shows the order for filling subshells. Recall that s orbitals hold a maximum of 2 electrons, a p orbital set holds 6 electrons, a d orbital set holds 10 electrons, and an f orbital set holds 14 electrons.
Solution:
a) Rb: $1s^2 2s^2 2p^6 3s^2 3p^6 4s^2 3d^{10} 4p^6 5s^1$
b) Ge: $1s^2 2s^2 2p^6 3s^2 3p^6 4s^2 3d^{10} 4p^2$
c) Ar: $1s^2 2s^2 2p^6 3s^2 3p^6$

7.25   Plan: The atomic number gives the number of electrons and the periodic table shows the order for filling subshells. Recall that s orbitals hold a maximum of 2 electrons, a p orbital set holds 6 electrons, a d orbital set holds 10 electrons, and an f orbital set holds 14 electrons.
Solution:
a) Cl: $1s^2 2s^2 2p^6 3s^2 3p^5$
b) Si: $1s^2 2s^2 2p^6 3s^2 3p^2$
c) Sr: $1s^2 2s^2 2p^6 3s^2 3p^6 4s^2 3d^{10} 4p^6 5s^2$

7.27   Plan: The atomic number gives the number of electrons and the periodic table shows the order for filling subshells. Recall that s orbitals hold a maximum of 2 electrons, a p orbital set holds 6 electrons, a d orbital set holds 10 electrons, and an f orbital set holds 14 electrons. Valence electrons are those in the highest energy level; in transition metals, the $(n-1)d$ electrons are also counted as valence electrons. For a condensed ground-state electron configuration, the electron configuration of the previous noble gas is shown by its element symbol in brackets, followed by the electron configuration of the energy level being filled.
Solution:
a) Ti ($Z = 22$); [Ar]$4s^2 3d^2$ (note that the 2 3d electrons can be placed in any of the 5 boxes as long as they have the same spin, which could be positive or negative).

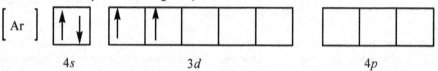

b) Cl ($Z = 17$); [Ne]$3s^2 3p^5$ (note that the unpaired electron could have positive or negative spin).

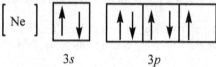

c) V ($Z = 23$); [Ar]$4s^2 3d^3$ (note that the 3 3d electrons can be placed in any of the 5 boxes as long as they have the same spin, which could be positive or negative).

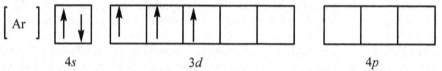

7.29   Plan: The atomic number gives the number of electrons and the periodic table shows the order for filling subshells. Recall that s orbitals hold a maximum of 2 electrons, a p orbital set holds 6 electrons, a d orbital set holds 10 electrons, and an f orbital set holds 14 electrons. Valence electrons are those in the highest energy level; in transition metals, the $(n-1)d$ electrons are also counted as valence electrons. For a condensed ground-state electron configuration, the electron configuration of the previous noble gas is shown by its element symbol in brackets, followed by the electron configuration of the energy level being filled.
Solution:
a) Mn ($Z = 25$); [Ar]$4s^2 3d^5$ (note that the 3d electrons could also ALL have negative spin).

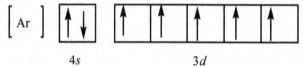

b) P ($Z = 15$); [Ne]$3s^2 3p^3$ (note that the 3p electrons could also ALL have negative spin).

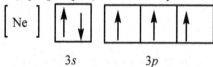

c) Fe ($Z = 26$); [Ar]$4s^2 3d^6$ (note that the unpaired electrons could also all have negative spins).

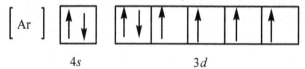

7.31   Plan: Add up all of the electrons in the electron configuration to obtain the atomic number of the element which is then used to identify the element and its position in the periodic table. When drawing the partial orbital diagram, only include electrons after those of the previous noble gas; remember to put one electron in each orbital in a set before pairing electrons.
Solution:
a) There are 8 electrons in the configuration; the element is O, Group 16, Period 2. (Note that the unpaired 2p electrons could both have negative spin.)

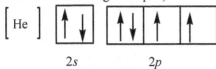

b) There are 15 electrons in the configuration; the element is P, Group 15, Period 3. (Note that the 3p electrons could all have negative spins as well.)

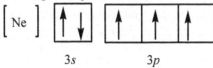

7.33   Plan: Add up all of the electrons in the electron configuration to obtain the atomic number of the element which is then used to identify the element and its position in the periodic table. When drawing the partial orbital diagram, only include electrons after those of the previous noble gas; remember to put one electron in each orbital in a set before pairing electrons.
Solution:
a) There are 17 electrons in the configuration; the element is Cl; Group 17; Period 3. Note that the single electron could have negative spin.

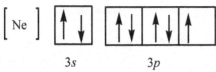

b) There are 33 electrons in the configuration; the element is As; Group 15; Period 4. Note that the 4p electrons could all have negative spin.

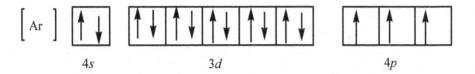

7.35   Plan: Use the periodic table and the partial orbital diagram to identify the element.
Solution:
a) The orbital diagram shows the element is in Period 4 ($n = 4$ as outer level). The configuration is $1s^22s^22p^63s^23p^64s^23d^{10}4p^1$ or $[Ar]4s^23d^{10}4p^1$. One electron in the p level indicates the element is in Group **13**. The element is Ga.
b) The orbital diagram shows the 2s and 2p orbitals filled which would represent the last element in Period 2, Ne. The configuration is $1s^22s^22p^6$ or $[He]2s^22p^6$. Filled s and p orbitals indicate Group **18**.

7.37   Plan: Core electrons are those seen in the previous noble gas and completed transition series (d orbitals). Valence electrons are those in the highest energy level (highest n value). For transition metals, valence electrons also include electrons in the outermost d set of orbitals. It is easiest to determine the types of electrons by writing a condensed electron configuration.

Solution:
a) O (Z = 8); [He]$2s^22p^4$. There are **2** core electrons (represented by [He]) and 4 valence electrons.
b) Sn (Z = 50); [Kr]$5s^24d^{10}5p^2$. There are 36 (from [Kr]) + 10 (from the filled 4d set) = **46** core electrons. The highest energy level is n = 5 so there are **4** valence electrons.
c) Ca (Z = 20); [Ar]$4s^2$. There are **2** valence electrons (the 4s electrons), and **18** core electrons (from [Ar]).
d) Fe (Z = 26); [Ar]$4s^23d^6$. There are **8** valence electrons (2 from n = 4 level and the d orbital electrons count in this case because the subshell is not full), and **18** core electrons (from [Ar]).
e) Se (Z = 34); [Ar]$4s^23d^{10}4p^4$. There are (2 + 4 in the n = 4 level), **6** valence electrons (filled d subshells count as core electrons), and **28** core electrons (18 from [Ar] and 10 from the filled 3d set).

7.39   Plan: Add up all of the electrons in the electron configuration to obtain the atomic number of the element which is then used to identify the element and its position in the periodic table.
        Solution:
        a) The electron configuration [He]$2s^22p^1$ has a total of 5 electrons (3 + 2 from He configuration) which is element boron with symbol **B**. Boron is in Group 13. Other elements in this group are **Al, Ga, In,** and **Tl.**
        b) The electrons in this element total 16, 10 from the neon configuration plus 6 from the rest of the configuration. Element 16 is sulfur, **S,** in Group16. Other elements in Group 16 are **O, Se, Te,** and **Po.**
        c) Electrons total 3 + 54 (from xenon) = 57. Element 57 is lanthanum, **La,** in Group 3. Other elements in this group are **Sc, Y,** and **Ac.**

7.41   Plan: Add up all of the electrons in the electron configuration to obtain the atomic number of the element which is then used to identify the element and its position in the periodic table.
        Solution:
        a) The electron configuration [He]$2s^22p^2$ has a total of 6 electrons (4 + 2 from He configuration) which is element carbon with symbol **C**; other Group 14 elements include **Si, Ge, Sn,** and **Pb.**
        b) Electrons total 5 + 18 (from argon) = 23 which is **vanadium**; other Group 5 elements include **Nb, Ta,** and **Db.**
        c) The electrons in this element total 15, 10 from the neon configuration plus 5 from the rest of the configuration. Element 15 is **phosphorus**; other Group 15 elements include **N, As, Sb,** and **Bi.**

7.43   Plan: Write the ground-state electron configuration of sodium; for the excited state, move the outermost electron to the next orbital.
        Solution:
        The ground-state configuration of Na is $1s^22s^22p^63s^1$. Upon excitation, the $3s^1$ electron is promoted to the 3p level, with configuration $1s^22s^22p^63p^1$. (Note that the electron in 3p can be in any of the 3 boxes and have positive or negative spin.)

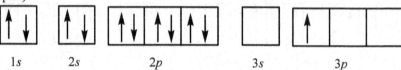

        1s   2s   2p   3s   3p

7.50   A high, endothermic IE_1 means it is very difficult to remove the first valence electron. This value would exclude any metal, because metals lose a valence electron easily. A very negative, exothermic EA_1 suggests that this element easily gains one electron. These values indicate that the element belongs to the halogens, Group 17, which form –1 ions.

7.53   Plan: Atomic size decreases up a main group and left to right across a period.
        Solution:
        a) Increasing atomic size: **K < Rb < Cs**; these three elements are all part of the same group, the alkali metals. Atomic size decreases up a main group (larger valence electron orbital), so potassium is the smallest and cesium is the largest.
        b) Increasing atomic size: **O < C < Be**; these three elements are in the same period and atomic size decreases across a period (increasing effective nuclear charge), so beryllium is the largest and oxygen the smallest.
        c) Increasing atomic size: **Cl < S < K**; chlorine and sulfur are in the same period so chlorine is smaller since it is further to the right in the period. Potassium is the first element in the next period so it is larger than either Cl or S.

d) Increasing atomic size: **Mg < Ca < K**; calcium is larger than magnesium because Ca is further down the alkaline earth metal group on the periodic table than Mg. Potassium is larger than calcium because K is further to the left than Ca in Period 4 of the periodic table.

7.55   Plan: Ionization energy increases up a group and left to right across a period.
Solution:
a) **Ba < Sr < Ca** The "group" rule applies in this case. Ionization energy increases up a main group. Barium's valence electron receives the most shielding; therefore, it is easiest to remove and has the lowest IE.
b) **B < N < Ne** These elements have the same n, so the "period" rule applies. Ionization energy increases from left to right across a period. B experiences the lowest Z_{eff} and has the lowest IE. Ne has the highest IE, because it's very difficult to remove an electron from the stable noble gas configuration.
c) **Rb < Se < Br** IE decreases with increasing atomic size, so Rb (largest atom) has the smallest IE. Se has a lower IE than Br because IE increases across a period.
d) **Sn < Sb < As** IE increases up a group, so Sn and Sb will have smaller IEs than As. The "period" rule applies for ranking Sn and Sb.

7.57   Plan: When a large jump between successive ionization energies is observed, the subsequent electron must come from a full lower energy level. Thus, by looking at a series of successive ionization energies, we can determine the number of valence electrons. The number of valence electrons identifies which group the element is in.
Solution:
The successive ionization energies show a very significant jump between the third and fourth IEs. This indicates that the element has three valence electrons. The fourth electron must come from the core electrons and thus has a very large ionization energy. The electron configuration of the Period 2 element with three valence electrons is $1s^2 2s^2 2p^1$ which represents boron, **B**.

7.59   Plan: For a given element, successive ionization energies always increase. As each successive electron is removed, the positive charge on the ion increases, which results in a stronger attraction between the leaving electron and the ion. A very large jump between successive ionization energies will occur when the electron to be removed comes from a full lower energy level. Examine the electron configurations of the atoms. If the IE_2 represents removing an electron from a full orbital, then the IE_2 will be very large. In addition, for atoms with the same valence electron configuration, IE_2 is larger for the smaller atom.
Solution:
a) **Na** would have the highest IE_2 because ionization of a second electron would require breaking the stable [Ne] configuration:
First ionization: Na ([Ne]$3s^1$) → Na$^+$ ([Ne]) + e$^-$ (low IE)
Second ionization: Na$^+$ ([Ne]) → Na^{+2} ([He]$2s^2 2p^5$) + e$^-$ (high IE)
b) **Na** would have the highest IE_2 because it has one valence electron and is smaller than K.
c) You might think that Sc would have the highest IE_2, because removing a second electron would require breaking the stable, filled 4s shell. However, **Be** has the highest IE_2 because Be's small size makes it difficult to remove a second electron.

7.61   Three of the ways that metals and nonmetals differ are: 1) metals conduct electricity, nonmetals do not; 2) when they form stable ions, metal ions tend to have a positive charge, nonmetal ions tend to have a negative charge; and 3) metal oxides are ionic and act as bases, nonmetal oxides are covalent and act as acids.

7.62   Metallic character decreases up a group and decreases toward the right across a period. These trends are the same as those for atomic size and opposite those for ionization energy.

7.63   Plan: Write the electron configurations for the two elements. Remember that these elements lose electrons to achieve pseudo-noble gas configurations.
Solution:
The two largest elements in Group 14, Sn and Pb, have atomic electron configurations that look like $ns^2(n-1)d^{10}np^2$. Both of these elements are metals so they will form positive ions. To reach the noble gas configuration of xenon the atoms would have to lose 14 electrons, which is not likely. Instead the atoms lose either 2 or 4 electrons to attain a stable configuration with either the ns and $(n-1)d$ filled for the 2+ ion or the $(n-1)d$ orbital filled for the 4+ ion. The Sn^{2+} and Pb^{2+} ions form by losing the two p electrons:

Sn ([Kr]$5s^24d^{10}5p^2$) $\rightarrow$ Sn^{2+} ([Kr]$5s^24d^{10}$) + 2 e$^-$
Pb ([Xe]$6s^25d^{10}6p^2$) $\rightarrow$ Pb^{2+} ([Xe]$6s^25d^{10}$) + 2 e$^-$
The Sn^{4+} and Pb^{4+} ions form by losing the two p and two s electrons:
Sn ([Kr]$5s^24d^{10}5p^2$) $\rightarrow$ Sn^{4+} ([Kr]$4d^{10}$) + 4 e$^-$
Pb ([Xe]$6s^25d^{10}6p^2$) $\rightarrow$ Pb^{4+} ([Xe]$5d^{10}$) + 4 e$^-$
Possible ions for tin and lead have **+2** and **+4** charges.

7.67   Plan: Metallic behavior decreases up a group and decreases left to right across a period.
        Solution:
        a) **Rb** is more metallic because it is to the left and below Ca.
        b) **Ra** is more metallic because it lies below Mg in Group 2.
        c) **I** is more metallic because it lies below Br in Group 17.

7.69   Plan: Metallic behavior decreases up a group and decreases left to right across a period.
        Solution:
        a) **As** should be less metallic than antimony because it lies above Sb in the same group of the periodic table.
        b) **P** should be less metallic because it lies to the right of silicon in the same period of the periodic table.
        c) **Be** should be less metallic since it lies above and to the right of sodium on the periodic table.

7.71   Plan: For main-group elements, the most stable ions have electron configurations identical to noble gas atoms.
        Write the electron configuration of the atom and then remove or add electrons until a noble gas configuration is
        achieved. Metals lose electrons and nonmetals gain electrons.
        Solution:
        a) Cl: $1s^22s^22p^63s^23p^5$; chlorine atoms are one electron short of a noble gas configuration, so a **–1** ion will form by
        adding an electron to have the same electron configuration as an argon atom: Cl$^-$, **$1s^22s^22p^63s^23p^6$**.
        b) Na: $1s^22s^22p^63s^1$; sodium atoms contain one more electron than the noble gas configuration of neon. Thus, a
        sodium atom loses one electron to form a **+1** ion: Na$^+$, **$1s^22s^22p^6$**.
        c) Ca: $1s^22s^22p^63s^23p^64s^2$; calcium atoms contain two more electrons than the noble gas configuration of argon.
        Thus, a calcium atom loses two electrons to form a **+2** ion: Ca^{2+}, **$1s^22s^22p^63s^23p^6$**.

7.73   Plan: For main-group elements, the most stable ions have electron configurations identical to noble gas atoms.
        Write the electron configuration of the atom and then remove or add electrons until a noble gas configuration is
        achieved. Metals lose electrons and nonmetals gain electrons.
        Solution:
        a) Al: $1s^22s^22p^63s^23p^1$; aluminum atoms contain three more electrons than the noble gas configuration of Ne.
        Thus, an aluminum atom loses its 3 valence shell electrons to form a **+3** ion: Al^{3+}, **$1s^22s^22p^6$**.
        b) S: $1s^22s^22p^63s^23p^4$; sulfur atoms are two electrons short of the noble gas configuration of argon. Thus, a
        sulfur atom gains two electrons to form a **–2** ion: S^{2-}, **$1s^22s^22p^63s^23p^6$**.
        c) Sr: $1s^22s^22p^63s^23p^64s^23d^{10}4p^65s^2$; strontium atoms contain two more electrons than the noble gas configuration
        of krypton. Thus, a strontium atom loses two electrons to form a **+2** ion: Sr^{2+}, **$1s^22s^22p^63s^23p^64s^23d^{10}4p^6$**.

7.75   Plan: To find the number of unpaired electrons look at the electron configuration expanded to include
        the different orientations of the orbitals, such as p_x and p_y and p_z. Remember that one electron will occupy every
        orbital in a set (p, d, or f) before electrons will pair in an orbital in that set. In the noble gas configurations, all
        electrons are paired because all orbitals are filled.
        Solution:
        a) Configuration of 2 group elements: [noble gas]ns^2, **no unpaired electrons**. The electrons in the ns
        orbital are paired.
        b) Configuration of 15 group elements: [noble gas]$ns^2np_x^1np_y^1np_z^1$. **Three** unpaired electrons, one each in p_x,
        p_y, and p_z. Spins can be all positive or all negative.
        c) Configuration of 18 group elements: noble gas configuration ns^2np^6 with no half-filled orbitals, **no unpaired
        electrons**.
        d) Configuration of 13 group elements: [noble gas]ns^2np^1. There is **one** unpaired electron in one of the p orbitals.
        The unpaired electron can be in any of the p orbitals and can have positive or negative spin.

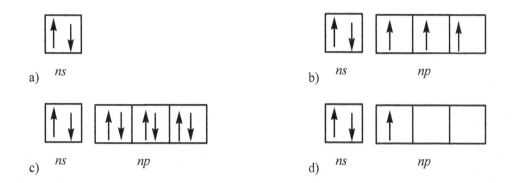

a) *ns* b) *ns* *np*

c) *ns* *np* d) *ns* *np*

7.77   Plan: Substances are paramagnetic if they have unpaired electrons. To find the number of unpaired electrons look at the electron configuration expanded to include the different orientations of the orbitals, such as p_x and p_y and p_z. Remember that all orbitals in a *p*, *d*, or *f* set will each have one electron before electrons pair in an orbital. In the noble gas configurations, all electrons are paired because all orbitals are filled.
Solution:
a) Ga ($Z = 31$) = [Ar]$4s^2 3d^{10} 4p^1$. The *s* and *d* subshells are filled, so all electrons are paired. The lone *p* electron is unpaired, so this element is **paramagnetic**.
b) Si ($Z = 14$) = [Ne]$3s^2 3p_x^1 3p_y^1 3p_z^0$. This element is **paramagnetic** with two unpaired electrons.

      Correct   Incorrect
c) Be ($Z = 4$) = [He]$2s^2$. The two *s* electrons are paired so Be is **not paramagnetic**.
d) Te ($Z = 52$) = [Kr]$5s^2 4d^{10} 5p_x^2 5p_y^1 5p_z^1$ is **paramagnetic** with two unpaired electrons in the *5p* set.

7.79   Plan: Substances are paramagnetic if they have unpaired electrons. Write the electron configuration of the atom and then remove the specified number of electrons. Remember that all orbitals in a *p*, *d*, or *f* set will each have one electron before electrons pair in an orbital. In the noble gas configurations, all electrons are paired because all orbitals are filled.
Solution:
a) V: [Ar]$4s^2 3d^3$; **V^{3+}: [Ar]$3d^2$** Transition metals first lose the *s* electrons in forming ions, so to form the +3 ion a vanadium atom loses two *4s* electrons and one *3d* electron. Note that the two d electrons can be in any of the boxes and can both have either positive or negative spins). **Paramagnetic**

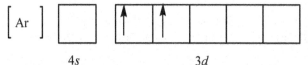

      4s   *3d*
b) Cd: [Kr]$5s^2 4d^{10}$; **Cd^{2+}: [Kr]$4d^{10}$** Cadmium atoms lose two electrons from the *4s* orbital to form the +2 ion. **Diamagnetic**

      5s   *4d*
c) Co: [Ar]$4s^2 3d^7$; **Co^{3+}: [Ar]$3d^6$** Cobalt atoms lose two *4s* electrons and one *3d* electron to form the +3 ion. Note that all the unpaired electrons can have either positive or negative spins. **Paramagnetic**

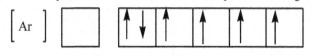

      4s   *3d*
d) Ag: [Kr]$5s^1 4d^{10}$; **Ag$^+$: [Kr]$4d^{10}$** Silver atoms lose the one electron in the *5s* orbital to form the +1 ion. **Diamagnetic**

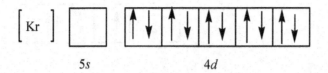

5s   4d

7.81   Plan: Substances are diamagnetic if they have no unpaired electrons. Draw the partial orbital diagrams,
        remembering that all orbitals in d set will each have one electron before electrons pair in an orbital.
        Solution:
        You might first write the condensed electron configuration for Pd as $[Kr]5s^24d^8$. However, the partial orbital
        diagram is not consistent with diamagnetism.

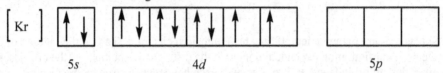

5s   4d   5p

        Promoting an s electron into the d subshell (as in (c) $[Kr]5s^14d^9$) still leaves two electrons unpaired.

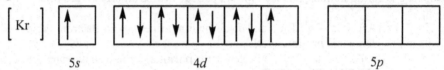

5s   4d   5p

        The only configuration that supports diamagnetism is **(b) $[Kr]4d^{10}$**.

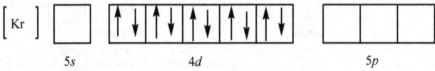

5s   4d   5p

7.83   Plan: The size of ions increases down a group. For ions that are isoelectronic (have the same electron
        configuration) size decreases with increasing atomic number.
        Solution:
        a) Increasing size: **$Li^+ < Na^+ < K^+$**, size increases down Group 1.
        b) Increasing size: **$Rb^+ < Br^- < Se^{2-}$**, these three ions are isoelectronic with the same electron configuration as
        krypton. Size decreases with increasing atomic number in an isoelectronic series.
        c) Increasing size: **$F^- < O^{2-} < N^{3-}$**, the three ions are isoelectronic with an electron configuration identical to neon.
        Size decreases with increasing atomic number in an isoelectronic series.

7.86   Plan: Write the electron configuration for each atom. Remove the specified number of electrons, given by
        the positive ionic charge, to write the configuration for the ions. Remember that electrons with the highest n
        value are removed first.
        Solution:
        Ce: $[Xe]6s^24f^15d^1$ Eu: $[Xe]6s^24f^7$
        Ce^{4+}: $[Xe]$ Eu^{2+}: $[Xe]4f^7$
        Ce^{4+} has a noble gas configuration and Eu^{2+} has a half-filled f subshell.

7.89   <u>Plan</u>: Remember that isoelectronic species have the same electron configuration. Atomic radius decreases up a group and left to right across a period.
<u>Solution</u>:
a) A chemically unreactive Period 4 element would be Kr in Group 18. Both the Sr^{2+} ion and Br^- ion are isoelectronic with Kr. Their combination results in **$SrBr_2$, strontium bromide**.
b) Ar is the Period 3 noble gas. Ca^{2+} and S^{2-} are isoelectronic with Ar. The resulting compound is **CaS, calcium sulfide**.
c) The smallest filled d subshell is the $3d$ shell, so the element must be in Period 4. Zn forms the Zn^{2+} ion by losing its two s subshell electrons to achieve a *pseudo–noble gas* configuration ($[Ar]3d^{10}$). The smallest halogen is fluorine, whose anion is F^-. The resulting compound is **ZnF_2, zinc fluoride**.
d) Ne is the smallest element in Period 2, but it is not ionizable. Li is the largest atom whereas F is the smallest atom in Period 2. The resulting compound is **LiF, lithium fluoride**.

7.90   <u>Plan</u>: Recall Hess's law: the enthalpy change of an overall process is the sum of the enthalpy changes of its individual steps. Both the ionization energies and the electron affinities of the elements are needed.
<u>Solution</u>:
a) F: ionization energy = 1681 kJ/mol   electron affinity = –328 kJ/mol
$\quad\quad F(g) \rightarrow F^+(g) + e^-$ $\Delta E = 1681$ kJ/mol
$\quad\quad F(g) + e^- \rightarrow F^-(g)$ $\Delta E = -328$ kJ/mol
Reverse the electron affinity reaction to give: $F^-(g) \rightarrow F(g) + e^-$ $\Delta E = +328$ kJ/mol
Summing the ionization energy reaction with the reversed electron affinity reaction (Hess's law):
$\quad\quad \cancel{F(g)} \rightarrow F^+(g) + e^-$ $\Delta E = 1681$ kJ/mol
$\quad\quad \underline{F^-(g) \rightarrow \cancel{F(g)} + e^-}$ $\underline{\Delta E = +328 \text{ kJ/mol}}$
$\quad\quad F^-(g) \rightarrow F^+(g) + 2\ e^-$ $\Delta E = $ **2009 kJ/mol**
b) Na: ionization energy = 496 kJ/mol   electron affinity = –52.9 kJ/mol
$\quad\quad Na(g) \rightarrow Na^+(g) + e^-$ $\Delta E = 496$ kJ/mol
$\quad\quad Na(g) + e^- \rightarrow Na^-(g)$ $\Delta E = -52.9$ kJ/mol
Reverse the ionization reaction to give: $Na^+(g) + e^- \rightarrow Na(g)$ $\Delta E = -496$ kJ/mol
Summing the electron affinity reaction with the reversed ionization reaction (Hess's law):
$\quad\quad \cancel{Na(g)} + e^- \rightarrow Na^-(g)$ $\Delta E = -52.9$ kJ/mol
$\quad\quad \underline{Na^+(g) + e^- \rightarrow \cancel{Na(g)}}$ $\underline{\Delta E = -496 \text{ kJ/mol}}$
$\quad\quad Na^+(g) + 2\ e^- \rightarrow Na^-(g)$ $\Delta E = -548.9$ kJ/mol= **–549 kJ/mol**

9.91   <u>Plan</u>: Determine the electron configuration for iron, and then begin removing one electron at a time. Remember that all orbitals in a d set will each have one electron before electrons pair in an orbital, and electrons with the highest n value are removed first. Ions with all electrons paired are diamagnetic. Ions with at least one unpaired electron are paramagnetic. The more unpaired electrons, the greater the attraction to a magnetic field.
<u>Solution</u>:

Fe	$[Ar]4s^23d^6$	partially filled $3d$ = **paramagnetic**	number of unpaired electrons = 4
Fe^+	$[Ar]4s^13d^6$	partially filled $3d$ = **paramagnetic**	number of unpaired electrons = 5
Fe^{2+}	$[Ar]3d^6$	partially filled $3d$ = **paramagnetic**	number of unpaired electrons = 4
Fe^{3+}	$[Ar]3d^5$	partially filled $3d$ = **paramagnetic**	number of unpaired electrons = 5
Fe^{4+}	$[Ar]3d^4$	partially filled $3d$ = **paramagnetic**	number of unpaired electrons = 4
Fe^{5+}	$[Ar]3d^3$	partially filled $3d$ = **paramagnetic**	number of unpaired electrons = 3
Fe^{6+}	$[Ar]3d^2$	partially filled $3d$ = **paramagnetic**	number of unpaired electrons = 2
Fe^{7+}	$[Ar]3d^1$	partially filled $3d$ = **paramagnetic**	number of unpaired electrons = 1
Fe^{8+}	$[Ar]$	filled orbitals = **diamagnetic**	number of unpaired electrons = 0
Fe^{9+}	$[Ne]3s^23p^5$	partially filled $3p$ = **paramagnetic**	number of unpaired electrons = 1
Fe^{10+}	$[Ne]3s^23p^4$	partially filled $3p$ = **paramagnetic**	number of unpaired electrons = 2
Fe^{11+}	$[Ne]3s^23p^3$	partially filled $3p$ = **paramagnetic**	number of unpaired electrons = 3
Fe^{12+}	$[Ne]3s^23p^2$	partially filled $3p$ = **paramagnetic**	number of unpaired electrons = 2
Fe^{13+}	$[Ne]3s^23p^1$	partially filled $3p$ = **paramagnetic**	number of unpaired electrons = 1
Fe^{14+}	$[Ne]3s^2$	filled orbitals = **diamagnetic**	number of unpaired electrons = 0

Fe^+ and **Fe^{3+}** would both be most attracted to a magnetic field. They each have 5 unpaired electrons.

CHAPTER 8 MODELS OF CHEMICAL BONDING

END–OF–CHAPTER PROBLEMS

8.1   a) Larger ionization energy decreases metallic character.
        b) Larger atomic radius increases metallic character.
        c) Larger number of outer electrons decreases metallic character.
        d) Larger effective nuclear charge decreases metallic character.

8.4   Plan: Metallic behavior increases to the left and down a group in the periodic table.
        Solution:
        a) **Cs** is more metallic since it is further down the alkali metal group than Na.
        b) **Rb** is more metallic since it is both to the left and down from Mg.
        c) **As** is more metallic since it is further down Group 15 than N.

8.6   Plan: Ionic bonding occurs between metals and nonmetals, covalent bonding between nonmetals, and metallic bonds between metals.
        Solution:
        a) Bond in CsF is **ionic** because Cs is a metal and F is a nonmetal.
        b) Bonding in N_2 is **covalent** because N is a nonmetal.
        c) Bonding in Na(s) is **metallic** because this is a monatomic, metal solid.

8.8   Plan: Ionic bonding occurs between metals and nonmetals, covalent bonding between nonmetals, and metallic bonds between metals.
        Solution:
        a) Bonding in O_3 would be **covalent** since O is a nonmetal.
        b) Bonding in $MgCl_2$ would be **ionic** since Mg is a metal and Cl is a nonmetal.
        c) Bonding in BrO_2 would be **covalent** since both Br and O are nonmetals.

8.10   Plan: Lewis electron-dot symbols show valence electrons as dots. Place one dot at a time on the four sides (this method explains the structure in b) and then pair up dots until all valence electrons are used. The group number of the elements in Groups 1-2 and the group number – 10 of the main-group elements in Groups 13-18 gives the number of valence electrons. Rb is Group 1, Si is a Group 14 element, and I is a Group 17 element.
        Solution:

        a)   Rb •   b) • Si •   c)   : I •

8.12   Plan: Lewis electron-dot symbols show valence electrons as dots. Place one dot at a time on the four sides (this method explains the structure in b) and then pair up dots until all valence electrons are used. The group number of the elements in Groups 1-2 and the group number – 10 of the main-group elements in Groups 13-18 gives the number of valence electrons. Sr is a Group 1 element, P is a Group 15 element, and S is a Group 16 element.
        Solution:

        a) • Sr •   b)   • P •   c)   : S •

8.14   <u>Plan:</u> Assuming X is a main-group element, the number of dots (valence electrons) equals the group number if this number is 1 or 2. If the number of dots (valence electrons) is 3 or more, then we add 10 to calculate the group number. Once the group number is known, the general electron configuration of the element can be written.
<u>Solution:</u>
a) Since there are 6 dots in the Lewis electron-dot symbol, element X has 6 valence electrons and is a Group 16 element. Its general electron configuration is **[noble gas]**ns^2np^4, where n is the energy level.
b) Since there are 3 dots in the Lewis electron-dot symbol, element X has 3 valence electrons and is a Group 13 element with general electron configuration **[noble gas]**ns^2np^1.

8.20   <u>Plan:</u> Write condensed electron configurations and draw the Lewis electron-dot symbols for the atoms. The group number of the elements in Groups 1-2 and the group number – 10 of the main-group elements in Groups 13-18 gives the number of valence electrons. Remove electrons from the metal and add electrons to the nonmetal to attain filled outer levels. The number of electrons lost by the metal must equal the number of electrons gained by the nonmetal.
<u>Solution:</u>
a) Barium is a metal and loses 2 electrons to achieve a noble gas configuration:
$$Ba\ ([Xe]6s^2) \rightarrow Ba^{2+}\ ([Xe]) + 2e^-$$

Chlorine is a nonmetal and gains 1 electron to achieve a noble gas configuration:
$$Cl\ ([Ne]3s^23p^5) + 1e^- \rightarrow Cl^-\ ([Ne]3s^23p^6)$$

Two Cl atoms gain the 2 electrons lost by Ba. The ionic compound formed is **BaCl₂**.

b) Strontium is a metal and loses 2 electrons to achieve a noble gas configuration:
$$Sr\ ([Kr]5s^2) \rightarrow Sr^{2+}\ ([Kr]) + 2e^-$$
Oxygen is a nonmetal and gains 2 electrons to achieve a noble gas configuration:
$$O\ ([He]2s^22p^4) + 2e^- \rightarrow O^{2-}\ ([He]2s^22p^6)$$
One O atom gains the two electrons lost by one Sr atom. The ionic compound formed is **SrO**.

c) Aluminum is a metal and loses 3 electrons to achieve a noble gas configuration:
$$Al\ ([Ne]3s^23p^1) \rightarrow Al^{3+}\ ([Ne]) + 3e^-$$
Fluorine is a nonmetal and gains 1 electron to achieve a noble gas configuration:
$$F\ ([He]2s^22p^5) + 1e^- \rightarrow F^-\ ([He]2s^22p^6)$$
Three F atoms gains the three electrons lost by one Al atom. The ionic compound formed is **AlF₃**.

d) Rubidium is a metal and loses 1 electron to achieve a noble gas configuration:

Rb ([Kr]$5s^1$) → Rb$^+$ ([Kr]) + 1e$^-$

Oxygen is a nonmetal and gains 2 electrons to achieve a noble gas configuration:

O ([He]$2s^2 2p^4$) + 2e$^-$ → O^{2-} ([He]$2s^2 2p^6$)

One O atom gains the two electrons lost by two Rb atoms. The ionic compound formed is **Rb$_2$O**.

8.22   Plan: Find the charge of the known atom and use that charge to find the ionic charge of element X.
For cations of groups 1 and 2, ion charge = the group number; for cations of groups 13 and higher, ion charge = the group number – 10. For anions, ion charge = the group number – 18. Once the ion charge of X is known, the group number can be determined.
Solution:
a) X in XF$_2$ is a cation with +2 charge since the anion is F$^-$ and there are two fluoride ions in the compound. **Group 2** metals form +2 ions.
b) X in MgX is an anion with – 2 charge since Mg^{2+} is the cation. Elements in **Group 16** form –2 ions (16 – 18 = –2).
c) X in X$_2$SO$_4$ must be a cation with +1 charge since the polyatomic sulfate ion has a charge of –2. X comes from **Group 1**.

8.24   Plan: Find the charge of the known atom and use that charge to find the ionic charge of element X.
For cations of groups 1 and 2, ion charge = the group number; for cations of groups 13 and higher, ion charge = the group number – 10. For anions, ion charge = the group number – 18. Once the ion charge of X is known, the group number can be determined.
Solution:
a) X in X$_2$O$_3$ is a cation with +3 charge. The oxygen in this compound has a –2 charge. To produce an electrically neutral compound, 2 cations with +3 charge bond with 3 anions with –2 charge: 2(+3) + 3(–2) = 0. Elements in **Group 13** form +3 ions.
b) The carbonate ion, CO$_3^{2-}$, has a –2 charge, so X has a +2 charge. **Group 2** elements form +2 ions.
c) X in Na$_2$X has a –2 charge, balanced with the +2 overall charge from the two Na$^+$ ions. **Group 16** elements gain 2 electrons to form –2 ions with a noble gas configuration.

8.26   Plan: The magnitude of the lattice energy depends on ionic size and ionic charge. For a particular arrangement of ions, the lattice energy increases as the charges on the ions increase and as their radii decrease.
Solution:
a) **BaS** would have the higher lattice energy since the charge on each ion (+2 for Ba and –2 for S) is twice the charge on the ions in CsCl (+1 for Cs and –1 for Cl) and lattice energy is greater when ionic charges are larger.
b) **LiCl** would have the higher lattice energy since the ionic radius of Li$^+$ is smaller than that of Cs$^+$ and lattice energy is greater when the distance between ions is smaller.

8.28   Plan: The magnitude of the lattice energy depends on ionic size and ionic charge. For a particular arrangement of ions, the lattice energy increases as the charges on the ions increase and as their radii decrease.
Solution:
a) **BaS** has the lower lattice energy because the ionic radius of Ba^{2+} is larger than Ca^{2+}. A larger ionic radius results in a greater distance between ions. The lattice energy decreases with increasing distance between ions.
b) **NaF** has the lower lattice energy since the charge on each ion (+1, –1) is half the charge on the Mg^{2+} and O^{2-} ions. Lattice energy increases with increasing ion charge.

8.30   Plan: The lattice energy of NaCl is represented by the equation $NaCl(s) \rightarrow Na^+(g) + Cl^-(g)$. Use Hess's law and arrange the given equations so that they sum up to give the equation for the lattice energy. You will need to reverse the last equation (and change the sign of $\Delta H°$); you will also need to multiply the second equation ($\Delta H°$) by ½.
Solution:

$$\Delta H°$$

~~$Na(s) \rightarrow Na(g)$~~	109 kJ/mol
~~$1/2Cl_2(g) \rightarrow Cl(g)$~~	(1/2)(243 kJ/mol) = 121.5 kJ/mol
~~$Na(g) \rightarrow Na^+(g) + e^-$~~	496 kJ/mol
~~$Cl(g) + e^- \rightarrow Cl^-(g)$~~	–349 kJ/mol
$NaCl(s) \rightarrow$ ~~$Na(s) + 1/2Cl_2(g)$~~	411 kJ/mol (Reaction is reversed; sign of $\Delta H°$ changed.)
$NaCl(s) \rightarrow Na^+(g) + Cl^-(g)$	788.5 kJ/mol = **788 kJ/mol**

The lattice energy for NaCl is less than that of LiF, which is expected since lithium and fluoride ions are smaller than sodium and chloride ions, resulting in a larger lattice energy for LiF.

8.33   Plan: The electron affinity of fluorine is represented by the equation $F(g) + e^- \rightarrow F^-(g)$. Use Hess's law and arrange the given equations so that they sum up to give the equation for the lattice energy, $KF(s) \rightarrow K^+(g) + F^-(g)$. You will need to reverse the last two given equations (and change the sign of $\Delta H°$); you will also need to multiply the third equation ($\Delta H°$) by ½. Solve for EA.
Solution:
An analogous Born-Haber cycle has been described in Figure 8.7 for LiF. Use Hess's law and solve for the EA of fluorine:

$$\Delta H°$$

~~$K(s) \rightarrow K(g)$~~	90 kJ/mol
~~$K(g) \rightarrow K^+(g) + e^-$~~	419 kJ/mol
~~$1/2F_2(g) \rightarrow F(g)$~~	(1/2)(159 kJ/mol) = 79.5 kJ/mol
~~$F(g) + e^- \rightarrow F^-(g)$~~	? = EA
$KF(s) \rightarrow$ ~~$K(s) + 1/2F_2(g)$~~	569 kJ/mol (Reverse the reaction and change the sign of $\Delta H°$.)

$KF(s) \rightarrow K^+(g) + F^-(g)$	821 kJ/mol (Reverse the reaction and change the sign of $\Delta H°$.)

821 kJ/mol = 90 kJ/mol + 419 kJ/mol + 79.5 kJ/mol + EA + 569 kJ/mol
EA = 821 kJ/mol – (90 + 419 + 79.5 + 569) kJ/mol
EA = –336.5 kJ/mol= **–336 kJ/mol**

8.34   When two chlorine atoms are far apart, there is no interaction between them. Once the two atoms move closer together, the nucleus of each atom attracts the electrons on the other atom. As the atoms move closer this attraction increases, but the repulsion of the two nuclei also increases. When the atoms are very close together the repulsion between nuclei is much stronger than the attraction between nuclei and electrons. The final internuclear distance for the chlorine molecule is the distance at which maximum attraction is achieved in spite of the repulsion. At this distance, the energy of the molecule is at its lowest value.

8.35   The bond energy is the energy required to overcome the attraction between H atoms and Cl atoms in one mole of HCl molecules in the gaseous state. Energy input is needed to break bonds, so bond energy is always absorbed (endothermic) and $\Delta_{\text{bond breaking}}H°$ is positive. The same amount of energy needed to break the bond is released upon its formation, so $\Delta_{\text{bond forming}}H°$ has the same magnitude as $\Delta_{\text{bond breaking}}H°$, but opposite in sign (always exothermic and negative).

8.39   Plan: Bond strength increases as the atomic radii of atoms in the bond decrease; bond strength also increases as bond order increases.
Solution:
a) **I–I < Br–Br < Cl–Cl**. Atomic radii decrease up a group in the periodic table, so I is the largest and Cl is the smallest of the three.

b) **S–Br < S–Cl < S–H**. H has the smallest radius and Br has the largest, so the bond strength for S–H is the greatest and that for S–Br is the weakest.

c) **C–N < C=N < C≡N**. Bond strength increases as the number of electrons in the bond increases. The triple bond is the strongest and the single bond is the weakest.

8.41   Plan: Bond strength increases as the atomic radii of atoms in the bond decrease; bond strength also increases as bond order increases.
Solution:
a) The C=O bond (bond order = 2) is stronger than the C–O bond (bond order = 1).
b) O is smaller than C so the O–H bond is shorter and stronger than the C–H bond.

8.43   Reaction between molecules requires the breaking of existing bonds and the formation of new bonds. Substances with weak bonds are more reactive than are those with strong bonds because less energy is required to break weak bonds.

8.45   Plan: Write the combustion reactions of methane and of formaldehyde. The reactants requiring the smaller amount of energy to break bonds will have the greater heat of reaction. Examine the bonds in the reactant molecules that will be broken. In general, more energy is required to break double bonds than to break single bonds.
Solution:
For methane: $CH_4(g) + 2O_2(g) \rightarrow CO_2(g) + 2H_2O(l)$ which requires that 4 C–H bonds and 2 O=O bonds be broken and 2 C=O bonds and 4 O–H bonds be formed.
For formaldehyde: $CH_2O(g) + O_2(g) \rightarrow CO_2(g) + H_2O(l)$ which requires that 2 C–H bonds, 1 C=O bond, and 1 O=O bond be broken and 2 C=O bonds and 2 O–H bonds be formed.
Methane contains more C–H bonds and fewer C=O bonds than formaldehyde. Since C–H bonds take less energy to break than C=O bonds, more energy is released in the combustion of methane than of formaldehyde.

8.47   Plan: To find the heat of reaction, add the energy required to break all the bonds in the reactants to the energy released to form all bonds in the product. Remember to use a negative sign for the energy of the bonds formed since bond formation is exothermic. The bond energy values are found in Table 8.2.
Solution:
Reactant bonds broken:
1 x C=C =1(614 kJ/mol) =   614 kJ/mol
4 x C–H =4(413 kJ/mol) = 1652 kJ/mol
1 x Cl–Cl = (243 kJ/mol) =   243 kJ/mol
$$\Sigma\Delta_{\text{bonds broken}} H^\circ = 2509 \text{ kJ/mol}$$

Product bonds formed:
1 x C–C = (–347 kJ/mol) =   –347 kJ/mol
4 x C–H = 4(–413 kJ/mol) = –1652 kJ/mol
2 x C–Cl = 2(–339 kJ/mol = –678 kJ/mol
$$\Sigma\Delta_{\text{bonds formed}} H^\circ = -2677 \text{ kJ/mol}$$

$\Delta_r H^\circ = \Sigma\Delta_{\text{bonds broken}} H^\circ + \Sigma\Delta_{\text{bonds formed}} H^\circ = 2509$ kJ/mol $+ (-2677$ kJ/mol$) = $**–168 kJ/mol**

8.49   Plan: To find the heat of reaction, add the energy required to break all the bonds in the reactants to the energy released to form all bonds in the product. Remember to use a negative sign for the energy of the bonds formed since bond formation is exothermic. The bond energy values are found in Table 8.2.

Solution:
The reaction:

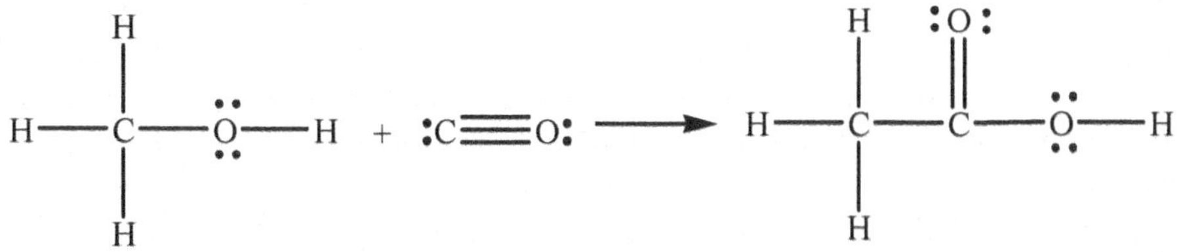

Reactant bonds broken:
1 x C–O = (358 kJ/mol) =   358 kJ/mol
3 x C–H = 3(413 kJ/mol) = 1239 kJ/mol
1 x O–H = (467 kJ/mol) =   467 kJ/mol
1 x C≡O = (1070 kJ/mol) =   1070 kJ/mol

$\Sigma\Delta_{bonds\ broken}H^° = 3134$ kJ/mol

Product bonds formed:
3 x C–H = 3(–413 kJ/mol) = –1239 kJ/mol
1 x C–C = (–347 kJ/mol) = –347 kJ/mol
1 x C=O = (–745 kJ/mol) = –745 kJ/mol
1 x C–O =)(–358 kJ/mol) = –358 kJ/mol
1 x O–H = (–467 kJ/mol) = –467 kJ/mol

$\Sigma\Delta_{bonds\ formed}H^° = -3156$ kJ/mol

$\Delta_r H^° = \Sigma\Delta_{bonds\ broken}H^° + \Sigma\Delta_{bonds\ formed}H^° = 3134$ kJ/mol + (–3156 kJ/mol) = **–22 kJ/mol**

8.50   Plan: To find the heat of reaction, add the energy required to break all the bonds in the reactants to the energy released to form all bonds in the product. Remember to use a negative sign for the energy of the bonds formed since bond formation is exothermic. The bond energy values are found in Table 8.2.
Solution:

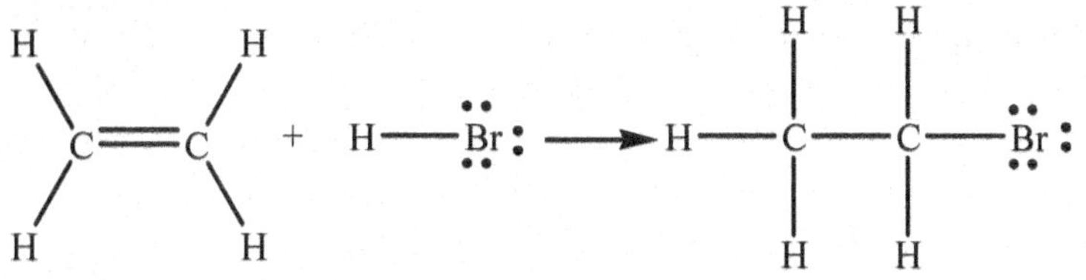

Reactant bonds broken:
1 x C=C = (614 kJ/mol) =   614 kJ/mol
4 x C–H = 4(413 kJ/mol) = 1652 kJ/mol
1 x H–Br = (363 kJ/mol) =   363 kJ/mol

$\Sigma\Delta_{bonds\ broken}H^°$ = 2629 kJ/mol

Product bonds formed:
5 x C–H = 5(–413 kJ/mol) = –2065 kJ/mol
1 x C–C = (–347 kJ/mol) = –347 kJ/mol
1 x C–Br = (–276 kJ/mol) = –276 kJ/mol

$\Sigma\Delta_{bonds\ formed}H^° = -2688$ kJ/mol

$\Delta_r H^° = \Sigma\Delta_{bonds\ broken}H^° + \Sigma\Delta_{bonds\ formed}H^° = 2629$ kJ/mol + (–2688 kJ/mol) = **–59 kJ/mol**

8.51   Electronegativity increases from left to right across a period (except for the noble gases) and increases from bottom to top within a group. Fluorine (F) and oxygen (O) are the two most electronegative elements. Cesium (Cs) and francium (Fr) are the two least electronegative elements.

8.53   Ionic bonds occur between two elements of very different electronegativity, generally
a metal with low electronegativity and a nonmetal with high electronegativity. Although electron sharing occurs
to a very small extent in some ionic bonds, the primary force in ionic bonds is attraction of opposite charges
resulting from electron transfer between the atoms. A nonpolar covalent bond occurs between two atoms with
identical electronegativity values where the sharing of bonding electrons is equal. A polar covalent bond is
between two atoms (generally nonmetals) of different electronegativities so that the bonding electrons are
unequally shared.
The H–O bond in water is **polar covalent**. The bond is between two nonmetals so it is covalent and not ionic, but
atoms with different electronegativity values are involved.

8.56   Plan: Electronegativity increases from left to right across a period (except for the noble gases) and increases from
bottom to top within a group.
Solution:
a) **Si < S < O**, sulfur is more electronegative than silicon since it is located further to the right in the table. Oxygen
is more electronegative than sulfur since it is located nearer the top of the table.
b) **Mg < As < P**, magnesium is the least electronegative because it lies on the left side of the periodic table and
phosphorus and arsenic on the right side. Phosphorus is more electronegative than arsenic because it is higher in
the table.

8.58   Plan: Electronegativity increases from left to right across a period (except for the noble gases) and increases from
bottom to top within a group.
Solution:
a) **N > P > Si**, nitrogen is above P in Group 15 and P is to the right of Si in Period 3.
b) **As > Ga > Ca**, all three elements are in Period 4, with As the rightmost element.

8.60   Plan: The polar arrow points toward the less electronegative atom. Electronegativity increases
from left to right across a period (except for the noble gases) and increases from bottom to top within a group.
Solution:

a) N ──── B   b) N ──── O   none c) C ──── S

d) S ──── O   e) N ──── H   f) Cl ──── O

8.62   Plan: The more polar bond will have a greater difference in electronegativity, $\Delta\chi$.
Solution:
a) N: $\chi = 3.0$; B: $\chi = 2.0$; $\Delta_a\chi = 3.0 - 2.0 = 1.0$
b) N: $\chi = 3.0$; O: $\chi = 3.5$; $\Delta_b\chi = 3.5 - 3.0 = 0.5$
c) C: $\chi = 2.5$; S: $\chi = 2.5$; $\Delta_c\chi = 2.5 - 2.5 = 0$
d) S: $\chi = 2.5$; O: $\chi = 3.5$; $\Delta_d\chi = 3.5 - 2.5 = 1.0$
e) N: $\chi = 3.0$; H: $\chi = 2.1$; $\Delta_e\chi = 3.0 - 2.1 = 0.9$
f) Cl: $\chi = 3.0$; O: $\chi = 3.5$; $\Delta_f\chi = 3.5 - 3.0 = 0.5$
(a), (d), and (e) have greater bond polarity.

8.64   Plan: Ionic bonds occur between two elements of very different electronegativity, generally a metal with low
electronegativity and a nonmetal with high electronegativity. Although electron sharing occurs to a very small
extent in some ionic bonds, the primary force in ionic bonds is attraction of opposite charges resulting from
electron transfer between the atoms. A nonpolar covalent bond occurs between two atoms with identical
electronegativity values where the sharing of bonding electrons is equal. A polar covalent bond is between two
atoms (generally nonmetals) of different electronegativities so that the bonding electrons are unequally shared.
For polar covalent bonds, the larger the $\Delta\chi$, the more polar the bond.
Solution:
a) Bonds in S_8 are **nonpolar covalent**. All the atoms are nonmetals so the substance is covalent and bonds are
nonpolar because all the atoms are of the same element and thus have the same electronegativity value. $\Delta\chi = 0$.

b) Bonds in RbCl are **ionic** because Rb is a metal and Cl is a nonmetal. $\Delta\chi$ is large.

c) Bonds in PF_3 are **polar covalent**. All the atoms are nonmetals so the substance is covalent. The bonds between P and F are polar because their electronegativity differs (by 1.9 units for P–F).

d) Bonds in SCl_2 are **polar covalent**. S and Cl are nonmetals and differ in electronegativity (by 0.5 units for S–Cl).

e) Bonds in F_2 are **nonpolar covalent**. F is a nonmetal. Bonds between two atoms of the same element are nonpolar since $\Delta\chi = 0$.

f) Bonds in SF_2 are **polar covalent**. S and F are nonmetals that differ in electronegativity (by 1.5 units for S–F).

Increasing bond polarity: $SCl_2 < SF_2 < PF_3$

8.66   Plan: Increasing ionic character occurs with increasing $\Delta\chi$. Electronegativity increases from left to right across a period (except for the noble gases) and increases from bottom to top within a group. The polar arrow points toward the less electronegative atom.

Solution:

a) H: $\chi = 2.1$; Cl: $\chi = 3.0$; Br: $\chi = 2.8$; I: $\chi = 2.5$

$\Delta_{HBr}\chi = 2.8 - 2.1 = 0.7$; $\Delta_{HCl}\chi = 3.0 - 2.1 = 0.9$; $\Delta_{HI}\chi = 2.5 - 2.1 = 0.4$

b) H: $\chi = 2.1$; O: $\chi = 3.5$; C: $\chi = 2.5$; F: $\chi = 4.0$

$\Delta_{HO}\chi = 3.5 - 2.1 = 1.4$; $\Delta_{CH}\chi = 2.5 - 2.1 = 0.4$; $\Delta_{HF}\chi = 4.0 - 2.1 = 1.9$

c) Cl: $\chi = 3.0$; S: $\chi = 2.5$; P: $\chi = 2.1$; Si: $\chi = 1.8$

$\Delta_{SCl}\chi = 3.0 - 2.5 = 0.5$; $\Delta_{PCl}\chi = 3.0 - 2.1 = 0.9$; $\Delta_{SiCl}\chi = 3.0 - 1.8 = 1.2$

a)   H——I   <   H——Br   <   H——Cl

b)   H——C   <   H——O   <   H——F

c)   S——Cl   <   P——Cl   <   Si——Cl

8.69   Plan: To be the central atom in a compound, an atom must be able to simultaneously bond to at least two other atoms.

Solution:

He, F, and H cannot serve as central atoms in a Lewis structure. Helium ($1s^2$) is a noble gas, and as such, it does not need to bond to any other atoms. Hydrogen ($1s^1$) and fluorine ($1s^2 2s^2 2p^5$) only need one electron to complete their valence shells. Thus, they can only bond to one other atom, and they do not have d orbitals available to expand their valence shells.

8.71   Plan: For an element to obey the octet rule it must be surrounded by eight electrons. To determine the number of electrons present, (1) count the individual electrons actually shown adjacent to a particular atom (lone pairs), and (2) add two times the number of bonds to that atom: number of electrons = individual electrons + 2(number of bonds).

Solution:

(a) $0 + 2(4) = 8$; (b) $2 + 2(3) = 8$; (c) $0 + 2(5) = 10$; (d) $2 + 2(3) = 8$; (e) $0 + 2(4) = 8$;
(f) $2 + 2(3) = 8$; (g) $0 + 2(3) = 6$; (h) $8 + 2(0) = 8$.

All the structures obey the octet rule except: c and g.

8.73   Plan: Count the valence electrons and draw Lewis structures.

Solution:

Total valence electrons: SiF_4: [1 x Si($4e^-$) + 4 x F($7e^-$)] = 32; $SeCl2$: [1 x Se($6e^-$)] + [2 x Cl($7e^-$)] = 20; COF_2: [1 x C($4e^-$)] + [1 x O($6e^-$)] + [2 x F($7e^-$)] = 24. The Si, Se, and the C are the central atoms, because these are the elements in their respective compounds with the lower group number (in addition, we are told C is central). Place the other atoms around the central atoms and connect each to the central atom with a single bond. SiF4: At this point, eight electrons ($2e^-$ in four Si–F bonds) have been used with $32 - 8 = 24$ remaining; the remaining electrons are placed around the fluorine atoms (three pairs each).   All atoms have an octet.

$SeCl_2$: The two bonds use $4e^-$ ($2e^-$ in two Se–Cl bonds) leaving $20 - 4 = 16e^-$. These $16e^-$ are used to complete the octets on Se and the Cl atoms.

COF_2: The three bonds to the C use $6e^-$ ($2e^-$ in three bonds) leaving $24 - 6 = 18 e^-$. These $18e^-$ are distributed to the surrounding atoms first to complete their octets. After the $18e^-$ are used, the central C is two electrons short of an octet. Forming a double bond to the O (change a lone pair on O to a bonding pair on C) completes the C octet.

(a) SiF_4 (b) $SeCl_2$

(c) COF_2

8.75   Plan: Count the valence electrons and draw Lewis structures.

Solution:

a) PF_3: $[1 \times P(5 e^-)] + [3 \times F(7e^-)] = 26$ valence electrons. P is the central atom. Draw single bonds from P to the three F atoms, using $2e^- \times 3$ bonds $= 6 e^-$. Remaining e^-: $26 - 6 = 20 e^-$. Distribute the $20 e^-$ around the P and F atoms to complete their octets.

b) H_2CO_3: $[2 \times H(1e^-)] + [1 \times C(4e^-) + 3 \times O(6e^-)] = 24$ valence electrons. C is the central atom with the H atoms attached to the O atoms. Place appropriate single bonds between all atoms using $2e^- \times 5$ bonds $= 10e^-$ so that $24 - 10 = 14e^-$ remain. Use these $14e^-$ to complete the octets of the O atoms (the H atoms already have their two electrons). After the $14e^-$ are used, the central C is two electrons short of an octet. Forming a double bond to the O that does not have an H bonded to it (change a lone pair on O to a bonding pair on C) completes the C octet.

c) CS_2: $[1 \times C(4e^-)] + [2 \times S(6e^-)] = 16$ valence electrons. C is the central atom. Draw single bonds from C to the two S atoms, using $2e^- \times 2$ bonds $= 4e^-$. Remaining e^-: $16 - 4 = 12e^-$. Use these $12e^-$ to complete the octets of the surrounding S atoms; this leaves C four electrons short of an octet. Form a double bond from each S to the C by changing a lone pair on each S to a bonding pair on C.

a) PF_3 (26 valence e^-)   b) H_2CO_3 (24 valence e^-)

c) CS_2 (16 valence e^-)

8.77   Plan: The problem asks for resonance structures, so there must be more than one answer for each part.
       Solution:
       a) NO_2^+ has $[1 \times N(5e^-)] + [2 \times O(6e^-)] - 1e^-$ (+ charge) = 16 valence electrons. Draw a single bond from N to
           each O, using $2e^- \times 2$ bonds = $4e^-$; $16 - 4 = 12e^-$ remain. Distribute these $12e^-$ to the O atoms to complete
           their octets.

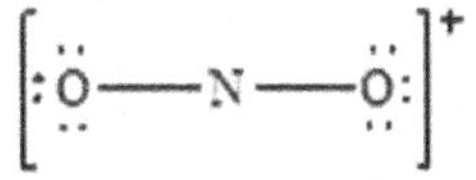

           This leaves N $4e^-$ short of an octet. Form a double bond from each O to the N by changing a lone pair on each
           O to a bonding pair on N. No resonance is required as all atoms can achieve an octet with double bonds.

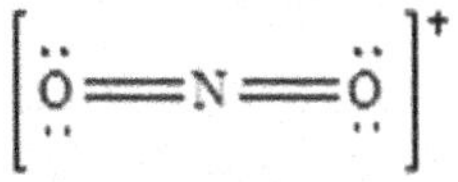

       b) NO_2F has $[1 \times N(5e^-)] + [2 \times O(6e^-)] + [1 \times F(7e^-)]$ = 24 valence electrons. Draw a single bond from N to
           each surrounding atom, using $2e^- \times 3$ bonds = $6e^-$; $24 - 6 = 18e^-$ remain. Distribute these $18e^-$ to the O and F
           atoms to complete their octets.

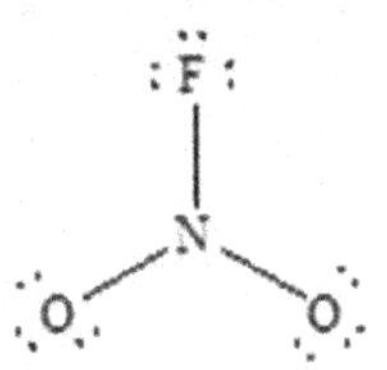

           This leaves N $2e^-$ short of an octet. Form a double bond from either O to the N by changing a lone pair on O
           to a bonding pair on N. There are two resonance structures since a lone pair from either of the two O atoms
           can be moved to a bonding pair with N:

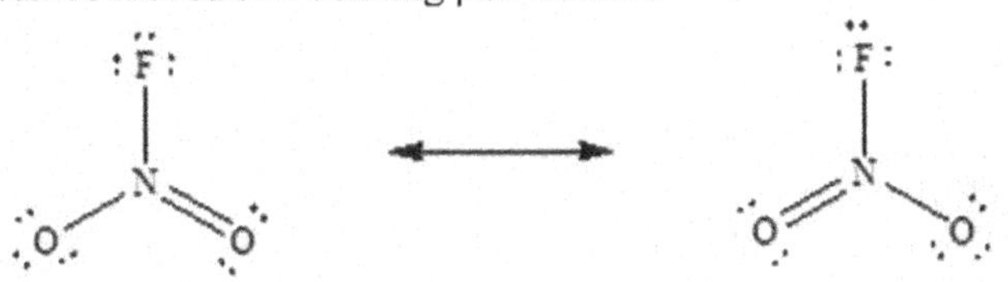

8.79   Plan: Count the valence electrons and draw Lewis structures. Additional structures are needed to show resonance.
       Solution:
       a) N_3^- has $[3 \times N(5e^-)] + [1 e^-(\text{from charge})]$ = 16 valence electrons. Place a single bond between the nitrogen
       atoms. This uses $2e^- \times 2$ bonds = 4 electrons, leaving $16 - 4 = 12$ electrons (6 pairs). Giving three pairs on each
       end nitrogen gives them an octet, but leaves the central N with only four electrons as shown below:

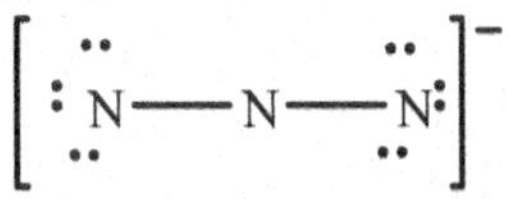

       The central N needs four electrons. There are three options to do this: (1) each of the end N atoms could form a
       double bond to the central N by sharing one of its pairs; (2) one of the end N atoms could form a triple bond by
       sharing two of its lone pairs; (3) the other end N atom could form the triple bond instead.

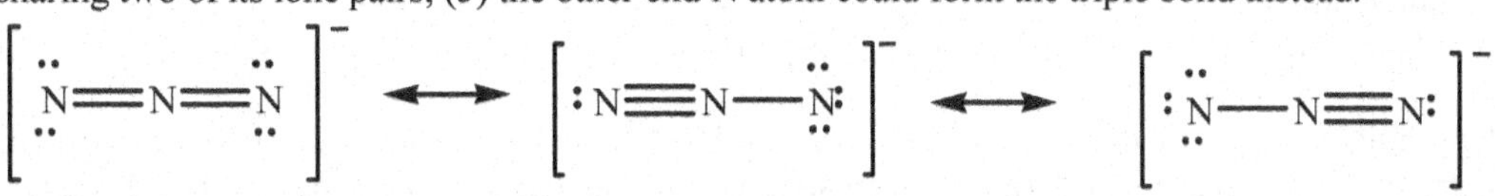

       b) NO_2^- has $[1 \times N(5e^-)] + [2 \times O(6e^-)] + [1 e^- \text{ (from charge)}]$ = 18 valence electrons. The nitrogen should be the
       central atom with each of the oxygen atoms attached to it by a single bond ($2e^- \times 2$ bonds = 4 electrons). This
       leaves $18 - 4 = 14$ electrons (seven pairs). If three pairs are given to each O and one pair is given to the N, then
       both O atoms have an octet, but the N atom only has six.

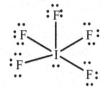

To complete an octet the N atom needs to gain a pair of electrons from one O atom or the other (form a double bond). The resonance structures are:

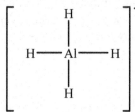

8.81   Plan: Initially, the method used in the preceding problems may be used to establish a Lewis structure. The total of the formal charges must equal the charge on an ion or be equal to 0 for a compound. The formal charge only needs to be calculated once for a set of identical atoms. Formal charge (FC) = no. of valence electrons − [no. of unshared valence electrons + ½ no. of shared valence electrons].
Solution:
a) IF_5 has $[1 \times I(7e^-)] + [5 \times F(7e^-)] = 42$ valence electrons. The presence of five F atoms around the central I means that the I atom will have a minimum of ten electrons; thus, this is an exception to the octet rule. The five I–F bonds use $2e^- \times 5$ bonds = 10 electrons leaving $42 − 10 = 32$ electrons (16 pairs). Each F needs three pairs to complete an octet. The five F atoms use fifteen of the sixteen pairs, so there is one pair left for the central I. This gives:

$$
\begin{array}{ccc}
 & :\!\ddot{F}\!\cdot & \\
:\!\ddot{F} & | & \ddot{F}: \\
 & I & \\
:\!\ddot{F} & | & \\
 & \ddot{F}: &
\end{array}
$$

Calculating formal charges:
FC = no. of valence electrons − [no. of unshared valence electrons + ½ no. of shared valence electrons].
For iodine: $FC_I = 7 − [2 + ½(10)] = 0$
For each fluorine: $FC_F = 7 − [6 + ½(2)] = 0$
Total formal charge = 0 = charge on the compound.

b) AlH_4^- has $[1 \times Al(3e^-)] + [4 \times H(1e^-)] + [1e^- \text{ (from charge)}] = 8$ valence electrons.
The four Al–H bonds use all the electrons and Al has an octet.

$$
\left[\begin{array}{c}
H \\
| \\
H\!-\!Al\!-\!H \\
| \\
H
\end{array}\right]^{-}
$$

FC = no. of valence electrons − [no. of unshared valence electrons + ½ no. of shared valence electrons].
For aluminum: $FC_{Al} = 3 − [0 + ½(8)] = −1$
For each hydrogen: $FC_H = 1 − [0 + ½(2)] = 0$

8.83   Plan: Initially, the method used in the preceding problems may be used to establish a Lewis structure. The total of the formal charges must equal the charge on an ion or be equal to 0 for a compound. The formal charge only needs to be calculated once for a set of identical atoms. Formal charge (FC) = no. of valence electrons − [no. of unshared valence electrons + ½ no. of shared valence electrons].
Solution:
a) CN^-: $[1 \times C(4e^-)] + [1 \times N(5e^-)] + [1 \ e^- \text{ from charge}] = 10$ valence electrons. Place a single bond between the carbon and nitrogen atoms. This uses $2e^- \times 1$ bond = 2 electrons, leaving $10 − 2 = 8$ electrons (four pairs). Giving three pairs of electrons to the nitrogen atom completes its octet but that leaves only one pair of electrons for the carbon atom which will not have an octet. The nitrogen could form a triple bond by sharing two of its lone pairs

with the carbon atom. A triple bond between the two atoms plus a lone pair on each atom satisfies the octet rule and uses all ten electrons.

$$\left[:C \equiv N: \right]^-$$

FC = no. of valence electrons – [no. of unshared valence electrons + ½ no. of shared valence electrons].
$FC_C = 4 – [2 + ½(6)] = –1;$ $FC_N = 5 – [2 + ½(6)] = 0$
Check: The total formal charge equals the charge on the ion (–1).

b) ClO^-: $[1 \times Cl(7e^-)] + [1 \times O(6e^-)] + [1e^-$ from charge$] = 14$ valence electrons. Place a single bond between the chlorine and oxygen atoms. This uses $2e^- \times 1$ bond $= 2$ electrons, leaving $14 – 2 = 12$ electrons (six pairs). Giving three pairs of electrons each to the carbon and oxygen atoms completes their octets.

$$\left[:\ddot{C}l - \ddot{O}: \right]^-$$

FC = no. of valence electrons – [no. of unshared valence electrons + ½ no. of shared valence electrons].
$FC_{Cl} = 7 – [6 + ½(2)] = 0$ $FC_O = 6 – [6 + ½(2)] = –1$
Check: The total formal charge equals the charge on the ion (–1).

8.85   Plan: The general procedure is similar to the preceding problems, plus the oxidation number determination.
Solution:
a) BrO_3^- has $[1 \times Br(7e^-)] + 3 \times O(6e^-)] + [1e^-$ (from charge)$] = 26$ valence electrons.
Placing the O atoms around the central Br and forming three Br–O bonds uses $2e^- \times 3$ bonds $= 6$ electrons and leaves $26 – 6 = 20$ electrons (ten pairs). Placing three pairs on each O ($3 \times 3 = 9$ total pairs) leaves one pair for the Br and yields structure I below. In structure I, all the atoms have a complete octet. Calculating formal charges:
$FC_{Br} = 7 – [2 + ½(6)] = +2$ $FC_O = 6 – [6 + ½(2)] = –1$
The FC_O is acceptable, but FC_{Br} is larger than is usually acceptable. Forming a double bond between any one of the O atoms gives structure II. Calculating formal charges:
$FC_{Br} = 7 – [2 + ½(8)] = +1$ $FC_O = 6 – [6 + ½(2)] = –1$ $FC_O = 6 – [4 + ½(4)] = 0$
                                                                                                                          (Double bonded O)
The FC_{Br} can be improved further by forming a second double bond to one of the other O atoms (structure III).
$FC_{Br} = 7 – [2 + ½(10)] = 0$ $FC_O = 6 – [6 + ½(2)] = –1$ $FC_O = 6 – [4 + ½(4)] = 0$
                                                                                                                          (Double bonded O atoms)

Structure III has the most reasonable distribution of formal charges.

                      I   II   III

Oxidation number = (No. of valence e-) – (no. of shared e- + no. of unshared e-)
(Note: when there are electrons in a bond, they are transferred completely to the more electronegative atom)

The oxidation numbers are: oxidation number of Br = +5 and oxidation number of O = –2.
                                                                                                                        +5 –2
Check: The total formal charge equals the charge on the ion (–1). BrO_3^-
b) SO_3^{2-} has $[1 \times S(6e^-)] + [3 \times O(6e^-)] + [2e^-$ (from charge)$] = 26$ valence electrons.
Placing the O atoms around the central S and forming three S–O bonds uses $2e^- \times 3$ bonds $= 6$ electrons and leaves $26 – 6 = 20$ electrons (ten pairs). Placing three pairs on each O ($3 \times 3 = 9$ total pairs) leaves one pair for the S and yields structure I below. In structure I all the atoms have a complete octet. Calculating formal charges:
$FC_S = 6 – [2 + ½(6)] = +1;$ $FC_O = 6 – [6 + ½(2)] = –1$

The FCO is acceptable, but FC$_S$ is larger than is usually acceptable. Forming a double bond between any one of the O atoms (structure II) gives:

FC$_S$ = 6 − [2 + ½(8)] = 0   FC$_O$ = 6 − [6 + ½(2)] = −1   FC$_O$ = 6 − [4 + ½(4)] = 0
(Double bonded O)

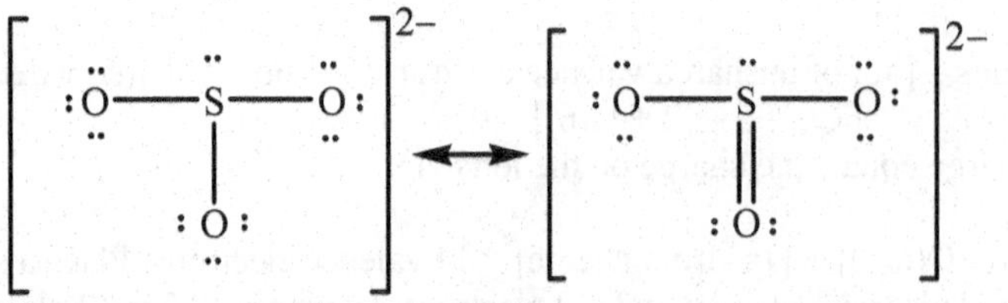

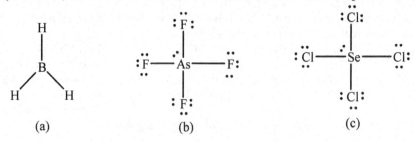

Structure II has the more reasonable distribution of formal charges.   +4 −2
The oxidation numbers (O.N.) are: O.N.$_S$ = +4 and O.N.$_O$ = −2.   SO$_3$$^{2-}$
Check: The total formal charge equals the charge on the ion (−2).

8.87   Plan: The octet rule states that when atoms bond, they share electrons to attain a filled outer shell of eight electrons. If an atom has fewer than eight electrons, it is electron deficient; if an atom has more than eight electrons around it, the atom has an expanded octet.
Solution:
a) BH$_3$ has [1 x B(3e$^-$)] + [3 x H(1e$^-$)] = 6 valence electrons. These are used in three B–H bonds. The B has six electrons instead of an octet; this molecule is **electron deficient**.
b) AsF$_4$– has [1 x As(5e$^-$)] +[4 x F(7e$^-$)] + [1e$^-$ (from charge)] = 34 valence electrons. Four As–F bonds use eight electrons leaving 34 − 8 = 26 electrons (13 pairs). Each F needs three pairs to complete its octet and the remaining pair goes to the As. The As has an **expanded octet** with ten electrons. The F cannot expand its octet.
c) SeCl$_4$ has [1 x Se(6e$^-$)] + 4 x Cl(7e$^-$)] = 34 valence electrons. The SeCl$_4$ is isoelectronic (has the same electron structure) as AsF4–, and so its Lewis structure looks the same. Se has an **expanded octet** of ten electrons.

(a)   (b)   (c)

8.89   Plan: The octet rule states that when atoms bond, they share electrons to attain a filled outer shell of eight electrons. If an atom has fewer than eight electrons, it is electron deficient; if an atom has more than eight electrons around it, the atom has an expanded octet.
Solution:
a) BrF$_3$ has [1 x Br(7e$^-$)] + [3 x F(7e$^-$)] = 28 valence electrons. Placing a single bond between Br and each F uses 2e$^-$ x 3 bonds = 6e$^-$, leaving 28 − 6 = 22 electrons (eleven pairs). After the F atoms complete their octets with three pairs each, the Br gets the last two lone pairs. The Br has an **expanded octet** of ten electrons.

b) ICl$_2$$^-$ has [1 x I(7e$^-$)] + [2 x Cl(7e$^-$)] + [1e$^-$ (from charge)] = 22 valence electrons. Placing a single bond between I and each Cl uses 2e$^-$ x 2 bond = 4e$^-$, leaving 22 − 4 = 18 electrons (nine pairs). After the Cl atoms complete their octets with three pairs each, the iodine finishes with the last three lone pairs. The iodine has an expanded octet of ten electrons.

c) BeF$_2$ has [1 x Be(2e$^-$)] + [2 x F(7e$^-$)] = 16 valence electrons. Placing a single bond between Be and each of the F atoms uses 2e$^-$ x 2 bonds = 4e$^-$, leaving 16 − 4 = 12 electrons (six pairs).The F atoms complete their octets with three pairs each, and there are no electrons left for the Be. Formal charges work against the formation of double bonds. Be, with only four electrons, is **electron deficient**.

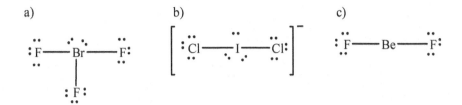

a)   b)   c)

8.91   Plan: Draw Lewis structures for the reactants and products.
Solution:
Beryllium chloride has the formula $BeCl_2$. $BeCl_2$ has $[1 \times Be(2e^-)] + [2 \times Cl(7e^-)] = 16$ valence electrons. Four of these electrons are used to place a single bond between Be and each of the Cl atoms, leaving $16 - 4 = 12$ electrons (six pairs). These six pairs are used to complete the octets of the Cl atoms, but Be does not have an octet – it is electron deficient.
Chloride ion has the formula Cl– with an octet of electrons.
$BeCl_4^{2-}$ has $[1 \times Be(2e^-)] + [4 \times Cl(7e^-)] + [2e^-$ (from charge)$] = 32$ valence electrons. Eight of these electrons are used to place a single bond between Be and each Cl atom, leaving $32 - 8 = 24$ electrons (twelve pairs). These twelve pairs complete the octet of the Cl atoms (Be already has an octet).

8.94   Plan: Use the structures in the text to determine the formal charges.
Formal charge (FC) = no. of valence electrons – [no. of unshared valence electrons + ½ no. of shared valence electrons].
Solution:
Structure **A**: $FC_C = 4 - [0 + ½(8)] = 0$; $FC_O = 6 - [4 + ½(4)] = 0$; $FC_{Cl} = 7 - [6 + ½(2)] = 0$
Total FC = 0
Structure **B**: $FC_C = 4 - [0 + ½(8)] = 0$; $FC_O = 6 - [6 + ½(2)] = -1$;
$FC_{Cl(double\ bonded)} = 7 - [4 + ½(4)] = +1$; $FC_{Cl(single\ bonded)} = 7 - [6 + ½(2)] = 0$
Total FC = 0
Structure **C**: $FC_C = 4 - [0 + ½(8)] = 0$; $FC_O = 6 - [6 + ½(2)] = -1$;
$FC_{Cl(double\ bonded)} = 7 - [4 + ½(4)] = +1$; $FC_{Cl(single\ bonded)} = 7 - [6 + ½(2)] = 0$
Total FC = 0
Structure **A** has the most reasonable set of formal charges.

8.95   a) A solid metal is a shiny solid that conducts heat, is malleable, and melts at high temperatures. (Other answers include relatively high boiling point and good conductor of electricity.)
b) Metals lose electrons to form positive ions

8.99   Plan: Write a balanced chemical reaction. The given heat of reaction is the sum of the energy required to break all the bonds in the reactants and the energy released to form all bonds in the product. Remember to use a negative sign for the energy of the bonds formed since bond formation is exothermic. The bond energy values are found in Table 8.2. Use the ratios from the balanced reaction between the heat of reaction and acetylene and between acetylene and CO_2 and O_2 to find the amounts needed. The ideal gas law is used to convert from moles of oxygen to volume of oxygen.
Solution:
a) $C_2H_2 + 5/2O_2 \rightarrow 2CO_2 + H_2O$ $\Delta_r H° = -1259$ kJ/mol
H–C≡C–H + 5/2O=O → 2O=C=O + H–O–H

$\Delta_r H^\circ = \Sigma\Delta_{\text{bonds broken}} H^\circ + \Sigma\Delta_{\text{bonds formed}} H^\circ$

$\Delta_r H^\circ = [2BE_{C-H} + BE_{C\equiv C} + 5/2BE_{O=O}] + [4(-BE_{C=O}) + 2(-BE_{O-H})]$

-1259 kJ/mol $= [2(413$ kJ/mol$) + BE_{C\equiv C} + 5/2(498$ kJ/mol$)] + [4(-799$ kJ/mol$) + 2(-467$ kJ/mol$)]$

-1259 kJ/mol $= [826$ kJ/mol $+ BE_{C\equiv C} + 1245$ kJ/mol$] + [-4130$kJ/mol$)]$

-1259 kJ/mol $= -2059$ kJ/mol $+ BE_{C\equiv C}$

$BE_{C\equiv C} = $ **800. kJ/mol**   Table 8.2 lists the value as 839 kJ/mol.

b) Heat (kJ) $= q = \left(500.0 \text{ g C}_2\text{H}_2\right)\left(\dfrac{1 \text{ mol C}_2\text{H}_2}{26.04 \text{ g C}_2\text{H}_2}\right)\left(\dfrac{-1259 \text{ kJ}}{1 \text{ mol C}_2\text{H}_2}\right) = -2.4174347\times10^4$ kJ $= $ **-2.417×10^4 kJ**

c) Mass (g) of $CO_2 = \left(500.0 \text{ g C}_2\text{H}_2\right)\left(\dfrac{1 \text{ mol C}_2\text{H}_2}{26.04 \text{ g C}_2\text{H}_2}\right)\left(\dfrac{2 \text{ mol CO}_2}{1 \text{ mol C}_2\text{H}_2}\right)\left(\dfrac{44.01 \text{ g CO}_2}{1 \text{ mol CO}_2}\right) = 1690.092$ g $= $ **1690 g CO_2**

d) Amount (mol) of $O_2 = \left(500.0 \text{ g C}_2\text{H}_2\right)\left(\dfrac{1 \text{ mol C}_2\text{H}_2}{26.04 \text{ g C}_2\text{H}_2}\right)\left(\dfrac{(5/2) \text{ mol O}_2}{1 \text{ mol C}_2\text{H}_2}\right) = 48.0030722$ mol O_2

$pV = nRT$

Volume (L) of $O_2 = \dfrac{nRT}{p} = \dfrac{\left(48.0030722 \text{ mol O}_2\right)\left(8.3144\dfrac{\text{L} \cdot \text{kPa}}{\text{mol} \cdot \text{K}}\right)(298 \text{ K})}{1823 \text{ kPa}} = 65.2423$ L $= $ **65.2 L O_2**

8.101   Plan: The heat of formation of MgCl is represented by the equation Mg(s) + 1/2Cl$_2$(g) → MgCl(s). Use Hess's law and arrange the given equations so that they sum up to give the equation for the heat of formation of MgCl. You will need to multiply the second equation by ½; you will need to reverse the equation for the lattice energy [MgCl(s) → Mg$^+$(g) + Cl$^-$(g)] and change the sign of the given lattice energy value. Negative heats of formation are energetically favored.
Solution:

a)   1) Mg(s) → ~~Mg(g)~~ $\Delta_1 H^\circ = 148$ kJ/mol

    2) 1/2Cl$_2$(g) → ~~Cl(g)~~ $\Delta_2 H^\circ = 1/2(243$ kJ/mol$) = 121.5$ kJ/mol

    3) ~~Mg(g)~~ → ~~Mg$^+$(g)~~ + e$^-$ $\Delta_3 H^\circ = 738$ kJ/mol

    4) ~~Cl(g)~~ + e$^-$ → ~~Cl$^-$(g)~~ $\Delta_4 H^\circ = -349$ kJ/mol

    5) ~~Mg$^+$(g)~~ + ~~Cl$^-$(g)~~ → MgCl(s) $\Delta_5 H^\circ = -783.5$ kJ/mol $(= - \Delta_{\text{lattice}} H^\circ$ (MgCl))
_____

    Mg(s) + 1/2Cl$_2$(g) → MgCl(s) $\Delta_f H^\circ$ (MgCl) = ?

$\Delta_f H^\circ$ (MgCl) $= \Delta_1 H^\circ + \Delta_2 H^\circ + \Delta_3 H^\circ + \Delta_4 H^\circ + \Delta_5 H^\circ$
                $= 148$ kJ/mol $+ 121.5$ kJ/mol $+ 738$ kJ/mol $+ (-349$ kJ/mol$) + (-783.5$ kJ/mol$)$
                $= -125$ kJ/mol

b) **Yes**, since $\Delta_f H^\circ$ for MgCl is negative, MgCl(s) is stable relative to its elements.

c) 2MgCl(s) → MgCl$_2$(s) + Mg(s)

$\Delta_r H^\circ = \Sigma m \Delta_{f(\text{products})} H^\circ - \Sigma n \Delta_{f(\text{reactants})} H^\circ$

$\Delta_r H^\circ = \{1 \Delta_f H^\circ$ [MgCl$_2$(s)] $+ 1 \Delta_f H^\circ$ [Mg(s)]$\} - \{2 \Delta_f H^\circ$ [MgCl(s)]$\}$

$\Delta_r H^\circ = [(-641.6$ kJ/mol$) + (0$ kJ/mol$)] - [2(-125$ kJ/mol$)]$

$\Delta_r H^\circ = -391.6$ kJ/mol $= $ **-392 kJ/mol**

d) **No**, $\Delta_f H^\circ$ for MgCl$_2$ is much more negative than that for MgCl. This makes the $\Delta_r H^\circ$ value for the above reaction very negative, and the formation of MgCl$_2$ would be favored.

8.103   <u>Plan:</u> Find the bond energy for an H–I bond from Table 8.2. For part a), calculate the wavelength with this energy using the relationship from Chapter 6: $E = hc/\lambda$. For part b), calculate the energy for a wavelength of 254 nm and then subtract the energy from part a) to get the excess energy.
For part c), speed can be calculated from the excess energy since $E_k = 1/2mu^2$.
<u>Solution:</u>
a) Bond energy for H–I is 295 kJ/mol (Table 8.2).

$$\text{Bond energy (J/photon)} = \left(\frac{295 \text{ kJ}}{\text{mol}}\right)\left(\frac{10^3 \text{ J}}{1 \text{ kJ}}\right)\left(\frac{1 \text{ mol}}{6.022\text{x}10^{23} \text{ photons}}\right) = 4.898705\text{x}10^{-19} \text{ J/photon}$$

$E = hc/\lambda$

$$\lambda \text{ (m)} = hc/E = \frac{\left(6.626\text{x}10^{-34} \text{ J}\bullet\text{s}\right)\left(3.00\text{x}10^8 \text{ m/s}\right)}{\left(4.898705\text{x}10^{-19} \text{ J}\right)} = 4.057807\text{x}10^{-7} \text{ m}$$

$$\lambda \text{ (nm)} = \left(4.057807\text{x}10^{-7} \text{ m}\right)\left(\frac{1 \text{ nm}}{10^{-9} \text{ m}}\right) = 405.7807 \text{ nm} = \textbf{406 nm}$$

b) E (HI) $= 4.898705\text{x}10^{-19}$ J

$$E \text{ (254 nm)} = hc/\lambda = \frac{\left(6.626\text{x}10^{-34} \text{ J}\bullet\text{s}\right)\left(3.00\text{x}10^8 \text{ m/s}\right)}{254 \text{ nm}}\left(\frac{1 \text{ nm}}{10^{-9} \text{ m}}\right) = 7.82598\text{x}10^{-19} \text{ J}$$

Excess energy $= 7.82598\text{x}10^{-19} \text{ J} - 4.898705\text{x}10^{-19} \text{ J} = 2.92728\text{x}10^{-19} \text{ J} = \textbf{2.93x10}^{\textbf{-19}} \textbf{ J}$

c) Mass (kg) of H $= \left(\frac{1.008 \text{ g H}}{\text{mol}}\right)\left(\frac{\text{mol}}{6.022\text{x}10^{23}}\right)\left(\frac{1 \text{ kg}}{10^3 \text{ g}}\right) = 1.67386\text{x}10^{-27} \text{ kg}$

$E_k = 1/2mu^2$ thus, $u = \sqrt{\dfrac{2E}{m}}$

$$u = \sqrt{\frac{2(2.92728\text{x}10^{-19} \text{ J})}{1.67386\text{x}10^{-27} \text{ kg}}\left(\frac{\text{kg}\bullet\text{m}^2/\text{s}^2}{\text{J}}\right)} = 1.8701965\text{x}10^4 \text{ m/s} = \textbf{1.87x10}^{\textbf{4}} \textbf{ m/s}$$

8.106   <u>Plan:</u> Find the appropriate bond energies in Table 8.2. Calculate the wavelengths using $E = hc/\lambda$.
<u>Solution:</u>
C–Cl bond energy = 339 kJ/mol

$$\text{Bond energy (J/photon)} = \left(\frac{339 \text{ kJ}}{\text{mol}}\right)\left(\frac{10^3 \text{ J}}{1 \text{ kJ}}\right)\left(\frac{1 \text{ mol}}{6.022\text{x}10^{23} \text{ photons}}\right) = 5.62936\text{x}10^{-19} \text{ J/photon}$$

$E = hc/\lambda$

$$\lambda \text{ (m)} = hc/E = \frac{\left(6.626\text{x}10^{-34} \text{ J}\bullet\text{s}\right)\left(3.00\text{x}10^8 \text{ m/s}\right)}{\left(5.62936\text{x}10^{-19} \text{ J}\right)} = 3.5311296\text{x}10^{-7} \text{ m} = \textbf{3.53x10}^{\textbf{-7}} \textbf{ m}$$

O_2 bond energy = 498 kJ/mol

$$\text{Bond energy (J/photon)} = \left(\frac{498 \text{ kJ}}{\text{mol}}\right)\left(\frac{10^3 \text{ J}}{1 \text{ kJ}}\right)\left(\frac{1 \text{ mol}}{6.022\text{x}10^{23} \text{ photons}}\right) = 8.269678\text{x}10^{-19} \text{ J/photon}$$

$E = hc/\lambda$

$$\lambda \text{ (m)} = hc/E = \frac{\left(6.626\text{x}10^{-34} \text{ J}\bullet\text{s}\right)\left(3.00\text{x}10^8 \text{ m/s}\right)}{\left(8.269678\text{x}10^{-19} \text{ J}\right)} = 2.40372\text{x}10^{-7} \text{ m} = \textbf{2.40x10}^{\textbf{-7}} \textbf{ m}$$

8.107 Plan: Write balanced chemical equations for the formation of each of the compounds. Obtain the bond energy of fluorine from Table 8.2 (159 kJ/mol). Determine the average bond energy from ΔH = bonds broken + bonds formed. Remember that the bonds formed (Xe–F) have negative values since bond formation is exothermic.
Solution:

$\Delta_r H° = \Sigma\Delta_{\text{bonds broken}} H° + \Sigma\Delta_{\text{bonds formed}} H°$

XeF_2 $Xe(g) + F_2(g) \rightarrow XeF_2(g)$

$\qquad\qquad \Delta_r H° = -105$ kJ/mol $= [(159$ kJ/mol$)] + [2(-Xe-F)]$

$\qquad\qquad -264$ kJ/mol $= 2(-Xe-F)$

$\qquad\qquad$ Xe–F = **132 kJ/mol**

XeF_4 $Xe(g) + 2F_2(g) \rightarrow XeF_4(g)$

$\qquad\qquad \Delta_r H° = -284$ kJ/mol $= [2(159$ kJ/mol$)] + [4(-Xe-F)]$

$\qquad\qquad -602$ kJ/mol $= 4(-Xe-F)$

$\qquad\qquad$ Xe–F = 150.5 kJ/mol = **150. kJ/mol**

XeF_6 $Xe(g) + 3F_2(g) \rightarrow XeF_6(g)$

$\qquad\qquad \Delta_r H° = -402$ kJ/mol $= [3(159$ kJ/mol$)] + [6(-Xe-F)]$

$\qquad\qquad -879$ kJ/mol $= 6(-Xe-F)$

$\qquad\qquad$ Xe–F = 146.5 kJ/mol = **146 kJ/mol**

8.109 a) The presence of the very electronegative fluorine atoms bonded to one of the carbon atoms in H_3C—CF_3 makes the C–C bond polar. This polar bond will tend to undergo heterolytic rather than homolytic cleavage. More energy is required to force heterolytic cleavage.
b) Since one atom gets both of the bonding electrons in heterolytic bond breakage, this results in the formation of ions. In heterolytic cleavage a cation is formed, involving ionization energy; an anion is also formed, involving electron affinity. The bond energy of the O_2 bond is 498 kJ/mol.
ΔH = (homolytic cleavage + electron affinity + first ionization energy)
ΔH = (498/2 kJ/mol + (–141 kJ/mol) + 1314 kJ/mol) = 1422 kJ/mol = **1420 kJ/mol**
It would require 1420 kJ to heterolytically cleave 1 mol of O_2.

8.112 Plan: The heat of formation of SiO_2 is represented by the equation $Si(s) + O_2(g) \rightarrow SiO_2(s)$. Use Hess's law and arrange the given equations so that they sum up to give the equation for the heat of formation. The lattice energy of SiO_2 is represented by the equation $SiO_2(s) \rightarrow Si^{4+}(g) + 2O^{2-}(g)$. You will need to reverse the lattice energy equation (and change the sign of $\Delta H°$); you will also need to multiply the fourth given equation by 2.
Solution:

Use Hess' law. $\Delta H_f°$ of SiO_2 is found in Appendix B.

1)	$Si(s) \rightarrow \cancel{Si(g)}$	$\Delta_1 H° = 454$ kJ/mol
2)	$\cancel{Si(g)} \rightarrow \cancel{Si^{4+}(g)} + \cancel{4e^-}$	$\Delta_2 H° = 9949$ kJ/mol
3)	$O_2(g) \rightarrow \cancel{2O(g)}$	$\Delta_3 H° = 498$ kJ/mol
4)	$\cancel{2O(g)} + \cancel{4e^-} \rightarrow \cancel{2O^{2-}(g)}$	$\Delta_4 H° = 2(737)$ kJ/mol
5)	$\cancel{Si^{4+}(g)} + \cancel{2O^{2-}(g)} \rightarrow SiO_2(s)$	$\Delta_5 H° = -\Delta_{\text{lattice}} H° (SiO_2) = ?$

$\qquad\qquad$ $Si(s) + O_2(g) \rightarrow SiO_2(s)$ $\qquad\qquad$ $\Delta_f H° (SiO_2) = -910.9$ kJ/mol

$\Delta_f H° = [\Delta_1 H° + \Delta_2 H° + \Delta_3 H° + \Delta_4 H° + (-\Delta_{\text{lattice}} H°)]$

-910.9 kJ/mol $= [454$ kJ/mol $+ 9949$ kJ/mol $+ 498$ kJ/mol $+ 2(737)$ kJ/mol $+ (-\Delta_{\text{lattice}} H°)]$

$-\Delta_{\text{lattice}} H° = -13,285.9$ kJ/mol

$\Delta_{\text{lattice}} H° = $ **13,286 kJ/mol**

8.114   Plan: Convert the bond energy in kJ/mol to units of J/photon. Use the equations $E = h\nu$, and
$E = hc/\lambda$ to find the frequency and wavelength of light associated with this energy.
Solution:

Bond energy (J/photon) = $\left(\dfrac{347 \text{ kJ}}{\text{mol}} \right)\left(\dfrac{10^3 \text{ J}}{1 \text{ kJ}} \right)\left(\dfrac{1 \text{ mol}}{6.022 \times 10^{23} \text{ photons}} \right)$ = 5.762205×10^{-19} J/photon

$E = h\nu$ or $\nu = \dfrac{E}{h}$

$\nu = \dfrac{E}{h} = \dfrac{5.762205 \times 10^{-19} \text{ J}}{6.626 \times 10^{-34} \text{ J} \cdot \text{s}}$ = 8.6963553×10^{14} s^{-1} = $\mathbf{8.70 \times 10^{14}}$ s^{-1}

$E = hc/\lambda$ or $\lambda = hc/E$

$\lambda \text{ (m)} = hc/E = \dfrac{\left(6.626 \times 10^{-34} \text{ J} \cdot \text{s} \right)\left(3.00 \times 10^8 \text{ m/s} \right)}{5.762205 \times 10^{-19} \text{ J}}$ = 3.44972×10^{-7} m = $\mathbf{3.45 \times 10^{-7}}$ **m**

This is in the **ultraviolet** region of the electromagnetic spectrum.

8.116   Plan: Write the balanced equations for the reactions. Determine the heat of reaction from
ΔH = bonds broken + bonds formed. Remember that the bonds formed have negative values since bond
formation is exothermic.
Solution:
a) $2CH_4(g) + O_2(g) \rightarrow CH_3OCH_3(g) + H_2O(g)$

$\Delta_r H^\circ = \Sigma \Delta_{\text{bonds broken}} H^\circ + \Sigma \Delta_{\text{bonds formed}} H^\circ$

$\Delta_r H^\circ = [8 \times (BE_{C-H}) + 1 \times (BE_{O=O})] + [6 \times (BE_{C-H}) + 2 \times (BE_{C-O}) + 2 \times (BE_{O-H})]$

$\Delta_r H^\circ = [8 \, (413 \text{ kJ/mol}) + (498 \text{ kJ/mol})]$
$\qquad\qquad\qquad\qquad + [6(-413 \text{ kJ/mol}) + 2(-358 \text{ kJ/mol}) + 2 \qquad (-467 \text{ kJ/mol})]$

$\Delta_r H^\circ = \mathbf{-326}$ **kJ/mol**

$2CH_4(g) + O_2(g) \rightarrow CH_3CH_2OH(g) + H_2O(g)$

$\Delta_r H^\circ = \Sigma \Delta_{\text{bonds broken}} H^\circ + \Sigma \Delta_{\text{bonds formed}} H^\circ$

$\Delta_r H^\circ = [8 \times (BE_{C-H}) + 1 \times (BE_{O=O})] + [5 \times (BE_{C-H}) + 1 \times (BE_{C-C}) + 1 \times (BE_{C-O}) + 3 \times (BE_{O-H})]$

$\Delta_r H^\circ = [8(413 \text{ kJ/mol}) + (498 \text{ kJ/mol})]$
$\qquad\qquad\qquad + [5(-413 \text{ kJ/mol}) + (-347 \text{ kJ/mol}) + (-358 \text{ kJ/mol}) + 3(-467 \text{ kJ/mol})]$

$\Delta_r H^\circ = \mathbf{-369}$ **kJ** /mol

b) The formation of gaseous **ethanol** is more exothermic.
c) The conversion reaction is $CH_3CH_2OH(g) \rightarrow CH_3OCH_3(g)$.
Use Hess's law:

$CH_3CH_2OH(g) + \cancel{H_2O(g)} \rightarrow \cancel{2CH_4(g)} + \cancel{O_2(g)}$ $\Delta_r H^\circ = -(-369 \text{ kJ}) = 369 \text{ kJ/mol}$

$\cancel{2CH_4(g)} + \cancel{O_2(g)} \rightarrow CH_3OCH_3(g) + \cancel{H_2O(g)}$ $\Delta_r H^\circ = -326 \text{ kJ/mol}$

$CH_3CH_2OH(g) \rightarrow CH_3OCH_3(g)$ $\Delta_r H^\circ = -326 \text{ kJ/mol} + 369 \text{ kJ/mol} = \mathbf{43}$ **kJ/mol**

8.118   Plan: The Lewis structures are needed to do this problem. A single bond (bond order = 1) is weaker and longer
than a double bond (bond order = 2) which is weaker and longer than a triple bond (bond order = 3). To find the
heat of reaction, add the energy required to break all the bonds in the reactants to the energy released to form all
bonds in the product. Remember to use a negative sign for the energy of the bonds formed since bond formation
is exothermic. The bond energy values are found in Table 8.2.
Solution:
a) The H atoms cannot be central, and they are evenly distributed on the N atoms.
N_2H_4 has $[2 \times N(5e^-)] + [4 \times H(1e^-)]$ = fourteen valence electrons, ten of which are used in the bonds between the
atoms. The remaining two pairs are used to complete the octets of the N atoms.

N_2H_2 has $[2 \times N(5e^-)] + (2 \times H(1e^-)] =$ twelve valence electrons, six of which are used in the bonds between the atoms. The remaining three pairs of electrons are not enough to complete the octets of both N atoms, so one lone pair is moved to a bonding pair between the N atoms.

N_2 has $[2 \times N(5\ e^-)] =$ ten valence electrons, two of which are used to place a single bond between the two N atoms. Since only four pairs of electrons remain and six pairs are required to complete the octets, two lone pairs become bonding pairs to form a triple bond.

Hydrazine   Diazene   Nitrogen

The **single (bond order = 1) N–N bond is weaker and longer** than any of the others are. The **triple bond (bond order = 3) is stronger and shorter** than any of the others. The **double bond (bond order = 2) has an intermediate strength and length**.

b) N_4H_4 has $[4 \times N(5e^-)] + [4 \times H(1e^-)] =$ twenty-four valence electrons, fourteen of which are used for single bonds between the atoms. When the remaining five pairs are distributed to complete the octets, one N atom lacks two electrons. A lone pair is moved to a bonding pair for a double bond.

Reactant bonds broken:

4 N–H = 4 (391 kJ/mol) = 1564 kJ /mol
2 N–N = 2 (160 kJ/mol) =   320 kJ/mol
1 N=N = (418 kJ/mol) =   418 kJ/mol

$$\Sigma\Delta_{\text{bonds broken}}H^\circ = 2302 \text{ kJ/mol}$$

Product bonds formed:

4 N–H = 4 (–391 kJ/mol) = –1564 kJ/mol
1 N–N = (–160 kJ/mol) =   –160 kJ/mol
1 N≡N = (–945 kJ/mol) = –945 kJ/mol

$$\Sigma\Delta_{\text{bonds formed}}H^\circ = -2669 \text{ kJ/mol}$$

$$\Delta_r H^\circ = \Sigma\Delta_{\text{bonds broken}}H^\circ + \Sigma\Delta_{\text{bonds formed}}H^\circ = 2302 \text{ kJ/mol} + (-2669 \text{ kJ/mol}) = \textbf{–367 kJ/mol}$$

8.122   Plan: Ethanol burns (combusts) with O_2 to produce CO_2 and H_2O. To find the heat of reaction in part a), add the energy required to break all the bonds in the reactants to the energy released to form all bonds in the product. Remember to use a negative sign for the energy of the bonds formed since bond formation is exothermic. The bond energy values are found in Table 8.2. The heat of vaporization of ethanol must be included for part b). The enthalpy change in part c) is the sum of the heats of formation of the products minus the sum of the heats of formation of the reactants. The calculation for part d) is the same as in part a).

Solution:

a) $CH_3CH_2OH(g) + 3O_2(g) \rightarrow 2CO_2(g) + 3H_2O(g)$

Reactant bonds broken:

1 x C–C = (347 kJ/mol) =   347 kJ/mol
5 x C–H = (5)(413 kJ/mol) = 2065 kJ/mol
1 x C–O = (358 kJ/mol) =   358 kJ/mol
1 x O–H = (467 kJ/mol) =   467 kJ/mol
3 x O=O = (3)(498 kJ/mol) = 1494 kJ/mol

$$\Sigma\Delta_{\text{bonds broken}}H^\circ = 4731 \text{ kJ/mol}$$

Product bonds formed:

4 x C=O = (4)(–799 kJ/mol) = –3196 kJ/mol
6 x O–H = (6)(–467 kJ/mol) = –2802 kJ/mol

$$\Sigma\Delta_{\text{bonds formed}}H^\circ = -5998 \text{ kJ/mol}$$

$\Delta_r H^\circ = \Sigma\Delta_{bonds\ broken}H^\circ + \Sigma\Delta_{bonds\ formed}H^\circ = 4731\ kJ/mol + (-5998\ kJ/mol) = $ **−1267 kJ/mol** (for each mole of ethanol burned).

b) If it takes 40.5 kJ/mol to vapourize the ethanol, part of the heat of combustion must be used to convert liquid ethanol to gaseous ethanol. The new value becomes:

$$\Sigma\Delta_{combustion(liquid)}H^\circ = -1267\ kJ/mol + (1)\cdot\left[\frac{40.5\ kJ}{1\ mol}\right] = -1226.5\ kJ/mol = \textbf{−1226 kJ/mol}$$ (of liquid ethanol

burned)

c) $\Delta_r H^\circ = \Sigma m\Delta_{f(products)}H^\circ - \Sigma n\Delta_{f(reactants)}H^\circ$

$\Delta_r H^\circ = \{2\,\Delta_f H^\circ\,[CO_2(g)] + 3\,\Delta_f H^\circ\,[H_2O(g)]\} - \{1\,\Delta_f H^\circ\,[C_2H_5OH(l)] + 3\,\Delta_f H^\circ\,[O_2(g)]\}$

$\quad = [(2)(-393.5\ kJ/mol) + (3)(-241.826\ kJ/mol)] - [(-277.63\ kJ/mol)$
$\quad\quad + 3\ (0\ kJ/mol)]$
$\quad = -1234.848\ kJ/mol = \textbf{−1234.8 kJ/mol}$

The two answers differ by less than 10 kJ/mol. This is a very good agreement since average bond energies were used to calculate the answers in a) and b).

d) $C_2H_4(g) + H_2O(g) \rightarrow CH_3CH_2OH(g)$

The Lewis structures for the reaction are:

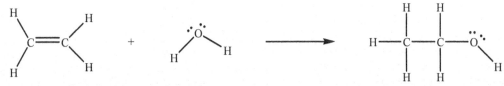

Reactant bonds broken:
1 x C=C =)(614 kJ/mol) =   614 kJ/mol
4 x C–H = (4)(413 kJ/mol) = 1652 kJ/mol
2 x O–H = (2)(467 kJ/mol) = 934 kJ/mol

$\quad\quad\quad \Sigma\Delta_{bonds\ broken}H^\circ = 3200\ kJ/mol$

Product bonds formed:
1 x C–C = (−347 kJ/mol) =   −347 kJ/mol
5 x C–H = (5)(−413 kJ/mol) = −2065 kJ/mol
1 x C–O = (−358 kJ/mol) =   −358 kJ/mol
1 x O–H = (−467 kJ/mol) =   −467 kJ/mol

$\quad\quad\quad \Sigma\Delta_{bonds\ formed}H^\circ = -3237\ kJ/mol$

$\Delta_r H^\circ = \Sigma\Delta_{bonds\ broken}H^\circ + \Sigma\Delta_{bonds\ formed}H^\circ = 3200\ kJ/mol + (-3237\ kJ/mol) = $ **−37 kJ/mol**

8.124   Plan: Determine the empirical formula from the percent composition (assuming 100 g of compound). Use the titration data to determine the mole ratio of acid to the NaOH. This ratio gives the amount of acidic H atoms in the formula of the acid. Finally, combine this information to construct the Lewis structure.
Solution:

$$\text{Moles of H} = (2.24\ g\ H)\left(\frac{1\ mol}{1.008\ g\ H}\right) = 2.222\ mol\ H$$

$$\text{Moles of C} = (26.7\ g\ C)\left(\frac{1\ mol}{12.01\ g\ C}\right) = 2.223\ mol\ C$$

$$\text{Moles of O} = (71.1\ g\ O)\left(\frac{1\ mol}{16.00\ g\ O}\right) = 4.444\ mol\ O$$

The preliminary formula is $H_{2.222}C_{2.223}O_{4.444}$.
Dividing all subscripts by the smallest subscript to obtain integer subscripts:

$$\frac{H_{2.222}}{2.222}\frac{C_{2.223}}{2.222}\frac{O_{4.444}}{2.222} = HCO_2$$

The empirical formula is HCO_2.

To determine the molecular formula, calculate the amount of NaOH required for the titration:

$$\text{mmoles of NaOH} = (50.0 \text{ mL})\left(\frac{0.040 \text{ mol NaOH}}{L}\right)\left(\frac{1000 \text{ mmol}}{mol}\right)\left(\frac{1 \text{ L}}{1000 \text{ mL}}\right) = 2.0 \text{ mmol NaOH}$$

Thus, the ratio is 2.0 mmole base/1.0 mmole acid, or each acid molecule has two hydrogen atoms to react (diprotic). The empirical formula indicates a monoprotic acid, so the formula must be doubled to: $H_2C_2O_4$. $H_2C_2O_4$ has $[2 \times H(1e^-)] + [2 \times C(4e^-)] + [4 \times O(6e^-)] = 34$ valence electrons to be used in the Lewis structure. Fourteen of these electrons are used to bond the atoms with single bonds, leaving $34 - 14 = 20$ electrons or ten pairs of electrons. When these ten pairs of electrons are distributed to the atoms to complete octets, neither C atom has an octet; a lone pair from the oxygen without hydrogen is changed to a bonding pair on C.

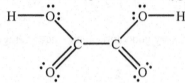

8.127   Plan: Write the balanced chemical equations for the reactions and draw the Lewis structures. To find the heat of reaction, add the energy required to break all the bonds in the reactants to the energy released to form all bonds in the product. Remember to use a negative sign for the energy of the bonds formed since bond formation is exothermic. The bond energy values are found in Table 8.2. Divide the heat of reaction by the amount of moles of oxygen gas appearing in each reaction to get the heat of reaction per mole of oxygen.
Solution:

$$CH_4(g) + 2O_2(g) \rightarrow CO_2(g) + 2H_2O(g)$$

Reactant bonds broken:
4 x C–H = (4)(413 kJ/mol) =   1652 kJ/mol
2 x O=O = (2)(498 kJ/mol) =   996 kJ/mol
$$\Sigma \Delta H^{\circ}_{\text{bonds broken}} = 2648 \text{ kJ/mol}$$

Product bonds formed:
2 x C=O = (2)(–799 kJ/mol) = –1598 kJ/mol
4 x O–H = (4)(–467 kJ/mol) = –1868 kJ/mol
$$\Sigma \Delta H^{\circ}_{\text{bonds formed}} = -3466 \text{ kJ/mol}$$

$$\Delta_r H^{\circ} = \Sigma \Delta_{\text{bonds broken}} H^{\circ} + \Sigma \Delta_{\text{bonds formed}} H^{\circ}$$
$$= 2648 \text{ kJ/mol} + (-3466 \text{ kJ/mol})$$
$$= -818 \text{ kJ/mol} \quad \text{Per mole of O}_2$$
$$= -818 \text{ kJ/mol} /2$$
$$= \mathbf{-409 \text{ kJ/mol O}_2}$$

$$2H_2S(g) + 3O_2(g) \rightarrow 2SO_2(g) + 2H_2O(g)$$

Reactant bonds broken:
4 x S–H = (4)(347 kJ/mol) = 1388 kJ/mol
3 x O=O = (3)(498 kJ/mol) = 1494 kJ/mol
$$\Sigma \Delta H^{\circ}_{\text{bonds broken}} = 2882 \text{ kJ/mol}$$

Product bonds formed:
4 x S=O = (4)(–552 kJ/mol) = –2208 kJ/mol
4 x O–H = (4)(–467 kJ/mol) = –1868 kJ/mol
$$\Sigma \Delta H^{\circ}_{\text{bonds formed}} = -4076 \text{ kJ/mol}$$

$$\Delta_r H^{\circ} = \Sigma\Delta_{\text{bonds broken}} H^{\circ} + \Sigma\Delta_{\text{bonds formed}} H^{\circ} = 2882 \text{ kJ/mol} + (-4076 \text{ kJ/mol})$$
$$= -1194 \text{ kJ/per mole of } O_2$$
$$= -(1194 \text{ kJ/mol})/3$$
$$= \mathbf{-398 \text{ kJ/mol } O_2}$$

8.129   Plan: Draw the Lewis structure of the OH species. The standard enthalpy of formation is the sum of the energy required to break all the bonds in the reactants and the energy released to form all bonds in the product. Remember to use a negative sign for the energy of the bonds formed since bond formation is exothermic. The bond energy values are found in Table 8.2.
Solution:
a) The OH molecule has [1 x O(6e⁻)] + [1 x H(1e⁻)] = 7 valence electrons to be used in the Lewis structure. Two of these electrons are used to bond the atoms with a single bond, leaving 7 – 2 = 5 electrons. Those five electrons are given to oxygen. But no atom can have an octet, and one electron is left unpaired. The Lewis structure is:

$$\cdot \ddot{O}\!\!-\!\!-H$$

b) The formation reaction is: $1/2 O_2(g) + 1/2 H_2(g) \rightarrow OH(g)$. The heat of reaction is:
$$\Delta_r H^{\circ} = \Sigma\Delta_{\text{bonds broken}} H^{\circ} + \Sigma\Delta_{\text{bonds formed}} H^{\circ} = 39.0 \text{ kJ}$$
[½ (BE$_{O=O}$) + ½ (BE$_{H-H}$)] + [BE$_{O-H}$] = 39.0 kJ/mol
[(½)(498 kJ/mol) + (½)(432 kJ/mol)] + [BE$_{O-H}$] = 39.0 kJ/mol
465 kJ/mol + [BE$_{O-H}$] = 39.0 kJ/mol
BE$_{O-H}$ = **–426 kJ/mol or 426 kJ/mol**
c) The average bond energy (from the bond energy table) is 467 kJ/mol. There are two O–H bonds in water for a total of 2 x 467 kJ/mol = 934 kJ/mol. The answer to part b) accounts for 426 kJ/mol of this, leaving:
934 kJ/mol – 426 kJ/mol = **508 kJ/mol**

8.132   Plan: Count the valence electrons and draw Lewis structures for the resonance forms.
Solution:
The $H_2C_2O_4$ molecule has [2 x H(1e⁻)] + [2 x C(4e⁻)] + [4 x O(6e⁻)] = 34 valence electrons to be used in the Lewis structure. Fourteen of these electrons are used to bond the atoms with a single bond, leaving 34 –14 = 20 electrons. If these twenty electrons are given to the oxygen atoms to complete their octet, the carbon atoms do not have octets. A lone pair from each of the oxygen atoms without hydrogen is changed to a bonding pair on C. The $HC_2O_4^-$ ion has [1 x H(1e⁻)] + [2 x C(4e⁻)] + [4 x O(6e⁻)] + [1e⁻ (from the charge)] = 34 valence electrons to be used in the Lewis structure. Twelve of these electrons are used to bond the atoms with a single bond, leaving 34 –12 = 22 electrons. If these twenty-two electrons are given to the oxygen atoms to complete their octet, the carbon atoms do not have octets. A lone pair from two of the oxygen atoms without hydrogen is changed to a bonding pair on C. There are two resonance structures.
The $C_2O_4^{2-}$ ion has [2 x C(4e⁻)] + [4 x O(6e⁻)] + [2e⁻ (from the charge)] = 34 valence electrons to be used in the Lewis structure. Ten of these electrons are used to bond the atoms with a single bond, leaving 34 –10 = 24 electrons. If these twenty-four electrons are given to the oxygen atoms to complete their octets, the carbon atoms do not have octets. A lone pair from two oxygen atoms is changed to a bonding pair on C. There are four resonance structures.

$H_2C_2O_4$:

$HC_2O_4^-$:

$C_2O_4^{2-}$:

In $H_2C_2O_4$, there are two shorter C=O bonds and two longer, weaker C—O bonds.

In $HC_2O_4^-$, the C—O bonds on the side retaining the H remain as one long C—O bond and one shorter, stronger C=O bond. The C—O bonds on the other side of the molecule have resonance forms with an average bond order of 1.5, so they are intermediate in length and strength.

In $C_2O_4^{2-}$, all the carbon to oxygen bonds are resonating and have an average bond order of 1.5.

8.135   Plan: Draw the Lewis structures. Calculate the heat of reaction using the bond energies in Table 8.2.
Solution:

$$SO_3(g) + H_2SO_4(l) \rightarrow H_2S_2O_7(l)$$

Reactant bonds broken:
5 x S=O = (5)(552 kJ/mol) = 2760 kJ/mol
2 x S–O = (2)(265 kJ/mol) =   530 kJ/mol
2 x O–H = (2)(467 kJ/mol) =   934 kJ/mol

$$\Sigma\Delta_{bonds\ broken} H° = 4224\ kJ/mol$$

Product bonds formed:
4 x S=O = (4)(–552 kJ/mol) = –2208 kJ/mol
4 x S–O = (4)(–265 kJ/mol) = –1060 kJ/mol
2 x O–H = (2)(–467 kJ/mol) =   –934 kJ/mol

$$\Sigma\Delta_{bonds\ formed} H° = -4202\ kJ/mol$$

$$\Delta_r H° = \Sigma\Delta_{bonds\ broken} H° + \Sigma\Delta_{bonds\ formed} H° = 4224\ kJ/mol + (-4202\ kJ/mol) = \mathbf{22\ kJ/mol}$$

CHAPTER 9 THE SHAPES OF MOLECULES

CHEMICAL CONNECTIONS BOXED READING PROBLEMS

B9.1   Plan: Examine the Lewis structure, noting the number of regions of electron density around the carbon and nitrogen atoms in the two resonance structures. The molecular shape is determined by the number of electron regions. An electron region is any type of bond (single, double, or triple) and an unshared pair of electrons.
Solution:
Resonance structure on the left:
Carbon has three electron regions (two single bonds and one double bond); three electron regions are arranged in a trigonal planar arrangement. The molecular shape around the C atom is **trigonal planar**. Nitrogen has four electron regions (three single bonds and an unshared pair of electrons); the four electron regions are arranged tetrahedrally; since one corner of the tetrahedron is occupied by an unshared electron pair, the shape around N is **trigonal pyramidal**.
Resonance structure on the right:
This C atom also has three electrons regions (two single bond and one double bond) so the molecular shape is again **trigonal planar**. The N atom also has three electron regions (two single bonds and one double bond); the molecular shape is **trigonal planar**.

END–OF–CHAPTER PROBLEMS

9.2   The molecular shape and the electron-group arrangement are the same when there are no lone pairs on the central atom.

9.4   Plan: Examine a list of all possible structures, and choose the ones with four electron groups since the tetrahedral electron-group arrangement has four electron groups.
Solution:
Tetrahedral AX_4
Trigonal pyramidal AX_3E
Bent or V shaped AX_2E_2

9.6   Plan: Begin with the basic structures and redraw them.
Solution:
a) A molecule that is V shaped has two bonds and generally has either one (AX_2E) or two (AX_2E_2) lone electron pairs.
b) A trigonal planar molecule follows the formula AX_3 with three bonds and no lone electron pairs.
c) A trigonal bipyramidal molecule contains five bonding pairs (single bonds) and no lone pairs (AX_5).
d) A T-shaped molecule has three bonding groups and two lone pairs (AX_3E_2).
e) A trigonal pyramidal molecule follows the formula AX_3E with three bonding pairs and one lone pair.
f) A square pyramidal molecule shape follows the formula AX_5E with five bonding pairs and one lone pair.

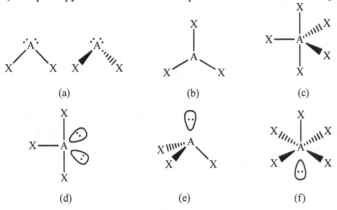

9-1

9.8   Plan: First, draw a Lewis structure, and then apply VSEPR.
Solution:
a) O_3: The molecule has $[3 \times O(6e^-)] = 18$ valence electrons. Four electrons are used to place single bonds between the oxygen atoms, leaving $18 - 4 = 14e^-$ (seven pairs). Six pairs are required to give the end oxygen atoms an octet; the last pair is distributed to the central oxygen, leaving this atom two electrons short of an octet. Form a double bond from one of the end O atoms to the central O by changing a lone pair on the end O to a bonding pair on the central O. This gives the following Lewis structure:

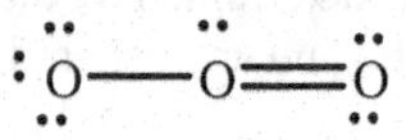

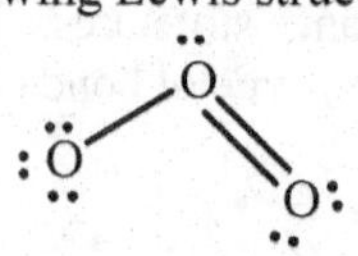

There are three electron groups around the central O, one of which is a lone pair. This gives a **trigonal planar** electron-group arrangement (AX_2E), a **bent** molecular shape, and an ideal bond angle of **120°**.

b) H_3O^+: This ion has $[3 \times H(1e^-)] + [1 \times O(6e^-)] - [1e^-$ (due to + charge)] = eight valence electrons. Six electrons are used to place a single bond between O and each H, leaving $8 - 6 = 2e^-$ (one pair). Distribute this pair to the O atom, giving it an octet (the H atoms only get two electrons). This gives the following Lewis structure:

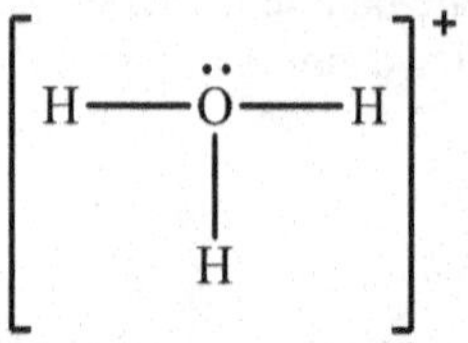

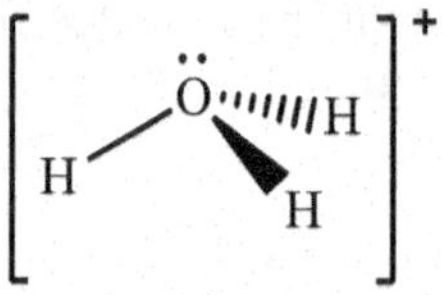

There are four electron groups around the O, one of which is a lone pair. This gives a **tetrahedral** electron-group arrangement (AX_3E), a **trigonal pyramidal** molecular shape, and an ideal bond angle of **109.5°**.

c) NF_3: The molecule has $[1 \times N(5e^-)] + [3 \times F(7e^-)] = 26$ valence electrons. Six electrons are used to place a single bond between N and each F, leaving $26 - 6 = 20$ e^- (ten pairs). These ten pairs are distributed to all of the F atoms and the N atoms to give each atom an octet. This gives the following Lewis structure:

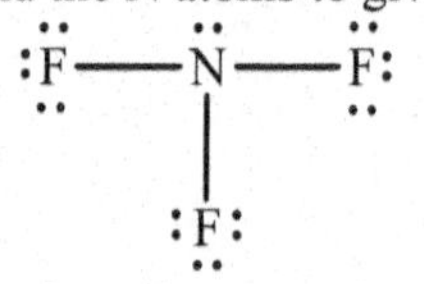

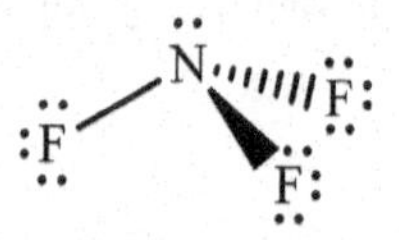

There are four electron groups around the N, one of which is a lone pair. This gives a **tetrahedral** electron-group arrangement (AX_3E), a **trigonal pyramidal** molecular shape, and an ideal bond angle of **109.5°**.

9.10   Plan: First, draw a Lewis structure, and then apply VSEPR.
Solution:
(a) CO_3^{2-}: This ion has $[1 \times C(4e^-)] + [3 \times O(6e^-)] + [2e^-$ (from charge)] = 24 valence electrons. Six electrons are used to place single bonds between C and each O atom, leaving $24 - 6 = 18$ e^- (nine pairs). These nine pairs are used to complete the octets of the three O atoms, leaving C two electrons short of an octet. Form a double bond from one of the O atoms to C by changing a lone pair on an O to a bonding pair on C. This gives the following Lewis structure:

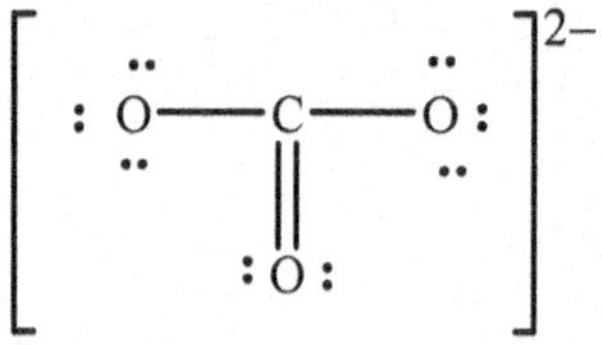

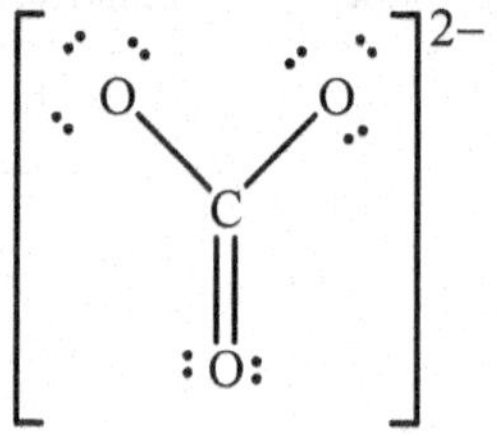

There are two additional resonance forms. There are three groups of electrons around the C, none of which are lone pairs. This gives a **trigonal planar** electron-group arrangement (AX_3), a **trigonal planar** molecular shape, and an ideal bond angle of **120°**.

(b) SO_2: This molecule has $[1 \times S(6e^-)] + [2 \times S(6e^-)] = 18$ valence electrons. Four electrons are used to place a single bond between S and each O atom, leaving $18 - 4 = 14e^-$ (seven pairs). Six pairs are needed to complete the octets of the O atoms, leaving a pair of electrons for S. S needs one more pair to complete its octet. Form a double bond from one of the end O atoms to the S by changing a lone pair on the O to a bonding pair on the S. This gives the following Lewis structure:

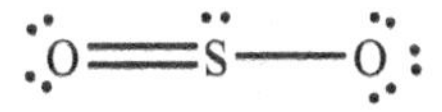

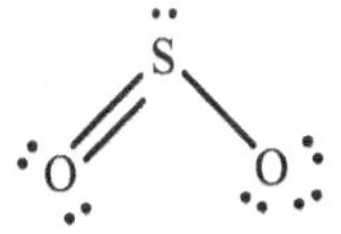

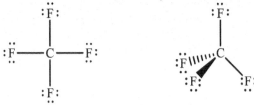

There are three groups of electrons around the C, one of which is a lone pair.
This gives a **trigonal planar** electron-group arrangement (AX_2E), a **bent (V-shaped)** molecular shape, and an ideal bond angle of **120°**.
(c) CF_4: This molecule has $[1 \times C(4e^-)] + [4 \times F(7e^-)] = 32$ valence electrons. Eight electrons are used to place a single bond between C and each F, leaving $32 - 8 = 24 \ e^-$ (twelve pairs). Use these twelve pairs to complete the octets of the F atoms (C already has an octet). This gives the following Lewis structure:

There are four groups of electrons around the C, none of which is a lone pair.
This gives a **tetrahedral** electron-group arrangement (AX_4), a **tetrahedral** molecular shape, and an ideal bond angle of **109.5°**.

9.12   Plan: Examine the structure shown, and then apply VSEPR.
Solution:
a) This structure shows three electron groups with three bonds around the central atom.
There appears to be no distortion of the bond angles so the shape is **trigonal planar**, the classification is AX_3, with an ideal bond angle of **120°**.
b) This structure shows three electron groups with three bonds around the central atom.
The bonds are distorted down indicating the presence of a lone pair. The shape of the molecule is **trigonal pyramidal** and the classification is AX_3E, with an ideal bond angle of **109.5°**.
c) This structure shows five electron groups with five bonds around the central atom.
There appears to be no distortion of the bond angles so the shape is **trigonal bipyramidal** and the classification is AX_5, with ideal bond angles of **90°** and **120°**.

9.14   Plan: The Lewis structures must be drawn, and VSEPR applied to the structures. Lone pairs on the central atom generally result in a deviation of the ideal bond angle.
Solution:
a) The ClO_2^- ion has $[1 \times Cl(7e^-)] + [2 \times O(6e^-)] + [1e^- \text{ (from charge)}] = 20$ valence electrons. Four electrons are used to place a single bond between the Cl and each O, leaving $20 - 4 = 16$ electrons (eight pairs). All eight pairs are used to complete the octets of the Cl and O atoms. There are two bonds (to the O atoms) and two lone pairs on the Cl for a total of four electron groups (AX_2E_2). The structure is based on a tetrahedral electron-group arrangement with an ideal bond angle of **109.5°**. The shape is **bent** (or V shaped). The presence of the lone pairs will cause the remaining angles to be **less than 109.5°**.
b) The PF_5 molecule has $[1 \times P(5 \ e^-)] + [5 \times F(7 \ e^-)] = 40$ valence electrons. Ten electrons are used to place single bonds between P and each F atom, leaving $40 - 10 = 30 \ e^-$ (fifteen pairs). The fifteen pairs are used to complete the octets of the F atoms. There are five bonds to the P and no lone pairs (AX_5). The electron-group arrangement and the shape is **trigonal bipyramidal**. The ideal bond angles are **90°** and **120°**. The absence of lone pairs means the **angles are ideal**.
c) The SeF_4 molecule has $[1 \times Se(6e^-)] + [4 \times F(7e^-)] = 34$ valence electrons. Eight electrons are used to place single bonds between Se and each F atom, leaving $34 - 8 = 26e^-$ (thirteen pairs). Twelve pairs are used to complete the octets of the F atoms which leaves one pair of electrons. This pair is placed on the central Se atom. There are four bonds to the Se which also has a lone pair (AX_4E). The structure is based on a trigonal bipyramidal

structure with ideal angles of **90° and 120°**. The shape is **seesaw**. The presence of the lone pairs means the angles are **less than ideal**.

d) The KrF_2 molecule has $[1 \times Kr(8e^-)] + [2 \times F(7e^-)] = 22$ valence electrons. Four electrons are used to place a single bond between the Kr atom and each F atom, leaving $22 - 4 = 18\ e^-$ (nine pairs). Six pairs are used to complete the octets of the F atoms. The remaining three pairs of electrons are placed on the Kr atom. The Kr is the central atom. There are two bonds to the Kr and three lone pairs (AX_2E_3). The structure is based on a trigonal bipyramidal structure with ideal angles of 90° and 120°. The shape is **linear**. The placement of the F atoms makes their ideal bond angle to be $2 \times 90° = \mathbf{180°}$. The placement of the lone pairs is such that they cancel each other's repulsion, thus the actual **bond angle is ideal**.

a)   b)   c)   d)

9.16   Plan: The Lewis structures must be drawn, and VSEPR applied to the structures.
        Solution:
        a) CH_3OH: This molecule has $[1 \times C(4e^-)] + [4 \times H(1e^-)] + [1 \times O(6e^-)] = $ fourteen valence electrons. In the CH_3OH molecule, both carbon and oxygen serve as central atoms. (H can never be central.) Use eight electrons to place a single bond between the C and the O atom and three of the H atoms and another two electrons to place a single bond between the O and the last H atom. This leaves $14 - 10 = 4\ e^-$ (two pairs). Use these two pairs to complete the octet of the O atom. C already has an octet and each H only gets two electrons. The carbon has four bonds and no lone pairs (AX_4), so it is **tetrahedral** with **no deviation** (no lone pairs) from the ideal angle of 109.5°. The oxygen has two bonds and two lone pairs (AX_2E_2), so it is **V shaped** or **bent** with the angles **less than the ideal** angle of 109.5°.

b) N_2O_4: This molecule has $[2 \times N(5e^-)] + [4 \times O(6e^-)] = 34$ valence electrons. Use ten electrons to place a single bond between the two N atoms and between each N and two of the O atoms. This leaves $34 - 10 = 24e^-$ (twelve pairs). Use the twelve pairs to complete the octets of the oxygen atoms. Neither N atom has an octet, however. Form a double bond from one O atom to one N atom by changing a lone pair on the O to a bonding pair on the N. Do this for the other N atom as well. In the N_2O_4 molecule, both nitrogen atoms serve as central atoms. This is the arrangement given in the problem. Both nitrogen atoms are equivalent with three groups and no lone pairs (AX_3), so the arrangement is **trigonal planar** with **no deviation** (no lone pairs) from the ideal angle of 120°. The same results arise from the other resonance structures.

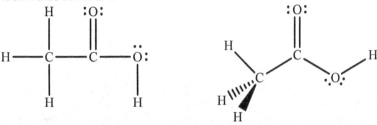

9.18   Plan: The Lewis structures must be drawn, and VSEPR applied to the structures.
        Solution:
        a) CH_3COOH has $[2 \times C(4e^-)] + [4 \times H(1e^-)] + [2 \times O(6e^-)]$ = twenty-four valence electrons. Use fourteen
        electrons to place a single bond between all of the atoms. This leaves $24 - 14 = 10$ e^- (five pairs). Use these five
        pairs to complete the octets of the O atoms; the C atom bonded to the H atoms has an octet but the other C atom
        does not have a complete octet. Form a double bond from the O atom (not bonded to H) to the C by changing a
        lone pair on the O to a bonding pair on the C. In the CH_3COOH molecule, the carbon atoms and the O with H
        attached serve as central atoms. The carbon bonded to the H atoms has four groups and no lone pairs (AX_4), so it
        is **tetrahedral** with **no deviation** from the ideal angle of 109.5°. The carbon bonded to the O atoms has three
        groups and no lone pairs (AX_3), so it is **trigonal planar** with **no deviation** from the ideal angle of 120°. The H
        bearing O has two bonds and two lone pairs (AX_2E_2), so the arrangement is **V shaped** or **bent** with an angle **less
        than the ideal** value of 109.5°.

        b) H_2O_2 has $[2 \times H(1e^-)] + [2 \times O(6e^-)]$ = fourteen valence electrons. Use six electrons to place single bonds
        between the O atoms and between each O atom and an H atom. This leaves $14 - 6 = 8$ e^- (four pairs). Use these
        four pairs to complete the octets of the O atoms. In the H_2O_2 molecule, both oxygen atoms serve as central atoms.
        Both O atoms have tw bonds and two2 lone pairs (AX_2E_2), so they are **V shaped** or **bent** with angles **less than
        the ideal** value of 109.5°.

9.20   Plan: First, draw a Lewis structure, and then apply VSEPR. The presence of lone pairs on the central atom
        generally results in a smaller than ideal bond angle.
        Solution:

                                                                    120°   180°   109.5°   < 109.5°   << 109.5°

        Bond angles: $OF_2 < NF_3 < CF_4 < BF_3 < BeF_2$
        BeF_2 is an AX_2 type molecule, so the angle is the ideal 180°. BF_3 is an AX_3 molecule, so the angle is the ideal
        120°. CF_4, NF_3, and OF_2 all have tetrahedral electron-group arrangements of the following types: AX_4, AX_3E, and
        AX_2E_2, respectively. The ideal tetrahedral bond angle is 109.5°, which is present in CF_4. The one lone pair in NF_3
        decreases the angle a little. The two lone pairs in OF_2 decrease the angle even more.

9.22   Plan: The ideal bond angles depend on the electron-group arrangement. Deviations depend on lone pairs.
        Solution:
        a) The C and N have three groups, so they are **ideally 120°**, and the O has four groups, so **ideally the angle is 109.5°**. The N and O have lone pairs, so the **angles are less than ideal**.
        b) All central atoms have four pairs, so ideally all the angles are **109.5°**. The lone pairs on the O **reduce** this value.
        c) The B has three groups (no lone pairs) leading to an **ideal bond angle of 120°**. All the O atoms have four pairs **(ideally 109.5°)**, two of which are lone, and **reduce the angle**.

9.25   Plan: The Lewis structures are needed to predict the ideal bond angles.
        Solution:
        The P atoms have no lone pairs in any case so the angles are ideal.

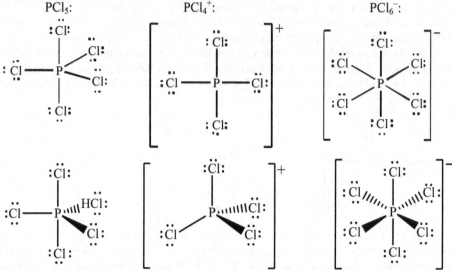

PCl₅: PCl₄⁺:   PCl₆⁻:

        The original PCl₅ is AX₅, so the shape is trigonal bipyramidal, and the angles are 120° and 90°.
        The PCl₄⁺ is AX₄, so the shape is tetrahedral, and the angles are 109.5°.
        The PCl₆⁻ is AX₆, so the shape is octahedral, and the angles are 90°.
        Half the PCl₅ (trigonal bipyramidal, 120° and 90°) become tetrahedral PCl₄⁺ (tetrahedral, 109.5°), and the other half become octahedral PCl₆⁻ (octahedral, 90°).

9.26   Molecules are polar if they have polar bonds that are not arranged to cancel each other. A polar bond is present any time there is a bond between elements with differing electronegativities.

9.29   Plan: To determine if a bond is polar, determine the electronegativity difference of the atoms participating in the bond. The greater the electronegativity difference, the more polar the bond. To determine if a molecule is polar (has a dipole moment), it must have polar bonds, and a certain shape determined by VSEPR.
        Solution:

a)

Molecule	Bond	Electronegativities	Electronegativity difference
SCl_2	S–Cl	S = 2.5 Cl = 3.0	3.0 − 2.5 = 0.5
F_2	F–F	F = 4.0 F = 4.0	4.0 − 4.0 = 0.0
CS_2	C–S	C = 2.5 S = 2.5	2.5 − 2.5 = 0.0
CF_4	C–F	C = 2.5 F = 4.0	4.0 − 2.5 = 1.5
BrCl	Br–Cl	Br = 2.8 Cl = 3.0	3.0 − 2.8 = 0.2

        The polarities of the bonds increase in the order: F–F = C–S < Br–Cl < S–Cl < C–F. Thus, **CF₄** has the most polar bonds.
        b) The F₂ and CS₂ cannot be polar since they do not have polar bonds. CF₄ is an AX₄ molecule, so it is tetrahedral with the four polar C–F bonds arranged to cancel each other giving an overall nonpolar molecule. **BrCl has a dipole moment** since there are no other bonds to cancel the polar Br–Cl bond. **SCl₂ has a dipole moment** (is polar) because it is a bent molecule, AX₂E₂, and the electron density in both S–Cl bonds is pulled towards the more electronegative chlorine atoms.

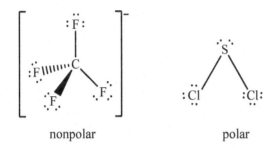

nonpolar   polar

9.31   Plan: If only two atoms are involved, only an electronegativity difference is needed. The greater the difference in electronegativity, the more polar the bond. If there are more than two atoms, the molecular geometry must be determined.
Solution:
a) All the bonds are polar covalent. The SO_3 molecule is trigonal planar, AX_3, so the bond dipoles cancel leading to a nonpolar molecule (no dipole moment). The SO_2 molecule is bent, AX_2E, so the polar bonds result in electron density being pulled towards one side of the molecule. **SO_2 has a greater dipole moment** because it is the only one of the pair that is polar.

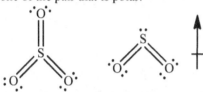

b) ICl and IF are polar, as are all diatomic molecules composed of atoms with differing electronegativities. The electronegativity difference for ICl $(3.0 – 2.5 = 0.5)$ is less than that for IF $(4.0 – 2.5 = 1.5)$. The greater difference means that **IF has a greater dipole moment**.
c) All the bonds are polar covalent. The SiF_4 molecule is nonpolar (has no dipole moment) because the bonds are arranged tetrahedrally, AX_4. SF_4 is AX_4E, so it has a see-saw shape, where the bond dipoles do not cancel. **SF_4 has the greater dipole moment**.

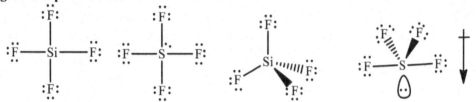

d) H_2O and H_2S have the same basic structure. They are both bent molecules, AX_2E_2, and as such, they are polar. The electronegativity difference in H_2O $(3.5 – 2.1 = 1.4)$ is greater than the electronegativity difference in H_2S $(2.5 – 2.1 = 0.4)$ so **H_2O has a greater dipole moment**.

9.33   Plan: Draw Lewis structures, and then apply VSEPR. A molecule has a dipole moment if polar bonds do not cancel.
Solution:
$C_2H_2Cl_2$ has $[2 \times C(4e^-)] + [2 \times H(1e^-)] + [2 \times Cl(7e^-)] = 24$ valence electrons. The two carbon atoms are bonded to each other. The H atoms and Cl atoms are bonded to the C atoms. Use ten electrons to place a single bond between all of the atoms. This leaves $24 – 10 = 14e^-$ (seven pairs). Use these seven pairs to complete the octets of the Cl atoms and one of the C atoms; the other C atom does not have a complete octet. Form a double bond between the carbon atoms by changing the lone pair on one C atom to a bonding pair. There are three possible structures for the compound $C_2H_2Cl_2$:

I   II   III

The presence of the double bond prevents rotation about the C=C bond, so the structures are "fixed." The C–Cl bonds are more polar than the C–H bonds, so the key to predicting the polarity is the positioning of the C–Cl bonds. Structure I has the C–Cl bonds arranged so that they cancel leaving I as a nonpolar molecule. Both II and III have C–Cl bonds on the same side so the bonds work together making both molecules polar. Both I and II will react with H_2 to give a compound with a Cl attached to each C (same product). Structure III will react with H_2 to give a compound with two Cl atoms on one C and none on the other (different product). **Structure I must be X** as it is the only one that is nonpolar (has no dipole moment). **Structure II must be Z** because it is polar and gives the same product as compound X. This means that **Structure III must be the remaining compound, Y. Compound Y (III) has a dipole moment**.

9.37   Plan: Use the Lewis structures shown in the text. The equation for formal charge (FC) is FC = no. of valence electrons – [no. of unshared valence electrons + ½ no. of shared valence electrons].
Solution:
a) Formal charges for Al_2Cl_6:
   $FC_{Al} = 3 – [0 + ½(8)] = –1$
   $FC_{Cl, ends} = 7 – [6 + ½(2)] = 0$
   $FC_{Cl, bridging} = 7 – [4 + ½(4)] = +1$
   (Check: Formal charges add to zero, the charge on the compound.)
   Formal charges for I_2Cl_6:
   $FC_I = 7 – [4 + ½(8)] = –1$
   $FC_{Cl, ends} = 7 – [6 + ½(2)] = 0$
   $FC_{Cl, bridging} = 7 – [4 + ½(4)] = +1$
   (Check: Formal charges add to zero, the charge on the compound.)
b) The aluminum atoms have no lone pairs and are AX_4, so they are tetrahedral. The two tetrahedral Al atoms cannot give a planar structure. The iodine atoms in I_2Cl_6 have two lone pairs each and are AX_4E_2 so they are square planar. Placing the square planar I atoms adjacent can give a planar molecule.

9.42   Plan: Draw the Lewis structures, and then use VSEPR to describe epoxypropane (propylene oxide).
Solution:
a)

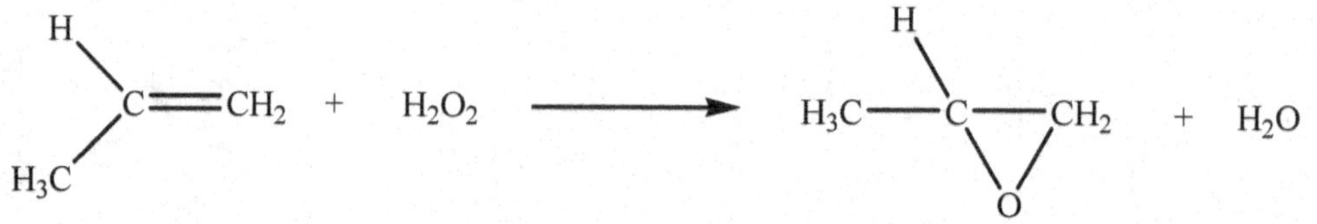

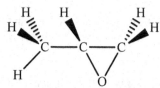

In epoxypropane , the C atoms are all AX_4. The C atoms do not have any unshared (lone) pairs. All of the ideal bond angles for the C atoms in epoxypropane are **109.5°** and the molecular shape around each carbon atom is **tetrahedral**.
b) In epoxypropane , the C that is not part of the three-membered ring should have an ideal angle. The atoms in the ring form an equilateral triangle. The angles in an equilateral triangle are 60°. The angles around the two carbon atoms in the rings are reduced from the ideal 109.5° to 60°.

9.45   Plan: The basic Lewis structure will be the same for all species. The Cl atoms are larger than the F atoms. All of the molecules are of the type AX_5 and have trigonal bipyramidal molecular shape. The equatorial positions are in the plane of the triangle and the axial positions above and below the plane of the triangle. In this molecular shape, there is more room in the equatorial positions.
Solution:
a) The F atoms will occupy the smaller axial positions first so that the larger Cl atoms can occupy the equatorial positions which are less crowded.

b) The molecule containing only F atoms is nonpolar (has no dipole moment), as all the polar bonds would cancel. The molecules with one F or one Cl would be polar since the P–F and P–Cl bonds are not equal in polarity and thus do not cancel each other. The presence of two axial F atoms means that their polarities will cancel (as would the three Cl atoms) giving a nonpolar molecule. The molecule with three F atoms is also polar.

Polar	Nonpolar No dipole moment	Polar	Polar	Nonpolar No dipole moment

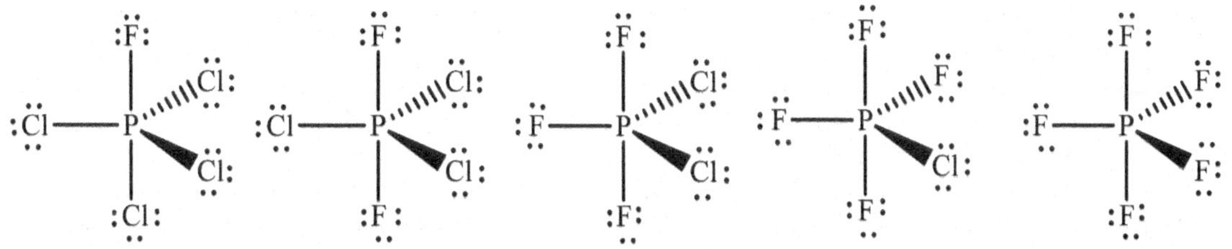

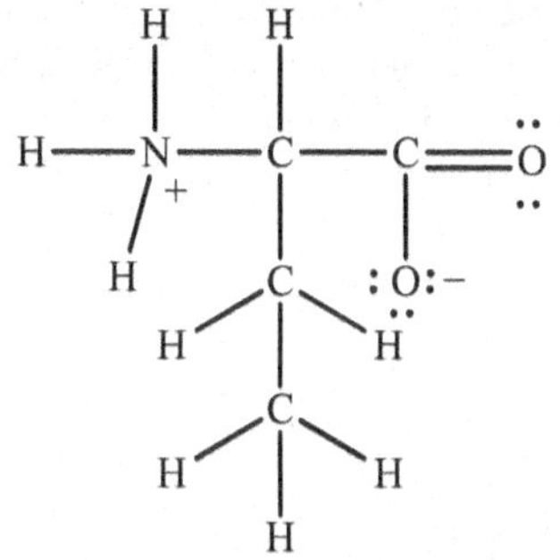

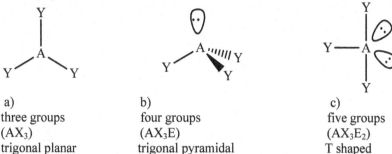

9.48 Plan: Pick the VSEPR structures for AY_3 substances. Then determine which are polar.

Solution:

The molecular shapes that have a central atom bonded to three other atoms are trigonal planar, trigonal pyramidal, and T shaped:

a)	b)	c)
three groups	four groups	five groups
(AX_3)	(AX_3E)	(AX_3E_2)
trigonal planar	trigonal pyramidal	T shaped

Trigonal planar molecules, such as a), are nonpolar, so it cannot be AY_3. Trigonal pyramidal molecules b) and T-shaped molecules c) are polar, so either could represent AY_3.

9.51 Plan: Draw the Lewis structure of each compound. Atoms 180° apart are separated by the sum of the bond's length. Atoms not at 180° apart must have their distances determined by geometrical relationships.

Solution:

(a) H—C≡C—H (b) (c)

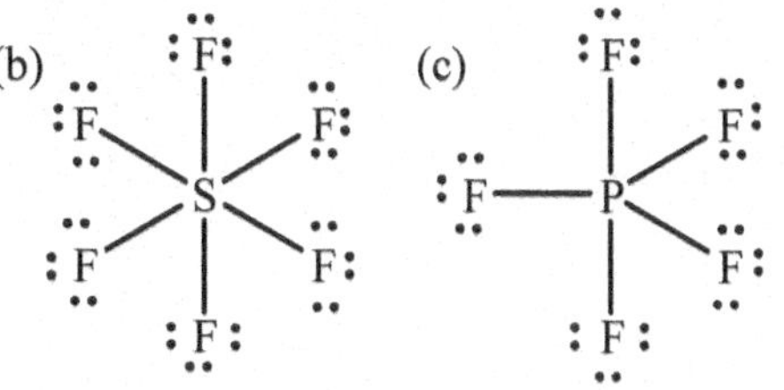

a) C_2H_2 has [2 x C(4e$^-$)] + [2 x H(1e$^-$)] = 10 valence electrons to be used in the Lewis structure. Six of these electrons are used to bond the atoms with a single bond, leaving 10 – 6 = 4 electrons. Giving one carbon atom the four electrons to complete its octet results in the other carbon atom not having an octet. The two lone pairs from the carbon with an octet are changed to two bonding pairs for a triple bond between the two carbon atoms. The molecular shape is linear. The H atoms are separated by two carbon-hydrogen bonds (109 pm) and a carbon-carbon triple bond (121 pm).

Total separation = 2(109 pm) + 121 pm = **339 pm**

b) SF_6 has [1 x S(6e$^-$)] + [6 x F(7e$^-$)] = 48 valence electrons to be used in the Lewis structure. Twelve of these electrons are used to bond the atoms with a single bond, leaving 48 – 12= 36 electrons. These thirty-six electrons are given to the fluorine atoms to complete their octets. The molecular shape is octahedral. The fluorine atoms on opposite sides of the S are separated by twice the sulfur-fluorine bond length (158 pm).

Total separation = 2(158 pm) = **316 pm**

Adjacent fluorines are at two corners of a right triangle, with the sulfur at the 90° angle. Two sides of the triangle are equal to the sulfur-fluorine bond length (158 pm). The separation of the fluorine atoms is at a distance equal to the hypotenuse of this triangle. This length of the hypotenuse may be found using the Pythagorean Theorem $(a^2 + b^2 = c^2)$. In this case a = b = 158 pm. Thus, $c^2 = (158 \text{ pm})^2 + (158 \text{ pm})^2$, and so c = 223.4457 pm = **223 pm**.

c) PF_5 has [1 x P(5e$^-$)] + [5 x F(7e$^-$)] = 40 valence electrons to be used in the Lewis structure. Ten of these electrons are used to bond the atoms with a single bond, leaving 40 – 10= 30 electrons. These thirty electrons are given to the fluorine atoms to complete their octets. The molecular shape is trigonal bipyramidal. Adjacent equatorial fluorine atoms are at two corners of a triangle with an F-P-F bond angle of 120°. The length of the P-F bond is 156 pm. If the 120° bond angle is A, then the F-F bond distance is a and the P-F bond distances are b and c. The F-F bond distance can be found using the Law of Cosines: $a^2 = b^2 + c^2 – 2bc (\cos A)$.

$a^2 = (156 \text{ pm})^2 + (156 \text{ pm})^2 – 2(156 \text{ pm})(156 \text{ pm})\cos 120°$.   a = 270.1999 pm = **270 pm**.

CHAPTER 10 THEORIES OF COVALENT BONDING

END–OF–CHAPTER PROBLEMS

10.1   Plan: Table 10.1 describes the types of hybrid orbitals that correspond to the various electron-group arrangements. The number of hybrid orbitals formed by a central atom is equal to the number of electron groups arranged around that central atom.
Solution:
a)   trigonal planar: three electron groups - three hybrid orbitals: sp^2
b)   octahedral: six electron groups - six hybrid orbitals: sp^3d^2
c)   linear: two electron groups - two hybrid orbitals: sp
d)   tetrahedral: four electron groups - four hybrid orbitals: sp^3
e)   trigonal bipyramidal: five electron groups - five hybrid orbitals: sp^3d

10.3   Carbon and silicon have the same number of valence electrons, but the outer level of electrons is $n = 2$ for carbon and $n = 3$ for silicon. Thus, silicon has $3d$ orbitals in addition to $3s$ and $3p$ orbitals available for bonding in its outer level, to form up to six hybrid orbitals, whereas carbon has only $2s$ and $2p$ orbitals available in its outer level to form up to four hybrid orbitals.

10.5   Plan: The *number* of hybrid orbitals is the same as the number of atomic orbitals before hybridization. The *type* depends on the orbitals mixed. The name of the type of hybrid orbital comes from the number and type of atomic orbitals mixed. The number of each type of atomic orbital appears as a superscript in the name of the hybrid orbital.
Solution:
a) There are six unhybridized orbitals, and therefore **six** hybrid orbitals result. The type is sp^3d^2 since one s, three p, and two d atomic orbitals were mixed.
b) **Four sp^3** hybrid orbitals form from three p and one s atomic orbitals.

10.7   Plan: To determine hybridization, draw the Lewis structure and count the number of electron groups around the central nitrogen atom. Hybridize that number of orbitals. Single, double, and triple bonds all count as one electron group. An unshared pair (lone pair) of electrons or one unshared electron also counts as one electron group.
Solution:
a) The three electron groups (one double bond, one lone pair, and one unpaired electron) around nitrogen require three hybrid orbitals. The hybridization is sp^2.

$\ddot{\text{N}} = \ddot{\text{O}}$

b) The nitrogen has three electron groups (one single bond, one double bond, and one unpaired electron), requiring three hybrid orbitals so the hybridization is sp^2.

c) The nitrogen has three electron groups (one single bond, one double bond, and one lone pair) so the hybridization is sp^2.

10.9   <u>Plan:</u> To determine hybridization, draw the Lewis structure and count the number of electron groups around the central chlorine atom. Hybridize that number of orbitals. Single, double, and triple bonds all count as one electron group. An unshared pair (lone pair) of electrons or one unshared electron also counts as one electron group.
<u>Solution:</u>
a) The Cl has four electron groups (one lone pair, one lone electron, and two double bonds) and therefore four hybrid orbitals are required; the hybridization is sp^3. Note that in ClO_2, the π bond is formed by the overlap of d orbitals from chlorine with p orbitals from oxygen.

b) The Cl has four electron groups (one lone pair and three bonds) and therefore four hybrid orbitals are required; the hybridization is sp^3.

c) The Cl has four electron groups (four bonds) and therefore four hybrid orbitals are required; the hybridization is sp^3.

10.11   <u>Plan:</u> Draw the Lewis structure and count the number of electron groups around the central atom. Hybridize that number of orbitals. Single, double, and triple bonds all count as one electron group. An unshared pair (lone pair) of electrons or one unshared electron also counts as one electron group. Once the type of hybridization is known, the types of atomic orbitals that will mix to form those hybrid orbitals are also known.
<u>Solution:</u>
a) Silicon has four electron groups (four bonds) requiring four hybrid orbitals; four sp^3 hybrid orbitals are made from **one s and three p atomic orbitals**.

b) Carbon has two electron groups (two double bonds) requiring two hybrid orbitals; two sp hybrid orbitals are made from **one s and one p orbital**.

c) Sulfur is surrounded by five electron groups (four bonding pairs and one lone pair), requiring five hybrid orbitals; five sp^3d hybrid orbitals are formed from **one s orbital, three p orbitals, and one d orbital**.

d) Nitrogen is surrounded by four electron groups (three bonding pairs and one lone pair) requiring four hybrid orbitals; four sp^3 hybrid orbitals are formed from **one s orbital and three p orbitals**.

10.13   Plan: To determine hybridization, draw the Lewis structure of the reactants and products and count the number of electron groups around the central atom. Hybridize that number of orbitals. Single, double, and triple bonds all count as one electron group. An unshared pair (lone pair) of electrons or one unshared electron also counts as one electron group. Recall that sp hybrid orbitals are oriented in a linear geometry, sp^2 in a trigonal planar geometry, sp^3 in a tetrahedral geometry, sp^3d in a trigonal bipyramidal geometry, and sp^3d^2 in an octahedral geometry.
Solution:
a) The P in PH_3 has four electron groups (one lone pair and three bonds) and therefore four hybrid orbitals are required; the hybridization is sp^3. The P in the product also has four electron groups (four bonds) and again four hybrid orbitals are required. The hybridization of P remains sp^3. There is no change in hybridization. Illustration **B** best shows the hybridization of P during the reaction as $sp^3 \rightarrow sp^3$.
b) The B in BH_3 has three electron groups (three bonds) and therefore three hybrid orbitals are required; the hybridization is sp^2. The B in the product has four electron groups (four bonds) and four hybrid orbitals are required. The hybridization of B is now sp^3. The hybridization of B changes from sp^2 **to** sp^3; this is best shown by illustration **A**.

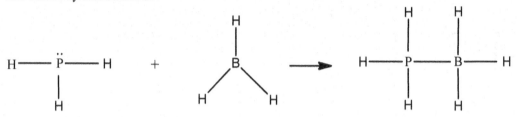

10.15   Plan: To determine hybridization, draw the Lewis structure and count the number of electron groups around the central atom. Hybridize that number of orbitals. Single, double, and triple bonds all count as one electron group. An unshared pair (lone pair) of electrons or one unshared electron also counts as one electron group. Write the electron configuration of the central atom and mix the appropriate atomic orbitals to form the hybrid orbitals.
Solution:
a) Germanium is the central atom in $GeCl_4$. Its electron configuration is $[Ar]4s^23d^{10}4p^2$. Ge has four electron groups (four bonds), requiring four hybrid orbitals. Hybridization is sp^3 around Ge. One of the $4s$ electrons is moved to a $4p$ orbital and the four orbitals are hybridized.

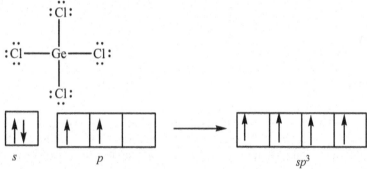

Isolated Ge atom   Hybridized Ge atom

b) Boron is the central atom in BCl_3. Its electron configuration is $[He]2s^22p^1$. B has three electron groups (three bonds), requiring three hybrid orbitals. Hybridization is sp^2 around B. One of the $2s$ electrons is moved to an empty $2p$ orbital and the three atomic orbitals are hybridized. One of the $2p$ atomic orbitals is not involved in the hybridization.

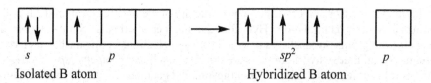

s   p sp^2 p

Isolated B atom   Hybridized B atom

c) Carbon is the central atom in CH_3^+. Its electron configuration is $[He]2s^22p^2$. C has three electron groups (three bonds), requiring three hybrid orbitals. Hybridization is sp^2 around C.
One of the 2s electrons is moved to an empty 2p orbital; three orbitals are hybridized and one electron is removed to form the +1 ion.

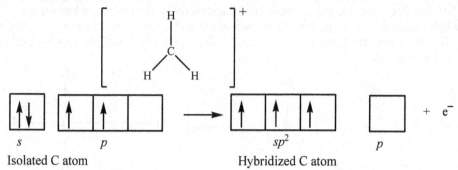

s   p sp^2 p

Isolated C atom   Hybridized C atom

10.17   <u>Plan:</u> To determine hybridization, draw the Lewis structure and count the number of electron groups around the central atom. Hybridize that number of orbitals. Single, double, and triple bonds all count as one electron group. An unshared pair (lone pair) of electrons or one unshared electron also counts as one electron group. Write the electron configuration of the central atom and mix the appropriate atomic orbitals to form the hybrid orbitals.
<u>Solution:</u>
a) In $SeCl_2$, Se is the central atom and has four electron groups (two single bonds and two lone pairs), requiring four hybrid orbitals so Se is sp^3 hybridized. The electron configuration of Se is $[Ar]4s^23d^{10}4p^4$. The 4s and 4p atomic orbitals are hybridized. Two sp^3 hybrid orbitals are filled with lone electron pairs and two sp^3 orbitals bond with the chlorine atoms.

$$: \overset{..}{\underset{..}{Cl}} \text{——} \overset{..}{\underset{..}{Se}} \text{——} \overset{..}{\underset{..}{Cl}} :$$

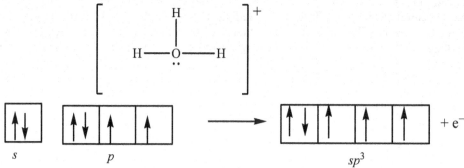

s   p sp^3

b) In H_3O^+, O is the central atom and has four electron groups (three single bonds and one lone pair), requiring four hybrid orbitals. O is sp^3 hybridized. The electron configuration of O is $[He]2s^22p^4$. The 2s and 2p orbitals are hybridized. One sp^3 hybrid orbital is filled with a lone electron pair and three sp^3 orbitals bond with the hydrogen atoms.

c) I is the central atom in IF_4^- with six electron groups (four single bonds and two lone pairs) surrounding it. Six hybrid orbitals are required and I has sp^3d^2 hybrid orbitals. The sp^3d^2 hybrid orbitals are composed of one s orbital, three *p* orbitals, and two *d* orbitals. Two sp^3d^2 orbitals are filled with a lone pair and four sp^3d^2 orbitals bond with the fluorine atoms.

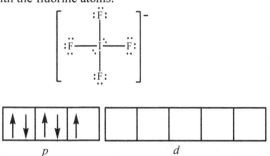

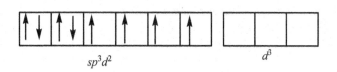

10.20   Plan: A single bond is a σ bond which is the result of two orbitals overlapping end to end; a double bond consists of one σ bond and one π bond; and a triple bond consists of one σ bond and two πbonds. A π bond is the result of orbitals overlapping side to side.
Solution:
a) **False**, a double bond is one σ and one π bond.
b) **False**, a triple bond consists of one σ and two π bonds.
c) **True**
d) **True**
e) **False**, a π bond consists of one pair of electrons; it occurs after a σ bond has been previously formed.
f) **False**, end-to-end overlap results in a bond with electron density along the bond axis.

10.21   Plan: To determine hybridization, draw the Lewis structure and count the number of electron groups around the central atom. Hybridize that number of orbitals. Single, double, and triple bonds all count as one electron group. An unshared pair (lone pair) of electrons or one unshared electron also counts as one electron group. A single bond is a σ bond which is the result of two orbitals overlapping end to end; a double bond consists of one σ bond and one π bond; and a triple bond consists of one σ bond and two π bonds.
Solution:
a) Nitrogen is the central atom in NO_3^-. Nitrogen has three surrounding electron groups (two single bonds and one double bond), so it is *sp^2* hybridized. Nitrogen forms **three σ bonds** (one each for the N–O bonds) and **one π bond** (part of the N=O double bond).

$$\left[:\overset{..}{\underset{..}{O}}\!\!-\!\!N\!\!=\!\!\overset{..}{\underset{..}{O}} \right]^-$$
$$\underset{\overset{|}{:\overset{..}{\underset{..}{O}}:}}{}$$

b) Carbon is the central atom in CS_2. Carbon has two surrounding electron groups (two double bonds), so it is *sp* hybridized. Carbon forms **two σ bonds** (one each for the C–S bonds) and **two π bonds** (part of the two C=S double bonds).

$$\overset{..}{\underset{..}{S}}\!\!=\!\!C\!\!=\!\!\overset{..}{\underset{..}{S}}$$

c) Carbon is the central atom in CH_2O. Carbon has three surrounding electron groups (two single bonds and one double bond), so it is *sp^2* hybridized. Carbon forms **three σ bonds** (one each for the two C–H bonds and one C–O bond) and **one π bond** (part of the C=O double bond).

10.23 <u>Plan:</u> To determine hybridization, draw the Lewis structure and count the number of electron groups around the central nitrogen atom. Hybridize that number of orbitals. Single, double, and triple bonds all count as one electron group. An unshared pair (lone pair) of electrons or one unshared electron also counts as one electron group. A single bond is a σ bond which is the result of two orbitals overlapping end to end; a double bond consists of one σ bond and one π bond; and a triple bond consists of one σ bond and two π bonds.
<u>Solution:</u>
a) In FNO, three electron groups (one lone pair, one single bond, and one double bond) surround the central N atom. Hybridization is ***sp²*** around nitrogen. One σ bond exists between F and N, and one σ and one π bond exist between N and O. Nitrogen participates in a total of **2 σ and 1 π bonds**.

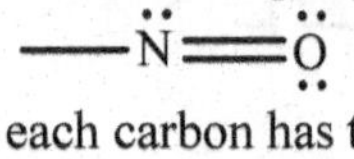

$$—\ddot{N}\!=\!\ddot{\ddot{O}}$$

b) In C_2F_4, each carbon has three electron groups (two single bonds and one double bond) with ***sp²*** hybridization. The bonds between C and F are σ bonds. The C–C bond consists of one σ and one π bond. Each carbon participates in a total of **three σ and one π bonds**.

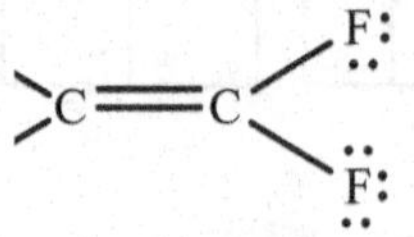

$$\text{>C}\!=\!\text{C<}\quad \overset{\ddot{F}:}{\underset{\ddot{F}:}{}}$$

c) In $(CN)_2$, each carbon has two electron groups (one single bond and one triple bond) and is ***sp*** hybridized with a σ bond between the two carbon atoms and a σ and two π bonds comprising each C–N triple bond. Each carbon participates in a total of **two σ and two π bonds**.

$$:\!N\!\equiv\!C\!-\!C\!\equiv\!N:$$

10.25 <u>Plan:</u> A single bond is a σ bond which is the result of two orbitals overlapping end to end; a double bond consists of one σ bond and one π bond; and a triple bond consists of one σ bond and two π bonds.
<u>Solution:</u>
The double bond in 2-butene restricts rotation of the molecule, so that *cis* and *trans* structures result. The two structures are shown below:

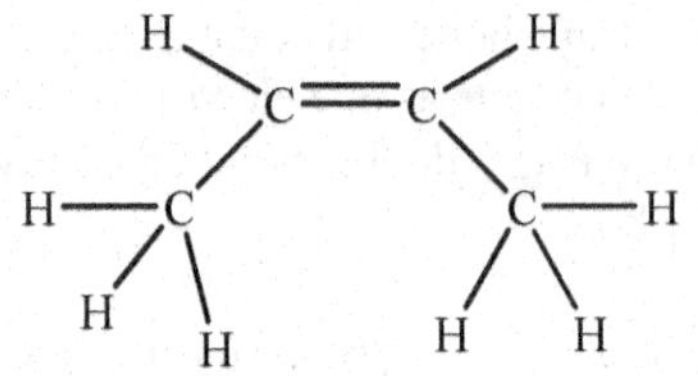

$$cis \qquad\qquad\qquad trans$$

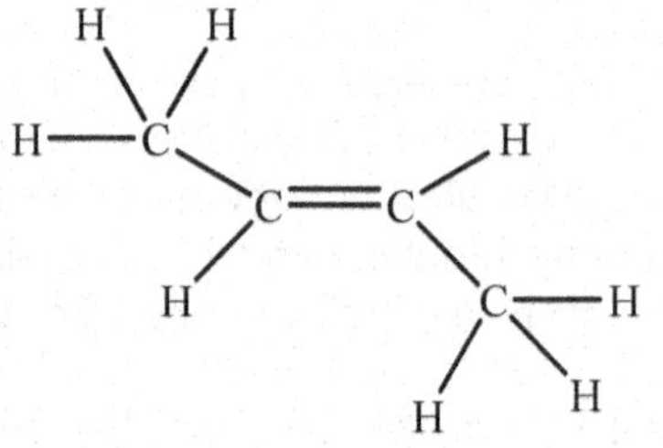

The carbon atoms participating in the double bond each have three surrounding groups, so they are *sp²* hybridized. The =C–H σ bonds result from the head-on overlap of a C *sp²* orbital and an H *s* orbital. The C–CH₃ bonds are also σ bonds, resulting from the head-on overlap of an *sp²* orbital and an *sp³* orbital. The C=C bond contains 1 σ bond (head on overlap of two *sp²* orbitals) and 1 π bond (sideways overlap of unhybridized *p* orbitals). Finally, C–H bonds in the methyl (–CH₃) groups are σ bonds resulting from the overlap of the *sp³* orbital of C with the *s* orbital of H.

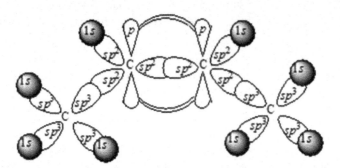

10.26   Four molecular orbitals form from the four p atomic orbitals. In forming molecular orbitals, the total number of molecular orbitals must equal the number of atomic orbitals. Two of the four molecular orbitals formed are bonding orbitals and two are antibonding.

10.28   a) Bonding MOs have lower energy than antibonding MOs. The bonding MO's lower energy, even lower than its constituent atomic orbitals, accounts for the stability of a molecule in relation to its individual atoms. However, the sum of energy of the MOs must equal the sum of energy of the AOs.
b) The node is the region of an orbital where the probability of finding the electron is zero, so the nodal plane is the plane that bisects the node perpendicular to the bond axis. There is no node along the bond axis (probability is positive between the two nuclei) for the bonding MO. The antibonding MO does have a nodal plane.
c) The bonding MO has higher electron density between nuclei than the antibonding MO.

10.30   <u>Plan:</u> Like atomic orbitals, any one MO holds a maximum of two electrons. Two atomic orbitals combine to form two molecular orbitals, a bonding and an antibonding MO.
<u>Solution:</u>
a) **Two** electrons are required to fill a σ-bonding molecular orbital. Each molecular orbital requires two electrons.
b) **Two** electrons are required to fill a π-antibonding molecular orbital. There are two π-antibonding orbitals, each holding a maximum of two electrons.
c) **Four** electrons are required to fill the two σ molecular orbitals (two electrons to fill the σ-bonding and two to fill the σ-antibonding) formed from two $1s$ atomic orbitals.

10.32   <u>Plan:</u> Recall that a bonding MO has a region of high electron density between the nuclei while an antibonding MO has a node, or region of zero electron density between the nuclei. MOs formed from s orbitals, or from p orbitals overlapping end to end, are called σ and MOs formed by the side-to-side overlap of p orbitals are called π. A superscript star (*) is used to designate an antibonding MO. To write the electron configuration of F_2^+, determine the number of valence electrons and write the sequence of MO energy levels, following the sequence order given in the text.

<u>Solution:</u>
a) A is the π^*_{2p} molecular orbital (two p orbitals overlapping side to side with a node between them); B is the σ_{2p} molecular orbital (two p orbitals overlapping end to end with no node); C is the π_{2p} molecular orbital (two p orbitals overlapping side to side with no node); D is the σ^*_{2p} molecular orbital (two p orbitals overlapping end to end with a node).
b) F_2^+ has thirteen valence electrons: $[2 \times F(7e^-) - 1$ (from + charge)]. The MO electron configuration is $(\sigma_{2s})^2(\sigma^*_{2s})^2(\sigma_{2p})^2(\pi_{2p})^2(\pi_{2p})^2(\pi^*_{2p})^2(\pi^*_{2p})^1$. The π^*_{2p} molecular orbital, A, σ_{2p} molecular orbital, B, and π_{2p} molecular orbital, C, are all occupied by at least one electron. The σ^*_{2p} molecular orbital is unoccupied.
c) A π^*_{2p} molecular orbital, A, has only one electron.

10.34   <u>Plan:</u> To write the electron configuration of Be_2^+, determine the number of electrons and write the sequence of MO energy levels, following the sequence order given in the text. Bond order = ½[(no. of electrons in bonding MO) – (no. of electrons in antibonding MO)]. Recall that a diamagnetic substance has no unpaired electrons.
<u>Solution:</u>
a) Be_2^+ has a total of seven electrons $[2 \times Be(4e^-) - 1$ (from + charge)]. The molecular orbital configuration is $(\sigma_{1s})^2(\sigma^*_{1s})^2(\sigma_{2s})^2(\sigma^*_{2s})^1$ and bond order = ½(4 – 3) = 1/2. With a bond order of 1/2 the Be_2^+ ion will be **stable**.
b) No, the ion has one unpaired electron in the σ^*_{2s} MO, so it is **paramagnetic**, not diamagnetic.
c) Valence electrons would be those in the molecular orbitals at the $n = 2$ level, so the valence electron configuration is $(\sigma_{2s})^2(\sigma^*_{2s})^1$.

10.36   <u>Plan:</u> Write the electron configuration of each species by determining the number of electrons and writing the sequence of MO energy levels, following the sequence order given in the text. Calculate the bond order: bond order = ½[(no. of electrons in bonding MO) – (no. of electrons in antibonding MO)]. Bond energy increases as bond order increases; bond length decreases as bond order increases.

Solution:

C_2^- Total electrons = 6 + 6 + 1 = 13

MO configuration: $(\sigma_{1s})^2(\sigma*_{1s})^2(\sigma_{2s})^2(\sigma*_{2s})^2(\pi_{2p})^4(\sigma_{2p})^1$

Bond order = 1/2(9 − 4) = 2.5

C_2 Total electrons = 6 + 6 = 12

MO configuration: $(\sigma_{1s})^2(\sigma*_{1s})^2(\sigma_{2s})^2(\sigma*_{2s})^2(\pi_{2p})^4$

Bond order = 1/2(8 − 4) = 2

C_2^+ Total electrons = 6 + 6 − 1 = 11

MO configuration: $(\sigma_{1s})^2(\sigma*_{1s})^2(\sigma_{2s})^2(\sigma*_{2s})^2(\pi_{2p})^3$

Bond order = 1/2(7 − 4) = 1.5

a) Bond energy increases as bond order increases: $\mathbf{C_2^+ < C_2 < C_2^-}$

b) Bond length decreases as bond energy increases, so the order of increasing bond length will be opposite that of increasing bond energy. Increasing bond length: $\mathbf{C_2^- < C_2 < C_2^+}$

10.40   Plan: To determine hybridization, count the number of electron groups around each of the C, O, and N atoms. Hybridize that number of orbitals. Single, double, and triple bonds all count as one electron group. An unshared pair (lone pair) of electrons or one unshared electron also counts as one electron group. A single bond is a σ bond which is the result of two orbitals overlapping end to end; a double bond consists of one σ bond and one π bond; and a triple bond consists of one σ bond and two π bonds.

Solution:

a) Each of the six C atoms in the ring has three electron groups (two single bonds and a double bond) and has $\mathbf{\mathit{sp}^2}$ hybridization; all of the other C atoms have four electron groups (four single bonds) and have $\mathbf{\mathit{sp}^3}$ hybridization; all of the O atoms have four electron groups (two single bonds and two lone pairs) and have $\mathbf{\mathit{sp}^3}$ hybridization; the N atom has four electron groups (three single bonds and a lone pair) and has $\mathbf{\mathit{sp}^3}$ hybridization.

b) Each of the single bonds is a σ bond; each of the double bonds has one σ bond for a total of **26 σ bonds**.

c) The ring has three double bonds each of which is composed of one σ bond and one π bond; so there are three π bonds each with two electrons for a total of **six π electrons.**

10.42   Plan: To determine hybridization, count the number of electron groups around each C and N atom. Hybridize that number of orbitals. Single, double, and triple bonds all count as one electron group. An unshared pair (lone pair) of electrons or one unshared electron also counts as one electron group. A single bond is a σ bond which is the result of two orbitals overlapping end to end; a double bond consists of one σ bond and one π bond; and a triple bond consists of one σ bond and two π bonds.

Solution:

a) Every single bond is a σ bond. There is one σ bond in each double bond as well. There are **17 σ** bonds in isoniazid. Every atom-to-atom connection contains a σ bond.

b) All carbon atoms have three surrounding electron groups (two single and one double bond), so their hybridization is $\mathbf{\mathit{sp}^2}$. The ring N also has three surrounding electron groups (one single bond, one double bond, and one lone pair), so its hybridization is also $\mathbf{\mathit{sp}^2}$. The other two N atoms have four surrounding electron groups (three single bonds and one lone pair) and are $\mathbf{\mathit{sp}^3}$ hybridized.

10.44   Plan: To determine the hybridization in each species, count the number of electron groups around the underlined atom. Hybridize that number of orbitals. Single, double, and triple bonds all count as one electron group. An unshared pair (lone pair) of electrons or one unshared electron also counts as one electron group.

Solution:

a) B changes from $\mathbf{\mathit{sp}^2 \rightarrow \mathit{sp}^3}$. Boron in BF_3 has three electron groups with sp^2 hybridization. In BF_4^-, four electron groups surround B with sp^3 hybridization.

b) P changes from $sp^3 \rightarrow sp^3d$. Phosphorus in PCl_3 is surrounded by four electron groups (three bonds to Cl and one lone pair) for sp^3 hybridization. In PCl_5, phosphorus is surrounded by five electron groups for sp^3d hybridization.

c) C changes from $sp \rightarrow sp^2$. Two electron groups surround C in C_2H_2 and three electron groups surround C in C_2H_4.

d) Si changes from $sp^3 \rightarrow sp^3d^2$. Four electron groups surround Si in SiF_4 and six electron groups surround Si in SiF_6^{2-}.

e) **No change**, S in SO_2 is surrounded by three electron groups (one single bond, one double bond, and one lone pair) and in SO_3 is surrounded by three electron groups (two single bonds and one double bond); both have sp^2 hybridization.

10.46   Plan: To determine the molecular shape and hybridization, count the number of electron groups around the P, N, and C atoms. Hybridize that number of orbitals. Single, double, and triple bonds all count as one electron group. An unshared pair (lone pair) of electrons or one unshared electron also counts as one electron group.
Solution:

P (3 single bonds and 1 double bond)	AX_4	tetrahedral	sp^3
N (3 single bonds and 1 lone pair)	AX_3E	trigonal pyramidal	sp^3
C_1 and C_2 (4 single bonds)	AX_4	tetrahedral	sp^3
C_3 (2 single bonds and 1 double bond)	AX_3	trigonal planar	sp^2

10.51   Plan: To determine the hybridization, count the number of electron groups around the atoms. Hybridize that number of orbitals. Single, double, and triple bonds all count as one electron group. An unshared pair (lone pair) of electrons or one unshared electron also counts as one electron group.
Solution:
a) **B and D** show hybrid orbitals that are present in the molecule. B shows sp^3 hybrid orbitals, used by atoms that have four groups of electrons. In the molecule, the C atom in the CH_3 group, the S atom, and the O atom all have four groups of electrons and would have sp^3 hybrid orbitals. D shows sp^2 hybrid orbitals, used by atoms that have three groups of electrons. In the molecule, the C bonded to the nitrogen atom, the C atoms involved in the C=C bond, and the nitrogen atom all have three groups of electrons and would have sp^2 hybrid orbitals.
b) The C atoms in the C≡C bond have only two electron groups and would have **sp hybrid orbitals**. These orbitals are not shown in the picture.
c) There are **two sets of sp** hybrid orbitals, **four sets of sp^2** hybrid orbitals, and **three sets of sp^3** hybrid orbitals in the molecule.

10.52   <u>Plan:</u> Draw a resonance structure that places the double bond between the C and N atoms.
<u>Solution:</u>
The resonance gives the C–N bond some double bond character, which hinders rotation about the C–N bond. The C–N single bond is a σ bond; the resonance interaction exchanges a C–O π bond for a C–N π bond.

10.55   <u>Plan:</u> To determine hybridization, count the number of electron groups around each C and O atom. Hybridize that number of orbitals. Single, double, and triple bonds all count as one electron group. An unshared pair (lone pair) of electrons or one unshared electron also counts as one electron group. A single bond is a σ bond which is the result of two orbitals overlapping end to end; a double bond consists of one σ bond and one π bond; and a triple bond consists of one σ bond and two π bonds.
<u>Solution:</u>
a) The six carbon atoms in the ring each have three surrounding electron groups (two single bonds and one double bond) with sp^2 hybrid orbitals. The two carbon atoms participating in the C=O bond are also sp^2 hybridized. The single carbon in the –CH$_3$ group has four electron groups (four single bonds) and is sp^3 hybridized. The two central oxygen atoms, one in a C–O–H configuration and the other in a C–O–C configuration, each have four surrounding electron groups (two single bonds and two lone pairs) and are sp^3 hybridized. The O atoms in the two C=O bonds have three electron groups (one double bond and two lone pairs) and are sp^2 hybridized.
Summary: C in –CH$_3$: ***sp***^{3}, all other C atoms (8 total): ***sp***^{2}, O in C=O (2 total): ***sp***^{2}, O in the C–O bonds (2 total): ***sp***^{3}.
b) The **two** C=O bonds are localized; the double bonds on the ring are delocalized as in benzene.
c) Each carbon with three surrounding groups has sp^2 hybridization and trigonal planar shape; therefore, **eight** carbon atoms have this shape. Only **one** carbon in the CH$_3$ group has four surrounding groups with sp^3 hybridization and tetrahedral shape.

10.56   <u>Plan:</u> In the *cis* arrangement, the two H atoms are on the same side of the double bond; in the *trans* arrangement, the two H atoms are on different sides of the double bond.
<u>Solution:</u>
a) **Four** different isomeric fatty acids: *trans-cis*, *cis-cis*, *cis-trans*, *trans-trans*.
b) With three double bonds, there are $2^n = 2^3 =$ **8 isomers** possible.

cis-cis-cis	*trans-trans-trans*
cis-trans-cis	*trans-cis-trans*
cis-cis-trans	*trans-cis-cis*
cis-trans-trans	*trans-trans-cis*

CHAPTER 11 INTERMOLECULAR FORCES: LIQUIDS, SOLIDS, AND PHASE CHANGES

TOOLS OF THE LABORATORY BOXED READING PROBLEMS

B11.1 Plan: The Bragg equation gives the relationship between the angle of incoming light, θ, the wavelength of the light, λ, and the distance between layers in a crystal, d.
Solution:
$n\lambda = 2d \sin\theta$
$n = 1;\quad \lambda = 0.709\text{x}10^{-10}\text{ m};\qquad \theta = 11.6°$
$1(0.709\text{x}10^{-10}\text{ m}) = 2d \sin 11.6°$
$0.709\text{x}10^{-10}\text{ m} = 0.4021558423\ d$
$d = 1.762998\text{x}10^{-10}\text{ m} = \mathbf{1.76\text{x}10^{-10}\ m}$

END–OF–CHAPTER PROBLEMS

11.1   The energy of attraction is a *potential* energy and denoted E_p. The energy of motion is *kinetic* energy and denoted E_k. The relative strength of E_p vs. E_k determines the phase of the substance. In the gas phase, $E_p \ll E_k$ because the gas particles experience little attraction for one another and the particles are moving very fast. In the solid phase, $E_p \gg E_k$ because the particles are very close together and are only vibrating in place.
Two properties that differ between a gas and a solid are the volume and density. The volume of a gas expands to fill the container it is in while the volume of a solid is constant no matter what container holds the solid. Density of a gas is much less than the density of a solid. The density of a gas also varies significantly with temperature and pressure changes. The density of a solid is only slightly altered by changes in temperature and pressure. Compressibility and ability to flow are other properties that differ between gases and solids.

11.4   a) Heat of fusion refers to the change between the solid and the liquid states and heat of vapourization refers to the change between liquid and gas states. In the change from solid to liquid, the kinetic energy of the molecules must increase only enough to partially offset the intermolecular attractions between molecules. In the change from liquid to gas, the kinetic energy of the molecules must increase enough to overcome the intermolecular forces. The energy to overcome the intermolecular forces for the molecules to move freely in the gaseous state is much greater than the amount of energy needed to allow the molecules to move more easily past each other but still stay very close together.
b) The net force holding molecules together in the solid state is greater than that in the liquid state. Thus, to change solid molecules to gaseous molecules in sublimation requires more energy than to change liquid molecules to gaseous molecules in vapourization.
c) At a given temperature and pressure, the magnitude of $\Delta_{vap}H$ is the same as the magnitude of $\Delta_{cond}H$. The only difference is in the sign: $\Delta_{vap}H = -\Delta_{cond}H$.

11.5   Plan: Intermolecular forces (nonbonding forces) are the forces that exist between molecules that attract the molecules to each other; these forces influence the physical properties of substances. Intramolecular forces (bonding forces) exist within a molecule and are the forces holding the atoms together in the molecule; these forces influence the chemical properties of substances.
Solution:
a) **Intermolecular** — Oil evaporates when individual oil molecules can escape the attraction of other oil molecules in the liquid phase.
b) **Intermolecular** — The process of butter (fat) melting involves a breakdown in the rigid, solid structure of fat molecules to an amorphous, less ordered system. The attractions between the fat molecules are weakened, but the bonds within the fat molecules are not broken.
c) **Intramolecular** — A process called oxidation tarnishes pure silver. Oxidation is a chemical change and involves the breaking of bonds and formation of new bonds.

d) **Intramolecular** — The decomposition of O_2 molecules into O atoms requires the breaking of chemical bonds, i.e., the force that holds the two O atoms together in an O_2 molecule.

Both a) and b) are physical changes, whereas c) and d) are chemical changes. In other words, intermolecular forces are involved in physical changes while intramolecular forces are involved in chemical changes.

11.7   a) **Condensation**   The water vapour in the air condenses to liquid when the temperature drops during the night.
b) **Fusion** (melting)   Solid ice melts to liquid water.
c) **Evaporation**   Liquid water on clothes evaporates to water vapour.

11.9   The propane gas molecules slow down as the gas is compressed. Therefore, much of the **kinetic energy** lost by the propane molecules is released to the surroundings upon liquefaction.

11.13   In closed containers, two processes, evaporation and condensation, occur simultaneously. Initially there are few molecules in the vapour phase, so more liquid molecules evaporate than gas molecules condense. Thus, the amount of molecules in the gas phase increases, causing the vapour pressure of hexane to increase. Eventually, the amount of molecules in the gas phase reaches a maximum where the amount of liquid molecules evaporating equals the amount of gas molecules condensing. In other words, the evaporation rate equals the condensation rate. At this point, there is no further change in the vapour pressure.

11.14   a) At the critical temperature, the molecules are moving so fast that they can no longer be condensed. This temperature decreases with weaker intermolecular forces because the forces are not strong enough to overcome molecular motion. Alternatively, as intermolecular forces increase, the **critical temperature increases**.
b) As intermolecular forces increase, the **boiling point increases** because it becomes more difficult and takes more energy to separate molecules from the liquid phase.
c) As intermolecular forces increase, the **vapour pressure decreases** for the same reason given in b). At any given temperature, strong intermolecular forces prevent molecules from easily going into the vapour phase and thus vapour pressure is decreased.
d) As intermolecular forces increase, the **heat of vapourization increases** because more energy is needed to separate molecules from the liquid phase.

11.18   When water at 100°C touches skin, the heat released is from the lowering of the temperature of the water. The specific heat of water is approximately 75 J/mol•K. When steam at 100°C touches skin, the heat released is from the condensation of the gas with a heat of condensation of approximately 41 kJ/mol. Thus, the amount of heat released from gaseous water condensing will be greater than the heat from hot liquid water cooling and the burn from the steam will be worse than that from hot water.

11.19   Plan: The total heat required is the sum of three processes: warming the ice to 0.00°C, the melting point; melting the ice to liquid water; warming the water to 0.500°C. The equation $q = c$ x mass x ΔT is used to calculate the heat involved in changing the temperature of the ice and of the water; the heat of fusion is used to calculate the heat involved in the phase change of ice to water.
Solution:
1) Warming the ice from –6.00°C to 0.00°C:
   $q_1 = c$ x mass x ΔT = (2.09 J/g•K)(22.00 g)[(0.0+273.2)K – (–6.00+273.2)K] = 275.88 J
2) Phase change of ice at 0.00°C to water at 0.00°C:

$$q_2 = n\left(\Delta_{\text{fus}}H^\circ\right) = \left(22.0\ \text{g}\right)\left(\frac{1\ \text{mol}}{18.02\ \text{g}}\right)\left(\frac{6.02\ \text{kJ}}{\text{mol}}\right)\left(\frac{10^3\ \text{J}}{1\ \text{kJ}}\right) = 7349.6115\ \text{J}$$

3) Warming the liquid from 0.00°C to 0.500°C:
   $q_3 = c$ x mass x ΔT = (4.21 J/g•K)(22.00 g)[(0.500+273.2)K – (0.0+273.2)K] = 46.31 J
The three heats are positive because each process takes heat from the surroundings (endothermic). The phase change requires much more energy than the two temperature change processes. The total heat is
$q_1 + q_2 + q_3$ = (275.88 J + 7349.6115 J + 46.31 J) = 7671.8015 J = **7.67×10^3 J**.

11.21 Plan: The Clausius-Clapeyron equation gives the relationship between vapour pressure and temperature. We aregiven $\Delta_{vap}H^\circ$, p_1, T_1, and T_2; these values are substituted into the equation to find the p_2, the vapour pressure.

Solution:

$p_1 = 101.3$ kPa $\qquad T_1 = 122°C + 273 = 395$ K

$p_2 = ?$ $\qquad\qquad T_2 = 113°C + 273 = 386$ K $\qquad\qquad \Delta_{vap}H^\circ = 35.5$ kJ/mol

$$\ln\frac{p_2}{p_1} = \frac{-\Delta_{vap}H^\circ}{R}\left(\frac{1}{T_2} - \frac{1}{T_1}\right)$$

$$\ln\frac{p_2}{101.3\ \text{kPa}} = \frac{-35.5\dfrac{\text{kJ}}{\text{mol}}}{8.314\ \text{J/mol•K}}\left(\frac{1}{386\ \text{K}} - \frac{1}{395\ \text{K}}\right)\left(\frac{10^3\ \text{J}}{1\text{kJ}}\right) = -0.2520440$$

$$\frac{p_2}{101.3\ \text{kPa}} = 0.7772105$$

$p_2 = (0.7772105)(101.3\ \text{kPa}) = 78.731424$ kPa $= \textbf{78.7 kPa}$

11.23 Plan: The Clausius-Clapeyron equation gives the relationship between vapour pressure and temperature. We are given p_1, p_2, T_1, and T_2; these values are substituted into the equation to find $\Delta_{vap}H^\circ$.

Solution:

$p_1 = 82.8$ kPa $\qquad T_1 = 85.2°C + 273.2 = 358.4$ K

$p_2 = 101.3$ kPa $\qquad T_2 = 95.6°C + 273.2 = 368.8$ K $\qquad \Delta_{vap}H^\circ = ?$ $\quad \ln\dfrac{p_2}{p_1} = \dfrac{-\Delta_{vap}H^\circ}{R}\left(\dfrac{1}{T_2} - \dfrac{1}{T_1}\right)$

$$\ln\frac{101.3\ \text{kPa}}{82.8\ \text{kPa}} = \frac{-\Delta_{vap}H^\circ}{8.314\ \text{J/mol•K}}\left(\frac{1}{368.8\ \text{K}} - \frac{1}{358.4\ \text{K}}\right)$$

$0.2016583 = -\Delta_{vap}H^\circ\ (-9.463775\times10^{-6})$ mol/J

$\Delta_{vap}H^\circ = 21{,}308.447$ kJ $= \textbf{21.3 kJ/mol}$

(The significant figures in the answer are limited by the 82.8 kPa in the problem.)

11.25

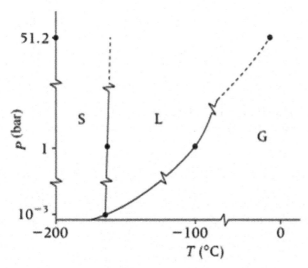

The pressure scale is distorted to represent the large range in pressures given in the problem, so the liquid-solid curve looks different from the one shown in the text. The important features of the graph include the distinction between the gas, liquid, and solid states, and the melting point T, which is located directly above the critical T. Solid ethene is denser than liquid ethene since the solid-liquid line slopes to the right with increasing pressure.

11.28   Plan: The Clausius-Clapeyron equation gives the relationship between vapour pressure and temperature. We are given $\Delta_{vap}H°$, p_1, T_1, and T_2; these values are substituted into the equation to find p_2. Convert the temperatures from °C to K and $\Delta_{vap}H°$ from kJ/mol to J/mol to allow cancellation with the units in R.

Solution:

$p_1 = 233$ kPa $T_1 = 25.0°C + 273 = 298$ K

$p_2 = ?$ $T_2 = 135°C + 273 = 408$ K $\Delta_{vap}H° = 24.3$ kJ/mol

$$\ln\frac{p_2}{p_1} = \frac{-\Delta_{vap}H°}{R}\left(\frac{1}{T_2} - \frac{1}{T_1}\right)$$

$$\ln\frac{p_2}{233\text{ kPa}} = \frac{-24.3\frac{\text{kJ}}{\text{mol}}}{8.314\text{ J/mol}\cdot\text{K}}\left(\frac{1}{408\text{ K}} - \frac{1}{298\text{ K}}\right)\left(\frac{10^3\text{ J}}{1\text{ kJ}}\right)$$

$$\ln\frac{p_2}{233\text{ kPa}} = 2.644311$$

$$\frac{p_2}{233\text{ kPa}} = 14.07374$$

$p_2 = (14.07374)(233$ kPa$) = 3279.18$ kPa $= \textbf{3280 kPa}$

11.32   To form hydrogen bonds, the atom bonded to hydrogen must have two characteristics: small size and high electronegativity (so that the atom has a very high electron density). With this high electron density, the attraction for a hydrogen on another molecule is very strong. Selenium is much larger than oxygen (atomic radius of 119 pm vs. 73 pm) and less electronegative than oxygen (2.4 for Se and 3.5 for O) resulting in an electron density on Se in H_2Se that is too small to form hydrogen bonds.

11.34   All particles (atoms and molecules) exhibit dispersion forces, but these are the weakest of intermolecular forces. The dipole-dipole forces in polar molecules dominate the dispersion forces.

11.37   Plan: Dispersion forces are the only forces between nonpolar substances; dipole-dipole forces exist between polar substances. Hydrogen bonds only occur in substances in which hydrogen is directly bonded to either oxygen, nitrogen, or fluorine.
Solution:
a) **Hydrogen bonding** will be the strongest force between methanol molecules since they contain O–H bonds. Dipole-dipole and dispersion forces also exist.
b) **Dispersion forces** are the only forces between nonpolar carbon tetrachloride molecules and, thus, are the strongest forces.
c) **Dispersion forces** are the only forces between nonpolar chlorine molecules and, thus, are the strongest forces.

11.39   Plan: Dispersion forces are the only forces between nonpolar substances; dipole-dipole forces exist between polar substances. Hydrogen bonds only occur in substances in which hydrogen is directly bonded to either oxygen, nitrogen, or fluorine.
Solution:
a) **Dipole-dipole** interactions will be the strongest forces between chloromethane molecules because the C–Cl bond has a dipole moment.
b) **Dispersion forces** dominate because CH_3CH_3 (ethane) is a symmetrical nonpolar molecule.
c) **Hydrogen bonding** dominates because hydrogen is bonded to nitrogen, which is one of the three atoms (N, O, or F) that participate in hydrogen bonding.

11.41 Plan: Hydrogen bonds are formed when a hydrogen atom is bonded to N, O, or F.
       Solution:
       a) The presence of an OH group leads to the formation of hydrogen bonds in **CH₃CH(OH)CH₃**.
       There are no hydrogen bonds in CH₃SCH₃.

       b) The presence of H attached to F in **HF** leads to the formation of hydrogen bonds. There are no hydrogen bonds in HBr.

11.43 Plan: In the vapourization process, intermolecular forces between particles in the liquid phase must be broken as the particles enter the vapour phase. In other words, the question is asking for the strongest interparticle force that must be broken to vapourize the liquid. Dispersion forces are the only forces between nonpolar substances; dipole-dipole forces exist between polar substances. Hydrogen bonds only occur in substances in which hydrogen is directly bonded to oxygen, nitrogen, or fluorine.
       Solution:
       a) **Dispersion forces**, because hexane, C_6H_{14}, is a nonpolar molecule.
       b) **Hydrogen bonding**; hydrogen is bonded to oxygen in water. A single water molecule can engage in as many as four hydrogen bonds.
       c) **Dispersion forces**, although the individual Si–Cl bonds are polar, the molecule has a symmetrical, tetrahedral shape and is therefore nonpolar.

11.45 Plan: Polarizability increases down a group and decreases from left to right because as atomic size increases, polarizability increases.
       Solution:
       a) **Iodide ion** has greater polarizability than the bromide ion because the iodide ion is larger. The electrons can be polarized over a larger volume in a larger atom or ion.
       b) **Ethene (CH₂=CH₂)** has greater polarizability than ethane (CH₃CH₃) because the electrons involved in π bonds are more easily polarized than electrons involved in σ bonds.
       c) **H₂Se** has greater polarizability than water because the selenium atom is larger than the oxygen atom.

11.47 Plan: Weaker attractive forces result in a higher vapour pressure because the molecules have a smaller energy barrier in order to escape the liquid and go into the gas phase. Decide which of the two substances in each pair has the weaker interparticle force. Dispersion forces are weaker than dipole-dipole forces, which are weaker than hydrogen bonds.
       Solution:
       a) **C₂H₆** C₂H₆ is a smaller molecule exhibiting weaker dispersion forces than C₄H₁₀.
       b) **CH₃CH₂F** CH₃CH₂F has no H–F bonds (F is bonded to C, not to H), so it only exhibits dipole-dipole forces, which are weaker than the hydrogen bonding in CH₃CH₂OH.
       c) **PH₃** PH₃ has weaker intermolecular forces (dipole-dipole) than NH₃ (hydrogen bonding).

11.49 Plan: The weaker the interparticle forces, the lower the boiling point. Decide which of the two substances in each pair has the weaker interparticle force. Dispersion forces are weaker than dipole-dipole forces, which are weaker than hydrogen bonds, which are weaker than ionic forces.

Solution:

a) **HCl** would have a lower boiling point than LiCl because the dipole-dipole intermolecular forces between hydrogen chloride molecules in the liquid phase are weaker than the significantly stronger ionic forces holding the ions in lithium chloride together.

b) **PH₃** would have a lower boiling point than NH₃ because the intermolecular forces in PH₃ are weaker than those in NH₃. Hydrogen bonding exists between NH₃ molecules but weaker dipole-dipole forces hold PH₃ molecules together.

c) **Xe** would have a lower boiling point than iodine. Both are nonpolar with dispersion forces, but the forces between xenon atoms would be weaker than those between iodine molecules since the iodine molecules are more polarizable because of their larger size.

11.51   Plan: The weaker the intermolecular forces, the lower the boiling point. Decide which of the two substances in each pair has the weaker intermolecular force. Dispersion forces are weaker than dipole-dipole forces, which are weaker than hydrogen bonds, which are weaker than ionic forces.
Solution:

a) **C_4H_8**, the cyclic molecule, cyclobutane, has less surface area exposed, so its dispersion forces are weaker than the straight chain molecule, C_4H_{10}.

b) **PBr_3**, the dipole-dipole forces of phosphorous tribromide are weaker than the ionic forces of sodium bromide.

c) **HBr**, the dipole-dipole forces of hydrogen bromide are weaker than the hydrogen bonding forces of water.

11.53   The trend in both atomic size and electronegativity predicts that the trend in increasing strength of hydrogen bonds is N–H < O–H < F–H. As the atomic size decreases and electronegativity increases, the electron density of the atom increases. High electron density strengthens the attraction to a hydrogen atom on another molecule. Fluorine is the smallest of the three and the most electronegative, so its hydrogen bonds would be the strongest. Oxygen is smaller and more electronegative than nitrogen, so hydrogen bonds for water would be stronger than hydrogen bonds for ammonia.

11.57   The shape of the drop depends upon the competing cohesive forces (attraction of molecules within the drop itself) and adhesive forces (attraction between molecules in the drop and the molecules of the waxed floor). If the cohesive forces are strong and outweigh the adhesive forces, the drop will be as spherical as gravity will allow. If, on the other hand, the adhesive forces are significant, the drop will spread out. Both water (hydrogen bonding) and mercury (metallic bonds) have strong cohesive forces, whereas cohesive forces in oil (dispersion) are relatively weak. Neither water nor mercury will have significant adhesive forces to the nonpolar wax molecules, so these drops will remain nearly spherical. The adhesive forces between the oil and wax can compete with the weak, cohesive forces of the oil (dispersion) and so the oil drop spreads out.

11.59   Surface tension is defined as the energy needed to increase the surface area by a given amount, so units of energy (J) per surface area (m^2) describe this property.

11.61   Plan: The stronger the intermolecular force, the greater the surface tension. Decide which of the substances has the weakest intermolecular force and which has the strongest. Dispersion forces are weaker than dipole-dipole forces, which are weaker than hydrogen bonds, which are weaker than ionic forces.
Solution:

All three molecules exhibit hydrogen bonding (H is bonded to O), but the extent of hydrogen bonding increases with the number of O–H bonds present in each molecule. $HOCH_2CH(OH)CH_2OH$ with three O–H groups can form more hydrogen bonds than $HOCH_2CH_2OH$ with two O–H groups, which in turn can form more hydrogen bonds than $CH_3CH_2CH_2OH$ with only one O–H group. The greater the number of hydrogen bonds, the stronger the intermolecular forces, and the higher the surface tension.

$CH_3CH_2CH_2OH$ < $HOCH_2CH_2OH$ < $HOCH_2CH(OH)CH_2OH$

11.63   Plan: Viscosity is a measure of the resistance of a liquid to flow, and is greater for molecules with stronger intermolecular forces. The stronger the force attracting the molecules to each other, the harder it is for one molecule to move past another. Thus, the substance will not flow easily if the intermolecular force is strong. Decide which of the substances has the weakest intermolecular force and which has the strongest. Dispersion

forces are weaker than dipole-dipole forces, which are weaker than hydrogen bonds, which are weaker than ionic forces.
Solution:
The ranking of decreasing viscosity is the opposite of that for increasing surface tension (Problem 11.61).
HOCH₂CH(OH)CH₂OH > HOCH₂CH₂OH > CH₃CH₂CH₂OH

The greater the number of hydrogen bonds, the stronger the intermolecular forces, and the higher the viscosity.

11.68   Water is a good solvent for polar and ionic substances and a poor solvent for nonpolar substances. Water is a polar molecule and dissolves polar substances because their intermolecular forces are of similar strength. Water is also able to dissolve ionic compounds and keep ions separated in solution through ion-dipole interactions. Nonpolar substances will not be very soluble in water since their dispersion forces are much weaker than the hydrogen bonds in water. A solute whose intermolecular attraction to a solvent molecule is less than the attraction between two solvent molecules will not dissolve because its attraction cannot replace the attraction between solvent molecules.

11.69   A single water molecule can form four hydrogen bonds. The two hydrogen atoms form a hydrogen bond each to oxygen atoms on neighboring water molecules. The two lone pairs on the oxygen atom form hydrogen bonds with hydrogen atoms on neighboring molecules.

11.72   Water exhibits strong capillary action, which allows it to be easily absorbed by the plant's roots and transported to the leaves.

11.78   The unit cell is a simple cubic cell. According to the bottom row in Figure 11.29 two atomic radii (or one atomic diameter) equal the width of the cell.

11.81   The energy gap is the energy difference between the highest filled energy level (valence band) and the lowest unfilled energy level (conduction band). In conductors and superconductors, the energy gap is zero because the valence band overlaps the conduction band. In semiconductors, the energy gap is small but greater than zero. In insulators, the energy gap is large and thus insulators do not conduct electricity.

11.83   The density of a solid depends on the atomic mass of the element (greater mass = greater density), the atomic radius (how many atoms can fit in a given volume, which determines the packing efficiency (how much of the volume is occupied by empty space).

11.84   Plan: The simple cubic structure unit cell contains one atom since the atoms at the eight corners are shared by eight cells for a total of 8 atoms x 1/8 atom per cell = 1 atom; the body-centered cell also has an atom in the center, for a total of two atoms; the face-centered cell has six atoms in the faces which are shared by two cells:
6 atoms x ½ atom per cell = 3 atoms plus another atom from the eight corners for a total of four atoms.
Solution:
a) Ni is **face-centered cubic** since there are four atoms/unit cell.
b) Cr is **body-centered cubic** since there are two atoms/unit cell.
c) Ca is **face-centered cubic** since there are four atoms/unit cell.

11.86   a) There is a change in unit cell from CdO in a sodium chloride structure to CdSe in a zinc blende structure.
b) **Yes**, the coordination number of Cd does change from six in the CdO unit cell to four in the CdSe unit cell.

11.88   Plan: Substances composed of individual atoms are atomic solids; molecular substances composed of covalent molecules form molecular solids; ionic compounds form ionic solids; metal elements form metallic solids; certain substances that form covalent bonds between atoms or molecules form network covalent solids.
Solution:
a) Nickel forms a **metallic solid** since nickel is a metal whose atoms are held together by metallic bonds.
b) Fluorine forms a **molecular solid** since the F_2 molecules have covalent bonds and the molecules are held to each other by dispersion forces.
c) Methanol forms a **molecular solid** since the covalently bonded CH_3OH molecules are held to each other by hydrogen bonds.
d) Tin forms a **metallic solid** since tin is a metal whose atoms are held together by metallic bonds.

e) Silicon is in the same group as carbon, so it exhibits similar bonding properties. Since diamond and graphite are both **network covalent** solids, it makes sense that Si forms the same type of bonds.
f) Xe is an **atomic** solid since individual atoms are held together by dispersion forces.

11.90   Figure P11.90 shows the face-centered cubic array of zinc blende, ZnS. Both ZnS and ZnO have a 1:1 ion ratio, so the ZnO unit cell will also contain **four** Zn^{2+} ions.

11.92   Plan: To determine the number of Zn^{2+} ions and Se^{2-} ions in each unit cell count the number of ions at the corners, faces, and center of the unit cell. Atoms at the eight corners are shared by eight cells for a total of 8 atoms x 1/8 atom per cell = 1 atom; atoms in the body of a cell are in that cell only; atoms at the faces are shared by two cells: 6 atoms x 1/2 atom per cell = 3 atoms. Add the masses of the total number of atoms in the cell to find the mass of the cell. Given the mass of one unit cell and the ratio of mass to volume (density) divide the mass, converted to grams (conversion factor is 1 u = $1.66054x10^{-24}$ g), by the density to find the volume of the unit cell. Since the volume of a cube is length x width x height, the edge length is found by taking the cube root of the cell volume.
Solution:
a) Looking at selenide ions, there is one ion at each corner and one ion on each face. The total number of selenide ions is 1/8 (8 corner ions) + 1/2 (6 face ions) = **4 Se^{2-} ions**. There are also **4 Zn^{2+} ions** due to the 1:1 ratio of Se ions to Zn ions.
b) Mass of unit cell = (4 x mass of Zn atom) + (4 x mass of Se atom)
$$= (4 \times 65.41 \text{ u}) + (4 \times 78.96 \text{ u}) = \textbf{577.48 u}$$

c) Volume $(cm^3) = \left(577.48 \text{ u}\right)\left(\dfrac{1.66054x10^{-24} \text{ g}}{1 \text{ u}}\right)\left(\dfrac{cm^3}{5.42 \text{ g}}\right) = 1.76924x10^{-22} \text{ cm}^3 = \textbf{1.77x10}^{-22} \textbf{ cm}^3$

d) The volume of a cube equals (length of edge)^3.
Edge length (cm) = $\sqrt[3]{1.76924 \times 10^{-22} \text{ cm}^3}$ = $5.6139x10^{-8}$ cm = **5.61x10^{-8} cm**

11.94   Plan: To classify a substance according to its electrical conductivity, first locate it on the periodic table as a metal, metalloid, or nonmetal. In general, metals are conductors, metalloids are semiconductors, and nonmetals are insulators.
Solution:
a) Phosphorous is a nonmetal and an **insulator**.
b) Mercury is a metal and a **conductor**.
c) Germanium is a metalloid in Group 14 and is beneath carbon and silicon in the periodic table. Pure germanium crystals are **semiconductors** and are used to detect gamma rays emitted by radioactive materials. Germanium can also be doped with phosphorous (similar to the doping of silicon) to form an n-type semiconductor or be doped with lithium to form a p-type semiconductor.

11.96   Plan: First, classify the substance as an insulator, conductor, or semiconductor. The electrical conductivity of conductors decreases with increasing temperature, whereas that of semiconductors increases with temperature. Temperature increases have little impact on the electrical conductivity of insulators.
Solution:
a) Antimony, Sb, is a metalloid, so it is a semiconductor. Its electrical conductivity **increases** as the temperature increases.
b) Tellurium, Te, is a metalloid, so it is a semiconductor. Its electrical conductivity **increases** as temperature increases.
c) Bismuth, Bi, is a metal, so it is a conductor. Its electrical conductivity **decreases** as temperature increases.

11.98   Plan: Use the molar mass and the density of Po to find the volume of one mole of Po. Divide by Avogadro's number to obtain the volume of one Po atom (and the volume of the unit cell). Since Po has a simple cubic unit cell, there is one Po atom in the cell (atoms at the eight corners are shared by eight cells for a total of 8 atoms x 1/8 atom = 1 atom per cell). Find the edge length of the cell by taking the cube root of the volume of the unit cell. The edge length of a simple cubic unit cell is twice the radius of the atom.

Solution:

$$\text{Volume (cm}^3\text{) of the unit cell} = \left(\frac{209 \text{ g Po}}{1 \text{ mol Po}}\right)\left(\frac{cm^3}{9.142 \text{ g}}\right)\left(\frac{1 \text{ mol Po}}{6.022 \times 10^{23} \text{ Po atoms}}\right)\left(\frac{1 \text{ Po atom}}{1 \text{ unit cell}}\right)$$

$$= 3.7963332 \times 10^{-23} \text{ cm}^3$$

Edge length (cm) of the unit cell $= \sqrt[3]{\left(3.7963332 \times 10^{-23} \text{ cm}^3\right)} = 3.3608937 \times 10^{-8} \text{ cm}$

$2r$ = edge length
$2r = 3.3608937 \times 10^{-8}$ cm
$r = 1.680447 \times 10^{-8}$ cm = **1.68x10^{-8} cm**

11.105   A substance whose physical properties are the same in all directions is called isotropic; an anisotropic substance has properties that depend on direction. Liquid crystals flow like liquids but have a degree of order that gives them the anisotropic properties of a crystal.

11.107   Plan: Germanium and silicon are elements in Group 14 with four valence electrons. If germanium or silicon is doped with an atom with more than four valence electrons, an n-type semiconductor is produced. If it is doped with an atom with fewer than four valence electrons, a p-type semiconductor is produced.
Solution:
a) Phosphorus has five valence electrons so an **n-type semiconductor** will form by doping Ge with P.
b) Indium has three valence electrons so a **p-type semiconductor** will form by doping Si with In.

11.110   Plan: The vapour pressure of water is temperature dependent. Table 4.2 gives the vapour pressure of water at various temperatures. Use $pV = nRT$ to find the moles and then mass of water in 5.0 L of nitrogen at 22°C; then find the mass of water in the 2.5 L volume of nitrogen and subtract the two masses to calculate the mass of water that condenses.
Solution:
At 22°C the vapour pressure of water is 2.6453 kPa (from Table 4.2).
a) Once compressed, the N_2 gas would still be saturated with water. The vapour pressure depends on the temperature, which has not changed. Therefore, the partial pressure of water in the compressed gas remains the same at **2.6453 kPa.**
b) $pV = nRT$
Moles of H_2O at 22°C and 5.00 L volume:

$$n = \frac{pV}{RT} = \frac{(2.6453 \text{ atm})(5.00 \text{ L})}{\left(8.31446 \frac{\text{L·kPa}}{\text{mol·K}}\right)\left((273 + 22)\text{K}\right)} = 0.0053925 \text{ mol } H_2O$$

The gas is compressed to half the volume: 5.00 L/2 = 2.50 L

$$\text{Mass (g) of } H_2O \text{ at 22°C and 5.00 L volume} = \left(0.0053925 \text{ mol } H_2O\right)\left(\frac{18.02 \text{ g } H_2O}{1 \text{ mol } H_2O}\right) = 0.097173 \text{ g}$$

Moles of H_2O at 22°C and 2.50 L volume:

$$n = \frac{pV}{RT} = \frac{(2.6453 \text{ atm})(2.50 \text{ L})}{\left(8.31446 \frac{\text{L·kPa}}{\text{mol·K}}\right)\left((273 + 22)\text{K}\right)} = 0.0026962 \text{ mol } H_2O$$

$$\text{Mass (g) of } H_2O \text{ at 22°C and 2.50 L volume} = \left(0.0026962 \text{ mol } H_2O\right)\left(\frac{18.02 \text{ g } H_2O}{1 \text{ mol } H_2O}\right) = 0.04859 \text{ g}$$

Mass (g) of H_2O condensed = (0.097173 g H_2O) − (0.04859 g H_2O) = 0.0485867 g = **0.0486 g H$_2$O**

11.115 <u>Plan:</u> The Clausius-Clapeyron equation gives the relationship between vapour pressure and temperature. We are given p_1, p_2, T_1, and $\Delta_{vap}H°$; these values are substituted into the equation to find T_2.

<u>Solution:</u>

$$\ln\frac{p_2}{p_1} = -\frac{\Delta H°_{vap}}{R}\left(\frac{1}{T_2} - \frac{1}{T_1}\right) \qquad p_1 = 0.160 \text{ Pa} \qquad T_1 = 20.0°C + 273 = 293 \text{ K}$$

$$p_2 = 6.67\text{x}10^{-3} \text{ Pa} \qquad T_2 = ? \qquad \Delta_{vap}H° = 59.1 \text{ kJ/mol}$$

$$\ln\frac{6.67\text{x}10^{-3} \text{ Pa}}{0.160 \text{ Pa}} = \frac{-59.1 \text{ kJ/mol}}{8.314 \text{ J/mol}\bullet\text{K}}\left(\frac{1}{T_2} - \frac{1}{293 \text{ K}}\right)\left(\frac{10^3 \text{ J}}{1 \text{ kJ}}\right)$$

$$-3.177554 = -7108.492 \text{ K}\left(\frac{1}{T_2} - \frac{1}{293 \text{ K}}\right)$$

$$(-3.177554)/(-7108.49 \text{ K}) = 4.47008\text{x}10^{-4} \text{ (1/K)} = \left(\frac{1}{T_2} - \frac{1}{293 \text{ K}}\right)$$

$4.47008\text{x}10^{-4}$ (1/K) + 1/293 K = 1/T_2
T_2 = 259.069 K = **259 K**

11.116 <u>Plan:</u> Use the volume of the liquid water and the density of water to find the moles of water present in the volume of the greenhouse. Find the pressure of this number of moles of water vapour using the ideal gas equation. Knowing that 4.20 L results in the calculated vapour pressure, the volume of water that would give a vapour pressure corresponding to 100% relative humidity can be calculated.

<u>Solution:</u>

a) Moles of water = $\left(4.20 \text{ L}\right)\left(\frac{1 \text{ mL}}{10^{-3} \text{ L}}\right)\left(\frac{1.00 \text{ g}}{\text{mL}}\right)\left(\frac{1 \text{ mol } H_2O}{18.02 \text{ g } H_2O}\right)$ = 233.0744 mol

$pV = nRT$

$$p = \frac{nRT}{V} = \frac{(233.0744 \text{ mol})\left(8.31446\frac{\text{L}\bullet\text{kPa}}{\text{mol}\bullet\text{K}}\right)((273 + 26)\text{K})}{\left(256 \text{ m}^3\right)}\left(\frac{10^{-3} \text{ m}^3}{1 \text{ L}}\right)$$

= 2.26338 kPa = **2.26 kPa**

b) 3.3639 kPa is needed to saturate the air (at 26°C).

$$\frac{4.20 \text{ L}}{2.26338 \text{ kPa}} = \frac{x}{3.3639 \text{ kPa}}$$

Volume (L) of water needed for 100% relative humidity = $\dfrac{(3.3639 \text{ kPa})(4.20 \text{ L})}{2.26338 \text{ kPa}}$ = 6.24216 L = **6.24 L H_2O**

11.119 <u>Plan:</u> Hydrogen bonds only occur in substances in which hydrogen is directly bonded to either oxygen, nitrogen, or fluorine.

<u>Solution:</u>

a) Both furfuryl alcohol and 2-furoic acid can form hydrogen bonds since these two molecules have hydrogen directly bonded to oxygen.

2-furoic acid

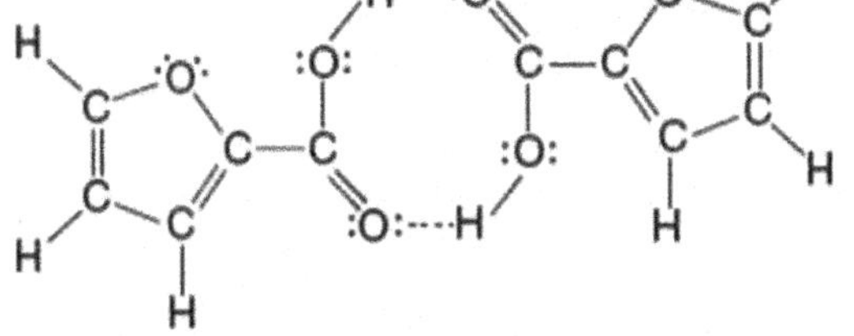

furfuryl alcohol

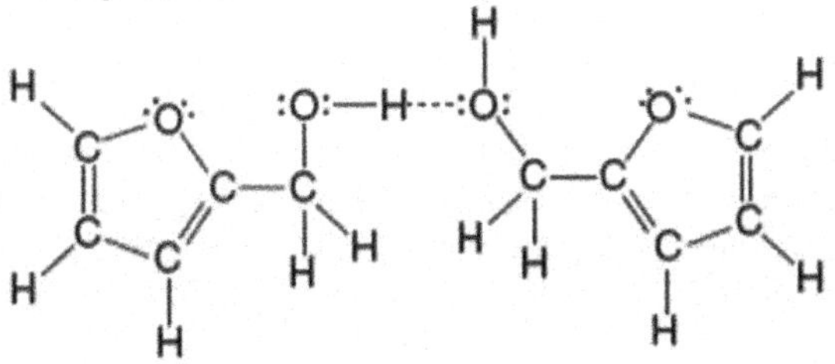

b) Both furfuryl alcohol and 2-furoic acid can form internal hydrogen bonds by forming a hydrogen bond between the O–H and the O in the ring.

2-furoic acid   furfuryl alcohol

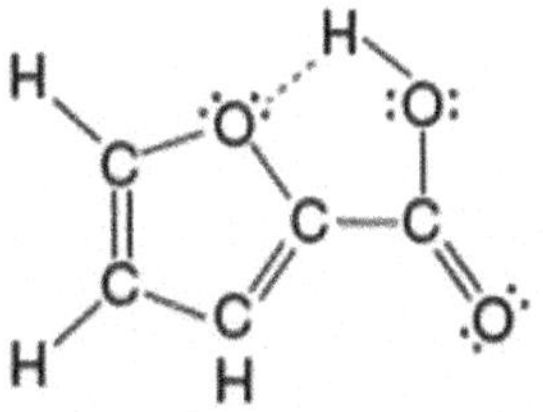

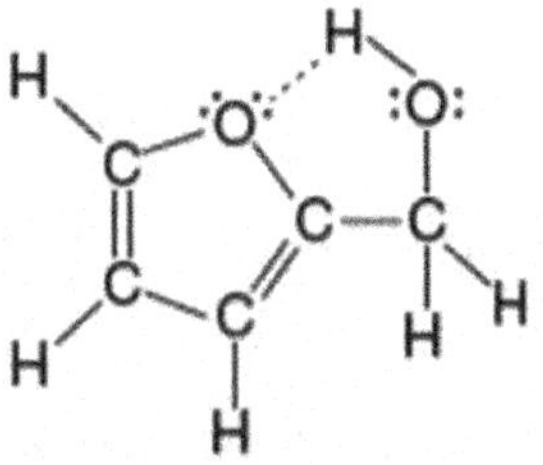

11.120   Plan: Determine the total mass of water, with a partial pressure of 4.133 kPa, contained in the air. This is done by using $pV = nRT$ to find the moles of water at 4.133 kPa and 22.0°C. Then calculate the total mass of water, with a partial pressure of 1.333 kPa, contained in the air. The difference between these two values is the amount of water removed. The mass of water and the heat of condensation are necessary to find the amount of energy removed from the water.

Solution:

a) $pV = nRT$

$$n = \frac{pV}{RT}$$

Convert volume to units of L: $V\,(L) = \left(2.4\text{x}10^6\ \text{m}^3\right)\left(\dfrac{1\ \text{L}}{10^{-3}\ \text{m}^3}\right) = 2.4\text{x}10^9\ \text{L}$

Moles of H_2O at 4.133 kPa = $\dfrac{\left(4.133\ \text{kPa}\right)\left(2.4\text{x}10^9\ \text{L}\right)}{\left(8.31446\dfrac{\text{L}\bullet\text{kPa}}{\text{mol}\bullet\text{K}}\right)\left((273.2 + 22.0)\,\text{K}\right)} = 4{,}041{,}348\ \text{mol}$

Mass (metric tons) of H_2O at 44.133 kPa = $\left(4{,}041{,}348\ \text{mol}\ H_2O\right)\left(\dfrac{18.02\ \text{g}}{1\ \text{mol}\ H_2O}\right)\left(\dfrac{1\ \text{kg}}{10^3\ \text{g}}\right)\left(\dfrac{1\ \text{t}}{10^3\ \text{kg}}\right)$

$$= 73.552533\ \text{t}\ H_2O$$

Moles of H_2O at 1.333 kPa = $\dfrac{\left(1.333\ \text{kPa}\right)\left(2.4\text{x}10^9\ \text{L}\right)}{\left(8.31446\dfrac{\text{L}\bullet\text{kPa}}{\text{mol}\bullet\text{K}}\right)\left((273.2 + 22.0)\,\text{K}\right)} = 1{,}303{,}440\ \text{mol}$

Mass (metric tons) of H_2O at 1.333 kPa $= (1{,}303{,}440 \text{ mol } H_2O)\left(\dfrac{18.02 \text{ g}}{1 \text{ mol } H_2O}\right)\left(\dfrac{1 \text{ kg}}{10^3 \text{ g}}\right)\left(\dfrac{1 \text{ t}}{10^3 \text{ kg}}\right)$

$$= 23.4880 \text{ tons } H_2O$$

Mass of water removed $= (73.5525 \text{ metric tons } H_2O) - (23.4880 \text{ metric tons } H_2O) = 50.0645 \text{ metric tons} =$ **50.1 metric tons H_2O**

b) The heat of condensation for water is –40.7 kJ/mol.

Heat (kJ) $= (50.0645 \text{ tons } H_2O)\left(\dfrac{10^3 \text{ kg}}{1 \text{ ton}}\right)\left(\dfrac{10^3 \text{ g}}{1 \text{ kg}}\right)\left(\dfrac{1 \text{ mol } H_2O}{18.02 \text{ g } H_2O}\right)\left(\dfrac{-40.7 \text{ kJ}}{1 \text{ mol } H_2O}\right)$

$$= -1.119574 \times 10^8 \text{ kJ} = \mathbf{-1.12 \times 10^8 \text{ kJ}}$$

11.121   Plan: At the boiling point, the vapour pressure equals the atmospheric pressure, so the two boiling points can be used to find the heat of vapourization for amphetamine using the Clausius-Clapeyron equation. Then use the Clausius-Clapeyron equation to find the vapour pressure of amphetamine at a different temperature, 20.°C. Then use $pV = nRT$ to find the concentration of amphetamine at this calculated pressure and 20.°C.
Solution:

$$\ln\frac{p_2}{p_1} = -\frac{\Delta_{vap}H°}{R}\left(\frac{1}{T_2} - \frac{1}{T_1}\right) \qquad \begin{array}{ll} p_1 = 101.3 \text{ kPa} & T_1 = 201°C + 273 = 474 \text{ K} \\ \\ p_2 = 1.733 \text{ kPa} & T_2 = 83°C + 273 = 356 \text{ K} \\ \\ \Delta_{vap}H° = ? \end{array}$$

$$\ln\frac{1.733 \text{ kPa}}{101.3 \text{ kPa}} = \frac{-\Delta_{vap}H°}{8.314 \text{ J/mol•K}}\left(\frac{1}{356 \text{ K}} - \frac{1}{474 \text{ K}}\right)$$

$-4.045413384 = -\Delta_{vap}H°\,(0.000084109 \text{ mol/J})$

$\Delta_{vap}H° = (-4.045413384)/(-0.000084109 \text{ mol/J}) = 48{,}097.271 \text{ J/mol}$

$$\ln\frac{p_2}{p_1} = -\frac{\Delta_{vap}H°}{R}\left(\frac{1}{T_2} - \frac{1}{T_1}\right) \qquad \begin{array}{ll} p_1 = 1.733 \text{ kPa} & T_1 = 83°C + 273 = 356 \text{ K} \\ \\ p_2 = ? & T_2 = 20°C + 273 = 293 \text{ K} \\ \\ \Delta_{vap}H° = 48{,}097.271 \text{ J/mol} \end{array}$$

$$\ln\frac{p_2}{1.733 \text{ kPa}} = \frac{-48{,}097.271 \text{ J/mol}}{8.314 \text{ J/mol•K}}\left(\frac{1}{293 \text{ K}} - \frac{1}{356 \text{ K}}\right) = -3.4940841$$

$$\frac{p_2}{1.733 \text{ kPa}} = 0.0303766$$

$p_2 = (0.0303766)(1.733 \text{ kPa}) = 0.05264 \text{ kPa}$

At this pressure and a temperature of 20.°C, use the ideal gas equation to calculate the concentration of amphetamine in the air. Use a volume of 1 m³. Moles from the ideal gas equation times the molar mass gives the mass in a cubic meter.

$$\text{Moles} = n = \frac{pV}{RT} = \frac{(0.05264 \text{ kPa})(1 \text{ m}^3)}{\left(8.31446\dfrac{\text{L•kPa}}{\text{mol•K}}\right)(293 \text{ K})}\left(\frac{1 \text{ L}}{10^{-3} \text{ m}^3}\right) = 0.02160904 \text{ mol amphetamine}$$

$$\text{Mass (g)} = (0.02160904 \text{ mol})\left(\frac{135.20 \text{ g amphetamine}}{1 \text{ mol}}\right) = 2.9215422 \text{ g/m}^3 = \mathbf{2.9 \text{ g/m}^3}$$

11.126 <u>Plan:</u> The equation $q = c$ x mass x ΔT is used to calculate the heat involved in changing the temperature of solid A, the temperature of liquid A after it melts, and the temperature of vapour A after the liquid boils; the heat of fusion is used to calculate the heat involved in the phase change of solid A to liquid A and the heat of vapourization is used to calculate the heat involved in the phase change of liquid A to A as a vapour.

<u>Solution:</u>

a) To heat the substance to the melting point the substance must be warmed from –40.°C to –20.°C:

$q = c$ x mass x ΔT = (25 g)(1.0 J/g•K)[(273+(–20))K –(273+ (–40.))K] = 500 J

Time (min) required $= \left(500 \text{ J}\right)\left(\dfrac{1 \text{ min}}{450 \text{ J}}\right) = 1.1111$ min = **1.1 min**

b) Phase change of the substance from solid at –20.°C to liquid at –20.°C:

$q = n\left(\Delta_{\text{fus}}H^{\circ}\right) = \left(25 \text{ g}\right)\left(\dfrac{180. \text{ J}}{1 \text{ g}}\right) = 4500$ J

Time (min) required $= \left(4500 \text{ J}\right)\left(\dfrac{1 \text{ min}}{450 \text{ J}}\right) =$ **10. min**

c) To heat the substance to the melting point the substance must be warmed from –20.°C to 85°C:

$q = c$ x mass x ΔT = (25 g)(2.5 J/g•K)[(273+85)K – (273+(–20.))K] = 6562.5 J

Time (min) required $= \left(6562.5 \text{ J}\right)\left(\dfrac{1 \text{ min}}{450 \text{ J}}\right) = 14.583$ min = **15 min**

To boil the sample at 85°C:

$q = n\left(\Delta_{\text{vap}}H^{\circ}\right) = \left(25 \text{ g}\right)\left(\dfrac{500. \text{ J}}{1 \text{ g}}\right) = 12,500$ J

Time (min) required $= \left(12,500 \text{ J}\right)\left(\dfrac{1 \text{ min}}{450 \text{ J}}\right) = 27.78$ min = **28 min**

Warming the vapour from 85°C to 100.°C:

$q = c$ x mass x ΔT = (25 g)(0.5 J/g•K)[(273+100)K –(273+ 85)K] = 187.5 J

Time (min) required $= \left(187.5 \text{ J}\right)\left(\dfrac{1 \text{ min}}{450 \text{ J}}\right) = 0.417$ min = **0.4 min**

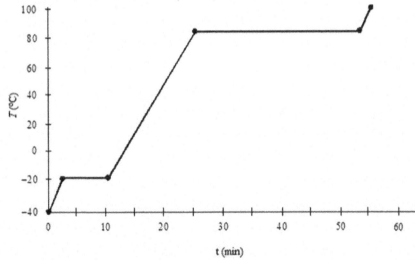

11.127 <u>Plan:</u> Balanced chemical equations are necessary. See the section on ceramic materials for the reactions. These equations may be combined to produce an overall equation with an overall yield. Find the limiting reactant which is then used to calculate the amount of boron nitride produced. The ideal gas law is used to calculate the moles of NH_3.

<u>Solution:</u>

Step 1 $B(OH)_3(s) + 3NH_3(g) \rightarrow \text{B(NH}_2)_3(s) + 3H_2O(g)$

Step 2 B̶(̶N̶H̶₂̶)̶₃̶(̶s̶)̶ → BN(*s*) + 2NH₃(*g*)

Overall reaction: $B(OH)_3(s) + NH_3(g) \rightarrow BN(s) + 3\ H_2O(g)$
Yields are 85.5% for step 1 and 86.8% for step 2.
Overall fractional yield = (85.5%/100%)(86.8%/100%) = 0.74214
Find the limiting reactant. Since the overall reaction has a 1:1 mole ratio, the reactant with the fewer moles will be limiting.

$$\text{Moles of } B(OH)_3 = \left(1.00\ \text{t}\ B(OH)_3\right)\left(\frac{10^3\ \text{kg}}{1\text{t}}\right)\left(\frac{10^3\ \text{g}}{1\ \text{kg}}\right)\left(\frac{1\ \text{mol}\ B(OH)_3}{61.83\ \text{g}\ B(OH)_3}\right)$$

$$= 1.6173379 \times 10^4\ \text{mol}\ B(OH)_3$$

$$V\ (\text{L}) = \left(12.5\ \text{m}^3\right)\left(\frac{1\ \text{L}}{10^{-3}\ \text{m}^3}\right) = 12{,}500\ \text{L}$$

$$\text{Moles of } NH_3 = pV/RT = \frac{\left(3.07 \times 10^3\ \text{kPa}\right)\left(12{,}500\ \text{L}\right)}{\left(8.31446\dfrac{\text{L}\bullet\text{kPa}}{\text{mol}\bullet\text{K}}\right)\left(275\ \text{K}\right)} = 1.6783466 \times 10^4\ \text{mol}\ NH_3$$

$B(OH)_3$ is the limiting reactant.

$$\text{Mass (g) of } BN = \left(1.6173379 \times 10^4\ \text{mol}\ B(OH)_3\right)\left(\frac{1\ \text{mol}\ BN}{1\ \text{mol}\ B(OH)_3}\right)\left(\frac{24.82\ \text{g}\ BN}{1\ \text{mol}\ BN}\right)\left(\frac{74.214\%}{100\%}\right)$$

$$= 2.97912 \times 10^5\ \text{g} = \mathbf{2.98 \times 10^5\ g\ BN}$$

11.130 Plan: A body-centered cubic unit cell has eight corner atoms; 8 atoms x 1/8 atom per cell = 1 atom. In addition, the body-centered cell has an atom in the center, for a total of two atoms.
Solution:

$$\text{Mass (u) of two Na atoms} = \left(2\ \text{Na atoms}\right)\left(\frac{22.99\ \text{u}}{1\ \text{Na atom}}\right) = \mathbf{45.98\ u}.$$

CHAPTER 12 THE PROPERTIES OF MIXTURES: SOLUTIONS AND COLLOIDS

CHEMICAL CONNECTIONS BOXED READING PROBLEMS

B12.1   a) The colloidal particles in water generally have negatively charged surfaces and so repel each other, slowing the settling process. Cake alum, $Al_2(SO_4)_3$, is added to coagulate the colloids. The Al^{3+} ions neutralize the negative surface charges and allow the particles to aggregate and settle.
b) Water that contains large amounts of divalent cations (such as Ca^{2+} and Mg^{2+}) is called hard water. During cleaning, these ions combine with the fatty-acid anions in soaps to produce insoluble deposits.
c) In reverse osmosis, a pressure greater than the osmotic pressure is applied to the solution, forcing the water back through the membrane and leaving the ions behind.
d) Chlorine may give the water an unpleasant odor, and can form carcinogenic chlorinated compounds.
e) The high concentration of NaCl displaces the divalent and polyvalent ions from the ion-exchange resin.

END–OF–CHAPTER PROBLEMS

12.2   When a salt such as NaCl dissolves, ion-dipole forces cause the ions to separate, and many water molecules cluster around each of them in hydration shells. Ion-dipole forces hold the outermost shell. Additional shells are held by hydrogen bonding to inner shells.

12.4   **Sodium octadecanoate (stearate)** would be a more effective soap because the hydrocarbon chain in the stearate ion is longer than the chain in the ethanoate (acetate) ion. A soap forms suspended particles called micelles with the polar end of the soap interacting with the water solvent molecules and the nonpolar ends forming a nonpolar environment inside the micelle. Oils dissolve in the nonpolar portion of the micelle. Thus, a better solvent for the oils in dirt is a more nonpolar substance. The long hydrocarbon chain in the stearate ion is better at dissolving oils in the micelle than the shorter hydrocarbon chain in the acetate ion.

12.7   <u>Plan:</u> A more concentrated solution will have more solute dissolved in the solvent. Determine the types of intermolecular forces in the solute and solvents. A solute tends to be more soluble in a solvent whose intermolecular forces are similar to its own.
<u>Solution:</u>
Potassium nitrate, KNO_3, is an ionic compound and can form ion-dipole forces with a polar solvent like water, thus dissolving in the water. Potassium nitrate is not soluble in the nonpolar solvent CCl_4. Because potassium nitrate dissolves to a greater extent in water, **a) KNO_3 in H_2O** will result in the more concentrated solution.

12.11   <u>Plan:</u> To identify the strongest type of intermolecular force, check the formula of the solute and identify the forces that could occur. Then look at the formula for the solvent and determine if the forces identified for the solute would occur with the solvent. Ionic forces are present in ionic compounds; dipole-dipole forces are present in polar substances, while nonpolar substances exhibit only dispersion forces. The strongest force is ion-dipole followed by dipole-dipole (including hydrogen bonds). Next in strength is ion–induced dipole force and then dipole–induced dipole force. The weakest intermolecular interactions are dispersion forces.
<u>Solution:</u>
a) **Hydrogen bonding** occurs between the H atom on water and the lone electron pair on the O atom in methoxymethane (CH_3OCH_3). However, none of the hydrogen atoms on methoxymethane participates in hydrogen bonding because the C–H bond does not have sufficient polarity.
b) The dipole in water induces a dipole on the Ne(g) atom, so **dipole–induced dipole** interactions are the strongest intermolecular forces in this solution.
c) Nitrogen gas and butane are both nonpolar substances, so **dispersion forces** are the principal attractive forces.

12.13   Plan: Ethoxyethane ($CH_3CH_2OCH_2CH_3$) is polar with dipole-dipole interactions as the dominant intermolecular forces. Examine the solutes to determine which has intermolecular forces more similar to those in ethoxyethane. This solute is the one that would be more soluble.
Solution:
a) **HCl** would be more soluble since it is a covalent compound with dipole-dipole forces, whereas NaCl is an ionic solid. Dipole-dipole forces between HCl and ethoxyethane are more similar to the dipole forces in ethoxyethane than the ion-dipole forces between NaCl and ethoxyethane.

b) **CH_3CHO** (ethanal, also known as acetaldehyde) would be more soluble. The dominant interactions in H_2O are hydrogen bonding, a stronger type of dipole-dipole force. The dominant interactions in CH_3CHO are dipole-dipole. The solute-solvent interactions between CH_3CHO and ethoxyethane are more similar to the solvent intermolecular forces than the forces between H_2O and ethoxyethane.
c) **CH_3CH_2MgBr** would be more soluble. CH_3CH_2MgBr has a polar end (–MgBr) and a nonpolar end (CH_3CH_2–), whereas $MgBr_2$ is an ionic compound. The nonpolar end of CH_3CH_2MgBr and ethoxyethane would interact with dispersion forces, while the polar end of CH_3CH_2MgBr and the dipole in ethoxyethane would interact with dipole-dipole forces.

12.16   Plan: Determine the types of intermolecular forces present in the two compounds and in water and hexane. Substances with similar types of forces tend to be soluble while substances with different type of forces tend to be insoluble.
Solution:
Gluconic acid is a very polar molecule because it has –OH groups attached to every carbon. The abundance of –OH bonds allows gluconic acid to participate in extensive hydrogen bonding with water, hence its great solubility in water. On the other hand, caproic acid has a five carbon, nonpolar, hydrophobic ("water hating") tail that does not easily dissolve in water. The dispersion forces in the nonpolar tail are more similar to the dispersion forces in hexane, hence its greater solubility in hexane.

12.18   For a general solvent, the energy changes needed to separate solvent into particles ($\Delta_{solvent}H$), and that needed to mix the solvent and solute particles ($\Delta_{mix}H$) would be combined to obtain $\Delta_{solution}H$.

12.22   This compound would be very **soluble** in water. A large exothermic value in $\Delta_{solution}H$ (enthalpy of solution) means that the solution has a much lower energy state than the isolated solute and solvent particles, so the system tends to the formation of the solution. Entropy that accompanies dissolution always favors solution formation. Entropy becomes important when explaining why solids with endothermic $\Delta_{solution}H$ values (and higher energy states) are still soluble in water.

12.23   Plan: $\Delta_{solution}H = \Delta_{lattice}H + \Delta_{hydration}H$. Lattice energy values are always positive as energy is required to separate the ions from each other. Hydration energy values are always negative as energy is released when intermolecular forces between ions and water form. Since the heat of solution for KCl is endothermic, the lattice energy must be greater than the hydration energy for an overall input of energy.
Solution:

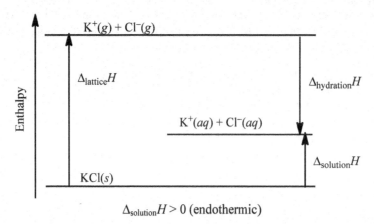

$\Delta_{solution}H > 0$ (endothermic)

12.25   Plan: Charge density is the ratio of an ion's charge (regardless of sign) to its volume. An ion's volume is related to its radius. For ions whose charges have the same sign (+ or –), ion size decreases as a group in the periodic table is ascended and as you proceed from left to right in the periodic table. Charge density increases with increasing charge and increases with decreasing size.
Solution:
a) Both ions have a +1 charge, but the volume of Na^+ is smaller, so it has the greater charge density.
b) Sr^{2+} has a greater ionic charge and a smaller size (because it has a greater Z_{eff}), so it has the greater charge density.
c) Na^+ has a smaller ion volume than Cl^-, so it has the greater charge density.
d) O^{2-} has a greater ionic charge and similar ion volume, so it has the greater charge density.
e) OH^- has a smaller ion volume than SH^- (O is smaller than S), so it has the greater charge density.
f) Mg^{2+} has the higher charge density because it has a smaller ion volume.
g) Mg^{2+} has the higher charge density because it has both a smaller ion volume and greater charge.
h) CO_3^{2-} has the higher charge density because it has both a smaller ion volume and greater charge.

12.27   Plan: The ion with the greater charge density will have the larger $\Delta_{hydration}H$.
Solution:
a) Na^+ would have a larger $\Delta_{hydration}H$ than Cs^+ since its charge density is greater than that of Cs^+.
b) Sr^{2+} would have a larger $\Delta_{hydration}H$ than Rb^+.
c) Na^+ would have a larger $\Delta_{hydration}H$ than Cl^-.
d) O^{2-} would have a larger $\Delta_{hydration}H$ than F^-.
e) OH^- would have a larger $\Delta_{hydration}H$ than SH^-.
f) Mg^{2+} would have a larger $\Delta_{hydration}H$ than Ba^{2+}.
g) Mg^{2+} would have a larger $\Delta_{hydration}H$ than Na^+.
h) CO_3^{2-} would have a larger $\Delta_{hydration}H$ than NO_3^-.

12.29   Plan: Use the relationship $\Delta_{solution}H = \Delta_{lattice}H + \Delta_{hydration}H$. Given $\Delta_{solution}H$ and $\Delta_{lattice}H$, $\Delta_{hydration}H$ can be calculated. $\Delta_{hydration}H$ increases with increasing charge density, and charge density increases with increasing charge and decreasing size.
Solution:
a) The two ions in potassium bromate are K^+ and BrO_3^-.

$\Delta_{solution}H = \Delta_{lattice}H + \Delta_{hydration}H$

$\Delta_{hydration}H = \Delta_{solution}H - \Delta_{lattice}H = 41.1$ kJ/mol – 745 kJ/mol = –703.9 kJ/mol = **–704 kJ/mol**

b) K^+ ion contributes more to the heat of hydration because it has a smaller size and, therefore, a greater charge density.

12.31   Plan: Entropy increases as the possible states for a system increase, which is related to the freedom of motion of its particles and the number of ways they can be arranged.
Solution:
a) Entropy **increases** as the gasoline is burned. Gaseous products at a higher temperature form.
b) Entropy **decreases** as the gold is separated from the ore. Pure gold has only the arrangement of gold atoms next to gold atoms, while the ore mixture has a greater number of possible arrangements among the components of the mixture.
c) Entropy **increases** as a solute dissolves in the solvent.

12.34   Add a pinch of the solid solute to each solution. A saturated solution contains the maximum amount of dissolved solute at a particular temperature. When additional solute is added to this solution, it will remain undissolved. An unsaturated solution contains less than the maximum amount of dissolved solute and so will dissolve added solute. A supersaturated solution is unstable and addition of a "seed" crystal of solute causes the excess solute to crystallize immediately, leaving behind a saturated solution.

12.37   Plan: The solubility of a gas in water decreases with increasing temperature and increases with increasing pressure.
Solution:
a) Increasing pressure for a gas **increases** the solubility of the gas according to Henry's law.

b) Increasing the volume of a gas causes a decrease in its pressure (Boyle's law), which **decreases** the solubility of the gas.

12.39   Plan: Solubility for a gas is calculated from Henry's law: $S_{gas} = k_H \times p_{gas}$. We know k_H and p_{gas}, so S_{gas} can be calculated with units of mol/L. To calculate the mass of oxygen gas, convert moles of O_2 to mass of O_2 using the molar mass.
Solution:
a) $S_{gas} = k_H \times p_{gas}$

$$S_{gas} = \left(1.26 \times 10^{-5} \frac{mol}{L \cdot kPa}\right)(101.3 \text{ kPa}) = 1.28 \times 10^{-3} \text{ mol/L}$$

$$\text{Mass (g) of } O_2 = \left(\frac{1.28 \times 10^{-3} \text{ mol } O_2}{L}\right)\left(\frac{32.0 \text{ g } O_2}{1 \text{ mol } O_2}\right)(2.50 \text{ L}) = 0.1024 \text{ g} = \textbf{0.102 g } O_2$$

b) The mass of gas that will dissolve in a given volume decreases proportionately with the partial pressure of the gas.

$$S_{gas} = \left(1.26 \times 10^{-5} \frac{mol}{L \cdot kPa}\right)(21.2 \text{ kPa}) = 2.6712 \times 10^{-4} \text{ mol/L}$$

$$\text{Mass (g) of } O_2 = \left(\frac{2.6712 \times 10^{-4} \text{ mol } O_2}{L}\right)\left(\frac{32.0 \text{ g } O_2}{1 \text{ mol } O_2}\right)(2.50 \text{ L}) = 0.0213696 \text{ g} = \textbf{0.0214 g } O_2$$

12.42   Plan: Solubility for a gas is calculated from Henry's law: $S_{gas} = k_H \times p_{gas}$. We know k_H and p_{gas}, so S_{gas} can be calculated with units of mol/L.
Solution:
$S_{gas} = k_H \times p_{gas} = (3.7 \times 10^{-4} \text{ mol/L} \cdot \text{kPa})(557.2 \text{ kPa}) = 0.2061 \text{ mol/L} = \textbf{0.21 mol/L}$

12.45   Plan: Refer to the table of concentration definitions for the different methods of expressing concentration.
Solution:
a) **Concentration (mol/L)** and **parts-by-volume** (% w/v or % v/v) include the volume of the solution.
b) **Parts-by-mass** (% w/w) include the mass of solution directly. (Others may involve the mass indirectly.)
c) **Molality** includes the mass of the solvent.

12.47   Converting between concentration (mol/L) and molality involves conversion between volume of solution and mass of solution. Both of these quantities are given so interconversion is possible. To convert to mole fraction requires that the mass of solvent be converted to moles of solvent. Since the identity of the solvent is not given, conversion to mole fraction is not possible if the molar mass is not known.

12.49   Plan: The concentration (mol/L) is the amount of solute (moles) in each litre of solution: $c = \dfrac{\text{mol of solute}}{V(L) \text{ of solution}}$.

Convert the masses to moles and the volumes to litres and divide moles by volume.
Solution:

$$\text{a) Concentration} = \left(\frac{32.3 \text{ g } C_{12}H_{22}O_{11}}{100. \text{ mL}}\right)\left(\frac{1 \text{ mL}}{10^{-3} \text{ L}}\right)\left(\frac{1 \text{ mol } C_{12}H_{22}O_{11}}{342.30 \text{ g } C_{12}H_{22}O_{11}}\right)$$

$$= 0.943617 \text{ mol/L} = \textbf{0.944 mol/L } C_{12}H_{22}O_{11}$$

$$\text{b) Concentration} = \left(\frac{5.80 \text{ g LiNO}_3}{505 \text{ mL}}\right)\left(\frac{1 \text{ mL}}{10^{-3} \text{ L}}\right)\left(\frac{1 \text{ mol LiNO}_3}{68.95 \text{ g LiNO}_3}\right) = 0.166572 \text{ mol/L} = \textbf{0.167 mol/L LiNO}_3$$

12.51 <u>Plan:</u> Dilution calculations can be done using $c_{conc}V_{conc} = c_{dil}V_{dil}$.
<u>Solution:</u>
a) $c_{conc} = 0.240$ mol/L NaOH $V_{conc} = 78.0$ mL $c_{dil} = ?$ $V_{dil} = 0.250$ L

$$c_{dil} = \frac{(c_{conc})(V_{conc})}{(V_{dil})} = \frac{(0.240 \text{ mol / L})(78.0 \text{ mL})}{(0.250 \text{ L})}\left(\frac{10^{-3} \text{ L}}{1 \text{ mL}}\right) = 0.07488 \text{ mol/L} = \textbf{0.0749 mol/L}$$

b) $c_{conc} = 1.2$ mol/L HNO_3 $V_{conc} = 38.5$ mL $c_{dil} = ?$ $V_{dil} = 0.130$ L

$$c_{dil} = \frac{(c_{conc})(V_{conc})}{(V_{dil})} = \frac{(1.2 \text{ mol / L})(38.5 \text{ mL})}{(0.130 \text{ L})}\left(\frac{10^{-3} \text{ L}}{1 \text{ mL}}\right) = 0.355385 \text{ mol/L} = \textbf{0.36 mol/L}$$

12.53 <u>Plan:</u> For part a), find the amount of KH_2PO_4 (moles) needed to make 365 mL of a solution of this concentration (mol/L). Convert moles to mass using the molar mass of KH_2PO_4. For part b), use the relationship $c_{conc}V_{conc} = c_{dil}V_{dil}$ to find the volume of 1.25 mol/L NaOH needed.
<u>Solution:</u>

a) Moles of $KH_2PO_4 = (365 \text{ mL})\left(\frac{10^{-3} \text{ L}}{1 \text{ mL}}\right)\left(\frac{8.55 \times 10^{-2} \text{ mol } KH_2PO_4}{L}\right) = 0.0312075 \text{ mol}$

Mass (g) of $KH_2PO_4 = (0.0312075 \text{ mol } KH_2PO_4)\left(\frac{136.09 \text{ g } KH_2PO_4}{1 \text{ mol } KH_2PO_4}\right) = 4.24703 \text{ g} = 4.25 \text{ g } KH_2PO_4$

Add enough water to **4.25 g KH_2PO_4** to make 365 mL of aqueous solution.
b) $c_{conc} = 1.25$ mol/L NaOH $V_{conc} = ?$ $c_{dil} = 0.335$ mol/L NaOH $V_{dil} = 465$ mL

$$V_{conc} = \frac{(c_{dil})(V_{dil})}{(c_{conc})} = \frac{(0.335 \text{ mol / L})(465 \text{ mL})}{(1.25 \text{ mol/L})} = 124.62 \text{ mL} = \textbf{125 mL}$$

Add enough water to **125 mL** of 1.25 mol/L NaOH to make 465 mL of solution.

12.55 <u>Plan:</u> To find the mass of KBr needed in part a), find the moles of KBr in 1.40 L of a 0.288 mol/L solution and convert to grams using the molar mass of KBr. To find the volume of the concentrated solution that will be diluted to 255 mL in part b), use $c_{conc}V_{conc} = c_{dil}V_{dil}$ and solve for V_{conc}.
<u>Solution:</u>

a) Moles of KBr = $(1.40 \text{ L})\left(\frac{0.288 \text{ mol KBr}}{L}\right) = 0.4032 \text{ mol}$

Mass (g) of KBr = $(0.4032 \text{ mol})\left(\frac{119.00 \text{ g KBr}}{1 \text{ mol KBr}}\right) = 47.9808 \text{ g} = 48.0 \text{ g KBr}$

To make the solution, weigh **48.0 g KBr** and then dilute to 1.40 L with distilled water.
b) $c_{conc} = 0.264$ mol/L $LiNO_3$ $V_{conc} = ?$ $c_{dil} = 0.0856$ mol/L $LiNO_3$ $V_{dil} = 255$ mL

$$V_{conc} = \frac{(c_{dil})(V_{dil})}{(c_{conc})} = \frac{(0.0856 \text{ mol/L})(255 \text{ mL})}{(0.264 \text{ mol/L})} = 82.68182 \text{ mL} = 82.7 \text{ mL}$$

To make the 0.0856 mol/L solution, measure **82.7 mL** of the 0.264 mol/L solution and add distilled water to make a total of 255 mL.

12.57 <u>Plan:</u> Molality, $m = \dfrac{\text{moles of solute}}{\text{kg of solvent}}$. Convert the mass of solute to moles and divide by the mass of solvent in units of kg.
<u>Solution:</u>

a) Moles of glycine = 85.4 g glycine $\left(\dfrac{1 \text{ mol glycine}}{75.07 \text{ g glycine}}\right) = 1.137605 \text{ mol}$

m glycine = $\dfrac{1.137605 \text{ mol glycine}}{1.270 \text{ kg}} = 0.895752 \text{ mol/kg} = \textbf{0.896 mol/kg glycine}$

b) Moles of glycerol = $8.59 \text{ g glycerol} \left(\dfrac{1 \text{ mol glycerol}}{92.09 \text{ g glycerol}} \right) = 0.093278 \text{ mol}$

Volume (kg) of solvent = $77.0 \text{ g} \left(\dfrac{1 \text{ kg}}{10^3 \text{ g}} \right) = 0.0770 \text{ kg}$

m glycerol = $\dfrac{0.093278 \text{ mol glycerol}}{0.0770 \text{ kg}} = 1.2114 \text{ mol/kg} = \textbf{1.21 mol/kg glycerol}$

12.59   <u>Plan:</u> Molality, $m = \dfrac{\text{moles of solute}}{\text{kg of solvent}}$. Use the density of benzene to find the mass and then the moles of benzene; use the density of hexane to find the mass of hexane and convert to units of kg. Divide the moles of benzene by the mass of hexane.
<u>Solution:</u>

Mass (g) of benzene = $\left(44.0 \text{ mL C}_6\text{H}_6 \right) \left(\dfrac{0.877 \text{ g}}{1 \text{ mL}} \right) = 38.588 \text{ g benzene}$

Moles of benzene = $\left(38.588 \text{ g C}_6\text{H}_6 \right) \left(\dfrac{1 \text{ mol C}_6\text{H}_6}{78.11 \text{ g C}_6\text{H}_6} \right) = 0.49402 \text{ mol benzene}$

Mass (kg) of hexane = $\left(167 \text{ mL C}_6\text{H}_{14} \right) \left(\dfrac{0.660 \text{ g}}{\text{mL}} \right) \left(\dfrac{1 \text{ kg}}{10^3 \text{ g}} \right) = 0.11022 \text{ kg hexane}$

$m = \dfrac{\text{moles of solute}}{\text{kg of solvent}} = \dfrac{\left(0.49402 \text{ mol C}_6\text{H}_6 \right)}{\left(0.11022 \text{ kg C}_6\text{H}_{14} \right)} = 4.48213 \text{ mol/kg} = \textbf{4.48 mol/kg C}_6\textbf{H}_6$

12.61   <u>Plan:</u> In part a), the total mass of the <u>solution</u> is 3.10×10^2 g, so mass$_{\text{solute}}$ + mass$_{\text{solvent}}$ = 3.10×10^2 g. Assume that you have 1000 g of the solvent water and find the mass of $C_2H_6O_2$ needed to make a 0.125 mol/kg solution. Then a ratio can be used to find the mass of $C_2H_6O_2$ needed to make 3.10×10^2 g of a 0.125 mol/kg solution. Part b) is a dilution problem. First, determine the amount of solute in your target solution and then determine the amount of the concentrated acid solution needed to get that amount of solute.
<u>Solution:</u>

a) Mass (g) of $C_2H_6O_2$ in 1000 g (1 kg) of H_2O = $\left(1 \text{ kg H}_2\text{O} \right) \left(\dfrac{0.125 \text{ mol C}_2\text{H}_6\text{O}_2}{1 \text{ kg H}_2\text{O}} \right) \left(\dfrac{62.07 \text{ g C}_2\text{H}_6\text{O}_2}{1 \text{ mol C}_2\text{H}_6\text{O}_2} \right)$

$= 7.75875 \text{ g C}_2\text{H}_6\text{O}_2 \text{ in } 1000 \text{ g H}_2\text{O}$

Mass (g) of this solution = 1000 g H_2O + 7.75875 g $C_2H_6O_2$ = 1007.75875 g

Mass (g) of $C_2H_6O_2$ for 3.10×10^2 g of solution = $\left(\dfrac{7.75875 \text{ g C}_2\text{H}_6\text{O}_2}{1007.75875 \text{ g solution}} \right) \left(3.10 \times 10^2 \text{ g solution} \right)$

$= 2.386695 \text{ g C}_2\text{H}_6\text{O}_2$

Mass$_{\text{solvent}}$ = 3.10×10^2 g − mass$_{\text{solute}}$ = 3.10×10^2 g − 2.386695 g $C_2H_6O_2$ = 307.613305 g = 308 g H_2O
Therefore, **add 2.39 g $C_2H_6O_2$ to 308 g of H_2O** to make a 0.125 mol/kg solution.

b) Mass (kg) of HNO_3 in the 2.20% solution = $\left(1.20 \text{ kg} \right) \left(\dfrac{2.20\%}{100\%} \right) = 0.0264 \text{ kg HNO}_3 \text{ (solute)}$

Mass % = $\dfrac{\text{mass of solute}}{\text{mass of solution}} (100)$

Mass of 52.0% solution containing 0.0264 kg HNO_3 = $\dfrac{\text{mass of solute} (100)}{\text{mass \%}} = \dfrac{0.0264 \text{ kg} (100)}{52.0\%}$

$= 0.050769 \text{ kg} = 0.0508 \text{ kg}$

Mass of water added = mass of 2.2% solution − mass of 52.0% solution

$= 1.20 \text{ kg} − 0.050769 \text{ kg} = 1.149231 \text{ kg} = 1.15 \text{ kg}$

Add 0.0508 kg of the 52.0% (w/w) HNO_3 to 1.15 kg H_2O to make 1.20 kg of 2.20% (w/w) HNO_3.

12.63   Plan: You know the moles of solute (C_3H_7OH) and the moles of solvent (H_2O). Divide moles of C_3H_7OH by the total moles of C_3H_7OH and H_2O to obtain mole fraction. To calculate mass percent, convert moles of solute and solvent to mass and divide the mass of solute by the total mass of solution (solute + solvent). For molality, divide the moles of C_3H_7OH by the mass of water expressed in units of kg.
Solution:
a) Mole fraction is moles of propan-2-ol (isopropanol) per total moles.

$$X_{\text{propan-2-ol}} = \frac{\text{moles of propan-2-ol}}{\text{moles of isopropanol} + \text{moles of water}} = \frac{0.35 \text{ mol propan-2-ol}}{(0.35 + 0.85) \text{ mol}} = 0.2916667 = \mathbf{0.29}$$

(Notice that mole fractions have no units.)

b) Mass percent $= \dfrac{\text{mass of solute}}{\text{mass of solution}}(100)$. From the mole amounts, find the masses

of propan-2-ol and water:

$$\text{Mass (g) of propan-2-ol} = (0.35 \text{ mol } C_3H_7OH)\left(\frac{60.09 \text{ g } C_3H_7OH}{1 \text{ mol } C_3H_7OH}\right) = 21.0315 \text{ g propan-2-ol}$$

$$\text{Mass (g) of water} = (0.85 \text{ mol } H_2O)\left(\frac{18.02 \text{ g } H_2O}{1 \text{ mol } H_2O}\right) = 15.317 \text{ g water}$$

$$\text{Mass percent} = \frac{\text{mass of solute}}{\text{mass of solution}}(100) = \frac{21.0315 \text{ g propan-2-ol}}{(21.0315 + 15.317) \text{ g}}(100) = 57.860710 \% = \mathbf{58\%}$$

c) Molality of propan-2-ol is moles of propan-2-ol per kg of water.

$$m = \frac{\text{moles of solute}}{\text{kg of solvent}} = \frac{0.35 \text{ mol propan-2-ol}}{15.317 \text{ g water}}\left(\frac{10^3 \text{ g}}{1 \text{ kg}}\right) = 22.85043 \text{ mol/kg} = \mathbf{23 \text{mol/kg}} \text{ prpan-2-ol}$$

12.65   Plan: Molality $= \dfrac{\text{moles of solute}}{\text{kg of solvent}}$. Use the density of water to convert the volume of water to mass. Multiply the

mass of water in kg by the molality to find moles of cesium bromide; convert moles to mass. To find the mole fraction, convert the masses of water and cesium bromide to moles and divide moles of cesium bromide by the total moles of cesium bromide and water. To calculate mass percent, divide the mass of cesium bromide by the total mass of solution and multiply by 100.
Solution:
The density of water is 1.00 g/mL. The mass of water is:

$$\text{Mass (g) of water} = (0.500 \text{ L})\left(\frac{1 \text{ mL}}{10^{-3} \text{ L}}\right)\left(\frac{1.00 \text{ g}}{1 \text{ mL}}\right)\left(\frac{1 \text{ kg}}{10^3 \text{ g}}\right) = 0.500 \text{ kg}$$

$$m = \frac{\text{moles of solute}}{\text{kg of solvent}}$$

$$0.400 \text{ ,mol/kg CsBr} = \frac{\text{moles CsBr}}{0.500 \text{ kg } H_2O}$$

Moles of CsBr = (0.400 mol/kg)(0.500 kg H_2O) = 0.200 mol

$$\text{Mass (g) of CsBr} = (0.200 \text{ mol CsBr})\left(\frac{212.8 \text{ g CsBr}}{1 \text{ mol CsBr}}\right) = 42.56 \text{ g} = \mathbf{42.6 \text{ g CsBr}}$$

$$\text{Mass (g) of water} = (0.500 \text{ kg})\left(\frac{10^3 \text{ g}}{1 \text{ kg}}\right) = 500. \text{ g water}$$

Mass of solution $=$ mass (g) H_2O + mass of CsBr = 500. g H_2O + 42.56 g CsBr = 542.56 g

$$\text{Moles of } H_2O = (500. \text{ g } H_2O)\left(\frac{1 \text{ mol } H_2O}{18.02 \text{ g } H_2O}\right) = 27.74695 \text{ mol } H_2O$$

$$X_{CsBr} = \frac{mol\ CsBr}{mol\ CsBr + mol\ H_2O} = \frac{0.2000\ mol\ CsBr}{(0.2000 + 27.74695)\,mol} = 7.156\times10^{-3} = \mathbf{7.16\times10^{-3}}$$

$$Mass\ percent\ CsBr = \frac{mass\ of\ CsBr}{mass\ of\ solution}(100) = \frac{(42.56\ g\ CsBr)}{(42.56 + 500.)g} \times 100\% = 7.84429\ \% = \mathbf{7.84\%\ CsBr}$$

12.67   Plan: You are given the mass percent of the solution. Assuming 100. g of solution allows us to express the mass % as the mass of solute, NH_3. To find the mass of solvent, subtract the mass of NH_3 from the mass of solution and convert to units of kg. To find molality, convert mass of NH_3 to moles and divide by the mass of solvent in kg. To find concentration (mol/L), you will need the volume of solution. Use the density of the solution to convert the 100. g of solution to volume in litres; divide moles of NH_3 by volume of solution. To find the mole fraction, convert mass of solvent to moles and divide moles of NH_3 by the total moles.
Solution:
Determine some fundamental quantities:

$$Mass\ (g)\ of\ NH_3 = (100\ g\ solution)\left(\frac{8.00\%\ NH_3}{100\%\ solution}\right) = 8.00\ g\ NH_3$$

$$Mass\ (g)\ H_2O = mass\ of\ solution - mass\ NH_3 = (100.00 - 8.00)\ g = 92.00\ g\ H_2O$$

$$Mass\ (kg)\ of\ H_2O = (92.00\ g\ H_2O)\left(\frac{1\ kg}{10^3\ g}\right) = 0.09200\ kg\ H_2O$$

$$Moles\ of\ NH_3 = (8.00\ g\ NH_3)\left(\frac{1\ mol\ NH_3}{17.03\ g\ NH_3}\right) = 0.469759\ mol\ NH_3$$

$$Moles\ of\ H_2O = (92.00\ g\ H_2O)\left(\frac{1\ mol\ H_2O}{18.02\ g\ H_2O}\right) = 5.1054\ mol\ H_2O$$

$$Volume\ (L)\ of\ solution = (100.00\ g\ solution)\left(\frac{1\ mL\ solution}{0.9651\ g\ solution}\right)\left(\frac{10^{-3}\ L}{1\ mL}\right) = 0.103616\ L$$

Using the above fundamental quantities and the definitions of the various units:

$$Molality = m = \frac{moles\ of\ solute}{kg\ of\ solvent} = \left(\frac{0.469759\ mol\ NH_3}{0.09200\ kg\ H_2O}\right) = 5.106076\ mol/Kg = \mathbf{5.11\,mol/kg\ NH_3}$$

$$Concentration = c = \frac{moles\ of\ solute}{L\ of\ solution} = \left(\frac{0.469759\ mol\ NH_3}{0.103616\ L}\right) = 4.53365\ mol/L = \mathbf{4.53\ mol/L\ NH_3}$$

$$Mole\ fraction = X = \frac{moles\ of\ NH_3}{total\ moles} = \frac{0.469759\ mol\ NH_3}{(0.469759 + 5.1054)\,mol} = 0.084259 = \mathbf{0.0843}$$

12.69   Plan: Use the equation for parts per million, ppm. Use the given density of solution to find the mass of solution; divide the mass of each ion by the mass of solution and multiply by 1×10^6.
Solution:

$$Mass\ (g)\ of\ solution\ is\ (100.0\ L\ solution)\left(\frac{1\ mL}{10^{-3}\ L}\right)\left(\frac{1.001\ g}{1\ mL}\right) = 1.001\times10^5\ g$$

$$ppm = \left(\frac{mass\ solute}{mass\ solution}\right) \times 10^6$$

$$ppm\ Ca^{2+} = \left(\frac{0.25\ g\ Ca^{2+}}{1.001\times10^5\ g\ solution}\right) \times 10^6 = 2.49750\ ppm = \mathbf{2.5\ ppm\ Ca^{2+}}$$

$$ppm\ Mg^{2+} = \left(\frac{0.056\ g\ Mg^{2+}}{1.001\times10^5\ g\ solution}\right) \times 10^6 = 0.5594406\ ppm = \mathbf{0.56\ ppm\ Mg^{2+}}$$

12.73   The "strong" in "strong electrolyte" refers to the ability of an electrolyte solution to conduct a large current. This conductivity occurs because solutes that are strong electrolytes dissociate completely into ions when dissolved in water.

12.75   The boiling point temperature is higher and the freezing point temperature is lower for the solution compared to the solvent because the addition of a solute lowers the freezing point and raises the boiling point of a liquid.

12.78   A dilute solution of an electrolyte behaves more ideally than a concentrated one. With increasing concentration, the effective concentration deviates from the molar concentration because of ionic attractions. Thus, the more dilute **0.050 mol/kg NaF** solution has a boiling point closer to its predicted value.

12.81   Plan: Strong electrolytes are substances that produce a large amount of ions when dissolved in water; strong acids and bases and soluble salts are strong electrolytes. Weak electrolytes produce few ions when dissolved in water; weak acids and bases are weak electrolytes. Nonelectrolytes produce no ions when dissolved in water. Molecular compounds other than acids and bases are nonelectrolytes.

   Solution:
   a) **Strong electrolyte** When hydrogen chloride is bubbled through water, it dissolves and dissociates completely into H^+ (or H_3O^+) ions and Cl^- ions. HCl is a strong acid.
   b) **Strong electrolyte** Potassium nitrate is a soluble salt and dissociates into K^+ and NO_3^- ions in water.
   c) **Nonelectrolyte** Glucose solid dissolves in water to form individual $C_6H_{12}O_6$ molecules, but these units are not ionic and therefore do not conduct electricity. Glucose is a molecular compound.
   d) **Weak electrolyte** Ammonia gas dissolves in water, but is a weak base that forms few NH_4^+ and OH^- ions.

12.83   Plan: To count solute particles in a solution of an ionic compound, count the amount of ions per mole and multiply by the amount of moles in solution. For a covalent compound, the amount of particles equals the amount of molecules.
   Solution:

   a) $\left(\dfrac{0.3 \text{ mol KBr}}{L}\right)\left(\dfrac{2 \text{ mol particles}}{1 \text{ mol KBr}}\right)(1 \text{ L}) =$ **0.6 mol of particles**

   Each KBr forms one K^+ ion and one Br^- ion, two particles for each KBr.

   b) $\left(\dfrac{0.065 \text{ mol HNO}_3}{L}\right)\left(\dfrac{2 \text{ mol particles}}{1 \text{ mol HNO}_3}\right)(1 \text{ L}) =$ **0.13 mol of particles**

   HNO$_3$ is a strong acid that forms $H^+(H_3O^+)$ ions and NO_3^- ions in aqueous solution.

   c) $\left(\dfrac{10^{-4} \text{ mol KHSO}_4}{L}\right)\left(\dfrac{2 \text{ mol particles}}{1 \text{ mol KHSO}_4}\right)(1 \text{ L}) =$ **2×10^{-4} mol of particles**

   Each KHSO$_4$ forms one K^+ ion and one HSO_4^- ion in aqueous solution, two particles for each KHSO$_4$.

   d) $\left(\dfrac{0.06 \text{ mol C}_2\text{H}_5\text{OH}}{L}\right)\left(\dfrac{1 \text{ mol particles}}{1 \text{ mol C}_2\text{H}_5\text{OH}}\right)(1 \text{ L}) =$ **0.06 mol of particles**

   Ethanol is not an ionic compound so each molecule dissolves as one particle. The amount of particles (moles) is the same as the amount of moles of molecules, **0.06 mol of particles** in 1 L.

12.85   Plan: The magnitude of freezing point depression is directly proportional to molality. Calculate the molality of solution by dividing the moles of solute by the mass of solvent in kg. The solution with the larger molality will have the lower freezing point.
   Solution:

   a) Molality of CH$_3$OH $= \dfrac{(11.0 \text{ g CH}_3\text{OH})}{(100. \text{ g H}_2\text{O})}\left(\dfrac{1 \text{ mol CH}_3\text{OH}}{32.04 \text{ g CH}_3\text{OH}}\right)\left(\dfrac{10^3 \text{ g}}{1 \text{ kg}}\right) = 3.4332085$ mol/kg

   $= 3.43$ mol/kg CH$_3$OH

$$\text{Molality of } CH_3CH_2OH = \frac{(22.0 \text{ g } CH_3CH_2OH)}{(200. \text{ g } H_2O)}\left(\frac{1 \text{ mol } CH_3CH_2OH}{46.07 \text{ g } CH_3CH_2OH}\right)\left(\frac{10^3 \text{ g}}{1 \text{ kg}}\right)$$

$$= 2.387671 \text{ mol/kg} = 2.39 \text{ mol/kg } CH_3CH_2OH$$

The molality of methanol, CH_3OH, in water is 3.43 mol/kg whereas the molality of ethanol, CH_3CH_2OH, in water is 2.39 mol/kg. Thus, **CH_3OH/H_2O solution** has the lower freezing point.

b) $\text{Molality of } H_2O = \dfrac{(20.0 \text{ g } H_2O)}{(1.00 \text{ kg } CH_3OH)}\left(\dfrac{1 \text{ mol } H_2O}{18.02 \text{ g } H_2O}\right) = 1.10988 \text{ mol/kg } H_2O = 1.11 \text{ mol/kg } H_2O$

$$\text{Molality of } CH_3CH_2OH = \frac{(20.0 \text{ g } CH_3CH_2OH)}{(1.00 \text{ kg } CH_3OH)}\left(\frac{1 \text{ mol } CH_3CH_2OH}{46.07 \text{ g } CH_3CH_2OH}\right) = 0.434122 \text{ mol/kg}$$

$$= 0.434 \text{ mol/kg } CH_3CH_2OH$$

The molality of H_2O in CH_3OH is 1.11 mol/kg, whereas CH_3CH_2OH in CH_3OH is 0.434 mol/kg. Therefore, **H_2O/CH_3OH solution** has the lower freezing point.

12.87   Plan: To rank the solutions in order of increasing osmotic pressure, boiling point, freezing point, and vapour pressure, convert the molality of each solute to molality of particles in the solution. The higher the molality of particles, the higher the osmotic pressure, the higher the boiling point, the lower the freezing point, and the lower the vapour pressure at a given temperature.

Solution:

(I) $(0.100 \text{ mol/kg } NaNO_3)\left(\dfrac{2 \text{ mol particles}}{1 \text{ mol } NaNO_3}\right) = 0.200 \text{ mol/kg ions}$

$NaNO_3$ consists of Na^+ ions and NO_3^- ions, two particles for each $NaNO_3$.

(II) $(0.100 \text{ mol/kg glucose})\left(\dfrac{1 \text{ mol particles}}{1 \text{ mol glucose}}\right) = 0.100 \text{ mol/kg molecules}$

Glucose is not an ionic compound so each molecule dissolves as one particle. The amount of particles (moles) is the same as the amount of moles of molecules.

(III) $(0.100 \text{ mol/kg } CaCl_2)\left(\dfrac{3 \text{ mol particles}}{1 \text{ mol } CaCl_2}\right) = 0.300 \text{ mol/kg ions}$

$CaCl_2$ consists of Ca^{+2} ions and Cl^- ions, three particles for each $CaCl_2$.
a) Osmotic pressure: $\Pi_{II} < \Pi_I < \Pi_{III}$
b) Boiling point: $bp_{II} < bp_I < bp_{III}$
c) Freezing point: $fp_{III} < fp_I < fp_{II}$
d) Vapour pressure at 50°C: $vp_{III} < vp_I < vp_{II}$

12.89   Plan: The mole fraction of solvent affects the vapour pressure according to the equation $p_{solvent} = X_{solvent}p°_{solvent}$. Convert the masses of glycerol and water to moles and find the mole fraction of water by dividing moles of water by the total amount of moles. Multiply the mole fraction of water by the vapour pressure of water to find the vapour pressure of the solution.
Solution:

$$\text{Moles of } C_3H_8O_3 = (34.0 \text{ g } C_3H_8O_3)\left(\frac{1 \text{ mol } C_3H_8O_3}{92.09 \text{ g } C_3H_8O_3}\right) = 0.369204 \text{ mol } C_3H_8O_3$$

$$\text{Moles of } H_2O = (500.0 \text{ g } H_2O)\left(\frac{1 \text{ mol } H_2O}{18.02 \text{ g } H_2O}\right) = 27.7469 \text{ mol } H_2O$$

$$X_{solvent} = \frac{\text{mol } H_2O}{\text{mol } H_2O + \text{mol glycerol}} = \frac{27.7469 \text{ mol } H_2O}{27.7469 \text{ mol } H_2O + 0.369204 \text{ mol glycerol}} = 0.9868686$$

$P_{solvent} = X_{solvent}p°_{solvent} = (0.9868686)(3168 \text{ Pa}) = 3126.4 \text{ Pa} = \textbf{3.13 kPa}$

12.91   Plan: The change in freezing point is calculated from $\Delta_f T = iK_f m$, where K_f is 1.86°C•kg/mol for aqueous solutions, i is the van't Hoff factor, and m is the molality of particles in solution. Since urea is a covalent compound and does not ionize in water, $i = 1$. Once $\Delta_f T$ is calculated, the freezing point is determined by subtracting it from the freezing point of pure water (0.00°C).
Solution:
$\Delta_f T = iK_f m = (1)(1.86°C•kg/mol)(0.251\ mol/kg) = 0.46686°C$
The freezing point is 0.00°C – 0.46686°C = –0.46686°C = **–0.467°C**.

12.93   Plan: The boiling point of a solution is increased relative to the pure solvent by the relationship $\Delta_b T = iK_b m$. Vanillin is a nonelectrolyte (it is a molecular compound) so $i = 1$. To find the molality, convert mass of vanillin to moles and divide by the mass of solvent expressed in units of kg. K_b is given (1.22°C•kg/mol).
Solution:

$$\text{Moles of vanillin} = \left(6.4\ \text{g vanillin}\right)\left(\frac{1\ \text{mol vanillin}}{152.14\ \text{g vanillin}}\right) = 0.0420665\ \text{mol}$$

$$\text{Molality of vanillin} = \frac{\text{moles of vanillin}}{\text{kg of solvent (ethanol)}} = \frac{0.042065\ \text{mol vanillin}}{50.0\ \text{g ethanol}}\left(\frac{10^3\ \text{g}}{1\ \text{kg}}\right)$$

$$= 0.8413\ \text{mol/kg vanillin}$$

$\Delta_b T = iK_b m = (1)(1.22°C•kg/mol)(0.8413\ kg/mol) = 1.026386°C$
The boiling point is 78.5°C + 1.026386°C = 79.5264°C = **79.5°C**.

12.95   Plan: The molality of the solution can be determined from the relationship $\Delta_f T = iK_f m$ with the value 1.86°C•kg/mol inserted for K_f and $i = 1$ for the nonelectrolyte ethylene glycol (ethylene glycol is a covalent compound that will form one particle per molecule when dissolved). Convert the freezing point of the solution to °C and find $\Delta_f T$ by subtracting the freezing point of the solvent from the freezing point of the solution. Once the molality of the solution is known, the mass of ethylene glycol needed for a solution of that molality can be found.
Solution:

$\Delta_f T = T_{f(\text{solution})} - T_{f(\text{solvent})} = (0.00 - (-24.44444))°C = 24.44444°C$
$\Delta_f T = iK_f m$

$$m = \frac{\Delta_f T}{K_f} = \frac{24.44444°C}{1.86°C•kg/mol} = 13.14217\ \text{mol/kg}$$

Ethylene glycol will be abbreviated as EG.

$$\text{Molality of EG} = \frac{\text{moles of EG}}{\text{kg of solvent (water)}}$$

$$\text{Moles of EG} = \text{molality} \times \text{kg of solvent} = \left(\frac{13.14217\ \text{mol EG}}{1\ \text{kg } H_2O}\right)(14.5\ \text{kg } H_2O) = 190.561465\ \text{mol EG}$$

$$\text{Mass (g) of ethylene glycol} = \left(190.561465\ \text{mol EG}\right)\left(\frac{62.07\ \text{g EG}}{1\ \text{mol EG}}\right)$$

$$= 1.18282 \times 10^4\ \text{g} = \mathbf{1.18 \times 10^4\ \text{g ethylene glycol}}$$

To prevent the solution from freezing, dissolve a minimum of 1.18×10^4 g ethylene glycol in 14.5 kg water.

12.97   Plan: Assume 100. g of solution so that the mass of solute = mass percent. Convert the mass of solute to moles. Subtract the mass of the solute from 100. g to obtain the mass of solution. Divide moles of solute by the mass of solvent in kg to obtain molality. Use $\Delta T = iK_f m$ to find the van't Hoff factor. K_f for water = 1.86°C•kg/mol.
Solution:
a) Assume exactly 100 g of solution.

$$\text{Mass (g) of NaCl} = \left(100.00\ \text{g solution}\right)\left(\frac{1.00\%\ \text{NaCl}}{100\%\ \text{solution}}\right) = 1.00\ \text{g NaCl}$$

Moles of NaCl $= (1.00 \text{ g NaCl})\left(\dfrac{1 \text{ mol NaCl}}{58.44 \text{ g NaCl}}\right) = 0.0171116$ mol NaCl

Mass of H_2O = 100.00 g solution − 1.00 g NaCl = 99.00 g H_2O

Molality of NaCl $= \dfrac{\text{moles of NaCl}}{\text{kg of } H_2O} = \dfrac{0.0171116 \text{ mol NaCl}}{99.00 \text{ g } H_2O}\left(\dfrac{10^3 \text{ g}}{1 \text{ kg}}\right) = 0.172844$ mol/kg = **0.173 mol/kg NaCl**

$\Delta_f T = T_{f(\text{solution})} - T_{f(\text{solvent})} = 0.000°C - (-0.593)°C = 0.593°C$
$\Delta_f T = iK_f m$

$i = \dfrac{\Delta_f T}{K_f m} = \dfrac{0.593°C}{(1.86°C \cdot \text{kg/mol})(0.172844 \text{ mol/kg})} = 1.844537 = \mathbf{1.84}$

The value of i should be close to two because NaCl dissociates into two particles when dissolving in water.
b) For ethanoic acid (acetic acid, CH_3COOH):
Assume exactly 100 g of solution.

Mass (g) of $CH_3COOH = (100.00 \text{ g solution})\left(\dfrac{0.500\% \text{ } CH_3COOH}{100\% \text{ solution}}\right) = 0.500$ g CH_3COOH

Moles of $CH_3COOH = (0.500 \text{ g } CH_3COOH)\left(\dfrac{1 \text{ mol } CH_3COOH}{60.05 \text{ g } CH_3COOH}\right) = 0.0083264$ mol CH_3COOH

Mass (g) of H_2O = 100.00 g solution − 0.500 g CH_3COOH = 99.500 g H_2O

Molality of $CH_3COOH = \dfrac{\text{moles of } CH_3COOH}{\text{kg of } H_2O} = \dfrac{0.0083264 \text{ mol } CH_3COOH}{99.500 \text{ g } H_2O}\left(\dfrac{10^3 \text{ g}}{1 \text{ kg}}\right)$

$= 0.083682$ mol/kg = **0.0837mol/kg CH_3COOH**

$\Delta_f T = T_{f(\text{solution})} - T_{f(\text{solvent})} = 0.000°C - (-0.159)°C = 0.159°C$
$\Delta_f T = iK_f m$

$i = \dfrac{\Delta_f T}{K_f m} = \dfrac{0.159°C}{(1.86°C \cdot \text{kg/mol})(0.083682 \text{ mol})} = 1.02153 = \mathbf{1.02}$

Acetic acid is a weak acid and dissociates to a small extent in solution, hence a van't Hoff factor that is close to 1.

12.100 Plan: The mole fraction of solvent affects the vapour pressure according to the equation $p_{\text{solvent}} = X_{\text{solvent}} p°_{\text{solvent}}$. Find the mole fraction of each substance by dividing moles of substance by the total amount of moles. Multiply the mole fraction of each compound by its vapour pressure to find the vapour pressure of the compounds above the solution.
Solution:

$X_{CH_2Cl_2} = \dfrac{\text{moles } CH_2Cl_2}{\text{moles } CH_2Cl_2 + \text{mol } CCl_4} = \dfrac{1.60 \text{ mol}}{1.60 + 1.10 \text{ mol}} = 0.592593$

$X_{CCl_4} = \dfrac{\text{moles } CCl_4}{\text{moles } CH_2Cl_2 + \text{mol } CCl_4} = \dfrac{1.10 \text{ mol}}{1.60 + 1.10 \text{ mol}} = 0.407407$

$p_A = X_A p°_A$
$= (0.592593)(46.9 \text{ kPa}) = 27.79261 \text{ kPa} = \textbf{27.8 kPa } CH_2Cl_2$
$= (0.407407)(15.7 \text{ kPa}) = 6.39629 \text{ kPa} = \textbf{6.40 kPa } CCl_4$

12.101 The fluid inside a bacterial cell is **both a solution and a colloid**. It is a solution of ions and small molecules, and a colloid of large molecules, proteins, and nucleic acids.

12.105 Soap micelles have nonpolar "tails" pointed inward and anionic "heads" pointed outward. The charges on the "heads" on one micelle repel the "heads" on a neighboring micelle because the charges are the same. This repulsion between soap micelles keeps them from coagulating. Soap is more effective in **freshwater** than in seawater because the divalent cations in seawater combine with the anionic "head" to form an insoluble precipitate.

12.109 Plan: To find the volume of seawater needed, substitute the given information into the equation that describes the ppb concentration, account for extraction efficiency, and convert mass to volume using the density of seawater.
Solution:
1 troy ounce = 31.1 g gold

$$1.1 \times 10^{-2} \text{ ppb} = \frac{\text{mass of gold}}{\text{mass of seawater}} \times 10^9$$

$$1.1 \times 10^{-2} \text{ ppb} = \frac{31.1 \text{ g Au}}{\text{mass seawater}} \times 10^9$$

$$\text{Mass (g) of seawater} = \left[\frac{31.1 \text{ g}}{1.1 \times 10^{-2}} \times 10^9 \right] = 2.827273 \times 10^{12} \text{ g (with 100\% efficiency)}$$

$$\text{Mass (g) of seawater} = \left(2.827273 \times 10^{12} \text{ g} \right)\left(\frac{100\%}{81.5\%} \right) = 3.46905 \times 10^{12} \text{ g seawater (81.5\% efficiency)}$$

$$\text{Volume (L) of seawater} = \left(3.46905 \times 10^{12} \text{ g} \right)\left(\frac{1 \text{ mL}}{1.025 \text{ g}} \right)\left(\frac{10^{-3} \text{ L}}{1 \text{ mL}} \right) = 3.384439 \times 10^9 \text{ L} = \mathbf{3.4 \times 10^9 \text{ L}}$$

12.113 Plan: Convert the mass of O_2 dissolved to moles of O_2. Use the density to convert the 1 kg mass of solution to volume in L. Divide moles of O_2 by volume of solution in L to obtain concentration (mol/L).
Solution:
0.0°C:

$$\text{Moles of } O_2 = \left(\frac{14.5 \text{ mg } O_2}{1 \text{ kg } H_2O} \right)\left(\frac{10^{-3} \text{ g}}{1 \text{ mg}} \right)\left(\frac{1 \text{ mol } O_2}{32.00 \text{ g } O_2} \right) = 4.53125 \times 10^{-4} \text{ mol } O_2$$

$$\text{Volume (L) of solution} = \left(1 \text{ kg} \right)\left(\frac{10^3 \text{ g}}{1 \text{kg}} \right)\left(\frac{1 \text{ mL}}{0.99987 \text{ g}} \right)\left(\frac{10^{-3} \text{ L}}{1 \text{mL}} \right) = 1.000130017 \text{ L}$$

$$c = \frac{\text{moles of } O_2}{\text{L of solution}} = \frac{4.53125 \times 10^{-4} \text{ mol}}{1.000130017 \text{ L}} = 4.53066 \times 10^{-4} \text{ mol/L} = \mathbf{4.53 \times 10^{-4} \text{ mol/L } O_2}$$

20.0°C:

$$\text{Moles of } O_2 = \left(\frac{9.07 \text{ mg } O_2}{1 \text{ kg } H_2O} \right)\left(\frac{10^{-3} \text{ g}}{1 \text{ mg}} \right)\left(\frac{1 \text{ mol } O_2}{32.00 \text{ g } O_2} \right) = 2.834375 \times 10^{-4} \text{ mol } O_2$$

$$\text{Volume (L) of solution} = \left(1 \text{ kg} \right)\left(\frac{10^3 \text{ g}}{1 \text{kg}} \right)\left(\frac{1 \text{ mL}}{0.99823 \text{ g}} \right)\left(\frac{10^{-3} \text{ L}}{1 \text{mL}} \right) = 1.001773138 \text{ L}$$

$$c = \frac{\text{moles of } O_2}{\text{L of solution}} = \frac{2.834375 \times 10^{-4} \text{ mol}}{1.001773138 \text{ L}} = 2.829358 \times 10^{-4} \text{ mol/L} = \mathbf{2.83 \times 10^{-4} \text{ mol/L } O_2}$$

40.0°C:

$$\text{Moles of } O_2 = \left(\frac{6.44 \text{ mg } O_2}{1 \text{ kg } H_2O} \right)\left(\frac{10^{-3} \text{ g}}{1 \text{ mg}} \right)\left(\frac{1 \text{ mol } O_2}{32.00 \text{ g } O_2} \right) = 2.0125 \times 10^{-4} \text{ mol } O_2$$

$$\text{Volume (L) of solution} = (1 \text{ kg})\left(\frac{10^3 \text{ g}}{1 \text{kg}}\right)\left(\frac{1 \text{ mL}}{0.99224 \text{ g}}\right)\left(\frac{10^{-3} \text{ L}}{1 \text{mL}}\right) = 1.007820689 \text{ L}$$

$$c = \frac{\text{moles of O}_2}{\text{L of solution}} = \frac{2.0125 \times 10^{-4} \text{ mol}}{1.007820689 \text{ L}} = 1.996883 \times 10^{-4} \text{ mol/L} = \textbf{2.00} \times \textbf{10}^{-4} \textbf{ mol/L O}_2$$

12.115 <u>Plan:</u> First, find the molality from the freezing point depression using the relationship $\Delta T = iK_f m$ and then use the molality, given mass of solute and volume of water, to calculate the molar mass of the solute compound. Assume the solute is a nonelectrolyte ($i = 1$). Use the mass percent data to find the empirical formula of the compound; the molar mass is used to convert the empirical formula to the molecular formula. A Lewis structure that forms hydrogen bonds must have H atoms bonded to O atoms.
<u>Solution:</u>
a) $\Delta_f T = iK_f m = 0.000\,°C - (-0.201\,°C) = 0.201\,°C$

$$m = \frac{\Delta_f T}{K_f i} = \frac{0.201\,°C}{(1.86\,°C \cdot \text{kg/mol})(1)} = 0.1080645 \text{ mol/kg}$$

$$\text{Mass (kg) of solvent} = (25.0 \text{ mL})\left(\frac{1.00 \text{ g}}{1 \text{ mL}}\right)\left(\frac{1 \text{ kg}}{10^3 \text{ g}}\right) = 0.0250 \text{ kg water}$$

$$m = \frac{\text{moles of solute}}{\text{kg of solvent}}$$

Moles of solute = (m)(kg solvent) = (0.1080656 mol/kg)(0.0250 kg) = 0.0027016 mol

$$\text{Molar mass} = \frac{0.243 \text{ g}}{0.0027016 \text{ mol}} = 89.946698 \text{ g/mol} = \textbf{89.9 g/mol}$$

b) Assume that 100.00 g of the compound gives 53.31 g carbon, 11.18 g hydrogen, and $100.00 - 53.31 - 11.18 = 35.51$ g oxygen.

$$\text{Moles C} = (53.31 \text{ g C})\left(\frac{1 \text{ mol C}}{12.01 \text{ g C}}\right) = 4.43880 \text{ mol C}; \qquad \frac{4.43880}{2.219375} = 2$$

$$\text{Moles H} = (11.18 \text{ g H})\left(\frac{1 \text{ mol H}}{1.008 \text{ g H}}\right) = 11.09127 \text{ mol H}; \qquad \frac{11.09127}{2.219375} = 5$$

$$\text{Moles O} = (35.51 \text{ g O})\left(\frac{1 \text{ mol O}}{16.00 \text{ g O}}\right) = 2.219375 \text{ mol O}; \qquad \frac{2.219375}{2.219375} = 1$$

Dividing the values by the lowest amount of moles (2.219375) gives an **empirical formula of C_2H_5O** with molar mass 45.06 g/mol.
Since the molar mass of the compound, 89.9 g/mol from part a), is twice the molar mass of the empirical formula, the **molecular formula is $2(C_2H_5O)$ or $C_4H_{10}O_2$.**
c) There is more than one example in each case. Possible Lewis structures:

Forms hydrogen bonds   Does not form hydrogen bonds

12.119 <u>Plan:</u> Find the moles of NaF required to form a 4.50×10^{-5} mol/L solution of F^- with a volume of 5000. L. Then convert moles of NaF to mass. Then use the concentration (mol/L) to find the mass of F^- in 2.0 L of solution.
<u>Solution:</u>

a) Moles of NaF = $(5000. \text{ L})\left(\frac{4.50 \times 10^{-5} \text{ mol F}^-}{\text{L}}\right)\left(\frac{1 \text{ mol NaF}}{1 \text{ mol F}^-}\right) = 0.225 \text{ mol NaF}$

$$\text{Mass (g) of NaF} = (0.225 \text{ mol})\left(\frac{41.99 \text{ g NaF}}{1 \text{ mol NaF}}\right) = 9.44775 \text{ g} = \textbf{9.45 g NaF}$$

b) $\text{Mass (g) of F}^- = (2.0 \text{ L})\left(\dfrac{4.50\times10^{-5} \text{ mol F}^-}{\text{L}}\right)\left(\dfrac{19.00 \text{ g F}^-}{1 \text{ mol F}}\right) = 0.00171\text{g} = \textbf{0.0017 g F}^-$

12.122 Plan: Use the boiling point elevation of 0.45°C to calculate the molality of the solution using the relationship $\Delta_b T = iK_b m$ and then use the molality, given mass of solute and volume of water, to calculate the molar mass of the solute compound. If the solute is a nonelectrolyte, $i = 1$. If the formula is AB_2 or A_2B, then $i = 3$. For part d), use the molar mass of CaN_2O_6 to calculate the molality of the compound. Then calculate i in the boiling point elevation formula.

Solution:

a) $\Delta_b T = iK_b m$ \qquad $i = 1$ (nonelectrolyte)

ΔT = boiling point of solution – boiling point of solvent = $(100.45 - 100.00)°C = 0.45°C$

$$m = \frac{\Delta_b T}{K_b i} = \frac{0.45°C}{(0.512°C \cdot \text{kg/mol})(1)} = 0.878906 \text{ mol/kg} = 0.878906 \text{ mol/kg}$$

$$\text{Mass (kg) of water} = (25.0 \text{ mL})\left(\frac{0.997 \text{ g}}{1 \text{ mL}}\right)\left(\frac{1 \text{ kg}}{10^3 \text{ g}}\right) = 0.0249250 \text{ kg water}$$

$$m = \frac{\text{moles of solute}}{\text{kg of solvent}}$$

Moles solute = (m)(kg solvent) = (0.878906 mol•kg/mol)(0.0249250 kg) = 0.0219067 mol

$$\text{Molar mass} = \frac{1.50 \text{ g}}{0.0219067 \text{ mol}} = 68.4722 \text{ g/mol} = \textbf{68 g/mol}$$

b) $\Delta_b T = iK_b m$ \qquad $i = 3 (AB_2$ or $A_2B)$

$$m = \frac{\Delta_b T}{K_b i} = \frac{0.45°C}{(0.512°C \cdot \text{kg/mol})(3)} = 0.29296875 \text{mol/kg}$$

$$m = \frac{\text{moles of solute}}{\text{kg of solvent}}$$

Moles solute = (mol solute/kg solvent)(kg solvent) = (0.29296875 mol/kg)(0.0249250 kg) = 0.00730225 mol

$$\text{Molar mass} = \frac{1.50 \text{ g}}{0.00730225 \text{ mol}} = 205.416 \text{ g/mol} = \textbf{2.1x10}^2 \textbf{ g/mol}$$

c) The molar mass of CaN_2O_6 is 164.10 g/mol. This molar mass is less than the 2.1×10^2 g/mol calculated when the compound is assumed to be a strong electrolyte and is greater than the 68 g/mol calculated when the compound is assumed to be a nonelectrolyte. Thus, the compound is an electrolyte, since it dissociates into ions in solution. However, the ions do not dissociate completely in solution.

d) $\text{Moles of } CaN_2O_6 = (1.50 \text{ g } CaN_2O_6)\left(\dfrac{1 \text{ mol}}{164.10 \text{ g } CaN_2O_6}\right) = 0.0091408 \text{ mol}$

$$m = \frac{\text{moles of solute}}{\text{kg of solvent}} = \frac{0.00914078 \text{ mol}}{0.0249250 \text{ kg}} = 0.3667314 \text{ mol/kg}$$

$\Delta_b T = iK_b m$

$$i = \frac{\Delta_b T}{K_b m} = \frac{(0.45°C)}{(0.512°C \cdot \text{kg / mol})(0.3667314 \text{ mol / kg})} = 2.39659 = \textbf{2.4}$$

12.126 Plan: From the osmotic pressure, the concentration (mol/L) of the solution can be found using the relationship $\Pi = cRT$. Convert the temperature from °C to K. Use the concentration of the solution to find moles of solute; divide the given mass of solute in grams by the moles of solute to obtain molar mass. To find the freezing point depression, the concentration of the solution must be converted to molality by using the density of the solution to convert volume of solution to mass of solution. Then use $\Delta_f T = iK_f m$. ($i = 1$).

Solution:

a) $\Pi = cRT$

Osmotic pressure, $\Pi = 45.3$ Pa

$T = 25°C + 273 = 298$ K

$$c = \frac{\Pi}{RT} = \frac{(45.3 \text{ Pa})}{\left(8.31446 \dfrac{\text{L•kPa}}{\text{mol•K}}\right)(298 \text{ K})} = 1.828302 \times 10^{-5} \text{ mol/L}$$

$(c)(V) = $ moles

$$\text{Moles} = \left(1.828302 \times 10^{-5} \text{ mol/L}\right)(30.0 \text{ mL})\left(\frac{10^{-3} \text{ L}}{1 \text{ mL}}\right) = 5.48491 \times 10^{-7} \text{ mol}$$

$$\text{Molar mass} = \frac{(10.0 \text{ mg})\left(\dfrac{10^{-3} \text{ g}}{1 \text{ mg}}\right)}{5.48491 \times 10^{-7} \text{ mol}} = 1.82318 \times 10^4 \text{ g/mol} = \mathbf{1.82 \times 10^4 \text{ g/mol}}$$

b) Mass (g) of solution $= (30.0 \text{ mL})\left(\dfrac{0.997 \text{ g}}{1 \text{ mL}}\right) = 29.91$ g

Mass (g) of solute $= (10.0 \text{ mg})\left(\dfrac{10^{-3} \text{ g}}{1 \text{ mg}}\right) = 0.0100$ g

Mass (kg) of solvent = mass of solution – mass of solute $= 29.91 \text{ g} - 0.0100 \text{ g}\left(\dfrac{1 \text{ kg}}{10^3 \text{ g}}\right) = 0.0299$ kg

Moles of solute $= 5.48563 \times 10^{-7}$ mol (from part a))

$$\text{Molality} = \frac{\text{moles of solute}}{\text{kg of solvent}} = \frac{5.48563 \times 10^{-7} \text{ mol}}{0.0299 \text{ kg}} = 1.83466 \times 10^{-5} \text{ mol/kg}$$

$\Delta_f T = iK_f m = (1)(1.86°C•kg/mol)(1.83466 \times 10^{-5} \text{ mol/kg}) = 3.412 \times 10^{-5} \ °C = \mathbf{3.41 \times 10^{-5} \ °C}$

(So the solution would freeze at $0 \ °C - (3.41 \times 10^{-5} \ °C) = -3.41 \times 10^{-5} \ °C$).

12.127 Plan: Henry's law expresses the relationship between gas pressure and the gas solubility (S_{gas}) in a given solvent. Use Henry's law to solve for pressure of 1,2-dichloroethene (assume that the constant (k_H) is given at 21°C), use the ideal gas law to find moles per unit volume, and convert moles/L to ng/L.

Solution:

$S_{gas} = k_H p_{gas}$

$$S_{gas} \text{ (mol/L)} = \left(\frac{0.65 \text{ mg } C_2H_2Cl_2}{L}\right)\left(\frac{10^{-3} \text{ g}}{1 \text{ mg}}\right)\left(\frac{1 \text{ mol } C_2H_2Cl_2}{96.94 \text{ g } C_2H_2Cl_2}\right) = 6.705178 \times 10^{-6} \text{ mol/L}$$

$$P_{gas} = \frac{S_{gas}}{k_H} = \left(\frac{6.705178 \times 10^{-6} \text{ mol/L}}{0.00033 \text{ mol/L•kPa}}\right) = 0.0203187 \text{ kPa}$$

$pV = nRT$

$$\frac{n}{V} = \frac{p}{RT} = \frac{(0.020318721 \text{ kPa})}{\left(8.31446 \dfrac{\text{L•kPa}}{\text{mol•K}}\right)((273 + 21)\text{K})} = 8.31218 \times 10^{-6} \text{ mol/L}$$

$$\text{Concentration (ng/L)} = \left(\frac{8.31218 \times 10^{-6} \text{ mol C}_2\text{H}_2\text{Cl}_2}{\text{L}}\right)\left(\frac{96.94 \text{ g C}_2\text{H}_2\text{Cl}_2}{1 \text{ mol C}_2\text{H}_2\text{Cl}_2}\right)\left(\frac{1 \text{ ng}}{10^{-9} \text{ g}}\right)$$

$$= 8.0578316035 \times 10^5 = \mathbf{8.1 \times 10^5 \text{ ng/L}}$$

12.131 Plan: Assume a concentration of 1 mol/m^3 for both ethanol and 2-butoxyethanol in the detergent solution. Then, from Henry's law, the partial pressures of the two substances can be calculated.

Solution:

a) $S_{gas} = k_H \times p_{gas}$

$p_{gas} = \dfrac{S_{gas}}{k_H}$

$$p_{ethanol} = \left(\frac{1 \text{ mol}}{\text{m}^3}\right)\left(\frac{5 \times 10^{-4} \text{ kPa} \cdot \text{m}^3}{\text{mol}}\right) = 5 \times 10^{-4} \text{ kPa}$$

$$p_{2\text{-butoxyethanol}} = \left(\frac{1 \text{ mol}}{\text{m}^3}\right)\left(\frac{1.6 \times 10^{-4} \text{ kPa} \cdot \text{m}^3}{\text{mol}}\right) = 1.6 \times 10^{-4} \text{ kPa}$$

$$\%_{2\text{-butoxyethanol}} = (5\%)\left(\frac{1.6 \times 10^{-4} \text{ kPa 2-butoxyethanol}}{5 \times 10^{-4} \text{ kPa ethanol}}\right) = 1.6\%$$

"Down-the-drain" factor is 0.016 = **0.02**

b) $k_{H(ethanol)} = \left(\dfrac{5 \times 10^{-4} \text{ kPa} \cdot \text{m}^3}{\text{mol}}\right)\left(\dfrac{1 \text{ L}}{10^{-3} \text{ m}^3}\right) = \mathbf{5 \times 10^{-1} \text{ kPa} \cdot \text{L/mol}}$

c) $k_{H(ethanol)} = \mathbf{0.64 \text{ Pa} \cdot \text{m}^3/\text{mol} = 0.64 \text{ kPa} \cdot \text{L/mol}}$

Considering the single significant figure in the measured value of 5×10^{-4}, the agreement is good.

12.133 Plan: Molality is defined as moles of solute per kg of solvent, so 0.150 mol/kg means 0.150 mol NaHCO$_3$ per kg of water. The total mass of the solution would be 1 kg + (0.150 mol x molar mass of NaHCO$_3$).

Solution:

$$0.150 \text{ mol/kg} = (0.150 \text{ mol NaHCO}_3)/(1 \text{ kg solvent}) = \frac{(0.150 \text{ mol NaHCO}_3)\left(\frac{84.01 \text{ g NaHCO}_3}{1 \text{ mol NaHCO}_3}\right)}{1 \text{ kg}}\left(\frac{1 \text{ kg}}{10^3 \text{ g}}\right)$$

$$= 12.6015 \text{ g NaHCO}_3/1000 \text{ g solvent}$$

$$\left(\frac{12.6015 \text{ g NaHCO}_3}{(1000 + 12.6015) \text{g solution}}\right)(250. \text{ g solution}) = 3.111 \text{ g NaHCO}_3$$

Mass (g) of H$_2$O = 250. g – 3.111 g = 246.889 g H$_2$O

To make 250. g of a 0.150 mol/kg solution of NaHCO$_3$, **weigh 3.11 g NaHCO$_3$ and dissolve in 247 g water.**

12.137 Concentration (mol/L) is moles solute/L solution and molality is moles solute/kg solvent.

Multiplying molality by concentration of solvent in kg solvent per litre of solution gives concentration (mol/L):

$$c = \frac{\text{mol of solute}}{\text{L of solution}} = \left(\frac{\text{mol of solute}}{\text{kg solvent}}\right)\left(\frac{\text{kg solvent}}{\text{L of solution}}\right)$$

$$c = m\left(\frac{\text{kg solvent}}{\text{L of solution}}\right)$$

For a very dilute solution, the assumption that mass of solvent $\cong$ mass of solution is valid. This equation then becomes

$c = m$ (kg solvent/L solution) $= m \times d_{solution}$

Thus, for very dilute solutions **molality x density = concentration (mol/L)**.

In an aqueous solution, the litres of solution have approximately the same value as the kg of solvent because the density of water is close to 1 kg/L, so $m = c$.

12.139 Plan: Use Henry's law, $S_{gas} = k_H \times P_{gas}$, to find the solubility of SO_2.
Solution:
a) $S_{gas} = k_H \times p_{gas} = (1.21 \times 10^{-2} \text{mol/L} \cdot \text{kPa})(0.203 \text{ kPa}) = 2.46 \times 10^{-3} \text{ mol/L} = \textbf{2.5} \times \textbf{10}^{-3} \textbf{ mol/L } \textbf{SO}_2$
b) The base reacts with the sulfur dioxide to produce calcium sulfite. The reaction of sulfur dioxide makes "room" for more sulfur dioxide to dissolve.

12.144 Plan: Use Henry's law, $S_{gas} = k_H \times P_{gas}$, to find k_H for O_2. Then use that value to find the concentration of O_2 at a pressure of 0.5 kPa. To calculate the mole fraction of O_2, assume a litre of solution. Divide the moles of O_2 in 1.0 L of sample by the total moles of O_2 and acrylic acid. To calculate ppm, convert moles of O_2 and acrylic acid to mass; divide the mass of O_2 by the total mass of the solution and multiply by 10^6.
Solution:
a) $S_{gas} = k_H \times p_{gas}$
$$k_H = \frac{S_{gas}}{p_{gas}} = \frac{1.64 \times 10^{-3} \text{ mol/L}}{21.2 \text{ kPa}} = 7.7358 \times 10^{-5} \text{ mol/L} \cdot \text{kPa} = \textbf{7.74} \times \textbf{10}^{-5} \textbf{ mol/L} \cdot \textbf{kPa}$$

b) $S_{gas} = k_H \times p_{gas}$
$S_{gas} = (7.7358 \times 10^{-5} \text{ mol/L} \cdot \text{kPa})(0.5 \text{ kPa})$
$S_{gas} = 3.8679 \times 10^{-5} \text{ mol/L} = \textbf{4} \times \textbf{10}^{-5} \textbf{ mol/L}$
c) Assume a 1.0 L sample. Acrylic acid is 14.6 mol/L or 14.6 mol in 1.0 L.
Oxygen is 4×10^{-5} mol/L or 4×10^{-5} mol in 1.0 L.

$$X_{O_2} = \frac{\text{moles of } O_2}{\text{moles of } O_2 + \text{moles of acrylic acid}} = \frac{4 \times 10^{-5} \text{ mol}}{\left((4 \times 10^{-5}) + 14.6 \right) \text{ mol}} = 2.73972 \times 10^{-6} = \textbf{3} \times \textbf{10}^{-6}$$

d) Mass (g) of acrylic acid $= \left(\dfrac{14.6 \text{ mol acrylic acid}}{L} \right)\left(\dfrac{72.06 \text{ g acrylic acid}}{1 \text{ mol acrylic acid}} \right) = 1052.076 \text{ g/L}$

Mass of oxygen $= \left(\dfrac{4 \times 10^{-5} \text{ mol } O_2}{L} \right)\left(\dfrac{32.0 \text{ g } O_2}{1 \text{ mol } O_2} \right) = 0.00128 \text{ g/L}$

ppm $= \dfrac{\text{mass of solute}}{\text{mass of solution}}\left(1 \times 10^6\right) = \dfrac{0.00128 \text{ g}}{0.00128 \text{ g} + 1052.176 \text{ g}}\left(1 \times 10^6\right) = 1.2165 \text{ ppm} = \textbf{1 ppm}$

12.148 Plan: Use the density of C_6F_{14} to find the mass and then moles of C_6F_{14} in 1 L. This is the concentration (mol/L) of C_6F_{14} which is then used to find the concentration (mol/L) of O_2 from its mole fraction. Then Henry's law can be used to find k_H. In part b), use Henry's law to find the solubility of O_2 at the given temperature.
Solution:

a) Moles of C_6F_{14} in 1 L $(c) = (1 \text{ L})\left(\dfrac{1 \text{ mL}}{10^{-3} \text{ L}} \right)\left(\dfrac{1.674 \text{ g } C_6F_{14}}{1 \text{ mL}} \right)\left(\dfrac{1 \text{ mol } C_6F_{14}}{338 \text{ g } C_6F_{14}} \right) = 4.9527 \text{ mol/L}$

$$X_{O_2} = \frac{\text{mol of } O_2}{\text{mol of } O_2 + \text{mol of } C_6F_{14}}$$

$$4.28 \times 10^{-3} = \frac{x \text{ mol } O_2}{4.9527 \text{ mol}}$$

Moles of $O_2 = 0.021198$ (The moles of O_2 is small enough to ignore in the denominator.)
$p_{gas} = = 101,325 \text{ Pa}$
$S_{gas} = k_H \times p_{gas}$
$$k_H = \frac{S_{gas}}{p_{gas}} = \frac{0.021198 \text{ mol/L}}{101,325 \text{ Pa}} = \frac{0.021198 \text{ mol/L}}{101.325 \text{ kPa}} = 2.0926 \times 10^{-4} \text{ mol/L} \cdot \text{kPa} = \textbf{2.09} \times \textbf{10}^{-4} \textbf{ mol/L} \cdot \textbf{kPa}$$

b) $S_{gas} = k_H \times p_{gas}$
$$k_H = \frac{1}{7.67 \times 10^4 \text{ L} \cdot \text{kPa/mol}} = 1.304 \times 10^{-5} \text{ mol/L} \cdot \text{kPa}$$
$p_{O_2} = 0.2095 \times 101.3 \text{ kPa} = 21.222 \text{ kPa}$ since O_2 is 20.95% of air

$S_{gas} = (1.304 \times 10^{-5} \text{ mol/L} \cdot \text{kPa})(21.222 \text{ kPa}) = 2.76357 \times 10^{-4} \text{ mol/L}$

$$\text{ppm} = \left(\frac{2.76357 \times 10^{-4} \text{ mol}}{\text{L}} \right)\left(\frac{32.0 \text{ g O}_2}{1 \text{ mol O}_2} \right) = 8.8434 \times 10^{-3} \text{ g/L} = (8.8434 \times 10^{-3} \text{ g/1000 g})(1 \times 10^6)$$

$= 8.8434 \text{ ppm} = \textbf{8.84 ppm}$

c) k_H: $\textbf{C}_6\textbf{F}_{14} > \textbf{C}_6\textbf{H}_{14} > \textbf{ethanol} > \textbf{water}$

To dissolve oxygen in a solvent, the solvent molecules must be moved apart to make room for the gas. The stronger the intermolecular forces in the solvent, the more difficult it is to separate solvent particles and the lower the solubility of the gas. Both C_6F_{14} and C_6H_{14} have weak dispersion forces, with C_6H_{14} having the weaker forces due to the electronegative fluorine atoms repelling each other. Both ethanol and water are held together by strong hydrogen bonds with those bonds being stronger in water as the boiling point indicates.

12.150   a) **Yes,** the phases of water can still coexist at some temperature and can therefore establish equilibrium.
b) The triple point would occur at a lower pressure and **lower temperature** because the dissolved air solute lowers the vapour pressure of the solvent.
c) **Yes,** this is possible because the gas-solid phase boundary exists below the new triple point.
d) **No,** the presence of the solute lowers the vapour pressure of the liquid.

12.152   Plan: Use the given percentages to find the volume of ethanol absorbed into the blood and then use the density of ethanol to convert volume of ethanol to mass and divide by the total volume of blood in mL. Use a ratio to find the volume of whiskey associated with the given blood alcohol level.
Solution:

a) Mass (g) of ethanol dissolved in the blood $= (28 \text{ mL})\left(\dfrac{40\%}{100\%} \right)\left(\dfrac{22\%}{100\%} \right)\left(\dfrac{0.789 \text{ g}}{\text{mL}} \right) = 1.944096 \text{ g}$

$\text{Concentration} = \left(\dfrac{1.944096 \text{ g ethanol}}{7.0 \text{ L}} \right)\left(\dfrac{10^{-3} \text{ L}}{1 \text{ mL}} \right) = 2.77728 \times 10^{-4} \text{ g/mL} = \textbf{2.8} \times \textbf{10}^{-4} \textbf{ g/mL}$

b) $\left(\dfrac{28 \text{ mL whiskey}}{2.77728 \times 10^{-4} \text{ g/mL}} \right)(8.0 \times 10^{-4} \text{ g/mL}) = 80.6545 \text{ mL} = \textbf{81 mL}$

CHAPTER 13 PERIODIC PATTERNS IN THE MAIN-GROUP ELEMENTS

END–OF–CHAPTER PROBLEMS

13.1 Ionization energy is defined as the energy required to remove the outermost electron from an atom. The further the outermost electron is from the nucleus, the less energy is required to remove it from the attractive force of the nucleus. In hydrogen, the outermost electron is in the $n = 1$ level and in lithium the outermost electron is in the $n = 2$ level. Therefore, the outermost electron in lithium requires less energy to remove, resulting in a lower ionization energy.

13.3 Plan: Recall that to form hydrogen bonds a compound must have H directly bonded to either N, O, or F.
Solution:
a) **NH₃** will form hydrogen bonds because H is bonded to N.

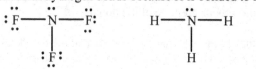

b) **CH₃CH₂OH** will form hydrogen bonds since H is bonded to O. CH₃OCH₃ has no O–H bonds, only C–H bonds.

$$CH_3OCH_3 \qquad\qquad CH_3CH_2OH$$

13.5 Plan: Active metals displace hydrogen from HCl by reducing the H^+ to H_2. In water, H^- (here in LiH) reacts as a strong base to form H_2 and OH^-.
Solution:
a) $2Al(s) + 6HCl(aq) \rightarrow 2AlCl_3(aq) + 3H_2(g)$
b) $LiH(s) + H_2O(l) \rightarrow LiOH(aq) + H_2(g)$

13.7 Plan: In metal hydrides, the oxidation state of hydrogen is –1.
Solution:
a)

Na = +1	B = +3	H = –1 in NaBH₄
Al = +3	B = +3	H = –1 in Al(BH₄)₃
Li = +1	Al = +3	H = –1 in LiAlH₄

b) The polyatomic ion in $NaBH_4$ is $[BH_4]^-$. There are $[1 \times B(3e^-)] + [4 \times H(1e^-)] + [1e^-$ from charge$] = 8$ valence electrons. All eight electrons are required to form the four bonds from the four hydrogen atoms to the boron atom. Boron is the central atom and has four surrounding electron groups; therefore, its shape is **tetrahedral**.

$$\left[\begin{array}{c} H \\ | \\ H - B - H \\ | \\ H \end{array} \right]^{-}$$

13.12   a) E must have an oxidation of +3 to form an oxide E_2O_3 or fluoride EF_3. E is in Group **13 or 3**.
b) If E were in Group 3, the oxide and fluoride would have more ionic character because Group 3 elements have lower electronegativity than Group 13 elements. The Group 3 oxides would be more basic.

13.15   a) Alkali metals generally lose electrons (act as **reducing agents**) in their reactions.
b) Alkali metals have relatively low ionization energies, meaning they easily lose the outermost electron. The electron configurations of alkali metals have one more electron than a noble gas configuration, so losing an electron gives a stable electron configuration.
c) $2Na(s) + 2H_2O(l) \rightarrow 2Na^+(aq) + 2OH^-(aq) + H_2(g)$
$2Na(s) + Cl_2(g) \rightarrow 2NaCl(s)$

13.17   a) Density increases down a group. The increasing atomic size (volume) is not offset by the increasing size of the nucleus (mass), so m/V increases.
b) Ionic size increases down a group. Electron shells are added down a group, so both atomic and ionic size increase.
c) E–E bond energy decreases down a group. Shielding of the outer electron increases as the atom gets larger, so the attraction responsible for the E–E bond decreases.
d) IE_1 decreases down a group. Increased shielding of the outer electron is the cause of the decreasing IE_1.
e) $\Delta_{hydr}H$ decreases down a group. $\Delta_{hydr}H$ is the heat released when the metal salt dissolves in, or is hydrated by, water. Hydration energy decreases as ionic size increases.
Increasing down: a and b;   Decreasing down: c, d, and e

13.19   Plan: Peroxides are oxides in which oxygen has a –1 oxidation state. Sodium peroxide has the formula Na_2O_2 and is formed from the elements Na and O_2.
Solution:
$2Na(s) + O_2(g) \rightarrow Na_2O_2(s)$

13.21   Plan: The problem specifies that an alkali halide is the desired product. The alkali metal is K (comes from potassium carbonate, $K_2CO_3(s)$) and the halide is I (comes from hydroiodic acid, $HI(aq)$). Treat the reaction as a double displacement reaction.
Solution:
$K_2CO_3(s) + 2HI(aq) \rightarrow 2KI(aq) + H_2CO_3(aq)$
However, $H_2CO_3(aq)$ is unstable and decomposes to $H_2O(l)$ and $CO_2(g)$, so the final reaction is:
$K_2CO_3(s) + 2HI(aq) \rightarrow 2KI(aq) + H_2O(l) + CO_2(g)$

13.25   Metal atoms are held together by metallic bonding, a sharing of valence electrons. Alkaline earth metal atoms have one more valence electron than alkali metal atoms, so the number of electrons shared is greater. Thus, metallic bonds in alkaline earth metals are stronger than in alkali metals. Melting requires overcoming the metallic bonds. To overcome the stronger alkaline earth metal bonds requires more energy (higher temperature) than to overcome the alkali earth metal bonds.
First ionization energy, density, and boiling points will be larger for alkaline earth metals than for alkali metals.

13.26   Plan: A base forms when a basic oxide, such as CaO (lime), is added to water. Alkaline earth metals reduce O_2 to form the oxide.
Solution:
a) $CaO(s) + H_2O(l) \rightarrow Ca(OH)_2(s)$
b) $2Ca(s) + O_2(g) \rightarrow 2CaO(s)$

13.29   Plan: The oxides of alkaline earth metals are strongly basic, but BeO is amphoteric. BeO will react with both acids and bases to form salts, but an amphoteric substance does not react with water. In part b), each chloride ion donates a lone pair of electrons to form a covalent bond with the Be in $BeCl_2$. Metal ions form similar covalent bonds with ions or molecules containing a lone pair of electrons. The difference in beryllium is that the orbital involved in the bonding is a *p* orbital, whereas in metal ions it is usually the *d* orbitals that are involved.
Solution:
a) Here, Be does not behave like other alkaline earth metals: $BeO(s) + H_2O(l) \rightarrow$ NR.

b) Here, Be does behave like other alkaline earth metals:

$$BeCl_2(l) + 2\ Cl^-\ (solvated) \rightarrow BeCl_4^{2-}\ (solvated)$$

13.32 The electron removed in Group 2 atoms is from the outer level s orbital, whereas in Group 13 atoms the electron is from the outer level p orbital. For example, the electron configuration for Be is $1s^22s^2$ and for B is $1s^22s^22p^1$. It is easier to remove the p electron of B than the s electron of Be, because the energy of a p orbital is slightly higher than that of the s orbital from the same level. Even though the atomic size decreases from increasing Z_{eff}, the IE decreases from Group 2 to 13.

13.33 a) Compounds of Group 13 elements, like boron, have only six electrons in their valence shell when combined with halogens to form three bonds. Having six electrons, rather than an octet, results in an "electron deficiency."
b) As an electron deficient central atom, B is trigonal planar. Upon accepting an electron pair to form a bond, the shape changes to tetrahedral.
$$BF_3(g) + NH_3(g) \rightarrow F_3B{-}NH_3(g)$$
$$B(OH)_3(aq) + OH^-\ (aq) \rightarrow B(OH)_4^-\ (aq)$$

13.35 Plan: Oxide acidity increases up a group; the less metallic an element, the more acidic is its oxide.
Solution:
$In_2O_3 < Ga_2O_3 < Al_2O_3$

13.37 Halogens typically have a -1 oxidation state in metal-halide combinations, so the apparent oxidation state of Tl = +3. However, the anion I_3^- combines with Tl in the +1 oxidation state. The anion I_3^- has [3 x (I)7e$^-$] + [1e$^-$ from the charge] = 22 valence electrons; four of these electrons are used to form the two single bonds between iodine atoms and sixteen electrons are used to give every atom an octet. The remaining two electrons belong to the central I atom; therefore the central iodine has five electron groups (two single bonds and three lone pairs) and has a general formula of AX_2E_3. The electrons are arranged in a trigonal bipyramidal with the three lone pairs in the trigonal plane. It is a linear ion with bond angles = 180°. $(Tl^{3+})\ (I^-)_3$ does not exist because of the low strength of the Tl–I bond.
O.N. = +3 (apparent); = +1 (actual)

13.42 Plan: To calculate the enthalpy of reaction, use the relationship $\Delta_r H^\circ = \Sigma m\,\Delta_{products}H^\circ - \Sigma n\,\Delta_{reactants}H^\circ$.

Convert the given amount of 1.0 kg of BN to moles, find the amount (mol) of B in that amount of BN, and then find the amount (mol) and then mass of borax that provides that amount (mol) of B.
Solution:
a) $B_2O_3(s) + 2NH_3(g) \rightarrow 2BN(s) + 3H_2O(g)$

b) $\Delta_r H^\circ = \Sigma m\,\Delta_{products}H^\circ - \Sigma n\,\Delta_{reactants}H^\circ$

$$= \{2\,\Delta_f H^\circ\ [BN(s)] + 3\,\Delta_f H^\circ\ [H_2O(g)]\} - \{1\,\Delta_f H^\circ\ [B_2O_3(s)] + 2\,\Delta_f H^\circ\ [NH_3(g)]\}$$
$$= [(2\ )(-254\ kJ/mol) + (3)(-241.826\ mol\ kJ/mol)]$$
$$- [(-1272\ kJ/mol) + (2\ )(-45.9\ kJ/mol)]$$
$$= 130.322\ kJ = \mathbf{1.30x10^2\ kJ/mol}$$

c) Mass (g) of borax =

$$(1.0\ kg\ BN)\left(\frac{10^3\ g}{1\ kg}\right)\left(\frac{1\ mol\ BN}{24.82\ g\ BN}\right)\left(\frac{1\ mol\ B}{1\ mol\ BN}\right)\left(\frac{1\ mol\ Na_2B_4O_7{\cdot}10\,H_2O}{4\ mol\ B}\right)\left(\frac{381.38\ g}{1\ mol}\right)\left(\frac{100\%}{72\%}\right)$$
$$= 5.335359x10^3\ g = \mathbf{5.3x10^3\ g\ borax}$$

13.43 Oxide basicity is greater for the oxide of a metal atom. Tin(IV) oxide is more basic than carbon dioxide since tin has more metallic character than carbon.

13.45 a) IE_1 values generally decrease down a group.

b) The increase in Z_{eff} from Si to Ge is larger than the increase from C to Si because more protons have been added. Between C and Si an additional eight protons have been added, whereas between Si and Ge an additional eighteen (includes the protons for the d-block) protons have been added. The same type of change takes place when going from Sn to Pb, when the fourteen f-block protons are added.

c) Group 13 would show greater deviations because the single p electron receives no shielding effect offered by other p electrons.

13.48 Atomic size increases moving down a group. As atomic size increases, ionization energy decreases so that it is easier to form a positive ion. An atom that is easier to ionize exhibits greater metallic character.

13.50 Plan: The silicate building unit is —SiO_4—. There are $[4 \times Si(4e^-)] + [12 \times O(6e^-)] + [8e^-$ from charge] = 96 valence electrons in $Si_4O_{12}{}^{8-}$. Thirty-two electrons are required to form the sixteen bonds in the ion; the remaining $96 - 32 = 64$ electrons are required to complete the octets of the oxygen atoms. In C_4H_8, there are $[4 \times C(4e^-)] + [8 \times H(1e^-)] = 24$ valence electrons. All twenty four electrons are used to form the bonds between the atoms in the molecule.

Solution:

a)

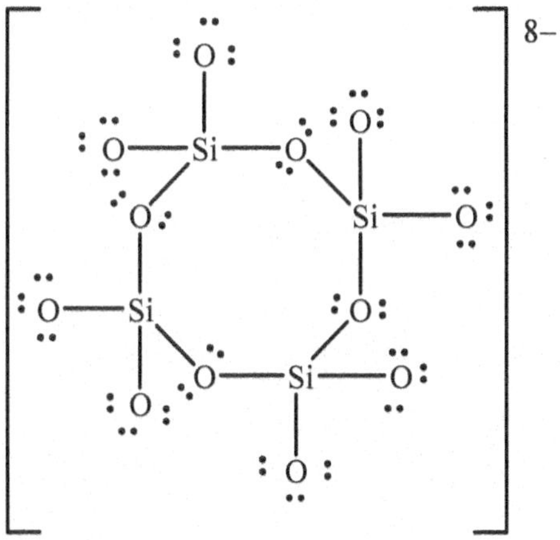

b)

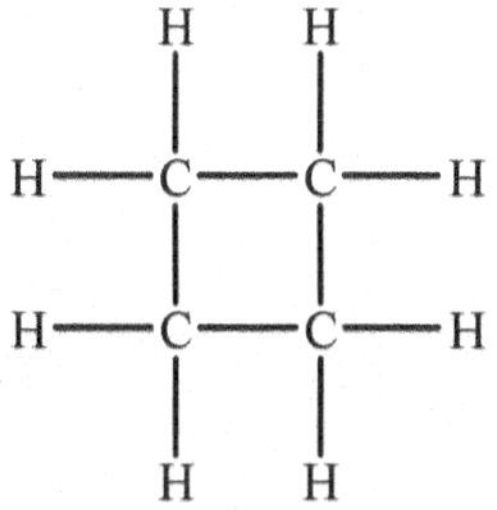

There is another answer possible for C_4H_8.

13.53 a) **Diamond, C**, a network covalent solid of carbon

b) **Calcium carbonate, $CaCO_3$** (Brands that use this compound as an antacid also advertise them as an important source of calcium.)

c) **Carbon dioxide, CO_2**, is the most widely known greenhouse gas; CH_4 is also implicated.

d) **Carbon monoxide, CO**, is formed in combustion when the amount of O_2 (air) is limited. CO_2 also binds coordinately to Fe(II) in blood in a manner similar to that of O_2, but much stronger. The preferential binding of carbon monoxide to Fe(II) is largely responsible for the asphyxiation that results from carbon monoxide poisoning.

e) **Silicon, Si**

13.57 a) In Group 15, all elements except bismuth have a range of oxidation states from –3 to +5.

b) For nonmetals, the range of oxidation states is from the lowest at group number -18, which is $15 - 18 = -3$ for Group 15, to the highest equal to the group number -10, which is +5 for Group 15.

13.60 Plan: Acid strength increases with increasing electronegativity of the central atom. Arsenic is less electronegative than phosphorus, which is less electronegative than nitrogen.

Solution:

Arsenic acid is the weakest acid and nitric acid is the strongest. Order of increasing strength:

$H_3AsO_4 < H_3PO_4 < HNO_3$

13.62   <u>Plan:</u> With excess oxygen, arsenic will form the oxide with arsenic in its highest possible oxidation state, +5. Trihalides are formed by direct combination of the elements (except N). Metal phosphides, arsenides, and antimonides react with water to form Group 15 hydrides.
<u>Solution:</u>
a) $4 As(s) + 5O_2(g) \rightarrow 2As_2O_5(s)$
b) $2Bi(s) + 3F_2(g) \rightarrow 2BiF_3(s)$
c) $Ca_3As_2(s) + 6H_2O(l) \rightarrow 3Ca(OH)_2(s) + 2AsH_3(g)$

13.64   a) Aluminum is not as active a metal as Li or Mg, so heat is needed to drive this reaction.
$$N_2(g) + 2Al(s) \xrightarrow{\Delta} 2AlN(s)$$
b) The Group 15 halides react with water to form the oxoacid with the same oxidation state as the original halide.
$$PF_5(g) + 4H_2O(l) \rightarrow H_3PO_4(aq) + 5HF(g)$$

13.66   <u>Plan:</u> There are $[1 \times P(5e^-)] + [2 \times F(7e^-)] + [3 \times Cl(7e^-)] = 40$ valence electrons in PF_2Cl_3. Ten electrons are required to form the five bonds between F or Cl to P; the remaining $40 - 10 = 30$ electrons are required to complete the octets of the fluorine and chlorine atoms. From the Lewis structure, the phosphorus has five electron groups for a trigonal bipyramidal molecular shape. In this shape, the three groups in the equatorial plane have greater bond angles ($120°$) than the two groups above and below this plane ($90°$). The chlorine atoms would occupy the planar sites where there is more space for the larger atoms.
<u>Solution:</u>

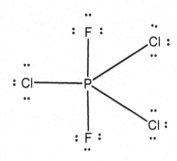

13.70   <u>Plan:</u> Set the atoms into the positions described, and then complete the Lewis structures.
a) and b) N_2O_2 has $[2 \times N(5e^-)] + [2 \times O(6e^-)] = 22$ valence electrons. Six of these electrons are used to make the single bonds between the atoms, leaving $22 - 6 = 16$ electrons. Since twenty electrons are needed to complete the octets of all of the atoms, two double bonds are needed.
c) N_2O_3 has $[2 \times N(5e^-)] + [3 \times O(6e^-)] = 28$ valence electrons. Eight of these electrons are used to make the single bonds between the atoms, leaving $28 - 8 = 20$ electrons. Since twenty-four electrons are needed to complete the octets of all of the atoms, two double bonds are needed.
d) NO^+ has $[1 \times N(5e^-)] + [1 \times O(6e^-)] - [1e^- \text{ (due to the + charge)}] = 10$ valence electrons. Two of these electrons are used to make the single bond between the atoms, leaving $10 - 2 = 8$ electrons. Since twelve electrons are needed to complete the octets of both atoms, a triple bond is needed.
NO_3^- has $[1 \times N(5e^-)] + [3 \times O(6e^-) + [1\ e^- \text{ (due to the} - \text{ charge)}] = 24$ valence electrons. Six of these electrons are used to make the single bond between the atoms, leaving $24 - 6 = 18$ electrons. Since twenty electrons are needed to complete the octets of all of the atoms, a double bond is needed.
<u>Solution:</u>

a)

$$\overset{..}{\underset{..}{O}} = \overset{..}{N} - \overset{..}{N} = \overset{..}{\underset{..}{O}}$$

b)

$$\overset{..}{\underset{..}{O}} = \overset{..}{N} - \overset{..}{\underset{..}{O}} = \overset{..}{N} :$$

c)

$$\overset{\displaystyle :\overset{..}{O}:}{\overset{|}{\underset{..}{O}} = \overset{..}{N} - \overset{..}{\underset{..}{O}} = \overset{..}{N}}$$

d)

$$\left[:N \equiv \overset{..}{O}: \right]^+ \qquad \left[\overset{..}{\underset{..}{O}} = \overset{..}{N} \underset{\displaystyle :\overset{..}{O}:}{\overset{\displaystyle \overset{..}{\cdot}\overset{..}{O}\overset{..}{\cdot}}{\diagup}} \right]^-$$

13.72   a) Thermal decomposition of KNO_3 at low temperatures:
$$2KNO_3(s) \xrightarrow{\Delta} 2KNO_2(s) + O_2(g)$$
b) Thermal decomposition of KNO_3 at high temperatures:
$$4KNO_3(s) \xrightarrow{\Delta} 2K_2O(s) + 2N_2(g) + 5O_2(g)$$

13.74   a) Both groups have elements that range from gas to metalloid to metal. Thus, their boiling points and conductivity vary in similar ways down a group.
b) The degree of metallic character and methods of bonding vary in similar ways down a group.
c) Both P and S have allotropes and both bond covalently with almost every other nonmetal.
d) Both nitrogen and oxigen are diatomic gases at normal temperature and pressure. Both N and O have very low melting and boiling points.
e) Oxygen, O_2, is a reactive gas whereas nitrogen, N_2, is not. Nitrogen can exist in six oxidation states, whereas oxygen has two.

13.76   a) To decide what type of reaction will occur, examine the reactants. Notice that sodium hydroxide is a strong base. Is the other reactant an acid? If we separate the salt, sodium hydrogen sulfate, into the two ions, Na^+ and HSO_4^-, then it is easier to see the hydrogen sulfate ion as the acid. The sodium ions could be left out for the net ionic reaction.
$$NaHSO_4(aq) + NaOH(aq) \rightarrow Na_2SO_4(aq) + H_2O(l)$$
b) As mentioned in the book, hexafluorides are known to exist for sulfur. These will form when excess fluorine is present.
$$S_8(s) + 24F_2(g) \rightarrow 8SF_6(g)$$
c) Group 16 elements, except oxygen, form hydrides in the following reaction.
$$FeS(s) + 2HCl(aq) \rightarrow H_2S(g) + FeCl_2(aq)$$
d) Tetraiodides, but not hexaiodides, of tellurium are known.
$$Te(s) + 2I_2(s) \rightarrow TeI_4(s)$$

13.78   Plan: The oxides of nonmetal elements are acidic, while the oxides metal elements are basic.
Solution:
a) Se is a nonmetal; its oxide is **acidic**.
b) N is a nonmetal; its oxide is **acidic**.
c) K is a metal; its oxide is **basic**.
d) Be is an alkaline earth metal, but all of its bonds are covalent; its oxide is **amphoteric**.
e) Ba is a metal; its oxide is **basic**.

13.80   Plan: Acid strength of binary acids increases down a group since bond energy decreases down the group.
Solution:
$H_2O < H_2S < H_2Te$

13.83   a) **O_3, ozone**
b) **SO_3, sulfur trioxide** (+6 oxidation state)
c) **SO_2, sulfur dioxide**
d) **H_2SO_4, sulfuric acid**
e) **$Na_2S_2O_3 \cdot 5H_2O$, sodium thiosulfate pentahydrate**

13.85 $S_2F_{10}(g) \rightarrow SF_4(g) + SF_6(g)$
O.N. of S in S_2F_{10}: $- (10 \times -1$ for F$)/2 = $ **+5**
O.N. of S in SF_4: $- (4 \times -1$ for F$) = $ **+4**
O.N. of S in SF_6: $- (6 \times -1$ for F$) = $ **+6**

13.87   a) Bonding with very electronegative elements: **+1, +3, +5, +7**. Bonding with other elements: **−1**
b) The electron configuration for Cl is $[Ne]3s^23p^5$. By adding one electron to form Cl^-, Cl achieves an octet similar to the noble gas Ar. By forming covalent bonds, Cl completes or expands its octet by maintaining its electrons paired in bonds or lone pairs.

c) Fluorine has only the –1 oxidation state because its small size and no access to d orbitals prevent it from forming multiple covalent bonds. Fluorine's high electronegativity also prevents it from sharing its electrons.

13.89   a) The **Cl–Cl bond** is stronger than the Br–Br bond since the chlorine atoms are smaller than the bromine atoms, so the shared electrons are held more tightly by the two nuclei.
b) The **Br–Br bond** is stronger than the I–I bond since the bromine atoms are smaller than the iodine atoms.
c) The **Cl–Cl bond** is stronger than the F–F bond. The fluorine atoms are smaller than the chlorine but they are so small that electron-electron repulsion of the lone pairs decreases the strength of the bond.

13.91   a) A substance that disproportionates serves as both an oxidizing and reducing agent. Assume that OH^- serves as the base. Write the reactants and products of the reaction, and balance like a redox reaction.
$$3\ Br_2(l) + 6OH^-(aq) \rightarrow 5Br^-(aq) + BrO_3^-(aq) + 3H_2O(l)$$
b) In the presence of base, instead of water, only the oxy*anion* (not oxo*acid*) and fluoride (not *hydro*fluoride) form. No oxidation or reduction takes place, because Cl maintains its +5 oxidation state and F maintains its –1 oxidation state.
$$ClF_5(l) + 6OH^-(aq) \rightarrow 5F^-(aq) + ClO_3^-(aq) + 3H_2O(l)$$

13.92   a) $2Rb(s) + Br_2(l) \rightarrow 2RbBr(s)$
b) $I_2(s) + H_2O(l) \rightarrow HI(aq) + HIO(aq)$
c) $Br_2(l) + 2I^-(aq) \rightarrow I_2(s) + 2Br^-(aq)$
d) $CaF_2(s) + H_2SO_4(l) \rightarrow CaSO_4(s) + 2HF(g)$

13.94   Plan: Acid strength increases with increasing electronegativity of the central atom and increasing number of oxygen atoms.
Solution:
Iodine is less electronegative than bromine, which is less electronegative than chlorine.
$HIO < HBrO < HClO < HClO_2$

13.98 $I_2 < Br_2 < Cl_2$, since Cl_2 is able to oxidize Re to the +6 oxidation state, Br_2 only to +5, and I_2 only to +4.

13.101   Whether a boiling point is high or low is a result of the strength of the forces between particles. Dispersion forces, the weakest of all the intermolecular forces, hold atoms of noble gases together. Only a relatively low temperature is required for the atoms to have enough kinetic energy to break away from the attractive force of other atoms and go into the gas phase. The boiling points are so low that all the noble gases are gases at room temperature.

13.105   Plan: To obtain the overall reaction, reverse the first reaction and the third reaction and add these two reactions to the second reaction, canceling substances that appear on both sides of the arrow. When a reaction is reversed, the sign of its enthalpy change is reversed. Add the three enthalpy values to obtain the overall enthalpy value.
Solution:

$H_3O^+(g) \rightarrow \cancel{H^+(g)} + \cancel{H_2O(g)}$ $\Delta H = +720$ kJ/mol

$\cancel{H^+(g)} + H_2O(l) \rightarrow H_3O^+(aq)$ $\Delta H = -1090$ kJ/mol
$\cancel{H_2O(g)} \rightarrow \cancel{H_2O(l)}$ $\Delta H = -40.7$ kJ/mol

Overall: $H_3O^+(g) \rightarrow H_3O^+(aq)$ $\Delta H = -410.7$ kJ/mol= **–411 kJ/mol**

13.109   Plan: Examine the outer electron configuration of the alkali metals. To calculate the $\Delta_r H^{\circ}$ in part b), use Hess's law.
Solution:
a) Alkali metals have an outer electron configuration of ns^1. The first electron lost by the metal is the ns electron, giving the metal a noble gas configuration. Second ionization energies for alkali metals are high because the electron being removed is from the next lower energy level and electrons in a lower level are more tightly held by the nucleus. The metal would also lose its noble gas configuration.
b) The reaction is $2CsF_2(s) \rightarrow 2CsF(s) + F_2(g)$.
You know the $\Delta_f H^{\circ}$ for the formation of CsF:

$$Cs(s) + 1/2F_2(g) \rightarrow CsF(s) \qquad\qquad \Delta_f H^\circ = -530 \text{ kJ/mol}$$

You also know the $\Delta_f H^\circ$ for the formation of CsF_2:

$$Cs(s) + F_2(g) \rightarrow CsF_2(s) \qquad\qquad \Delta_f H^\circ = -125 \text{ kJ/mol}$$

To obtain the heat of reaction for the breakdown of CsF_2 to CsF, combine the formation reaction of CsF with the reverse of the formation reaction of CsF_2, both multiplied by 2:

$$2\cancel{Cs(s)} + \cancel{F_2(g)} \rightarrow 2CsF(s) \qquad \Delta_f H^\circ = 2 \text{ x } (-530 \text{ kJ/mol}) = -1060 \text{ kJ/mol}$$

$$2CsF_2(s) \rightarrow \cancel{2Cs(s)} + 2F_2(g) \qquad \Delta_f H^\circ = 2 \text{ x } (+125 \text{ kJ/mol}) = 250 \text{ kJ/mol (Note sign change)}$$

$$\overline{2\,CsF_2(s) \rightarrow 2CsF(s) + F_2(g) \qquad \Delta_r H^\circ = -810 \text{ kJ/mol}}$$

810 kJ/mol of energy are released when two moles of CsF_2 convert to two moles of CsF, so heat of reaction for one mole of CsF is ½(–810 kJ/mol) or **–405 kJ/mol**.

13.111 Plan: To find the molecular formula, divide the molar mass of each compound by the molar mass of the empirical formula, HNO. The result of this gives the factor by which the empirical formula is multiplied to obtain the molecular formula.

Solution:
a) Empirical formula HNO has a molar mass of 31.02 g/mol. Hyponitrous acid has a molar mass of 62.04 g/mol, twice the mass of the empirical formula; its molecular formula is twice as large as the empirical formula, $2(HNO) = H_2N_2O_2$. The molecular formula of nitroxyl would be the same as the empirical formula, HNO, since the molar mass of nitroxyl is the same as the molar mass of the empirical formula.
b) $H_2N_2O_2$ has $[2 \times H(1e^-)] + [2 \times N(5e^-)] + [2 \times O(6e^-)] = 24$ valence e^-. Ten electrons are used for single bonds between the atoms, leaving $24 - 10 = 14\ e^-$. Sixteen electrons are needed to give every atom an octet; since only fourteen electrons are available, one double bond (between the N atoms) is needed.
HNO has $[1 \times H(1e^-)] + [1 \times N(5e^-)] + [1 \times O(6e^-)] = 12$ valence e^-. Four electrons are used for single bonds between the atoms, leaving $12 - 4 = 8e^-$. Ten electrons are needed to give every atom an octet; since only eight electrons are available, one double bond is needed between the N and O atoms.

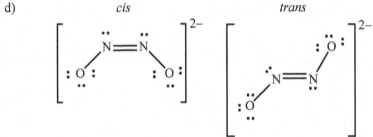

c) In both hyponitrous acid and nitroxyl, the nitrogens are surrounded by three electron groups (one single bond, one double bond, and one unshared pair), so the electron arrangement is trigonal planar and the molecular shape is **bent**.
d)

13.115 Plan: Carbon monoxide and carbon dioxide would be formed from the reaction of coke (carbon) with the oxygen in the air. The nitrogen in the producer gas would come from the nitrogen already in the air. So, the calculation of mass of product is based on the mass of CO and CO_2 that can be produced from 1.75 metric tons of coke.

Solution:

Using 100 g of sample, the percentages simply become grams.

Since 5.0 g of CO_2 is produced for each 25 g of CO, we can calculate a mass ratio of carbon that produces each:

$$\frac{(25 \text{ g CO})\left(\dfrac{12.01 \text{ g C}}{28.01 \text{ g CO}}\right)}{(5.0 \text{ g CO}_2)\left(\dfrac{12.01 \text{ g C}}{44.01 \text{ g CO}_2}\right)} = 7.85612/1$$

Using the ratio of carbon that reacts as 7.85612:1, the total C reacting is 7.85612 + 1 = 8.85612. The mass fraction of the total carbon that produces CO is 7.85612/8.85612 and the mass fraction of the total carbon reacting that produces CO_2 is 1.00/8.85612. To find the mass of CO produced from 1.75 metric tons of carbon with an 87% yield:

$$\text{Mass (g) of CO} = \left(\frac{7.85612}{8.85612}\right)(1.75 \text{ t})\left(\frac{28.01 \text{ t CO}}{12.01 \text{ t C}}\right)\left(\frac{87\%}{100\%}\right) = 3.1498656 \text{ t CO}$$

$$\text{Mass (g) of CO}_2 = \left(\frac{1}{8.85612}\right)(1.75 \text{ t})\left(\frac{44.01 \text{ t CO}_2}{12.01 \text{ t C}}\right)\left(\frac{87\%}{100\%}\right) = 0.6299733 \text{ t CO}_2$$

The mass of CO and CO_2 represent a total of 30% (100% − 70.% N_2) of the mass of the producer gas, so the total mass would be (3.1498656 + 0.6299733)t(100%/30%) = 12.59946 t= **13 metric tons**.

13.117 In a disproportionation reaction, a substance acts as both a reducing agent and oxidizing agent because an atom within the substance reacts to form atoms with higher and lower oxidation states.

$\quad\quad$ 0 $\quad\quad$ −1 $\quad\quad\quad$ −1/3

a) $\quad I_2(s) + KI(aq) \rightarrow KI_3(aq)$

I in I_2 reduces to I in KI_3. I in KI oxidizes to I in KI_3. This is not a disproportionation reaction since different substances have atoms that reduce or oxidize. The *reverse* direction would be a disproportionation reaction because a single substance (I in KI) both oxidizes and reduces.

$\quad\quad$ +4 $\quad\quad\quad\quad\quad$ +5 $\quad\quad\quad$ +3

b) $2ClO_2(g) + H_2O(l) \rightarrow HClO_3(aq) + HClO_2(aq)$

Yes, ClO_2 disproportionates, as the chlorine reduces from +4 to +3 and oxidizes from +4 to +5.

$\quad\quad$ 0 $\quad\quad\quad\quad\quad\quad$ −1 $\quad\quad$ +1

c) $Cl_2(g) + 2NaOH(aq) \rightarrow NaCl(aq) + NaClO(aq) + H_2O(l)$

Yes, Cl_2 disproportionates, as the chlorine reduces from 0 to −1 and oxidizes from 0 to +1.

$\quad$ −3 $\quad$ +3 $\quad\quad\quad$ 0

d) $NH_4NO_2(s) \rightarrow N_2(g) + 2H_2O(g)$

Yes, NH_4NO_2 disproportionates; the ammonium (NH_4^+) nitrogen oxidizes from −3 to 0, and the nitrite (NO_2^-) nitrogen reduces from +3 to 0.

$\quad\quad$ +6 $\quad\quad\quad\quad\quad\quad$ +7 $\quad\quad\quad$ +4

e) $3MnO_4^{2-}(aq) + 2H_2O(l) \rightarrow 2MnO_4^-(aq) + MnO_2(s) + 4OH^-(aq)$

Yes, MnO_4^{2-} disproportionates; the manganese oxidizes from +6 to +7 and reduces from +6 to +4.

$\quad$ +1 $\quad\quad\quad$ +3 $\quad\quad\quad$ 0

f) $3 AuCl(s) \rightarrow AuCl_3(s) + 2 Au(s)$

Yes, AuCl disproportionates; the gold oxidizes from +1 to +3 and reduces from +1 to 0.

13.119 a) Group **15** elements have five valence electrons and typically form three bonds with a lone pair to complete the octet. An example is NH_3.

b) Group **17** elements readily gain an electron causing the other reactant to be oxidized. They form monatomic ions of formula X^- and oxoanions. Examples would be Cl^- and ClO^-.

c) Group **16** elements have six valence electrons and gain a complete octet by forming two covalent bonds. An example is H_2O.

d) Group **1** elements are the strongest reducing agents because they most easily lose an electron. As the least electronegative and most metallic of the elements, they are not likely to form covalent bonds. Group **2** elements have similar characteristics. Thus, either Na or Ca could be an example.

e) Group **13** elements have only three valence electrons to share in covalent bonds, but with an empty orbital they can accept an electron pair from another atom. Boron would be an example of an element of this type.

f) Group **18**, the noble gases, are the least reactive of all the elements. Xenon is an example that forms compounds, while helium does not form compounds.

13.121   Plan: Find $\Delta_r H°$ for the reaction $2BrF(g) \rightarrow Br_2(g) + F_2(g)$ by applying Hess's law to the equations given. Recall that when an equation is reversed, the sign of its $\Delta_r H°$ is changed.

Solution:

1)	$3BrF(g) \rightarrow Br_2(g) + BrF_3(l)$	$\Delta_r H = -125.3$ kJ/mol
2)	$5BrF(g) \rightarrow 2Br_2(g) + BrF_5(l)$	$\Delta_r H = -166.1$ kJ/mol
3)	$BrF_3(l) + F_2(g) \rightarrow BrF_5(l)$	$\Delta_r H = -158.0$ kJ/mol

Reverse equations 1 and 3, and add to equation 2:

1)	~~$Br_2(g) + BrF_3(l)$~~ $\rightarrow 3BrF(g)$	$\Delta_r H = +125.3$ kJ/mol (note sign change)
2)	$5BrF(g) \rightarrow$ ~~$2Br_2(g) + BrF_5(l)$~~	$\Delta_r H = -166.1$ kJ/mol
3)	~~$BrF_5(l)$~~ $\rightarrow$ ~~$BrF_3(l)$~~ $+ F_2(g)$	$\Delta_r H = +158.0$ kJ/mol (note sign change)

Total: $2BrF(g) \rightarrow Br_2(g) + F_2(g)$ **$\Delta_r H = +117.2$ kJ/mol**

13.126   Plan: Nitrite ion, NO_2^-, has [1 x N(5e⁻)] + [2 x O(6e⁻)] + [1e⁻ from charge] = 18 valence electrons. Four electrons are used in the single bonds between the atoms, leaving 18 – 4 = 14 electrons. Since sixteen electrons are required to complete the octets of the atoms, one double bond is needed. There are two resonance structures. Nitrogen dioxide, NO_2, has [1 x N(5e⁻)] + [2 x O(6e⁻)] = 17 valence electrons. Four electrons are used in the single bonds between the atoms, leaving 17 – 4 = 13 electrons. Since sixteen electrons are required to complete the octets of the atoms, one double bond is needed and one atom must have an unpaired electron. There are two resonance structures. The nitronium ion, NO_2^+, has [1 x N(5e⁻)] + [2 x O(6e⁻)] – [1e⁻ due to + charge] = 16 valence electrons. Four electrons are used in the single bonds between the atoms, leaving 16 – 4 = 12 electrons. Since sixteen electrons are required to complete the octets of the atoms, two double bonds are needed.

Solution:
The Lewis structures are

$$\left[\overset{..}{O}=\overset{..}{N}-\overset{..}{\underset{..}{O}}\colon \right]^- \longleftrightarrow \left[\colon\overset{..}{\underset{..}{O}}-\overset{..}{N}=\overset{..}{O} \right]^-$$

$$\overset{..}{O}=\overset{\bullet}{N}-\overset{..}{\underset{..}{O}}\colon \longleftrightarrow \colon\overset{..}{\underset{..}{O}}-\overset{\bullet}{N}=\overset{..}{O}$$

$$\left[\overset{..}{O}=N=\overset{..}{O} \right]^+$$

The nitronium ion (NO_2^+) has a linear shape because the central N atom has two surrounding electron groups, which achieve maximum repulsion at 180°. Both the nitrite ion (NO_2^-) and nitrogen dioxide (NO_2) have a central N surrounded by three electron groups. The electron-group arrangement would be trigonal planar with an ideal bond angle of 120°. The bond angle in NO_2^- is more compressed than that in NO_2 since the lone pair of electrons in NO_2^- takes up more space than the lone electron in NO_2. Therefore the bond angle in NO_2^- is smaller (115°) than that of NO_2 (134°)

13.128 **Plan:** To find the limiting reactant, find the amount (mol) of UF_6 that can be produced from the given amount of uranium and then from the given amount of ClF_3, use the mole ratios in the balanced equation. The density of ClF_3 is used to find the mass of ClF_3. The limiting reactant determines the amount of UF_6 that can be produced.
Solution:

$U(s) + 3ClF_3(l) \rightarrow UF_6(l) + 3ClF(g)$
(1 metric ton = 1 t = 1000 kg)

$$\text{Amount of } UF_6 \text{ from } U = (1.00 \text{ t ore})\left(\frac{10^3 \text{ kg}}{1 \text{ t}}\right)\left(\frac{10^3 \text{ g}}{1 \text{ kg}}\right)\left(\frac{1.55\%}{100\%}\right)\left(\frac{1 \text{ mol U}}{238.0 \text{ g U}}\right)\left(\frac{1 \text{ mol } UF_6}{1 \text{ mol U}}\right)$$

$$= 65.12605 \text{ mol } UF_6$$

$$\text{Amount of } UF_6 \text{ from } ClF_3 = (12.75 \text{ L})\left(\frac{1 \text{ mL}}{10^{-3} \text{ L}}\right)\left(\frac{1.88 \text{ g } ClF_3}{1 \text{ mL}}\right)\left(\frac{1 \text{ mol } ClF_3}{92.45 \text{ g } ClF_3}\right)\left(\frac{1 \text{ mol } UF_6}{3 \text{ mol } ClF_3}\right)$$

$$= 86.42509 \text{ mol } UF_6$$

Since the amount of uranium will produce less uranium hexafluoride, it is the limiting reactant.

$$\text{Mass (g) of } UF_6 = (65.12605 \text{ mol } UF_6)\left(\frac{352.0 \text{ g } UF_6}{1 \text{ mol } UF_6}\right) = 2.2924 \times 10^4 \text{ g} = \mathbf{2.29 \times 10^4 \text{ g } UF_6}$$

13.132 **Plan:** Determine the electron configuration of each species. Partially filled orbitals lead to paramagnetism (unpaired electrons).
Solution:

O^+	$1s^2 2s^2 2p^3$	**paramagnetic**	odd number of electrons
O^-	$1s^2 2s^2 2p^5$	**paramagnetic**	odd number of electrons
O^{2-}	$1s^2 2s^2 2p^6$	diamagnetic	all orbitals filled (all electrons paired)
O^{2+}	$1s^2 2s^2 2p^2$	**paramagnetic**	Two of the $2p$ orbitals have one electron each. These electrons have parallel spins (Hund's rule).

13.133 **Plan:** To determine mass percent, divide the mass of As in 1 mole of compound by the molar mass of the compound and multiply by 100. Find the volume of the room (length x width x height) and use the toxic concentration to find the mass of As required. The mass percent of As in $CuHAsO_3$ is used to convert that mass of As to mass of compound.
Solution:

a) $\text{Mass percent} = \dfrac{\text{mass of As}}{\text{mass of compound}}(100\%)$

$$\% \text{ As in } CuHAsO_3 = \frac{74.92 \text{ g As}}{187.48 \text{ g } CuHAsO_3}(100\%) = 39.96160\% = \mathbf{39.96\% \text{ As}}$$

$$\% \text{ As in } (CH_3)_3As = \frac{74.92 \text{ g As}}{120.02 \text{ g } (CH_3)_3As}(100\%) = 62.4229 \% = \mathbf{62.42\% \text{ As}}$$

b) $\text{Volume (m}^3\text{) of room} = (12.35 \text{ m})(7.52 \text{ m})(2.98 \text{ m}) = 276.75856 \text{ m}^3$

$$\text{Mass (g) of As} = (276.75856 \text{ m}^3)\left(\frac{0.50 \text{ mg As}}{\text{m}^3}\right)\left(\frac{10^{-3} \text{ g}}{1 \text{ mg}}\right) = 0.13838 \text{ g As}$$

$$\text{Mass (g) of } CuHAsO_3 = (0.13838 \text{ g As})\left(\frac{100 \text{ g } CuHAsO_3}{39.96160 \text{ g As}}\right) = 0.346282 \text{ g} = \mathbf{0.35 \text{ g } CuHAsO_3}$$

CHAPTER 14 KINETICS: RATES AND MECHANISMS OF CHEMICAL REACTIONS

END–OF–CHAPTER PROBLEMS

14.2   Rate is proportional to concentration. An increase in pressure will increase the number of gas molecules per unit volume. In other words, the gas concentration increases due to increased pressure, so the **reaction rate increases**. Increased pressure also causes more collisions between gas molecules.

14.3   The addition of more water will dilute the concentrations of all solutes dissolved in the reaction vessel. If any of these solutes are reactants, the **rate of the reaction will decrease**.

14.5   An increase in temperature affects the rate of a reaction by increasing the number of collisions, but more importantly, the energy of collisions increases. As the energy of collisions increases, more collisions result in reaction (i.e., reactants → products), so the **rate of reaction increases**.

14.8   a) For most reactions, the rate of the reaction changes as a reaction progresses. The instantaneous rate is the rate at one point, or instant, during the reaction. The average rate is the average of the instantaneous rates over a period of time. On a graph of reactant concentration vs. time of reaction, the instantaneous rate is the slope of the tangent to the curve at any one point. The average rate is the slope of the line connecting two points on the curve. The closer together the two points (shorter the time interval), the more closely the average rate agrees with the instantaneous rate.
b) The initial rate is the instantaneous rate at the point on the graph where time = 0, that is when reactants are mixed.

14.10   At time $t = 0$, no product has formed, so the B(g) curve must start at the origin. Reactant concentration (A(g)) decreases with time; product concentration (B(g)) increases with time. Many correct graphs can be drawn. Two examples are shown below. The graph on the left shows a reaction that proceeds nearly to completion, i.e., [products] >> [reactants] at the end of the reaction. The graph on the right shows a reaction that does not proceed to completion, i.e., [reactants] > [products] at reaction end.

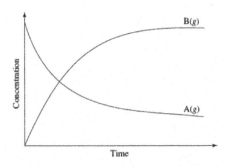 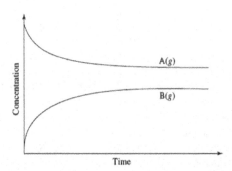

14.12   <u>Plan:</u> The average rate is the total change in concentration divided by the total change in time.
<u>Solution:</u>
a) The average rate from $t = 0$ s to $t = 20.0$ s is proportional to the slope of the line connecting these two points:

$$\text{Rate} = -\frac{1}{2}\frac{\Delta[AX_2]}{\Delta t} = -\frac{1}{2}\frac{(0.0088 \text{ mol/L} - 0.0500 \text{ mol/L})}{(20.0 \text{ s} - 0 \text{ s})} = 0.00103 \text{ mol/L·s} = \textbf{0.0010 mol/L·s}$$

The negative of the slope is used because rate is defined as the change in product concentration with time. If a reactant is used, the rate is the negative of the change in reactant concentration. The 1/2 factor is included to account for the stoichiometric coefficient of 2 for AX_2 in the reaction.

14-1

(b)

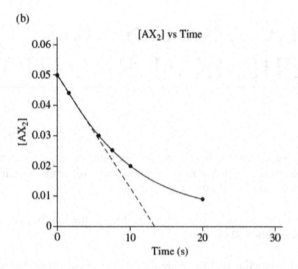

The slope of the tangent to the curve (dashed line) at $t = 0$ s is approximately –0.004 mol/L•s. This initial rate is greater than the average rate as calculated in part a). The **initial rate is greater than the average rate** because rate decreases as reactant concentration decreases.

14.14   Plan: Use Equation 14.2 to describe the rate of this reaction in terms of reactant disappearance and product appearance. A negative sign is used for the rate in terms of reactant A since A is reacting and [A] is decreasing over time. Positive signs are used for the rate in terms of products B and C since B and C are being formed and [B] and [C] increase over time. Reactant A decreases twice as fast as product C increases because two molecules of A disappear for every molecule of C that appears.
Solution:
Expressing the rate in terms of each component:
$$\text{Rate} = -\frac{1}{2}\frac{\Delta[A]}{\Delta t} = \frac{\Delta[B]}{\Delta t} = \frac{\Delta[C]}{\Delta t}$$
Calculating the rate of change of [A]:
$$-\frac{1}{2}\frac{\Delta[A]}{\Delta t} = \frac{\Delta[C]}{\Delta t}$$
$$\left(2 \text{ mol C/L•s}\right)\left(\frac{2 \text{ mol A/L•s}}{1 \text{ mol C/L•s}}\right) = -4 \text{ mol/L•s}$$

The negative value indicates that [A] is decreasing as the reaction progresses. The rate of reaction is always expressed as a positive number, so [A] is decreasing at a rate of **4 mol/L•s**.

14.16   Plan: Use Equation 14.2 to describe the rate of this reaction in terms of reactant disappearance and product appearance. A negative sign is used for the rate in terms of reactants A and B since A and B are reacting and [A] and [B] are decreasing over time. A positive sign is used for the rate in terms of product C since C is being formed and [C] increases over time. The 1/2 factor is included for reactant B to account for the stoichiometric coefficient of 2 for B in the reaction. Reactant A decreases half as fast as reactant B decreases because one molecule of A disappears for every two molecules of B that disappear.
Solution:
Expressing the rate in terms of each component:
$$\text{Rate} = -\frac{\Delta[A]}{\Delta t} = -\frac{1}{2}\frac{\Delta[B]}{\Delta t} = \frac{\Delta[C]}{\Delta t}$$
Calculating the rate of change of [A]:
$$\left(0.5 \text{ mol B/L•s}\right)\left(\frac{1 \text{ mol A/L•s}}{2 \text{ mol B/L•s}}\right) = -0.25 \text{ mol/L•s} = -0.2 \text{ mol/L•s}$$

The negative value indicates that [A] is decreasing as the reaction progresses. The rate of reaction is always expressed as a positive number, so [A] is decreasing at a rate of **0.2 mol/L•s**.

14.18 <u>Plan:</u> A term with a negative sign is a reactant; a term with a positive sign is a product. The inverse of the fraction becomes the coefficient of the molecule.
<u>Solution:</u>
N_2O_5 is the reactant; NO_2 and O_2 are products.
$2N_2O_5(g) \rightarrow 4NO_2(g) + O_2(g)$

14.21 <u>Plan:</u> Use Equation 14.2 to describe the rate of this reaction in terms of reactant disappearance and product appearance. A negative sign is used for the rate in terms of reactants N_2 and H_2 since these substances are reacting and $[N_2]$ and $[H_2]$ are decreasing over time. A positive sign is used for the rate in terms of the product NH_3 since it is being formed and $[NH_3]$ increases over time.
<u>Solution:</u>

$$\text{Rate} = -\frac{\Delta[N_2]}{\Delta t} = -\frac{1}{3}\frac{\Delta[H_2]}{\Delta t} = \frac{1}{2}\frac{\Delta[NH_3]}{\Delta t}$$

14.22 <u>Plan:</u> Use Equation 14.2 to describe the rate of this reaction in terms of reactant disappearance and product appearance. A negative sign is used for the rate in terms of the reactant O_2 since it is reacting and $[O_2]$ is decreasing over time. A positive sign is used for the rate in terms of the product O_3 since it is being formed and $[O_3]$ increases over time. O_3 increases 2/3 as fast as O_2 decreases because two molecules of O_3 are formed for every three molecules of O_2 that disappear.
<u>Solution:</u>
a) Rate = $-\dfrac{1}{3}\dfrac{\Delta[O_2]}{\Delta t} = \dfrac{1}{2}\dfrac{\Delta[O_3]}{\Delta t}$
b) Use the mole ratio in the balanced equation:

$$\left(\frac{2.17\times10^{-5} \text{ mol } O_2 \text{ /L}\cdot s}{}\right)\left(\frac{2 \text{ mol } O_3 \text{ /L}\cdot s}{3 \text{ mol } O_2\text{/L}\cdot s}\right) = \textbf{1.45}\times\textbf{10}^{-5} \textbf{ mol/L}\cdot\textbf{s}$$

14.23 a) k is the rate constant, the proportionality constant in the rate law. k represents the fraction of successful collisions which includes the fraction of collisions with sufficient energy and the fraction of collisions with correct orientation. k is a constant that varies with temperature.
b) m represents the order of the reaction with respect to $[A]$ and n represents the order of the reaction with respect to $[B]$. The order is the exponent in the relationship between rate and reactant concentration and defines how reactant concentration influences rate.
The order of a reactant does not necessarily equal its stoichiometric coefficient in the balanced equation. If a reaction is an elementary reaction, meaning the reaction occurs in only one step, then the orders and stoichiometric coefficients are equal. However, if a reaction occurs in a series of elementary reactions, called a mechanism, then the rate law is based on the slowest elementary reaction in the mechanism. The orders of the reactants will equal the stoichiometric coefficients of the reactants in the slowest elementary reaction but may not equal the stoichiometric coefficients in the overall reaction.
c) For the rate law rate = $k[A][B]^2$ substitute in the units:

$$\text{Rate (mol/L}\cdot\text{min)} = k[A]^1[B]^2$$

$$k = \frac{\text{rate}}{[A]^1[B]^2} = \frac{\text{mol/L}\cdot\text{min}}{\left[\dfrac{\text{mol}}{L}\right]^1\left[\dfrac{\text{mol}}{L}\right]^2} = \frac{\text{mol/L}\cdot\text{min}}{\dfrac{\text{mol}^3}{L^3}}$$

$$k = \frac{\text{mol}}{L\cdot\text{min}}\left(\frac{L^3}{\text{mol}^3}\right)$$

$$\boldsymbol{k = L^2/\text{mol}^2\cdot\text{min}}$$

14.25 a) The **rate doubles**. If rate = $k[A]^1$ and [A] is doubled, then the rate law becomes rate = $k[2 \times A]^1$. The rate increases by 2^1 or 2.

b) The **rate decreases by a factor of four**. If rate = $k[B]^2$ and [B] is halved, then the rate law becomes rate = $k[1/2 \times B]^2$. The rate decreases to $(1/2)^2$ or 1/4 of its original value.

c) The **rate increases by a factor of nine**. If rate = $k[C]^2$ and [C] is tripled, then the rate law becomes rate = $k[3 \times C]^2$. The rate increases to 3^2 or 9 times its original value.

14.26 <u>Plan:</u> The order for each reactant is the exponent on the reactant concentration in the rate law. The individual orders are added to find the overall reaction order.
<u>Solution:</u>
The orders with respect to $[BrO_3^-]$ and to $[Br^-]$ are both 1 since both have an exponent of 1. The order with respect to $[H^+]$ is 2 (its exponent in the rate law is 2). The overall reaction order is $1 + 1 + 2 = 4$.
First order with respect to BrO_3^-, first order with respect to Br^-, second order with respect to H^+, fourth order overall

14.28 a) The rate is first order with respect to $[BrO_3^-]$. If $[BrO_3^-]$ is doubled, rate = $k[2 \times BrO_3^-]$, then rate increases to 2^1 or 2 times its original value. The rate **doubles**.

b) The rate is first order with respect to $[Br^-]$. If $[Br^-]$ is halved, rate = $k[1/2 \times Br^-]$, then rate decreases by a factor of $(1/2)^1$ or 1/2 times its original value. The rate is **halved**.

c) The rate is second order with respect to $[H^+]$. If $[H^+]$ is quadrupled, rate = $k[4 \times H^+]^2$, then rate increases to 4^2 or **16 times** its original value.

14.30 <u>Plan:</u> The order for each reactant is the exponent on the reactant concentration in the rate law. The individual orders are added to find the overall reaction order.
<u>Solution:</u>
The order with respect to **$[NO_2]$ is 2**, and the order with respect to **$[Cl_2]$ is 1**. The **overall order is:** $2 + 1 = 3$

14.32 a) The rate is second order with respect to $[NO_2]$. If $[NO_2]$ is tripled, rate = $k[3 \times NO_2]^2$, then rate increases to 3^2 or 9 times its original value. The rate **increases by a factor of 9.**

b) The rate is second order with respect to $[NO_2]$ and first order with respect to $[Cl_2]$. If $[NO_2]$ and $[Cl_2]$ are doubled, rate = $k[2 \times NO_2]^2[2 \times Cl_2]^1$, then the rate **increases by a factor of $2^2 \times 2^1 = 8$**.

c) The rate is first order with respect to $[Cl_2]$. If Cl_2 is halved, rate = $k[1/2 \times Cl_2]^1$, then rate decreases to 1/2 times its original value. The rate is **halved.**

14.34 <u>Plan:</u> The rate law is rate = $[A]^m[B]^n$ where m and n are the orders of the reactants. To find the order of each reactant, take the ratio of the rate laws for two experiments in which only the reactant in question changes. Once the rate law is known, any experiment can be used to find the rate constant k.
<u>Solution:</u>
a) To find the order for reactant A, first identify the reaction experiments in which [A] changes but [B] is constant. Use experiments 1 and 2 (or 3 and 4 would work) to find the order with respect to [A].
Set up a ratio of the rate laws for experiments 1 and 2 and fill in the values given for rates and concentrations and solve for m, the order with respect to [A].

$$\frac{\text{rate}_{\text{exp 2}}}{\text{rate}_{\text{exp 1}}} = \left(\frac{[A]_{\text{exp 2}}}{[A]_{\text{exp 1}}}\right)^m$$

$$\frac{45.0 \text{ mol/L} \cdot \text{min}}{5.00 \text{ mol/L} \cdot \text{min}} = \left(\frac{0.300 \text{ mol/L}}{0.100 \text{ mol/L}}\right)^m$$

$9.00 = (3.00)^m$

$\log(9.00) = m \log(3.00)$

$m = 2$

Using experiments 3 and 4 also gives **second order with respect to [A]**.
To find the order for reactant B, first identify the reaction experiments in which [B] changes but [A] is constant. Use experiments 1 and 3 (or 2 and 4 would work) to find the order with respect to [B].
Set up a ratio of the rate laws for experiments 1 and 3 and fill in the values given for rates and concentrations and solve for n, the order with respect to [B].

$$\frac{\text{rate}_{\text{exp 3}}}{\text{rate}_{\text{exp 1}}} = \left(\frac{[B]_{\text{exp 3}}}{[B]_{\text{exp 1}}}\right)^{n}$$

$$\frac{10.0 \text{ mol/L} \cdot \text{min}}{5.00 \text{ mol/L} \cdot \text{min}} = \left(\frac{0.200 \text{ mol/L}}{0.100 \text{ mol/L}}\right)^{n}$$

$$2.00 = (2.00)^{n}$$
$$\log (2.00) = n \log (2.00)$$
$$n = 1$$

The reaction is **first order with respect to [B].**

b) The rate law, without a value for k, is **rate $= k[A]^2[B]$.**

c) Using experiment 1 to calculate k (the data from any of the experiments can be used):

Rate $= k[A]^2[B]$

$$k = \frac{\text{rate}}{[A]^2[B]} = \frac{5.00 \text{ mol/L} \cdot \text{min}}{[0.100 \text{ mol/L}]^2[0.100 \text{ mol/L}]} = \mathbf{5.00 \times 10^3 \ L^2/mol^2 \cdot min}$$

14.36 Plan: Write the appropriate rate law and enter the units for rate and concentrations to find the units of k. The units of k are dependent on the reaction orders and the unit of time.

Solution:

a) A first-order rate law follows the general expression, rate $= k[A]$. The reaction rate is expressed as a change in concentration per unit time with units of mol/L·time. Since [A] has units of mol/L, k **has units of time^{-1}**:

Rate $= k[A]$

$$\frac{\text{mol}}{\text{L} \cdot \text{time}} = k \frac{\text{mol}}{\text{L}}$$

$$k = \frac{\dfrac{\text{mol}}{\text{L} \cdot \text{time}}}{\dfrac{\text{mol}}{\text{L}}} = \frac{\text{mol}}{\text{L} \cdot \text{time}} \times \frac{\text{L}}{\text{mol}} = \frac{1}{\text{time}} = \mathbf{time^{-1}}$$

b) A second-order rate law follows the general expression, rate $= k[A]^2$. The reaction rate is expressed as a change in concentration per unit time with units of mol/L·time. Since [A] has units of mol^2/L^2, k **has units of L/mol·time**:

Rate $= k[A]^2$

$$\frac{\text{mol}}{\text{L} \cdot \text{time}} = k \left(\frac{\text{mol}}{\text{L}}\right)^{2}$$

$$k = \frac{\dfrac{\text{mol}}{\text{L} \cdot \text{time}}}{\dfrac{\text{mol}^2}{\text{L}^2}} = \frac{\text{mol}}{\text{L} \cdot \text{time}} \times \frac{\text{L}^2}{\text{mol}^2} = \mathbf{\frac{L}{mol \cdot time}}$$

c) A third-order rate law follows the general expression, rate $= k[A]^3$. The reaction rate is expressed as a change in concentration per unit time with units of mol/L·time. Since [A] has units of mol^3/L^3, k **has units of L^2/mol^2·time**:

Rate $= k[A]^3$

$$\frac{\text{mol}}{\text{L} \cdot \text{time}} = k \left(\frac{\text{mol}}{\text{L}}\right)^{3}$$

$$k = \frac{\dfrac{\text{mol}}{\text{L} \cdot \text{time}}}{\dfrac{\text{mol}^3}{\text{L}^3}} = \frac{\text{mol}}{\text{L} \cdot \text{time}} \times \frac{\text{L}^3}{\text{mol}^3} = \mathbf{\frac{L^2}{mol^2 \cdot time}}$$

d) A 5/2-order rate law follows the general expression, rate = $k[A]^{5/2}$. The reaction rate is expressed as a change in concentration per unit time with units of mol/L·time. Since [A] has units of $mol^{5/2}/L^{5/2}$, **k has units of $L^{3/2}/mol^{3/2}$·time**:

$$\frac{mol}{L \cdot time} = k\left(\frac{mol}{L}\right)^{5/2}$$

$$k = \frac{\dfrac{mol}{L \cdot time}}{\dfrac{mol^{5/2}}{L^{5/2}}} = \frac{mol}{L \cdot time} \times \frac{L^{5/2}}{mol^{5/2}} = \frac{\mathbf{L^{3/2}}}{\mathbf{mol^{3/2} \cdot time}}$$

14.39   The integrated rate law can be used to plot a graph. If the plot of [reactant] vs. time is linear, the order is zero. If the plot of ln[reactant] vs. time is linear, the order is first. If the plot of inverse concentration (1/[reactant]) vs. time is linear, the order is second.
a) The reaction is **first order** since ln[reactant] vs. time is linear.
b) The reaction is **second order** since 1/[reactant] vs. time is linear.
c) The reaction is **zero order** since [reactant] vs. time is linear.

14.41   Plan: The rate expression indicates that this reaction is second order overall (the order of [AB] is 2), so use the second-order integrated rate law to find time. We know k (0.2 L/mol·s), $[AB]_0$ (1.50 M), and $[AB]_t$ (1/3$[AB]_0$ = 1/3(1.50 mol/L) = 0.500 mol/L), so we can solve for t.
Solution:

$$\frac{1}{[AB]_t} - \frac{1}{[AB]_0} = kt$$

$$t = \frac{\left(\dfrac{1}{[AB]_t} - \dfrac{1}{[AB]_0}\right)}{k}$$

$$t = \frac{\left(\dfrac{1}{0.500\,mol\,/\,L} - \dfrac{1}{1.50\,mol\,/\,L}\right)}{0.2\,L/mol \cdot s}$$

$$t = 6.6667 = \mathbf{7\ s}$$

14.43   Plan: This is a first-order reaction so use the first-order integrated rate law. In part a), we know t (10.5 min). Let $[A]_0$ = 1 mol/L and then $[A]_t$ = 50% of 1 M = 0.5 mol/L. Solve for k. In part b), use the value of k to find the time necessary for 75.0% of the compound to react. If 75.0% of the compound has reacted, 100–75 = 25% remains at time t. Let $[A]_0$ = 1 mol/L and then $[A]_t$ = 25% of 1 mol/L = 0.25 mol/L.
Solution:
a) ln $[A]_t$ = ln $[A]_0 - kt$
ln [0.5] = ln [1] – k(10.5 min)
–0.693147 = 0 – k(10.5 min)
0.693147 = k(10.5 min)
k = 0.0660 min^{-1}
Alternatively, 50.0% decomposition means that one half-life has passed. Thus, the first-order half-life equation may be used:

$$t_{1/2} = \frac{\ln 2}{k} \qquad k = \frac{\ln 2}{t_{1/2}} = \frac{\ln 2}{10.5\ min} = 0.066014\ min^{-1} = \mathbf{0.0660\ min^{-1}}$$

b) ln $[A]_t$ = ln $[A]_0 - kt$

$$\frac{\ln[A]_t - \ln[A]_0}{-k} = t$$

$$\frac{\ln[0.25] - \ln[1]}{-0.0660 \text{ min}^{-1}} = t$$

$t = 21.0045$ min= **21.0 min**

If you recognize that 75.0% decomposition means that two half-lives have passed, then

$t = 2 (10.5 \text{ min}) = $ **21.0 min.**

14.45   <u>Plan:</u> In a first-order reaction, ln [NH_3] vs. time is a straight line with slope equal to k. The half-life can be determined using the first-order half-life equation.
<u>Solution:</u>
a) A new data table is constructed: (Note that additional significant figures are retained in the calculations.)

x-axis (time, s)	[NH₃]	y-axis (ln [NH₃])
0	4.000 mol/L	1.38629
1.000	3.986 mol/L	1.38279
2.000	3.974 mol/L	1.37977

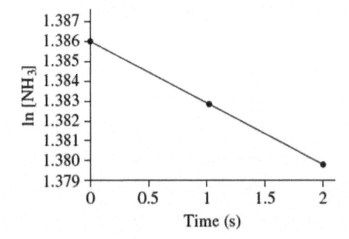

k = slope = rise/run = $(y_2 - y_1)/(x_2 - x_1)$
$k = (1.37977 - 1.38629)/(2.000 - 0) = (0.00652)/(2) = 3.260 \times 10^{-3} \text{ s}^{-1} = $ **3x10⁻³ s⁻¹**
(Note that the starting time is not exact, and hence, limits the significant figures.)

b) $t_{1/2} = \dfrac{\ln 2}{k} = \dfrac{\ln 2}{3.260 \times 10^{-3} \text{ s}^{-1}} = 212.62 \text{ s} = $ **2x10² s**

14.47   **No**, collision frequency is not the only factor affecting reaction rate. The collision frequency is a count of the total number of collisions between reactant molecules. Only a small number of these collisions lead to a reaction. Other factors that influence the fraction of collisions that lead to reaction are the energy and orientation of the collision. A collision must occur with a minimum energy (activation energy) to be successful. In a collision, the orientation, that is, which ends of the reactant molecules collide, must bring the reacting atoms in the molecules together in order for the collision to lead to a reaction.

14.50   The Arrhenius equation, $k = Ae^{-E_a/RT}$, can be used directly to solve for activation energy at a specified temperature if the rate constant, k, and the pre-exponential factor, A, are known. However, the pre-exponential factor is usually not known. To find E_a without knowing A, rearrange the Arrhenius equation to put it in the form of a linear plot: ln k = ln $A - E_a/RT$ where the y value is ln k and the x value is $1/T$. Measure the rate constant at a series of temperatures and plot ln k vs. $1/T$. The slope equals $-E_a/R$.

14.53   **No**. For 4×10^{-5} moles of EF to form, every collision must result in a reaction and no EF molecule can decompose back to AB and CD. Neither condition is likely. All collisions will not result in product as some collisions will occur with an energy that is lower than the activation energy. In principle, all reactions are reversible, so some EF molecules decompose. Even if all AB and CD molecules did combine, the reverse decomposition rate would result in an amount of EF that is less than 4×10^{-5} moles.

14.54   Collision frequency is proportional to the velocity of the reactant molecules. At the same temperature, both reaction mixtures have the same average kinetic energy, but not the same velocity. Kinetic energy equals $1/2 \ mv^2$, where m is mass and v velocity. The trimethylamine ($N(CH_3)_3$) molecule has a greater mass than the ammonia molecule, so trimethylamine molecules will collide less often than ammonia molecules, because of their slower velocities. Collision energy thus is less for the $N(CH_3)_3(g) + HCl(g)$ reaction than for the $NH_3(g) + HCl(g)$ reaction. Therefore, the **rate of the reaction between ammonia and hydrogen chloride is greater** than the rate of the reaction between methylamine and hydrogen chloride.

The fraction of successful collisions also differs between the two reactions. In both reactions the hydrogen from HCl is bonding to the nitrogen in NH_3 or $N(CH_3)_3$. The difference between the reactions is in how easily the H can collide with the N, the correct orientation for a successful reaction. The groups (H) bonded to nitrogen in ammonia are less bulky than the groups bonded to nitrogen in trimethylamine (CH_3). So, collisions with correct orientation between HCl and NH_3 occur more frequently than between HCl and $N(CH_3)_3$ and the reaction $NH_3(g) + HCl(g) \rightarrow NH_4Cl(s)$ occurs at a higher rate than $N(CH_3)_3(g) + HCl(g) \rightarrow (CH_3)_3NHCl(s)$. Therefore, the **rate of the reaction between ammonia and hydrogen chloride is greater** than the rate of the reaction between methylamine and hydrogen chloride.

14.55   Each A particle can collide with three B particles, so $(4 \times 3) = $ **12 unique collisions** are possible.

14.57   Plan: The fraction of collisions with a specified energy is equal to the $e^{-E_a/RT}$ term in the Arrhenius equation.
Solution:

$f = e^{-E_a/RT}$ $T = 25°C + 273 = 298$ K
$E_a = 100.$ kJ/mol $R = 8.314$ J/mol•K $= 8.314 \times 10^{-3}$ kJ/mol•K

$$-\frac{E_a}{RT} = -\frac{100. \ \text{kJ/mol}}{\left(8.314 \times 10^{-3} \ \text{kJ/mol•K}\right)\left(298 \ \text{K}\right)} = -40.362096$$

Fraction $= e^{-E_a/RT} = e^{-40.362096} = 2.9577689 \times 10^{-18} = \mathbf{2.96 \times 10^{-18}}$

14.59   Plan: You are given one rate constant k_1 at one temperature T_1 and the activation energy E_a. Substitute these values into the Arrhenius equation and solve for k_2 at the second temperature.
Solution:

$k_1 = 4.7 \times 10^{-3}$ s^{-1} $T_1 = 25°C + 273 = 298$ K
$k_2 = ?$ $T_2 = 75°C + 273 = 348$ K
$E_a = 33.6$ kJ/mol $= 33,600$ J/mol

$$\ln\frac{k_2}{k_1} = -\frac{E_a}{R}\left(\frac{1}{T_2} - \frac{1}{T_1}\right)$$

$$\ln\frac{k_2}{4.7 \times 10^{-3} \ \text{s}^{-1}} = -\frac{33,600 \ \text{J/mol}}{8.314 \ \text{J/mol•K}}\left(\frac{1}{348 \ \text{K}} - \frac{1}{298 \ \text{K}}\right)$$

$$\ln\frac{k_2}{4.7 \times 10^{-3} \ \text{s}^{-1}} = 1.948515 \text{ (unrounded)}\qquad \text{Raise each side to } e^x$$

$$\frac{k_2}{4.7 \times 10^{-3} \ \text{s}^{-1}} = 7.0182577$$

$k_2 = (4.7 \times 10^{-3} \ \text{s}^{-1})(7.0182577) = 0.0329858 \ \text{s}^{-1} = \mathbf{0.033 \ s^{-1}}$

14.61   Plan: The reaction is exothermic (ΔH is negative), so the energy of the products must be lower than that of the reactants. Use the relationship $\Delta_r H = E_{a(fwd)} - E_{a(rev)}$ to solve for $E_{a(rev)}$. To draw the transition state, note that the bond between B and C will be breaking while a bond between C and D will be forming.
Solution:
a)

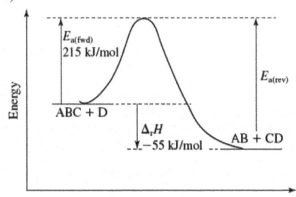

b) $\Delta_r H = E_{a(fwd)} - E_{a(rev)}$
$E_{a(rev)} = E_{a(fwd)} - \Delta_r H = 215 \text{ kJ/mol} - (-55 \text{ kJ/mol}) = \mathbf{2.70x10^2 \text{ kJ/mol}}$
c)

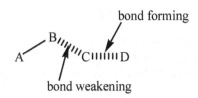

14.64   Plan: The reaction is endothermic (ΔH is positive), so the energy of the products must be higher than that of the reactants. Use the relationship $\Delta_r H = E_{a(fwd)} - E_{a(rev)}$ to solve for $E_{a(rev)}$. To draw the transition state, note that the bond in Cl_2 will be breaking while the bond between N and Cl will be forming.
Solution:
a)

$E_a \text{ (fwd)} = +86 \text{ kJ}$
$\Delta_r H = +83 \text{ kJ}$

b) $\Delta_r H = E_{a(fwd)} - E_{a(rev)}$
$E_{a(rev)} = E_{a(fwd)} - \Delta H_{rxn} = 86 \text{ kJ} - 83 \text{ kJ} = \mathbf{3 \text{ kJ}}$.
c) To draw the transition state, look at structures of reactants and products:

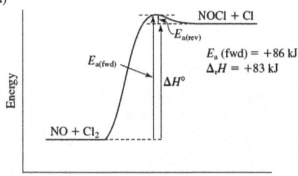

The collision must occur between one of the chlorine atoms and the nitrogen. The transition state would have weak bonds between the nitrogen and chlorine and between the two chlorine atoms.

14.65   The rate of an overall reaction depends on the slowest step. Each individual step's reaction rate can vary widely, so the rate of the slowest step, and hence the overall reaction, will be **slower than the average of the individual rates** because the average contains faster rates as well as the rate-determining step.

14.69   A bimolecular step (a collision between two particles) is more reasonable physically than a termolecular step (a collision involving three particles) because the likelihood that two reactant molecules will collide with the proper energy and orientation is much greater than the likelihood that three reactant molecules will collide simultaneously with the proper energy and orientation.

14.70   **No**, the overall rate law must contain reactants only (no intermediates) and is determined by the slow step. If the first step in a reaction mechanism is slow, the rate law for that step is the overall rate law.

14.72   <u>Plan:</u> The overall reaction can be obtained by adding the three steps together. An intermediate is a substance that is formed in one step and consumed in a subsequent step. The molecularity of each step is the total number of reactant particles; the molecularities are used as the orders in the rate law for each step. The overall rate law for the mechanism is determined from the slowest step (the rate-determining step) and can be compared to the actual rate law.
<u>Solution:</u>
a)
$$(1)\ A(g) + B(g) \rightarrow X(g)\quad \text{fast}$$
$$(2)\ X(g) + C(g) \rightarrow Y(g)\quad \text{slow}$$
$$\underline{(3)\ Y(g) \rightarrow D(g)\quad \text{fast}}$$
Total: $A(g) + B(g) + \cancel{X(g)} + C(g) + \cancel{Y(g)} \rightarrow \cancel{X(g)} + \cancel{Y(g)} + D(g)$
Overall: $A(g) + B(g) + C(g) \rightarrow D(g)$

b) Both X and Y are intermediates in the given mechanism. Intermediate X is produced in the first step and consumed in the second step; intermediate Y is produced in the second step and consumed in the third step. Notice that neither X nor Y were included in the overall reaction.
c)

Step	Molecularity	Rate law
$A(g) + B(g) \rightarrow X(g)$	bimolecular	$rate_1 = k_1[A][B]$
$X(g) + C(g) \rightarrow Y(g)$	bimolecular	$rate_2 = k_2[X][C]$
$Y(g) \rightarrow D(g)$	unimolecular	$rate_3 = k_3[Y]$

d) **Yes**, the mechanism is consistent with the actual rate law. The slow step in the mechanism is the second step with rate law: rate = $k_2[X][C]$. Since X is an intermediate, it must be replaced by using the first step. For an equilibrium, rate$_{\text{forward rxn}}$ = rate$_{\text{reverse rxn}}$. For step 1 then, $k_1[A][B] = k_{-1}[X]$. Rearranging to solve for [X] gives [X] = $(k_1/k_{-1})[A][B]$. Substituting this value for [X] into the rate law for the second step gives the overall rate law as rate = $(k_2k_1/k_{-1})[A][B][C]$ which is identical to the actual rate law with $k = k_2k_1/k_{-1}$.
e) **Yes**, The one step mechanism $A(g) + B(g) + C(g) \rightarrow D(g)$ would have a rate law of rate = $k[A][B][C]$, which is the actual rate law.

14.74   <u>Plan:</u> Use the rate-determining step to find the rate law for the mechanism. The concentration of the intermediate in the rate law must be expressed in terms of a true reactant which is then substituted into the rate law for the concentration of the intermediate.
<u>Solution:</u>
Nitrosyl bromide is $NOBr(g)$. The reactions sum to the equation $2NO(g) + Br_2(g) \rightarrow 2NOBr(g)$, so criterion 1 (elementary steps must add to overall equation) is satisfied. Both elementary steps are bimolecular and chemically reasonable, so criterion 2 (steps are physically reasonable) is met. The reaction rate is determined by the slow step; however, rate expressions do not include reaction intermediates ($NOBr_2$). The slow step in the

mechanism is the second step with rate law: rate = $k_2[NOBr_2][NO]$. Since $NOBr_2$ is an intermediate, it must be replaced by using the first step. For an equilibrium like step 1, $rate_{forward\ rxn} = rate_{reverse\ rxn}$.

       Solve for $[NOBr_2]$ in step 1:

       $Rate_1$ (forward) = $rate_1$ (reverse)

       $k_1[NO][Br_2] = k_{-1}[NOBr_2]$

       $[NOBr_2] = (k_1/k_{-1})[NO][Br_2]$

Rate of the slow step: $Rate_2 = k_2[NOBr_2][NO]$

Substitute the expression for $[NOBr_2]$ into this equation, the slow step:

       $Rate_2 = k_2(k_1/k_{-1})[NO][Br_2][NO]$

Combine the separate constants into one constant: $k = k_2(k_1/k_{-1})$

       $Rate_2 = k[NO]^2[Br_2]$

The derived rate law equals the known rate law, so criterion 3 is satisfied. The proposed mechanism is valid.

14.77   **No**, a catalyst changes the mechanism of a reaction to one with lower activation energy. Lower activation energy means a faster reaction. An increase in temperature does not influence the activation energy, but instead increases the fraction of collisions with sufficient energy to react.

14.78   a) **No**, by definition, a catalyst is a substance that increases reaction rate without being consumed. The spark provides energy that is absorbed by the H_2 and O_2 molecules to achieve the threshold energy needed for reaction.
b) **Yes**, the powdered metal acts like a heterogeneous catalyst, providing a surface upon which the reaction between O_2 and H_2 becomes more favorable because the activation energy is lowered.

14.83   Plan: An intermediate is a substance that is formed in one step and consumed in a subsequent step. The coefficients of the reactants in each elementary step are used as the orders in the rate law for the step. The overall rate law for the mechanism is determined from the slowest step (the rate-determining step) and can be compared to the actual rate law. Reactants that appear in the mechanism after the slow step do not determine the rate and therefore do not appear in the rate law.
Solution:
a) Water does not appear as a reactant in the rate-determining step.
Note that as a solvent in the reaction, the concentration of the water is assumed not to change even though some water is used up as a reactant. This assumption is valid as long as the solute concentrations are low (~1 M or less). So, even if water did appear as a reactant in the rate-determining step, it would not appear in the rate law. See rate law for step 2 below.

    b)   Rate law for step (1): $rate_1 = k_1[(CH_3)_3CBr]$
              Rate law for step (2): $rate_2 = k_2[(CH_3)_3C^+]$
              Rate law for step (3): $rate_3 = k_3[(CH_3)_3COH_2^+]$

c) The intermediates are $(CH_3)_3C^+$ and $(CH_3)_3COH_2^+$. $(CH_3)_3C^+$ is formed in step 1 and consumed in step 2; $(CH_3)_3COH_2^+$ is formed in step 2 and consumed in step 3.
d) The rate-determining step is the slow step, (1). The rate law for this step is rate = $k_1[(CH_3)_3CBr]$ since the coefficient of the reactant in this slow step is 1. The rate law for this step agrees with the actual rate law with $k = k_1$.

14.85   Plan: The activation energy can be calculated using the Arrhenius equation. Although the rate constants, k_1 and k_2, are not expressly stated, the relative times give an idea of the rate. The reaction rate is proportional to the rate constant. At $T_1 = 20°C$, the rate of reaction is 1 apple/4 days while at $T_2 = 0°C$, the rate is 1 apple/16 days. Therefore, $rate_1 = 1$ apple/4 days and $rate_2 = 1$ apple/16 days are substituted for k_1 and k_2, respectively.
Solution:

$k_1 = 1/4$ $T_1 = 20°C + 273 = 293$ K

$k_2 = 1/16$ $T_2 = 0°C + 273 = 273$ K

$E_a = ?$

$$\ln \frac{k_2}{k_1} = -\frac{E_a}{R}\left(\frac{1}{T_2} - \frac{1}{T_1}\right)$$

$$E_a = -\dfrac{R\left(\ln\dfrac{k_2}{k_1}\right)}{\left(\dfrac{1}{T_2} - \dfrac{1}{T_1}\right)} = -\dfrac{\left(8.314\dfrac{J}{mol\bullet K}\right)\left(\ln\dfrac{1/16}{1/4}\right)}{\left(\dfrac{1}{273\ K} - \dfrac{1}{293\ K}\right)}$$

$E_a = 4.6096266 \times 10^4$ J/mol = **4.61×10^4 J/mol**   The significant figures are based on the Kelvin temperatures.

14.89   Plan: Use the given rate law, rate $= k[H^+][sucrose]$, and enter the given values. The glucose and fructose are not in the rate law, so they may be ignored.
Solution:
a) The rate is first order with respect to [sucrose]. The [sucrose] is changed from 1.0 mol/L to 2.5 mol/L , or is increased by a factor of 2.5/1.0 or 2.5. Then the rate $= k[H^+][2.5$ x sucrose]; the rate **increases by a factor of 2.5.**
b) The [sucrose] is changed from 1.0 mol/L to 0.5 mol/L , or is decreased by a factor of 0.5/1.0 or 0.5. Then the rate $= k[H^+][0.5$ x sucrose]; the rate decreases by a factor of ½ or **half the original rate.**
c) The rate is first order with respect to $[H^+]$. The $[H^+]$ is changed from 0.01 mol/L to 0.0001 mol/L , or is decreased by a factor of 0.0001/0.01 or 0.01. Then the rate $= k[0.01$ x $H^+][sucrose]$; the rate **decreases by a factor of 0.01.**
Thus, the reaction will decrease to **1/100 the original.**
d) The [sucrose] decreases from 1.0 mol/L to 0.1 mol/L , or by a factor of (0.1 mol/L /1.0 mol/L) = 0.1. $[H^+]$ increases from 0.01 mol/L to 0.1 mol/L , or by a factor of (0.1 mol/L /0.01 mol/L) = 10. Then the rate will increase by $k[10$ x $H^+][0.1$ x sucrose]= 1.0 times as fast. Thus, there will be **no change.**

14.90   Plan: The overall order is equal to the sum of the individual orders. Since the reaction is eleventh order overall, the sum of the exponents equals eleven. Add up the known orders and subtract that sum from eleven to find the unknown order.
Solution:
Sum of known orders = $1 + 4 + 2 + 2 = 9$
Overall order – sum of known orders = $11 – 9 = 2$.
The reaction is **second order** with respect to NAD.

14.93   Plan: First, find the rate constant, k, for the reaction by solving the first-order half-life equation for k. Then use the first-order integrated rate law expression to find t, the time for decay.
Solution:
Rearrange $t_{1/2} = \dfrac{\ln 2}{k}$ to $k = \dfrac{\ln 2}{t_{1/2}}$

$$k = \dfrac{\ln 2}{12\ yr} = 5.7762 \times 10^{-2}\ yr^{-1}$$

Use the first-order integrated rate law: $\ln\dfrac{[DDT]_t}{[DDT]_0} = -kt$

$$\ln\dfrac{[10.\ ppbm]_t}{[275\ ppbm]_0} = -(5.7762 \times 10^{-2}\ yr^{-1})\,t$$

$t = 57.3765798$ yr= **57 yr**

14.96   Plan: The rate constant can be determined from the slope of the integrated rate law plot. To find the correct order, the data should be plotted as 1) [sucrose] vs. time – linear for zero order, 2) ln [sucrose] vs. time – linear for first order, and 3) 1/[sucrose] vs. time – linear for second order. Once the order is established, use the appropriate integrated rate law to find the time necessary for 75.0% of the sucrose to react. If 75.0% of the sucrose has reacted, $100–75 = 25\%$ remains at time t. Let $[sucrose]_0 = 100\%$ and then $[sucrose]_t = 25\%$.
Solution:
a) All three graphs are linear, so picking the correct order is difficult. One way to select the order is to compare correlation coefficients (R^2) — you may or may not have experience with this. The best correlation coefficient is

the one closest to a value of 1.00. Based on this selection criterion, the plot of ln [sucrose] vs. time for the first-order reaction is the best.

Another method when linearity is not obvious from the graphs is to examine the reaction and decide which order fits the reaction. For the reaction of one molecule of sucrose with one molecule of liquid water, the rate law would most likely include sucrose with an order of one and would not include water.

The plot for a first-order reaction is described by the equation $\ln [A]_t = -kt + \ln [A]_0$. The slope of the plot of ln [sucrose] vs. t equals $-k$. The equation for the straight line in the first-order plot is $y = -0.21x - 0.6936$.
So, $k = -(-0.21 \text{ h}^{-1}) = \mathbf{0.21 \text{ h}^{-1}}$.
Solve the first-order half-life equation to find $t_{1/2}$:

$$t_{1/2} = \frac{\ln 2}{k} = \frac{\ln 2}{0.21 \text{ hr}^{-1}} = 3.3007 \text{ h} = \mathbf{3.3 \text{ h}}$$

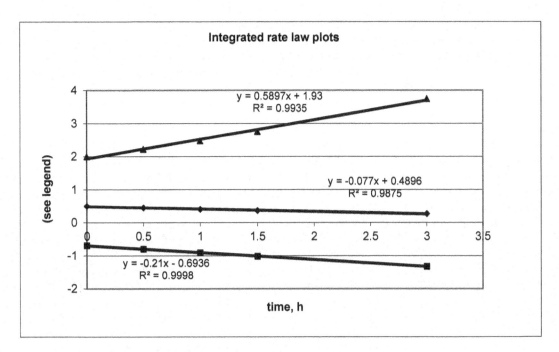

Legend: ♦ y-axis is [sucrose]
        ■ y-axis is ln [sucrose]
        ▲ y-axis is 1/[sucrose]

b) If 75% of the sucrose has been reacted, 25% of the sucrose remains. Let [sucrose]$_0$ = 100% and [sucrose]$_t$ = 25% in the first-order integrated rate law equation:

$$\ln \frac{[\text{sucrose}]_t}{[\text{sucrose}]_0} = -kt$$

$$\ln \frac{[25\%]_t}{[100\%]_0} = -(0.21 \text{ h}^{-1})\, t$$

$$t = 6.6014 \text{ h} = \mathbf{6.6 \text{ h}}$$

c) The reaction might be second order overall with first order in sucrose and first order in water. If the concentration of sucrose is relatively low, the concentration of water remains constant even with small changes in the amount of water. This gives an apparent zero-order reaction with respect to water. Thus, the reaction appears to be first order overall because the rate does not change with changes in the amount of water.

14.99 Plan: To find concentration of reactant at a later time, given the initial concentration and the rate constant k, use an integrated rate law expression. Since the units on k are s^{-1}, this is a first-order reaction. Use the first-order integrated rate law. Since the time unit in k is seconds, time t must also be expressed in units of seconds. To find the fraction of reactant that has decomposed, divide that amount of reactant that has decomposed $([N_2O_5]_0 - [N_2O_5]_t)$ by the initial concentration.

Solution:

a) Converting t in min to s: $(5.00 \text{ min})\left(\dfrac{60 \text{ s}}{1 \text{ min}}\right) = 300. \text{ s}$

$$\ln\frac{\left[N_2O_5\right]_t}{\left[N_2O_5\right]_0} = -kt \text{ or}$$

$\ln [N_2O_5]_t = \ln [N_2O_5]_0 - kt$

$\ln [N_2O_5]_t = \ln [1.58 \text{ mol/L}] - (2.8 \times 10^{-3} \text{ s}^{-1})(300. \text{ s})$

$\ln [N_2O_5]_t = -0.382575$

$[N_2O_5]_t = 0.68210 \text{ mol/L} = \textbf{0.68 mol/L}$

b) Fraction decomposed $= \dfrac{[N_2O_5]_0 - [N_2O_5]_t}{[N_2O_5]_0} = \dfrac{1.58 - 0.68210 \text{ mol/L}}{1.58 \text{ mol/L}} = 0.56829 = \textbf{0.57}$

14.102 Plan: To solve this problem, a clear picture of what is happening is useful. Initially only N_2O_5 is present at a pressure of 125 kPa. Then a reaction takes place that consumes the gas N_2O_5 and produces the gases NO_2 and O_2. The balanced equation gives the change in the number of moles of gas as N_2O_5 decomposes. Since the number of moles of gas is proportional to the pressure, this change mirrors the change in pressure. The total pressure at the end, 178 kPa, equals the sum of the partial pressures of the three gases.

Solution:

Balanced equation: $N_2O_5(g) \rightarrow 2NO_2(g) + 1/2O_2(g)$

Therefore, for each mole of dinitrogen pentaoxide that is consumed, 2.5 moles of gas are produced.

	$N_2O_5(g) \rightarrow$	$2NO_2(g)$	$+ 1/2O_2(g)$	
Initial P (kPa)	125	0	0	total $P_{\text{initial}} = 125$ kPa
Final P (kPa)	$125 - x$	$2x$	$1/2x$	total $P_{\text{final}} = 178$ kPa

Solve for x:

$$P_{N2O5} + P_{NO2} + P_{O2} = (125 - x) + 2x + 1/2x = 178$$

$x = 35.3333$ kPa (unrounded)

Partial pressure of NO_2 equals $2x = 2(35.3333 \text{ kPa}) = 70.667 \text{kPa} = \textbf{71 kPa}$.

Check: Substitute values for all partial pressures to find total final pressure:

$(125 - 35.3333)\text{kPa} + (2 \times 35.3333 \text{ kPa}) + ((1/2) \times 35.3333 \text{ kPa}) = 178$ kPa

The result agrees with the given total final pressure.

14.106 Plan: The activation energy can be calculated using the Arrhenius equation. Although the rate constants, k_1 and k_2, are not expressly stated, the relative times give an idea of the rate. The reaction rate is proportional to the rate constant. At $T_1 = 90.0°C$, the rate of reaction is 1 egg/4.8 min while at $T_2 = 100.0°C$, the rate is 1 egg/4.5 min. Therefore, $\text{rate}_1 = 1$ egg/4.8 min and $\text{rate}_2 = 1$ egg/4.5 min are substituted for k_1 and k_2, respectively.

Solution:

$k_1 = 1$ egg/4.8 min $T_1 = 90.0°C + 273.2 = 363.2$ K

$k_2 = 1$ egg/4.5 min $T_2 = 100.0°C + 273.2 = 373.2$ K

$E_a = ?$

$$\ln\frac{k_2}{k_1} = -\frac{E_a}{R}\left(\frac{1}{T_2} - \frac{1}{T_1}\right)$$

The number of eggs (1) is exact, and has no bearing on the significant figures.

$$E_a = -\frac{R\left(\ln\frac{k_2}{k_1}\right)}{\left(\frac{1}{T_2}-\frac{1}{T_1}\right)} = -\frac{\left(8.314\frac{J}{mol \cdot K}\right)\left(\ln\frac{(1\ egg/4.5\ min)}{(1\ egg/4.8\ min)}\right)}{\left(\frac{1}{373.2\ K}-\frac{1}{363.2\ K}\right)}$$

$E_a = 7.2730\text{x}10^3$ J/mol = **7.3x10³ J/mol**

14.108 Plan: Starting with the fact that rate of formation of O (rate of step 1) equals the rate of consumption of O (rate of step 2), set up an equation to solve for [O] using the given values of k_1, k_2, [NO₂], and [O₂].
Solution:
a)   Rate₁ = k_1[NO₂]   Rate₂ = k_2[O][O₂}
        Rate₁ = rate₂
        k_1[NO₂] = k_2[O][O₂]

$$[O] = \frac{k_1[NO_2]}{k_2[O_2]} = \frac{(6.0\times10^{-3}\ s^{-1})[4.0\times10^{-9}\ mol\ /\ L]}{(1.0\times10^6\ L/mol\bullet s)[1.0\times10^{-2}\ mol\ /\ L]} = \textbf{2.4x10}^{-15}\ \text{mol / L}$$

b) Since the rate of the two steps is equal, either can be used to determine rate of formation of ozone.
        Rate₂ = k_2[O][O₂] = (1.0x10⁶ L/mol•s)(2.4x10⁻¹⁵ mol/L)(1.0x10⁻² mol/L) = **2.4x10⁻¹¹ mol/L·s**

14.111 Plan: This problem involves the first-order integrated rate law ($\ln [A]_t/[A]_0 = -kt$). The temperature must be part of the calculation of the rate constant. The concentration of the ammonium ion is directly related to the ammonia concentration. Use the given values of $[NH_3]_0$ and $[NH_3]_t$ and the calculated values of k to find time, t.
Solution:
a) $[NH_3]_0 = 3.0$ mol/m³ $[NH_3]_t = 0.35$ mol/m³ $T = 20°C$
$k_1 = 0.47e^{0.095(T-15°C)} = 0.47e^{0.095(20-15°C)} = 0.75576667$ d⁻¹

$$\ln\frac{[NH_3]_t}{[NH_3]_0} = -kt$$

$$t = -\frac{\ln\dfrac{[NH_3]_t}{[NH_3]_0}}{k}$$

$$t = -\frac{\ln\dfrac{[0.35\ mol/m^3]_t}{[3.0\ mol/m^3]_0}}{0.75576667\ d^{-1}} = 2.84272\ d = \textbf{2.8 d}$$

b) Repeating the calculation at the different temperature:
$[NH_3]_0 = 3.0$ mol/m³ $[NH_3]_t = 0.35$ mol/m³ $T = 10°C$
$k_1 = 0.47e^{0.095(T-15°C)} = 0.47e^{0.095(10-15°C)} = 0.292285976$ d⁻¹

$$t = -\frac{\ln\dfrac{[NH_3]_t}{[NH_3]_0}}{k}$$

$$t = -\frac{\ln\dfrac{[0.35\ mol/m^3]_t}{[3.0\ mol/m^3]_0}}{0.292285976\ d^{-1}}$$

$t = 7.35045$ d = **7.4 d**
c) For NH₄⁺ the rate = k_1[NH₄⁺]
        From the balanced chemical equation:

$$-\frac{\Delta[NH_4^+]}{\Delta t} = -\frac{1}{2}\frac{\Delta[O_2]}{\Delta t}$$

Thus, for O_2: Rate $= 2\,k_1[NH_4^+]$

$$\text{Rate} = (2)(0.75576667)\left[3.0\ \text{mol/m}^3\right] = 4.5346 = \mathbf{4.5\ mol/m^3}$$

14.114 Plan: Rate is the change in concentration divided by change in time. To find the average rate for each trial in part a), the change in concentration of $S_2O_3^{2-}$ is divided by the time required to produce the colour. The rate law is rate $= k[I^-]^m[S_2O_8^{2-}]^n$ where m and n are the orders of the reactants. To find the order of each reactant, take the ratio of the rate laws for two experiments in which only the reactant in question changes. Once the rate law is known, any experiment can be used to find the rate constant k. Since several solutions are mixed, final concentrations of each solution must be found with dilution calculations using $c_iV_i = c_fV_f$ in the form: $c_f = c_iV_i/V_f$.

Solution:
a) $c_f\ S_2O_3^{2-} = [(10.0\ \text{mL})(0.0050\ \text{mol/L})]/50.0\ \text{mL} = 0.0010\ \text{mol/L}\ S_2O_3^{2-}$

$$-\frac{\Delta[I_2]}{\Delta t} = -\frac{1}{2}\frac{\Delta\left[S_2O_3^{2-}\right]}{\Delta t} = [1/2(0.0010\ \text{mol/L})]/\text{time} = [0.00050\ \text{mol/L}]/\text{time} = \text{rate}$$

Average rates:

Rate$_1$ = (0.00050 mol/L)/29.0 s = 1.724×10^{-5} mol/L•s= $\mathbf{1.7\times10^{-5}}$ **mol/L•s**

Rate$_2$ = (0.00050 mol/L)/14.5 s = 3.448×10^{-5} mol/L•s = $\mathbf{3.4\times10^{-5}}$ **mol/L•s**

Rate$_3$ = (0.00050 mol/L)/14.5 s = 3.448×10^{-5} mol/L•s = $\mathbf{3.4\times10^{-5}}$ **mol/L•s**

b) $c_f\ KI = c_f\ I^- = [(10.0\ \text{mL})(0.200\ \text{mol/L})]/50.0\ \text{mL} = 0.0400\ \text{mol/L}\ I^-$ (Experiment 1)

$c_f\ I^- = [(20.0\ \text{mL})(0.200\ \text{mol/L})]/50.0\ \text{mL} = 0.0800\ \text{mol/L}\ I^-$ (Experiments 2 and 3)

$c_f\ Na_2S_2O_8 = c_f\ S_2O_8^{2-} = [(20.0\ \text{mL})(0.100\ \text{mol/L})]/50.0\ \text{mL}$
$= 0.0400\ \text{mol/L}\ S_2O_8^{2-}$ (Experiments 1 and 2)

$c_f\ S_2O_8^{2-} = [(10.0\ \text{mL})(0.100\ \text{mol/L})]/50.0\ \text{mL} = 0.0200\ \text{mol/L}\ S_2O_8^{2-}$ (Experiment 3)

Generic rate law equation: Rate $= k\,[I^-]^m[S_2O_8^{2-}]^n$

To find the order for I^-, use experiments 1 and 2 in which $[S_2O_8^{2-}]$ is constant while $[I^-]$ changes. Set up a ratio of the rate laws for experiments 1 and 2 and fill in the values given for rates and concentrations and solve for m, the order with respect to $[I^-]$.

$$\frac{\text{Rate}_2}{\text{Rate}_1} = \frac{k_2\left[I^-\right]^m\left[S_2O_8^{2-}\right]^n}{k_1\left[I^-\right]^m\left[S_2O_8^{2-}\right]^n} \qquad \text{Concentration (mol/L) of } S_2O_8^{2-}\text{ is constant.}$$

$$\frac{3.4\times10^{-5}\ \text{mol / L•s}}{1.7\times10^{-5}\ \text{mol / L•s}} = \frac{[0.0800]^m}{[0.0400]^m}$$

$2.0 = (2.00)^m$

$m = 1$

The reaction is **first order with respect to I^-**.

To find the order for $S_2O_8^{2-}$, use experiments 2 and 3 in which $[I^-]$ is constant while $[S_2O_8^{2-}]$ changes. Set up a ratio of the rate laws for experiments 2 and 3 and fill in the values given for rates and concentrations and solve for n, the order with respect to $[S_2O_8^{2-}]$.

$$\frac{\text{Rate}_3}{\text{Rate}_2} = \frac{k_3\left[I^-\right]^m\left[S_2O_8^{2-}\right]^n}{k_2\left[I^-\right]^m\left[S_2O_8^{2-}\right]^n} \qquad \text{Concentration (mol/L) of } I^-\text{ is constant.}$$

$$\frac{3.4\times10^{-5}\ \text{mol / L•s}}{3.4\times10^{-5}\ \text{mol / L•s}} = \frac{[0.0200]^n}{[0.0400]^n}$$

$1.0 = (0.500)^n$

$n = 0$

The reaction is **zero order with respect to $S_2O_8^{2-}$**.

c) Rate $= k[I^-]$

$k = \text{rate}/[I^-]$

Using experiment 2 (unrounded rate value)

$k = (3.448 \times 10^{-5} \text{ mol/L·s})/(0.0800 \text{ mol/L}) = 4.31 \times 10^{-4} \text{ s}^{-1} = \mathbf{4.3 \times 10^{-4} \text{ s}^{-1}}$

d) **Rate = $(4.3 \times 10^{-4} \text{ s}^{-1})[\text{I}^-]$**

14.117   Plan: This is a first-order process so use the first-order integrated rate law. The increasing cell density changes the integrated rate law from $-kt$ to $+kt$. In part a), we know $t(2 \text{ h})$, k, and $[A]_0$ so $[A]_t$ can be found. Treat the concentration of the cells as you would molarity. Since the rate constant is expressed in units of min^{-1}, the time interval of 2 h must be converted to a time in minutes. In part b), $[A]_0$, $[A]_t$, and k are known and time t is calculated.
Solution:

a) Converting time in h to min: $(2 \text{ h})\left(\dfrac{60 \text{ min}}{1 \text{ h}}\right) = 120 \text{ min}$

$\ln [A]_t = \ln [A]_0 + kt$
$\ln [A]_t = \ln [1.0 \times 10^3] + (0.035 \text{ min}^{-1})(120 \text{ min})$
$\ln [A]_t = 11.107755$
$[A]_t = 6.6686 \times 10^4 \text{ cells/L} = \mathbf{7 \times 10^4 \text{ cells/L}}$

b) $\ln [A]_t = \ln [A]_0 + kt$

$\dfrac{\ln [A]_t - \ln [A]_0}{k} = t$

$\dfrac{\ln [2 \times 10^3 \text{ cells/L}] - \ln [1 \times 10^3 \text{ cells/L}]}{0.035 \text{ min}^{-1}} = t$

$t = 19.804 \text{ min} = \mathbf{2.0 \times 10^1 \text{ min}}$

14.120   Plan: For part a), use the Monod equation to calculate μ for values of S between 0.0 and 1.0 kg/m^3 and then graph. For parts b) and c), use the Monod equation to calculate μ at the given conditions. The value of μ is the rate constant k in the first-order integrated rate law. The increasing population density changes the integrated rate law from $-kt$ to $+kt$. We know $t(1 \text{ h})$, k, and $[A]_0$ so $[A]_t$ can be found. Treat the density of the cells as you would molarity.
Solution:

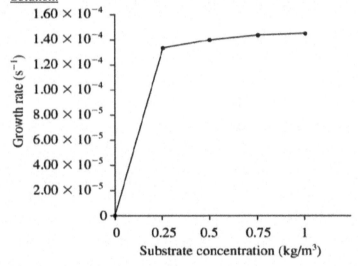

$\mu = \dfrac{\mu_{\max} S}{K_s + S} = \dfrac{\left(1.5 \times 10^{-4} \text{ s}^{-1}\right)\left(0.25 \text{ kg/m}^3\right)}{\left(0.03 \text{ kg/m}^3\right) + \left(0.25 \text{ kg/m}^3\right)} = 1.34 \times 10^{-4} \text{ s}^{-1}$

$\mu = \dfrac{\mu_{\max} S}{K_s + S} = \dfrac{\left(1.5 \times 10^{-4} \text{ s}^{-1}\right)\left(0.50 \text{ kg/m}^3\right)}{\left(0.03 \text{ kg/m}^3\right) + \left(0.50 \text{ kg/m}^3\right)} = 1.42 \times 10^{-4} \text{ s}^{-1}$

$$\mu = \frac{\mu_{max}S}{K_s + S} = \frac{\left(1.5 \times 10^{-4}\ s^{-1}\right)\left(0.75\ kg/m^3\right)}{\left(0.03\ kg/m^3\right) + \left(0.75\ kg/m^3\right)} = 1.44 \times 10^{-4}\ s^{-1}$$

$$\mu = \frac{\mu_{max}S}{K_s + S} = \frac{\left(1.5 \times 10^{-4}\ s^{-1}\right)\left(1.0\ kg/m^3\right)}{\left(0.03\ kg/m^3\right) + \left(1.0\ kg/m^3\right)} = 1.46 \times 10^{-4}\ s^{-1}$$

b) $\mu = \dfrac{\mu_{max}S}{K_s + S} = \dfrac{\left(1.5 \times 10^{-4}\ s^{-1}\right)\left(0.30\ kg/m^3\right)}{\left(0.03\ kg/m^3\right) + \left(0.30\ kg/m^3\right)} = 1.3636 \times 10^{-4}\ s^{-1}$

Converting time in h to seconds: $(1\ h)\left(\dfrac{3600\ s}{1\ h}\right) = 3600\ s$

$\ln [A]_t = \ln [A]_0 + kt$
$\ln [A]_t = \ln [5.0 \times 10^3] + (1.3636 \times 10^{-4}\ s^{-1})(3600\ s)$
$\ln [A]_t = 9.00808919$
$[A]_t = 8.1689 \times 10^3$ cells/m³= **8.2x10³ cells/m³**

c) $\mu = \dfrac{\mu_{max}S}{K_s + S} = \dfrac{\left(1.5 \times 10^{-4}\ s^{-1}\right)\left(0.70\ kg/m^3\right)}{\left(0.03\ kg/m^3\right) + \left(0.70\ kg/m^3\right)} = 1.438356 \times 10^{-4}\ s^{-1}$

$\ln [A]_t = \ln [A]_0 + kt$
$\ln [A]_t = \ln [5.0 \times 10^3] + (1.438356 \times 10^{-4}\ s^{-1})(3600\ s)$
$\ln [A]_t = 9.03500135$
$[A]_t = 8.39172 \times 10^3$ cells/m³= **8.4x10³ cells/m³**

14.125   Plan: This is a first-order reaction so use the first-order integrated rate law. In part a), use the first-order half-life equation and the given value of k to find the half-life. In parts b) and c), solve the first-order integrated rate law to find the time necessary for 40.% and 90.% of the acetone to decompose. If 40.% of the acetone has decomposed, $100 - 40. = 60.\%$ remains at time t. If 90.% of the acetone has decomposed, $100 - 90. = 10.\%$ remains at time t.
Solution:

a) $t_{1/2} = \dfrac{\ln 2}{k} = \dfrac{\ln 2}{8.7 \times 10^{-3}\ s^{-1}} = 79.672\ s =$ **8.0x10¹ s**

b) $\ln [acetone]_t = \ln [acetone]_0 - kt$

$\dfrac{\ln [acetone]_t\ -\ \ln [acetone]_0}{-k} = t$ 40.% of acetone has decomposed; $[acetone]_t = 100 - 40. = 60.\%$

$\dfrac{\ln [60.]\ -\ \ln [100]}{-8.7 \times 10^{-3}\ s^{-1}} = t = 58.71558894 s = $ **59 s**

c) $\ln [acetone]_t = \ln [acetone]_0 - kt$

$\dfrac{\ln [acetone]_t\ -\ \ln [acetone]_0}{-k} = t$ 90.% of acetone has decomposed; $[acetone]_t = 100 - 90. = 10.\%$

$\dfrac{\ln [10.]\ -\ \ln [100]}{-8.7 \times 10^{-3}\ s^{-1}} = t = 264.66\ s = $ **2.6x10² s**

CHAPTER 15 EQUILIBRIUM: THE EXTENT OF CHEMICAL REACTIONS

CHEMICAL CONNECTIONS BOXED READING PROBLEM

B15.1   Plan: To control the pathways, the first enzyme specific for a branch is inhibited by the end product of that branch.
Solution:
a) The enzyme that is inhibited by F is the first enzyme in that branch, which is **enzyme 3**.
b) Enzyme **6** is inhibited by I.
c) If F inhibited enzyme 1, then neither branch of the reaction would take place once enough F was produced.
d) If F inhibited enzyme 6, then the second branch would not take place when enough F was made.

END–OF–CHAPTER PROBLEMS

15.1   If the rate of the forward reaction exceeds the rate of reverse reaction, products are formed faster than they are consumed. The change in reaction conditions results in more products and less reactants. A change in reaction conditions can result from a change in concentration or a change in temperature. If concentration changes, product concentration increases while reactant concentration decreases, but the K_c remains unchanged because the *ratio* of products and reactants remains the same. If the increase in the forward rate is due to a change in temperature, the rate of the reverse reaction also increases. The equilibrium ratio of product concentration to reactant concentration is no longer the same. Since the rate of the forward reaction increases more than the rate of the reverse reaction, K_c increases (numerator, [products], is larger and denominator, [reactants], is smaller).

$$K_c = \frac{[\text{products}]}{[\text{reactants}]}$$

15.7   The equilibrium constant expression is $K = p_{O_2}$ (remember the activity of solids is 1). If the temperature remains constant, K remains constant. If the initial amount of Li_2O_2 present was sufficient to reach equilibrium, the pressure of O_2 obtained will be constant, regardless of how much $Li_2O_2(s)$ is present.

15.8   a) On the graph, the concentration of HI increases at twice the rate that H_2 decreases because the stoichiometric ratio in the balanced equation is $1H_2 : 2HI$. Q for a reaction is the ratio of concentrations of products to concentrations of reactants. As the reaction progresses the concentration of reactants H_2 and I_2 decrease and the concentration of product HI increases, which means that Q increases as a function of time.

$$H_2(g) + I_2(g) \rightleftharpoons 2HI(g) \qquad Q = \frac{p_{HI}^2}{p_{H_2}\, p_{I_2}}$$

The value of Q increases as a function of time until it reaches the value of K.
b) No, Q would still increase with time because the $[I_2]$ would decrease in exactly the same way as $[H_2]$ decreases.

15.11 <u>Plan:</u> Write the reaction and then the expression for Q.
<u>Solution:</u>
The balanced equation for the first reaction is
$$3/2H_2(g) + 1/2N_2(g) \rightleftharpoons NH_3(g) \quad (1)$$
The coefficient in front of NH_3 is fixed at 1 mole according to the description. The reaction quotient for this

reaction is $Q_1 = \dfrac{p_{NH_3}}{p_{H_2}^{3/2} p_{N_2}^{1/2}}$.

In the second reaction, the coefficient in front of N_2 is fixed at 1 mole.
$$3H_2(g) + N_2(g) \rightleftharpoons 2NH_3(g) \quad (2)$$

The reaction quotient for this reaction is $Q_2 = \dfrac{p_{NH_3}^2}{p_{H_2}^3 p_{N_2}}$

Q_2 is equal to $Q_1{}^2$.

15.12 <u>Plan:</u> Remember that $Q = \dfrac{a_C^c a_D^d}{a_A^a a_B^b}$ where A and B are reactants, C and D are products, and a, b, c, and d are the

stoichiometric coefficients in the balanced equation.
<u>Solution:</u>
a) $4NO(g) + O_2(g) \rightleftharpoons 2N_2O_3(g)$

$$Q = \dfrac{p_{N_2O_3}^2}{p_{NO}^4 p_{O_2}}$$

b) $SF_6(g) + 2SO_3(g) \rightleftharpoons 3SO_2F_2(g)$

$$Q = \dfrac{p_{SO_2F_2}^3}{p_{SF_6} p_{SO_3}^2}$$

c) $2SClF_5(g) + H_2(g) \rightleftharpoons S_2F_{10}(g) + 2HCl(g)$

$$Q = \dfrac{p_{S_2F_{10}} p_{HCl}^2}{p_{SClF_5}^2 p_{H_2}}$$

15.14 <u>Plan:</u> Remember that Q will be determined using pressures in place of activities when the species in the chemical reaction are all gases.
<u>Solution:</u>
a) $2NO_2Cl(g) \rightleftharpoons 2NO_2(g) + Cl_2(g)$

$$Q = \dfrac{p_{NO_2}^2 p_{Cl_2}}{p_{NO_2Cl}^2}$$

b) $2POCl_3(g) \rightleftharpoons 2PCl_3(g) + O_2(g)$

$$Q = \dfrac{p_{PCl_3}^2 p_{O_2}}{p_{POCl_3}^2}$$

c) $4NH_3(g) + 3O_2(g) \rightleftharpoons 2N_2(g) + 6H_2O(g)$

$$Q = \dfrac{p_{N_2}^2 p_{H_2O}^6}{p_{NH_3}^4 p_{O_2}^3}$$

15.16 Plan: Compare each equation with the reference equation to see how the direction and coefficients have changed. If a reaction has been reversed, the K value is the reciprocal of the K value for the reference reaction. If the coefficients have been changed by a factor n, the K value is equal to the original K value raised to the nth power.
Solution:

a) The K for the original reaction is $K = \dfrac{p_{H_2}^2 \, p_{S_2}}{p_{H_2S}^2}$

The given reaction $1/2 S_2(g) + H_2(g) \rightleftharpoons H_2S(g)$ is the reverse reaction of the original reaction and the coefficients of the original reaction have been multiplied by a factor of 1/2. The equilibrium constant for the reverse reaction is the reciprocal $(1/K)$ of the original constant. The K value of the original reaction is raised to the 1/2 power.

$$K_{(a)} = (1/K)^{1/2} = \frac{p_{H_2S}}{p_{H_2} \, p_{S_2}^{1/2}}$$

$$K_{(a)} = (1/1.6 \times 10^{-2})^{1/2} = 7.90569 = \textbf{7.9}$$

b) The given reaction $5H_2S(g) \rightleftharpoons 5H_2(g) + 5/2 S_2(g)$ is the original reaction multiplied by 5/2. Take the original K to the 5/2 power to find K of given reaction.

$$K_{(b)} = (K_c)^{5/2} = \frac{p_{H_2}^5 \, p_{S_2}^{5/2}}{p_{H_2S}^5}$$

$$K_{(b)} = (1.6 \times 10^{-2})^{5/2} = 3.23817 \times 10^{-5} = \textbf{3.2} \times \textbf{10}^{-5}$$

15.18 Plan: The activity of pure solids and pure liquids is 1, so they do not appear in the reaction quotient expression. Remember that stoichiometric coefficients are used as exponents in the expression for the reaction quotient.
Solution:

a) $2Na_2O_2(s) + 2CO_2(g) \rightleftharpoons 2Na_2CO_3(s) + O_2(g)$

$$Q = \frac{p_{O_2}}{p_{CO_2}^2}$$

b) $H_2O(l) \rightleftharpoons H_2O(g)$

$$Q = p_{H_2O}$$

c) $NH_4Cl(s) \rightleftharpoons NH_3(g) + HCl(g)$

$$Q = p_{NH_3} \, p_{HCl}$$

15.20 Plan: The activity of pure solids and pure liquids is 1, so they do not appear in the reaction quotient expression. Remember that stoichiometric coefficients are used as exponents in the expression for the reaction quotient.
Solution:

a) $2NaHCO_3(s) \rightleftharpoons Na_2CO_3(s) + CO_2(g) + H_2O(g)$

$$Q = p_{CO_2} \, p_{H_2O}$$

b) $SnO_2(s) + 2H_2(g) \rightleftharpoons Sn(s) + 2H_2O(g)$

$$Q = \frac{p_{H_2O}^2}{p_{H_2}^2}$$

c) $H_2SO_4(l) + SO_3(g) \rightleftharpoons H_2S_2O_7(l)$

$$Q = \frac{1}{p_{SO_3}}$$

15.23   Plan: Add the two equations, canceling substances that appear on both sides of the equation. Write the Q_c expression for each of the steps and for the overall equation. Since the individual steps are added, their Q_c's are multiplied and common terms are canceled to obtain the overall Q_c.
Solution:
a) The balanced equations and corresponding reaction quotients are given below. Note the second equation must be multiplied by 2 to get the appropriate overall equation.

$$(1)\ Cl_2(g) + F_2(g) \rightleftharpoons 2ClF(g) \qquad\qquad Q_1 = \frac{p_{ClF}^2}{p_{Cl_2}\,p_{F_2}}$$

$$(2)\ 2ClF(g) + 2F_2(g) \rightleftharpoons 2ClF_3(g) \qquad\qquad Q_2 = \frac{p_{ClF_3}^2}{p_{ClF}^2\,p_{F_2}^2}$$

$$\text{Overall: } Cl_2(g) + 3F_2(g) \rightleftharpoons 2ClF_3(g) \qquad\qquad Q_{overall} = \frac{p_{ClF_3}^2}{p_{Cl_2}\,p_{F_2}^3}$$

b) The reaction quotient for the overall reaction, $Q_{overall}$, determined from the reaction is:

$$Q_{overall} = \frac{p_{ClF_3}^2}{p_{Cl_2}\,p_{F_2}^3}$$

$$Q_{overall} = Q_1 Q_2^2 = \left(\frac{p_{ClF}^2}{p_{Cl_2}\,p_{F_2}}\right)\left(\frac{p_{ClF_3}^2}{p_{ClF}^2\,p_{F_2}^2}\right) = \frac{p_{ClF_3}^2}{p_{Cl_2}\,p_{F_2}^3}$$

15.25 K_c and K are related by the equation $K = K_c(RT)^{\Delta n}$, where Δn represents the change in amount (mol) of gas in the reaction (amount (mol) gaseous products – amount (mol) gaseous reactants). When Δn is zero (no change in amount (mol) of gas), the term $(RT)^{\Delta n}$ equals 1 and $K_c = K$. When Δn is not zero, meaning that there is a change in the amount (mol) of gas in the reaction, then $K_c \neq K$.

15.26   a) $K = K_c(RT)^{\Delta n}$. Since Δn = amount (mol) gaseous products – amount (mol) gaseous reactants, Δn is a positive integer for this reaction. If Δn is a positive integer, then $(RT)^{\Delta n}$ is greater than 1. Thus, K_c is multiplied by a number that is greater than 1 to give K. **K_c is smaller than K.**
b) Assuming that $RT > 1$ (which occurs when $T > 12.0\ K$, because $0.08314\ (R) \times 12.0 = 1$), **$K > K_c$** if the amount (mol) of gaseous products exceeds the amount (mol) of gaseous reactants. $K < K_c$ when the amount (mol) of gaseous reactants exceeds the amount (mol) of gaseous product.

15.27   Plan: Δn_{gas} = moles gaseous products – moles gaseous reactants.
Solution:
a) Amount (mol) of gaseous reactants = 0; amount (mol) of gaseous products = 3; $\Delta n_{gas} = 3 - 0 = $ **3**
b) Amount (mol) of gaseous reactants = 1; amount (mol) of gaseous products = 0; $\Delta n_{gas} = 0 - 1 = $ **–1**
c) Amount (mol) of gaseous reactants = 0; amount (mol) of gaseous products = 3; $\Delta n_{gas} = 3 - 0 = $ **3**

15.29   Plan: First, determine Δn for the reaction and then calculate K_c using $K = K_c(RT)^{\Delta n}$.
Solution:
a) Δn = moles gaseous products – moles gaseous reactants = $1 - 2 = -1$
$$K = K_c(RT)^{\Delta n}$$
$$K_c = \frac{K}{(RT)^{\Delta n}} = \frac{3.9 \times 10^{-2}}{[(0.08314)(1000.)]^{-1}} = 3.24246 = \textbf{3.2}$$
b) Δn = moles gaseous products – moles gaseous reactants = $1 - 1 = 0$
$$K_c = \frac{K}{(RT)^{\Delta n}} = \frac{28.5}{[(0.08314)(500.)]^{0}} = \textbf{28.5}$$

15.31   Plan: First, determine Δn for the reaction and then calculate K using $K = K_c(RT)^{\Delta n}$.

Solution:

a) Δn = moles gaseous products – moles gaseous reactants = 2 – 1 = 1

$$K = K_c(RT)^{\Delta n} = (6.1 \times 10^{-3})[(0.08314)(298)]^1 = 0.15113 = \mathbf{0.15}$$

b) Δn = moles gaseous products – moles gaseous reactants = 2 – 4 = – 2

$$K = K_c(RT)^{\Delta n} = (2.4 \times 10^{-3})[(0.08314)(1000.)]^{-2} = 3.4721 \times 10^{-7} = \mathbf{3.5 \times 10^{-7}}$$

15.33   When $Q < K$, the reaction proceeds to the **right** to form more products. The reaction quotient and equilibrium constant are determined by [products]/[reactants]. For Q to increase and reach the value of K, the concentration of products (numerator) must increase in relation to the concentration of reactants (denominator).

15.35   Plan: To decide if the reaction is at equilibrium, calculate Q and compare it to K. If $Q = K$, then the reaction is at equilibrium. If $Q > K$, then the reaction proceeds to the left to produce more reactants. If $Q < K$, then the reaction proceeds to the right to produce more products.

Solution:

$$Q = \frac{p_{H_2} p_{Br_2}}{p_{HBr}^2} = \frac{(0.010)(0.010)}{(0.20)^2} = 2.5 \times 10^{-3} > K = 4.18 \times 10^{-9}$$

$Q > K$, thus, the reaction is **not** at equilibrium and will proceed to the **left** (towards the reactants). Thus, the numerator will decrease in size as products are consumed and the denominator will increase in size as more reactant is produced. Q will decrease until $Q = K$.

15.38   At equilibrium, equal concentrations of $CFCl_3$ and HCl exist, regardless of starting reactant concentrations. The equilibrium concentrations of $CFCl_3$ and HCl would still be equal if unequal concentrations of CCl_4 and HF were used. This occurs only when the two products have the same coefficients in the balanced equation. Otherwise, more of the product with the larger coefficient will be produced.

15.40   a) The approximation applies when the change in concentration from initial to equilibrium is so small that it is insignificant. This occurs when K is small and initial concentration is large.

b) This approximation will not work when the change in concentration is greater than 5%. This can occur when [reactant]$_{initial}$ is very small, or when [reactant]$_{change}$ is relatively large due to a large K.

15.41   Plan: Since all equilibrium concentrations are given in mol/L and the reaction is balanced, construct an equilibrium expression and substitute the equilibrium concentrations to find K_c.

Solution:

$$K_c = \frac{[HI]^2}{[H_2][I_2]} = \frac{[1.87 \times 10^{-3}]^2}{[6.50 \times 10^{-5}][1.06 \times 10^{-3}]} = 50.753 = \mathbf{50.8}$$

15.43   Plan: Calculate the initial concentration of PCl_5 from the given amount (mol) and the container volume; the reaction is proceeding to the right, consuming PCl_5 and producing products. There is a 1:1:1 mole ratio between the reactants and products.

Solution:

Initial $[PCl_5]$ = 0.15 mol/2.0 L = 0.075 mol/L

Since there is a 1:1:1 mole ratio in this reaction:

    x = $[PCl_5]$ reacting (–x), and the amount of PCl_3 and of Cl_2 forming (+x).

Concentration (M)	$PCl_5(g)$	$\rightleftharpoons$	$PCl_3(g)$	+	$Cl_2(g)$
Initial	0.075		0		0
Change	–x		+x		+x
Equilibrium	0.075 – x		x		x

15.45   Plan: Two of the three equilibrium pressures are known, as is K. Construct an equilibrium expression and solve for p_{NOCl}.
Solution:

$$K = 6.5 \times 10^4 = \frac{p_{NOCl}^2}{p_{NO}^2 \, p_{Cl_2}}$$

$$6.5 \times 10^4 = \frac{P_{NOCl}^2}{(0.35)^2 (0.10)}$$

$$P_{NOCl} = \sqrt{(6.5 \times 10^4)(0.35)^2 (0.10)} = 28.2179 \text{ bar} = \textbf{28 bar}$$

A high pressure for NOCl is expected because the large value of K indicates that the reaction proceeds largely to the right, i.e., to the formation of products.

15.47   Plan: Use the balanced equation to write an equilibrium expression and to define x. Set up a reaction table, substitute into the K expression, and solve for x.
Solution:

$$NH_4HS(s) \rightleftharpoons H_2S(g) + NH_3(g)$$

x = [NH₄HS] reacting (–x), and the amount of H₂S and of NH₃ forming (+x) since there is a 1:1:1 mole ratio between the reactant and products.
(It is not necessary to include the NH₄HS as it is a solid with activity=1).

Pressure (bar)	$NH_4HS(s)$	$\rightleftharpoons$	$H_2S(g)$	+	$NH_3(g)$
Initial	—		0		0
Change	—		+x		+x
Equilibrium	—		x		x

$$K = 0.11 = (p_{H_2S})(p_{NH_3}) \qquad \text{(The solid NH}_4\text{HS is not included.)}$$
$$0.11 = (x)(x)$$
$$x = p_{NH_3} = 0.33166 = \textbf{0.33 bar}$$

15.49   Plan: Use the balanced equation to write an equilibrium expression. Find the initial concentration of each reactant from the given amounts and container volume, use the balanced equation to define x and set up a reaction table, substitute into the equilibrium expression, and solve for x, from which the concentration of NO is calculated.
Solution:
The initial concentrations of N₂ and O₂ are (0.20 mol/1.0 L) = 0.20 mol/L and (0.15 mol/1.0 L) = 0.15 mol/L, respectively.

$$N_2(g) + O_2(g) \rightleftharpoons 2NO(g) \qquad \text{There is a 1:1:2 mole ratio between reactants and products.}$$

Concentration (mol/L)	$N_2(g)$	+	$O_2(g)$	$\rightleftharpoons$	$2NO(g)$	
Initial	0.20		0.15		0	
Change	–x		–x		+2x	(1:1:2 mole ratio)
Equilibrium	0.20 – x		0.15 – x		2x	

$$K_c = 4.10 \times 10^{-4} = \frac{[NO]^2}{[N_2][O_2]} = \frac{[2x]^2}{[0.20 - x][0.15 - x]}$$

Assume 0.20 mol/L – x ≈ 0.20 mol/L   and   0.15 mol/L – x ≈ 0.15 mol/L

$$4.10 \times 10^{-4} = \frac{4x^2}{[0.20][0.15]}$$

x = 1.753568×10⁻³ mol/L
[NO] = 2x = 2(1.753568×10⁻³ mol/L) = 3.507136×10⁻³ mol/L = **3.5×10⁻³ mol/L**
(Since (1.8×10⁻³)/(0.15) < 0.05, the assumption is OK.)

15.51   Plan: Find the initial concentration of each reactant and product from the given amounts and container volume, use the balanced equation to define x, and set up a reaction table. The equilibrium concentration of H_2 is known, so x can be calculated and used to find the other equilibrium concentrations.
Solution:
Initial concentrations:
   [HI] = (0.0244 mol)/(1.50 L) = 0.0162667 mol/L
   $[H_2]$ = (0.00623 mol)/(1.50 L) = 0.0041533 mol/L
   $[I_2]$ = (0.00414 mol)/(1.50 L) = 0.00276 mol/L
Equilibrium concentration of H_2 is greater than the initial, so the reaction moves in the forward direction.
$2 HI(g) \rightleftharpoons \quad H_2(g) + I_2(g)$ There is a 2:1:1 mole ratio between reactants and products.

Concentration (mol/L)	2 HI(g)	$\rightleftharpoons$	$H_2(g)$	+	$I_2(g)$	
Initial	0.0162667		0.0041533		0.00276	
Change	−2x		+x		+x	(2:1:1 mole ratio)
Equilibrium	0.0162667 − 2x		0.0041533 + x		0.00276 + x	

$[H_2]_{eq}$ = 0.00467 = 0.0041533 + x
        x = 0.0005167 mol/L
$[I_2]_{eq}$ = 0.00276 + x = 0.00276 + 0.0005167 = 0.0032767 mol/L= **0.00328 mol/L I_2**
$[HI]_{eq}$ = 0.0162667 − 2x = 0.0162667 − 2(0.0005167) = 0.0152333 mol/L= **0.0152 mol/L HI**

15.53   Plan: Use the balanced equation to write an equilibrium expression. Find the initial concentration of ICl from the given amount and container volume, use the balanced equation to define x and set up a reaction table, substitute into the equilibrium expression, and solve for x, from which the equilibrium concentrations can be calculated.
Solution:
$[ICl]_{init}$ = (0.500 mol/5.00 L) = 0.100 mol/L

Concentration (mol/L)	2ICl(g)	$\rightleftharpoons$	$I_2(g)$	+	$Cl_2(g)$	
Initial	0.100		0		0	
Change	−2x		+x		+x	(2:1:1 mole ratio)
Equilibrium	0.100 − 2x		x		x	

$$K_c = 0.110 = \frac{[I_2][Cl_2]}{[ICl]^2} = \frac{(x)(x)}{(0.100 - 2x)^2}$$

$$0.110 = \frac{(x)^2}{(0.100 - 2x)^2}$$ Take the square root of each side:

$$0.331662 = \frac{(x)}{(0.100 - 2x)}$$

x = 0.0331662 − 0.663324x
1.663324x = 0.0331662
x = 0.0199397
$[I_2]_{eq}$ = $[Cl_2]_{eq}$ = x = 0.0199397 mol/L= **0.0200 mol/L**
$[ICl]_{eq}$ = 0.100 − 2x = 0.100 − 2(0.0199397) = 0.0601206 mol/L= **0.060 mol/L ICl**

15.55   Plan: Use the balanced equation to write an equilibrium expression. Find the initial concentration of each reactant from the given amounts and container volume, use the balanced equation to define x, and set up a reaction table. The equilibrium concentration of N_2 is known, so x can be calculated and used to find the other equilibrium concentrations. Substitute the equilibrium concentrations into the equilibrium expression to find K_c.
Solution:
$4NH_3(g) + 3O_2(g) \rightleftharpoons 2N_2(g) + 6H_2O(g)$

Initial $[NH_3]$ = Initial $[O_2]$ = (0.0150 mol)/(1.00 L) = 0.0150 mol/L

Concentration (mol/L)	$4NH_3(g)$	+	$3O_2(g)$	$\rightleftharpoons$	$2N_2(g)$	+	$6H_2O(g)$
Initial	0.0150		0.0150		0		0
Change	$-4x$		$-3x$		$+2x$		$+6x$
Equilibrium	$0.0150 - 4$		$0.0150 - 3x$		$+2x$		$+6x$

$[N_2]_{eq} = 2x = 1.96 \times 10^{-3}$ mol/L

$x = (1.96 \times 10^{-3} \text{ mol/L})/2 = 9.80 \times 10^{-4}$ mol/L

$[H_2O]_{eq} = 6x = 6(9.80 \times 10^{-4}) = 5.8800 \times 10^{-3}$ mol/L

$[NH_3]_{eq} = 0.0150 - 4x = 0.0150 - 4(9.80 \times 10^{-4}) = 1.1080 \times 10^{-2}$ mol/L

$[O_2]_{eq} = 0.0150 - 3x = 0.0150 - 3(9.80 \times 10^{-4}) = 1.2060 \times 10^{-2}$ mol/L

$$K_c = \frac{[N_2]^2[H_2O]^6}{[NH_3]^4[O_2]^3} = \frac{\left(1.96 \times 10^{-3}\right)^2\left(5.8800 \times 10^{-3}\right)^6}{\left(1.1080 \times 10^{-2}\right)^4\left(1.2060 \times 10^{-2}\right)^3} = 6.005859 \times 10^{-6} = \mathbf{6.01 \times 10^{-6}}$$

15.58 Equilibrium position refers to the specific concentrations or pressures of reactants and products that exist at equilibrium, whereas equilibrium constant refers to the overall ratio of equilibrium concentrations and not to specific concentrations. Changes in reactant concentration cause changes in the specific equilibrium concentrations of reactants and products (equilibrium position), but not in the equilibrium constant.

15.59 A positive $\Delta_r H$ indicates that the reaction is endothermic, and that heat is consumed in the reaction:

$NH_4Cl(s) + \mathbf{heat} \rightleftharpoons NH_3(g) + HCl(g)$

a) The addition of heat (high temperature) causes the reaction to proceed to the right to counterbalance the effect of the added heat. Therefore, more products form at a higher temperature and container **(B)** with the largest number of product molecules best represents the mixture.
b) When heat is removed (low temperature), the reaction shifts to the left to produce heat to offset that disturbance. Therefore, NH_3 and HCl molecules combine to form more reactant and container **(A)** with the smallest number of product gas molecules best represents the mixture.

15.63 Plan: If the concentration of a substance in the reaction increases, the equilibrium position will shift to consume some of it. If the concentration of a substance in the reaction decreases, the equilibrium position will shift to produce more of it.
Solution:
a) Equilibrium position shifts **towards products**. Adding a reactant (CO) causes production of more products as the system will act to reduce the increase in reactant by proceeding toward the product side, thereby consuming additional CO.
b) Equilibrium position shifts **towards products**. Removing a product (CO_2) causes production of more products as the system acts to replace the removed product.
c) Equilibrium position **does not shift**. The amount of a solid reactant or product does not impact the equilibrium as long as there is some solid present.
d) Equilibrium position shifts **towards reactants**. When product is added, the system will act to reduce the increase in product by proceeding toward the reactant side, thereby consuming additional CO_2; dry ice is solid carbon dioxide that sublimes to carbon dioxide gas. At very low temperatures, CO_2 solid will not sublime, but since the reaction lists carbon dioxide as a gas, the assumption that sublimation takes place is reasonable.

15.65 Plan: An increase in container volume results in a decrease in pressure (Boyle's law). Le Châtelier's principle states that the equilibrium will shift in the direction that forms more moles of gas to offset the decrease in pressure.
Solution:
a) **More F** forms (two moles of gas) and **less F_2** (one mole of gas) is present as the reaction shifts towards the right.
b) **More C_2H_2 and H_2** form (four moles of gas) and **less CH_4** (two moles of gas) is present as the reaction shifts towards the right.

15.67   Plan: Decreasing container volume increases the pressure (Boyle's law). Le Châtelier's principle states that the equilibrium will shift in the direction that forms a smaller amount (mol) of gas to offset the increase in pressure.
Solution:
a) There are two moles of reactant gas (H_2 and Cl_2) and two moles of product gas (HCl). Since there is the same amount (mol) of reactant and product gas , there is **no effect** on the amounts of reactants or products.
b) There are three moles of reactant gases (H_2 and O_2) and zero moles of product gas. The reaction will shift to the right to produce a smaller amount (mol) of gas to offset the increase in pressure. **H_2 and O_2 will decrease** from their initial values before the volume was changed. **More H_2O** will form because of the shift in equilibrium position.

15.69   Plan: The purpose of adjusting the volume is to cause a shift in equilibrium to the right for increased product yield. Increasing the volume of the container results in a shift in the direction that forms a larger amount (mol) of gas, while decreasing the container volume results in a shift in the direction that forms a smaller amount (mol) of gas.
Solution:
a) Because the amount (mol) of reactant gas ($4H_2$) equals the amount (mol) of product gas ($4H_2O$), a change in volume will have **no effect** on the yield.
b) The moles of gaseous product (2CO) exceed the moles of gaseous reactant ($1O_2$). A decrease in pressure favors the reaction direction that forms more moles of gas, so **increase** the reaction vessel volume.

15.71   Plan: An increase in temperature (addition of heat) causes a shift in the equilibrium <u>away</u> from the side of the reaction with heat. Recall that a negative value of $\Delta_r H°$ indicates an exothermic reaction, while a positive value of $\Delta_r H°$ indicates an endothermic reaction.
Solution:
a) $CO(g) + 2H_2(g) \rightleftharpoons CH_3OH(g) + heat$ $\Delta_r H° = -90.7$ kJ/mol
The reaction is exothermic, so heat is written as a product. The equilibrium shifts to the left, away from heat, towards the reactants, so amount of product **decreases**.
b) $C(s) + H_2O(g) + heat \rightleftharpoons CO(g) + H_2(g)$ $\Delta_r H° = 131$ kJ/mol
The reaction is endothermic, so heat is written as a reactant. The equilibrium shifts to the right, away from heat, towards the products, so amounts of products **increase**.
c) $2NO_2(g) + heat \rightleftharpoons 2NO(g) + O_2(g)$
The reaction is endothermic, so heat is written as a reactant. The equilibrium shifts to the right, away from heat, towards the product, so amounts of products **increase**.
d) $2C(s) + O_2(g) \rightleftharpoons 2CO(g) + heat$
The reaction is exothermic, so heat is written as a product. The equilibrium shifts to the left, away from heat, towards the reactants; amount of product **decreases**.

15.73   Plan: The van't Hoff equation shows how the equilibrium constant is affected by a change in temperature. Substitute the given variables into the equation and solve for K_2.
Solution:

$K_{298} = K_1 = 1.80$ $T_1 = 298$ K
$K_{500} = K_2 = ?$ $T_2 = 500.$ K $R = 8.314$ J/mol•K

$$\Delta_r H° = \left(\frac{0.32 \text{ kJ}}{1 \text{ mol DH}} \right)(2 \text{ DH})\left(\frac{10^3 \text{ J}}{1 \text{ kJ}} \right) = 6.4 \times 10^2 \text{ J/mol}$$

$$\ln \frac{K_2}{K_1} = -\frac{\Delta_r H°}{R}\left(\frac{1}{T_2} - \frac{1}{T_1} \right)$$

$$\ln \frac{K_2}{1.80} = -\frac{6.4 \times 10^2 \text{ J / mol}}{8.314 \text{ J/mol•K}}\left(\frac{1}{500. \text{ K}} - \frac{1}{298 \text{ K}} \right)$$

$$\ln \frac{K_2}{1.80} = 0.104360$$

$$\frac{K_2}{1.80} = 1.110$$

$$K_2 = (1.80)(1.110) = 1.998 = \textbf{2.0}$$

15.76   Plan: An increase in temperature (addition of heat) causes a shift in the equilibrium away from the side of the reaction with heat, while a decrease in temperature (removal of heat) causes a shift in the equilibrium towards the side with heat.   Increasing the volume of the container (pressure decreases) results in a shift in the direction that forms a larger amount (mol) of gas, while decreasing the container volume (pressure increases) results in a shift in the direction that forms a smaller amount (mol) of gas. Adding a reactant causes a shift in the direction of products.
Solution:

a) $SO_2(g) + 1/2O_2(g) \rightleftharpoons SO_3(g) +$ heat

The forward reaction is exothermic ($\Delta_r H°$ is negative), so it is favored by **lower temperatures**. Lower temperatures will cause a shift to the right, the heat side of the reaction. The amount (mol) of gas as products ($1SO_3$) is smaller than as reactants ($1SO_2(g) + 1/2O_2$), so products are favored by **higher pressure**. High pressure will cause a shift in equilibrium to the side with the smaller amount (mol) of gas.

b) Addition of O_2 would **decrease Q** since $Q = \dfrac{p_{SO_3}}{p_{SO_2} \, p_{O_2}^{1/2}}$, and have **no impact on K**.

c) To enhance yield of SO_3, a low temperature is used. Reaction rates are slower at lower temperatures, so a catalyst is used **to speed up the reaction**.

15.78   a) $3H_2(g) + N_2(g) \rightleftharpoons 2NH_3(g)$ The mole ratio $H_2:N_2 = 3:1$; at equilibrium, if $N_2 = x$, $H_2 = 3x$;

$p_{NH_3} = 50.$ bar

$$K = \frac{\left(p_{NH_3}\right)^2}{\left(p_{N_2}\right)\left(p_{H_2}\right)^3} = 1.00 \times 10^{-4}$$

$$K = \frac{(50.)^2}{(x)(3x)^3} = 1.00 \times 10^{-4}$$

$x = 31.02016 = \textbf{31 bar } N_2$
$3x = 3(31.02016) = 93.06049 = \textbf{93 bar } H_2$
$p_{total} = p_{nitrogen} + p_{hydrogen} + p_{ammonia} = (31.02016 \text{ bar}) + (93.06049 \text{ bar}) + (50. \text{ bar})$
$= 174.08065 \text{ bar} = \textbf{174 bar total}$

b) The mole ratio $H_2:N_2 = 6:1$; at equilibrium, if $N_2 = x$, $H_2 = 6x$; $p_{NH_3} = 50.$ bar

$$K = \frac{(50.)^2}{(x)(6x)^3} = 1.00 \times 10^{-4}$$

$x = 18.445 = \textbf{18 bar } N_2$
$6x = 6(18.445) = 110.67 = \textbf{111 bar } H_2$
$p_{total} = p_{nitrogen} + p_{hydrogen} + p_{ammonia} = (18.445 \text{ bar}) + (110.67 \text{ bar}) + (50. \text{ bar})$
$= 179.115 \text{ bar} = \textbf{179 bar total}$

This is not a valid argument. The total pressure in b) is greater than in a) to produce the same amount of NH_3.

15.81   Plan: Use the balanced equation to write an equilibrium expression and to define x. Set up a reaction table, substitute into the K_c expression, and solve for x. Once the total concentration of the gases at equilibrium is known, the pressure can be found with $pV = nRT$.
Solution:

Concentration (mol/L)	$NH_2COONH_4(s)$	$\rightleftharpoons$	$2NH_3(g)$	$+$	$CO_2(g)$
Initial	7.80 g		0		0
Change	—		$+2x$		$+x$
Equilibrium	—		$2x$		x

The solid has an activity of 1 and, as long as some is present, is not included in the K_c expression.

$K_c = [NH_3]^2[CO_2]$
$K_c = 1.58\times10^{-8} = (2x)^2(x)$
$x = 1.580759\times10^{-3}$ mol/L
Total concentration of gases $= 2x + x = 2(1.580759\times10^{-3}$ mol/L$) + 1.580759\times10^{-3}$ mol/L $= 4.742277\times10^{-3}$ mol/L
To find total pressure use the ideal gas equation: $PV = nRT$

$$p = \frac{nRT}{V} = \left(\frac{n}{V}\right)RT = cRT$$

$P = (4.742277\times10^{-3}$ mol/L$)(0.08314$ L•bar/mol•K$)(273 + 250.)$K $= 0.206205$ bar $= \textbf{0.206 bar}$

15.84   Plan: Write the equilibrium expression. You are given a value of K_c but the amounts of reactant and product are given in units of pressure. Convert K_c to K and use the equilibrium pressures of C_2H_5OH and H_2O to obtain the equilibrium pressure of C_2H_4. An increase in temperature (addition of heat) causes a shift in the equilibrium away from the side of the reaction with heat, while a decrease in temperature (removal of heat) causes a shift in the equilibrium towards the side with heat. Increasing the volume of the container (pressure decreases) results in a shift in the direction that forms more moles of gas, while decreasing the container volume (pressure increases) results in a shift in the direction that forms fewer moles of gas. The van't Hoff equation shows how the equilibrium constant is affected by a change in temperature. Substitute the given variables into the equation and solve for K at 450. K.
Solution:
a) $K = K_c(RT)^{\Delta n}$

$\Delta n =$ amount (mol) gaseous products – amount (mol) gaseous reactants $= 1 - 2 = -1$ (one mol of product, C_2H_5OH, and two mol of reactants, $C_2H_4 + H_2O$)
$K = K_c(RT)^{-1} = (9\times10^3)[(0.08314$ L•bar/mol•K$)(600.$ K$)]^{-1} = 1.8042\times10^2$
Substitute the given values into the equilibrium expression and solve for $p_{C_2H_4}$.

$$K = \frac{p_{C_2H_5OH}}{p_{C_2H_4}\,p_{H_2O}} = \frac{200.}{p_{C_2H_4}\,(400.)} = 1.8042\times10^2$$

$p_{C_2H_4} = 2.7713\times10^{-3} = \textbf{3}\times\textbf{10}^{\textbf{-3}}\textbf{ bar}$

b) Since $\Delta_r H°$ is negative, the reaction is exothermic and heat is written as a product. To shift the reaction towards the right to yield more ethanol, heat must be removed. A **low temperature** favors an exothermic reaction. The forward direction, towards the production of ethanol, produces the smaller amount (mol) of gas and is favored by **high pressure**.

c) $K_1 = 9\times10^3$ $T_1 = 600.$ K $\Delta_r H° = (-47.8$ kJ/mol$)\left(\dfrac{10^3 \text{ J}}{1 \text{ kJ}}\right) = -4.78\times10^4$ J/mol

$K_2 = ?$ $T_2 = 450.$ K $R = 8.314$ J/mol•K

$$\ln\frac{K_2}{K_1} = -\frac{\Delta_r H°}{R}\left(\frac{1}{T_2} - \frac{1}{T_1}\right)$$

$$\ln\frac{K_2}{9\times10^3} = -\frac{-4.78\times10^4 \text{ J / mol}}{8.314 \text{ J/mol•K}}\left(\frac{1}{450. \text{ K}} - \frac{1}{600. \text{ K}}\right)$$

$$\ln \frac{K_2}{9 \times 10^3} = 3.1940769$$

$$\frac{K_2}{9 \times 10^3} = 24.38765$$

$$K_2 = (9 \times 10^3)(24.38765) = 2.1949 \times 10^5 = \mathbf{2 \times 10^5}$$

d) **No**, condensing the C_2H_5OH would not increase the yield. Ethanol has a lower boiling point (78.5°C) than water (100°C). Decreasing the temperature to condense the ethanol would also condense the water, so moles of gas from each side of the reaction are removed. The direction of equilibrium (yield) is unaffected when there is no net change in the amount (mol) of gas.

15.87   <u>Plan:</u> Write the equilibrium expression. You are given a value of K_c but the amounts of reactants and product are given in units of pressure. Convert K_c to K and use the equilibrium pressures of SO_3 and O_2 to obtain the equilibrium pressure of SO_2. For part b), set up a reaction table and solve for x. The equilibrium concentrations can then be used to find the K_c value at the higher temperature. The concentration of SO_2 is converted to pressure using the ideal gas law, $pV = nRT$.
<u>Solution:</u>
a) $K = K_c(RT)^{\Delta n}$

Δn = amount (mol) of gaseous products – amount (mol) of gaseous reactants = 2 – 3 = –1 (two mol of product, SO_3, and three mol of reactants, $2\ SO_2 + O_2$)

$$K = K_c(RT)^{\Delta n} = K_c(RT)^{-1} = (1.7 \times 10^8)[(0.08314\ \text{L} \cdot \text{bar/mol} \cdot \text{K})(600.\ \text{K})]^{-1} = 3.4079 \times 10^6$$

$$K = \frac{p_{SO_3}^2}{p_{SO_2}^2 \, p_{O_2}} = \frac{(300.)^2}{p_{SO_2}^2 \, (100.)} = 3.4079 \times 10^6$$

$$p_{SO_2} = 0.016251 = \mathbf{0.016\ bar}$$

b) Create a reaction table that describes the reaction conditions. Since the volume is 1.0 L, the amount (mol) equals the concentration (mol/L). Note the 2:1:2 mole ratio between SO_2:O_2:SO_3.

Concentration (mol/L)	$2SO_2(g)$	+	$O_2(g)$	$\rightleftharpoons$	$2SO_3(g)$	
Initial	0.0040		0.0028		0	
Change	–2x		–x		+2x	(2:1:2 mole ratio)
Equilibrium	0.0040 – 2x		0.0028 – x		2x = 0.0020	(given)

x = 0.0010, therefore:

[SO_2] = 0.0040 – 2x = 0.0040 – 2(0.0010) = 0.0020 mol/L
[O_2] = 0.0028 – x = 0.0028 – 0.0010 = 0.0018 mol/L
[SO_3] = 2(0.0010) = 0.0020 mol/L

Substitute equilibrium concentrations into the equilibrium expression and solve for K_c.

$$K_c = \frac{[SO_3]^2}{[SO_2]^2 [O_2]} = \frac{(0.0020)^2}{(0.0020)^2 (0.0018)} = 555.5556 = \mathbf{5.6 \times 10^2}$$

The pressure of SO_2 is estimated using the concentration of SO_2 and the ideal gas law (although the ideal gas law is not well behaved at high pressures and temperatures).

$$pV = nRT$$

$$p_{SO_2} = \frac{nRT}{V} = \frac{(0.0020\ \text{mol})\left(0.08314\ \dfrac{\text{L} \cdot \text{bar}}{\text{mol} \cdot \text{K}}\right)(1000.\ \text{K})}{(1.0\ \text{L})} = 0.1663 = \mathbf{0.17\ bar}$$

15.89   <u>Plan:</u> Set up a reaction table to find the equilibrium amount of $CaCO_3$ after the first equilibrium is established and then the equilibrium amount after the second equilibrium is established.
<u>Solution:</u>
The equilibrium pressure of $CO_2 = p_{CO_2} = 0.220$ bar.

	$CaCO_3(s)$	$\rightleftharpoons$	$CaO(s)$	$+$	$CO_2(g)$
Initial	0.100 mol		0.100 mol		0
Change	$-x$		$-x$		$+x$
Equilibrium	$0.100 - x$		$0.100 - x$		$x = 0.220$ bar (given)

The amount of calcium carbonate solid in the container at the first equilibrium equals the original amount, 0.100 mol, minus the amount reacted to form 0.220 bar of carbon dioxide. The amount (mol) of $CaCO_3$ reacted is equal to the amount (mol) of carbon dioxide produced. Use the pressure of CO_2 and the ideal gas equation to calculate the amount (mol) of CO_2 produced:

$pV = nRT$

Amount (mol) of $CO_2 = n = \dfrac{pV}{RT}$

$$n = \frac{(0.220 \text{ bar})(10.0 \text{ L})}{\left(0.08314 \dfrac{\text{L·bar}}{\text{mol·K}}\right)(385 \text{ K})} = 0.068731 \text{ mol } CO_2$$

Amount (mol) of $CaCO_3$ reacted = amount (mol) of CO_2 produced = 0.068731 mol
Amount (mol) of $CaCO_3$ remaining = initial amount (mol) amount (mol) reacted = 0.100 mol $CaCO_3$ – 0.068731 mol $CaCO_3$

$= 0.0313$ mol $CaCO_3$ at first equilibrium

As more carbon dioxide gas is added, the system returns to equilibrium by shifting to the left to convert the added carbon dioxide to calcium carbonate to maintain the partial pressure of carbon dioxide at 0.220 bar (K). Convert the added 0.300 bar of CO_2 to moles using the ideal gas equation. The amount (mol) of CO_2 reacted equals the amount (mol) of $CaCO_3$ formed.

Amount (mol) of $CO_2 = n = \dfrac{pV}{RT}$

$$n = \frac{(0.300 \text{ bar})(10.0 \text{ L})}{\left(0.08314 \dfrac{\text{L·bar}}{\text{mol·K}}\right)(385 \text{ K})} = 0.09372 \text{ mol } CO_2$$

Amount (mol) of $CaCO_3$ produced = amount (mol) of CO_2 reacted = 0.09372 mol $CaCO_3$
Add the amount (mol) of $CaCO_3$ formed in the second equilibrium to the amount (mol) of $CaCO_3$ at the first equilibrium position.
Amount (mol) of $CaCO_3$ = amount (mol) at first equilibrium + amount (mol) formed in second equilibrium

$= 0.0313$ mol $+ 0.09372 = 0.12502$ mol $CaCO_3$

Mass (g) of $CaCO_3 = (0.12502 \text{ mol } CaCO_3)\left(\dfrac{100.09 \text{ g } CaCO_3}{1 \text{ mol } CaCO_3}\right) = 12.514 = \textbf{12.5 g } \mathbf{CaCO_3}$

15.93   <u>Plan:</u> Use the balanced reaction to write the equilibrium expression. The equilibrium concentration of S_2F_{10} is used to write an expression for the equilibrium concentrations of SF_4 and SF_6.
<u>Solution:</u>
$S_2F_{10}(g) \rightleftharpoons SF_4(g) + SF_6(g)$

The reaction is described by the following equilibrium expression:

$K_c = \dfrac{[SF_4][SF_6]}{[S_2F_{10}]}$

At the first equilibrium, $[S_2F_{10}] = 0.50$ mol/L and $[SF_4] = [SF_6] = x$ ($[SF_4]:[SF_6] = 1:1$).

$K_c = \dfrac{[SF_4][SF_6]}{[S_2F_{10}]} = \dfrac{(x)(x)}{(0.50)}$

$$x^2 = 0.50K_c$$
$$[SF_4] = [SF_6] = x = \sqrt{0.50K_c}$$

At the second equilibrium, $[S_2F_{10}] = 2.5$ mol/L and $[SF_4] = [SF_6] = x$.

$$K_c = \frac{[SF_4][SF_6]}{[S_2F_{10}]} = \frac{(x)(x)}{(2.5)}$$
$$x^2 = 2.5K_c$$
$$[SF_4] = [SF_6] = x = \sqrt{2.5K_c}$$

Thus, the concentrations of SF_4 and SF_6 increase by a factor of:

$$\frac{\sqrt{2.5K_c}}{\sqrt{0.50K_c}} = \frac{\sqrt{2.5}}{\sqrt{0.50}} = 2.236 = \mathbf{2.2}$$

15.95 Plan: Use the volume fraction of O_2 and CO_2 to find the partial pressure of each gas and substitute these pressures into the equilibrium expression to find the partial pressure of CO. Use $pV = nRT$ to convert the partial pressure of CO to moles per liter and then convert to pg/L.
Solution:
a) Calculate the partial pressures of oxygen and carbon dioxide because volumes are proportional to the amount (mol) of gas, so volume fraction equals mole fraction. Assume that the amount of carbon monoxide gas is small relative to the other gases, so the total volume of gases equals $V_{CO_2} + V_{O_2} + V_{N_2} = 10.0 + 1.00 + 50.0 = 61.0$.

$$p_{CO_2} = \left(\frac{10.0 \text{ mol } CO_2}{61.0 \text{ mol gas}}\right)(4.0 \text{ bar}) = 0.6557377 \text{ bar}$$

$$p_{O_2} = \left(\frac{1.00 \text{ mol } O_2}{61.0 \text{ mol gas}}\right)(4.0 \text{ bar}) = 0.06557377 \text{ bar}$$

Use the partial pressures and given K to find p_{CO}.
$$2CO_2(g) \rightleftharpoons 2CO(g) + O_2(g)$$

$$K = \frac{p_{CO}^2 p_{O_2}}{p_{CO_2}^2} = \frac{p_{CO}^2 (0.06557377)}{(0.6557377)^2} = 1.4\times10^{-28}$$
$$p_{CO} = 3.0299\times10^{-14} = \mathbf{3.0\times10^{-14} \text{ bar}}$$
b) $pV = nRT$

$$\frac{n_{CO}}{V} = \frac{p}{RT} = \frac{(3.0299\times10^{-14} \text{ bar})}{\left(0.08314\dfrac{\text{L}\cdot\text{bar}}{\text{mol}\cdot\text{K}}\right)(800 \text{ K})} = 4.55542\times10^{-16} \text{ mol/L}$$

$$\text{Concentration (pg/L) of CO} = \left(\frac{4.55572\times10^{-16} \text{ mol CO}}{\text{L}}\right)\left(\frac{28.01 \text{ g CO}}{1 \text{ mol CO}}\right)\left(\frac{1 \text{ pg}}{10^{-12} \text{ g}}\right) = 0.01276 \text{ pg/L} = \mathbf{0.013 \text{ pg}}$$

CO/L

15.97 Plan: Write a reaction table given that p_{CH_4} (init) $= p_{CO_2}$ (init) $= 10.0$ bar, substitute equilibrium values into the equilibrium expression, and solve for p_{H_2}.

Solution:

a) Pressure (bar)	$CH_4(g)$	+	$CO_2(g)$	$\rightleftharpoons$	$2CO(g)$	+	$2H_2(g)$
Initial	10.0		10.0		0		0
Change	$-x$		$-x$		$+2x$		$+2x$
Equilibrium	$10.0 - x$		$10.0 - x$		$2x$		$2x$

$$K = \frac{p_{CO}^2 p_{H_2}^2}{p_{CH_4} p_{CO_2}} = \frac{(2x)^2 (2x)^2}{(10.0 - x)(10.0 - x)} = \frac{(2x)^4}{(10.0 - x)^2} = 3.548\times10^6 \quad \text{(take square root of each side)}$$

$$\frac{(2x)^2}{(10.0 - x)} = 1.8836135 \times 10^3$$

A quadratic is necessary:
$$4x^2 + (1.8836135 \times 10^3 \, x) - 1.8836135 \times 10^4 = 0$$
$$a = 4 \quad b = 1.8836135 \times 10^3 \quad c = -1.8836135 \times 10^4$$

$$x = \frac{-b \pm \sqrt{b^2 - 4ac}}{2a}$$

$$x = \frac{-1.8836135 \times 10^3 \pm \sqrt{\left(1.8836135 \times 10^3\right)^2 - 4(4)\left(-1.8836135 \times 10^4\right)}}{2(4)}$$

$$x = 9.796209$$
$$p_{H_2} = 2x = 2(9.796209) = 19.592419 \text{ bar}$$

If the reaction proceeded entirely to completion, the partial pressure of H_2 would be 20.0 bar (pressure is proportional to amount (mol), and twice as many moles of H_2 form for each mole of CH_4 or CO_2 that reacts).

The percent yield is $\dfrac{19.592418 \text{ bar}}{20.0 \text{ bar}}(100\%) = 97.96209 \% = \mathbf{98.0\%}$.

b) Repeat the calculations for part a) with the new K value. The reaction table is the same.

$$K = \frac{p_{CO}^2 \, p_{H_2}^2}{p_{CH_4} \, p_{CO_2}} = \frac{(2x)^2 (2x)^2}{(10.0 - x)(10.0 - x)} = \frac{(2x)^4}{(10.0 - x)^2} = 2.626 \times 10^7$$

$$\frac{(2x)^2}{(10.0 - x)} = 5.124451 \times 10^3$$

A quadratic is needed:
$$4x^2 + (5.124451 \times 10^3 \, x) - 5.124451 \times 10^4 = 0$$
$$a = 4 \quad\quad b = 5.124451 \times 10^3 \quad\quad c = -5.124451 \times 10^4$$

$$x = \frac{-5.124451 \times 10^3 \pm \sqrt{\left(5.124451 \times 10^3\right)^2 - 4(4)\left(-5.124451 \times 10^4\right)}}{2(4)}$$

$$x = 9.923144$$
$$p_{H_2} = 2x = 2(9.923144) = 19.84629 \text{ bar}$$

If the reaction proceeded entirely to completion, the partial pressure of H_2 would be 20.0 bar (pressure is proportional to moles, and twice as many moles of H_2 form for each mole of CH_4 or CO_2 that reacts).

The percent yield is $\dfrac{19.84629 \text{ bar}}{20.0 \text{ bar}}(100\%) = 99.23145 \% = \mathbf{99.0\%}$.

c) van't Hoff equation:

$$K_1 = 3.548 \times 10^6 \quad\quad\quad T_1 = 1200. \text{ K} \quad\quad \Delta_r H^\circ = ?$$
$$K_2 = 2.626 \times 10^7 \quad\quad\quad T_2 = 1300. \text{ K} \quad\quad R = 8.314 \text{ J/mol·K}$$

$$\ln \frac{K_2}{K_1} = -\frac{\Delta_r H^\circ}{R}\left(\frac{1}{T_2} - \frac{1}{T_1}\right)$$

$$\ln \frac{2.626 \times 10^7}{3.548 \times 10^6} = -\frac{\Delta_r H^\circ}{\left(8.314 \dfrac{\text{J}}{\text{mol·K}}\right)}\left(\frac{1}{1200. \text{ K}} - \frac{1}{1300. \text{ K}}\right)$$

$$2.0016628 = \Delta_r H^\circ \, (7.710195 \times 10^{-6}) \text{mol/J}$$

$$\Delta_r H^\circ = 2.0016628/(7.710195 \times 10^{-6} \text{ mol/J}) = 2.5961247 \times 10^5 \text{ J/mol} = \mathbf{2.60 \times 10^5 \text{ J/mol}}$$

(The subtraction of the $1/T$ terms limits the answer to three significant figures.)

15.99 Plan: Add the two reactions to obtain the overall reaction. Multiply the second equation by 2 to cancel the amount (mol) of CO produced in the first reaction. K for the second reaction is then $(K)^2$. K for the overall reaction is equal to the product of the K values for the two individual reactions. Calculate K_c using $K = K_c(RT)^{\Delta n}$.
Solution:

a)

$$2CH_4(g) + O_2(g) \rightleftharpoons \cancel{2CO}(g) + 4H_2(g) \qquad K = 9.34\text{x}10^{28}$$

$$\cancel{2CO}(g) + 2H_2O(g) \rightleftharpoons 2CO_2(g) + 2H_2(g) \qquad K = (1.374)^2 = 1.888$$

$$\mathbf{2CH_4(g) + O_2(g) + 2H_2O(g) \rightleftharpoons 2CO_2(g) + 6H_2(g)}$$

b) $K = (9.34\text{x}10^{28})(1.888) = 1.76339\text{x}10^{29} = \mathbf{1.76\text{x}10^{29}}$

c) Δn = amount (mol) of gaseous products – amount (mol) of gaseous reactants = 8 – 5 = 3
(8 moles of product gas – 5 moles of reactant gas)

$$K = K_c(RT)^{\Delta n}$$

$$K_c = \frac{K}{(RT)^{\Delta n}} = \frac{1.76339\text{x}10^{29}}{[(0.08314 \text{ bar•L/mol•K})(1000)]^3} = 3.01713\text{x}10^{23} = \mathbf{3.02\text{x}10^{23}}$$

d) The initial total pressure is given as 30. bar. To find the final pressure use the relationship between pressure and amount (mol) of gas: $n_{initial}/P_{initial} = n_{final}/P_{final}$
Total amount (mol) of gas initial = 2.0 mol CH_4 + 1.0 mol O_2 + 2.0 mol H_2O = 5.0 mol
Total amount (mol) of gas final = 2.0 mol CO_2 + 6.0 mol H_2 = 8.0 mol   (from mole ratios)

$$P_{final} = (30. \text{ bar reactants})\left(\frac{8 \text{ mol products}}{5 \text{ mol reactants}}\right) = \mathbf{48 \text{ bar}}$$

15.100 Plan: Write an equilibrium expression. Use the balanced equation to define x and set up a reaction table, substitute into the equilibrium expression, and solve for x, from which the pressure of N or H is calculated. Convert log K to K. Convert pressures to amount (mol) using the ideal gas law, $pV = nRT$. Convert amount (mol) to atoms using Avogadro's number.
Solution:
a) The initial pressure of N_2 is 200. bar.   log K = –43.10; $K = 10^{-43.10} = 7.94328\text{x}10^{-44}$

Pressure (bar)	$N_2(g)$	$\rightleftharpoons$	$2N(g)$
Initial	200.		0
Change	–x		+2x
Equilibrium	200 – x		2x

$$K = \frac{(p_N)^2}{(p_{N_2})} = 7.94328\text{x}10^{-44}$$

$$\frac{(2x)^2}{(200. - x)} = 7.94328\text{x}10^{-44} \qquad \text{Assume } 200. - x \cong 200.$$

$$\frac{(2x)^2}{(200)} = 7.94328\text{x}10^{-44}$$

$$4x^2 = 1.588656\text{x}10^{-41}$$
$$x = 1.992897\text{x}10^{-21}$$
$$p_N = 2x = 2(1.992897\text{x}10^{-21}) = 3.985795\text{x}10^{-21} = \mathbf{4.0\text{x}10^{-21} \text{ bar}}$$

b) Log K = –17.30; $K = 10^{-17.30} = 5.01187\text{x}10^{-18}$

Pressure (bar)	$H_2(g)$	$\rightleftharpoons$	$2H(g)$
Initial	600.		0
Change	–x		+2x
Equilibrium	600 – x		2x

$$K = \frac{(p_H)^2}{(p_{H_2})} = 5.01187\text{x}10^{-18}$$

$$\frac{(2x)^2}{(600. - x)} = 5.01187 \times 10^{-18} \qquad \text{Assume } 600. - x \cong 600.$$

$$\frac{(2x)^2}{(600)} = 5.01187 \times 10^{-18}$$

$$4x^2 = 3.007122 \times 10^{-15}$$

$$x = 2.741862 \times 10^{-8}$$

$$p_H = 2x = 2(2.741862 \times 10^{-8}) = 5.48372 \times 10^{-8} = \mathbf{5.5 \times 10^{-8} \ bar}$$

c) $pV = nRT$

$$\text{Moles of N atoms} = \frac{pV}{RT} = \frac{(3.985795 \times 10^{-21} \, \text{bar})(1.00 \, \text{L})}{\left(0.08314 \dfrac{\text{L} \cdot \text{bar}}{\text{mol} \cdot \text{K}}\right)(1000.\, \text{K})} = 4.794076 \times 10^{-23} \ \text{mol}$$

$$\text{Number of N atoms} = (4.794076 \times 10^{-23} \ \text{mol N atoms})\left(\frac{6.022 \times 10^{23} \ \text{N atoms}}{1 \ \text{mol N atoms}}\right) = 28.8699 \ \text{atoms/L} = \mathbf{29 \ N}$$

atoms/L

$$\text{Moles of H atoms} = \frac{pV}{RT} = \frac{(5.48372 \times 10^{-8} \, \text{bar})(1.00 \, \text{L})}{\left(0.08314 \dfrac{\text{L} \cdot \text{bar}}{\text{mol} \cdot \text{K}}\right)(1000.\, \text{K})} = 6.595766 \times 10^{-10} \ \text{mol}$$

$$\text{Number of H atoms} = (6.595766 \times 10^{-10} \ \text{mol H atoms})\left(\frac{6.022 \times 10^{23} \ \text{H atoms}}{1 \ \text{mol H atoms}}\right)$$

$$= 3.97197 \times 10^{14} = \mathbf{4.0 \times 10^{14} \ H \ atoms/L}$$

d) The more reasonable step is $\mathbf{N_2(g) + H(g) \rightarrow NH(g) + N(g)}$. With only twenty-nine N atoms in 1.0 L, the first reaction would produce virtually no NH(g) molecules. There are orders of magnitude more N_2 molecules than N atoms, so the second reaction is the more reasonable step.

15.103   Plan: Write an equilibrium expression. Use the balanced equation to define x and set up a reaction table, substitute into the equilibrium expression, and solve for x, from which the equilibrium pressures of the gases are calculated. Add the equilibrium pressures of the three gases to obtain the total pressure. Use the relationship $K = K_c(RT)^{\Delta n}$ to find K_c.
Solution:

a)

Pressure (bar)	$N_2(g)$	+	$O_2(g)$	$\rightleftharpoons$	$2NO(g)$
Initial	0.780		0.210		0
Change	$-x$		$-x$		$+2x$
Equilibrium	$0.780 - x$		$0.210 - x$		$2x$

$$K = \frac{(p_{NO})^2}{(p_{N_2})(p_{O_2})} = 4.35 \times 10^{-31}$$

$$\frac{(2x)^2}{(0.780 - x)(0.210 - x)} = 4.35 \times 10^{-31} \ \text{Assume x is small because } K \text{ is small.}$$

$$\frac{(2x)^2}{(0.780)(0.210)} = 4.35 \times 10^{-31}$$

$$x = 1.33466 \times 10^{-16}$$

Based on the small amount of nitrogen monoxide formed, the assumption that the partial pressures of nitrogen and oxygen change to an insignificant degree holds.

$p_{nitrogen}$ (equilibrium) = $(0.780 - 1.33466 \times 10^{-16})$ bar = **0.780 bar N_2**

p_{oxygen} (equilibrium) = $(0.210 - 1.33466 \times 10^{-16})$ bar = **0.210 bar O_2** (assumption justified)

p_{NO} (equilibrium) = $2(1.33466 \times 10^{-16})$ bar = 2.66933×10^{-16} = **2.67×10⁻¹⁶ bar NO**

b) The total pressure is the sum of the three partial pressures:

$$0.780 \text{ bar} + 0.210 \text{ bar} + 2.67 \times 10^{-16} \text{ bar} = \textbf{0.990 bar}$$

c) $K = K_c(RT)^{\Delta n}$

Δn = amount (mol) of gaseous products – amount (mol) of gaseous reactants = $2 - 2 = 0$

(two moles of product NO and two moles of reactants N_2 and O_2)

$K = K_c(RT)^0$

$K_c = K = \textbf{4.35} \times \textbf{10}^{-\textbf{31}}$ because there is no net increase or decrease in the amount (mol) of gas in the course of the reaction.

15.105 Plan: Use the equation $K = K_c(RT)^{\Delta n}$ to find K. The value of K_c for the formation of HI is the reciprocal of the K_c value for the decomposition of HI. Use the equation $\Delta_r H° = \sum[\Delta_{f(products)} H°] - \sum[\Delta_{f(reactants)} H°]$ to find the value of $\Delta_r H°$. Use the van't Hoff equation as a second method of calculating $\Delta_r H°$.

Solution:

a) $K = K_c(RT)^{\Delta n}$

Δn = amount (mol) of gaseous products – amount (mol) of gaseous reactants = $2 - 2 = 0$

(2 mol product ($1H_2 + 1I_2$) – 2 mol reactant (HI) = 0)

$K = K_c(RT)^0 = 1.26 \times 10^{-3}(RT)^0 = \textbf{1.26} \times \textbf{10}^{-\textbf{3}}$

b) The equilibrium constant for the reverse reaction is the reciprocal of the equilibrium constant for the forward reaction:

$$K_{formation} = \frac{1}{K_{decomposition}} = \frac{1}{1.26 \times 10^{-3}} = 793.65 = \textbf{794}$$

c) $\Delta_r H° = \sum[\Delta_{f(products)} H°] - \sum[\Delta_{f(reactants)} H°]$

$\Delta_r H° = \{1\,\Delta_f H° \,[H_2(g)] + 1\,\Delta_f H° \,[I_2(g)]\} - \{2\,\Delta_f H° \,[HI(g)]\}$

$\Delta_r H° = [(0 \text{ kJ/mol}) + (62.442 \text{ kJ/mol})] - [(2)(25.9 \text{ kJ/mol})]$

$\Delta_r H° = \textbf{10.6 kJ/mol}$

d) $\ln \dfrac{K_2}{K_1} = -\dfrac{\Delta_r H°}{R}\left(\dfrac{1}{T_2} - \dfrac{1}{T_1}\right)$

$K_1 = 1.26 \times 10^{-3}$; $K_2 = 2.0 \times 10^{-2}$, $T_1 = 298$ K; $T_2 = 729$ K

$\ln \dfrac{2.0 \times 10^{-2}}{1.26 \times 10^{-3}} = -\dfrac{\Delta_r H°}{8.314 \text{ J/mol·K}}\left(\dfrac{1}{729 \text{ K}} - \dfrac{1}{298 \text{ K}}\right)$

$2.764621 = (2.38629 \times 10^{-4} \text{ mol/J})\,\Delta_r H°$

$\Delta_r H° = 1.1585 \times 10^4 \text{ J/mol} = \textbf{1.2} \times \textbf{10}^{\textbf{4}} \text{ J/mol}$

15.109 Plan: Use the balanced equation to write an equilibrium expression. Find the initial concentration of each reactant from the given amounts and container volume, use the balanced equation to define x, and set up a reaction table. The equilibrium concentration of CO is known, so x can be calculated and used to find the other equilibrium concentrations. Substitute the equilibrium concentrations into the equilibrium expression to find K_c. Add the molarities of all of the gases at equilibrium, use $(c)(V)$ to find the total amount (mol), and then use $pV = nRT$ to find the total pressure. To find $[CO]_{eq}$ after the pressure is doubled, set up another reaction table in which the initial concentrations are equal to the final concentrations from part a) and add in the additional CO.

Solution:

The reaction is: $CO(g) + H_2O(g) \rightleftharpoons CO_2(g) + H_2(g)$

a) Initial [CO] and initial [H$_2$O] = 0.100 mol/20.00 L = 0.00500 mol/L.

concentrations	CO	H$_2$O	$\rightleftharpoons$	CO$_2$	H$_2$
Initial	0.00500 mol/L	0.00500 mol/L		0	0
Change	−x	−x		+x	+x
Equilibrium	0.00500 − x	0.00500 − x		x	x

15-18

$[CO]_{equilibrium} = 0.00500 - x = 2.24 \times 10^{-3}$ mol/L $= [H_2O]$ (given in problem)

$\qquad$ x = 0.00276 mol/L $= [CO_2] = [H_2]$

$$K_c = \frac{[CO_2][H_2]}{[CO][H_2O]} = \frac{(0.00276)(0.00276)}{(0.00224)(0.00224)} = 1.518176 = \mathbf{1.52}$$

b) $c_{total} = [CO] + [H_2O] + [CO_2] + [H_2] = (0.00224 \text{ mol/L}) + (0.00224 \text{ mol/L}) + (0.00276 \text{ mol/L}) + (0.00276$ mol/L)

$\qquad$ = 0.01000 mol/L

$n_{total} = (c_{total})(V) = (0.01000 \text{ mol/L})(20.00 \text{ L}) = 0.2000$ mol total

$pV = nRT$

$$p_{total} = n_{total}RT/V = \frac{(0.2000\,\text{mol})\left(0.08314\dfrac{\text{L}\cdot\text{bar}}{\text{mol}\cdot\text{K}}\right)\big((273+900.)\text{K}\big)}{(20.00\ \text{L})} = 0.9752322 \text{ bar} = \mathbf{0.975\ bar}$$

c) Initially, an equal amount (mol) must be added = **0.2000 mol CO**

d) Set up a table with the initial concentrations equal to the final concentrations from part a), and then add 0.2000 mol CO/20.00 L = 0.01000 mol/L to compensate for the added CO.

	CO	H_2O	CO_2	H_2
Initial	0.00224 mol/L	0.00224 mol/L	0.00276 mol/L	0.00276 mol/L
Added CO	0.01000 mol/L			
Change	−x	−x	+x	+x
Equilibrium	0.01224 − x	0.00224 − x	0.00276 + x	0.00276 + x

$$K_c = \frac{[CO_2][H_2]}{[CO][H_2O]} = \frac{(0.00276 + x)(0.00276 + x)}{(0.00224 - x)(0.00224 - x)} = 1.518176$$

$$\frac{7.6176 \times 10^{-6} + 5.52 \times 10^{-3}\,x + x^2}{2.74176 \times 10^{-5} - 1.448 \times 10^{-2}\,x + x^2} = 1.518176$$

$7.6176 \times 10^{-6} + 5.52 \times 10^{-3}x + x^2 = (1.518176)(2.74176 \times 10^{-5} - 1.448 \times 10^{-2}x + x^2)$

$7.6176 \times 10^{-6} + 5.52 \times 10^{-3}x + x^2 = 4.162474 \times 10^{-5} - 0.021983x + 1.518176x^2$

$0.518176x^2 - 0.027503x + 3.400714 \times 10^{-5} = 0$

$a = 0.518176 \qquad b = -0.027503 \qquad c = 3.400714 \times 10^{-5}$

$$x = \frac{-b \pm \sqrt{b^2 - 4ac}}{2a}$$

$$x = \frac{-(-0.027503) \pm \sqrt{(-0.027503)^2 - 4(0.518176)(3.400714 \times 10^{-5})}}{2(0.518176)}$$

$x = 1.31277 \times 10^{-3}$

$[CO] = 0.01224 - x = 0.01224 - (1.31277 \times 10^{-3}) = 0.01092723 = \mathbf{0.01093\ mol/L}$

CHAPTER 16 ACID-BASE EQUILIBRIA

END–OF–CHAPTER PROBLEMS

16.2   (a) All Arrhenius acids contain hydrogen and produce hydronium ion (H_3O^+) in aqueous solution. All Arrhenius bases contain an OH group and produce hydroxide ion (OH^-) in aqueous solution.
(b) Neutralization occurs when each H_3O^+ molecule combines with an OH^- molecule to form two molecules of H_2O. Chemists found that the Δ_rH was independent of the combination of strong acid with strong base. In other words, the reaction of any strong base with any strong acid always produced 56 kJ/mol ($\Delta H = -56$ kJ/mol). This was consistent with Arrhenius's hypothesis describing neutralization, because all other counter ions (those present from the dissociation of the strong acid and base) were spectators and did not participate in the overall reaction.

16.4   (a) The Brønsted-Lowry theory defines acids as proton donors and bases as proton acceptors, while the Arrhenius definition looks at acids as containing ionizable H atoms and at bases as containing hydroxide ions. In both definitions, an acid produces hydronium ions and a base produces hydroxide ions when added to water.
(b) Ammonia, NH_3, and carbonate ion, CO_3^{2-}, are two Brønsted-Lowry bases that are not Arrhenius bases because they do not contain hydroxide ions. Brønsted-Lowry acids must contain an ionizable H atom in order to be proton donors, so a Brønsted-Lowry acid that is not an Arrhenius acid cannot be identified. (Other examples are also acceptable.)

16.7   An amphoteric substance can act as either an acid or a base. In the presence of a strong base (OH^-), the dihydrogen phosphate ion acts like an acid by donating hydrogen:
$H_2PO_4^-(aq) + OH^-(aq) \rightarrow H_2O(aq) + HPO_4^{2-}(aq)$
In the presence of a strong acid (HCl), the dihydrogen phosphate ion acts like a base by accepting hydrogen:
$H_2PO_4^-(aq) + HCl(aq) \rightarrow H_3PO_4(aq) + Cl^-(aq)$

16.8   (a) Strong acids and bases dissociate completely into their ions when dissolved in water. Weak acids and bases only partially dissociate.
(b) The characteristic property of all weak acids and bases is that a significant number of the molecules are not dissociated. For a strong acid, the concentration of hydronium ions produced by dissolving the acid is equal to the initial concentration of the undissociated acid. For a weak acid, the concentration of hydronium ions produced when the acid dissolves is less than the initial concentration of the acid. The same is true for bases. A strong base dissociates to produce the same concentration of OH^- ion as that of the strong base. The concentration of OH^- that results from dissociation of a weak base is much less than the concentration of the original base.

16.9   Plan: Recall that an Arrhenius acid contains hydrogen and produces hydrogen ion (H^+) (hydronium ion, H_3O^+) in aqueous solution.
Solution:
a) Water, H_2O, is an **Arrhenius acid** because it produces H_3O^+ ion in aqueous solution. Water is also an Arrhenius base because it produces the OH^- ion as well.
b) Calcium hydroxide, $Ca(OH)_2$ is a base, not an acid.
c) Phosphorous acid, H_3PO_3, is a weak **Arrhenius acid**. It is weak because the number of O atoms equals the number of ionizable H atoms.
d) Hydroiodic acid, HI, is a strong **Arrhenius acid**.

16.11   Plan: All Arrhenius bases contain an OH group and produce hydroxide ion (OH^-) in aqueous solution.
Solution:
Barium hydroxide, $Ba(OH)_2$, and potassium hydroxide, KOH, (**b and d**) are Arrhenius bases because they contain hydroxide ions and form OH^- when dissolved in water. H_3AsO_4 and HClO, (a) and (c), are Arrhenius acids, not bases.

16.13   Plan: K_a is the equilibrium constant for an acid dissociation which has the generic equation

$HA(aq) + H_2O(l) \rightleftharpoons H_3O^+(aq) + A^-(aq)$. The K_a expression is $\dfrac{\left[H_3O^+\right]\left[A^-\right]}{\left[HA\right]}$. $H_2O(l)$ has an activity of 1 and

thus does not appear in the expression. Write the acid-dissociation reaction for each acid, following the generic equation, and then write the K_a expression.
Solution:
a) $HCN(aq) + H_2O(l) \rightleftharpoons H_3O^+(aq) + CN^-(aq)$

$$K_a = \dfrac{\left[H_3O^+\right]\left[CN^-\right]}{\left[HCN\right]}$$

b) $HCO_3^-(aq) + H_2O(l) \rightleftharpoons H_3O^+(aq) + CO_3^{2-}(aq)$

$$K_a = \dfrac{\left[H_3O^+\right]\left[CO_3^{2-}\right]}{\left[HCO_3^-\right]}$$

c) $HCOOH(aq) + H_2O(l) \rightleftharpoons H_3O^+(aq) + HCOO^-(aq)$

$$K_a = \dfrac{\left[H_3O^+\right]\left[HCOO^-\right]}{\left[HCOOH\right]}$$

16.15   Plan: K_a is the equilibrium constant for an acid dissociation which has the generic equation

$HA(aq) + H_2O(l) \rightleftharpoons H_3O^+(aq) + A^-(aq)$. The K_a expression is $\dfrac{\left[H_3O^+\right]\left[A^-\right]}{\left[HA\right]}$. $H_2O(l)$ has an activity of 1 and

thus does not appear in the expression. Write the acid-dissociation reaction for each acid, following the generic equation, and then write the K_a expression.
Solution:
a) $HNO_2(aq) + H_2O(l) \rightleftharpoons H_3O^+(aq) + NO_2^-(aq)$

$$K_a = \dfrac{\left[H_3O^+\right]\left[NO_2^-\right]}{\left[HNO_2\right]}$$

b) $CH_3COOH(aq) + H_2O(l) \rightleftharpoons H_3O^+(aq) + CH_3COO^-(aq)$

$$K_a = \dfrac{\left[H_3O^+\right]\left[CH_3COO^-\right]}{\left[CH_3COOH\right]}$$

c) $HBrO_2(aq) + H_2O(l) \rightleftharpoons H_3O^+(aq) + BrO_2^-(aq)$

$$K_a = \dfrac{\left[H_3O^+\right]\left[BrO_2^-\right]}{\left[HBrO_2\right]}$$

16.17   Plan: K_a is the equilibrium constant for an acid dissociation which has the generic equation

$HA(aq) + H_2O(l) \rightleftharpoons H_3O^+(aq) + A^-(aq)$. The K_a expression is $\dfrac{\left[H_3O^+\right]\left[A^-\right]}{\left[HA\right]}$. $H_2O(l)$ has an activity of 1 and

thus does not appear in the expression. Write the acid-dissociation reaction for each acid, following the generic equation, and then write the K_a expression.
Solution:
a) When phosphoric acid is dissolved in water, a proton is donated to the water and dihydrogen phosphate ions are generated.

$H_3PO_4(aq) + H_2O(l) \rightleftharpoons H_2PO_4^-(aq) + H_3O^+(aq)$

$$K_a = \frac{\left[H_3O^+\right]\left[H_2PO_4^-\right]}{\left[H_3PO_4\right]}$$

b) Benzoic acid is an organic acid and has only one proton to donate from the carboxylic acid group. The H atoms bonded to the benzene ring are not acidic hydrogens.

$$C_6H_5COOH(aq) + H_2O(l) \rightleftharpoons C_6H_5COO^-(aq) + H_3O^+(aq)$$

$$K_a = \frac{\left[H_3O^+\right]\left[C_6H_5COO^-\right]}{\left[C_6H_5COOH\right]}$$

c) Hydrogen sulfate ion donates a proton to water and forms the sulfate ion.

$$HSO_4^-(aq) + H_2O(l) \rightleftharpoons SO_4^{2-}(aq) + H_3O^+(aq)$$

$$K_a = \frac{\left[H_3O^+\right]\left[SO_4^{2-}\right]}{\left[HSO_4^-\right]}$$

16.19   Plan: To derive the conjugate base, remove one H from the acid and decrease the charge by 1 (acids donate H^+).
Since each formula in this problem is neutral, the conjugate base will have a charge of -1.
Solution:
a) Cl^- b) HCO_3^- c) OH^-

16.21   Plan: To derive the conjugate acid, add an H and increase the charge by 1 (bases accept H^+).
Solution:
a) NH_4^+ b) NH_3 c) $C_{10}H_{14}N_2H^+$

16.23   Plan: The acid donates the proton to form its conjugate base; the base accepts a proton to form its conjugate acid.
Solution:
a) HCl + H_2O $\rightleftharpoons$ Cl^- + H_3O^+
   acid   base   conjugate base   conjugate acid
      Conjugate acid-base pairs: HCl/Cl^- and H_3O^+/H_2O
b) $HClO_4$ + H_2SO_4 $\rightleftharpoons$ ClO_4^- + $H_3SO_4^+$
   acid   base   conjugate base   conjugate acid
      Conjugate acid-base pairs: $HClO_4/ClO_4^-$ and $H_3SO_4^+/H_2SO_4$
Note: Perchloric acid is able to protonate another strong acid, H_2SO_4, because perchloric acid is a stronger acid. ($HClO_4$'s oxygen atoms exceed its hydrogen atoms by one more than H_2SO_4.)
c) HPO_4^{2-} + H_2SO_4 $\rightleftharpoons$ $H_2PO_4^-$ + HSO_4^-
   base   acid   conjugate acid   conjugate base
      Conjugate acid-base pairs: H_2SO_4/HSO_4^- and $H_2PO_4^-/HPO_4^{2-}$

16.25   Plan: The acid donates the proton to form its conjugate base; the base accepts a proton to form its conjugate acid.
Solution:
a) NH_3 + H_3PO_4 $\rightleftharpoons$ NH_4^+ + $H_2PO_4^-$
   base   acid   conjugate acid   conjugate base
      Conjugate acid-base pairs: $H_3PO_4/H_2PO_4^-$; NH_4^+/NH_3
b) CH_3O^- + NH_3 $\rightleftharpoons$ CH_3OH + NH_2^-
   base   acid   conjugate acid   conjugate base
      Conjugate acid-base pairs: NH_3/NH_2^-; CH_3OH/CH_3O^-
c) HPO_4^{2-} + HSO_4^- $\rightleftharpoons$ $H_2PO_4^-$ + SO_4^{2-}
   base   acid   conjugate acid   conjugate base
      Conjugate acid-base pairs: HSO_4^-/SO_4^{2-}; $H_2PO_4^-/HPO_4^{2-}$

16.27   <u>Plan:</u> Write total ionic equations (show all soluble ionic substances as dissociated into ions) and then remove the spectator ions to write the net ionic equations. The (aq) subscript denotes that each species is soluble and dissociates in water. The acid donates the proton to form its conjugate base; the base accepts a proton to form its conjugate acid.
<u>Solution:</u>
a) ~~$Na^+(aq)$~~ $+ OH^-(aq) +$ ~~$Na^+(aq)$~~ $+ H_2PO_4^-(aq) \rightleftharpoons H_2O(l) +$ ~~$2Na^+(aq)$~~ $+ HPO_4^{2-}(aq)$

       Net: $OH^-(aq) + H_2PO_4^-(aq) \rightleftharpoons H_2O(l) + HPO_4^{2-}(aq)$

          base   acid   conjugate acid   conjugate base
         Conjugate acid-base pairs: $H_2PO_4^-/HPO_4^{2-}$ and H_2O/OH^-
b) ~~$K^+(aq)$~~ $+ HSO_4^-(aq) +$ ~~$2K^+(aq)$~~ $+ CO_3^{2-}(aq) \rightleftharpoons$ ~~$2K^+(aq)$~~ $+ SO_4^{2-}(aq) +$ ~~$K^+(aq)$~~ $+ HCO_3^-(aq)$

       Net: $HSO_4^-(aq) + CO_3^{2-}(aq) \rightleftharpoons SO_4^{2-}(aq) + HCO_3^-(aq)$

          acid   base   conjugate base   conjugate acid
         Conjugate acid-base pairs: HSO_4^-/SO_4^{2-} and HCO_3^-/CO_3^{2-}

16.29   <u>Plan:</u> The two possible reactions involve reacting the acid from one conjugate pair with the base from the other conjugate pair. The reaction that favors the products ($K > 1$) is the one in which the stronger acid produces the weaker acid. The reaction that favors reactants ($K < 1$) is the reaction is which the weaker acid produces the stronger acid.
<u>Solution:</u>
The conjugate pairs are H_2S (acid)/HS^- (base) and HCl (acid)/Cl^- (base). Two reactions are possible:
       (1) $HS^- + HCl \rightleftharpoons H_2S + Cl^-$ and   (2) $H_2S + Cl^- \rightleftharpoons HS^- + HCl$

The first reaction is the reverse of the second. HCl is a strong acid and H_2S a weak acid. Reaction (1) with the stronger acid producing the weaker acid favors products and $K > 1$. Reaction (2) with the weaker acid forming the stronger acid favors the reactants and $K < 1$.

16.31   <u>Plan:</u> An acid-base reaction that favors the products ($K > 1$) is one in which the stronger acid produces the weaker acid. Use the figure to decide which of the two acids is the stronger acid.
<u>Solution:</u>
a) HCl + NH_3 $\rightleftharpoons$ NH_4^+ + Cl^-

strong acid   stronger base   weak acid   weaker base
         HCl is ranked above NH_4^+ in the list of conjugate acid-base pair strength and is the stronger acid. NH_3 is ranked above Cl^- and is the stronger base. NH_3 is shown as a "stronger" base because it is stronger than Cl^-, but is not considered a "strong" base. The reaction proceeds toward the production of the weaker acid and base, i.e., the reaction as written proceeds to the right and **$K > 1$**. The stronger acid is more likely to donate a proton than the weaker acid.
b) H_2SO_3 + NH_3 $\rightleftharpoons$ HSO_3^- + NH_4^+

stronger acid   stronger base   weaker base   weaker acid
         H_2SO_3 is ranked above NH_4^+ and is the stronger acid. NH_3 is a stronger base than HSO_3^-. The reaction proceeds toward the production of the weaker acid and base, i.e., the reaction as written proceeds to the right and **$K > 1$**.

16.33   <u>Plan:</u> An acid-base reaction that favors the reactants ($K < 1$) is one in which the weaker acid produces the stronger acid. Use the figure to decide which of the two acids is the weaker acid.
<u>Solution:</u>
a) NH_4^+ + HPO_4^{2-} $\rightleftharpoons$ NH_3 + $H_2PO_4^-$

weaker acid   weaker base   stronger base   stronger acid
         $K < 1$ The reaction proceeds toward the production of the weaker acid and base, i.e., the reaction as written proceeds to the left.

b) $HSO_3^- + HS^- \rightleftharpoons H_2SO_3 + S^{2-}$
weaker base   weaker acid   stronger acid   stronger base

$K < 1$ The reaction proceeds toward the production of the weaker acid and base, i.e., the reaction as written proceeds to the left.

16.35   Plan: K_a values are listed in the Appendix. The larger the K_a value, the stronger the acid. The K_a value for hydroiodic acid, HI, is not shown because K_a approaches infinity for strong acids and is not meaningful.
Solution:
HI is the strongest acid (it is one of the six strong acids), and acetic acid, CH_3COOH, is the weakest:
$CH_3COOH < HF < HIO_3 < HI$

16.37   Plan: Strong acids are the hydrohalic acids HCl, HBr, HI, and oxoacids in which the number of O atoms exceeds the number of ionizable protons by two or more; these include HNO_3, H_2SO_4, and $HClO_4$. All other acids are weak acids. Strong bases are metal hydroxides (or oxides) in which the metal is a Group 1 metal or Ca, Sr, or Ba in Group 2. Weak bases are NH_3 and amines.
Solution:
a) Arsenic acid, H_3AsO_4, is a **weak acid**. The number of O atoms is four, which exceeds the number of ionizable H atoms, three, by one. This identifies H_3AsO_4 as a weak acid.
b) Strontium hydroxide, $Sr(OH)_2$, is a **strong base**. Soluble compounds containing OH^- ions are strong bases. Sr is a Group 2 metal.
c) HIO is a **weak acid**. The number of O atoms is one, which is equal to the number of ionizable H atoms identifying HIO as a weak acid.
d) Perchloric acid, $HClO_4$, is a **strong acid**. $HClO_4$ is one example of the type of strong acid in which the number of O atoms exceeds the number of ionizable H atoms by more than two.

16.39   Plan: Strong acids are the hydrohalic acids HCl, HBr, HI, and oxoacids in which the number of O atoms exceeds the number of ionizable protons by two or more; these include HNO_3, H_2SO_4, and $HClO_4$. All other acids are weak acids. Strong bases are metal hydroxides (or oxides) in which the metal is a Group 1 metal or Ca, Sr, or Ba in Group 2. Weak bases are NH_3 and amines.
Solution:
a) Rubidium hydroxide, RbOH, is a **strong base** because Rb is a Group 1 metal.
b) Hydrobromic acid, HBr, is a **strong acid**, because it is one of the listed hydrohalic acids.
c) Hydrogen telluride, H_2Te, is a **weak acid**, because H is not bonded to an oxygen or halide.
d) Hypochlorous acid, HClO, is a **weak acid**. The number of O atoms is one, which is equal to the number of ionizable H atoms identifying HClO as a weak acid.

16.44   Plan: The lower the concentration of hydrogen (H^+) ions, the higher the pH. pH increases as K_a or the concentration (mol/L) of acid decreases. Recall that $pK_a = -\log K_a$.
Solution:
a) At equal concentrations, the acid with the larger K_a will ionize to produce more hydronium ions than the acid with the smaller K_a. The solution of an **acid with the smaller $K_a = 4\times10^{-5}$** has a lower $[H_3O^+]$ and higher pH.
b) pK_a is equal to $-\log K_a$. The smaller the K_a, the larger the pK_a is. So the **acid with the larger pK_a**, 3.5, has a lower $[H^+]$ and higher pH.
c) **Lower concentration** of the same acid means lower concentration of hydrogen ions produced. The 0.01 mol/L solution has a lower $[H^+]$ and higher pH.
d) At the same concentration, strong acids dissociate to produce more hydrogen ions than weak acids. The 0.1 mol/l solution of a **weak acid** has a lower $[H^+]$ and higher pH.
e) Bases produce OH^- ions in solution, so the concentration of hydrogen ion for a solution of a base solution is lower than that for a solution of an acid. The 0.01 mol/L **base solution** has the higher pH.
f) pOH equals $-\log [OH^-]$. At 25°C, the equilibrium constant for water ionization, K_w, equals 1×10^{-14} so 14 = pH + pOH. As pOH decreases, pH increases. The solution of **pOH = 6.0** has the higher pH.

16.45   <u>Plan:</u> Part a) can be approached two ways. Because NaOH is a strong base, the $[OH^-]_{eq} = [NaOH]_{init}$. One method involves calculating $[H^+]$ using $K_w = [H^+][OH^-]$, then calculating pH from the relationship $pH = -\log [H^+]$. The other method involves calculating pOH and then using $pH + pOH = 14.00$ to calculate pH. Part b) also has two acceptable methods analogous to those in part a); only one method will be shown.
<u>Solution:</u>
a) First method:
$K_w = [H^+][OH^-]$

$[H^+] = \dfrac{K_w}{[OH^-]} = \dfrac{1.0 \times 10^{-14}}{0.0111} = 9.0090 \times 10^{-13}$ mol/L

$pH = -\log [H^+] = -\log (9.0090 \times 10^{-13}) = 12.04532 = \mathbf{12.05}$
Second method:
$pOH = -\log [OH^-] = -\log (0.0111) = 1.954677$
$pH = 14.00 - pOH = 14.00 - 1.954677 = 12.04532 = \mathbf{12.05}$
With a pH > 7, the solution is **basic**.
b) For a strong acid such as HCl:
$[H^+] = [HCl] = 1.35 \times 10^{-3}$ mol/L
$pH = -\log (1.35 \times 10^{-3}) = 2.869666$
$pOH = 14.00 - 2.869666 = 11.130334 = \mathbf{11.13}$ With a pH < 7, the solution is **acidic**.

16.47   <u>Plan:</u> HI is a strong acid, so $[H^+] = [HI]$ and the pH can be calculated from the relationship $pH = -\log [H_3O^+]$. $Ba(OH)_2$ is a strong base, so $[OH^-] = 2 \times [Ba(OH)_2]$ and $pOH = -\log [OH^-]$.
<u>Solution:</u>
a) $[H^+] = [HI] = 6.14 \times 10^{-3}$ mol/L.
          $pH = -\log (6.14 \times 10^{-3}) = 2.211832 = \mathbf{2.212.}$ Solution is **acidic**.

b) $[OH^-] = 2 \times [Ba(OH)_2] = 2(2.55 \; M) = 5.10$ mol/L
          $pOH = -\log (5.10) = -0.70757 = \mathbf{-0.708.}$ Solution is **basic**.

16.49   <u>Plan:</u> The relationships are: $pH = -\log [H^+]$ and $[H^+] = 10^{-pH}$; $pOH = -\log [OH^-]$ and $[OH^-] = 10^{-pOH}$; and $14 = pH + pOH$.
<u>Solution:</u>
a) $[H^+] = 10^{-pH} = 10^{-9.85} = 1.4125375 \times 10^{-10} = \mathbf{1.4 \times 10^{-10}}$ **mol/L** $\mathbf{H^+}$
          $pOH = 14.00 - pH = 14.00 - 9.85 = \mathbf{4.15}$
          $[OH^-] = 10^{-pOH} = 10^{-4.15} = 7.0794578 \times 10^{-5} = \mathbf{7.1 \times 10^{-5}}$ **mol/L** $\mathbf{OH^-}$
b) $pH = 14.00 - pOH = 14.00 - 9.43 = \mathbf{4.57}$
          $[H^+] = 10^{-pH} = 10^{-4.57} = 2.691535 \times 10^{-5} = \mathbf{2.7 \times 10^{-5}}$ **mol/L** $\mathbf{H^+}$
          $[OH^-] = 10^{-pOH} = 10^{-9.43} = 3.7153523 \times 10^{-10} = \mathbf{3.7 \times 10^{-10}}$ **mol/L** $\mathbf{OH^-}$

16.51   <u>Plan:</u> The relationships are: $pH = -\log [H^+]$ and $[H^+] = 10^{-pH}$; $pOH = -\log [OH^-]$ and $[OH^-] = 10^{-pOH}$; and $14 = pH + pOH$.
<u>Solution:</u>
a) $[H^+] = 10^{-pH} = 10^{-4.77} = 1.69824 \times 10^{-5} = \mathbf{1.7 \times 10^{-5}}$ **mol/L** $\mathbf{H^+}$
          $pOH = 14.00 - pH = 14.00 - 4.77 = \mathbf{9.23}$
          $[OH^-] = 10^{-pOH} = 10^{-9.23} = 5.8884 \times 10^{-10} = \mathbf{5.9 \times 10^{-10}}$ **mol/L** $\mathbf{OH^-}$
b) $pH = 14.00 - pOH = 14.00 - 5.65 = \mathbf{8.35}$
          $[H^+] = 10^{-pH} = 10^{-8.35} = 4.46684 \times 10^{-9} = \mathbf{4.5 \times 10^{-9}}$ **mol/L** $\mathbf{H_3O^+}$
          $[OH^-] = 10^{-pOH} = 10^{-5.65} = 2.23872 \times 10^{-6} = \mathbf{2.2 \times 10^{-6}}$ **mol/L** $\mathbf{OH^-}$

16.53   <u>Plan:</u> The pH is increasing, so the solution is becoming more basic. Therefore, OH^- ion is added to increase the pH. Since one mole of H_3O^+ will react with one mole of OH^-, the difference in $[H^+]$ would be equal to the $[OH^-]$ added. Use the relationship $[H^+] = 10^{-pH}$ to find $[H^+]$ at each pH.
<u>Solution:</u>
                    $[H^+] = 10^{-pH} = 10^{-3.15} = 7.07946 \times 10^{-4}$ mol/L H^+
                    $[H^+] = 10^{-pH} = 10^{-3.65} = 2.23872 \times 10^{-4}$ mol/L H^+
Add $(7.07946 \times 10^{-4}$ mol/L $- 2.23872 \times 10^{-4}$ mol/L$) = 4.84074 \times 10^{-4} = \mathbf{4.8 \times 10^{-4}}$ **mol of** $\mathbf{OH^-}$ **per litre**

16.55   Plan: The pH is increasing, so the solution is becoming more basic. Therefore, OH^- ion is added to increase the pH. Since one mole of H^+ will react with one mole of OH^-, the difference in $[H^+]$ would be equal to the $[OH^-]$ added. Use the relationship $[H^+] = 10^{-pH}$ to find $[H^+]$ at each pH.
Solution:
$$[H^+] = 10^{-pH} = 10^{-4.52} = 3.01995 \times 10^{-5} \text{ mol/L } H^+$$
$$[H^+] = 10^{-pH} = 10^{-5.25} = 5.623413 \times 10^{-6} \text{ mol/L } H^+$$
$$3.01995 \times 10^{-5} \text{ mol/L} - 5.623413 \times 10^{-6} \text{ mol/L} = 2.4576 \times 10^{-5} \text{ mol/L } OH^- \text{ must be added.}$$

$$\text{Moles of } OH^- = \frac{2.4576 \times 10^{-5} \text{ mol}}{L}(5.6 \text{ L}) = 1.3763 \times 10^{-4} \text{ mol} = \textbf{1.4} \times \textbf{10}^{-4} \textbf{ mol of } OH^-$$

16.58   Plan: Apply Le Chatelier's principle in part a). In part b), given that the pH is 6.80, $[H^+]$ can be calculated by using the relationship $[H^+] = 10^{-pH}$. The problem specifies that the solution is neutral (pure water), meaning $[H^+] = [OH^-]$. A new K_w can then be calculated.
Solution:
a) Heat is absorbed in an endothermic process: $2H_2O(l) + \text{heat} \rightarrow H_3O^+(aq) + OH^-(aq)$. As the temperature increases, the reaction shifts to the formation of products. Since the products are in the numerator of the K_w expression, rising temperature **increases** the value of K_w.
b) $[H^+] = 10^{-pH} = 10^{-6.80} = 1.58489 \times 10^{-7} \text{ mol/L } H^+ = \textbf{1.6} \times \textbf{10}^{-7} \textbf{ mol/L}$ $[H^+] = [OH^-]$
$K_w = [H^+][OH^-] = (1.58489 \times 10^{-7})(1.58489 \times 10^{-7}) = 2.511876 \times 10^{-14} = \textbf{2.5} \times \textbf{10}^{-14}$
For a neutral solution: pH = **pOH = 6.80**

16.70   a) The concentration of a strong acid is **<u>very different</u>** before and after dissociation since a strong acid exhibits 100% dissociation. After dissociation, the concentration of the strong acid approaches 0, or $[HA] \approx 0$.
b) A weak acid dissociates to a very small extent (<<100%), so the acid concentration after dissociation is **<u>nearly the same</u>** as before dissociation.
c) Same as b), but the percent, or extent, of dissociation is greater than in b).
d) Same as a)

16.71   **No**, HCl and CH_3COOH are never of equal strength because HCl is a strong acid with $K_a > 1$ and CH_3COOH is a weak acid with $K_a < 1$. The K_a of the acid, not the concentration of H_3O^+ in a solution of the acid, determines the strength of the acid.

16.74   Plan: Write the acid-dissociation reaction and the expression for K_a. Set up a reaction table and substitute the given value of $[H_3O^+]$ for x; solve for K_a.
Solution:
Butanoic acid dissociates according to the following equation:

$$CH_3CH_2CH_2COOH(aq) + H_2O(l) \rightleftharpoons H_3O^+(aq) + CH_3CH_2CH_2COO^-(aq)$$

Initial:	0.15 mol/L	0	0
Change:	−x	+x	+x
Equilibrium:	0.15 − x	x	x

According to the information given in the problem, $[H_3O^+]_{eq} = 1.51 \times 10^{-3} \text{ mol/L} = x$
Thus, $[H_3O^+] = [CH_3CH_2CH_2COO^-] = 1.51 \times 10^{-3} \text{ mol/L}$
$[CH_3CH_2CH_2COOH] = (0.15 - x) = (0.15 - 1.51 \times 10^{-3}) \text{ mol/L} = 0.14849 \text{ mol/L}$

$$K_a = \frac{\left[H_3O^+\right]\left[CH_3CH_2CH_2COO^-\right]}{\left[CH_3CH_2CH_2COOH\right]}$$

$$K_a = \frac{\left(1.51 \times 10^{-3}\right)\left(1.51 \times 10^{-3}\right)}{(0.14849)} = 1.53552 \times 10^{-5} = \textbf{1.5} \times \textbf{10}^{-5}$$

16.76   Plan: Write the balanced equation for the base reaction and the expression for K_b. Set up a reaction table in which x = the concentration of reacted base and also [OH$^-$]. Use the expression for K_b to solve for x, [OH$^-$], and then calculate [H$^+$] and pH.

Solution:

The formula of dimethylamine has two methyl (CH$_3$$^-$) groups attached to a nitrogen:

$$CH_3 \overset{..}{-\!\!-} N \overset{|}{\underset{|}{-\!\!-}} H$$
$$\quad\quad\quad CH_3$$

The nitrogen has a lone pair of electrons that will accept the proton from water in the base-dissociation reaction:
The value for the dissociation constant is from Appendix C.

Concentration (mol/L)	$(CH_3)_2NH(aq) + H_2O(l) \rightleftharpoons OH^-(aq) + (CH_3)_2NH_2^+(aq)$		
Initial	0.070	0	0
Change	$-x$	$+x$	$+x$
Equilibrium	$0.070 - x$	x	x

$$K_b = 5.9 \times 10^{-4} = \frac{\left[(CH_3)_2 NH_2^+\right]\left[OH^-\right]}{\left[(CH_3)_2 NH\right]}$$

$$K_b = 5.9 \times 10^{-4} = \frac{[x][x]}{[0.070 - x]} \quad\quad \text{Assume } 0.070 - x = 0.070$$

$$5.9 \times 10^{-4} = \frac{[x][x]}{[0.070]}$$

$$x = 6.4265 \times 10^{-3} \text{ mol/L}$$

Check assumption that x is small compared to 0.070:

$$\frac{6.4265 \times 10^{-3}}{0.070}(100\%) = 9\% \text{ error, so the assumption is not valid.}$$

The problem will need to be solved as a quadratic.

$$5.9 \times 10^{-4} = \frac{[x][x]}{[0.070 - x]}$$

$$x^2 = (5.9 \times 10^{-4})(0.070 - x) = 4.13 \times 10^{-5} - 5.9 \times 10^{-4} x$$
$$x^2 + 5.9 \times 10^{-4} x - 4.13 \times 10^{-5} = 0$$
$$a = 1 \quad\quad b = 5.9 \times 10^{-4} \quad\quad c = -4.13 \times 10^{-5}$$

$$x = \frac{-b \pm \sqrt{b^2 - 4ac}}{2a}$$

$$x = \frac{-5.9 \times 10^{-4} \pm \sqrt{\left(5.9 \times 10^{-4}\right)^2 - 4(1)\left(-4.13 \times 10^{-5}\right)}}{2(1)} = 6.13827 \times 10^{-3} \text{ mol/L OH}^-$$

$$[H^+] = \frac{K_w}{\left[OH^-\right]} = \frac{1.0 \times 10^{-14}}{6.13827 \times 10^{-3}} = 1.629124 \times 10^{-12} \text{ mol/L H}^+$$

$$pH = -\log [H^+] = -\log (1.629124 \times 10^{-12}) = 11.7880 = \textbf{11.79}$$

16.78   Plan: Write the balanced equation for the base reaction and the expression for K_b. Set up a reaction table in which x = the concentration of reacted base and also [OH$^-$]. Use the expression for K_b to solve for x, [OH$^-$], and then calculate [H$_3$O$^+$] and pH.

Solution:

Concentration (mol/L)	$HOCH_2CH_2NH_2(aq) + H_2O(l) \rightleftharpoons OH^-(aq) + HOCH_2CH_2NH_3^+(aq)$		
Initial	0.25	0	0
Change	$-x$	$+x$	$+x$
Equilibrium	$0.25 - x$	x	x

$$K_b = 3.2 \times 10^{-5} = \frac{\left[HOCH_2CH_2NH_3^+\right]\left[OH^-\right]}{\left[HOCH_2CH_2NH_2\right]}$$

$$K_b = 3.2 \times 10^{-5} = \frac{[x][x]}{[0.25 - x]} \qquad \text{Assume x is small compared to 0.25.}$$

$$K_b = 3.2 \times 10^{-5} = \frac{(x)(x)}{(0.25)}$$

$$x = 2.8284 \times 10^{-3} \text{ mol/L OH}^-$$

Check assumption that x is small compared to 0.25:

$$\frac{2.8284 \times 10^{-3}}{0.25}(100\%) = 1\% \text{ error, so the assumption is valid.}$$

$$[H]^+ = \frac{K_w}{\left[OH^-\right]} = \frac{1.0 \times 10^{-14}}{2.8284 \times 10^{-3}} = 3.535568 \times 10^{-12} \text{ mol/L H}^+$$

$$pH = -\log [H^+] = -\log (3.535568 \times 10^{-12}) = 11.4515 = \textbf{11.45}$$

16.80   Plan: Write the acid-dissociation reaction and the expression for K_a. Set up a reaction table in which x = the concentration of the dissociated HNO_2 and also $[H_3O^+]$. Use the expression for K_a to solve for x ($[H^+]$).
Solution:
For a solution of a weak acid, the acid-dissociation equilibrium determines the concentrations of the weak acid, its conjugate base and H_3O^+. The acid-dissociation reaction for HNO_2 is:

Concentration (mol/L)	$HNO_2(aq)$	+	$H_2O(l)$	$\rightleftharpoons$	$H_3O^+(aq)$	+	$NO_2^-(aq)$
Initial	0.60		—		0		0
Change	−x				+x		+x
Equilibrium	0.60 − x				x		x

(The H_3O^+ contribution from water has been neglected.)

$$K_a = 7.1 \times 10^{-4} = \frac{\left[H_3O^+\right]\left[NO_2^-\right]}{\left[HNO_2\right]}$$

$$K_a = 7.1 \times 10^{-4} = \frac{(x)(x)}{(0.60 - x)} \qquad \text{Assume x is small compared to 0.60: } 0.60 - x = 0.60$$

$$K_a = 7.1 \times 10^{-4} = \frac{(x)(x)}{(0.60)}$$

$$x = 0.020639767$$

Check assumption that x is small compared to 0.60:

$$\frac{0.020639767}{0.60}(100\%) = 3.4\% \text{ error, so the assumption is valid.}$$

$$[H^+] = [NO_2^-] = \textbf{2.1} \times \textbf{10}^{-2} \textbf{ mol/L}$$

The concentration of hydroxide ion is related to concentration of hydronium ion through the equilibrium for water: $2H_2O(l) \rightleftharpoons H_3O^+(aq) + OH^-(aq)$ with $K_w = 1.0 \times 10^{-14}$

$$K_w = 1.0 \times 10^{-14} = [H^+][OH^-]$$
$$[OH^-] = 1.0 \times 10^{-14}/0.020639767 = 4.84502 \times 10^{-13} = \textbf{4.8} \times \textbf{10}^{-13} \textbf{ mol/L OH}^-$$

16.82   Plan: Write the acid-dissociation reaction and the expression for K_a. Set up a reaction table in which x = the concentration of the dissociated acid and also $[H_3O^+]$. Use the expression for K_a to solve for x ($[H^+]$). K_a is found from the pK_a by using the relationship $K_a = 10^{-pKa}$.
Solution:
$K_a = 10^{-pKa} = 10^{-2.87} = 1.34896 \times 10^{-3}$

Concentration (mol/L) $ClCH_2COOH(aq) + H_2O(l) \rightleftharpoons H_3O^+(aq) + ClCH_2COO^-(aq)$

Initial	1.25	0	0
Change	−x	+x	+x
Equilibrium	1.25 − x	x	x

$$K_a = 1.34896 \times 10^{-3} = \frac{\left[H_3O^+\right]\left[ClCH_2COO^-\right]}{\left[ClCH_2COOH\right]}$$

$$K_a = 1.34896 \times 10^{-3} = \frac{(x)(x)}{(1.25 - x)}$$ Assume x is small compared to 1.25.

$$K_a = 1.34896 \times 10^{-3} = \frac{(x)(x)}{(1.25)}$$

x = 0.04106337

Check assumption that x is small compared to 1.25:

$$\frac{0.04106337}{1.25}(100\%) = 3.3\%. \text{ The assumption is good.}$$

$[H^+] = [ClCH_2COO^-] = \textbf{0.041 mol/L}$

$[ClCH_2COOH] = 1.25 - 0.04106337 = 1.20894 = \textbf{1.21 mol/L}$

$pH = -\log[H^+] = -\log(0.04106337) = 1.3865 = \textbf{1.39}$

16.84   Plan: In part a), potassium cyanide, when placed in water, dissociates into potassium ions, K^+, and cyanide ions, CN^-. Potassium ion is the conjugate acid of a strong base, KOH, so K^+ does not react with water. Cyanide ion is the conjugate base of a weak acid, HCN, so it does react with a base-dissociation reaction. To find the pH first set up a reaction table and use K_b for CN^- to calculate $[OH^-]$. Find the K_b for CN^- from the equation $K_w = K_a \times K_b$. In part b), the salt triethylammonium chloride in water dissociates into two ions: $(CH_3CH_2)_3NH^+$ and Cl^-. Chloride ion is the conjugate base of a strong acid so it will not influence the pH of the solution. Triethylammonium ion is the conjugate acid of a weak base, so an acid-dissociation reaction determines the pH of the solution. To find the pH first set up a reaction table and use K_a for $(CH_3CH_2)_3NH^+$ to calculate $[H^+]$. Find the K_a for $(CH_3CH_2)_3NH^+$ from the equation $K_w = K_a \times K_b$.

Solution:

a) $CN^-(aq) + H_2O(l) \rightleftharpoons HCN(aq) + OH^-(aq)$

Concentration (mol/L)	$CN^-(aq)$ +	$H_2O(l)$ $\rightleftharpoons$	$HCN(aq)$ +	$OH^-(aq)$
Initial	0.150	—	0	0
Change	−x		+x	+x
Equilibrium	0.150 − x		x	x

$$K_b \text{ of } CN^- = \frac{K_w}{K_a} = \frac{1.0 \times 10^{-14}}{6.2 \times 10^{-10}} = 1.612903 \times 10^{-5}$$

$$K_b = 1.612903 \times 10^{-5} = \frac{[HCN]\left[OH^-\right]}{\left[CN^-\right]}$$

$$K_b = 1.612903 \times 10^{-5} = \frac{[x][x]}{[0.150 - x]}$$ Assume x is small compared to 0.150.

$$K_b = 1.612903 \times 10^{-5} = \frac{(x)(x)}{(0.150)}$$

x = 1.555 × 10⁻³ mol/L OH⁻

Check assumption that x is small compared to 0.150:

$$\frac{1.555 \times 10^{-3}}{0.150}(100\%) = 1\% \text{ error, so the assumption is valid.}$$

$$[H]^+ = \frac{K_w}{\left[OH^-\right]} = \frac{1.0 \times 10^{-14}}{1.555 \times 10^{-3}} = 6.430868 \times 10^{-12} \text{ mol/L } H^+$$

$$pH = -\log [H^+] = -\log (6.430868 \times 10^{-12}) = 11.19173 = \mathbf{11.19}$$

b) $(CH_3CH_2)_3NH^+(aq) + H_2O(l) \rightleftharpoons (CH_3CH_2)_3N(aq) + H_3O^+(aq)$

Concentration (mol/L)	$(CH_3CH_2)_3NH^+(aq)$ + $H_2O(l)$	$\rightleftharpoons$	$(CH_3CH_2)_3N(aq)$ +	$H_3O^+(aq)$
Initial	0.40	—	0	0
Change	−x		+x	+x
Equilibrium	0.40 − x		x	x

$$K_a \text{ of } (CH_3CH_2)_3NH^+ = \frac{K_w}{K_b} = \frac{1.0 \times 10^{-14}}{5.2 \times 10^{-4}} = 1.9230769 \times 10^{-11}$$

$$K_a = 1.9230769 \times 10^{-11} = \frac{\left[H_3O^+\right]\left[(CH_3CH_2)_3N\right]}{\left[(CH_3CH_2)_3NH^+\right]}$$

$$K_a = 1.9230769 \times 10^{-11} = \frac{(x)(x)}{(0.40 - x)} \qquad \text{Assume x is small compared to 0.40.}$$

$$K_a = 1.9230769 \times 10^{-11} = \frac{(x)(x)}{(0.40)}$$

$[H^+] = x = 2.7735 \times 10^{-6}$ mol/L

Check assumption that x is small compared to 0.40:

$$\frac{2.7735 \times 10^{-6}}{0.40}(100\%) = 0.0007\% \text{ error, so the assumption is valid.}$$

$$pH = -\log [H^+] = -\log (2.7735 \times 10^{-6}) = 5.55697 = \mathbf{5.56}$$

16.86   Plan: In part a), potassium formate, when placed in water, dissociates into potassium ions, K^+, and formate ions, $HCOO^-$. Potassium ion is the conjugate acid of a strong base, KOH, so K^+ does not react with water. Formate ion is the conjugate base of a weak acid, HCOOH, so it does react with a base-dissociation reaction. To find the pH first set up a reaction table and use K_b for $HCOO^-$ to calculate $[OH^-]$. Find the K_b for $HCOO^-$ from the equation $K_w = K_a \times K_b$. In part b), the salt ammonium bromide in water dissociates into two ions: NH_4^+ and Br^-. Bromide ion is the conjugate base of a strong acid so it will not influence the pH of the solution. Ammonium ion is the conjugate acid of the weak base NH_3, so an acid-dissociation reaction determines the pH of the solution. To find the pH first set up a reaction table and use K_a for NH_4^+ to calculate $[H_3O^+]$. Find the K_a for NH_4^+ from the equation $K_w = K_a \times K_b$.

Solution:

a) $HCOO^-(aq) + H_2O(l) \rightleftharpoons HCOOH(aq) + OH^-(aq)$

Concentration (mol/L)	$HCOO^-(aq)$ +	$H_2O(l)$	$\rightleftharpoons$	$HCOOH(aq)$ +	$OH^-(aq)$
Initial	0.65	—		0	0
Change	−x			+x	+x
Equilibrium	0.65 − x			x	x

$$K_b \text{ of } HCOO^- = \frac{K_w}{K_a} = \frac{1.0 \times 10^{-14}}{1.8 \times 10^{-4}} = 5.55556 \times 10^{-11}$$

$$K_b = 5.55556 \times 10^{-11} = \frac{[HCOOH]\left[OH^-\right]}{\left[HCOO^-\right]}$$

$$K_b = 5.55556 \times 10^{-11} = \frac{[x][x]}{[0.65 - x]} \qquad \text{Assume x is small compared to 0.65.}$$

$$K_b = 5.55556 \times 10^{-11} = \frac{(x)(x)}{(0.65)}$$

$x = 6.00925 \times 10^{-6}$ mol/L OH^-

Check assumption that x is small compared to 0.65:

$$\frac{6.00925\times10^{-6}}{0.65}(100\%) = 0.0009\% \text{ error, so the assumption is valid.}$$

$$[\text{H}]^+ = \frac{K_w}{\left[\text{OH}^-\right]} = \frac{1.0\times10^{-14}}{6.00925\times10^{-6}} = 1.66410\times10^{-9} \text{ mol/L H}^+$$

$$\text{pH} = -\log[\text{H}^+] = -\log(1.66410\times10^{-9}) = 8.7788 = \textbf{8.78}$$

b) $\text{NH}_4^+(aq) + \text{H}_2\text{O}(l) \rightleftharpoons \text{H}_3\text{O}^+(aq) + \text{NH}_3(aq)$

Concentration (mol/L)	$\text{NH}_4^+(aq)$	+	$\text{H}_2\text{O}(l)$	$\rightleftharpoons$	$\text{NH}_3(aq)$	+	$\text{H}_3\text{O}^+(aq)$
Initial	0.85		—		0		0
Change	−x				+x		+x
Equilibrium	0.85 − x				x		x

$$K_a \text{ of NH}_4^+ = \frac{K_w}{K_b} = \frac{1.0\times10^{-14}}{1.76\times10^{-5}} = 5.681818\times10^{-10}$$

$$K_a = 5.681818\times10^{-10} = \frac{\left[\text{H}_3\text{O}^+\right]\left[\text{NH}_3\right]}{\left[\text{NH}_4^+\right]}$$

$$K_a = 5.681818\times10^{-10} = \frac{[x][x]}{[0.85 - x]} \qquad \text{Assume x is small compared to 0.85.}$$

$$K_a = 5.681818\times10^{-10} = \frac{[x][x]}{[0.85]}$$

$[\text{H}^+] = x = 2.1976\times10^{-5} \text{ mol/L}$

Check assumption that x is small compared to 0.85:

$$\frac{2.1976\times10^{-5}}{0.85}(100\%) = 0.003\% \text{ error, so the assumption is valid.}$$

$$\text{pH} = -\log[\text{H}^+] = -\log(2.1976\times10^{-5}) = 4.65805 = \textbf{4.66}$$

16.88 Plan: Write the acid-dissociation reaction and the expression for K_a. Percent dissociation refers to the amount of the initial concentration of the acid that dissociates into ions. Use the percent dissociation to find the concentration of acid dissociated, which also equals $[\text{H}_3\text{O}^+]$. HA will be used as the formula of the acid. Set up a reaction table in which x = the concentration of the dissociated acid and $[\text{H}_3\text{O}^+]$. pH and $[\text{OH}^-]$ are determined from $[\text{H}_3\text{O}^+]$. Substitute [HA], [A$^-$], and $[\text{H}_3\text{O}^+]$ into the expression for K_a to find the value of K_a.
Solution:
a) $\text{HA}(aq) + \text{H}_2\text{O}(l) \rightleftharpoons \text{H}_3\text{O}^+(aq) + \text{A}^-(aq)$

$$\text{Percent HA} = \frac{\text{dissociated acid}}{\text{initial acid}}(100\%)$$

$$3.0\% = \frac{x}{0.20}(100\%)$$

[Dissociated acid] = x = 6.0×10^{-3} mol/L

Concentration (mol/L)	$\text{HA}(aq)$	+	$\text{H}_2\text{O}(l)$	$\rightleftharpoons$	$\text{H}_3\text{O}^+(aq)$	+	$\text{A}^-(aq)$
Initial:	0.20				0		0
Change:	−x				+x		+x
Equilibrium:	0.20 − x				x		x

[Dissociated acid] = x = $[\text{A}^-]$ = $[\text{H}_3\text{O}^+]$ = $\textbf{6.0}\times\textbf{10}^{-3}$ **mol/L**
$\text{pH} = -\log[\text{H}^+] = -\log(6.0\times10^{-3}) = 2.22185 = \textbf{2.22}$
$K_w = 1.0\times10^{-14} = [\text{H}^+][\text{OH}^-]$

$$[\text{OH}^-] = \frac{K_w}{\left[\text{H}^+\right]} = \frac{1.0\times10^{-14}}{6.0\times10^{-3}} = 1.6666667\times10^{-12} = \textbf{1.7}\times\textbf{10}^{-12} \text{ mol/L}$$

$pOH = -\log [OH^-] = -\log (1.6666667 \times 10^{-12}) = 11.7782 = \textbf{11.78}$

b) In the equilibrium expression, substitute the concentrations above and calculate K_a.

$$K_a = \frac{\left[H_3O^+\right]\left[A^-\right]}{\left[HA\right]} = \frac{\left(6.0 \times 10^{-3}\right)\left(6.0 \times 10^{-3}\right)}{\left(0.20 - 6.0 \times 10^{-3}\right)} = 1.85567 \times 10^{-4} = \textbf{1.9} \times \textbf{10}^{-4}$$

16.90   Plan: Write the acid-dissociation reaction and the expression for K_a. Calculate the concentration (mol/L) of HX by dividing moles by volume. Convert pH to $[H_3O^+]$, set up a reaction table in which x = the concentration of the dissociated acid and also $[H_3O^+]$, and substitute into the equilibrium expression to find K_a.

$$\text{Concentration (mol/L) of HX} = \left(\frac{0.250 \text{ mol}}{655 \text{ mL}}\right)\left(\frac{1 \text{ mL}}{10^{-3} \text{ L}}\right) = 0.381679 \text{ mol/L}$$

Concentration (mol/L)	$HX(aq) + H_2O(l)$	$\rightleftharpoons$	$H_3O^+(aq) +$	$X^-(aq)$
Initial:	0.381679		0	0
Change:	$-x$		$+x$	$+x$
Equilibrium:	$0.381679 - x$		x	x

$[H^+] = 10^{-pH} = 10^{-3.54} = 2.88403 \times 10^{-4} \text{ mol/L} = x$

Thus, $[H^+] = [X^-] = 2.88403 \times 10^{-4}$ mol/L, and $[HX] = (0.381679 - 2.88403 \times 10^{-4})$ mol/L

$$K_a = \frac{\left[H_3O^+\right]\left[X^-\right]}{\left[HX\right]} = \frac{\left(2.88403 \times 10^{-4}\right)\left(2.88403 \times 10^{-4}\right)}{\left(0.381679 - 2.88403 \times 10^{-4}\right)} = 2.18087 \times 10^{-7} = \textbf{2.2} \times \textbf{10}^{-7}$$

16.92   Plan: Write the acid-dissociation reaction and the expression for K_a. Set up a reaction table in which x = the concentration of the dissociated acid and also $[H_3O^+]$. Use the expression for K_a to solve for x ($[H^+]$). OH^- and then pOH can be found from $[H^+]$.
Solution:

a)

Concentration(mol/L)	$HZ(aq) +$	$H_2O(l)$	$\rightleftharpoons$	$H_3O^+(aq) +$	$Z^-(aq)$
Initial	0.075	—		0	0
Change	$-x$			$+x$	$+x$
Equilibrium	$0.075 - x$			x	x

(The H^+ contribution from water has been neglected.)

$$K_a = 2.55 \times 10^{-4} = \frac{\left[H_3O^+\right]\left[Z^-\right]}{\left[HZ\right]}$$

$$K_a = 2.55 \times 10^{-4} = \frac{(x)(x)}{(0.075 - x)} \qquad \text{Assume x is small compared to 0.075.}$$

$$K_a = 2.55 \times 10^{-4} = \frac{(x)(x)}{(0.075)}$$

$[H^+] = x = 4.3732 \times 10^{-3}$

Check assumption that x is small compared to 0.075:

$$\frac{4.3732 \times 10^{-3}}{0.075}(100\%) = 6\% \text{ error, so the assumption is not valid.}$$

Since the error is greater than 5%, it is not acceptable to assume x is small compared to 0.075, and it is necessary to use the quadratic equation.

$$K_a = 2.55 \times 10^{-4} = \frac{(x)(x)}{(0.075 - x)}$$

$$x^2 + 2.55 \times 10^{-4} x - 1.9125 \times 10^{-5} = 0$$

$$a = 1 \qquad b = 2.55 \times 10^{-4} \qquad c = -1.9125 \times 10^{-5}$$

$$x = \frac{-b \pm \sqrt{b^2 - 4ac}}{2a}$$

$$x = \frac{-(2.55 \times 10^{-4}) \pm \sqrt{(2.55 \times 10^{-4})^2 - 4(1)(-1.9125 \times 10^{-5})}}{2(1)}$$

x = 0.00425 or –0.004503

(The –0.004503 value is not possible.)

pH = –log [H$^+$] = –log (0.00425) = 2.3716 = **2.37**

b) Concentration (mol/L) HZ(*aq*)   +   H$_2$O(*l*) $\rightleftharpoons$ H$_3$O$^+$(*aq*)   +   Z$^-$(*aq*)

Initial	0.045	—	0	0
Change	–x		+x	+x
Equilibrium	0.045 – x		x	x

(The H$^+$ contribution from water has been neglected.)

$$K_a = 2.55 \times 10^{-4} = \frac{[H_3O^+][Z^-]}{[HZ]}$$

$$K_a = 2.55 \times 10^{-4} = \frac{(x)(x)}{(0.045 - x)} \qquad \text{Assume x is small compared to 0.045.}$$

$$K_a = 2.55 \times 10^{-4} = \frac{(x)(x)}{(0.045)}$$

[H$^+$] = x = 3.3875 × 10^{-3}

Check assumption that x is small compared to 0.045:

$$\frac{3.3875 \times 10^{-3}}{0.045}(100\%) = 7.5\% \text{ error, so the assumption is not valid.}$$

Since the error is greater than 5%, it is not acceptable to assume x is small compared to 0.045, and it is necessary to use the quadratic equation.

$$K_a = 2.55 \times 10^{-4} = \frac{(x)(x)}{(0.045 - x)}$$

$$x^2 = (2.55 \times 10^{-4})(0.045 - x) = 1.1475 \times 10^{-5} - 2.55 \times 10^{-4} x$$

$$x^2 + 2.55 \times 10^{-4} x - 1.1475 \times 10^{-5} = 0$$

a = 1   b = 2.55 × 10^{-4} c = –1.1475 × 10^{-5}

$$x = \frac{-b \pm \sqrt{b^2 - 4ac}}{2a}$$

$$x = \frac{-2.55 \times 10^{-4} \pm \sqrt{(2.55 \times 10^{-4})^2 - 4(1)(-1.1475 \times 10^{-5})}}{2(1)}$$

x = 3.26238 × 10^{-3} mol/L H$^+$

$$[OH^-] = \frac{K_w}{[H_3O^+]} = \frac{1.0 \times 10^{-14}}{3.26238 \times 10^{-3}} = 3.0652468 \times 10^{-12} \text{ mol/L}$$

pOH = –log [OH$^-$] = –log (3.0652468 × 10^{-12}) = 11.51353 = **11.51**

16.94   Plan: Write the acid-dissociation reaction and the expression for K_a. Set up a reaction table in which x = the concentration of the dissociated acid and also [H$^+$]. Use the expression for K_a to solve for x ([H$^+$]). OH$^-$ and then pOH can be found from [H$^+$].

Solution:

a) Concentration (mol/L) HY(*aq*)   +   H$_2$O(*l*) $\rightleftharpoons$ H$_3$O$^+$(*aq*)   +   Y$^-$(*aq*)

Initial	0.175	—	0	0
Change	–x		+x	+x
Equilibrium	0.175 – x		x	x

(The H$_3$O$^+$ contribution from water has been neglected.)

$$K_a = 1.50\text{x}10^{-4} = \frac{\left[H_3O^+\right]\left[Y^-\right]}{\left[HY\right]}$$

$$K_a = 1.50\text{x}10^{-4} = \frac{(x)(x)}{(0.175 - x)}$$ Assume x is small compared to 0.175.

$$K_a = 1.50\text{x}10^{-4} = \frac{(x)(x)}{(0.175)}$$

$[H^+] = x = 5.1235\text{x}10^{-3}$ mol/L

Check assumption that x is small compared to 0.175:

$$\frac{5.1235\text{x}10^{-3}}{0.175}(100\%) = 3\% \text{ error, so the assumption is valid.}$$

$\text{pH} = -\log [H^+] = -\log (5.1235\text{x}10^{-3}) = 2.29043 = \mathbf{2.290}$

b)

Concentration (mol/L)	HX(aq)	+	H$_2$O(l)	$\rightleftharpoons$	H$_3$O$^+$(aq)	+	X$^-$(aq)
Initial	0.175		—		0		0
Change	−x				+x		+x
Equilibrium	0.175 − x				x		x

(The H$_3$O$^+$ contribution from water has been neglected.)

$$K_a = 2.00\text{x}10^{-2} = \frac{\left[H_3O^+\right]\left[X^-\right]}{\left[HX\right]}$$

$$K_a = 2.00\text{x}10^{-2} = \frac{(x)(x)}{(0.175 - x)}$$ Assume x is small compared to 0.175.

$$K_a = 2.00\text{x}10^{-2} = \frac{(x)(x)}{(0.175)}$$

$[H^+] = x = 5.9161\text{x}10^{-2}$ mol/L

Check assumption that x is small compared to 0.175:

$$\frac{5.9161\text{x}10^{-2}}{0.175}(100\%) = 34\% \text{ error, so the assumption is not valid.}$$

Since the error is greater than 5%, it is not acceptable to assume x is small compared to 0.175, and it is necessary to use the quadratic equation.

$$K_a = 2.00\text{x}10^{-2} = \frac{(x)(x)}{(0.175 - x)}$$

$x^2 = = (2.00\text{x}10^{-2})(0.175 - x) = 0.0035 - 2.00\text{x}10^{-2}x$

$x^2 + 2.00\text{x}10^{-2}x - 0.0035 = 0$

        a = 1   b = 2.00x10^{-2} c = −0.0035

$$x = \frac{-b \pm \sqrt{b^2 - 4ac}}{2a}$$

$$x = \frac{-2.00\text{x}10^{-2} \pm \sqrt{\left(2.00\text{x}10^{-2}\right)^2 - 4(1)(-0.0035)}}{2(1)}$$

$x = 5.00\text{x}10^{-2}$ mol/L H$^+$

$$[OH^-] = \frac{K_w}{\left[H^+\right]} = \frac{1.0\text{x}10^{-14}}{5.00\text{x}10^{-2}} = 2.00\text{x}10^{-13} \text{ mol/L}$$

$\text{pOH} = -\log [OH^-] = -\log (2.00\text{x}10^{-13}) = 12.69897 = \mathbf{12.699}$

16.96 <u>Plan:</u> Write the acid-dissociation reaction and the expression for K_a. Set up a reaction table in which x = the concentration of the dissociated acid and also [H_3O^+]. Use the expression for K_a to solve for x, the concentration of benzoate ion at equilibrium. Then use the initial concentration of benzoic acid and the equilibrium concentration of benzoate to find % dissociation.

<u>Solution:</u>

Concentration (mol/L)	$C_6H_5COOH(aq)$	+	$H_2O(l)$	$\rightleftharpoons$	$H_3O^+(aq)$	+	$C_6H_5COO^-(aq)$
Initial	0.55		—		0		0
Change	−x				+x		+x
Equilibrium	0.55 − x				x		x

$$K_a = 6.3 \times 10^{-5} = \frac{\left[H_3O^+ \right]\left[C_6H_5COO^- \right]}{\left[C_6H_5COOH \right]}$$

$$K_a = 6.3 \times 10^{-5} = \frac{[x][x]}{[0.55 - x]} \qquad \text{Assume x is small compared to 0.55.}$$

$$K_a = 6.3 \times 10^{-5} = \frac{[x][x]}{[0.55]}$$

$$x = 5.8864 \times 10^{-3} \text{ mol/L}$$

$$\text{Percent } C_6H_5COOH \text{ dissociated} = \frac{[C_6H_5COOH]_{\text{dissociated}}}{[C_6H_5COOH]_{\text{initial}}}(100)$$

$$\text{Percent } C_6H_5COOH \text{ dissociated} = \frac{5.8864 \times 10^{-3} \text{ mol/L}}{0.55 \text{ mol/L}}(100\%) = 1.07025 = \textbf{1.1\%}$$

16.98 <u>Plan:</u> Write balanced chemical equations and corresponding equilibrium expressions for dissociation of hydrosulfuric acid, H_2S, and HS^-. Since $K_{a_1} \gg K_{a_2}$, assume that almost all of the H_3O^+ comes from the first dissociation. Set up reaction tables in which x = the concentration of dissociated acid and [H_3O^+].

<u>Solution:</u>

$H_2S(aq) + H_2O(l) \rightleftharpoons H_3O^+(aq) + HS^-(aq)$ $\qquad$ $HS^-(aq) + H_2O(l) \rightleftharpoons H_3O^+(aq) + S^{2-}(aq)$

$$K_{a_1} = 9 \times 10^{-8} = \frac{\left[H_3O^+ \right]\left[HS^- \right]}{\left[H_2S \right]} \qquad\qquad K_{a_2} = 1 \times 10^{-17} = \frac{\left[H_3O^+ \right]\left[S^{2-} \right]}{\left[HS^- \right]}$$

Concentration (mol/L)	$H_2S(aq)$	+	$H_2O(l)$	$\rightleftharpoons$	$H_3O^+(aq)$	+	$HS^-(aq)$
Initial	0.10		—		0		0
Change	−x				+x		+x
Equilibrium	0.10 − x				x		x

$$K_{a_1} = 9 \times 10^{-8} = \frac{\left[H_3O^+ \right]\left[HS^- \right]}{\left[H_2S \right]}$$

$$K_{a_1} = 9 \times 10^{-8} = \frac{[x][x]}{[0.10 - x]} \qquad \text{Assume x is small compared to 0.10.}$$

$$K_{a_1} = 9 \times 10^{-8} = \frac{[x][x]}{[0.10]}$$

$$x = 9.48683 \times 10^{-5}$$

[H^+] = [HS^-] = x = **9x10^{-5} mol/L**

pH = −log [H^+] = −log (9.48683×10^{-5}) = 4.022878 = **4.0**

$$[OH^-] = \frac{K_w}{\left[H^+ \right]} = \frac{1.0 \times 10^{-14}}{9.48683 \times 10^{-5}} = 1.05409 \times 10^{-10} = \textbf{1x10}^{-10} \textbf{ mol/L}$$

$pOH = -\log [OH^-] = -\log (1.05409 \times 10^{-10}) = 9.9771 = \textbf{10.0}$

$[H_2S] = 0.10 - x = 0.10 - 9.48683 \times 10^{-5} = 0.099905 = \textbf{0.10 mol/L}$

Concentration is limited to one significant figure because K_a is given to only one significant figure. The pH is given to what appears to be two significant figures because the number before the decimal point (4) represents the exponent and the number after the decimal point represents the significant figures in the concentration.

Calculate $[S^{2-}]$ by using the K_{a_2} expression and assuming that $[HS^-]$ and $[H_3O^+]$ come mostly from the first dissociation. This new calculation will have a new x value.

Concentration (mol/L)	$HS^-(aq)$	+	$H_2O(l)$	$\rightleftharpoons$	$H_3O^+(aq)$	+	$S^{2-}(aq)$
Initial	9.48683×10^{-5}		—		9.48683×10^{-5}		0
Change	$-x$				$+x$		$+x$
Equilibrium	$9.48683 \times 10^{-5} - x$				$9.48683 \times 10^{-5} + x$		x

$$K_{a_2} = 1 \times 10^{-17} = \frac{\left[H_3O^+\right]\left[S^{2-}\right]}{\left[HS^-\right]}$$

$$K_{a_2} = 1 \times 10^{-17} = \frac{\left(9.48683 \times 10^{-5} + x\right)(x)}{\left(9.48683 \times 10^{-5} - x\right)} \qquad \text{Assume x is small compared to } 9.48683 \times 10^{-5}.$$

$$K_{a_2} = 1 \times 10^{-17} = \frac{\left(9.48683 \times 10^{-5}\right)(x)}{\left(9.48683 \times 10^{-5}\right)}$$

$$x = [S^{2-}] = \textbf{1} \times \textbf{10}^{-17} \textbf{ mol/L}$$

The small value of x means that it is not necessary to recalculate the $[H^+]$ and $[HS^-]$ values.

16.101   Plan: Write the acid-dissociation reaction and the expression for K_a. Set up a reaction table in which x = the concentration of the dissociated acid and also $[H_3O^+]$. Use the expression for K_a to solve for x, the concentration of formate ion at equilibrium. Then use the initial concentration of formic acid and the equilibrium concentration of formate to find % dissociation.

Solution:

Concentration (mol/L)	$HCOOH(aq)$	+	$H_2O(l)$	$\rightleftharpoons$	$H_3O^+(aq)$	+	$HCOO^-(aq)$
Initial	0.75				0		0
Change	$-x$				$+x$		$+x$
Equilibrium	$0.75 - x$				x		x

$$K_a = 1.8 \times 10^{-4} = \frac{\left[H_3O^+\right]\left[HCOO^-\right]}{\left[HCOOH\right]}$$

$$K_a = 1.8 \times 10^{-4} = \frac{(x)(x)}{(0.75 - x)} \qquad \text{Assume x is small compared to 0.75.}$$

$$K_a = 1.8 \times 10^{-4} = \frac{(x)(x)}{(0.75)}$$

$$x = 1.161895 \times 10^{-2}$$

$$\text{Percent HCOOH dissociated} = \frac{\left[HCOOH\right]_{\text{dissociated}}}{\left[HCOOH\right]_{\text{initial}}}(100\%)$$

$$\text{Percent HCOOH dissociated} = \frac{1.161895 \times 10^{-2} \text{ mol/L}}{0.75 \text{ mol/L}}(100\%) = 1.54919 \% = \textbf{1.5\%}$$

16.102　Plan: First, calculate the initial concentration (mol/L) of ClO^- from the mass percent. Then, set up reaction table with base dissociation of ClO^-. Find the K_b for ClO^- from the equation $K_w = K_a \times K_b$, using the K_a for HClO from Appendix C.

Solution:

Concentration (mol/L) of ClO^- =

$$\left(\frac{1 \text{ mL solution}}{10^{-3} \text{ L solution}}\right)\left(\frac{1.0 \text{ g solution}}{1 \text{ mL solution}}\right)\left(\frac{6.5\% \text{ NaClO}}{100\% \text{ Solution}}\right)\left(\frac{1 \text{ mol NaClO}}{74.44 \text{ g NaClO}}\right)\left(\frac{1 \text{ mol ClO}^-}{1 \text{ mol NaClO}}\right)$$

$$= 0.873186 \text{ mol/L } ClO^-$$

The sodium ion is from a strong base; therefore, it will not affect the pH, and can be ignored.

Concentration (mol/L)	$ClO^-(aq)$	+	$H_2O(l)$	$\rightleftharpoons$	$HClO(aq)$	+	$OH^-(aq)$
Initial	0.873186		—		0		0
Change	$-x$				$+x$		$+x$
Equilibrium	$0.873186 - x$				x		x

$$K_b \text{ of } ClO^- = \frac{K_w}{K_a} = \frac{1.0 \times 10^{-14}}{2.9 \times 10^{-8}} = 3.448275862 \times 10^{-7}$$

$$K_b = 3.448275862 \times 10^{-7} = \frac{[HClO]\left[OH^-\right]}{\left[ClO^-\right]}$$

$$K_b = 3.448275862 \times 10^{-7} = \frac{[x][x]}{[0.873186 - x]} \qquad \text{Assume x is small compared to 0.873186.}$$

$$K_b = 3.448275862 \times 10^{-7} = \frac{(x)(x)}{(0.873186)}$$

$$x = 5.4872 \times 10^{-4} = \textbf{5.5} \times \textbf{10}^{-4} \textbf{ mol/L OH}^-$$

Check assumption that x is small compared to 0.873186:

$$\frac{5.4872 \times 10^{-4}}{0.873186}(100\%) = 0.006\% \text{ error, so the assumption is valid.}$$

$$[H]^+ = \frac{K_w}{\left[OH^-\right]} = \frac{1.0 \times 10^{-14}}{5.4872 \times 10^{-4}} = 1.82242 \times 10^{-11} \text{ mol/L H}^+$$

$$pH = -\log [H^+] = -\log (1.82242 \times 10^{-11}) = 10.73935 = \textbf{10.74}$$

16.104　Electronegativity increases left to right across a period. As the nonmetal becomes more electronegative, the acidity of the binary hydride increases. The electronegative nonmetal attracts the electrons more strongly in the polar bond, shifting the electron density away from H^+ and making the H^+ more easily transferred to a surrounding water molecule to make H_3O^+.

16.107　The two factors that explain the greater acid strength of $HClO_4$ are:
1) Chlorine is more electronegative than iodine, so chlorine more strongly attracts the electrons in the bond with oxygen. This makes the H in $HClO_4$ less tightly held by the oxygen than the H in HIO.
2) Perchloric acid has more oxygen atoms than HIO, which leads to a greater shift in electron density from the hydrogen atom to the oxygen atoms making the H in $HClO_4$ more susceptible to transfer to a base.

16.108　Plan: For oxyacids, acid strength increases with increasing number of oxygen atoms and increasing electronegativity of the nonmetal in the acid. For binary acids, acid strength increases with increasing electronegativity across a row and increases with increasing size of the nonmetal down a column.

Solution:
a) Selenic acid, $\textbf{H}_2\textbf{SeO}_4$, is the stronger acid because it contains more oxygen atoms.
b) Phosphoric acid, $\textbf{H}_3\textbf{PO}_4$, is the stronger acid because P is more electronegative than As.
c) Hydrotelluric acid, $\textbf{H}_2\textbf{Te}$, is the stronger acid because Te is larger than S and so the Te–H bond is weaker.

16.110 <u>Plan:</u> For oxyacids, acid strength increases with increasing number of oxygen atoms and increasing electronegativity of the nonmetal in the acid. For binary acids, acid strength increases with increasing electronegativity across a row and increases with increasing size of the nonmetal in a column.
<u>Solution:</u>
a) **H_2Se**, hydrogen selenide, is a stronger acid than H_3As, arsenic hydride, because Se is more electronegative than As.
b) **$B(OH)_3$**, boric acid also written as H_3BO_3, is a stronger acid than $Al(OH)_3$, aluminum hydroxide, because boron is more electronegative than aluminum.
c) **$HBrO_2$**, bromous acid, is a stronger acid than HBrO, hypobromous acid, because there are more oxygen atoms in $HBrO_2$ than in HBrO.

16.112 <u>Plan:</u> Acidity increases as the value of K_a increases. Determine the ion formed from each salt and compare the corresponding K_a values from Appendix C.
<u>Solution:</u>
a) Copper(II) bromide, $CuBr_2$, contains Cu^{2+} ion with $K_a = 3 \times 10^{-8}$. Aluminum bromide, $AlBr_3$, contains Al^{3+} ion with $K_a = 1 \times 10^{-5}$. The concentrations of Cu^{2+} and Al^{3+} are equal, but the K_a of $AlBr_3$ is almost three orders of magnitude greater. Therefore, **0.5 mol/L $AlBr_3$** is the stronger acid and would have the lower pH.
b) Zinc chloride, $ZnCl_2$, contains the Zn^{2+} ion with $K_a = 1 \times 10^{-9}$. Tin(II) chloride, $SnCl_2$, contains the Sn^{2+} ion with $K_a = 4 \times 10^{-4}$. Since both solutions have the same concentration, and $K_a (Sn^{2+}) > K_a (Zn^{2+})$, **0.3 mol/L $SnCl_2$** is the stronger acid and would have the lower pH.

16.114 <u>Plan:</u> A higher pH (more basic solution) results when an acid has a smaller K_a (from the Appendix). Determine the ion formed from each salt and compare the corresponding K_a values from Appendix C.
<u>Solution:</u>
a) The **$Ni(NO_3)_2$** solution has a higher pH than the $Co(NO_3)_2$ solution because K_a of Ni^{2+} (1×10^{-10}) is smaller than the K_a of Co^{2+} (2×10^{-10}). Note that nitrate ion is the conjugate base of a strong acid and therefore does not influence the pH of the solution.
b) The **$Al(NO_3)_3$** solution has a higher pH than the $Cr(NO_3)_2$ solution because K_a of Al^{3+} (1×10^{-5}) is smaller than the K_a of Cr^{3+} (1×10^{-4}).

16.117 Sodium fluoride, NaF, contains the cation of a strong base, NaOH, and anion of a weak acid, HF.
This combination yields a salt that is basic in aqueous solution as the F^- ion acts as a base:
$$F^-(aq) + H_2O(l) \rightleftharpoons HF(aq) + OH^-(aq)$$
Sodium chloride, NaCl, is the salt of a strong base, NaOH, and strong acid, HCl. This combination yields a salt that is neutral in aqueous solution as neither Na^+ or Cl^- react in water to change the $[H_3O^+]$.

16.119 <u>Plan:</u> For each salt, first break into the ions present in solution and then determine if either ion acts as a weak acid or weak base to change the pH of the solution. Cations are neutral if they are from a strong base; other cations will be weakly acidic. Anions are neutral if they are from a strong acid; other anions are weakly basic.
<u>Solution:</u>
a) $KBr(s) \xrightarrow{H_2O} K^+(aq) + Br^-(aq)$
K^+ is the conjugate acid of a strong base, so it does not influence pH.
Br^- is the conjugate base of a strong acid, so it does not influence pH.
Since neither ion influences the pH of the solution, it will remain at the **neutral** pH of pure water.
b) $NH_4I(s) \xrightarrow{H_2O} NH_4^+(aq) + I^-(aq)$
NH_4^+ is the conjugate acid of a weak base, so it will act as a weak acid in solution and produce H_3O^+ as represented by the acid-dissociation reaction:
$$NH_4^+(aq) + H_2O(l) \rightleftharpoons NH_3(aq) + H_3O^+(aq)$$
I^- is the conjugate base of a strong acid, so it will not influence the pH.
The production of H_3O^+ from the ammonium ion makes the solution of NH_4I **acidic**.

c) $KCN(s) \xrightarrow{H_2O} K^+(aq) + CN^-(aq)$

K^+ is the conjugate acid of a strong base, so it does not influence pH.

CN^- is the conjugate base of a weak acid, so it will act as a weak base in solution and impact pH by the base-dissociation reaction:

$$CN^-(aq) + H_2O(l) \rightleftharpoons HCN(aq) + OH^-(aq)$$

Hydroxide ions are produced in this equilibrium so solution will be **basic**.

16.121 Plan: For each salt, first break into the ions present in solution and then determine if either ion acts as a weak acid or weak base to change the pH of the solution. Cations are neutral if they are from a strong base; other cations will be weakly acidic. Anions are neutral if they are from a strong acid; other anions are weakly basic.

Solution:

a) The two ions that comprise sodium carbonate, Na_2CO_3, are sodium ion, Na^+, and carbonate ion, CO_3^{2-}.

$$Na_2CO_3(s) \xrightarrow{H_2O} 2Na^+(aq) + CO_3^{2-}(aq)$$

Sodium ion is derived from the strong base NaOH. Carbonate ion is derived from the weak acid HCO_3^-. A salt derived from a strong base and a weak acid produces a **basic** solution.

Na^+ does not react with water.

$$CO_3^{2-}(aq) + H_2O(l) \rightleftharpoons HCO_3^-(aq) + OH^-(aq)$$

b) The two ions that comprise calcium chloride, $CaCl_2$, are calcium ion, Ca^{2+}, and chloride ion, Cl^-.

$$CaCl_2(s) \xrightarrow{H_2O} Ca^{2+}(aq) + 2Cl^-(aq)$$

Calcium ion is derived from the strong base $Ca(OH)_2$. Chloride ion is derived from the strong acid HCl. A salt derived from a strong base and strong acid produces a **neutral** solution.

Neither Ca^{2+} nor Cl^- reacts with water.

c) The two ions that comprise cupric nitrate, $Cu(NO_3)_2$, are the cupric ion, Cu^{2+}, and the nitrate ion, NO_3^-.

$$Cu(NO_3)_2(s) \xrightarrow{H_2O} Cu^{2+}(aq) + 2NO_3^-(aq)$$

Small metal ions are acidic in water (assume the hydration of Cu^{2+} is 6):

$$Cu(H_2O)_6^{2+}(aq) + H_2O(l) \rightleftharpoons Cu(H_2O)_5OH^+(aq) + H_3O^+(aq)$$

Nitrate ion is derived from the strong acid HNO_3. Therefore, NO_3^- does not react with water. A solution of cupric nitrate is **acidic**.

16.123 Plan: For each salt, first break into the ions present in solution and then determine if either ion acts as a weak acid or weak base to change the pH of the solution. Cations are neutral if they are from a strong base; other cations will be weakly acidic. Anions are neutral if they are from a strong acid; other anions are weakly basic.

Solution:

a) A solution of strontium bromide is **neutral** because Sr^{2+} is the conjugate acid of a strong base, $Sr(OH)_2$, and Br^- is the conjugate base of a strong acid, HBr, so neither change the pH of the solution.

b) A solution of barium acetate is **basic** because CH_3COO^- is the conjugate base of a weak acid and therefore forms OH^- in solution whereas Ba^{2+} is the conjugate acid of a strong base, $Ba(OH)_2$, and does not influence solution pH. The base-dissociation reaction of acetate ion is

$$CH_3COO^-(aq) + H_2O(l) \rightleftharpoons CH_3COOH(aq) + OH^-(aq).$$

c) A solution of dimethylammonium bromide is **acidic** because $(CH_3)_2NH_2^+$ is the conjugate acid of a weak base and therefore forms H_3O^+ in solution whereas Br^- is the conjugate base of a strong acid and does not influence the pH of the solution. The acid-dissociation reaction for methylammonium ion is

$$(CH_3)_2NH_2^+(aq) + H_2O(l) \rightleftharpoons (CH_3)_2NH(aq) + H_3O^+(aq).$$

16.125 Plan: For each salt, first break into the ions present in solution and then determine if either ion acts as a weak acid or weak base to change the pH of the solution. Cations are neutral if they are from a strong base; other cations will be weakly acidic. Anions are neutral if they are from a strong acid; other anions are weakly basic.

Solution:

a) The two ions that comprise ammonium phosphate, $(NH_4)_3PO_4$, are the ammonium ion, NH_4^+, and the phosphate ion, PO_4^{3-}.

$$NH_4^+(aq) + H_2O(l) \rightleftharpoons NH_3(aq) + H_3O^+(aq) \qquad K_a = K_w/K_b\,(NH_3) = 5.7 \times 10^{-10}$$

$$PO_4^{3-}(aq) + H_2O(l) \rightleftharpoons HPO_4^{2-}(aq) + OH^-(aq) \qquad K_b = K_w/K_{a3} \ (H_3PO_4) = 2.4\text{x}10^{-2}$$

A comparison of K_a and K_b is necessary since both ions are derived from a weak base and weak acid. The K_a of NH_4^+ is determined by using the K_b of its conjugate base, NH_3 (Appendix). The K_b of PO_4^{3-} is determined by using the K_a of its conjugate acid, HPO_4^{2-}. The K_a of HPO_4^{2-} comes from K_{a3} of H_3PO_4 (Appendix). Since $K_b > K_a$, a solution of $(NH_4)_3PO_4$ is **basic**.
b) The two ions that comprise sodium sulfate, Na_2SO_4, are sodium ion, Na^+, and sulfate ion, SO_4^{2-}. The sodium ion is derived from the strong base NaOH. The sulfate ion is derived from the weak acid, HSO_4^-.

$$SO_4^{2-}(aq) + H_2O(l) \rightleftharpoons HSO_4^-(aq) + OH^-(aq)$$

A solution of sodium sulfate is **basic**.
c) The two ions that comprise lithium hypochlorite, LiClO, are lithium ion, Li^+, and hypochlorite ion, ClO^-. Lithium ion is derived from the strong base LiOH. Hypochlorite ion is derived from the weak acid, HClO (hypochlorous acid).

$$ClO^-(aq) + H_2O(l) \rightleftharpoons HClO(aq) + OH^-(aq)$$

A solution of lithium hypochlorite is **basic**.

16.127   Plan: For each salt, first break into the ions present in solution and then determine if either ion acts as a weak acid or weak base to change the pH of the solution. Cations are neutral if they are from a strong base; other cations will be weakly acidic. Anions are neutral if they are from a strong acid; other anions are weakly basic. Use K_a and K_b values to rank the pH; the larger the K_a value, the lower the pH and the larger the K_b value, the higher the pH.
Solution:
a) Order of increasing pH: $\mathbf{Fe(NO_3)_2 < KNO_3 < K_2SO_3 < K_2S}$ (assuming concentrations equivalent)
Iron(II) nitrate, $Fe(NO_3)_2$, is an acidic solution because the iron ion is a small, highly charged metal ion that acts as a weak acid and nitrate ion is the conjugate base of a strong acid, so it does not influence pH.
Potassium nitrate, KNO_3, is a neutral solution because potassium ion is the conjugate acid of a strong base and nitrate ion is the conjugate base of a strong acid, so neither influences solution pH.
Potassium sulfite, K_2SO_3, and potassium sulfide, K_2S, are similar in that the potassium ion does not influence solution pH, but the anions do because they are conjugate bases of weak acids. K_a for HSO_3^- is $6.5\text{x}10^{-8}$, so K_b for SO_3^- is $1.5\text{x}10^{-7}$, which indicates that sulfite ion is a weak base. K_a for HS^- is $1\text{x}10^{-17}$ (see the table of K_a values for polyprotic acids), so sulfide ion has a K_b equal to $1\text{x}10^3$. Sulfide ion is thus a strong base. The solution of a strong base will have a greater concentration of hydroxide ions (and higher pH) than a solution of a weak base of equivalent concentrations.
b) In order of increasing pH: $\mathbf{NaHSO_4 < NH_4NO_3 < NaHCO_3 < Na_2CO_3}$
In solutions of ammonium nitrate, only the ammonium will influence pH by dissociating as a weak acid:

$$NH_4^+(aq) + H_2O(l) \rightleftharpoons NH_3(aq) + H_3O^+(aq)$$

with $K_a = 1.0\text{x}10^{-14}/1.8\text{x}10^{-5} = 5.6\text{x}10^{-10}$
Therefore, the solution of ammonium nitrate is acidic.
In solutions of sodium hydrogen sulfate, only HSO_4^- will influence pH. The hydrogen sulfate ion is amphoteric so both the acid and base dissociations must be evaluated for influence on pH. As a base, HSO_4^- is the conjugate base of a strong acid, so it will not influence pH. As an acid, HSO_4^- is the conjugate acid of a weak base, so the acid dissociation applies:

$$HSO_4^-(aq) + H_2O(l) \rightleftharpoons SO_4^{2-}(aq) + H_3O^+(aq) \ K_{a2} = 1.2\text{x}10^{-2}$$

In solutions of sodium hydrogen carbonate, only the HCO_3^- will influence pH and it, like HSO_4^-, is amphoteric:

As an acid: $HCO_3^-(aq) + H_2O(l) \rightleftharpoons CO_3^{2-}(aq) + H_3O^+(aq)$

$K_a = 4.7\text{x}10^{-11}$, the second K_a for carbonic acid

As a base: $HCO_3^-(aq) + H_2O(l) \rightleftharpoons H_2CO_3(aq) + OH^-(aq)$

$K_b = 1.0\text{x}10^{-14}/4.5\text{x}10^{-7} = 2.2\text{x}10^{-8}$

Since $K_b > K_a$, a solution of sodium hydrogen carbonate is basic.
In a solution of sodium carbonate, only CO_3^{2-} will influence pH by acting as a weak base:

$$CO_3^{2-}(aq) + H_2O(l) \rightleftharpoons HCO_3^-(aq) + OH^-(aq)$$

$K_b = 1.0\text{x}10^{-14}/4.7\text{x}10^{-11} = 2.1\text{x}10^{-4}$

Therefore, the solution of sodium carbonate is basic.

Two of the solutions are acidic. Since the K_a of HSO_4^- is greater than that of NH_4^+, the solution of sodium hydrogen sulfate has a lower pH than the solution of ammonium nitrate, assuming the concentrations are relatively close.

Two of the solutions are basic. Since the K_b of CO_3^{2-} is greater than that of HCO_3^-, the solution of sodium carbonate has a higher pH than the solution of sodium hydrogen carbonate, assuming concentrations are not extremely different.

16.129 (a) Both methoxide ion and amide ion produce OH^- in aqueous solution. In water, the strongest base possible is OH^-. Since both bases produce OH^- in water, both bases appear equally strong.

(b) $CH_3O^-(aq) + H_2O(l) \rightarrow OH^-(aq) + CH_3OH(aq)$
         $NH_2^-(aq) + H_2O(l) \rightarrow OH^-(aq) + NH_3(aq)$

16.131 Ammonia, NH_3, is a more basic solvent than H_2O. In a more basic solvent, weak acids like HF act like strong acids and are 100% dissociated.

16.133 A Lewis acid is defined as an electron-pair acceptor, while a Brønsted-Lowry acid is a proton donor. If only the proton in a Brønsted-Lowry acid is considered, then every Brønsted-Lowry acid fits the definition of a Lewis acid since the proton is accepting an electron pair when it bonds with a base. There are Lewis acids that do not include a proton, so all Lewis acids are not Brønsted-Lowry acids.

A Lewis base is defined as an electron-pair donor and a Brønsted-Lowry base is a proton acceptor. In this case, the two definitions are essentially the same.

16.134 a) **No**, a weak Brønsted-Lowry base is not necessarily a weak Lewis base. For example, water molecules solvate metal ions very well:

$$Ni^{2+}(aq) + 4H_2O(l) \rightleftharpoons Ni(H_2O)_4^{2+}(aq)$$

Water is a very weak Brønsted-Lowry base, but forms the Zn complex fairly well and is a reasonably strong Lewis base.

b) The **cyanide ion** has a lone pair to donate from either the C or the N, and donates an electron pair to the $Cu(H_2O)_6^{2+}$ complex. It is the Lewis base for the forward direction of this reaction. In the reverse direction, **water** donates one of the electron pairs on the oxygen to the $Cu(CN)_4^{2-}$ and is the Lewis base.

c) Because $K_c > 1$, the reaction proceeds in the direction written (left to right) and is driven by the stronger Lewis base, the **cyanide ion**.

16.137 Plan: A Lewis acid is an electron-pair acceptor and therefore must be able to accept an electron pair. A Lewis base is an electron-pair donor and therefore must have an electron pair to donate.
Solution:
a) Cu^{2+} is a **Lewis acid** because it accepts electron pairs from molecules such as water.
b) Cl^- is a **Lewis base** because it has lone pairs of electrons it can donate to a Lewis acid.
c) Tin(II) chloride, $SnCl_2$, is a compound with a structure similar to carbon dioxide, so it will act as a **Lewis acid** to form an additional bond to the tin.
d) Oxygen difluoride, OF_2, is a **Lewis base** with a structure similar to water, where the oxygen has lone pairs of electrons that it can donate to a Lewis acid.

16.139 Plan: A Lewis acid is an electron-pair acceptor and therefore must be able to accept an electron pair. A Lewis base is an electron-pair donor and therefore must have an electron pair to donate.
Solution:
a) The boron atom in boron trifluoride, BF_3, is electron deficient (has six electrons instead of eight) and can accept an electron pair; it is a **Lewis acid**.
b) The sulfide ion, S^{2-}, can donate any of four electron pairs and is a **Lewis base**.
c) The Lewis dot structure for the sulfite ion, SO_3^{2-}, shows lone pairs on the sulfur and on the oxygen atoms. The sulfur atom has a lone electron pair that it can donate more easily than the electronegative oxygen in the formation of an adduct. The sulfite ion is a **Lewis base**.
d) Sulfur trioxide, SO_3, acts as a **Lewis acid**.

16.141 Plan: A Lewis acid is an electron-pair acceptor while a Lewis base is an electron-pair donor.
Solution:
a) Sodium ion is the Lewis acid because it is accepting electron pairs from water, the Lewis base.

$$Na^+ \quad + \quad 6H_2O \quad \rightleftharpoons \quad Na(H_2O)_6^+$$

Lewis acid   Lewis base   adduct

b) The oxygen from water donates a lone pair to the carbon in carbon dioxide. Water is the Lewis base and carbon dioxide the Lewis acid.

$$CO_2 \quad + \quad H_2O \quad \rightleftharpoons \quad H_2CO_3$$

Lewis acid   Lewis base   adduct

c) Fluoride ion donates an electron pair to form a bond with boron in BF_4^-. The fluoride ion is the Lewis base and the boron trifluoride is the Lewis acid.

$$F^- \quad + \quad BF_3 \quad \rightleftharpoons \quad BF_4^-$$

Lewis base   Lewis acid   adduct

16.143 Plan: In an Arrhenius acid-base reaction, H^+ ions react with OH^- ions to produce H_2O. In a Brønsted-Lowry acid-base reaction, an acid donates H^+ to a base. In a Lewis acid-base reaction, an electron pair is donated by the base and accepted by the acid.
Solution:
a) Since neither H^+ nor OH^- is involved, this is not an Arrhenius acid-base reaction. Since there is no exchange of protons, this is not a Brønsted-Lowry reaction. This reaction is only classified as **Lewis acid-base reaction**, where Ag^+ is the acid and NH_3 is the base.
b) Again, no OH^- is involved, so this is not an Arrhenius acid-base reaction. This is an exchange of a proton, from H_2SO_4 to NH_3, so it is a **Brønsted-Lowry acid-base reaction**. Since the Lewis definition is most inclusive, anything that is classified as a Brønsted-Lowry (or Arrhenius) reaction is automatically classified as a **Lewis acid-base reaction**.
c) This is not an acid-base reaction.
d) For the same reasons listed in a), this reaction is only classified as **Lewis acid-base reaction**, where $AlCl_3$ is the acid and Cl^- is the base.

16.146 Plan: Calculate the $[H^+]$ using the pH values given. Determine the value of K_w from the pK_w given. The $[H^+]$ is combined with the K_w value at 37°C to find $[OH^-]$ using $K_w = [H^+][OH^-]$.
Solution:

$$K_w = 10^{-pK_w} = 10^{-13.63} = 2.34423 \times 10^{-14}$$
$$K_w = [H^+][OH^-] = 2.34423 \times 10^{-14} \text{ at } 37°C$$

$[H^+]$ range
High value (low pH) = $10^{-pH} = 10^{-7.35} = 4.46684 \times 10^{-8} = 4.5 \times 10^{-8}$ mol/L H^+
Low value (high pH) = $10^{-pH} = 10^{-7.45} = 3.54813 \times 10^{-8} = 3.5 \times 10^{-8}$ mol/L H^+
Range: 3.5×10^{-8} to 4.5×10^{-8} mol/L H^+

$[OH^-]$ range
$$K_w = [H_3O^+][OH^-] = 2.34423 \times 10^{-14} \text{ at } 37°C$$

$$[OH^-] = \frac{K_w}{[H_3O]^+}$$

High value (high pH) = $\dfrac{2.34423 \times 10^{-14}}{3.54813 \times 10^{-8}} = 6.60695 \times 10^{-7} = 6.6 \times 10^{-7}$ mol/L OH^-

Low value (low pH) = $\dfrac{2.34423 \times 10^{-14}}{4.46684 \times 10^{-8}} = 5.24807 \times 10^{-7} = 5.2 \times 10^{-7}$ mol/L OH^-

Range: 5.2×10^{-7} to 6.6×10^{-7} mol/L OH^-

16.147   a) Acids will vary in the amount they dissociate (acid strength) depending on the acid-base character of the solvent. Water and methanol have different acid-base characters.
b) The K_a is the measure of an acid's strength. A stronger acid has a smaller pK_a. Therefore, phenol is a stronger acid in water than it is in methanol. In other words, water more readily accepts a proton from phenol than does methanol, i.e., methanol is a weaker base than water.
c) $C_6H_5OH(solvated) + CH_3OH(l) \rightleftharpoons CH_3OH_2^+(solvated) + C_6H_5O^-(solvated)$

The term "*solvated*" is analogous to "*aqueous*." "*Aqueous*" would be incorrect in this case because the reaction does not take place in water.
d) In the autoionization process, one methanol molecule is the proton donor while another methanol molecule is the proton acceptor.

$$CH_3OH(l) + CH_3OH(l) \rightleftharpoons CH_3O^-(solvated) + CH_3OH_2^+(solvated)$$

In this equation "(*solvated*)" indicates that the molecules are solvated by methanol.
The equilibrium constant for this reaction is the autoionization constant of methanol:
$$K = [CH_3O^-][CH_3OH_2^+]$$

16.150   Plan: A Lewis acid is an electron-pair acceptor and a Lewis base is an electron-pair donor. Recall that n is the main energy level and l is the orbital type.
Solution:
a) $SnCl_4$ is the Lewis acid accepting an electron pair from $(CH_3)_3N$, the Lewis base.
b) Tin is the element in the Lewis acid accepting the electron pair. The electron configuration of tin is $[Kr]5s^24d^{10}5p^2$. The four bonds to tin are formed by sp^3 hybrid orbitals, which completely fill the $5s$ and $5p$ orbitals. The **5d** orbitals are empty and available for the bond with trimethylamine.

16.151   Plan: A 10-fold dilution means that the chemist takes 1 mL of the 1.0×10^{-5} mol/L solution and dilutes it to 10 mL (or dilute 10 mL to 100 mL). The chemist then dilutes the diluted solution in a 1:10 ratio, and repeats this process for the next two successive dilutions. $c_1V_1 = c_2V_2$ can be used to find the concentration (mol/L) after each dilution. After each dilution, find $[H^+]$ and calculate the pH.
Solution:
Hydrochloric acid is a strong acid that completely dissociates in water. Therefore, the concentration of H^+ is the same as the starting acid concentration: $[H^+] = [HCl]$. The original solution pH:
$\quad\quad$ pH $= -\log(1.0 \times 10^{-5}) = \textbf{5.00} = \textbf{pH}$
Dilution 1: $c_1V_1 = c_2V_2$
$\quad\quad$ $(1.0 \times 10^{-5}$ mol/L$)(1.0$ mL$) = (x)(10.$ mL$)$
$\quad\quad$ $[H^+]_{HCl} = 1.0 \times 10^{-6}$ mol/L H^+
$\quad\quad$ pH $= -\log(1.0 \times 10^{-6}) = \textbf{6.00}$
Dilution 2:
$\quad\quad$ $(1.0 \times 10^{-6}$ mol/L$)(1.0$ mL$) = (x)(10.$ mL$)$
$\quad\quad$ $[H^+]_{HCl} = 1.0 \times 10^{-7}$ mol/L H^+
Once the concentration of strong acid is close to the concentration of H_3O^+ from water autoionization, the $[H_3O^+]$ in the solution does not equal the initial concentration of the strong acid. The calculation of $[H_3O^+]$ must be based on the water ionization equilibrium:
$$H_2O(l) + H_2O(l) \rightleftharpoons H_3O^+(aq) + OH^-(aq) \text{ with } K_w = 1.0 \times 10^{-14} \text{ at } 25°C.$$

The dilution gives an initial $[H_3O^+]$ of 1.0×10^{-7} mol/L. Assuming that the initial concentration of hydroxide ions is zero, a reaction table is set up.

Concentration (mol/L)	$2H_2O(l)$	$\rightleftharpoons$	$H_3O^+(aq)$	+	$OH^-(aq)$
Initial	—		1×10^{-7}		0
Change	—		$+x$		$+x$
Equilibrium	—		$1 \times 10^{-7} + x$		x

$K_w = [H^+][OH^-] = (1 \times 10^{-7} + x)(x) = 1.0 \times 10^{-14}$
Set up as a quadratic equation: $x^2 + 1.0 \times 10^{-7} x - 1.0 \times 10^{-14} = 0$
$\quad\quad\quad\quad$ $a = 1 \quad\quad b = 1.0 \times 10^{-7} \quad\quad c = -1.0 \times 10^{-14}$

$$x = \frac{-1.0\times10^{-7} \pm \sqrt{\left(1.0\times10^{-7}\right)^2 - 4(1)\left(-1.0\times10^{-14}\right)}}{2(1)}$$

$x = 6.18034\times10^{-8}$

$[H^+] = (1.0\times10^{-7} + x)\ mol/L = (1.0\times10^{-7} + 6.18034\times10^{-8})\ mol/L = 1.618034\times10^{-7}\ mol/L\ H^+$

$pH = -\log [H^+] = -\log (1.618034\times10^{-7}) = 6.79101 = \mathbf{6.79}$

Dilution 3:

$(1.0\times10^{-7}\ mol/L)(1.0\ mL) = (x)(10.\ mL)$

$[H^+]_{HCl} = 1.0\times10^{-8}\ mol/L\ H^+$

The dilution gives an initial $[H^+]$ of 1.0×10^{-8} mol/L. Assuming that the initial concentration of hydroxide ions is zero, a reaction table is set up.

Concentration (mol/L)	$2H_2O(l)$	$\rightleftharpoons$	$H_3O^+(aq)$	+	$OH^-(aq)$
Initial	—		1×10^{-8}		0
Change			+x		+x
Equilibrium	—		$1\times10^{-8} + x$		x

$K_w = [H^+][OH^-] = (1\times10^{-8} + x)(x) = 1.0\times10^{-14}$

Set up as a quadratic equation: $x^2 + 1.0\times10^{-8}\,x - 1.0\times10^{-14} = 0$

$a = 1 \qquad b = 1.0\times10^{-8} \qquad c = -1.0\times10^{-14}$

$$x = \frac{-1.0\times10^{-8} \pm \sqrt{\left(1.0\times10^{-8}\right)^2 - 4(1)\left(-1.0\times10^{-14}\right)}}{2(1)}$$

$x = 9.51249\times10^{-8}$

$[H^+] = (1.0\times10^{-8} + x)\ mol/L = (1.0\times10^{-8} + 9.51249\times10^{-8})\ mol/L = 1.051249\times10^{-7}\ mol/L\ H^+$

$pH = -\log [H^+] = -\log (1.051249\times10^{-7}) = 6.97829 = \mathbf{6.98}$

Dilution 4:

$(1.0\times10^{-8}\ mol/L)(1.0\ mL) = (x)(10.\ mL)$

$[H^+]_{HCl} = 1.0\times10^{-9}\ mol/L\ H^+$

The dilution gives an initial $[H^+]$ of 1.0×10^{-9} mol/L. Assuming that the initial concentration of hydroxide ions is zero, a reaction table is set up.

Concentration (mol/L)	$2H_2O(l)$	$\rightleftharpoons$	$H_3O^+(aq)$	+	$OH^-(aq)$
Initial	—		1×10^{-9}		0
Change	—		+x		+x
Equilibrium	—		$1\times10^{-9} + x$		x

$K_w = [H^+][OH^-] = (1\times10^{-9} + x)(x) = 1.0\times10^{-14}$

Set up as a quadratic equation: $x^2 + 1.0\times10^{-9}\,x - 1.0\times10^{-14} = 0$

$a = 1 \qquad b = 1.0\times10^{-9} \qquad c = -1.0\times10^{-14}$

$$x = \frac{-1.0\times10^{-9} \pm \sqrt{\left(1.0\times10^{-9}\right)^2 - 4(1)\left(-1.0\times10^{-14}\right)}}{2(1)}$$

$x = 9.95012\times10^{-8}$

$[H^+] = (1.0\times10^{-9} + x)\ mol/L = (1.0\times10^{-9} + 9.95012\times10^{-8})\ mol/L = 1.005012\times10^{-7}\ mol/L\ H^+$

$pH = -\log [H^+] = -\log (1.005012\times10^{-7}) = 6.9978 = \mathbf{7.00}$

As the HCl solution is diluted, the pH of the solution becomes closer to 7.0. Continued dilutions will not significantly change the pH from 7.0. Thus, a solution with a basic pH cannot be made by adding acid to water.

16.157   Plan: Determine the hydrogen ion concentration from the pH. The concentration (mol/L) and the volume will give the number of moles, and with the aid of Avogadro's number, the number of ions may be found.
Solution:

$c\ H^+ = 10^{-pH} = 10^{-6.2} = 6.30957\times10^{-7}\ mol/L$

$$\left(\frac{6.30957\times10^{-7}\ mol\ H_3O^+}{L}\right)\left(\frac{10^{-3}\ L}{1\ mL}\right)\left(\frac{1250.\ mL}{d}\right)\left(\frac{7\ d}{1\ wk}\right)\left(\frac{6.022\times10^{23}\ H_3O^+}{1\ mol\ H_3O^+}\right) = 3.32467\times10^{18} = \mathbf{3\times10^{18}\ H^+}$$

The pH has only one significant figure, and limits the significant figures in the final answer.

16.160 Plan: Determine K_b using the relationship $K_b = 10^{-pK_b}$. Write the base-dissociation equation and set up a reaction table in which x = the amount of OH^- produced. Use the K_b expression to find x. From $[OH^-]$, $[H_3O^+]$ and then pH can be calculated.

Solution:

$K_b = 10^{pK_b} = 10^{-5.91} = 1.23027 \times 10^{-6}$

	TRIS(aq)	+ H_2O(l)	$\rightleftharpoons$	OH^-(aq) +	$HTRIS^+$(aq)
Initial	0.075	—		0	0
Change	$-x$			$+x$	$+x$
Equilibrium	$0.075 - x$			x	x

$$K_b = 1.23027 \times 10^{-6} = \frac{\left[HTRIS^+\right]\left[OH^-\right]}{\left[TRIS\right]}$$

$$K_b = 1.23027 \times 10^{-6} = \frac{[x][x]}{[0.075 - x]} \qquad \text{Assume x is small compared to 0.075.}$$

$$K_b = 1.23027 \times 10^{-6} = \frac{[x][x]}{[0.075]}$$

$x = [OH^-] = 3.03760 \times 10^{-4}$ mol/L OH^-

Check assumption that x is small compared to 0.075:

$$\frac{3.03760 \times 10^{-4}}{0.075}(100\%) = 0.40\% \text{ error, so the assumption is valid.}$$

$$[H]^+ = \frac{K_w}{\left[OH^-\right]} = \frac{1.0 \times 10^{-14}}{3.03760 \times 10^{-4}} = 3.292073 \times 10^{-11} \text{ mol/L}$$

$pH = -\log[H^+] = -\log(3.292073 \times 10^{-11}) = 10.4825 = \mathbf{10.48}$

16.162 The pH is dependent on the *molar* concentration of H_3O^+. Convert % w/v to concentration (mol/L), and use the K_a of acetic acid to determine $[H_3O^+]$ from the equilibrium expression.

Convert % w/v to concentration (mol/L)using the molecular weight of acetic acid (CH_3COOH):

$$\text{Concentration (mol/L)} = \left(\frac{5.0 \text{ g } CH_3COOH}{100 \text{ mL solution}}\right)\left(\frac{1 \text{ mol } CH_3COOH}{60.05 \text{ g } CH_3COOH}\right)\left(\frac{1 \text{ mL}}{10^{-3} \text{ L}}\right) = 0.832639 \text{ mol/L } CH_3COOH$$

Acetic acid dissociates in water according to the following equation and equilibrium expression:

$$CH_3COOH(aq) + H_2O(l) \rightleftharpoons CH_3COO^-(aq) + H_3O^+(aq)$$

Initial	0.832639	—	0	0
Change	$-x$		$+x$	$+x$
Equilibrium	$0.832639 - x$		x	x

$$K_a = 1.8 \times 10^{-5} = \frac{\left[H_3O^+\right]\left[CH_3COO^-\right]}{\left[CH_3COOH\right]}$$

$$K_a = 1.8 \times 10^{-5} = \frac{[x][x]}{[0.832639 - x]} \qquad \text{Assume x is small compared to 0.832639.}$$

$$K_a = 1.8 \times 10^{-5} = \frac{[x][x]}{[0.832639]}$$

$x = 3.8714 \times 10^{-3}$ mol/L = $[H^+]$

Check assumption: $[3.871 \times 10^{-3}/0.832639]$ x 100% = 0.46%, therefore the assumption is good.

$pH = -\log[H^+] = -\log(3.8714 \times 10^{-3}) = 2.412132 = \mathbf{2.41}$

16.164 <u>Plan:</u> Assuming that the pH in the specific cellular environment is equal to the optimum pH for the enzyme, the hydronium ion concentrations are $[H^+] = 10^{-pH}$.
<u>Solution:</u>
Salivary amylase, mouth: $[H^+] = 10^{-6.8} = 1.58489 \times 10^{-7} = \mathbf{2 \times 10^{-7}\ mol/L}$
Pepsin, stomach: $[H^+] = 10^{-2.0} = \mathbf{1 \times 10^{-2}\ mol/L}$
Trypsin, pancreas: $[H^+] = 10^{-9.5} = 3.1623 \times 10^{-10} = \mathbf{3 \times 10^{-10}\ mol/L}$

16.168   The freezing point depression equation is required to determine the molality of the solution.
$$\Delta T = [0.00 - (-1.93°C)] = 1.93°C = iK_f m$$
Temporarily assume $i = 1$.

$$m = \frac{\Delta T}{iK_f} = \frac{1.93°C}{(1)(1.86°C/m)} = 1.037634\ m = 1.037634\ mol/L$$

This molality is the total molality of all species in the solution, and is equal to their concentration (mol/L). From the equilibrium:

$$ClCH_2COOH(aq) + H_2O(l) \rightleftharpoons H_3O^+(aq) + ClCH_2COO^-(aq)$$

Initial	1.000 mol/L	x	x
Change	−x	+x	+x
Equilibrium	1.000 − x	x	x

The total concentration of all species is:
$[ClCH_2COOH] + [H_3O^+] + [ClCH_2COO^-] = 1.037634\ mol/L$
$[1.000 - x] + [x] + [x] = 1.000 + x = 1.037634\ mol/L$
$x = 0.037634\ mol/L$

$$K_a = \frac{\left[H_3O^+\right]\left[CH_3COO^-\right]}{\left[CH_3COOH\right]}$$

$$K_a = \frac{(0.037634)(0.037634)}{(1.000 - 0.037634)} = 0.0014717 = \mathbf{0.00147}$$

16.170   a) The two ions that comprise this salt are Ca^{2+} (derived from the strong base $Ca(OH)_2$) and $CH_3CH_2COO^-$ (derived from the weak acid, propionic acid, CH_3CH_2COOH). A salt derived from a strong base and weak acid produces a **basic** solution.
        Ca^{2+} does not react with water.
        $$CH_3CH_2COO^-(aq) + H_2O(l) \rightleftharpoons CH_3CH_2COOH(aq) + OH^-(aq)$$

b) Calcium propionate is a soluble salt and dissolves in water to yield two propionate ions:
        $$Ca(CH_3CH_2COO)_2(s) + H_2O(l) \rightarrow Ca^{2+}(aq) + 2CH_3CH_2COO^-(aq)$$
        The concentration (mol/L)of the solution is:
Concentration (mol/L) =

$$\left(\frac{8.75\ g\ Ca(CH_3CH_2COO)_2}{0.500\ L}\right)\left(\frac{1\ mol\ Ca(CH_3CH_2COO)_2}{186.22\ g\ Ca(CH_3CH_2COO)_2}\right)\left(\frac{2\ mol\ CH_3CH_2COO^-}{1\ mol\ Ca(CH_3CH_2COO)_2}\right)$$

        $= 0.1879497\ mol/L\ CH_3CH_2COO^-$

$$CH_3CH_2COO^- + H_2O \rightleftharpoons CH_3CH_2COOH + OH^-$$

Initial	0.1879497 mol/L	0	0
Change	−x	+x	+x
Equilibrium	0.1879497 − x	x	x

$K_b = K_w/K_a = (1.0 \times 10^{-14})/(1.3 \times 10^{-5}) = 7.69231 \times 10^{-10}$

$$K_b = 7.69231 \times 10^{-10} = \frac{\left[CH_3CH_2COOH\right]\left[OH^-\right]}{\left[CH_3CH_2COO^-\right]}$$

$$K_b = 7.69231 \times 10^{-10} = \frac{(x)(x)}{(0.1879497 - x)} \qquad \text{Assume x is small compared to 0.1879497.}$$

$$K_b = 7.69231 \times 10^{-10} = \frac{(x)(x)}{(0.1879497)}$$

$$x = 1.202401 \times 10^{-5} \text{ mol/L} = [OH^-]$$

Check assumption: $[1.202401 \times 10^{-5}/0.1879497] \times 100\% = 0.006\%$, therefore the assumption is good.

$$[H]^+ = K_w/[OH^-] = (1.0 \times 10^{-14})/(1.202401 \times 10^{-5}) = 8.31669 \times 10^{-10} \text{ mol/L } H^+$$

$$pH = -\log [H^+] = -\log (8.31669 \times 10^{-10}) = 9.0800 = \textbf{9.08}$$

16.176 $NH_2(CH_2)_4NH_2(aq) + H_2O(l) \rightleftharpoons NH_2(CH_2)_4NH_3^+(aq) + OH^-(aq)$

           $0.10 - x$ x x

$$x = [OH^-] = 2.1 \times 10^{-3}$$

$$K_b = \frac{\left[NH_2(CH_2)_4 NH_3^+\right]\left[OH^-\right]}{\left[NH_2(CH_2)_4 NH_2\right]} = \frac{\left[2.1 \times 10^{-3}\right]\left[2.1 \times 10^{-3}\right]}{\left[0.10 - 2.1 \times 10^{-3}\right]} = 4.5045965 \times 10^{-5} = \textbf{4.5} \times \textbf{10}^{-5}$$

16.179 Plan: Use Le Chatelier's principle.
Solution:
a) The concentration of oxygen is higher in the lungs so the equilibrium shifts to the right.
b) In an oxygen deficient environment, the equilibrium would shift to the left to release oxygen.
c) A decrease in the $[H_3O^+]$ concentration would shift the equilibrium to the right. More oxygen is absorbed, but it will be more difficult to remove the O_2.
d) An increase in the $[H_3O^+]$ concentration would shift the equilibrium to the left. Less oxygen is absorbed, but it will be easier to remove the O_2.

16.181 Plan: The concentration (mol/L) of the acid is calculated by dividing moles of acid by the volume of solution. Set up a reaction table for the dissociation of the acid, in which x = the amount of propanoate ion at equilibrium. The freezing point depression is used to calculate the apparent molality and thus the apparent concentration (mol/L)of the solution. The total concentration of all species at equilibrium equals the apparent concentration (mol/L)and is used to find x. Percent dissociation is the concentration of dissociated acid divided by the initial concentration of the acid and multiplied by 100.
Solution:
a) Calculate the concentration (mol/L)of the solution (before acid dissocation).

$$c = \left(\frac{7.500 \text{ g } CH_3CH_2COOH}{100.0 \text{ mL solution}}\right)\left(\frac{1 \text{ mL}}{10^{-3} \text{ L}}\right)\left(\frac{1 \text{ mol } CH_3CH_2COOH}{74.08 \text{ g } CH_3CH_2COOH}\right) = 1.012419 \text{ mol/L}$$

$$= \textbf{1.012 mol/L } CH_3CH_2COOH$$

b) The freezing point depression equation is required to determine the molality of the solution.

$$\Delta T = iK_f m = [0.000 - (-1.890°C)] = 1.890°C$$

Temporarily assume $i = 1$.

$$m = \frac{\Delta T}{iK_f} = \frac{1.890°C}{(1)(1.86°C/m)} = 1.016129032 \, m = 1.016129032 \text{ mol/L}$$

This molality is the total molality of all species in the solution, and is equal to their concentration.
From the equilibrium:

              $CH_3CH_2COOH(aq) + H_2O(l) \rightleftharpoons H_3O^+(aq) + CH_3CH_2COO^-(aq)$

Initial	1.012419 mol/L	0	0
Change	$-x$	$+x$	$+x$
Equilibrium	$1.012419 - x$	x	x

The total concentration of all species is:

$$[CH_3CH_2COOH] + [H_3O^+] + [CH_3CH_2COO^-] = 1.016129032 \text{ mol/L}$$

$$[1.012419 - x] + [x] + [x] = 1.012419 + x = 1.016129032 \text{ mol/L}$$

$$x = 0.00371003 = \textbf{0.004 mol/L } CH_3CH_2COO^-$$

c) The percent dissociation is the amount dissociated (x from part b)) divided by the original concentration from part a).

$$\text{Percent dissociation} = \frac{0.00371003 \text{ mol / L}}{1.012419 \text{ mol / L}} (100\%) = 0.366452 \% = \textbf{0.4\%}$$

16.182 Plan: For parts a) and b), write the base-dissociation reaction and the K_b expression. Set up a reaction table in which x = the amount of reacted base and the concentration of OH^-. Solve for x, calculate $[H_3O]^+$, and find the pH. For parts c) and d), write the acid-dissociation reaction for the conjugate acid of quinine. Find the K_a value from $K_w = K_a \times K_b$. Set up a reaction table in which x = dissociated acid and the concentration of $[H_3O]^+$, and find the pH.
Solution:
Note that both pK_b values only have one significant figure. This will limit the final answers.
$K_{b \text{ (tertiary amine N)}} = 10^{-pK_b} = 10^{-5.1} = 7.94328\times10^{-6}$
$K_{b \text{ (aromatic ring N)}} = 10^{-pK_b} = 10^{-9.7} = 1.995262\times10^{-10}$
a) Ignoring the smaller K_b:

$$C_{20}H_{24}N_2O_2(aq) + H_2O(l) \rightleftharpoons OH^-(aq) + HC_{20}H_{24}N_2O_2^+(aq)$$

Initial	1.6×10^{-3} mol/L	0	0
Change	$-x$	$+x$	$+x$
Equilibrium	$1.6\times10^{-3} - x$	x	x

$$K_b = 7.94328\times10^{-6} = \frac{\left[HC_{20}H_{24}N_2O_2^+\right]\left[OH^-\right]}{\left[H_2C_{20}H_{24}N_2O_2\right]}$$

$$K_b = 7.94328\times10^{-6} = \frac{[x][x]}{\left[1.6\times10^{-3} - x\right]} \qquad \text{Assume x is small compared to } 1.6\times10^{-3}.$$

$$K_b = 7.94328\times10^{-6} = \frac{[x][x]}{\left[1.6\times10^{-3}\right]}$$

$$x = 1.127353\times10^{-4}$$

Check assumption that x is small compared to 1.6×10^{-3}:

$$\frac{1.127353\times10^{-4}}{1.6 \times 10^{-3}} (100\%) = 7\% \text{ error, so the assumption is not valid.}$$

Since the error is greater than 5%, it is not acceptable to assume x is small compared to 1.6×10^{-3}, and it is necessary to use the quadratic equation.
$x^2 = (7.94328\times10^{-6})(1.6\times10^{-3} - x) = 1.27092\times10^{-8} - 7.94328\times10^{-6}x$
$x^2 + 7.94328\times10^{-6} x - 1.270925\times10^{-8} = 0$
$\qquad a = 1 \qquad b = 7.94328\times10^{-6} \qquad c = -1.27092\times10^{-8}$

$$x = \frac{-b \pm \sqrt{b^2 - 4ac}}{2a}$$

$$x = \frac{-7.94328\times10^{-6} \pm \sqrt{\left(7.94328\times10^{-6}\right)^2 - 4(1)\left(-1.270925\times10^{-8}\right)}}{2(1)} = 1.08834\times10^{-4} \text{ mol/L } OH^-$$

$$[H]^+ = \frac{K_w}{[OH^-]} = \frac{1.0\times10^{-14}}{1.08834\times10^{-4}} = 9.18830513\times10^{-11} \text{ mol/L } H^+$$

$$pH = -\log[H^+] = -\log(9.18830513\times10^{-11}) = 10.03676 = \textbf{10.0}$$

b) (Assume the aromatic N is unaffected by the tertiary amine N.) Use the K_b value for the aromatic nitrogen.

$$C_{20}H_{24}N_2O_2(aq) + H_2O(l) \rightleftharpoons OH^-(aq) + HC_{20}H_{24}N_2O_2^+(aq)$$

Initial	1.6×10^{-3} mol/L	0	0
Change	$-x$	$+x$	$+x$
Equilibrium	$1.6\times10^{-3} - x$	x	x

$$K_b = 1.995262 \times 10^{-10} = \frac{\left[HC_{20}H_{24}N_2O_2^+ \right]\left[OH^- \right]}{\left[C_{20}H_{24}N_2O_2 \right]}$$

$$K_b = 1.995262 \times 10^{-10} = \frac{[x][x]}{\left[1.6 \times 10^{-3} - x \right]}$$ Assume x is small compared to 1.6×10^{-3}.

$$K_b = 1.995262 \times 10^{-10} = \frac{[x][x]}{\left[1.6 \times 10^{-3} \right]}$$

x = 5.65015×10^{-7} mol/L OH$^-$

The hydroxide ion from the smaller K_b is much smaller than the hydroxide ion from the larger K_b (compare the powers of ten in the concentration).

c) $HC_{20}H_{24}N_2O_2^+(aq) + H_2O(l) \rightleftharpoons H_3O^+(aq) + C_{20}H_{24}N_2O_2(aq)$

Initial	0.33 mol/L	0	0
Change	$-x$	$+x$	$+x$
Equilibrium	0.33 $-$ x	x	x

$$K_a = \frac{K_w}{K_b} = \frac{1.0 \times 10^{-14}}{7.94328 \times 10^{-6}} = 1.25893 \times 10^{-9}$$

$$K_a = 1.25893 \times 10^{-9} = \frac{\left[H_3O^+ \right]\left[C_{20}H_{24}N_2O_2 \right]}{\left[HC_{20}H_{24}N_2O_2^+ \right]}$$

$$K_a = 1.25893 \times 10^{-9} = \frac{(x)(x)}{(0.33 - x)}$$ Assume x is small compared to 0.33.

$$K_a = 1.25893 \times 10^{-9} = \frac{(x)(x)}{(0.33)}$$

$[H^+]$ = x = 2.038252×10^{-5} mol/L

Check assumption that x is small compared to 0.33:

$$\frac{2.038252 \times 10^{-5}}{0.33}(100\%) = 0.006\%.$$ The assumption is good.

pH = $-\log [H^+]$ = $-\log (2.038252 \times 10^{-5})$ = 4.69074 = **4.7**

d) Quinine hydrochloride will be indicated as QHCl.

$$M = \left(\frac{1.5\%}{100\%} \right)\left(\frac{1.0 \text{ g}}{\text{mL}} \right)\left(\frac{1 \text{ mL}}{10^{-3} \text{ L}} \right)\left(\frac{1 \text{ mol QHCl}}{360.87 \text{ g QHCl}} \right) = 0.041566 \text{ mol/L}$$

$HC_{20}H_{24}N_2O_2^+(aq) + H_2O(l) \rightleftharpoons H_3O^+(aq) + C_{20}H_{24}N_2O_2(aq)$

Initial	0.041566 mol/L	0	0
Change	$-x$	$+x$	$+x$
Equilibrium	0.041566 $-$ x	x	x

$$K_a = 1.25893 \times 10^{-9} = \frac{\left[H_3O^+ \right]\left[C_{20}H_{24}N_2O_2 \right]}{\left[HC_{20}H_{24}N_2O_2^+ \right]}$$

$$K_a = 1.25893 \times 10^{-9} = \frac{(x)(x)}{(0.041566 - x)}$$ Assume x is small compared to 0.041566.

$$K_a = 1.25893 \times 10^{-9} = \frac{(x)(x)}{(0.041566)}$$

$[H_3O^+]$ = x = 7.233857×10^{-6} mol/L

Check assumption that x is small compared to 0.33:

$$\frac{7.233857 \times 10^{-6}}{0.041566}(100\%) = 0.02\%. \quad \text{The assumption is good.}$$

$$pH = -\log [H^+] = -\log (7.233857 \times 10^{-6}) = 5.1406 = \textbf{5.1}$$

CHAPTER 17 IONIC EQUILIBRIA IN AQUEOUS SYSTEMS

CHEMICAL CONNECTIONS BOXED READING PROBLEMS

B17.2 Plan: Find the volume of the rain received by multiplying the surface area of the lake by the depth of rain. Find the volume of the lake before the rain. Express both volumes in litres. The pH of the rain is used to find the concentration (mol/L) of H^+; this concentration (mol/L) multiplied by the volume of rain gives the amount (mol) of H^+. The amount (mol) of H^+ divided by the volume of the lake plus rain gives the concentration (mol/L) of H^+ and the pH of the lake.

Solution:

a) To find the volume of rain, multiply the surface area in square kilometers by the depth of rain. Convert the volume to cm^3 and then to L using the density of water.

$$\text{Volume (L) of rain} = \left(0.040 \text{ km}^2\right)\left(\frac{1000 \text{ m}}{1 \text{ km}}\right)^2\left(\frac{100 \text{ cm}}{1 \text{ m}}\right)^2 (25.4 \text{ mm})\left(\frac{1 \text{ cm}}{10 \text{ mm}}\right)\left(\frac{1 \text{ mL}}{1 \text{ cm}^3}\right)\left(\frac{10^{-3} \text{ L}}{1 \text{ mL}}\right)$$

$$= 1.016 \times 10^6 \text{ L}$$

At pH = 4.20, $[H^+] = 10^{-4.20} = 6.3095734 \times 10^{-5}$ mol/L

$$\text{amount (mol) of } H^+ = \left(1.016 \times 10^6 \text{ L}\right)\left(\frac{6.3095734 \times 10^{-5} \text{ mol}}{L}\right) = 64.105266 = \textbf{64 mol}$$

b) $$\text{Volume (L) of the lake} = \left(0.040 \text{ km}^2\right)\left(\frac{1000 \text{ m}}{1 \text{ km}}\right)^2\left(\frac{100 \text{ cm}}{1 \text{ m}}\right)^2 (3.05 \text{ m})\left(\frac{100 \text{ cm}}{1 \text{ m}}\right)\left(\frac{1 \text{ mL}}{1 \text{ cm}^3}\right)\left(\frac{10^{-3} \text{ L}}{1 \text{ mL}}\right)$$

$$= 1.22 \times 10^8 \text{ L}$$

Total volume of lake after rain = 1.22×10^8 L + 1.016×10^6 L = 1.23016×10^8 L

$$[H^+] = \frac{\text{mol } H_3O^+}{L} = \frac{64.105266 \text{ mol}}{1.23016 \times 10^8 \text{ L}} = 5.211132 \times 10^{-7} \text{ mol/L}$$

pH = $-\log (5.211132 \times 10^{-7}) = 6.28307 = \textbf{6.28}$

c) Each mol of H^+ requires one mole of HCO_3^- for neutralization.

$$\text{Mass (g)} = (64.105266 \text{ mol } H^+)\left(\frac{1 \text{ mol } HCO_3^-}{1 \text{ mol } H_3O^+}\right)\left(\frac{61.02 \text{ g } HCO_3^-}{1 \text{ mol } HCO_3^-}\right)$$

$$= 3.9117 \times 10^3 = \textbf{3.9} \times \textbf{10}^3 \textbf{ g } HCO_3^-$$

END–OF–CHAPTER PROBLEMS

17.2   The weak-acid component neutralizes added base and the weak-base component neutralizes added acid so that the pH of the buffer solution remains relatively constant. The components of a buffer do not neutralize one another when they are a conjugate acid-base pair.

17.7   The buffer-component ratio refers to the ratio of concentrations of the acid and base that make up the buffer. When this ratio is equal to 1, the buffer resists changes in pH with added acid to the same extent that it resists changes in pH with added base. The buffer range extends equally in both the acidic and basic direction. When the ratio shifts with higher [base] than [acid], the buffer is more effective at neutralizing added acid than base so the range extends further in the acidic than basic direction. The opposite is true for a buffer where [acid] > [base]. Buffers with a ratio equal to 1 have the greatest buffer range. The more the buffer-component ratio deviates from 1, the smaller the buffer range.

17.9   Plan: Remember that the weak-acid buffer component neutralizes added base and the weak-base buffer component neutralizes added acid.
Solution:
a) The buffer-component ratio and pH **increase** with added base. The OH⁻ reacts with HA to decrease its concentration and increase [NaA]. The ratio [NaA]/[HA] thus increases. The pH of the buffer will be more basic because the concentration of base, A⁻, has increased and the concentration of acid, HA, decreased.
b) Buffer-component ratio and pH **decrease** with added acid. The H_3O^+ reacts with A⁻ to decrease its concentration and increase [HA]. The ratio [NaA]/[HA] thus decreases. The pH of the buffer will be more acidic because the concentration of base, A⁻, has decreased and the concentration of acid, HA, increased.
c) Buffer-component ratio and pH **increase** with the added sodium salt. The additional NaA increases the concentration of both NaA and HA, but the relative increase in [NaA] is greater. Thus, the ratio increases and the solution becomes more basic. Whenever base is added to a buffer, the pH always increases, but only slightly if the amount of base is not too large.
d) Buffer-component ratio and pH **decrease**. The concentration of HA increases more than the concentration of NaA, so the ratio is less and the solution is more acidic.

17.11   Plan: The buffer components are propanoic acid and propanoate ion, the concentrations of which are known. The sodium ion is a spectator ion and is ignored because it is not involved in the buffer. Write the propanoic acid-dissociation reaction and its K_a expression. Set up a reaction table in which x equals the amount of acid that dissociates; solving for x will result in [H⁺], from which the pH can be calculated. Alternatively, the pH can be calculated from the Henderson-Hasselbalch equation.
Solution:

Concentration (mol/L)	$CH_3CH_2COOH(aq) + H_2O(l)$		$\rightleftharpoons$ $CH_3CH_2COO^-(aq)$	$+ H_3O^+(aq)$
Initial	0.15	—	0.35	0
Change	– x	—	+x	+x
Equilibrium	0.15 – x	—	0.35 + x	x

Assume that x is negligible with respect to both 0.15 and 0.35 since both concentrations are much larger than K_a.
Check assumption: $0.15/1.3 \times 10^{-5} = 12\ 000 > 400$, the assumption is justified.

$$K_a = 1.3 \times 10^{-5} = \frac{[H_3O^+][CH_3CH_2COO^-]}{[CH_3CH_2COOH]} = \frac{(x)(0.35 + x)}{(0.15 - x)} = \frac{(x)(0.35)}{(0.15)}$$

$$x = [H_3O^+] = K_a \frac{[CH_3CH_2COOH]}{[CH_3CH_2COO^-]} = (1.3 \times 10^{-5})\left(\frac{0.15}{0.35}\right) = 5.57143 \times 10^{-6} = \textbf{5.6} \times \textbf{10}^{-6} \textbf{ mol/L}$$

$$pH = -\log [H^+] = -\log (5.57143 \times 10^{-6}) = 5.2540 = \textbf{5.25}$$

Another solution path to find pH is using the Henderson-Hasselbalch equation:

$$pH = pK_a + \log\left(\frac{[base]}{[acid]}\right) \qquad pK_a = -\log (1.3 \times 10^{-5}) = 4.886$$

$$pH = 4.886 + \log\left(\frac{[CH_3CH_2COO^-]}{[CH_3CH_2COOH]}\right) = 4.886 + \log\left(\frac{[0.35]}{[0.15]}\right)$$

$$pH = 5.25398 = 5.25$$

17.13   Plan: The buffer components are HNO_2 and NO_2^-, the concentrations of which are known. The potassium ion is a spectator ion and is ignored because it is not involved in the buffer. Write the HNO_2 acid-dissociation reaction and its K_a expression. Set up a reaction table in which x equals the amount of acid that dissociates; solving for x will result in [H_3O^+], from which the pH can be calculated. Alternatively, the pH can be calculated from the Henderson-Hasselbalch equation.
Solution:

Concentration (mol/L)	$HNO_2(aq)$	$+ H_2O(l) \rightleftharpoons$	$NO_2^-(aq)$	$+ H_3O^+(aq)$
Initial	0.55	—	0.75	0
Change	–x	—	+x	+x
Equilibrium	0.55 – x	—	0.75 + x	x

Assume that x is negligible with respect to both 0.55 and 0.75 since both concentrations are much larger than K_a.

$$K_a = 7.1 \times 10^{-4} = \frac{\left[H_3O^+\right]\left[NO_2^-\right]}{\left[HNO_2\right]} = \frac{(x)(0.75+x)}{(0.55-x)} = \frac{(x)(0.75)}{(0.55)}$$

$$x = [H_3O^+] = K_a \frac{\left[HNO_2\right]}{\left[NO_2^-\right]} = \left(7.1 \times 10^{-4}\right)\frac{(0.55)}{(0.75)} = 5.2066667 \times 10^{-4} = \mathbf{5.2 \times 10^{-4} \ mol/L}$$

Check assumption: Percent error = $(5.2066667 \times 10^{-4}/0.55)100\% = 0.095\%$. The assumption is valid.
$$pH = -\log [H^+] = -\log (5.2066667 \times 10^{-4}) = 3.28344 = \mathbf{3.28}$$

Using the Henderson-Hasselbalch equation instead:

$$pH = pK_a + \log\left(\frac{[base]}{[acid]}\right) \qquad pK_a = -\log(7.1 \times 10^{-4}) = 3.149$$

$$pH = 3.149 + \log\left(\frac{[NO_2^-]}{[HNO_2]}\right) = 3.149 + \log\left(\frac{[0.75]}{[0.55]}\right)$$

$$pH = 3.2837 = \mathbf{3.28}$$

17.15   **Plan:** The buffer components are formic acid, HCOOH, and formate ion, HCOO⁻, the concentrations of which are known. The sodium ion is a spectator ion and is ignored because it is not involved in the buffer. Write the HCOOH acid-dissociation reaction and its K_a expression. Set up a reaction table in which x equals the amount of acid that dissociates; solving for x will result in $[H_3O^+]$, from which the pH can be calculated. Alternatively, the pH can be calculated from the Henderson-Hasselbalch equation.
Solution:
$$K_a = 10^{-pK_a} = 10^{-3.74} = 1.8197 \times 10^{-4}$$

Concentration (mol/L)	HCOOH(aq) +	H₂O(l) ⇌	HCOO⁻(aq) +	H₃O⁺(aq)
Initial	0.45	—	0.63	0
Change	−x	—	+x	+x
Equilibrium	0.45 − x	—	0.63 + x	x

Assume that x is negligible because both concentrations are much larger than K_a.

$$K_a = 1.8197 \times 10^{-4} = \frac{\left[H_3O^+\right]\left[HCOO^-\right]}{\left[HCOOH\right]} = \frac{(x)(0.63+x)}{(0.45-x)} = \frac{(x)(0.63)}{(0.45)}$$

$$x = [H_3O^+] = K_a \frac{\left[HCOOH\right]}{\left[HCOO^-\right]} = \left(1.8197 \times 10^{-4}\right)\frac{(0.45)}{(0.63)} = 1.29979 \times 10^{-4} = \mathbf{1.3 \times 10^{-4} \ mol/L}$$

Check assumption: Percent error = $(1.29979 \times 10^{-4}/0.45)100\% = 0.029\%$. The assumption is valid.
$$pH = -\log [H^+] = -\log (1.29979 \times 10^{-4}) = 3.886127 = \mathbf{3.89}$$
Alternatively, using the Henderson-Hasselbalch equation.

$$pH = pK_a + \log\left(\frac{[base]}{[acid]}\right)$$

$$pH = 3.74 + \log\left(\frac{[HCOO^-]}{[HCOOH]}\right) = 3.74 + \log\left(\frac{[0.63]}{[0.45]}\right)$$

$$pH = 3.8861 = \mathbf{3.89}$$

17.17   **Plan:** The buffer components phenol, C₆H₅OH, and phenolate ion, C₆H₅O⁻, the concentrations of which are known. The sodium ion is a spectator ion and is ignored because it is not involved in the buffer. Write the C₆H₅OH acid-dissociation reaction and its K_a expression. Set up a reaction table in which x equals the amount of acid that dissociates; solving for x will result in $[H_3O^+]$, from which the pH can be calculated. Alternatively, the pH can be calculated from the Henderson-Hasselbalch equation.

<u>Solution:</u>

$K_a = 10^{-pK_a} = 10^{-10.00} = 1.0 \times 10^{-10}$

Concentration (mol/L)	$C_6H_5OH(aq)$ +	$H_2O(l)$	$\rightleftharpoons$	$C_6H_5O^-(aq)$ +	$H_3O^+(aq)$
Initial	1.2	—		1.3	0
Change	–x	—		+x	+x
Equilibrium	1.2 – x	—		1.3 + x	x

Assume that x is negligible with respect to both 1.0 and 1.2 because both concentrations are much larger than K_a.

$$K_a = 1.0 \times 10^{-10} = \frac{\left[H_3O^+\right]\left[C_6H_5O^-\right]}{\left[C_6H_5OH\right]} = \frac{(x)(1.3 + x)}{(1.2 - x)} = \frac{(x)(1.3)}{(1.2)}$$

$$x = [H_3O^+] = K_a \frac{\left[C_6H_5OH\right]}{\left[C_6H_5O^-\right]} = \left(1.0 \times 10^{-10}\right)\left(\frac{1.2}{1.3}\right) = 9.23077 \times 10^{-11} \text{ mol/L}$$

Check assumption: Percent error = $(9.23077 \times 10^{-11}/1.2)100\% = 7.7 \times 10^{-9}\%$. The assumption is valid.

$$pH = -\log(9.23077 \times 10^{-11}) = 10.03476 = \mathbf{10.03}$$

Using the Henderson-Hasselbalch equation:

$$pH = pK_a + \log\left(\frac{[\text{base}]}{[\text{acid}]}\right)$$

$$pH = 10.00 + \log\left(\frac{[C_6H_5O^-]}{[C_6H_5OH]}\right) = 10.00 + \log\left(\frac{[1.3]}{[1.2]}\right) = \mathbf{10.03}$$

17.19 <u>Plan:</u> The buffer components ammonia, NH_3, and ammonium ion, NH_4^+, the concentrations of which are known. The chloride ion is a spectator ion and is ignored because it is not involved in the buffer. Write the NH_4^+ acid-dissociation reaction and its K_a expression. Set up a reaction table in which x equals the amount of acid that dissociates; solving for x will result in $[H_3O^+]$, from which the pH can be calculated. Alternatively, the pH can be calculated from the Henderson-Hasselbalch equation. The K_a of NH_4^+ will have to be calculated from the pK_b.

<u>Solution:</u>

$14 = pK_a + pK_b$

$pK_a = 14 - pK_b = 14 - 4.75 = 9.25$

$K_a = 10^{-pK_a} = 10^{-9.25} = 5.62341325 \times 10^{-10}$

Concentration (mol/L)	$NH_4^+(aq)$ +	$H_2O(l)$	$\rightleftharpoons$	$NH_3(aq)$ +	$H_3O^+(aq)$
Initial	0.15	—		0.25	0
Change	–x	—		+x	+x
Equilibrium	0.15 – x	—		0.25 + x	x

Assume that x is negligible with respect to both 0.25 and 0.15 because both concentrations are much larger than K_a.

$$K_a = .62341325 \times 10^{-10} = \frac{\left[NH_3\right]\left[H_3O^+\right]}{\left[NH_4^+\right]} = \frac{(0.25 + x)\left[H_3O^+\right]}{(0.15 - x)} = \frac{(0.25)[H_3O^+]}{(0.15)}$$

$$X = [H_3O^+] = K_a \frac{\left[NH_4^+\right]}{\left[NH_3\right]} = \left(5.62341325 \times 10^{-10}\right)\left(\frac{0.15}{0.25}\right) = 3.374048 \times 10^{-10} \text{ mol/L}$$

Check assumption: Percent error = $(3.374048 \times 10^{-10}/0.15)100\% = 2 \times 10^{-7}\%$. The assumption is valid.

$$pH = -\log[H^+] = -\log[3.374048 \times 10^{-10}] = 9.4718 = \mathbf{9.47}$$

Using the Henderson-Hasselbalch equation:

$$pH = pK_a + \log\left(\frac{[\text{base}]}{[\text{acid}]}\right)$$

$$pH = 9.25 + \log\left(\frac{[NH_3]}{[NH_4^+]}\right) = 9.25 + \log\left(\frac{[0.25]}{[0.15]}\right) = \mathbf{9.47}$$

17.21   <u>Plan:</u> The buffer components are HCO_3^- from the salt $KHCO_3$ and CO_3^{2-} from the salt K_2CO_3. Choose the K_a value that corresponds to the equilibrium with these two components. The potassium ion is a spectator ion and is ignored because it is not involved in the buffer. Write the acid-dissociation reaction and its K_a expression. Set up a reaction table in which x equals the amount of acid that dissociates; solving for x will result in $[H_3O^+]$, from which the pH can be calculated. Alternatively, the pH can be calculated from the Henderson-Hasselbalch equation.
<u>Solution:</u>
a) K_{a1} refers to carbonic acid, H_2CO_3, losing one proton to produce HCO_3^-. This is not the correct K_a because H_2CO_3 is not involved in the buffer. **K_{a2}** is the correct K_a to choose because it is the equilibrium constant for the loss of the second proton to produce CO_3^{2-} from HCO_3^-.
b) Set up the reaction table and use K_{a2} to calculate pH.

Concentration (mol/L)	$HCO_3^-(aq)$	+	$H_2O(l)$	$\rightleftharpoons$	$CO_3^{2-}(aq)$	+	$H_3O^+(aq)$
Initial	0.22		—		0.37		0
Change	−x		—		+x		+x
Equilibrium	0.22 − x		—		0.37 + x		x

Assume that x is negligible with respect to both 0.22 and 0.37 because both concentrations are much larger than K_a.

$$K_a = 4.7 \times 10^{-11} = \frac{\left[H_3O^+\right]\left[CO_3^{2-}\right]}{\left[HCO_3^-\right]} = \frac{(x)(0.37 + x)}{(0.22 - x)} = \frac{(x)(0.37)}{(0.22)}$$

$$[H_3O^+] = K_a \frac{\left[HCO_3^-\right]}{\left[CO_3^{2-}\right]} = \left(4.7 \times 10^{-11}\right)\left(\frac{0.22}{0.37}\right) = 2.79459 \times 10^{-11} \text{ mol/L}$$

Check assumption: Percent error = $(2.79459 \times 10^{-11}/0.22)100\% = 1.3 \times 10^{-8}\%$. The assumption is valid.
$$pH = -\log [H^+] = -\log (2.79459 \times 10^{-11}) = 10.5537 = \mathbf{10.55}$$
Using the Henderson-Hasselbalch equation:

$$pH = pK_a + \log\left(\frac{[base]}{[acid]}\right) \qquad\qquad pK_a = -\log (4.7 \times 10^{-11}) = 10.328$$

$$pH = 10.328 + \log\left(\frac{[CO_3^{2-}]}{[HCO_3^-]}\right) = 10.328 + \log\left(\frac{[0.37]}{[0.22]}\right)$$

pH = 10.55

17.23   <u>Plan:</u> Given the pH and K_a of an acid, the buffer-component ratio can be calculated from the Henderson-Hasselbalch equation. Convert K_a to pK_a.
<u>Solution:</u>
$$pK_a = -\log K_a = -\log (1.3 \times 10^{-5}) = 4.8860566$$
$$pH = pK_a + \log\left(\frac{[base]}{[acid]}\right)$$
$$5.44 = 4.8860566 + \log\left(\frac{[EtCOO^-]}{[EtCOOH]}\right)$$
$$0.5539434 = \log\left(\frac{[EtCOO^-]}{[EtCOOH]}\right) \qquad \text{Raise each side to } 10^x.$$
$$\frac{[EtCOO^-]}{[EtCOOH]} = 3.5805 = \mathbf{3.6}$$

17.25   <u>Plan:</u> Given the pH and K_a of an acid, the buffer-component ratio can be calculated from the Henderson-Hasselbalch equation. Convert K_a to pK_a.
<u>Solution:</u>
$$pK_a = -\log K_a = -\log (2.3 \times 10^{-9}) = 8.63827$$

$$pH = pK_a + \log\left(\frac{[base]}{[acid]}\right)$$

$$7.95 = 8.63827 + \log\left(\frac{[BrO^-]}{[HBrO]}\right)$$

$$-0.68827 = \log\left(\frac{[BrO^-]}{[HBrO]}\right) \qquad \text{Raise each side to } 10^x.$$

$$\frac{[BrO^-]}{[HBrO]} = 0.204989 = \textbf{0.20}$$

17.27 <u>Plan:</u> Determine the pK_a of the acid from the concentrations of the conjugate acid and base, and the pH of the solution. This requires the Henderson-Hasselbalch equation. Set up a reaction table that shows the stoichiometry of adding the strong base NaOH to the weak acid in the buffer. Calculate the new concentrations of the buffer components and use the Henderson-Hasselbalch equation to find the new pH.
<u>Solution:</u>

$$pH = pK_a + \log\left(\frac{[base]}{[acid]}\right)$$

$$3.35 = pK_a + \log\left(\frac{[A^-]}{[HA]}\right) = pK_a + \log\left(\frac{[0.1500]}{[0.2000]}\right)$$

$$3.35 = pK_a - 0.1249387$$
$$pK_a = 3.474939 = \textbf{3.47}$$

Determine the amount (mol) of conjugate acid (HA) and conjugate base (A$^-$) using $(c)(V)$ = amount (mol) .

$$\text{amount (mol) of HA} = (0.5000 \text{ L})\left(\frac{0.2000 \text{ mol HA}}{1 \text{ L}}\right) = 0.1000 \text{ mol HA}$$

$$\text{amount (mol) of A}^- = (0.5000 \text{ L})\left(\frac{0.1500 \text{ mol A}^-}{1 \text{ L}}\right) = 0.07500 \text{ mol A}^-$$

The reaction is:

	HA(aq)	+	NaOH(aq)	→	Na$^+$(aq)	+	A$^-$(aq)	+	H$_2$O(l)
Initial	0.1000 mol		0.0015 mol				0.07500 mol		
Change	−0.0015 mol		−0.0015 mol				+ 0.0015 mol		
Final	0.0985 mol		0 mol				0.0765 mol		

NaOH is the limiting reagent. The addition of 0.0015 mol NaOH produces an additional 0.0015 mol A$^-$ and consumes 0.0015 mol of HA.
Then:

$$[A^-] = \frac{0.0765 \text{ mol A}^-}{0.5000 \text{ L}} = 0.153 \text{ mol/L A}^-$$

$$[HA] = \frac{0.0985 \text{ mol HA}}{0.5000 \text{ L}} = 0.197 \text{ mol/L HA}$$

$$pH = pK_a + \log\left(\frac{[base]}{[acid]}\right)$$

$$pH = 3.474939 + \log\left(\frac{[0.153]}{[0.197]}\right) = 3.365164 = \textbf{3.37}$$

Note: Since the volume is identical for the conjugate base and acid, we can substitute the amount (moles) directly into the ratio (i.e., n_A/V divided by n_{HA}/V is the same as n_A/n_{HA}), i.e.,

$$pH = pK_a + \log\left(\frac{n_{base}}{n_{acid}}\right) = 3.474939 + \log\left(\frac{[0.0765]}{[0.0985]}\right) = 3.37$$

17.29   Plan: Determine the pK_a of the acid from the concentrations of the conjugate acid and base, and the pH of the solution. This requires the Henderson-Hasselbalch equation. Set up a reaction table that shows the stoichiometry of adding the strong base $Ba(OH)_2$ to the weak acid in the buffer. Calculate the new concentrations of the buffer components and use the Henderson-Hasselbalch equation to find the new pH.
Solution:

$$pH = pK_a + \log\left(\frac{[base]}{[acid]}\right)$$

$$8.77 = pK_a + \log\left(\frac{[Y^-]}{[HY]}\right) = pK_a + \log\left(\frac{[0.220]}{[0.110]}\right)$$

$8.77 = pK_a + 0.3010299957$
$pK_a = 8.46897 = 8.47$

Determine the amount (mol) of conjugate acid (HY) and conjugate base (Y^-) using $(c)(V)$ = amount (mol) .

$$\text{amount (mol) of HY} = \left(0.350\ L\right)\left(\frac{0.110\ \text{mol HY}}{1\ L}\right) = 0.0385\ \text{mol HY}$$

$$\text{amount (mol) of } Y^- = \left(0.350\ L\right)\left(\frac{0.220\ \text{mol } Y^-}{1\ L}\right) = 0.077\ \text{mol } Y^-$$

The reaction is:

	$2HY(aq)$ +	$Ba(OH)_2(aq)$ →	$Ba^{2+}(aq)$ +	$2Y^-(aq) + 2H_2O(l)$
Initial	0.0385 mol	0.0015 mol		0.077 mol
Change	–0.0030 mol	–0.0015 mol		+0.0030 mol
Final	0.0355 mol	0 mol		0.0800 mol

$Ba(OH)_2$ is the limiting reagent. The addition of 0.0015 mol $Ba(OH)_2$ will produce 2 x 0.0015 mol Y^- and consume 2 x 0.0015 mol of HY.

$$pH = pK_a + \log\left(\frac{n_{base}}{n_{acid}}\right)$$

$$pH = 8.46897 + \log\left(\frac{[0.0800]}{[0.0355]}\right) = 8.82183 = \textbf{8.82}$$

17.31   Plan: The hydrochloric acid will react with the sodium acetate, $NaC_2H_3O_2$, to form acetic acid, $HC_2H_3O_2$. Calculate the amount (mol) of HCl and $NaC_2H_3O_2$. Set up a reaction table that shows the stoichiometry of the reaction of HCl and $NaC_2H_3O_2$. All of the HCl will be consumed to form $HC_2H_3O_2$, and the amount (mol) of $C_2H_3O_2^-$ will decrease. Find the new concentrations of $NaC_2H_3O_2$ and $HC_2H_3O_2$ and use the Henderson-Hasselbalch equation to find the pH of the buffer. Add 0.15 to find the pH of the buffer after the addition of the KOH. Use the Henderson-Hasselbalch equation to find the [base]/[acid] ratio needed to achieve that pH.
Solution:

a) $$\text{Initial amount (mol) of HCl} = \left(\frac{0.452\ \text{mol HCl}}{L}\right)\left(\frac{10^{-3}\ L}{1\ mL}\right)\left(204\ mL\right) = 0.092208\ \text{mol HCl}$$

$$\text{Initial amount (mol) of } NaC_2H_3O_2 = \left(\frac{0.400\ \text{mol } NaC_2H_3O_2}{L}\right)\left(0.500\ L\right) = 0.200\ \text{mol } NaC_2H_3O_2$$

	HCl +	$NaC_2H_3O_2$ →	$HC_2H_3O_2$ +	NaCl
Initial	0.092208 mol	0.200 mol	0 mol	
Change	–0.092208 mol	–0.092208 mol	+0.092208 mol	
Final	0 mol	0.107792 mol	0.092208 mol	

$$pK_a = -\log K_a = -\log\left(1.8 \times 10^{-5}\right) = 4.744727495$$

$$pH = pK_a + \log\left(\frac{n_{base}}{n_{acid}}\right)$$

17-7

$$pH = 4.744727495 + \log\left(\frac{[0.1531136]}{[0.1309773]}\right) = 4.812545 = \textbf{4.81}$$

b) The addition of base would increase the pH, so the new pH is $(4.81 + 0.15) = 4.96$.

The new $[C_2H_3O_2^-]/[HC_2H_3O_2]$ ratio is calculated using the Henderson-Hasselbalch equation.

$$pH = pK_a + \log\left(\frac{[C_2H_3O_2^-]}{[HC_2H_3O_2]}\right)$$

$$4.96 = 4.744727495 + \log\left(\frac{[C_2H_3O_2^-]}{[HC_2H_3O_2]}\right)$$

$$0.215272505 = \log\left(\frac{[C_2H_3O_2^-]}{[HC_2H_3O_2]}\right)$$

$$\frac{[C_2H_3O_2^-]}{[HC_2H_3O_2]} = 1.64162$$

From part a), we know that $[HC_2H_3O_2] + [C_2H_3O_2^-] = (0.1309773 \text{ mol/L} + 0.1531136 \text{ mol/L}) = 0.2840909 \text{ mol/L}$. Although the *ratio* of $[C_2H_3O_2^-]$ to $[HC_2H_3O_2]$ can change when acid or base is added, the *absolute amount* does not change unless acetic acid or an acetate salt is added.

Given that $[C_2H_3O_2^-]/[HC_2H_3O_2] = 1.64162$ and $[HC_2H_3O_2] + [C_2H_3O_2^-] = 0.2840909 \text{ mol/L}$, solve for $[C_2H_3O_2^-]$ and substitute into the second equation.

$[C_2H_3O_2^-] = 1.64162[HC_2H_3O_2]$ and $[HC_2H_3O_2] + 1.64162[HC_2H_3O_2] = 0.2840909 \text{ mol/L}$

$[HC_2H_3O_2] = 0.1075441 \text{ mol/L}$ and $[C_2H_3O_2^-] = 0.176547 \text{ mol/L}$

amount (mol) of $C_2H_3O_2^-$ needed $= (0.176547 \text{ mol } C_2H_3O_2^-/\text{L})(0.500 \text{ L}) = 0.0882735 \text{ mol}$

amount (mol) of $C_2H_3O_2^-$ initially $= (0.1531136 \text{ mol } C_2H_3O_2^-/\text{L})(0.500 \text{ L}) = 0.0765568 \text{ mol}$

This would require the addition of $(0.0882735 \text{ mol} - 0.0765568 \text{ mol}) = 0.0117167 \text{ mol } C_2H_3O_2^-$

The KOH added reacts with $HC_2H_3O_2$ to produce additional $C_2H_3O_2^-$:

$$HC_2H_3O_2 + KOH \rightarrow C_2H_3O_2^- + K^+ + H_2O(l)$$

To produce $0.0117167 \text{ mol } C_2H_3O_2^-$ would require the addition of $0.0117167 \text{ mol KOH}$.

$$\text{Mass (g) of KOH} = \left(0.0117167 \text{ mol KOH}\right)\left(\frac{56.11 \text{ g KOH}}{1 \text{ mol KOH}}\right) = 0.657424 = \textbf{0.66 g KOH}$$

17.33 <u>Plan:</u> Select conjugate pairs with K_a values close to the desired $[H^+]$. Convert pH to $[H^+]$ for easy comparison to K_a values in the Appendix. Determine an appropriate base by $[OH^-] = K_w/[H^+]$.
<u>Solution:</u>
a) For pH ≈ 4.5, $[H^+] = 10^{-4.5} = 3.2\times10^{-5} \text{ mol/L}$. Some good selections are the $HOOC(CH_2)_4COOH/HOOC(CH_2)_4COO^-$ conjugate pair with K_a equal to 3.8×10^{-5} or $C_6H_5CH_2COOH/C_6H_5CH_2COO^-$ conjugate pair with K_a equal to 4.9×10^{-5}. From the base list, the $C_6H_5NH_2/C_6H_5NH_3^+$ conjugate pair comes close with $K_a = K_w/K_b = 1.0\times10^{-14}/4.0\times10^{-10} = 2.5\times10^{-5}$.
b) For pH ≈ 7.0, $[H^+] = 10^{-7.0} = 1.0\times10^{-7} \text{ mol/L}$. Two choices are the $H_2PO_4^-/HPO_4^{2-}$ conjugate pair with K_a of 6.3×10^{-8} and the $H_2AsO_4^-/HAsO_4^{2-}$ conjugate pair with K_a of 1.1×10^{-7}.

17.35 <u>Plan:</u> Select conjugate pairs with pK_a values close to the desired pH. Convert pH to $[H^+]$ for easy comparison to K_a values in the Appendix. Determine an appropriate base by $[OH^-] = K_w/[H^+]$.
<u>Solution:</u>
a) For pH ≈ 3.5 ($[H^+] = 10^{-pH} = 10^{-3.5} = 3.2\times10^{-4}$), the best selection is the $HOCH_2CH(OH)COOH/HOCH_2CH(OH)COO^-$ conjugate pair with a $K_a = 2.9\times10^{-4}$. The $CH_3COOC_6H_4COOH/CH_3COOC_6H_4COO^-$ pair, with $K_a = 3.6\times10^{-4}$, is also a good choice. The $[OH^-] = K_w/[H^+] = 1.0\times10^{-14}/3.2\times10^{-4} = 3.1\times10^{-11}$, results in no reasonable K_b values from the Appendix.
b) For pH ≈ 5.5 ($[H^+] = 10^{-pH} = 3\times10^{-6}$), no K_{a1} gives an acceptable pair; the K_{a2} values for adipic acid, malonic acid, and succinic acid are reasonable. The $[OH^-] = K_w/[H^+] = 1.0\times10^{-14}/3\times10^{-6} = 3\times10^{-9}$; the K_b selection is $C_5H_5N/C_5H_5NH^+$.

17.38   Plan: Given the pH and K_a of an acid, the buffer-component ratio can be calculated from the Henderson-Hasselbalch equation. Convert K_a to pK_a.

Solution:

The value of the K_a from the Appendix: $K_a = 6.3 \times 10^{-8}$ (We are using K_{a2} since we are dealing with the equilibrium in which the second hydrogen ion is being lost.)

$pK_a = -\log K_a = -\log (6.3 \times 10^{-8}) = 7.200659451$

Use the Henderson-Hasselbalch equation:

$$pH = pK_a + \log\left(\frac{[HPO_4^{2-}]}{[H_2PO_4^{-}]}\right)$$

$$7.40 = 7.200659451 + \log\left(\frac{[HPO_4^{2-}]}{[H_2PO_4^{-}]}\right)$$

$$0.19934055 = \log\left(\frac{[HPO_4^{2-}]}{[H_2PO_4^{-}]}\right)$$

$$\frac{[HPO_4^{2-}]}{[H_2PO_4^{-}]} = 1.582486 = \mathbf{1.6}$$

17.42   To see a distinct colour in a mixture of two colours, you need one colour to be about 10 times the intensity of the other. For this to take place, the concentration ratio $[HIn]/[In^-]$ needs to be greater than 10:1 or less than 1:10. This will occur when $pH = pK_a - 1$ or $pH = pK_a + 1$, respectively, giving a transition range of about two units.

17.44   The equivalence point in a titration is the point at which the amount (mol) of OH^- equals the amount (mol) of H_3O^+ (be sure to account for stoichiometric ratios, e.g., one mol of $Ca(OH)_2$ produces two moles of OH^-). The end point is the point at which the added indicator changes colour. If an appropriate indicator is selected, the end point is close to the equivalence point, but not normally the same. Using an indicator that changes colour at a pH after the equivalence point means the equivalence point is reached first. However, if an indicator is selected that changes colour at a pH before the equivalence point, then the end point is reached first.

17.46   a) The initial pH is lowest for the flask solution of the strong acid, followed by the weak acid and then the weak base. In other words, *strong acid*–strong base < *weak acid*–strong base < strong acid–*weak base* in terms of initial pH.

b) At the equivalence point, the amount (mol) of H^+ equals the amount (mol) of OH^-, regardless of the type of titration. However, the strong acid–strong base equivalence point occurs at pH = 7.00 because the resulting cation-anion combination does not react with water. An example is the reaction $NaOH + HCl \rightarrow H_2O + NaCl$. Neither Na^+ nor Cl^- ions dissociate in water.

The weak acid–strong base equivalence point occurs at pH > 7, because the anion of the weak acid is weakly basic, whereas the cation of the strong base does not react with water. An example is the reaction $HCOOH + NaOH \rightarrow HCOO^- + H_2O + Na^+$. The conjugate base, $HCOO^-$, reacts with water according to this reaction: $HCOO^- + H_2O \rightarrow HCOOH + OH^-$.

The strong acid–weak base equivalence point occurs at pH < 7, because the anion of the strong acid does not react with water, whereas the cation of the weak base is weakly acidic. An example is the reaction $HCl + NH_3 \rightarrow NH_4^+ + Cl^-$. The conjugate acid, NH_4^+, dissociates slightly in water: $NH_4^+ + H_2O \rightarrow NH_3 + H_3O^+$.

In rank order of pH at the equivalence point, strong acid–*weak base* < *strong acid*–strong base < *weak acid*–strong base.

17.48   At the very centre of the buffer region of a weak acid–strong base titration, the concentration of the weak acid and its conjugate base are equal. If equal values for concentration are put into the Henderson-Hasselbalch equation, the [base]/[acid] ratio is 1, the log of 1 is 0, and the pH of the solution equals the pK_a of the weak acid.

$$pH = pK_a + \log\left(\frac{[base]}{[acid]}\right)$$

$$pH = pK_a + \log 1$$

17.52   Plan: Indicators have a pH range that is approximated by $pK_a \pm 1$. Find the pK_a of the indicator by using the relationship $pK_a = -\log K_a$.
Solution:
The pK_a of cresol red is $-\log (3.5 \times 10^{-9}) = 8.5$, so the indicator changes colour over an approximate range of 8.5 ± 1 or **7.5 to 9.5**.

17.54   Plan: Choose an indicator that changes colour at a pH close to the pH of the equivalence point.
Solution:
a) The equivalence point for a strong acid–strong base titration occurs at pH = 7.0. **Bromthymol blue** is an indicator that changes colour around pH 7.
b) The equivalence point for a weak acid–strong base is above pH 7. Estimate the pH at equivalence point from equilibrium calculations.
At the equivalence point, all of the HCOOH and NaOH have been consumed; the solution is 0.050 mol/L $HCOO^-$. (The volume doubles because equal volumes of base and acid are required to reach the equivalence point. When the volume doubles, the concentration is halved.) The weak base $HCOO^-$ undergoes a base reaction:

Concentration, mol/L	$COOH^-(aq)$ + $H_2O(l)$	$\rightleftharpoons$	$HCOOH(aq)$ +	$OH^-(aq)$
Initial	0.050 mol/L	—	0	0
Change	–x		+x	+x
Equilibrium	0.050 – x		x	x

The K_a for HCOOH is 1.8×10^{-4}, so $K_b = 1.0 \times 10^{-14}/1.8 \times 10^{-4} = 5.5556 \times 10^{-11}$

$$K_b = 5.5556 \times 10^{-11} = \frac{[HCOOH][OH^-]}{[HCOO^-]} = \frac{(x)(x)}{(0.050-x)} = \frac{(x)(x)}{(0.050)}$$

$[OH^-] = x = 1.666673 \times 10^{-6}$ mol/L
$pOH = -\log (1.666673 \times 10^{-6}) = 5.7781496$
$pH = 14.00 - pOH = 14.00 - 5.7781496 = 8.2218504 = 8.22$
Choose **thymol blue** or **phenolphthalein**.

17.58   Plan: The reaction occurring in the titration is the neutralization of H_3O^+ (from HCl) by OH^- (from NaOH):
       $HCl(aq) + NaOH(aq) \rightarrow H_2O(l) + NaCl(aq)$ or, omitting spectator ions:
       $H_3O^+(aq) + OH^-(aq) \rightarrow 2H_2O(l)$
For the titration of a strong acid with a strong base, the pH before the equivalence point depends on the excess concentration of acid and the pH after the equivalence point depends on the excess concentration of base. At the equivalence point, there is not an excess of either acid or base so the pH is 7.0. The equivalence point occurs when 40.00 mL of base has been added. Use $(c)(V)$ to determine the amount (mol) of acid and base. Note that the NaCl product is a neutral salt that does not affect the pH.
Solution:
The initial amount (mol) of HCl = (0.1000 mol HCl/L)(10^{-3} L/1 mL)(40.00 mL) = 4.000×10^{-3} mol HCl
a) At 0 mL of base added, the concentration of hydronium ion equals the original concentration of HCl.
       $pH = -\log (0.1000 \text{ mol/L}) = \mathbf{1.0000}$
b) Determine the amount (mol) of NaOH added:
       amount (mol) of added NaOH = (0.1000 mol NaOH/L)(10^{-3} L/1 mL)(25.00 mL)
                         = 2.500×10^{-3} mol NaOH

	$HCl(aq)$ +	$NaOH(aq)$	$\rightarrow$	$H_2O(l)$ +	$NaCl(aq)$
Initial	4.000×10^{-3} mol	2.500×10^{-3} mol		–	0
Change	-2.500×10^{-3} mol	-2.500×10^{-3} mol		–	$+2.500 \times 10^{-3}$ mol
Final	1.500×10^{-3} mol	0			2.500×10^{-3} mol

The volume of the solution at this point is $[(40.00 + 25.00) \text{ mL}](10^{-3}$ L/1 mL) = 0.06500 L
The concentration (mol/L) of the excess HCl is $(1.500 \times 10^{-3}$ mol HCl)/(0.06500 L) = 0.023077 mol/L
       $pH = -\log (0.023077) = \mathbf{1.6368}$
c) Determine the amount (mol) of NaOH added:
       amount (mol) of added NaOH = (0.1000 mol NaOH/L)(10^{-3} L/1 mL)(39.00 mL)
                         = 3.900×10^{-3} mol NaOH

	HCl(aq)	+	NaOH(aq)	→	H$_2$O(l)	+	NaCl(aq)
Initial	4.000x10^{-3} mol		4.900x10^{-3} mol		–		0
Change	–3.900x10^{-3} mol		–3.900x10^{-3} mol		–		+3.900x10^{-3} mol
Final	1.000x10^{-4} mol		0				3.900x10^{-3} mol

The volume of the solution at this point is [(40.00 + 39.00) mL](10^{-3} L/1 mL) = 0.07900 L

The concentration (mol/L) of the excess HCl is (1.00x 10^{-4}mol HCl)/(0.07900 L) = 0.0012658 mol/L

pH = –log (0.0012658) = **2.898**

d) Determine the amount (mol) of NaOH added:

amount (mol) of added NaOH = (0.1000 mol NaOH/L)(10^{-3} L/1 mL)(39.90 mL)

= 3.990x10^{-3} mol NaOH

	HCl(aq)	+	NaOH(aq)	→	H$_2$O(l)	+	NaCl(aq)
Initial	4.000x10^{-3} mol		3.990x10^{-3} mol		–		0
Change	–3.990x10^{-3} mol		–3.990x10^{-3} mol		–		+3.990x10^{-3} mol
Final	1.000x10^{-5} mol		0				3.900x10^{-3} mol

The volume of the solution at this point is [(40.00 + 39.90) mL](10^{-3} L/1 mL) = 0.07990 L

The concentration (mol/L) of the excess HCl is (1.0x10^{-5} mol HCl)/(0.07990 L) = 0.000125156 mol/L

pH = –log (0.000125156) = **3.903**

e) Determine the amount (mol) of NaOH added:

amount (mol) of added NaOH = (0.1000 mol NaOH/L)(10^{-3} L/1 mL)(40.00 mL)

= 4.000x10^{-3} mol NaOH

	HCl(aq)	+	NaOH(aq)	→	H$_2$O(l)	+	NaCl(aq)
Initial	4.000x10^{-3} mol		4.000x10^{-3} mol		–		0
Change	–4.000x10^{-3} mol		–4.000x10^{-3} mol		–		+4.000x10^{-3} mol
Final	0		0				4.000x10^{-3} mol

The NaOH will react with an equal amount of the acid and 0.0 mol HCl will remain. This is the equivalence point of a strong acid–strong base titration, thus, the pH is **7.00**. Only the neutral salt NaCl is in solution at the equivalence point.

f) The NaOH is now in excess. It will be necessary to calculate the excess base after reacting with the HCl. The excess strong base will give the pOH, which can be converted to the pH.

Determine the amount (mol) of NaOH added:

amount (mol) of added NaOH = (0.1000 mol NaOH/L)(10^{-3} L/1 mL)(40.10 mL)

= 4.010x10^{-3} mol NaOH

The HCl will react with an equal amount of the base, and 1.0x10^{-5} mol NaOH will remain.

	HCl(aq)	+	NaOH(aq)	→	H$_2$O(l)	+	NaCl(aq)
Initial	4.000x10^{-3} mol		4.010x10^{-3} mol		–		0
Change	–4.000x10^{-3} mol		–4.000x10^{-3} mol		–		+4.000x10^{-3} mol
Final	0		1.000x10^{-5} mol				4.000x10^{-3} mol

The volume of the solution at this point is [(40.00 + 40.10) mL](10^{-3} L/1 mL) = 0.08010 L

The concentration (mol/L) of the excess NaOH is (1.0x10^{-5} mol NaOH)/(0.08010 L) = 0.00012484 mol/L

pOH = –log (0.00012484) = 3.9036

pH = 14.00 – pOH = 14.00 – 3.9036 = 10.09637 = **10.10**

g) Determine the amount (mol) of NaOH added:

amount (mol) of NaOH = (0.1000 mol NaOH/L)(10^{-3} L/1 mL)(50.00 mL) = 5.000x10^{-3} mol NaOH

The HCl will react with an equal amount of the base, and 1.000x10^{-3} mol NaOH will remain.

	HCl(aq)	+	NaOH(aq)	→	H$_2$O(l)	+	NaCl(aq)
Initial	4.000x10^{-3} mol		5.000x10^{-3} mol		–		0
Change	–4.000x10^{-3} mol		–4.000x10^{-3} mol		–		+4.000x10^{-3} mol
Final	0		1.000x10^{-3} mol				4.000x10^{-3} mol

The volume of the solution at this point is [(40.00 + 50.00) mL](10^{-3} L/ 1 mL) = 0.09000 L

The concentration (mol/L) of the excess NaOH is (1.000x10^{-3} mol NaOH)/(0.09000 L) = 0.011111 mol/L

pOH = –log (0.011111) = 1.95424

pH = 14.00 – pOH = 14.00 – 1.95424 = 12.04576 = **12.05**

17.60　Plan: This is a titration between a weak acid and a strong base. The pH before addition of the base is dependent on the K_a of the acid (labeled HBut). Prior to reaching the equivalence point, the added base reacts with the acid to form butanoate ion (labeled But⁻). The equivalence point occurs when 20.00 mL of base is added to the acid because at this point, amount (mol) acid = amount (mol) base. Addition of base beyond the equivalence point is simply the addition of excess OH⁻.

Solution:

a) At 0 mL of base added, the concentration of $[H_3O^+]$ is dependent on the dissociation of butanoic acid:

	HBut	+	H_2O	⇌	H_3O^+	+	But⁻
Initial	0.1000 mol/L				0		0
Change	–x				+x		+x
Equilibrium	0.1000 – x				x		x

$$K_a = 1.54 \times 10^{-5} = \frac{\left[H_3O^+\right]\left[But^-\right]}{\left[HBut\right]} = \frac{x^2}{0.1000 - x} = \frac{x^2}{0.1000}$$

$$x = [H_3O^+] = 1.2409674 \times 10^{-3} \text{ mol/L}$$
$$pH = -\log[H^+] = -\log(1.2409674 \times 10^{-3}) = 2.9062 = \mathbf{2.91}$$

b) The initial amount (mol) of HBut = $(c)(V)$ = (0.1000 mol HBut/L)(10^{-3} L/1 mL)(20.00 mL)
$$= 2.000 \times 10^{-3} \text{ mol HBut}$$

Determine the amount (mol) of NaOH added:

Amount (mol) of added NaOH = (0.1000 mol NaOH/L)(10^{-3} L/1 mL)(10.00 mL) = 1.000×10^{-3} mol NaOH

The NaOH will react with an equal amount of the acid, and 1.000×10^{-3} mol HBut will remain. An equal amount (mol) of But⁻ will form.

	HBut(aq)	+	NaOH(aq)	→	H_2O(l)	+	But⁻(aq)	+	Na⁺(aq)
Initial	2.000×10^{-3} mol		1.000×10^{-3} mol		–		0		–
Change	-1.000×10^{-3} mol		-1.000×10^{-3} mol		–		$+1.000 \times 10^{-3}$ mol		–
Final	1.000×10^{-3} mol		0				1.000×10^{-3} mol		

The volume of the solution at this point is [(20.00 + 10.00) mL](10^{-3} L/1 mL) = 0.03000 L
The concentration (mol/L) of the excess HBut is (1.000×10^{-3} mol HBut)/(0.03000 L) = 0.03333 mol/L
The concentration (mol/L) of the But⁻ formed is (1.000×10^{-3} mol But⁻ /(0.03000 L) = 0.03333 mol/L

Using a reaction table for the equilibrium reaction of HBut:

	HBut	+	H_2O	⇌	H_3O^+	+	But⁻
Initial	0.03333 mol/L		–		0		0.03333 mol/L
Change	–x				+x		+x
Equilibrium	0.03333 – x				x		0.03333 + x

$$K_a = 1.54 \times 10^{-5} = \frac{\left[H_3O^+\right]\left[But^-\right]}{\left[HBut\right]} = \frac{x(0.0333 + x)}{0.03333 - x} = \frac{x(0.03333)}{0.03333}$$

$$x = [H_3O^+] = 1.54 \times 10^{-5} \text{ mol/L}$$
$$pH = -\log[H^+] = -\log(1.54 \times 10^{-5}) = 4.812479 = \mathbf{4.81}$$

c) Determine the amount (mol) of NaOH added:

amount (mol) of added NaOH = (0.1000 mol NaOH/L)(10^{-3} L/1 mL)(15.00 mL)
$$= 1.500 \times 10^{-3} \text{ mol NaOH}$$

The NaOH will react with an equal amount of the acid, and 5.00×10^{-4} mol HBut will remain, and 1.500×10^{-3} moles of But⁻ will form.

	HBut(aq)	+	NaOH(aq)	→	H_2O(l)	+	But⁻(aq)	+	Na⁺(aq)
Initial	2.000×10^{-3} mol		1.500×10^{-3} mol		–		0		–
Change	-1.500×10^{-3} mol		-1.500×10^{-3} mol		–		$+1.500 \times 10^{-3}$ mol		–
Final	5.000×10^{-4} mol		0				1.500×10^{-3} mol		

The volume of the solution at this point is [(20.00 + 15.00) mL](10^{-3} L/1 mL) = 0.03500 L
The concentration (mol/L) of the excess HBut is (5.00×10^{-4} mol HBut)/(0.03500 L) = 0.0142857 mol/L
The concentration (mol/L) of the But⁻ formed is (1.500×10^{-3} mol But⁻)/(0.03500 L) = 0.042857 mol/L
Using a reaction table for the equilibrium reaction of HBut:

	HBut	+	H_2O	⇌	H_3O^+	+	But⁻

Initial	0.0142857 mol/L	–		0	0.042857 mol/L
Change		$-x$		$+x$	$+x$
Equilibrium	0.0142857 $-$ x			x	0.042857 $+$ x

$$K_a = 1.54 \times 10^{-5} = \frac{\left[H_3O^+\right]\left[But^-\right]}{\left[HBut\right]} = \frac{x(0.042857 + x)}{0.0142857 - x} = \frac{x(0.042857)}{0.0142857}$$

$$x = [H_3O^+] = 5.1333 \times 10^{-6} \text{ mol/L}$$
$$pH = -\log[H^+] = -\log(5.1333 \times 10^{-6}) = 5.2896 = \mathbf{5.29}$$

d) Determine the amount (mol) of NaOH added:

amount (mol) of added NaOH = (0.1000 mol NaOH/L)(10^{-3} L/1 mL)(19.00 mL)
= 1.900×10^{-3} mol NaOH

The NaOH will react with an equal amount of the acid, and 1.00×10^{-4} mol HBut will remain, and 1.900×10^{-3} moles of But$^-$ will form.

	HBut(*aq*)	+	NaOH(*aq*)	→	H$_2$O(*l*)	+	But$^-$(*aq*)	+	Na$^+$(*aq*)
Initial	2.000×10^{-3} mol		1.900×10^{-3} mol		–		0		–
Change	-1.900×10^{-3} mol		-1.900×10^{-3} mol		–		$+1.900 \times 10^{-3}$ mol		–
Final	1.000×10^{-4} mol		0				1.900×10^{-3} mol		

The volume of the solution at this point is [(20.00 + 19.00) mL](10^{-3} L/1 mL) = 0.03900 L
The concentration (mol/L) of the excess HBut is (1.00×10^{-4} mol HBut)/(0.03900 L) = 0.0025641 mol/L
The concentration (mol/L) of the But$^-$ formed is (1.900×10^{-3} mol But$^-$)/(0.03900 L) = 0.0487179 mol/L
Using a reaction table for the equilibrium reaction of HBut:

	HBut	+	H$_2$O	⇌	H$_3$O$^+$	+	But$^-$
Initial	0.0025641 mol/L		–		0		0.0487179 mol/L
Change	$-x$		–		$+x$		$+x$
Equilibrium	0.0025641 $-$ x				$+x$		0.0487179 $+$ x

$$K_a = 1.54 \times 10^{-5} = \frac{\left[H_3O^+\right]\left[But^-\right]}{\left[HBut\right]} = \frac{x(0.0487179 + x)}{0.0025641 - x} = \frac{x(0.0487179)}{0.0025641}$$

$$x = [H_3O^+] = 8.1052632 \times 10^{-7} \text{ mol/L}$$
$$pH = -\log[H^+] = -\log(8.1052632 \times 10^{-7}) = 6.09123 = \mathbf{6.09}$$

e) Determine the amount (mol) of NaOH added:

amount (mol) of added NaOH = (0.1000 mol NaOH/L)(10^{-3} L/1 mL)(19.95 mL)
= 1.995×10^{-3} mol NaOH

The NaOH will react with an equal amount of the acid, and 5×10^{-6} mol HBut will remain, and 1.995×10^{-3} moles of But$^-$ will form.

	HBut(*aq*)	+	NaOH(*aq*)	→	H$_2$O(*l*)	+	But$^-$(*aq*)	+	Na$^+$(*aq*)
Initial	2.000×10^{-3} mol		1.995×10^{-3} mol		–		0		–
Change	-1.995×10^{-3} mol		-1.995×10^{-3} mol		–		$+1.995 \times 10^{-3}$ mol		–
Final	5.000×10^{-6} mol		0				1.995×10^{-3} mol		

The volume of the solution at this point is [(20.00 + 19.95) mL](10^{-3} L/1 mL) = 0.03995 L
The concentration (mol/L) of the excess HBut is (5×10^{-6} mol HBut)/(0.03995 L) = 0.000125156 mol/L
The concentration (mol/L) of the But$^-$ formed is (1.995×10^{-3} mol But$^-$)/(0.03995 L) = 0.0499374 mol/L
Using a reaction table for the equilibrium reaction of HBut:

	HBut	+	H$_2$O	⇌	H$_3$O$^+$	+	But$^-$
Initial	0.000125156 mol/L		–		0		0.0499374 mol/L
Change	$-x$		–		$+x$		$+x$
Equilibrium	0.000125156 $-$ x				x		0.0499374 $+$ x

$$K_a = 1.54 \times 10^{-5} = \frac{\left[H_3O^+\right]\left[But^-\right]}{\left[HBut\right]} = \frac{x(0.0499374 + x)}{0.000125156 - x} = \frac{x(0.0499374)}{0.000125156}$$

$$x = [H_3O^+] = 3.859637 \times 10^{-8} \text{ mol/L}$$
$$pH = -\log[H^+] = -\log(3.859637 \times 10^{-8}) = 7.41345 = \mathbf{7.41}$$

f) Determine the amount (mol) of NaOH added:

amount (mol) of added NaOH = (0.1000 mol NaOH/L)(10^{-3} L/1 mL)(20.00 mL)
$$= 2.000 \times 10^{-3} \text{ mol NaOH}$$

The NaOH will react with an equal amount of the acid, and 0 mol HBut will remain, and 2.000×10^{-3} moles of But⁻ will form. This is the equivalence point.

	HBut(aq)	+	NaOH(aq)	→	H₂O(l)	+	But⁻(aq)	+	Na⁺(aq)
Initial	2.000×10^{-3} mol		2.000×10^{-3} mol		–		0		–
Change	-2.000×10^{-3} mol		-2.000×10^{-3} mol		–		$+2.000 \times 10^{-3}$ mol		–
Final	0		0				2.000×10^{-3} mol		

The K_b of But⁻ is now important.

The volume of the solution at this point is [(20.00 + 20.00) mL](10^{-3} L/1 mL) = 0.04000 L

The concentration (mol/L) of the But⁻ formed is $(2.000 \times 10^{-3}$ mol But⁻)/(0.04000 L) = 0.05000 mol/L

$$K_b = K_w/K_a = (1.0 \times 10^{-14})/(1.54 \times 10^{-5}) = 6.49351 \times 10^{-10}$$

Using a reaction table for the equilibrium reaction of But⁻:

	But⁻	+	H₂O	⇌	HBut	+	OH⁻
Initial	0.05000 mol/L		–		0		0
Change	–x		–		+x		+x
Equilibrium	0.05000 – x				x		x

$$K_b = 6.49351 \times 10^{-10} = \frac{[\text{HBut}][\text{OH}^-]}{[\text{But}^-]} = \frac{(x)(x)}{(0.05000 - x)} = \frac{(x)(x)}{(0.05000)}$$

[OH⁻] = x = 5.6980304×10^{-6} mol/L

pOH = –log $(5.6980304 \times 10^{-6})$ = 5.244275238

pH = 14.00 – pOH = 14.00 – 5.244275238 = 8.7557248 = **8.76**

g) After the equivalence point, the excess strong base is the primary factor influencing the pH.

Determine the amount (mol) of NaOH added:

amount (mol) of added NaOH = (0.1000 mol NaOH/L)(10^{-3} L/1 mL)(20.05 mL)
$$= 2.005 \times 10^{-3} \text{ mol NaOH}$$

The NaOH will react with an equal amount of the acid, 0 mol HBut will remain, and 5×10^{-6} moles of NaOH will be in excess. There will be 2.000×10^{-3} mol of But⁻ produced, but this weak base will not affect the pH compared to the excess strong base, NaOH.

	HBut(aq)	+	NaOH(aq)	→	H₂O(l)	+	But⁻(aq)	+	Na⁺(aq)
Initial	2.000×10^{-3} mol		2.005×10^{-3} mol		–		0		–
Change	-2.000×10^{-3} mol		-2.000×10^{-3} mol		–		$+2.000 \times 10^{-3}$ mol		–
Final	0		5.000×10^{-6} mol				2.000×10^{-3} mol		

The volume of the solution at this point is [(20.00 + 20.05) mL](10^{-3} L/1 mL) = 0.04005 L

The concentration (mol/L) of the excess OH⁻ is $(5 \times 10^{-6}$ mol OH⁻)/(0.04005 L) = 1.2484×10^{-4} mol/L

pOH = –log (1.2484×10^{-4}) = 3.9036

pH = 14.00 – pOH = 14.00 – 3.9036 = 10.0964 = **10.10**

h) Determine the amount (mol) of NaOH added:

amount (mol) of added NaOH = (0.1000 mol NaOH/L)(10^{-3} L/1 mL)(25.00 mL)
$$= 2.500 \times 10^{-3} \text{ mol NaOH}$$

The NaOH will react with an equal amount of the acid, 0 mol HBut will remain, and 5.00×10^{-4} moles of NaOH will be in excess.

	HBut(aq)	+	NaOH(aq)	→	H₂O(l)	+	But⁻(aq)	+	Na⁺(aq)
Initial	2.000×10^{-3} mol		2.500×10^{-3} mol		–		0		–
Change	-2.000×10^{-3} mol		-2.000×10^{-3} mol		–		$+2.000 \times 10^{-3}$ mol		–
Final	0		5.000×10^{-4} mol				2.000×10^{-3} mol		

The volume of the solution at this point is [(20.00 + 25.00) mL](10^{-3} L/1 mL) = 0.04500 L

The concentration (mol/L) of the excess OH⁻ is $(5.00 \times 10^{-4}$ mol OH⁻/(0.04500 L) = 1.1111×10^{-2} mol/L

pOH = –log (1.1111×10^{-2}) = 1.9542

pH = 14.00 – pOH = 14.00 – 1.9542 = 12.0458 = **12.05**

17.62 <u>Plan:</u> Use $(c)(V)$ to find the initial amount (mol) of acid and then use the mole ratio in the balanced equation to find amount (mol) of base; dividing amount (mol) of base by the concentration (mol/L) of the base gives the volume. At the equivalence point, the conjugate base of the weak acid is present; set up a reaction table for the base dissociation in which x = the amount of dissociated base. Use the K_b expression to solve for x from which pOH and then pH is obtained.

<u>Solution:</u>

a) The balanced chemical equation is:

$$NaOH(aq) + CH_3COOH(aq) \rightarrow Na^+(aq) + CH_3COO^-(aq) + H_2O(l)$$

The sodium ions on the product side are written as separate species because they have no effect on the pH of the solution. Calculate the volume of NaOH needed:

Volume (mL) of NaOH =

$$\left(\frac{0.0520 \text{ mol CH}_3\text{COOH}}{L}\right)\left(\frac{10^{-3} \text{ L}}{1 \text{ mL}}\right)(42.2 \text{ mL})\left(\frac{1 \text{ mol NaOH}}{1 \text{ mol CH}_3\text{COOH}}\right)\left(\frac{L}{0.0372 \text{ mol NaOH}}\right)\left(\frac{1 \text{ mL}}{10^{-3} \text{ L}}\right)$$

$$= 58.989247 \text{ mL} = \textbf{59.0 mL NaOH}$$

Determine the amount (mol) of initially CH_3COOH present:

$$\text{amount (mol) of CH}_3\text{COOH} = \left(\frac{0.0520 \text{ mol CH}_3\text{COOH}}{L}\right)\left(\frac{10^{-3} \text{ L}}{1 \text{ mL}}\right)(42.2 \text{ mL}) = 0.0021944 \text{ mol CH}_3\text{COOH}$$

At the equivalence point, 0.0021944 mol NaOH will be added so the amount (mol) acid = amount (mol) base. The NaOH will react with an equal amount of the acid, 0 mol CH_3COOH will remain, and 0.0021944 moles of CH_3COO^- will be formed.

	$CH_3COOH(aq)$	+	$NaOH(aq)$	$\rightarrow$	$H_2O(l)$	+	$CH_3COO^-(aq)$	+	$Na^+(aq)$
Initial	0.0021944 mol		0.0021944 mol		–		0		–
Change	−0.0021944 mol		−0.0021944 mol		–		+0.0021944 mol		–
Final	0		0				0.0021944 mol		

Determine the volume of solution in litre present at the equivalence point:

$$\text{Volume} = [(42.2 + 58.989247) \text{ mL}](10^{-3} \text{ L}/1 \text{ mL}) = 0.101189247 \text{ L}$$

Concentration of CH_3COO^- at equivalence point:

$$\text{concentration (mol/L)} = (0.0021944 \text{ mol CH}_3\text{COO}^-)/(0.101189247 \text{ L}) = 0.0216861 \text{ mol/L}$$

Calculate K_b for CH_3COO^-: K_a $CH_3COOH = 1.8 \times 10^{-5}$

$$K_b = K_w/K_a = (1.0 \times 10^{-14})/(1.8 \times 10^{-5}) = 5.556 \times 10^{-10}$$

Using a reaction table for the equilibrium reaction of CH_3COO^-:

	CH_3COO^-	+	H_2O	$\rightleftharpoons$	CH_3COOH	+	OH^-
Initial	0.0216861 mol/L		–		0		0
Change	−x				+x		+x
Equilibrium	0.0216861 − x				x		x

Determine the hydroxide ion concentration from the K_b, and then determine the pH from the pOH.

$$K_b = 5.556 \times 10^{-10} = \frac{[CH_3COOH][OH^-]}{[CH_3COO^-]} = \frac{(x)(x)}{(0.0216861 - x)} = \frac{(x)(x)}{(0.0216861)}$$

$[OH^-] = x = 3.471138 \times 10^{-6}$ mol/L

pOH = −log $(3.471138 \times 10^{-6}) = 5.459528$

pH = 14.00 − pOH = 14.00 − 5.459528 = 8.54047 = **8.54**

b) The balanced chemical equations are:

$$NaOH(aq) + H_2SO_3(aq) \rightarrow Na^+(aq) + HSO_3^-(aq) + H_2O(l)$$
$$NaOH(aq) + HSO_3^-(aq) \rightarrow Na^+(aq) + SO_3^{2-}(aq) + H_2O(l)$$

The sodium ions on the product side are written as separate species because they have no effect on the pH of the solution. Calculate the volume of NaOH needed:

Volume (mL) of NaOH =

$$\left(\frac{0.0850 \text{ mol H}_2\text{SO}_3}{L}\right)\left(\frac{10^{-3} \text{ L}}{1 \text{ mL}}\right)(28.9 \text{ mL})\left(\frac{1 \text{ mol NaOH}}{1 \text{ mol H}_2\text{SO}_3}\right)\left(\frac{L}{0.0372 \text{ mol NaOH}}\right)\left(\frac{1 \text{ mL}}{10^{-3} \text{ L}}\right)$$

$$= 66.034946 \text{ mL} = \textbf{66.0 mL NaOH}$$

It will require an equal volume to reach the second equivalence point for a total of 2 x 66.034946 mL = **132.1 mL**.
Determine the amount (mol) of HSO_3^- produced:

$$\text{amount (mol)} \text{ of } HSO_3^- = \left(\frac{0.0850 \text{ mol } H_2SO_3}{L}\right)\left(\frac{10^{-3} \text{ L}}{1 \text{ mL}}\right)(28.9 \text{ mL})\left(\frac{1 \text{ mol } HSO_3^{2-}}{1 \text{ mol } H_2SO_3}\right) = 0.0024565 \text{ mol } HSO_3^-$$

An equal amount (mol) of SO_3^{2-} will be present at the second equivalence point.
Determine the volume of solution in litre present at the first equivalence point:
Volume = [(28.9 + 66.034946) mL](10^{-3} L/1 mL) = 0.094934946 L
Determine the volume of solution in litre present at the second equivalence point:
Volume = [(28.9 + 66.034946 + 66.034946) mL](10^{-3} L/1 mL) = 0.160969892 L
Concentration of HSO_3^- at equivalence point:
concentration (mol/L) = (0.0024565 moles HSO_3^-)/(0.094934946 L) = 0.0258756 mol/LM
Concentration of SO_3^{2-} at equivalence point:
concentration (mol/L) = (0.0024565 moles SO_3^{2-})/(0.160969892 L) = 0.0152606 mol/L
Calculate K_b for HSO_3^-: $\qquad$ K_a $H_2SO_3 = 1.4 \times 10^{-2}$
$K_b = K_w/K_a = (1.0 \times 10^{-14})/(1.4 \times 10^{-2}) = 7.142857 \times 10^{-13}$
Calculate K_b for SO_3^{2-}: $\qquad$ K_a $HSO_3^- = 6.5 \times 10^{-8}$
$K_b = K_w/K_a = (1.0 \times 10^{-14})/(6.5 \times 10^{-8}) = 1.53846 \times 10^{-7}$
For the first equivalence point:
Using a reaction table for the equilibrium reaction of HSO_3^-:

	HSO_3^-	+	H_2O	$\rightleftharpoons$	H_2SO_3	+	OH^-
Initial	0.0258756 mol/L				0		0
Change	$-x$				$+x$		$+x$
Equilibrium	0.0258756 – x				x		x

Determine the hydroxide ion concentration from the K_b, and then determine the pH from the pOH.

$$K_b = 7.142857 \times 10^{-13} = \frac{[H_2SO_3][OH^-]}{[HSO_3^-]} = \frac{(x)(x)}{(0.0258756 - x)} = \frac{(x)(x)}{(0.0258756)}$$

$[OH^-] = x = 1.359506 \times 10^{-7}$ mol/L
$\quad$ pOH = $-\log(1.359506 \times 10^{-7}) = 6.8666189$
$\quad$ pH = 14.00 – pOH = 14.00 – 6.8666189 = 7.13338 = **7.13**
For the second equivalence point:
Using a reaction table for the equilibrium reaction of SO_3^{2-}:

	SO_3^{2-}	+	H_2O	$\rightleftharpoons$	HSO_3^-	+	OH^-
Initial	0.0152606 mol/L				0		0
Change	$-x$				$+x$		$+x$
Equilibrium	0.0152606 – x				x		x

Determine the hydroxide ion concentration from the K_b, and then determine the pH from the pOH.

$$K_b = 1.53846 \times 10^{-7} = \frac{[HSO_3^-][OH^-]}{[SO_3^{2-}]} = \frac{(x)(x)}{(0.0152606 - x)} = \frac{(x)(x)}{(0.0152606)}$$

$[OH^-] = x = 4.84539 \times 10^{-5}$ mol/L
$\quad$ pOH = $-\log(4.84539 \times 10^{-5}) = 4.31467$
$\quad$ pH = 14.00 – pOH = 14.00 – 4.31467 = 9.68533 = **9.69**

17.64 $\quad$ Plan: Use $(c)(V)$ to find the initial amount (mol) of base and then use the mole ratio in the balanced equation to find amount (mol) of acid; dividing amount (mol) of acid by the concentration (mol/L) of the acid gives the volume. At the equivalence point, the conjugate acid of the weak base is present; set up a reaction table for the acid dissociation in which x = the amount of dissociated acid. Use the K_a expression to solve for x from which pH is obtained.
Solution:
a) The balanced chemical equation is:
$\qquad$ $HCl(aq) + NH_3(aq) \rightarrow NH_4^+(aq) + Cl^-(aq)$

The chloride ions on the product side are written as separate species because they have no effect on the pH of the solution. Calculate the volume of HCl needed:

Volume (mL) of HCl =

$$\left(\frac{0.234\ \text{mol NH}_3}{\text{L}}\right)\left(\frac{10^{-3}\ \text{L}}{1\ \text{mL}}\right)(65.5\ \text{mL})\left(\frac{1\ \text{mol HCl}}{1\ \text{mol NH}_3}\right)\left(\frac{\text{L}}{0.125\ \text{mol HCl}}\right)\left(\frac{1\ \text{mL}}{10^{-3}\ \text{L}}\right) = 122.616\ \textbf{mL}= \textbf{123 mL HCl}$$

Determine the amount (mol) of NH_3 present:

$$\text{amount (mol)} = \left(\frac{0.234\ \text{mol NH}_3}{\text{L}}\right)\left(\frac{10^{-3}\ \text{L}}{1\ \text{mL}}\right)(65.5\ \text{mL}) = 0.015327\ \text{mol NH}_3$$

At the equivalence point, 0.015327 mol HCl will be added so the amount (mol) acid = amount (mol) base. The HCl will react with an equal amount of the base, 0 mol NH_3 will remain, and 0.015327 moles of NH_4^+ will be formed.

	$HCl(aq)$	+	$NH_3(aq)$	$\rightarrow$	$NH_4^+(aq)$	+	$Cl^-(aq)$
Initial	0.015327 mol		0.015327 mol		0		–
Change	–0.015327 mol		–0.015327 mol		+0.015327 mol		–
Final	0		0		0.015327 mol		

Determine the volume of solution in litre present at the equivalence point:

Volume = [(65.5 + 122.616) mL](10^{-3} L/1 mL) = 0.188116 L

Concentration of NH_4^+ at equivalence point:

concentration (mol/L) = (0.015327 mol NH_4^+)/(0.188116 L) = 0.081476 mol/L

Calculate K_a for NH_4^+: $\quad K_b\ NH_3 = 1.76\text{x}10^{-5}$

$K_a = K_w/K_b = (1.0\text{x}10^{-14})/(1.76\text{x}10^{-5}) = 5.6818\text{x}10^{-10}$

Using a reaction table for the equilibrium reaction of NH_4^+:

	NH_4^+	+	H_2O	$\rightleftharpoons$	NH_3	+	H_3O^+
Initial	0.081476 mol/L		–		0		0
Change	–x				+x		+x
Equilibrium	0.081476 – x				x		x

Determine the hydrogen ion concentration from the K_a, and then determine the pH.

$$K_a= 5.6818\text{x}10^{-10} = \frac{\left[H_3O^+\right]\left[NH_3\right]}{\left[NH_4^+\right]} = \frac{(x)(x)}{(0.081476 - x)} = \frac{(x)(x)}{(0.081476)}$$

x = $[H_3O^+]$ = $6.803898\text{x}10^{-6}$ mol/L

pH = –log $[H^+]$ = –log $(6.803898\text{x}10^{-6})$ = 5.1672 = **5.17**

b) The balanced chemical equation is:

$HCl(aq) + CH_3NH_2(aq) \rightarrow CH_3NH_3^+(aq) + Cl^-(aq)$

The chloride ions on the product side are written as separate species because they have no effect on the pH of the solution. Calculate the volume of HCl needed:

Volume (mL) of HCl =

$$\left(\frac{1.11\ \text{mol CH}_3\text{NH}_2}{\text{L}}\right)\left(\frac{10^{-3}\ \text{L}}{1\ \text{mL}}\right)(21.8\ \text{mL})\left(\frac{1\ \text{mol HCl}}{1\ \text{mol CH}_3\text{NH}_2}\right)\left(\frac{\text{L}}{0.125\ \text{mol HCl}}\right)\left(\frac{1\ \text{mL}}{10^{-3}\ \text{L}}\right)$$

$$= 193.584\ \text{mL}= \textbf{194 mL HCl}$$

Determine the amount (mol) of CH_3NH_2 present:

$$\text{amount (mol)} = \left(\frac{1.11\ \text{mol CH}_3\text{NH}_2}{\text{L}}\right)\left(\frac{10^{-3}\ \text{L}}{1\ \text{mL}}\right)(21.8\ \text{mL}) = 0.024198\ \text{mol CH}_3\text{NH}_2$$

At the equivalence point, 0.024198 mol HCl will be added so the amount (mol) acid = amount (mol) base. The HCl will react with an equal amount of the base, 0 mol CH_3NH_2 will remain, and 0.024198 moles of $CH_3NH_3^+$ will be formed.

	$HCl(aq)$	+	$CH_3NH_2(aq)$	$\rightarrow$	$CH_3NH_3^+(aq)$	+	$Cl^-(aq)$
Initial	0.024198 mol		0.024198 mol		0		–
Change	–0.024198 mol		–0.024198 mol		+0.024198 mol		–
Final	0		0		0.024198 mol		

Determine the volume of solution in litre present at the equivalence point:

Volume = $[(21.8 + 193.584)$ mL$](10^{-3}$ L/1 mL$) = 0.215384$ L
Concentration of $CH_3NH_3^+$ at equivalence point:
concentration (mol/L) = $(0.024198$ mol $CH_3NH_3^+)/(0.215384$ L$) = 0.1123482$ mol/L
Calculate K_a for $CH_3NH_3^+$: K_b $CH_3NH_2 = 4.4 \times 10^{-4}$
$K_a = K_w/K_b = (1.0 \times 10^{-14})/(4.4 \times 10^{-4}) = 2.2727 \times 10^{-11}$
Using a reaction table for the equilibrium reaction of $CH_3NH_3^+$:

	$CH_3NH_3^+$	+	H_2O	$\rightleftharpoons$	CH_3NH_2	+	H_3O^+
Initial	0.1123482 mol/L		–		0		0
Change	–x				+x		+x
Equilibrium	0.1123482 – x				x		x

Determine the hydrogen ion concentration from the K_a, and then determine the pH.

$$K_a = 2.2727 \times 10^{-11} = \frac{\left[H_3O^+\right]\left[CH_3NH_2\right]}{\left[CH_3NH_3^+\right]} = \frac{(x)(x)}{(0.1123482 - x)} = \frac{(x)(x)}{(0.1123482)}$$

$x = [H_3O^+] = 1.5979 \times 10^{-6}$ mol/L
pH $= -\log [H^+] = -\log (1.5979 \times 10^{-6}) = 5.7964 = $ **5.80**

17.72   Fluoride ion in BaF_2 is the conjugate base of the weak acid HF. The base hydrolysis reaction of fluoride ion
$\quad\quad$ $F^-(aq) + H_2O(l) \rightleftharpoons HF(aq) + OH^-(aq)$

therefore is influenced by the pH of the solution. As the pH increases, $[OH^-]$ increases and the equilibrium shifts to the left to decrease $[OH^-]$ and increase $[F^-]$. As the pH decreases, $[OH^-]$ decreases and the equilibrium shifts to the right to increase $[OH^-]$ and decrease $[F^-]$. The changes in $[F^-]$ influence the solubility of BaF_2.
Chloride ion is the conjugate base of a strong acid so it does not react with water. Thus, its concentration is not influenced by pH, and solubility of $BaCl_2$ does not change with pH.

17.74   Consider the reaction $AB(s) \rightleftharpoons A^+(aq) + B^-(aq)$, where $Q_{sp} = [A^+][B^-]$. If $Q_{sp} > K_{sp}$, then there are more ions dissolved than expected at equilibrium, and the equilibrium shifts to the left and the compound AB precipitates. The excess ions precipitate as solid from the solution.

17.75   Plan: Write an equation that describes the solid compound dissolving to produce its ions. The ion-product expression follows the equation $K_{sp} = [M^{n+}]^p[X^{z-}]^q$ where p and q are the subscripts of the ions in the compound's formula.
Solution:
a) $Ag_2CO_3(s) \rightleftharpoons 2Ag^+(aq) + CO_3^{2-}(aq)$
$\quad\quad$ Ion-product expression: $K_{sp} = [Ag^+]^2[CO_3^{2-}]$
b) $BaF_2(s) \rightleftharpoons Ba^{2+}(aq) + 2F^-(aq)$
$\quad\quad$ Ion-product expression: $K_{sp} = [Ba^{2+}][F^-]^2$
c) $CuS(s) + H_2O(l) \rightleftharpoons Cu^{2+}(aq) + HS^-(aq) + OH^-(aq)$
$\quad\quad$ Ion-product expression: $K_{sp} = [Cu^{2+}][HS^-][OH^-]$

17.77   Plan: Write an equation that describes the solid compound dissolving to produce its ions. The ion-product expression follows the equation $K_{sp} = [M^{n+}]^p[X^{z-}]^q$ where p and q are the subscripts of the ions in the compound's formula.
Solution:
a) $CaCrO_4(s) \rightleftharpoons Ca^{2+}(aq) + CrO_4^{2-}(aq)$
$\quad\quad$ Ion-product expression: $K_{sp} = [Ca^{2+}][CrO_4^{2-}]$
b) $AgCN(s) \rightleftharpoons Ag^+(aq) + CN^-(aq)$
$\quad\quad$ Ion-product expression: $K_{sp} = [Ag^+][CN^-]$
c) $NiS(s) + H_2O(l) \rightleftharpoons Ni^{2+}(aq) + HS^-(aq) + OH^-(aq)$
$\quad\quad$ Ion-product expression: $K_{sp} = [Ni^{2+}][HS^-][OH^-]$

17.79   <u>Plan:</u> Write an equation that describes the solid compound dissolving in water and then write the ion-product expression. Write a reaction table, where S is the molar solubility of Ag_2CO_3. Substitute the given solubility, S, into the ion-expression and solve for K_{sp}.
<u>Solution:</u>

Concentration (mol/L)	$Ag_2CO_3(s)$	$\rightleftharpoons$	$2Ag^+(aq)$	$+$	$CO_3^{2-}(aq)$
Initial	—		0		0
Change	—		$+2S$		$+S$
Equilibrium	—		$2S$		S

$S = [Ag_2CO_3] = 0.032$ mol/L so $[Ag^+] = 2S = 0.064$ mol/L and $[CO_3^{2-}] = S = 0.032$ mol/L
$K_{sp} = [Ag^+]^2[CO_3^{2-}] = (0.064)^2(0.032) = 1.31072 \times 10^{-4} = \mathbf{1.3 \times 10^{-4}}$

17.81   <u>Plan:</u> Write an equation that describes the solid compound dissolving in water and then write the ion-product expression. Write a reaction table, where S is the molar solubility of $Ag_2Cr_2O_7$. Substitute the given solubility, S, converted from mass/volume to concentration (mol/L), into the ion-expression and solve for K_{sp}.
<u>Solution:</u>
The solubility of $Ag_2Cr_2O_7$, converted from g/100 mL to mol/L is:

Molar solubility $= S = \left(\dfrac{8.3 \times 10^{-3} \text{ g Ag}_2\text{Cr}_2\text{O}_7}{100 \text{ mL}} \right)\left(\dfrac{1 \text{ mL}}{10^{-3} \text{ L}} \right)\left(\dfrac{1 \text{ mol Ag}_2\text{Cr}_2\text{O}_7}{431.8 \text{ g Ag}_2\text{Cr}_2\text{O}_7} \right) = 0.00019221862$ mol/L

The equation for silver dichromate, $Ag_2Cr_2O_7$, is:

Concentration (mol/L)	$Ag_2Cr_2O_7(s)$	$\rightleftharpoons$	$2Ag^+(aq)$	$+$	$Cr_2O_7^{2-}(aq)$
Initial	—		0		0
Change	—		$+2S$		$+S$
Equilibrium	—		$2S$		S

$2S = [Ag^+] = 2(0.00019221862$ mol/L$) = 0.00038443724$ mol/L
$S = [Cr_2O_7^{2-}] = 0.00019221862$ mol/L
$K_{sp} = [Ag^+]^2[Cr_2O_7^{2-}] = (2S)^2(S) = (0.00038443724)^2(0.00019221862) = 2.8408 \times 10^{-11} = \mathbf{2.8 \times 10^{-11}}$

17.83   <u>Plan:</u> Write the equation that describes the solid compound dissolving in water and then write the ion-product expression. Set up a reaction table that expresses $[Sr^{2+}]$ and $[CO_3^{2-}]$ in terms of S, substitute into the ion-product expression, and solve for S. In part b), the $[Sr^{2+}]$ that comes from the dissolved $Sr(NO_3)_2$ must be included in the reaction table.
<u>Solution:</u>
a) The equation and ion-product expression for $SrCO_3$ is:
$$SrCO_3(s) \rightleftharpoons Sr^{2+}(aq) + CO_3^{2-}(aq) \qquad K_{sp} = [Sr^{2+}][CO_3^{2-}]$$
The solubility, S, in pure water equals $[Sr^{2+}]$ and $[CO_3^{2-}]$
Write a reaction table, where S is the molar solubility of $SrCO_3$:

Concentration (mol/L)	$SrCO_3(s)$	$\rightleftharpoons$	$Sr^{2+}(aq)$	$+$	$CO_3^{2-}(aq)$
Initial	—		0		0
Change	—		$+S$		$+S$
Equilibrium	—		S		S

$K_{sp} = 5.4 \times 10^{-10} = [Sr^{2+}][CO_3^{2-}] = [S][S] = S^2$
$S = 2.32379 \times 10^{-5} = \mathbf{2.3 \times 10^{-5}}$ **mol/L**
b) In 0.13 mol/L $Sr(NO_3)_2$, the initial concentration of Sr^{2+} is 0.13 mol/L.
Equilibrium $[Sr^{2+}] = 0.13 + S$ and equilibrium $[CO_3^{2-}] = S$ where S is the solubility of $SrCO_3$.

Concentration (mol/L)	$SrCO_3(s)$	$\rightleftharpoons$	$Sr^{2+}(aq)$	$+$	$CO_3^{2-}(aq)$
Initial	—		0.13		0
Change	—		$+S$		$+S$
Equilibrium	—		$0.13 + S$		S

$K_{sp} = 5.4 \times 10^{-10} = [Sr^{2+}][CO_3^{2-}] = (0.13 + S)S$
This calculation may be simplified by assuming S is small and setting $0.13 + S = 0.13$.
$K_{sp} = 5.4 \times 10^{-10} = (0.13)S$
$S = 4.1538 \times 10^{-9} = \mathbf{4.2 \times 10^{-9}}$ **mol/L**

17.85   Plan: Write the equation that describes the solid compound dissolving in water and then write the ion-product expression. Set up a reaction table that expresses $[Ca^{2+}]$ and $[IO_3^-]$ in terms of S, substitute into the ion-product expression, and solve for S. The $[Ca^{2+}]$ that comes from the dissolved $Ca(NO_3)_2$ and the $[IO_3^-]$ that comes from $NaIO_3$ must be included in the reaction table.
Solution:
a) The equilibrium is: $Ca(IO_3)_2(s) \rightleftharpoons Ca^{2+}(aq) + 2IO_3^-(aq)$. From the Appendix, $K_{sp}(Ca(IO_3)_2) = 7.1x10^{-7}$.
Write a reaction table that reflects an initial concentration of $Ca^{2+} = 0.060$ mol/L. In this case, Ca^{2+} is the common ion.

Concentration (mol/L)	$Ca(IO_3)_2(s)$	$\rightleftharpoons$	$Ca^{2+}(aq)$	+	$2IO_3^-(aq)$
Initial	—		0.060		0
Change	—		$+S$		$+2S$
Equilibrium	—		$0.060 + S$		$2S$

Assume that $0.060 + S \approx 0.060$ because the amount of compound that dissolves will be negligible in comparison to 0.060 mol/L.
$$K_{sp} = [Ca^{2+}][IO_3^-]^2 = (0.060)(2S)^2 = 7.1x10^{-7}$$
$$S = 1.71998x10^{-3} = 1.7x10^{-3} \text{ mol/L}$$
Check assumption: $(1.71998x10^{-3}$ mol/L$)/(0.060$ mol/L$) \times 100\% = 2.9\% < 5\%$, so the assumption is good.
S represents both the molar solubility of Ca^{2+} and $Ca(IO_3)_2$, so the molar solubility of $Ca(IO_3)_2$ is **$1.7x10^{-3}$ mol/L**.
b) Write a reaction table that reflects an initial concentration of $IO_3^- = 0.060$ mol/L. IO_3^- is the common ion.

Concentration (mol/L)	$Ca(IO_3)_2(s)$	$\rightleftharpoons$	$Ca^{2+}(aq)$	+	$2IO_3^-(aq)$
Initial	—		0		0.060
Change	—		$+S$		$+2S$
Equilibrium	—		S		$0.060 + 2S$

The equilibrium concentration of Ca^{2+} is S, and the IO_3^- concentration is $0.060 + 2S$.
Assume that $0.060 + 2S \approx 0.060$
$$K_{sp} = [Ca^{2+}][IO_3^-]^2 = (S)(0.060)^2 = 7.1x10^{-7}$$
$$S = 1.97222x10^{-4} = 2.0x10^{-4} \text{ mol/L}$$
Check assumption: $(1.97222x10^{-4}$ mol/L$)/(0.060$ mol/L$) \times 100\% = 0.3\% < 5\%$, so the assumption is good.
S represents both the molar solubility of Ca^{2+} and $Ca(IO_3)_2$, so the molar solubility of $Ca(IO_3)_2$ is **$2.0x10^{-4}$ mol/L**.

17.87   Plan: The larger the K_{sp}, the larger the molar solubility if the number of ions are equal.
Solution:
a) **$Mg(OH)_2$** with $K_{sp} = 6.3x10^{-10}$ has higher molar solubility than $Ni(OH)_2$ with $K_{sp} = 6x10^{-16}$.
b) **PbS** with $K_{sp} = 3x10^{-25}$ has higher molar solubility than CuS with $K_{sp} = 8x10^{-34}$.
c) **Ag_2SO_4** with $K_{sp} = 1.5x10^{-5}$ has higher molar solubility than MgF_2 with $K_{sp} = 7.4x10^{-9}$.

17.89   Plan: The larger the K_{sp}, the more water soluble the compound if the number of ions are equal.
Solution:
a) **$CaSO_4$** with $K_{sp} = 2.4x10^{-5}$ is more water soluble than $BaSO_4$ with $K_{sp} = 1.1x10^{-10}$.
b) **$Mg_3(PO_4)_2$** with $K_{sp} = 5.2x10^{-24}$ is more water soluble than $Ca_3(PO_4)_2$ with $K_{sp} = 1.2x10^{-29}$.
c) **$PbSO_4$** with $K_{sp} = 1.6x10^{-8}$ is more water soluble than $AgCl$ with $K_{sp} = 1.8x10^{-10}$.

17.91   Plan: If a compound contains an anion that is the weak conjugate base of a weak acid, the concentration of that anion, and thus the solubility of the compound, is influenced by pH.
Solution:
a) $AgCl(s) \rightleftharpoons Ag^+(aq) + Cl^-(aq)$

The chloride ion is the anion of a strong acid, so it does not react with H_3O^+. The solubility is not affected by pH.
b) $SrCO_3(s) \rightleftharpoons Sr^{2+}(aq) + CO_3^{2-}(aq)$

The strontium ion is the cation of a strong base, so pH will not affect its solubility.
The carbonate ion is the conjugate base of a weak acid and will act as a base:
$$CO_3^{2-}(aq) + H_2O(l) \rightleftharpoons HCO_3^-(aq) + OH^-(aq)$$
$$\text{and } HCO_3^-(aq) + H_2O(l) \rightleftharpoons H_2CO_3(aq) + OH^-(aq)$$

The H_2CO_3 will decompose to $CO_2(g)$ and $H_2O(l)$. The gas will escape and further shift the equilibrium. Changes in pH will change the $[CO_3^{2-}]$, so the solubility of $SrCO_3$ is affected. **Solubility increases with addition of H_3O^+ (decreasing pH)**. A decrease in pH will decrease $[OH^-]$, causing the base equilibrium to shift to the right which decreases $[CO_3^{2-}]$, causing the solubility equilibrium to shift to the right, dissolving more solid.

17.93 Plan: If a compound contains an anion that is the weak conjugate base of a weak acid, the concentration of that anion, and thus the solubility of the compound, is influenced by pH.
Solution:
a) $Fe(OH)_2(s) \rightleftharpoons Fe^{2+}(aq) + 2OH^-(aq)$

The hydroxide ion reacts with added H_3O^+:
$$OH^-(aq) + H_3O^+(aq) \rightarrow 2H_2O(l)$$
The added H_3O^+ consumes the OH^-, driving the equilibrium toward the right to dissolve more $Fe(OH)_2$. **Solubility increases with addition of H_3O^+ (decreasing pH)**.
b) $CuS(s) + H_2O(l) \rightleftharpoons Cu^{2+}(aq) + HS^-(aq) + OH^-(aq)$

Both HS^- and OH^- are anions of weak acids, so both ions react with added H_3O^+. **Solubility increases with addition of H_3O^+ (decreasing pH)**.

17.95 Plan: Find the initial molar concentrations of Cu^{2+} and OH^-. The concentration (mol/L) of the KOH is calculated by converting mass to the amount (mol) and dividing by the volume. Put these concentrations in the ion-product expression, solve for Q_{sp}, and compare Q_{sp} with K_{sp}. If $Q_{sp} > K_{sp}$, precipitate forms.
Solution:
The equilibrium is: $Cu(OH)_2(s) \rightleftharpoons Cu^{2+}(aq) + 2OH^-(aq)$. The ion-product expression is $K_{sp} = [Cu^{2+}][OH^-]^2$ and, from the Appendix, K_{sp} equals 2.2×10^{-20}.
$$[Cu^{2+}] = \left(\frac{1.0 \times 10^{-3} \text{ mol } Cu(NO_3)_2}{L}\right)\left(\frac{1 \text{ mol } Cu^{2+}}{1 \text{ mol } Cu(NO_3)_2}\right) = 1.0 \times 10^{-3} \text{ mol/L } Cu^{2+}$$
$$[OH^-] = \left(\frac{0.075 \text{ g KOH}}{1.0 \text{ L}}\right)\left(\frac{1 \text{ mol KOH}}{56.11 \text{ g KOH}}\right)\left(\frac{1 \text{ mol } OH^-}{1 \text{ mol KOH}}\right) = 1.33666 \times 10^{-3} \text{ mol/L } OH^-$$
$Q_{sp} = [Cu^{2+}][OH^-]^2 = (1.0 \times 10^{-3})(1.33666 \times 10^{-3})^2 = 1.786660 \times 10^{-9}$
Q_{sp} is greater than K_{sp} ($1.8 \times 10^{-9} > 2.2 \times 10^{-20}$), so **$Cu(OH)_2$ will precipitate**.

17.97 Plan: Find the initial molar concentrations of Ba^{2+} and IO_3^-. The concentration (mol/L) of the $BaCl_2$ is calculated by converting mass to amount (mol) and dividing by the volume. Put these concentrations in the ion-product expression, solve for Q_{sp}, and compare Q_{sp} with K_{sp}. If $Q_{sp} > K_{sp}$, precipitate forms.
Solution:
The equilibrium is: $Ba(IO_3)_2(s) \rightleftharpoons Ba^{2+}(aq) + 2IO_3^-(aq)$. The ion-product expression is $K_{sp} = [Ba^{2+}][IO_3^-]^2$ and, from the Appendix, K_{sp} equals 1.5×10^{-9}.
$$[Ba^{2+}] = \left(\frac{7.5 \text{ mg } BaCl_2}{500. \text{ mL}}\right)\left(\frac{10^{-3} \text{ g}}{1 \text{ mg}}\right)\left(\frac{1 \text{ mL}}{10^{-3} \text{ L}}\right)\left(\frac{1 \text{ mol } BaCl_2}{208.2 \text{ g } BaCl_2}\right)\left(\frac{1 \text{ mol } Ba^{2+}}{1 \text{ mol } BaCl_2}\right) = 7.204611 \times 10^{-5} \text{ mol/L } Ba^{2+}$$
$$[IO_3^-] = \left(\frac{0.023 \text{ mol } NaIO_3}{L}\right)\left(\frac{1 \text{ mol } IO_3^-}{1 \text{ mol } NaIO_3}\right) = 0.023 \text{ mol/L } IO_3^-$$
$Q_{sp} = [Ba^{2+}][IO_3^-]^2 = (7.204611 \times 10^{-5})(0.023)^2 = 3.81124 \times 10^{-8}$
Since $Q_{sp} > K_{sp}$ ($3.8 \times 10^{-8} > 1.5 \times 10^{-9}$), **$Ba(IO_3)_2$ will precipitate**.

17.100 Plan: When $Fe(NO_3)_3$ and $Cd(NO_3)_2$ mix with NaOH, the insoluble compounds $Fe(OH)_3$ and $Cd(OH)_2$ form. The compound with the smaller value of K_{sp} precipitates first. Calculate the initial concentrations of Fe^{3+} and Cd^{2+} from the dilution formula $c_{conc}V_{conc} = c_{dil}V_{dil}$. Use the ion-product expressions to find the minimum OH^- concentration required to cause precipitation of each compound.
Solution:
a) **$Fe(OH)_3$** will precipitate first because its K_{sp} (1.6×10^{-39}) is smaller than the K_{sp} for $Cd(OH)_2$ at 7.2×10^{-15}.

The precipitation reactions are:

$$Fe^{3+}(aq) + 3OH^-(aq) \rightarrow Fe(OH)_3(s) \qquad K_{sp} = [Fe^{3+}][OH^-]^3$$
$$Cd^{2+}(aq) + 2OH^-(aq) \rightarrow Cd(OH)_2(s) \qquad K_{sp} = [Cd^{2+}][OH^-]^2$$

The concentrations of Fe^{3+} and Cd^{2+} in the mixed solution are found from $c_{conc}V_{conc} = c_{dil}V_{dil}$

$[Fe^{3+}] = [(0.50 \text{ mol/L})(50.0 \text{ mL})]/[(50.0 + 125) \text{ mL}] = 0.142857 \text{ mol/L } Fe^{3+}$

$[Cd^{2+}] = [(0.25 \text{ mol/L})(125 \text{ mL})]/[(50.0 + 125) \text{ mL}] = 0.178571 \text{ mol/L } Cd^{2+}$

The hydroxide ion concentration required to precipitate the metal ions comes from the metal ion concentrations and the K_{sp}.

$$[OH^-]_{Fe} = \sqrt[3]{\frac{K_{sp}}{[Fe^{3+}]}} = \sqrt[3]{\frac{1.6 \times 10^{-39}}{[0.142857]}} = 2.237 \times 10^{-13} = 2.2 \times 10^{-13} \text{ mol/L}$$

$$[OH^-]_{Cd} = \sqrt{\frac{K_{sp}}{[Cd^{2+}]}} = \sqrt{\frac{7.2 \times 10^{-15}}{[0.178571]}} = 2.0079864 \times 10^{-7} = 2.0 \times 10^{-7} \text{ mol/L}$$

A lower hydroxide ion concentration is required to precipitate the Fe^{3+}.

b) The two ions are separated by adding just enough NaOH to precipitate the iron(III) hydroxide, but precipitating no more than 0.01% of the cadmium. The Fe^{3+} is found in the solid precipitate while the Cd^{2+} remains in the solution.

c) A hydroxide concentration between the values calculated in part a) will work. The best separation would be when $Q_{sp} = K_{sp}$ for $Cd(OH)_2$. This occurs when $[OH^-] = \mathbf{2.0 \times 10^{-7}}$ **mol/L**.

17.103 In the context of this equilibrium only, the increased solubility with added OH^- appears to be a violation of Le Châtelier's principle. Adding OH^- should cause the equilibrium to shift towards the left, decreasing the solubility of PbS. Before accepting this conclusion, other possible equilibria must be considered. Lead is a metal ion and hydroxide ion is a ligand, so it is possible that a complex ion forms between the lead ion and hydroxide ion:

$$Pb^{2+}(aq) + nOH^-(aq) \rightleftharpoons Pb(OH)_n^{2-n}(aq)$$

This decreases the concentration of Pb^{2+}, shifting the solubility equilibrium to the right to dissolve more PbS.

17.104 Plan: In many cases, a hydrated metal complex (e.g., $Hg(H_2O)_4^{2+}$) will exchange ligands when placed in a solution of another ligand (e.g., CN^-).
Solution:

$$Hg(H_2O)_4^{2+}(aq) + 4CN^-(aq) \rightleftharpoons Hg(CN)_4^{2-}(aq) + 4H_2O(l)$$

Note that both sides of the equation have the same "overall" charge of −2. The mercury complex changes from +2 to −2 because water is a neutral *molecular* ligand, whereas cyanide is an *ionic* ligand.

17.106 Plan: In many cases, a hydrated metal complex (e.g., $Ag(H_2O)_4^+$) will exchange ligands when placed in a solution of another ligand (e.g., $S_2O_3^{2-}$).
Solution:
The two water ligands are replaced by two thiosulfate ion ligands. The +1 charge from the silver ion plus the −4 charge from the two thiosulfate ions gives a net charge on the complex ion of −3.

$$Ag(H_2O)_2^+(aq) + 2S_2O_3^{2-}(aq) \rightleftharpoons Ag(S_2O_3)_2^{3-}(aq) + 2H_2O(l)$$

17.108 Plan: Write the formation reaction and the K_f expression. The initial concentrations of Ag^+ and $S_2O_3^{2-}$ may be determined from $c_{conc}V_{conc} = c_{dil}V_{dil}$. Set up a reaction table and use the limiting reactant to find the amounts of species in the mixture, assuming a complete reaction. A second reaction table is then written, with x representing the amount of complex ion that dissociates. Use the K_f expression to solve for x.
Solution:

$$Ag^+(aq) + 2S_2O_3^{2-}(aq) \rightleftharpoons Ag(S_2O_3)_2^{3-}(aq)$$

$[Ag^+] = (0.044 \text{ mol/L})(25.0 \text{ mL})/((25.0 + 25.0) \text{ mL}) = 0.022 \text{ mol/L } Ag^+$

$[S_2O_3^{2-}] = (0.57 \text{ mol/L})(25.0 \text{ mL})/((25.0 + 25.0) \text{ mL}) = 0.285 \text{ mol/L } S_2O_3^{2-}$

The reaction gives:

Concentration (mol/L) $\qquad Ag^+(aq) \quad + \quad 2S_2O_3^{2-}(aq) \quad \rightarrow \quad Ag(S_2O_3)_2^{3-}(aq)$

Initial	0.022	0.285	0
Change	−0.022	−2(0.022)	+0.022
Equilibrium	0	0.241	0.022

1:2:1 mole ratio

To reach equilibrium:

Concentration (mol/L)	$Ag^+(aq)$ +	$2S_2O_3^{2-}(aq)$ ⇌	$Ag(S_2O_3)_2^{3-}(aq)$
Initial	0	0.241	0.022
Change	+x	+2x	−x
Equilibrium	+ x	0.241 + 2x	0.022 − x

K_f is large, so $[Ag(S_2O_3)_2^{3-}] \approx 0.022$ mol/L and $[S_2O_3^{2-}]_{equil} \approx 0.241$ mol/L

$$K_f = 4.7\times10^{13} = \frac{\left[Ag(S_2O_3)_2^{3-}\right]}{\left[Ag^+\right]\left[S_2O_3^{2-}\right]^2} = \frac{(0.022)}{(x)(0.022)^2}$$

$x = [Ag^+] = 8.0591778\times10^{-15} = \textbf{8.1}\times\textbf{10}^{-15}$ **mol/L**

17.110 <u>Plan:</u> Write the ion-product equilibrium reaction and the complex-ion equilibrium reaction. Add the two reactions to yield an overall reaction; multiply the two constants to obtain $K_{overall}$. Write a reaction table where $S = [Cr(OH)_3]_{dissolved} = [Cr(OH)_4^-]$.
<u>Solution:</u>

Solubility-product:	$Cr(OH)_3(s) \rightleftharpoons \cancel{Cr^{3+}(aq)} + 3OH^-(aq)$	$K_{sp} = 6.3\times10^{-31}$
Complex-ion	$\cancel{Cr^{3+}(aq)} + 4OH^-(aq) \rightleftharpoons Cr(OH)_4^-(aq)$	$K_f = 8.0\times10^{29}$

Overall:	$Cr(OH)_3(s) + OH^-(aq) \rightleftharpoons Cr(OH)_4^-(aq)$	$K = K_{sp}K_f = 0.504$

At pH 13.0, the pOH is 1.0 and $[OH^-] = 10^{-1.0} = 0.1$ mol/L.
Reaction table:

Concentration (mol/L)	$Cr(OH)_3(s)$ +	$OH^-(aq)$ ⇌	$Cr(OH)_4^-(aq)$
Initial	——	0.1	0
Change	——	− S	+S
Equilibrium	——	0.1 − S	S

Assume that $0.1 - S \approx 0.1$.

$$K_{overall} = 0.504 = \frac{\left[Cr(OH)_4^-\right]}{\left[OH^-\right]} = \frac{(S)}{(0.1)}$$

$S = [Cr(OH)_4^-] = 0.0504 = \textbf{0.05 mol/L}$

17.112 <u>Plan:</u> First, calculate the initial amount (mol) of Zn^{2+} and CN^-, then set up reaction table assuming that the reaction first goes to completion, and then calculate back to find the reactant concentrations.
<u>Solution:</u>
The complex formation equilibrium is:

$$Zn^{2+}(aq) + 4CN^-(aq) \rightleftharpoons Zn(CN)_4^{2-}(aq) \qquad K_f = 4.2\times10^{19}$$

$$\text{amount (mol) of } Zn^{2+} = \left(0.84 \text{ g } ZnCl_2\right)\left(\frac{1 \text{ mol } ZnCl_2}{136.31 \text{ g } ZnCl_2}\right)\left(\frac{1 \text{ mol } Zn^{2+}}{1 \text{ mol } ZnCl_2}\right) = 0.0061624 \text{ mol } Zn^{2+}$$

$$\text{amount (mol) of } CN^- = \left(\frac{0.150 \text{ mol NaCN}}{L}\right)\left(\frac{10^{-3} \text{ L}}{1 \text{ mL}}\right)(245 \text{ mL})\left(\frac{1 \text{ mol } CN^-}{1 \text{ mol NaCN}}\right) = 0.03675 \text{ mol } CN^-$$

The Zn^{2+} is limiting because the amount (mol) of this ion is significantly smaller, thus, $[Zn^{2+}] = 0$.

$$\text{amount (mol) of } CN^- \text{ reacting} = \left(0.0061624 \text{ mol } Zn^{2+}\right)\left(\frac{4 \text{ mol } CN^-}{1 \text{ mol } Zn^{2+}}\right) = 0.0246496 \text{ mol } CN^-$$

amount (mol) of CN^- remaining are: $0.03675 - 0.0246496 = 0.0121004$ mol CN^-

$$[CN^-] = \frac{\left(0.0121004 \text{ mol } CN^-\right)}{\left(245 \text{ mL}\right)}\left(\frac{1 \text{ mL}}{10^{-3} \text{ L}}\right) = 0.0493894 \text{ mol/L } CN^-$$

The Zn^{2+} will produce an equal amount (mol) of the complex with the concentration:

$$[Zn(CN)_4^{2-}] = \left(\frac{0.0061624 \text{ mol } Zn^{2+}}{245 \text{ mL}}\right)\left(\frac{1 \text{ mL}}{10^{-3} \text{ L}}\right)\left(\frac{1 \text{ mol } Zn(CN)_4^{2-}}{1 \text{ mol } Zn^{2+}}\right) = 0.025153 \text{ mol/L } Zn(CN)_4^{2-}$$

Concentration (mol/L)	$Zn^{2+}(aq)$	+	$4CN^-(aq)$	$\rightleftharpoons$	$Zn(CN)_4^{2-}(aq)$
Initial	0		0.0493894		0.025153
Change	+x		+4x		–x
Equilibrium	x		0.0493894 + 4x		0.025153 – x

Assume the –x and the +4x do not significantly change the associated concentrations.

$$K_f = 4.2 \times 10^{19} = \frac{\left[Zn(CN)_4^{2-}\right]}{\left[Zn^{2+}\right]\left[CN^-\right]^4} = \frac{(0.025153 - x)}{(x)(0.0493894 + 4x)^4} = \frac{(0.025153)}{(x)(0.0493894)^4}$$

$x = 1.006481 \times 10^{-16} = 1.0 \times 10^{-16}$
$[Zn^{2+}] = \mathbf{1.0 \times 10^{-16} \text{ mol/L } Zn^{2+}}$
$[Zn(CN)_4^{2-}] = 0.025153 - x = 0.025153 - 1.0 \times 10^{-16} = 0.025153 = \mathbf{0.025 \text{ mol/L } Zn(CN)_4^{2-}}$
$[CN^-] = 0.0493894 + 4x = 0.0493894 + 4(1.0 \times 10^{-16}) = 0.0493894 = \mathbf{0.049 \text{ mol/L } CN^-}$

17.114 Plan: The NaOH will react with the benzoic acid, C_6H_5COOH, to form the conjugate base benzoate ion, $C_6H_5COO^-$. Calculate the amount (mol) of NaOH and C_6H_5COOH. Set up a reaction table that shows the stoichiometry of the reaction of NaOH and C_6H_5COOH. Since NaOH is a limiting reagent, all of the NaOH will be consumed to form $C_6H_5COO^-$, and the amount (mol) of C_6H_5COOH will decrease. Find the new amount (mol) of C_6H_5COOH and $C_6H_5COO^-$ and use the Henderson-Hasselbalch equation to find the pH of this buffer. Once the pH of the benzoic acid/benzoate buffer is known, the Henderson-Hasselbalch equation can be used to find the ratio of formate ion and formic acid that will produce a buffer of that same pH. From the ratio, the volumes of HCOOH and NaOH are calculated.
Solution:
The K_a for benzoic acid is 6.3×10^{-5} (from the Appendix). The pK_a is $-\log(6.3 \times 10^{-5}) = 4.201$. The reaction of benzoic acid with sodium hydroxide is:
$C_6H_5COOH(aq) + NaOH(aq) \rightarrow Na^+(aq) + C_6H_5COO^-(aq) + H_2O(l)$

$$\text{amount (mol) of } C_6H_5COOH = \left(\frac{0.200 \text{ mol } C_6H_5COOH}{L}\right)\left(\frac{10^{-3} \text{ L}}{1 \text{ mL}}\right)(475 \text{ mL}) = 0.0950 \text{ mol } C_6H_5COOH$$

$$\text{amount (mol) of NaOH} = \left(\frac{2.00 \text{ mol NaOH}}{L}\right)\left(\frac{10^{-3} \text{ L}}{1 \text{ mL}}\right)(25 \text{ mL}) = 0.050 \text{ mol NaOH}$$

NaOH is the limiting reagent:
The reaction table gives:

	$C_6H_5COOH(aq)$ +	NaOH(aq)	$\rightarrow$ Na$^+(aq)$ +	$C_6H_5COO^-(aq)$ +	H$_2$O(l)
Initial	0.0950 mol	0.050 mol	—	0	—
Reacting	–0.050 mol	–0.050 mol		+ 0.050 mol	
Final	0.045 mol	0 mol		0.050 mol	

Calculating the pH from the Henderson-Hasselbalch equation:

$$pH = pK_a + \log\left(\frac{n_{C_6H_5COO^-}}{n_{C_6H_5COOH}}\right) = 4.201 + \log\left(\frac{0.050}{0.045}\right) = 4.24676 = 4.2$$

Calculations on formic acid (HCOOH) also use the Henderson-Hasselbalch equation. The K_a for formic acid is 1.8×10^{-4} and the $pK_a = -\log(1.8 \times 10^{-4}) = 3.7447$.
The formate to formic acid ratio may now be determined:

$$pH = pK_a + \log\left(\frac{[HCOO^-]}{[HCOOH]}\right) = pK_a + \log\left(\frac{n_{HCOO^-}}{n_{HCOOH}}\right)$$

$$4.24676 = 3.7447 + \log\left(\frac{n_{HCOO^-}}{n_{HCOOH}}\right)$$

$$0.50206 = \log\left(\frac{n_{HCOO^-}}{n_{HCOOH}}\right)$$

$$\left(\frac{n_{HCOO^-}}{n_{HCOOH}}\right) = 3.177313$$

$$n_{HCOO^-} = 3.177313 \times n_{HCOOH} \qquad \text{(eqn 1)}$$

The total volume of the solution is $(500.\ mL)(10^{-3}\ L/1\ mL) = 0.500\ L$

Let V_a = volume of acid solution added, and V_b = volume of base added. Thus:

$V_a + V_b = 0.500\ L \qquad$ (eqn 2)

The reaction between the formic acid and the sodium hydroxide is:

$HCOOH(aq) + NaOH(aq) \rightarrow HCOONa(aq) + H_2O(l)$

The amount (mol) of NaOH added equal the amount (mol) of HCOOH reacted and the amount (mol) of HCOONa formed.

amount (mol) NaOH = (2.00 mol NaOH/L)(V_b) = 2.00V_b mol

Total amount (mol) HCOOH = (0.200 mol HCOOH/L)(V_a) = 0.200V_a mol

The stoichiometric ratios in this reaction are all 1:1.

amount (mol) of HCOOH remaining after the reaction = (0.200V_a – 2.00V_b) mol $\qquad$ (eqn 3)

amount (mol) of HCOO⁻ = amount (mol) ofHCOONa = amount (mol) of NaOH = 2.00 V_b $\quad$ (eqn 4)

Using these amounts (mol) and the mole ratio determined for the buffer gives:

amount (mol) of HCOO⁻ = 3.177313 mol HCOOH $\quad$ Substituting equations 3 and 4 into 1 gives:

2.00V_b mol = 3.177313(0.200V_a – 2.00V_b) mol

2.00V_b = 0.6354626V_a – 6.354626V_b

8.354626 V_b = 0.6354626 V_a $\qquad$ (eqn 5)

Rearranging equation 2 gives $V_a = (0.500 - V_b)$ L $\qquad$ (eqn 2b)

Substituting equation 2b into equation 5 gives:

8.354626 V_b = 0.6354626 (0.500 – V_b)

Solving for Vb:

8.354626 V_b = 0.3177313 – 0.6354626 V_b

8.9900886 V_b = 0.3177313

V_b = 0.0353424 = **0.035 L NaOH**

Substituting Vb into equation 2b:

V_a = 0.500 – 0.0353424 = 0.4646576 = **0.465 L HCOOH**

Limitations due to the significant figures lead to a solution with only an approximately correct pH.

17.116   Plan: A formate buffer contains formate (HCOO⁻) as the base and formic acid (HCOOH) as the acid. The Henderson-Hasselbalch equation gives the component ratio, [HCOO⁻]/[HCOOH]. The ratio is used to find the volumes of acid and base required to prepare the buffer.

Solution:

From the Appendix, the K_a for formic acid is 1.8×10^{-4} and the $pK_a = -\log(1.8 \times 10^{-4}) = 3.7447$.

a) $pH = pK_a + \log\left(\frac{[HCOO^-]}{[HCOOH]}\right)$

$3.74 = 3.7447 + \log\left(\frac{[HCOO^-]}{[HCOOH]}\right)$

$$-0.0047 = \log\left(\frac{[\text{HCOO}^-]}{[\text{HCOOH}]}\right)$$

$$\left(\frac{[\text{HCOO}^-]}{[\text{HCOOH}]}\right) = 0.989236 = \mathbf{0.99}$$

b) To prepare solutions, set up equations for concentrations of formate and formic acid with x equal to the volume, in L, of 1.0 mol/L HCOOH added. The equations are based on the neutralization reaction between HCOOH and NaOH that produces HCOO⁻.

$$\text{HCOOH}(aq) + \text{NaOH}(aq) \rightarrow \text{HCOO}^-(aq) + \text{Na}^+(aq) + \text{H}_2\text{O}(l)$$

$$[\text{HCOO}^-] = (1.0\,\text{mol / L NaOH})\left(\frac{(0.700 - x)\text{L NaOH}}{0.700\text{ L solution}}\right)\left(\frac{1\text{ mol HCOO}^-}{1\text{ mol NaOH}}\right)$$

$$[\text{HCOOH}] = (1.0\text{ mol / L HCOOH})\left(\frac{x\text{ L HCOOH}}{0.700\text{ L solution}}\right) -$$

$$(1.0\text{ mol / L NaOH})\left(\frac{(0.700 - x)\text{L NaOH}}{0.700\text{ L solution}}\right)\left(\frac{1\text{ mol HCOO}^-}{1\text{ mol NaOH}}\right)$$

The component ratio equals 0.99 (from part a)). Simplify the above equations and plug into ratio:

$$\frac{[\text{HCOO}^-]}{[\text{HCOOH}]} = \frac{\left[\left(\frac{0.700 - x}{0.700}\right)\text{mol / L HCOO}^-\right]}{\left[\left(x - \frac{(0.700 - x)}{0.700}\right)\text{mol / L HCOOH}\right]} = \frac{0.700 - x}{2x - 0.700} = 0.989236$$

Solving for x:
$$x = 0.46751 = 0.468\text{ L}$$

Mixing **0.468 L of 1.0 mol/L HCOOH** and 0.700 − 0.468 = **0.232 L of 1.0 mol/L NaOH** gives a buffer of pH 3.74.

c) The final concentration of HCOOH from the equation in part b):

$$[\text{HCOOH}] = (1.0\text{ mol / L HCOOH})\left(\frac{0.468\text{ L HCOOH}}{0.700\text{ L solution}}\right) -$$

$$(1.0\text{ mol / L NaOH})\left(\frac{0.232\text{ L NaOH}}{0.700\text{ L solution}}\right)\left(\frac{1\text{ mole HCOO}^-}{1\text{ mole NaOH}}\right) = 0.33714\text{mol/L} = \mathbf{0.34\text{ mol/L HCOOH}}$$

17.119   Plan: The minimum urate ion concentration necessary to cause a deposit of sodium urate is determined by the K_{sp} for the salt. Convert solubility in g/100. mL to molar solubility and calculate K_{sp}. Substituting [Na⁺] and K_{sp} into the ion-product expression allows one to find [Ur⁻].
Solution:
Molar solubility of NaUr:

$$[\text{NaUr}] = \left(\frac{0.085\text{ g NaUr}}{100.\text{ mL}}\right)\left(\frac{1\text{ mL}}{10^{-3}\text{ L}}\right)\left(\frac{1\text{ mol NaUr}}{190.10\text{ mol NaUr}}\right) = 4.4713309 \times 10^{-3}\text{ mol/L NaUr}$$

4.4713309×10^{-3} mol/L NaUr = [Na⁺] = [Ur⁻]
$K_{sp} = [\text{Na}^+][\text{Ur}^-] = (4.4713309 \times 10^{-3})(4.4713309 \times 10^{-3}) = 1.99927998 \times 10^{-5}$ mol/L
When [Na⁺] = 0.15 mol/L:
$K_{sp} = 1.99927998 \times 10^{-5}$ mol/L = [0.15][Ur⁻]
[Ur⁻] = 1.33285×10^{-4}
The minimum urate ion concentration that will cause precipitation of sodium urate is **1.3×10^{-4} mol/L**.

17.122 <u>Plan:</u> Substitute the given molar solubility of KCl into the ion-product expression to find the K_{sp} of KCl. Determine the total concentration of chloride ion in each beaker after the HCl has been added. This requires the amount (mol) originally present and the amount (mol) added. Determine a Q_{sp} value to see if K_{sp} is exceeded. If $Q_{sp} < K_{sp}$, nothing will precipitate.

<u>Solution:</u>

a) The solubility equilibrium for KCl is: $KCl(s) \rightleftharpoons K^+(aq) + Cl^-(aq)$

The solubility of KCl is 3.7 mol/L.

$K_{sp} = [K^+][Cl^-] = (3.7)(3.7) = 13.69 = \mathbf{14}$

b) Find the amount (mol) of Cl^-:

Original amount (mol) from the KCl:

amount (mol) of K^+ = amount (mol) of Cl^-

$$= \left(\frac{3.7 \text{ mol KCl}}{1 \text{ L}} \right)\left(\frac{10^{-3} \text{ L}}{1 \text{ mL}} \right)(100. \text{ mL})\left(\frac{1 \text{ mol } Cl^- \text{ ion}}{1 \text{ mol KCl}} \right) = 0.37 \text{ mol } Cl^-$$

Original amount (mol) from the 6.0 mol/L HCl in the first beaker:

$$\text{amount (mol) of } Cl^- = \left(\frac{6.0 \text{ mol HCl}}{1 \text{ L}} \right)\left(\frac{10^{-3} \text{ L}}{1 \text{ mL}} \right)(100. \text{ mL})\left(\frac{1 \text{ mol } Cl^-}{1 \text{ mol HCl}} \right) = 0.60 \text{ mol } Cl^-$$

This results in $(0.37 + 0.60)$ mol = 0.97 mol Cl^-.

Original amount (mol) from the 12 mol/L HCl in the second beaker:

$$\text{amount (mol) of } Cl^- = \left(\frac{12 \text{ mol HCl}}{1 \text{ L}} \right)\left(\frac{10^{-3} \text{ L}}{1 \text{ mL}} \right)(100. \text{ mL})\left(\frac{1 \text{ mol } Cl^-}{1 \text{ mol HCl}} \right) = 1.2 \text{ mol } Cl^-$$

This results in $(0.37 + 1.2)$ mol = 1.57 mol Cl^-.

Volume of mixed solutions = $(100. \text{ mL} + 100. \text{ mL})(10^{-3} \text{ L}/1 \text{ mL}) = 0.200 \text{ L}$

After the mixing:

$[K^+] = (0.37 \text{ mol } K^+)/(0.200 \text{ L}) = 1.85 \text{ mol/L } K^+$

From 6.0 mol/L HCl in the first beaker:

$[Cl^-] = (0.97 \text{ mol } Cl^-)/(0.200 \text{ L}) = 4.85 \text{ mol/L } Cl^-$

From 12 mol/L HCl in the second beaker:

$[Cl^-] = (1.57 \text{ mol } Cl^-)/(0.200 \text{ L}) = 7.85 \text{ mol/L } Cl^-$

Determine a Q_{sp} value to see if K_{sp} is exceeded. If $Q_{sp} < K_{sp}$, nothing will precipitate.

From 6.0 mol/L HCl in the first beaker:

$Q_{sp} = [K^+][Cl^-] = (1.85)(4.85) = 8.9725 = 9.0 < 14$, so no KCl will precipitate.

From 12 mol/L HCl in the second beaker:

$Q_{sp} = [K^+][Cl^-] = (1.85)(7.85) = 14.5225 = 15 > 14$, so KCl will precipitate.

The mass of KCl that will precipitate when 12 mol/L HCl is added:

Equal amounts of K and Cl will precipitate. Let x be the concentration (mol/L) change.

$K_{sp} = [K^+][Cl^-] = (1.85 - x)(7.85 - x) = 13.69$

$x = 0.08659785 = 0.09$ This is the change in the concentration (mol/L) of each of the ions.

$$\text{Mass (g) of KCl} = \left(\frac{0.08659785 \text{ mol } K^+}{\text{L}} \right)(0.200 \text{ L})\left(\frac{1 \text{ mol KCl}}{1 \text{ mol } K^+} \right)\left(\frac{74.55 \text{ g KCl}}{1 \text{ mol KCl}} \right) = 1.291174 \text{ g} = \mathbf{1 \text{ g KCl}}$$

17.125 <u>Plan:</u> Use the Henderson-Hasselbalch equation to find the ratio of $[HCO_3^-]/[H_2CO_3]$ that will produce a buffer with a pH of 7.40 and a buffer of 7.20.

<u>Solution:</u>

a) $K_{a1} = 4.5 \times 10^{-7}$

$pK_a = -\log K_a = -\log (4.5 \times 10^{-7}) = 6.34679$

$$pH = pK_a + \log\left(\frac{[HCO_3^-]}{[H_2CO_3]} \right)$$

$$7.40 = 6.34679 + \log\left(\frac{[HCO_3^-]}{[H_2CO_3]}\right)$$

$$1.05321 = \log\left(\frac{[HCO_3^-]}{[H_2CO_3]}\right)$$

$$\frac{[HCO_3^-]}{[H_2CO_3]} = 11.30342352$$

$$\frac{[H_2CO_3]}{[HCO_3^-]} = 0.0884688 = \mathbf{0.088}$$

b)
$$pH = pK_a + \log\left(\frac{[HCO_3^-]}{[H_2CO_3]}\right)$$

$$7.20 = 6.34679 + \log\left(\frac{[HCO_3^-]}{[H_2CO_3]}\right)$$

$$0.85321 = \log\left(\frac{[HCO_3^-]}{[H_2CO_3]}\right)$$

$$\frac{[HCO_3^-]}{[H_2CO_3]} = 7.131978$$

$$\frac{[H_2CO_3]}{[HCO_3^-]} = 0.14021 = \mathbf{0.14}$$

17.126 <u>Plan:</u> The buffer components will be TRIS, $(HOCH_2)_3CNH_2$, and its conjugate acid TRISH$^+$, $(HOCH_2)_3CNH_3^+$. The conjugate acid is formed from the reaction between TRIS and HCl. Since HCl is the limiting reactant in this problem, the concentration of conjugate acid will equal the starting concentration of HCl, 0.095 mol/L. The concentration of TRIS is the initial concentration minus the amount reacted. Once the concentrations of the TRIS-TRISH$^+$ acid-base pair are known, the Henderson-Hasselbalch equation can be used to find the pH.
<u>Solution:</u>

$$\text{amount (mol) of TRIS} = \left(43.0 \text{ g TRIS}\right)\left(\frac{1 \text{ mol TRIS}}{121.14 \text{ g TRIS}}\right) = 0.354961 \text{ mol}$$

$$\text{amount (mol) of HCl added} = \left(\frac{0.095 \text{ mol HCl}}{L}\right)(1.00 \text{ L}) = 0.095 \text{ mol HCl} = \text{mol TRISH}^+$$

$$(HOCH_2)_3CNH_2(aq) + HCl(aq) \rightleftharpoons (HOCH_2)_3CNH_3^+(aq) + Cl^-(aq)$$

Initial	0.354961 mol	0.095 mol	0	0
Reacting	−0.095 mol	−0.095 mol	+0.095 mol	—
Final	0.259961 mol	0 mol	0.095 mol	

Since there is 1.00 L of solution, the amount (mol) of TRIS and TRISH$^+$ equal their concentrations (mol/L).
pK_a of TRISH$^+$ = $14 - pK_b = 14 - 5.91 = 8.09$

$$pH = pK_a + \log\left(\frac{[TRIS]}{[TRISH^+]}\right) = 8.09 + \log\left(\frac{[0.259961]}{[0.095]}\right) = 8.527185 = \mathbf{8.53}$$

17.128 Zinc sulfide, ZnS, is much less soluble than manganese sulfide, MnS. Convert $ZnCl_2$ and $MnCl_2$ to ZnS and MnS by saturating the solution with H_2S; $[H_2S]_{sat'd} = 0.10$ mol/L. Adjust the pH so that the greatest amount of ZnS will precipitate and not exceed the solubility of MnS as determined by $K_{sp}(MnS)$.
$K_{sp}(MnS) = [Mn^{2+}][HS^-][OH^-] = 3\times10^{-11}$
$\qquad [Mn^{2+}] = [MnCl_2] = 0.020$ mol/L
$[HS^-]$ is calculated using the K_{a1} expression:

Concentration (mol/L): $H_2S(aq) + H_2O(l) \rightleftharpoons H_3O^+(aq) + HS^-(aq)$

Initial	0.10 mol/L	0	0
Reacting	−x	+x	+x
Final	0.10 − x	x	x

$$K_{a1} = 9 \times 10^{-8} = \frac{\left[H_3O^+\right]\left[HS^-\right]}{\left[H_2S\right]} = \frac{\left[H_3O^+\right]\left[HS^-\right]}{(0.10-x)} \qquad \text{Assume } 0.10 - x = 0.10.$$

$[H_3O^+][HS^-] = 9 \times 10^{-9}$

$[HS^-] = 9 \times 10^{-9}/[H_3O^+]$

Substituting $[Mn^{2+}]$ and $[HS^-]$ into the $K_{sp}(MnS)$ above gives:

$K_{sp}(MnS) = [Mn^{2+}][HS^-][OH^-] = 3 \times 10^{-11}$

$K_{sp}(MnS) = [Mn^{2+}](9 \times 10^{-9}/[H_3O^+])[OH^-] = 3 \times 10^{-11}$

Substituting $K_w/[H_3O^+]$ for $[OH^-]$:

$$K_{sp}(MnS) = 3 \times 10^{-11} = \left[Mn^{2+}\right]\left(\frac{9 \times 10^{-9}}{\left[H_3O^+\right]}\right)\left(\frac{K_w}{\left[H_3O^+\right]}\right)$$

$$3 \times 10^{-11} \times [H_3O^+]^2 = \left[Mn^{2+}\right]\left(9 \times 10^{-9}\right)\left(K_w\right)$$

$$[H_3O^+] = \sqrt{\frac{\left[Mn^{2+}\right]\left[9 \times 10^{-9}\right]K_w}{3 \times 10^{-11}}} = \sqrt{\frac{(0.020)\left(9 \times 10^{-9}\right)\left(1.0 \times 10^{-14}\right)}{3 \times 10^{-11}}} = 2.4494897 \times 10^{-7}$$

$pH = -\log [H^+] = -\log (2.4494897 \times 10^{-7}) = 6.610924 = \mathbf{6.6}$

Maintain the pH below 6.6 to separate the ions as their sulfides.

17.132 <u>Plan:</u> An indicator changes colour when the buffer-component ratio of the two forms of the indicator changes from a value greater than 1 to a value less than 1. The pH at which the ratio equals 1 is equal to pK_a. The midpoint in the pH range of the indicator is a good estimate of the pK_a of the indicator.
<u>Solution:</u>

$pK_a = (3.4 + 4.8)/2 = 4.1 \qquad K_a = 10^{-4.1} = 7.943 \times 10^{-5} = \mathbf{8 \times 10^{-5}}$

17.133

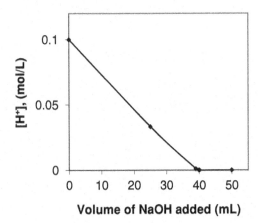

Due to the large range of $[H^+]$, this plot is difficult to prepare and does not easily show the end point. A logarithmic scale (pH vs. mL OH$^-$ added) shows this more clearly.

17.134 <u>Plan:</u> A spreadsheet will help you to quickly calculate $\Delta pH/\Delta V$ and average volume for each data point. At the equivalence point, the pH changes drastically when only a small amount of base is added, therefore, $\Delta pH/\Delta V$ is at a maximum at the equivalence point.

Solution:

a) Example calculation: For the first two lines of data: $\Delta pH = 1.22 - 1.00 = 0.22$; $\Delta V = 10.00 - 0.00 = 10.00$

$$\frac{\Delta pH}{\Delta V} = \frac{0.22}{10.00} = 0.022 \qquad V_{average}(mL) = (0.00 + 10.00)/2 = 5.00$$

V(mL)	pH	$\dfrac{\Delta pH}{\Delta V}$	$V_{average}$(mL)
0.00	1.00		
10.00	1.22	0.022	5.00
20.00	1.48	0.026	15.00
30.00	1.85	0.037	25.00
35.00	2.18	0.066	32.50
39.00	2.89	0.18	37.00
39.50	3.20	0.62	39.25
39.75	3.50	1.2	39.63
39.90	3.90	2.67	39.83
39.95	4.20	6	39.93
39.99	4.90	18	39.97
40.00	7.00	200	40.00
40.01	9.40	200	40.01
40.05	9.80	10	40.03
40.10	10.40	10	40.08
40.25	10.50	0.67	40.18
40.50	10.79	1.2	40.38
41.00	11.09	0.60	40.75
45.00	11.76	0.17	43.00
50.00	12.05	0.058	47.50
60.00	12.30	0.025	55.00
70.00	12.43	0.013	65.00
80.00	12.52	0.009	75.00

b)

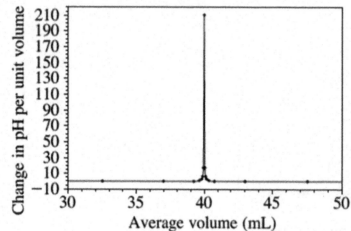

17.136 Use HLac to indicate lactic acid and Lac⁻ to indicate the lactate ion. The Henderson-Hasselbalch equation gives the pH of the buffer. Determine the final concentrations of the buffer components from $c_{conc}V_{conc} = c_{dil}V_{dil}$. Determine the pK_a of the acid from the K_a.

$$pK_a = -\log K_a = -\log (1.38\times10^{-4}) = 3.86012$$

Determine the concentration (mol/L) of the diluted buffer component as $c_{dil} = c_{conc}V_{conc}/V_{dil}$.

[HLac] = [(0.85 M) (225 mL)]/[(225 + 435) mL] = 0.28977 mol/L HLac

[Lac⁻] = [(0.68 M) (435 mL)]/[(225 + 435) mL] = 0.44818 mol/L Lac⁻

$$pH = pK_a + \log\left(\frac{[Lac^-]}{[HLac]}\right) = pK_a + \log\left(\frac{n_{Lac^-}}{n_{HLac}}\right)$$

$$pH = 3.86012 + \log\left(\frac{[0.44818]}{[0.28977]}\right) = 4.049519 = \mathbf{4.05}$$

17.142 Plan: To determine which species are present from a buffer system of a polyprotic acid, check the pK_a values for the one that is closest to the pH of the buffer. The two components involved in the equilibrium associated with this K_a are the principle species in the buffer. Use the Henderson-Hasselbalch equation to find the ratio of the phosphate species that will produce a buffer with a pH of 7.4.
Solution:
For carbonic acid, pK_{a1} [$-\log (8\times10^{-7}) = 6.1$] is closer to the pH of 7.4, so H_2CO_3 and HCO_3^- are the species present. For phosphoric acid, pK_{a2} [$-\log (2.3\times10^{-7}) = 6.6$] is closest to the pH, so $H_2PO_4^-$ and HPO_4^{2-} are the principle species present.

$$H_2PO_4^-(aq) \;+\; H_2O(l) \;\rightleftharpoons\; HPO_4^{2-}(aq) \;+\; H_3O^+(aq)$$

$$pH = pK_a + \log\left(\frac{[HPO_4^{2-}]}{[H_2PO_4^-]}\right)$$

$$7.4 = 6.6383 + \log\left(\frac{[HPO_4^{2-}]}{[H_2PO_4^-]}\right)$$

$$\frac{[HPO_4^{2-}]}{[H_2PO_4^-]} = 5.77697 = \mathbf{5.8}$$

17.143 Plan: Mercury sulfide, HgS, is much less soluble than nickel sulfide, NiS. Adjust the pH so that the greatest amount of HgS will precipitate and not exceed the solubility of NiS as determined by K_{sp} of NiS. Determine the minimum pH needed to cause the initial precipitation of NiS. Use the K_a expression for H_2S to express [HS^-] in terms of [H_3O^+]; use the K_w expression for water to express [OH^-] in terms of [H_3O^+].
Solution:

$$NiS(s) + H_2O(l) \rightleftharpoons Ni^{2+}(aq) + HS^-(aq) + OH^-(aq)$$

K_{sp} (NiS) = 3×10^{-16} = [Ni^{2+}][HS^-][OH^-]
[Ni^{2+}] = 0.15 mol/L, so [HS^-] and [OH^-] must be found.
From [H_2S] = 0.050 mol/L and K_{a1} in the Appendix:

$$H_2S\,(aq) + H_2O(l) \rightleftharpoons HS^-(aq) + H_3O^+(aq)$$

$$K_{a1} = \frac{\left[H_3O^+\right]\left[HS^-\right]}{\left[H_2S\right]} = \frac{\left[H_3O^+\right]\left[HS^-\right]}{(0.050 - x)} = \frac{\left[H_3O^+\right]\left[HS^-\right]}{(0.050)} = 9\times10^{-8}$$

[HS^-][H_3O^+] = 4.5×10^{-9} or [HS^-] = 4.5×10^{-9}/[H_3O^+]
[OH^-] = K_w/[H_3O^+]
K_{sp} (NiS) = 3×10^{-16} = [Ni^{2+}][HS^-][OH^-]

$$K_{sp}\text{ (NiS)} = 3\times10^{-16} = (0.15)\left(\frac{4.5\times10^{-9}}{[H_3O]^+}\right)\left(\frac{1.0\times10^{-14}}{[H_3O]^+}\right)$$

$$3\times10^{-16} = \frac{(0.15)\left(4.5\times10^{-9}\right)\left(1.0\times10^{-14}\right)}{\left([H_3O]^+\right)^2}$$

[H_3O^+]^2 = [$(0.15)(4.5\times10^{-9})(1.0\times10^{-14})$]/($3\times10^{-16}$) = 2.25×10^{-8}
[H_3O^+] = 1.5×10^{-4} mol/L
pH = $-\log$ [H^+] = $-\log (1.5\times10^{-4}$ mol/L) = $3.8239 = \mathbf{3.8}$

17.145   Plan: Find the amount (mol) of quinidine initially present in the sample by dividing its mass in grams by the molar mass. Use the molar ratio between quinidine and HCl to find the amount (mol) of HCl that would react with the amount (mol) of quinidine and subtract the reacted HCl from the initial amount (mol) of HCl to find the excess. Use the molar ratio between HCl and NaOH to find the volume of NaOH required to react with the excess HCl. Then use the molar ratio between NaOH and quinidine to find the volume of NaOH required to react with the quinidine.

Solution:

a) To find the concentration of HCl after neutralizing the quinidine, calculate the concentration of quinidine and the amount of HCl required to neutralize it, remembering that the mole ratio for the neutralization is 2 mol HCl/1 mol quinidine.

$$\text{amount (mol) of quinidine} = (33.85 \text{ mg quinidine})\left(\frac{10^{-3} \text{ g}}{1 \text{ mg}}\right)\left(\frac{1 \text{ mol quinidine}}{324.41 \text{ g quinidine}}\right)$$

$$= 1.0434327\times10^{-4} \text{ mol quinidine}$$

$$\text{amount (mol) of HCl excess} = (6.55 \text{ mL})\left(\frac{10^{-3} \text{ L}}{1 \text{ mL}}\right)\left(\frac{0.150 \text{ mol HCl}}{\text{L}}\right)$$

$$- (1.0434327\times10^{-4} \text{ mol quinidine})\left(\frac{2 \text{ mol HCl}}{1 \text{ mol quinidine}}\right) = 7.7381346\times10^{-4} \text{ mol HCl}$$

$$\text{Volume (mL) of NaOH needed} = (7.7381346\times10^{-4} \text{ mol HCl})\left(\frac{1 \text{ mol NaOH}}{1 \text{ mol HCl}}\right)\left(\frac{1 \text{ L}}{0.0133 \text{ mol NaOH}}\right)\left(\frac{1 \text{ mL}}{10^{-3} \text{ L}}\right)$$

$$= 58.18146 \text{ mL} = \textbf{58.2 mL NaOH solution}$$

b) Use the amount (mol) of quinidine and the concentration of the NaOH to determine the volume in millilitre.

$$\text{Volume} = (1.0434327\times10^{-4} \text{ mol quinidine})\left(\frac{1 \text{ mol NaOH}}{1 \text{ mol quinidine}}\right)\left(\frac{1 \text{ L}}{0.0133 \text{ mol NaOH}}\right)\left(\frac{1 \text{ mL}}{10^{-3} \text{ L}}\right)$$

$$= 7.84536 \text{ mL} = \textbf{7.85 mL NaOH solution}$$

c) When quinidine (QNN) is first acidified, it has the general form $QNH^{+}NH^{+}$. At the first equivalence point, one of the acidified nitrogen atoms has completely reacted, leaving a singly protonated form, $QNNH^{+}$. This form of quinidine can react with water as either an acid or a base, so both must be considered. If the concentration of quinidine at the first equivalence point is greater than K_{b1}, then the $[OH^-]$ at the first equivalence point can be estimated as:

$$[OH^-] = \sqrt{K_{b1}K_{b2}} = \sqrt{(4.0\times10^{-6})(1.0\times10^{-10})} = 2.0\times10^{-8} \text{ mol/L}$$

$$[H_3O^+] = K_w/[OH^-] = (1.0\times10^{-14})/(2.0\times10^{-8}) = 5.0\times10^{-7} \text{ mol/L}$$

$$pH = -\log[H^+] = -\log(5.0\times10^{-7} \text{ mol/L}) = 6.3010 = \textbf{6.30}$$

17.147   Plan: The Henderson-Hasselbalch equation demonstrates that the pH changes when the ratio of acid to base in the buffer changes (pK_a is constant at a given temperature).

Solution:

$$pH = pK_a + \log\left(\frac{[A^-]}{[HA]}\right)$$

The pH of the A^-/HA buffer cannot be calculated because the identity of "A" and, thus, the value of pK_a are unknown. However, the change in pH can be described:

$$\Delta pH = \log\left(\frac{[A^-]}{[HA]}\right)_{final} - \log\left(\frac{[A^-]}{[HA]}\right)_{initial}$$

Since both [HA] and $[A^-] = 0.10$ mol/L, $\log\left(\frac{[A^-]}{[HA]}\right)_{initial} = 0$ because $[HA] = [A^-]$, and $\log(1) = 0$

So the change in pH is equal to the concentration ratio of base to acid after the addition of H_3O^+.
Consider the buffer prior to addition to the medium.

$$H_3O^+ (aq) \quad + \quad A^- (aq) \quad \rightarrow \quad HA(aq)$$

0.0010 mol	0.10 mol	0.10 mol
-0.0010 mol	-0.0010 mol	+0.0010 mol
0	0.099 mol	0.101 mol

When 0.0010 mol H_3O^+ is added to 1 L of the undiluted buffer, the $[A^-]/[HA]$ ratio changes from 0.10/0.10 to (0.099)/(0.101). The change in pH is:

$$\Delta pH = \log (0.099/0.101) = -0.008686$$

If the undiluted buffer changes 0.009 pH units with addition of 0.0010 mol H_3O^+, how much can the buffer be diluted and still not change by 0.05 pH units ($\Delta pH < 0.05$)?

Let x = fraction by which the buffer can be diluted. Assume 0.0010 mol H_3O^+ is added to 1 L.

$$\log \frac{[base]}{[acid]} = \log \left(\frac{(0.10x - 0.0010)}{(0.10x + 0.0010)} \right) = -0.05$$

$$\left(\frac{(0.10x - 0.0010)}{(0.10x + 0.0010)} \right) = 10^{-0.05} = 0.89125$$

$$0.10x - 0.0010 = 0.89125 (0.10x + 0.0010)$$

$$x = 0.173908 = 0.17$$

The buffer concentration can be decreased by a factor of 0.17, or **170 mL** of buffer can be diluted to 1 L of medium. At least this amount should be used to adequately buffer the pH change.

17.151 <u>Plan:</u> Use the ideal gas law to calculate the amount (mol) of CO_2 dissolved in water. Use the K_a expression for H_2CO_3 to find the $[H_3O^+]$ associated with that CO_2 concentration.

<u>Solution:</u>
Carbon dioxide dissolves in water to produce H_3O^+ ions:

$$CO_2(g) \rightleftharpoons CO_2(aq)$$

$$CO_2(aq) + H_2O(l) \rightleftharpoons H_2CO_3(aq)$$

$$H_2CO_3(aq) \rightleftharpoons H_3O^+(aq) + HCO_3^-(aq) \qquad K_{a1} = 4.5 \times 10^{-7}$$

The molar concentration of CO_2, $[CO_2]$, depends on how much $CO_2(g)$ from the atmosphere can dissolve in pure water. Since air is not pure CO_2, account for the volume fraction of air (0.033 L/100 L) when determining the amount (mol).

$$\text{Volume (L) of } CO_2 = (88 \text{ mL}) \left(\frac{10^{-3} \text{ L}}{1 \text{ mL}} \right) \left(\frac{0.033\%}{100\%} \right) = 2.904 \times 10^{-5} \text{ L } CO_2$$

$$\text{amount (mol) of dissolved } CO_2 = \frac{PV}{RT} = \frac{(1 \text{ bar})(2.904 \times 10^{-5} \text{ L})}{\left(0.08314 \frac{\text{bar} \cdot \text{L}}{\text{mol} \cdot \text{K}} \right)((273 + 25)\text{K})} = 1.172115 \times 10^{-6} \text{ mol } CO_2$$

$[CO_2] = (1.172115 \times 10^{-6} \text{ mol } CO_2)/[(100 \text{ mL})(10^{-3} \text{ L/1 mL})] = 1.172115 \times 10^{-5} \text{ mol/L } CO_2$

$$K_{a1} = 4.5 \times 10^{-7} = \frac{\left[H_3O^+ \right]\left[HCO_3^- \right]}{\left[H_2CO_3 \right]} = \frac{\left[H_3O^+ \right]\left[HCO_3^- \right]}{\left[CO_2 \right]} \qquad \text{Let } x = [H_3O^+] = [HCO_3^-]$$

$$4.5 \times 10^{-7} = \frac{(x)(x)}{(1.172115 \times 10^{-5} - x)} \qquad \text{Check assumption: } 1.172115 \times 10^{-5}/4.5 \times 10^{-7} = 26 < 400$$

The assumption is not justified and it is necessary to use the quadratic equation.

$$4.5 \times 10^{-7} = \frac{(x)(x)}{(1.172115 \times 10^{-5} - x)}$$

$$x^2 + 4.5 \times 10^{-7}x - 5.27452 \times 10^{-12} = 0$$

$$a = 1 \qquad\qquad b = 4.5 \times 10^{-7} \qquad\qquad c = -5.27452 \times 10^{-12}$$

$$x = \frac{-b \pm \sqrt{b^2 - 4ac}}{2a}$$

$$x = \frac{-(4.5 \times 10^{-7}) \pm \sqrt{(4.5 \times 10^{-7})^2 - 4(1)(-5.27452 \times 10^{-12})}}{2(1)}$$

$x = 2.0826276 \times 10^{-6}$ mol/L = [H$^+$]

pH = $-\log (2.0826276 \times 10^{-6})$ = 5.68139 = **5.68**

17.153 Initial concentrations of Pb^{2+} and Ca(EDTA)$^{2-}$ before reaction based on mixing 100. mL of 0.10 mol/L Na$_2$Ca(EDTA) with 1.5 L blood:

$$[Pb^{2+}] = \left(\frac{120 \ \mu g \ Pb^{2+}}{100 \ mL}\right)\left(\frac{1 \ mL}{10^{-3} \ L}\right)\left(\frac{1.5 \ L \ blood}{1.6 \ L \ mixture}\right)\left(\frac{10^{-6} \ g}{1 \ \mu g}\right)\left(\frac{1 \ mol \ Pb^{2+}}{207.2 \ g \ Pb^{2+}}\right) = 5.42953668 \times 10^{-6} \ mol/L \ Pb^{2+}$$

$c_{conc}V_{conc} = c_{dil}V_{dil}$

$[Ca(EDTA)^{2-}] = c_{conc}V_{conc}/V_{dil} = [(0.10 \ mol/L \ (100 \ mL)(10^{-3} \ L/1 \ mL)]/(1.6 \ L)$
$\quad\quad\quad\quad = 6.25 \times 10^{-3}$ mol/L

Set up a reaction table assuming the reaction goes to completion:

Concentration (mol/L)	[Ca(EDTA)]$^{2-}$(aq)	+	Pb^{2+}(aq)	⇌	[Pb(EDTA)]$^{2-}$(aq)	+	Ca^{2+}(aq)
Initial	6.25×10^{-3}		$5.42953668 \times 10^{-6}$		0		0
React	$-5.42953668 \times 10^{-6}$		$-5.42953668 \times 10^{-6}$		$+5.42953668 \times 10^{-6}$		$+5.42953668 \times 10^{-6}$
	6.24457×10^{-3}		0		$5.42953668 \times 10^{-6}$		$5.42953668 \times 10^{-6}$

Now set up a reaction table for the equilibrium process:

Concentration (mol/L)	[Ca(EDTA)]$^{2-}$(aq)	+	Pb^{2+}(aq)	⇌	[Pb(EDTA)]$^{2-}$(aq)	+	Ca^{2+}(aq)
Initial	6.24457×10^{-3}		0		$5.42953668 \times 10^{-6}$		$5.42953668 \times 10^{-6}$
Change	$+x$		$+x$		$-x$		$-x$
Equilibrium	$6.24457 \times 10^{-3} + x$		x		$5.4295366 \times 10^{-6} - x$		$5.4295366 \times 10^{-6} - x$

Assuming that x is much smaller than all the numerical quantities and hence the change caused by x is negligible,:

$$K_c = 2.5 \times 10^7 = \frac{\left[Pb(EDTA)^{2-}\right]\left[Ca^{2+}\right]}{\left[Ca(EDTA)^{2-}\right]\left[Pb^{2+}\right]} = \frac{(5.42953668 \times 10^{-6})(5.42953668 \times 10^{-6})}{(6.24457 \times 10^{-3})(x)}$$

$x = [Pb^{2+}] = 1.8883522 \times 10^{-16}$ mol/L

$$\text{Mass } (\mu g) \text{ of } Pb^{2+} \text{ in } 100 \ mL = \left(\frac{1.8883522 \times 10^{-16} \ mol \ Pb^{2+}}{L}\right)\left(\frac{10^{-3} \ L}{1 \ mL}\right)(100 \ mL)\left(\frac{207.2 \ g \ Pb^{2+}}{1 \ mol \ Pb^{2+}}\right)\left(\frac{1 \ \mu g}{10^{-6} \ g}\right)$$

$$= 3.9126658 \times 10^{-9} \ \mu g \ Pb^{2+}$$

The final concentration is **3.9×10^{-9} μg/100 mL.**

17.155 <u>Plan:</u> Convert the solubility of NaCl from g/L to mol/l (concentration). Use the solubility to find the K_{sp} value for NaCl. Find the amount (mol) of Na$^+$ and Cl$^-$ in the original solution; find the amount (mol) of added Cl$^-$ (from the added HCl). The concentration (mol/L) of the Na$^+$ and Cl$^-$ ions are then found by dividing amount (mol) of each by the total volume after mixing. Using the concentrations (mol/L) of the two ions, determine a Q value and compare this value to the K_{sp} to determine if precipitation will occur.
<u>Solution:</u>

$$\text{Concentration (mol/L) of NaCl} = \left(\frac{317 \ g \ NaCl}{L}\right)\left(\frac{1 \ mol \ NaCl}{58.44 \ g \ NaCl}\right) = 5.42436687 \ mol/L \ NaCl$$

Determine the K_{sp} from the concentration (mol/L) just calculated.

NaCl(s) ⇌ Na$^+$(aq) + Cl$^-$(aq)

$K_{sp} = [Na^+][Cl^-] = S^2 = (5.42436687)^2 = 29.42375594 = 29.4$

$$\text{amount (mol) of Cl}^- \text{ initially} = \left(\frac{5.42436687 \ mol \ NaCl}{L}\right)(0.100 \ L)\left(\frac{1 \ mol \ Cl^-}{1 \ mol \ NaCl}\right) = 0.542436687 \ mol \ Cl^-$$

This is the same as the moles of Na$^+$ in the solution.

amount (mol) of Cl^- added $= \left(\dfrac{8.65 \text{ mol HCl}}{L}\right)\left(\dfrac{10^{-3} \text{ L}}{1 \text{ mL}}\right)(28.5 \text{ mL})\left(\dfrac{1 \text{ mol } Cl^-}{1 \text{ mol HCl}}\right) = 0.246525 \text{ mol } Cl^-$

0.100 L of saturated solution contains 0.542 mol each Na^+ and Cl^-, to which you are adding 0.246525 mol of additional Cl^- from HCl.

Volume of mixed solutions = 0.100 L + (28.5 mL)(10^{-3} L/1 mL) = 0.1285 L

concentration (mol/L)of Cl^- in mixture = [(0.542436687 + 0.246525) mol Cl^-]/(0.1285 L) = 6.13978 mol/L Cl^-

concentration (mol/L)of Na^+ in mixture = (0.542436687 mol Na^+)/(0.1285 L) = 4.22130 mol/L Na^+

Determine a Q value and compare this value to the K_{sp} to determine if precipitation will occur.

$Q_{sp} = [Na^+][Cl^-] = (4.22130)(6.13978) = 25.9179 = 25.9$

Since $Q_{sp} < K_{sp}$, no NaCl will precipitate.

17.156   Plan: A buffer contains a weak acid conjugate base pair. A K_a expression is used to calculate the pH of a weak acid while a K_b expression is used to calculate the pH of a weak base. The Henderson-Hasselbalch equation is used to calculate the pH when both the weak acid and conjugate base are present (a buffer).

Solution:

a) For the solution to be a buffer, both HA and A^- must be present in the solution. This situation occurs in **A** and **D**.

b) Scene A:

The amounts of HA and A^- are equal.

$pH = pK_a + \log\left(\dfrac{[A^-]}{[HA]}\right)$ $\left(\dfrac{[A^-]}{[HA]}\right) = 1$ when the amounts of HA and A^- are equal

$pH = pK_a + \log 1$

$pH = pK_a = -\log(4.5 \times 10^{-5}) = 4.346787 = \mathbf{4.35}$

Scene B:

Only A^- is present at a concentration of 0.10 mol/L.

The K_b for A^- is needed.

$K_b = K_w/K_a = 1.0 \times 10^{-14}/4.5 \times 10^{-5} = 2.222 \times 10^{-10}$

$A^-(aq) + H_2O(l) \rightleftharpoons OH^-(aq) + HA(aq)$

Initial:	0.10 mol/L	0	0
Change:	$-x$	$-x$	$-x$
Equilibrium:	$0.10 - x$	x	x

$K_b = 2.222 \times 10^{-10} = \dfrac{[HA][OH^-]}{[A^-]}$

$K_b = 2.222 \times 10^{-10} = \dfrac{(x)(x)}{(0.10 - x)}$ Assume that x is small compared to 0.10

$K_b = 2.222 \times 10^{-10} = \dfrac{(x)(x)}{(0.10)}$

$x = 4.7138095 \times 10^{-6}$ mol/L OH^-

Check assumption: $(4.7138095 \times 10^{-6}/0.10) \times 100\% = 0.005\%$ error, so the assumption is valid.

$[H_3O]^+ = K_w/[OH^-] = (1.0 \times 10^{-14})/(4.7138095 \times 10^{-6}) = 2.1214264 \times 10^{-9}$ mol/L H_3O^+

$pH = -\log[H^+] = -\log(2.1214264 \times 10^{-9}) = 8.67337 = \mathbf{8.67}$

Scene C:

This is a 0.10 mol/L HA solution. The hydrogen ion, and hence the pH, can be determined from the K_a.

Concentration (mol/L)	HA(aq) +	$H_2O(l)$	$\rightleftharpoons$	$H_3O^+(aq)$ +	$A^-(aq)$
Initial	0.10 mol/L	—		0	0
Change	$-x$			$+x$	$+x$
Equilibrium	$0.10 - x$			x	x

(The H_3O^+ contribution from water has been neglected.)

$$K_a = 4.5 \times 10^{-5} = \frac{\left[H_3O^+ \right]\left[A^- \right]}{\left[HA \right]}$$

$$K_a = 4.5 \times 10^{-5} = \frac{(x)(x)}{(0.10 - x)} \qquad \text{Assume that x is small compared to 0.10.}$$

$$K_a = 4.5 \times 10^{-5} = \frac{(x)(x)}{(0.10)}$$

$[H_3O^+] = x = 2.12132 \times 10^{-3}$

Check assumption: $(2.12132 \times 10^{-3}/0.10) \times 100\% = 2\%$ error, so the assumption is valid.

$pH = -\log [H^+] = -\log (2.12132 \times 10^{-3}) = 2.67339 = \mathbf{2.67}$

Scene D:

This is a buffer with a ratio of $[A^-]/[HA] = 5/3$.

$$pH = pK_a + \log \left(\frac{[A^-]}{[HA]} \right) = -\log (4.5 \times 10^{-5}) + \log \left(\frac{5}{3} \right) = 4.568636 = \mathbf{4.57}$$

c) The initial stage in the titration would only have HA present. The amount of HA will decrease, and the amount of A⁻ will increase until only A⁻ remains. The sequence will be: **C, A, D, and B**.

d) At the equivalence point, all the HA will have reacted with the added base. This occurs in scene **B**.

CHAPTER 18 THERMODYNAMICS: ENTROPY, GIBBS ENERGY, AND THE DIRECTION OF CHEMICAL REACTIONS

CHEMICAL CONNECTIONS BOXED READING PROBLEMS

B18.2   Plan: Add the two reactions to obtain the overall process; the values of the two reactions are then added to obtain for the overall reaction.
Solution:

creatine phosphate → creatine + ~~phosphate~~	$\Delta G° = -43.1$ kJ/mol
ADP + ~~phosphate~~ → ATP	$\Delta G° = +30.5$ kJ/mol
creatine phosphate + ADP → creatine + ATP	

$\Delta G = -43.1$ kJ/mol $+ 30.5$ kJ/mol $= \mathbf{-12.6}$ **kJ/mol**

END–OF–CHAPTER PROBLEMS

18.2   (a) A spontaneous process occurs by itself (possibly requiring an initial input of energy), whereas a nonspontaneous process requires a continuous supply of energy to make it happen. (b) It is possible to cause a nonspontaneous process to occur, but the process stops once the energy source is removed. A reaction that is found to be nonspontaneous under one set of conditions may be spontaneous under a different set of conditions (different temperature, different concentrations).

18.5   Vapourization is the change of a liquid substance to a gas so $\Delta_{vap}S = S_{gas} - S_{liquid}$. Fusion is the change of a solid substance into a liquid so $\Delta_{fus}S = S_{liquid} - S_{solid}$. Vapourization involves a greater change in volume than fusion. Thus, the transition from liquid to gas involves a greater entropy change than the transition from solid to liquid.

18.6   (a) (i) In an exothermic process, the *system* releases heat to its *surroundings*. The entropy of the surroundings increases because the temperature of the surroundings increases ($\Delta_{surr}S > 0$).
        (ii) In an endothermic process, the system absorbs heat from the surroundings and the surroundings become cooler. Thus, the entropy of the surroundings decreases ($\Delta_{surr}S < 0$).
        (b) A chemical cold pack for injuries is an example of a spontaneous, endothermic chemical reaction as is the melting of ice cream at room temperature.

18.8   Plan: A process is thermodynamically allowed if it is a spontaneous process. A spontaneous process is one that occurs by itself without a continuous input of energy.
Solution:
a) **Thermodynamically allowed (spontaneous),** evaporation occurs because a few of the liquid molecules have enough energy to break away from the intermolecular forces of the other liquid molecules and move spontaneously into the gas phase.
b) **Thermodynamically allowed (spontaneous),** a lion spontaneously chases an antelope without added force. This assumes that the lion has not just eaten.
c) **Thermodynamically allowed (spontaneous),** an unstable substance decays spontaneously to a more stable substance.

18.10   Plan: A process is thermodynamically allowed if it is a spontaneous process. A spontaneous process is one that occurs by itself without a continuous input of energy.
Solution:
a) **Thermodynamically allowed (spontaneous),** with a small amount of energy input, methane will continue to burn without additional energy (the reaction itself provides the necessary energy) until it is used up.

b) **Thermodynamically allowed (spontaneous)**, the dissolved sugar molecules have more states they can occupy than the crystalline sugar, so the reaction proceeds in the direction of dissolution.

c) **Not thermodynamically allowed (spontaneous)**, a cooked egg will not become raw again, no matter how long it sits or how many times it is mixed.

18.12   Plan: Particles with more freedom of motion have higher entropy. Therefore, $S_{gas} > S_{liquid} > S_{solid}$. If the products of the process have more entropy than the reactants, $\Delta_{sys}S$ is positive. If the products of the process have less entropy than the reactants, $\Delta_{sys}S$ is negative.
Solution:
a) $\Delta_{sys}S$ **positive**, melting is the change in state from solid to liquid. The solid state of a particular substance always has lower entropy than the same substance in the liquid state. Entropy increases during melting.
b) $\Delta_{sys}S$ **negative**, the entropy of most salt solutions is greater than the entropy of the solvent and solute separately, so entropy decreases as a salt precipitates.
c) $\Delta_{sys}S$**negative**, dew forms by the condensation of water vapour to liquid. Entropy of a substance in the gaseous state is greater than its entropy in the liquid state. Entropy decreases during condensation.

18.14   Plan: Particles with more freedom of motion have higher entropy. Therefore, $S_{gas} > S_{liquid} > S_{solid}$. If the products of the process have more entropy than the reactants, $\Delta_{sys}S$ is positive. If the products of the process have less entropy than the reactants, $\Delta_{sys}S$ is negative.
Solution:
a) $\Delta_{sys}S$ **positive**, the process described is liquid alcohol becoming gaseous alcohol. The gas molecules have greater entropy than the liquid molecules.
b) $\Delta_{sys}S$ **positive**, the process described is a change from solid to gas, an increase in possible energy states for the system.
c) $\Delta_{sys}S$ **positive**, the perfume molecules have more possible locations in the larger volume of the room than inside the bottle. A system that has more possible arrangements has greater entropy.

18.16   Plan: $\Delta_{sys}S$ is the entropy of the products – the entropy of the reactants. Use the fact that $S_{gas} > S_{liquid} > S_{solid}$; also, the greater the number of particles of a particular phase of matter, the higher the entropy.
Solution:
a) $\Delta_{sys}S$ **negative**, reaction involves a gaseous reactant and no gaseous products, so entropy decreases. The number of particles also decreases, indicating a decrease in entropy.
b) $\Delta_{sys}S$ **negative**, gaseous reactants form solid product and number of particles decreases, so entropy decreases.
c) $\Delta_{sys}S$ **positive**, when a solid salt dissolves in water, entropy generally increases since the entropy of the aqueous mixture has higher entropy than the solid.

18.18   Plan: $\Delta_{sys}S$ is the entropy of the products – the entropy of the reactants. Use the fact that $S_{gas} > S_{liquid} > S_{solid}$; also, the greater the number of particles of a particular phase of matter, the higher the entropy.
Solution:
a) $\Delta_{sys}S$ **positive**, the reaction produces gaseous CO_2 molecules that have greater entropy than the physical states of the reactants.
b) $\Delta_{sys}S$ **negative**, the reaction produces a net decrease in the number of gaseous molecules, so the system's entropy decreases.
c) $\Delta_{sys}S$ **positive**, the reaction produces a gas from a solid.

18.20   Plan: Particles with more freedom of motion have higher entropy. In general the entropy of gases is greater than that of liquids, and the entropy of liquids is greater than that of solids. Entropy increases with temperature. For substances in the same phase, entropy increases with atomic size and molecular complexity. If the entropy of the products is greater than that of the reactants, ΔS is positive.
Solution:
a) $\Delta_{sys}S$ **positive**, decreasing the pressure increases the volume available to the gas molecules so entropy of the system increases.

b) $\Delta_{sys}S$ **negative**, gaseous nitrogen molecules have greater entropy (more possible states) than dissolved nitrogen molecules.

c) $\Delta_{sys}S$ **positive**, dissolved oxygen molecules have lower entropy than gaseous oxygen molecules.

18.22 Plan: Particles with more freedom of motion have higher entropy. In general the entropy of gases is greater than that of liquids, and the entropy of liquids is greater than that of solids. Entropy increases with temperature. For substances in the same phase, entropy increases with atomic size and molecular complexity.
Solution:
a) **Butane** has the greater molar entropy because it has two additional C–H bonds that can vibrate and has greater rotational freedom around its bond. The presence of the double bond in 2-butene restricts rotation.
b) **Xe(g)** has the greater molar entropy because entropy increases with atomic size.
c) **CH$_4$(g)** has the greater molar entropy because gases in general have greater entropy than liquids.

18.24 Plan: Particles with more freedom of motion have higher entropy. In general the entropy of gases is greater than that of liquids, and the entropy of liquids is greater than that of solids. Entropy increases with temperature. For substances in the same phase, entropy increases with atomic size and molecular complexity.
Solution:
a) Ethanol, **C$_2$H$_5$OH(l)**, is a more complex molecule than methanol, CH_3OH, and has the greater molar entropy.
b) When a salt dissolves, there is an increase in the number of possible states for the ions. Thus, **KClO$_3$(aq)** has the greater molar entropy.
c) **K(s)** has greater molar entropy because K(s) has greater mass than Na(s).

18.26 Plan: Particles with more freedom of motion have higher entropy. In general the entropy of gases is greater than that of liquids, and the entropy of liquids is greater than that of solids. Entropy increases with temperature. For substances in the same phase, entropy increases with atomic size and molecular complexity.
Solution:
a) **Diamond < graphite < charcoal**. Diamond has an ordered, three-dimensional crystalline shape, followed by graphite with an ordered two-dimensional structure, followed by the amorphous (disordered) structure of charcoal.
b) **Ice < liquid water < water vapour**. Entropy increases as a substance changes from solid to liquid to gas.
c) **O atoms < O$_2$ < O$_3$**. Entropy increases with molecular complexity because there are more modes of movement (e.g., bond vibration) available to the complex molecules.

18.28 Plan: Particles with more freedom of motion have higher entropy. In general the entropy of gases is greater than that of liquids, and the entropy of liquids is greater than that of solids. Entropy increases with temperature. For substances in the same phase, entropy increases with atomic size and molecular complexity.
Solution:
a) **ClO$_4^-$(aq) > ClO$_3^-$(aq) > ClO$_2^-$(aq)**. The decreasing order of molar entropy follows the order of decreasing molecular complexity.
b) **NO$_2$(g) > NO(g) > N$_2$(g)**. N_2 has lower molar entropy than NO because N_2 consists of two of the same atoms while NO consists of two different atoms. NO_2 has greater molar entropy than NO because NO_2 consists of three atoms while NO consists of only two.
c) **Fe$_3$O$_4$(s) > Fe$_2$O$_3$(s) > Al$_2$O$_3$(s)**. Fe_3O_4 has greater molar entropy than Fe_2O_3 because Fe_3O_4 is more complex and more massive. Fe_2O_3 and Al_2O_3 contain the same number of atoms but Fe_2O_3 has greater molar entropy because iron atoms are more massive than aluminum atoms.

18.31 A system at equilibrium does not spontaneously produce more products or more reactants. For either reaction direction, the entropy change of the system is exactly offset by the entropy change of the surroundings. Therefore, for system at equilibrium, $\Delta_{univ}S = \Delta_{sys}S + \Delta_{surr}S = 0$. However, for a system moving to equilibrium, $\Delta_{univ}S > 0$, because the second law states that for any spontaneous process, the entropy of the universe increases.

18.32 Plan: Since entropy is a state function, the entropy changes can be found by summing the entropies of the products and subtracting the sum of the entropies of the reactants.
Solution:
$$\Delta_r S° = [(2)(S° \text{ of HClO})] - [(S° \text{ of } H_2O) + (S° \text{ of } Cl_2O)]$$

Rearranging this expression to solve for $S°$ of Cl_2O gives: $S°$ of $Cl_2O = 2(S°$ of $HClO) - S°$ of $H_2O - \Delta_r S°$

18.33   Plan: To calculate the standard entropy change, use the relationship $\Delta_r S° = \sum m\, S°_{products} - \sum n\, S°_{reactants}$.

To predict the sign of entropy recall that in general $S_{gas} > S_{liquid} > S_{solid}$, and entropy increases as the number of particles of a particular phase of matter increases, and with increasing atomic size and molecular complexity.
Solution:
a) Prediction: $\Delta S°$ **negative** because the amount (mol) of gas (Δn) decreases.
$\Delta S° = (S°$ of $N_2O) + (S°$ of $NO_2)] - [(3)(S°$ of $NO)]$
$\Delta S° = [\,(219.7\ \text{J/mol•K}) + (239.9\ \text{J/mol•K})] - [(3)(210.65\ \text{J/mol•K})]$
$\Delta S° = -172.35\ \text{J/ mol•K} = $ **–172.4 J/ mol•K**
b) Prediction: Sign difficult to predict because $\Delta n = 0$, but **possibly $\Delta S°$ positive** because water vapour has greater complexity than H_2 gas.
$\Delta S° = [(2)(S°$ of $Fe) + (3)(S°$ of $H_2O)] - [(3)(S°$ of $H_2) + (S°$ of $Fe_2O_3)]$
$\Delta S° = [(2)(27.3\ \text{J/mol•K}) + (3)(188.72\ \text{J/mol•K})] - [(3)(130.6\ \text{J/mol•K}) + (87.400\ \text{J/mol•K})]$
$\Delta S° = 141.56\ \text{J/ mol•K} = $ **141.6 J/ mol•K**
c) Prediction: $\Delta S°$ **negative** because a gaseous reactant forms a solid product and also because the amount (mol)of gas (Δn) decreases.
$\Delta S° = [\,(S°$ of $P_4O_{10})] - [\,(S°$of $P_4) + (5)(S°$ of $O)]$
$\Delta S° = [\,(229\ \text{J/mol•K})] - [\,(41.1\ \text{J/mol•K}) + (5)(205.0\ \text{J/mol•K})]$
$\Delta S° = -837.1\ \text{J/ mol•K} = $ **–837 J/ mol•K**

18.35   Plan: Write the balanced equation. To calculate the standard entropy change, use the relationship
$\Delta_r S° = \sum m\, S°_{products} - \sum n\, S°_{reactants}$. To predict the sign of entropy recall that in general $S_{gas} > S_{liquid} > S_{solid}$, entropy increases as the number of particles of a particular phase of matter increases, and entropy increases with increasing atomic size and molecular complexity.
Solution:
The balanced combustion reaction is:
$$2C_2H_6(g) + 7O_2(g) \rightarrow 4CO_2(g) + 6H_2O(g)$$
$\Delta S° = [(4)(S°$ of $CO_2) + (6)(S°$ of $H_2O)] - [(2)(S°$ of $C_2H_6) + (7)(S°$ of $O_2)]$
$\Delta S° = [(4)(213.7\ \text{J/mol•K}) + (6)(188.72\ \text{J/mol•K})] - [(2)(229.5\ \text{J/mol•K}) + (7)(205.0\ \text{J/mol•K})]$
$\Delta S° = 93.12\ \text{J/mol•K} = $ **93.1 J/mol•K**
The entropy value is not per mole of C_2H_6 but per two moles. Divide the calculated value by two to obtain entropy per mole of C_2H_6.
Yes, the positive sign of $\Delta S°$ is expected because there is a net increase in the number of gas molecules from nine moles as reactants to ten moles as products.

18.37   Plan: Write the balanced equation. To calculate the standard entropy change, use the relationship
$\Delta_r S° = \sum m\, S°_{products} - \sum n\, S°_{reactants}$. To predict the sign of entropy recall that in general $S_{gas} > S_{liquid} > S_{solid}$, entropy increases as the number of particles of a particular phase of matter increases, and entropy increases with increasing atomic size and molecular complexity.
Solution:
The balanced chemical equation for the described reaction is:
$$2NO(g) + 5H_2(g) \rightarrow 2NH_3(g) + 2H_2O(g)$$
Because the amount (mol) of gas decreases, i.e., $\Delta n = 4 - 7 = -3$, the entropy is expected to decrease.
$\Delta S° = [(2)(S°$ of $NH_3) + (2)(S°$ of $H_2O)] - [(2)(S°$ of $NO) + (5)(S°$ of $H_2)]$
$\Delta S° = [(2)(193\ \text{J/mol•K}) + (2)(188.72\ \text{J/mol•K})] - [(2)(210.65\ \text{J/mol•K}) + (5)(130.6\ \text{J/mol•K})]$
$\Delta S° = -310.86\ \text{J/mol•K} = $ **–311 J/mol•K**
Yes, the calculated entropy matches the predicted decrease.

18.39   Plan: Write the balanced equation. To calculate the standard entropy change, use the relationship
$\Delta_r S^\circ = \sum m S^\circ_{products} - \sum n S^\circ_{reactants}$.

Solution:

The reaction for forming Cu_2O from copper metal and oxygen gas is

$$2Cu(s) + 1/2O_2(g) \rightarrow Cu_2O(s)$$

$\Delta S^\circ = [(S^\circ \text{ of } Cu_2O)] - [(2)(S^\circ \text{ of } Cu) + (1/2)(S^\circ \text{ of } O_2)]$

$\Delta S^\circ = [(93.1 \text{ J/mol•K})] - [(2)(33.1 \text{ J/mol•K}) + (1/2)(205.0 \text{ J/mol•K})]$

$\Delta S^\circ = \textbf{–75.6 J/mol•K}$

18.41   Plan: Write the balanced equation. To calculate the standard entropy change, use the relationship
$\Delta_r S^\circ = \sum m S^\circ_{products} - \sum n S^\circ_{reactants}$.

Solution:

One mole of methanol is formed from its elements in their standard states according to the following equation:

$C(g) + 2H_2(g) + 1/2O_2(g) \rightarrow CH_3OH(l)$

$\Delta S^\circ = [(S^\circ \text{ of } CH_3OH)] - [(S^\circ \text{ of } C) + (2)(S^\circ \text{ of } H_2) + (1/2)(S^\circ \text{ of } O_2)]$

$\Delta S^\circ = [(127 \text{ J/mol•K})] - [(5.686 \text{ J/mol•K}) + (2)(130.6 \text{ J/mol•K}) + (1/2)(205.0 \text{ J/mol•K})]$

$\Delta S^\circ = -242.386 \text{ J/mol•K} = \textbf{–242 J/mol•K}$

18.44   Plan: Write the balanced equation. To calculate the standard entropy change, use the relationship
$\Delta_r S^\circ = \sum m S^\circ_{products} - \sum n S^\circ_{reactants}$.

Solution:

Complete combustion of a hydrocarbon includes oxygen as a reactant and carbon dioxide and water as the products.

$C_2H_2(g) + 5/2O_2(g) \rightarrow 2CO_2(g) + H_2O(g)$

$\Delta S^\circ = [(2)(S^\circ \text{ of } CO_2) + (S^\circ \text{ of } H_2O)] - [(S^\circ \text{ of } C_2H_2) + (5/2)(S^\circ \text{ of } O_2)]$

$\Delta S^\circ = [(2)(213.7 \text{ J/mol•K}) + (188.72 \text{ J/mol•K})]$

$\qquad\qquad - [(200.85 \text{ J/mol•K}) + (5/2l)(205.0 \text{ J/mol•K})]$

$\Delta S^\circ = -97.23 \text{ J/mol•K} = \textbf{–97.2 J/mol•K}$

18.46   A spontaneous process has $\Delta_{univ}S > 0$. Since the temperature in Kelvin is always positive, $\Delta_{sys}G$ must be negative ($\Delta_{sys}G < 0$) for a spontaneous process.

18.48 $\boldsymbol{\Delta H^\circ}$ **is positive and** $\boldsymbol{\Delta S^\circ}$ **is positive.** The reaction is endothermic ($\Delta H^\circ > 0$) and requires a lot of heat from its surroundings to be spontaneous. The removal of heat from the surroundings results in $\Delta_{surr}S < 0$. The only way an endothermic reaction can proceed spontaneously is if $\Delta S^\circ > 0$, effectively offsetting the decrease in surroundings entropy. In summary, the values of ΔH° and ΔS° are both positive for this reaction. Melting is an example.

18.49   For a given substance, the entropy changes greatly from one phase to another, e.g., from liquid to gas. However, the entropy changes little within a phase. As long as the substance does not change phase, the value of ΔS° is relatively unaffected by temperature.

18.50   Plan: ΔG° can be calculated with the relationship $\sum m \Delta_{f(products)}G^\circ - \sum n \Delta_{f(reactants)}G^\circ$.

Solution:

a) $\Delta G^\circ = [(2)(\Delta_f G^\circ \text{ of } MgO)] - [(2)(\Delta_f G^\circ \text{ of } Mg) + (\Delta_f G^\circ \text{ of } O_2)]$

Both $Mg(s)$ and $O_2(g)$ are the standard-state forms of their respective elements, so their $\Delta_f G^\circ$ values are zero.

$\Delta G^\circ = [(2)(-569.0 \text{ kJ/mol})] - [(2)(0 \text{ kJ/mol}) + (1)(0 \text{ kJ/mol})] = \textbf{–1138.0 kJ/mol}$

b) $\Delta G^\circ = [(2)(\Delta_f G^\circ \text{ of } CO_2) + (4)(\Delta_f G^\circ \text{ of } H_2O)]$

$\qquad\qquad - [(2)(\Delta_f G^\circ \text{ of } CH_3OH) + (3)(\Delta_f G^\circ \text{ of } O_2)]$

$\Delta G° = [(2)(-394.4 \text{ kJ/mol}) + (4)(-228.60 \text{ kJ/mol})] - [(2)(-161.9 \text{ kJ/mol}) + (3)(0)]$

$\Delta G° = -1379.4 \text{ kJ/mol}$

c) $\Delta G° = [(\Delta_f G° \text{ of BaCO}_3)] - [(\Delta_f G° \text{ of BaO}) + (\Delta_f G° \text{ of CO}_2)]$

$\Delta G° = [(-1139 \text{ kJ/mol})] - (-520.4 \text{ kJ/mol}) + (-394.4 \text{ kJ/mol})]$

$\Delta G° = -224.2 \text{ kJ/mol} = -224 \text{ kJ/mol}$

18.52   Plan: $\Delta_r H°$ can be calculated from the individual $\Delta_f H°$ values of the reactants and products by using the relationship $\Delta_r H° = \sum m \Delta_{f \text{(products)}} H° - \sum n \Delta_{f \text{(reactants)}} H°$. $\Delta_r S°$ can be calculated from the individual $S°$ values of the reactants and products by using the relationship $\Delta_r S° = \sum m S°_{\text{products}} - \sum n S°_{\text{reactants}}$. Once $\Delta H°_{\text{rxn}}$ and $\Delta_r S°$ are known, $\Delta G°$ can be calculated with the relationship $\Delta_r G° = \Delta_r H° - T\Delta_r S°$. $\Delta_r S°$ values in J/K must be converted to units of kJ/K to match the units of $\Delta_r H°$.

Solution:

a) $\Delta_r H° = [(2)(\Delta_f H° \text{ of MgO})] - [(2)(\Delta_f H° \text{ of Mg}) + (\Delta_f H° \text{ of O}_2)]$

$\Delta_r H° = [(2)(-601.2 \text{ kJ/mol})] - [(2)(0 \text{ kJ/mol}) + (0 \text{ kJ/mol})]$

$\Delta_r H° = -1202.4 \text{ kJ/mol}$

$\Delta_r S° = [(2)(S° \text{ of MgO})] - [(2)(S° \text{ of Mg}) + (S° \text{ of O}_2)]$

$\Delta_r S° = [(2)(26.9 \text{ J/mol•K})] - [(2)(32.69 \text{ J/mol•K}) + (205.0 \text{ J/mol•K})]$

$\Delta_r S° = -216.58 \text{ J/mol•K}$

$\Delta_r G° = \Delta_r H° - T\Delta_r S° = -1202.4 \text{ kJ/mol} - [(298 \text{ K})(-216.58 \text{ J/mol•K})(1 \text{ kJ}/10^3 \text{ J})] = -1137.859 \text{ kJ/mol}$
$= -1138 \text{ kJ/mol}$

b) $\Delta_r H° = [(2)(\Delta_f H° \text{ of CO}_2) + (4)(\Delta_f H° \text{ of H}_2\text{O})]$
$\qquad\qquad\qquad - [(2)(\Delta_f H° \text{ of CH}_3\text{OH}) + (3)(\Delta_f H° \text{ of O}_2)]$

$\Delta_r H° = [(2)(-393.5 \text{ kJ/mol}) + (4)(-241.826 \text{ kJ/mol})] - [(2)(-201.2 \text{ kJ/mol}) + (3)(0 \text{ kJ/mol})]$

$\Delta_r H° = -1351.904 \text{ kJ/mol}$

$\Delta_r S° = [(2)(S° \text{ of CO}_2) + (4)(S° \text{ of H}_2\text{O})]$
$\qquad\qquad\qquad - [(2)(S° \text{ of CH}_3\text{OH}) + (3)(S° \text{ of O}_2)]$

$\Delta_r S° = [(2)(213.7 \text{ J/mol•K}) + (4)(188.72 \text{ J/mol•K})]$
$\qquad\qquad - [(2)(238 \text{ J/mol•K}) + (3)(205.0 \text{ J/mol•K})] = 91.28 \text{ J/mol•K}$

$\Delta_r G° = \Delta_r H° - T\Delta_r S° = -1351.904 \text{ kJ/mol} - [(298 \text{ K})(91.28 \text{ J/mol•K})(1 \text{ kJ}/10^3 \text{ J})] = -1379.105 \text{kJ/mol}$
$= -1379 \text{ kJ/mol}$

c) $\Delta_r H° = [(\Delta_f H° \text{ of BaCO}_3)] - [(\Delta_f H° \text{ of BaO}) + (\Delta_f H° \text{ of CO}_2)]$

$\Delta_r H° = [(-1219 \text{ kJ/mol})] - [(-548.1 \text{ kJ/mol}) + (-393.5 \text{ kJ/mol})]$

$\Delta_r H° = -277.4 \text{ kJ/mol}$

$\Delta_r S° = [(S° \text{ of BaCO}_3)] - [(S° \text{ of BaO}) + (S° \text{ of CO}_2)]$

$\Delta_r S° = [(112 \text{ J/mol•K})] - [(72.07 \text{ J/mol•K}) + (213.7 \text{ J/mol•K})]$

$\Delta_r S° = -173.77 \text{ J/mol•K}$

$\Delta_r G° = \Delta_r H° - T\Delta_r S° = -277.4 \text{ kJ/mol} - [(298 \text{ K})(-173.77 \text{ J/mol•K})(1 \text{ kJ}/10^3 \text{ J})] = -225.6265 \text{ kJ/mol}$
$= -226 \text{ kJ/mol}$

18.54   <u>Plan:</u> $\Delta_r G°$ can be calculated with the relationship $\sum m\,\Delta_{f\,(products)}G° - \sum n\,\Delta_{f\,(reactants)}G°$. Alternatively, $\Delta_r G°$ can be calculated with the relationship $\Delta_r G° = \Delta_r H° - T\Delta_r S°$. Entropy decreases (is negative) when there are fewer moles of gaseous products than there are of gaseous reactants.

<u>Solution:</u>

a) Entropy decreases ($\Delta S°$ **negative**) because the amount (mol) of gas decreases from reactants (1 1/2 mol) to products (1 mole). The oxidation (combustion) of CO requires initial energy input to start the reaction, but then releases energy (exothermic, $\Delta H°$ **negative**) which is typical of all combustion reactions.

b) Method 1: Calculate $\Delta_r G°$ from $\Delta_f G°$ values of products and reactants.

$\Delta_r G° = \sum m\,\Delta_{f\,(products)}G° - \sum n\,\Delta_{f\,(reactants)}G°$

$\Delta_r G° = [(\Delta G_f° \text{ of } CO_2)] - [(\Delta G_f° \text{ of } CO) + (1/2)(\Delta G_f° \text{ of } O_2)]$

$\Delta_r G° = [(-394.4 \text{ kJ/mol})] - [(-137.2 \text{ kJ/mol}) + (1/2)(0 \text{ kJ/mol})] = \textbf{–257.2 kJ/mol}$

Method 2: Calculate $\Delta_r G°$ from $\Delta_r H°$ and $\Delta_r S°$ at 298 K (the degree superscript indicates a reaction at standard state, given in the Appendix at 25°C).

$\Delta_r H° = \sum m\,\Delta_{f\,(products)}H° - \sum n\,\Delta_{f\,(reactants)}H°$

$\Delta_r H° = [(\Delta H_f° \text{ of } CO_2)] - [(\Delta H_f° \text{ of } CO) + (1/2)(\Delta H_f° \text{ of } O_2)]$

$\Delta_r H° = [(-393.5 \text{ kJ/mol})] - [(-110.5 \text{ kJ/mol}) + (1/2l)(0 \text{ kJ/mol})] = -283.0 \text{ kJ/mol}$

$\Delta_r S° = \sum m\,S°_{products} - \sum n\,S°_{reactants}$

$\Delta_r S° = [(S° \text{ of } CO_2)] - [(S° \text{ of } CO) + (1/2)(S° \text{ of } O_2)]$

$\Delta_r S° = [(213.7 \text{ J/mol•K})] - [(197.5 \text{ J/mol•K}) + (1/2)(205.0 \text{ J/mol•K})] = -86.3 \text{ J/mol•K}$

$\Delta_r G° = \Delta_r H° - T\Delta_r S° = (-283.0 \text{ kJ/mol}) - [(298 \text{ K})(-86.3 \text{ J/mol•K})(1 \text{ kJ}/10^3 \text{ J})] = -257.2826 \text{ kJ/mol}$
        $= \textbf{–257.3 kJ/mol}$

18.56   <u>Plan:</u> Use the relationship $\Delta_r G° = \Delta_r H° - T\Delta_r S°$ to find $\Delta_r S°$, knowing $\Delta_r H°$ and $\Delta_r G°$. This relationship is also used to find $\Delta_r G°$ at a different temperature.

<u>Solution:</u>

Reaction is $Xe(g) + 3F_2(g) \rightarrow XeF_6(g)$

a) $\Delta_r G° = \Delta_r H° - T\Delta_r S°$

$\Delta S° = \dfrac{\Delta H° - \Delta G°}{T} = \dfrac{-402 \text{ kJ/mol} - (-280.\text{ kJ/mol})}{298 \text{ K}} = -0.40939597 \text{ kJ/mol•K} = \textbf{–0.409 kJ/mol•K}$

b) $\Delta_r G° = \Delta_r H° - T\Delta_r S° = (-402 \text{ kJ/mol}) - [(500.\text{ K})(-0.40939597 \text{ kJ/mol•K})] = -197.302 \text{ kJ/mol}$
        $= \textbf{–197 kJ/mol}$

18.58   <u>Plan:</u> $\Delta_r H°$ can be calculated from the individual $\Delta_f H°$ values of the reactants and products by using the relationship $\Delta_r H° = \sum m\,\Delta_{f\,(products)}H° - \sum n\,\Delta_{f\,(reactants)}H°$. $\Delta_r S°$ can be calculated from the individual $S°$ values of the reactants and products by using the relationship $\Delta_r S° = \sum m\,S°_{products} - \sum n\,S°_{reactants}$. Once $\Delta_r H°$ and $\Delta_r S°$ are known, $\Delta G°$ can be calculated with the relationship $\Delta_r G° = \Delta_r H° - T\Delta_{rxn}S°$. $\Delta_r S°$ values in J/mol·K must be converted to units of kJ/mol·K to match the units of $\Delta_r H°$.

<u>Solution:</u>

a) $\Delta_r H° = [(\Delta_f H° \text{ of } CO) + (2)(\Delta_f H° \text{ of } H_2)] - [(\Delta_f H° \text{ of } CH_3OH)]$

$\Delta_r H^\circ = [(-110.5 \text{ kJ/mol}) + (2)(0 \text{ kJ/mol})] - [(-201.2 \text{ kJ/mol})]$

$\Delta_r H^\circ = \mathbf{90.7 \text{ kJ} / \text{mol}}$

$\Delta_r S^\circ = [(S^\circ \text{ of CO}) + (2)(S^\circ \text{ of } H_2)] - [(S^\circ \text{ of } CH_3OH)]$

$\Delta_r S^\circ = [(197.5 \text{ J/mol} \cdot K) + (2)(130.6 \text{ J/mol} \cdot K)] - [(238 \text{ J/mol} \cdot K)]$

$\Delta_r S^\circ = 220.7 \text{ J/mol} \cdot K = \mathbf{221 \text{ J/mol} \cdot K}$

b) $\Delta_r G^\circ = \Delta_r H^\circ - T\Delta_r S^\circ$

$T_1 = 28 + 273 = 301 \text{ K}$ $\Delta G^\circ = 90.7 \text{ kJ/mol} - [(301 \text{ K})(220.7 \text{ J/mol} \cdot K)(1 \text{ kJ/10}^3 \text{ J})] = 24.2693 \text{ kJ/mol}$
    $= \mathbf{24.3 \text{ kJ/mol}}$

$T_2 = 128 + 273 = 401 \text{ K}$ $\Delta G^\circ = 90.7 \text{ kJ/mol} - [(401 \text{ K})(220.7 \text{ J/mol} \cdot K)(1 \text{ kJ/10}^3 \text{ J})] = 2.1993 \text{ kJ/mol}$
    $= \mathbf{2.2 \text{ kJ/mol}}$

$T_3 = 228 + 273 = 501 \text{ K}$ $\Delta G^\circ = 90.7 \text{ kJ/mol} - [(501 \text{ K})(220.7 \text{ J/mol} \cdot K)(1 \text{ kJ/10}^3 \text{ J})] = -19.8707 \text{ kJ/mol}$
    $= \mathbf{-19.9 \text{ kJ/mol}}$

c) For the substances in their standard states, the reaction is nonspontaneous at 28°C, near equilibrium at 128°C, and spontaneous at 228°C. Reactions with positive values of $\Delta_r H^\circ$ and $\Delta_r S^\circ$ become spontaneous at high temperatures.

18.60   Plan: At the normal boiling point, defined as the temperature at which the vapour pressure of the liquid equals 1 bar, the phase change from liquid to gas is at equilibrium. For a system at equilibrium, the change in Gibbs free energy is zero. Since the gas is at 1 bar and the liquid assumed to be pure, the system is at standard state and $\Delta G^\circ = 0$. The temperature at which this occurs can be found from $\Delta_r G^\circ = 0 = \Delta_r H^\circ - T\Delta_r S^\circ$. $\Delta_r H^\circ$ can be calculated from the individual $\Delta_f H^\circ$ values of the reactants and products by using the relationship $\Delta_r H^\circ = \Sigma m \Delta_{f \text{(products)}} H^\circ - \Sigma n \Delta_{f \text{(reactants)}} H^\circ$. $\Delta_r S^\circ$ can be calculated from the individual S° values of the reactants and products by using the relationship $\Delta_r S^\circ = \Sigma m S^\circ_{\text{products}} - \Sigma n S^\circ_{\text{reactants}}$.
Solution:
$Br_2(l) \rightleftharpoons Br_2(g)$

$\Delta_r H^\circ = \Sigma m \Delta_{f \text{(products)}} H^\circ - \Sigma n \Delta_{f \text{(reactants)}} H^\circ$

$\Delta_r H^\circ = [(\Delta_f H^\circ \text{ of } Br_2(g))] - [(\Delta_f H^\circ \text{ of } Br_2(l))]$

$\Delta_r H^\circ = [(30.91 \text{ kJ/mol})] - [(0 \text{ kJ/mol})] = 30.91 \text{ kJ/mol}$

$\Delta_r S^\circ = \Sigma m S^\circ_{\text{products}} - \Sigma n S^\circ_{\text{reactants}}$

$\Delta_r S^\circ = [(S^\circ \text{ of } Br_2(g))] - [(S^\circ \text{ of } Br_2(l))]$

$\Delta_r S^\circ = [(245.38 \text{ J/K} \cdot \text{mol})] - [(152.23 \text{ J/K} \cdot \text{mol})] = 93.15 \text{ J/K} \cdot \text{mol} = 0.09315 \text{ kJ/K} \cdot \text{mol}$

$\Delta_r G^\circ = 0 = \Delta_r H^\circ - T\Delta_r S^\circ$

$\Delta_r H^\circ = T\Delta_r S^\circ$

$T = \dfrac{\Delta H^\circ}{\Delta S^\circ} = \dfrac{30.91 \text{ kJ/mol}}{0.09315 \text{ kJ/K} \cdot \text{mol}} = 331.830 \text{ K} = \mathbf{331.8 \text{ K}}$

18.62   Plan: $\Delta_r H^\circ$ can be calculated from the individual $\Delta_f H^\circ$ values of the reactants and products by using the relationship $\Delta_r H^\circ = \Sigma m \Delta_{f \text{(products)}} H^\circ - \Sigma n \Delta_{f \text{(reactants)}} H^\circ$. $\Delta_r S^\circ$ can be calculated from the individual S° values of the reactants and products by using the relationship $\Delta_r S^\circ = \Sigma m S^\circ_{\text{products}} - \Sigma n S^\circ_{\text{reactants}}$. Once $\Delta_r H^\circ$ and $\Delta_r S^\circ$ are known, ΔG° can be calculated with the relationship $\Delta_r G^\circ = \Delta_r H^\circ - T\Delta_r S^\circ$. $\Delta_r S^\circ$ values in

J/mol•K must be converted to units of kJ/mol•K to match the units of $\Delta_r H°$. To find the temperature at which the reaction becomes spontaneous, use $\Delta_r G° = 0 = \Delta_r H° - T\Delta_r S°$ and solve for temperature.

Solution:
a) The reaction for this process is $H_2(g) + 1/2O_2(g) \rightarrow H_2O(g)$. The coefficients are written this way (instead of $2H_2(g) + O_2(g) \rightarrow 2H_2O(g)$) because the problem specifies thermodynamic values "per (1) mol H_2," not per 2 mol H_2.

$\Delta_r H° = \Sigma m \Delta_{f(products)} H° - \Sigma n \Delta_{f(reactants)} H°$

$\Delta_r H° = [(\Delta_f H° \text{ of } H_2O)] - [(\Delta_f H° \text{ of } H_2) + (1/2)(\Delta_f H° \text{ of } O_2)]$

$\Delta_r H° = [(-241.826 \text{ kJ/mol})] - [(0 \text{ kJ/mol}) + (1/2)(0 \text{ kJ/mol})]$

$\Delta_r H° = \textbf{-241.826 kJ/mol}$

$\Delta_r S° = \Sigma m S°_{products} - \Sigma n S°_{reactants}$

$\Delta_r S° = [(S° \text{ of } H_2O)] - [(S° \text{ of } H_2) + (1/2)(S° \text{ of } O_2)]$

$\Delta_r S° = [(188.72 \text{ J/mol•K})] - [(130.6 \text{ J/mol•K}) + (1/2)(205.0 \text{ J/mol•K})]$

$\Delta_r S° = -44.38 \text{ J/mol•K} = \textbf{-44.4 J/mol•K} = \textbf{-0.0444 kJ/mol•K}$ $\Delta_r G° = \Delta_r H° - T\Delta_r S°$

$\Delta_r G° = -241.826 \text{ kJ/mol} - [(298 \text{ K})(-0.0444 \textbf{ kJ/mol•K})]$

$\Delta_r G° = \textbf{-228.6 kJ/mol}$

b) Because $\Delta H < 0$ and $\Delta S < 0$, the reaction will become nonspontaneous at higher temperatures because the positive $(-T\Delta S)$ term becomes larger than the negative ΔH term.

c) The reaction becomes spontaneous below the temperature where $\Delta_r G° = 0$

$\Delta_r G° = 0 = \Delta_r H° - T\Delta_r S°$

$\Delta_r H° = T\Delta_r S°$

$T = \dfrac{\Delta H°}{\Delta S°} = \dfrac{-241.826 \text{ kJ/mol}}{-0.0444 \text{ kJ/K•mol}} = 5446.53 \text{ K} = \textbf{5.45x10}^3 \textbf{ K}$

18.64   a) An equilibrium constant that is much less than one indicates that very little product is made to reach equilibrium. The reaction, thus, is not spontaneous in the forward direction and $\Delta G°$ is a relatively large positive value.
b) A large negative $\Delta G°$ indicates that the reaction is quite spontaneous and goes almost to completion. At equilibrium, much more product is present than reactant so $K > 1$. Q depends on initial conditions, not equilibrium conditions, so its value cannot be predicted from $\Delta G°$.

18.67   The standard free energy change, $\Delta G°$, occurs when all components of the system are in their standard states. Standard state is defined as 1 bar for gases, 1 mol/L for solutes, and pure solids and liquids. Standard state does not specify a temperature because standard state can occur at any temperature. $\Delta G° = \Delta G$ when all concentrations equal 1 mol/L and all partial pressures equal 1 bar. This occurs because the value of $Q = 1$ and $\ln Q = 0$ in the equation $\Delta G = \Delta G° + RT \ln Q$.

18.68   Plan: For each reaction, first find $\Delta G°$, then calculate K from $\Delta G° = -RT \ln K$. Calculate $\Delta_r G°$ using $\Delta_f G°$ values in the relationship $\Delta_r G° = \Sigma m \Delta_{f(products)} G° - \Sigma n \Delta_{f(reactants)} G°$.

Solution:
a) $\Delta_r G° = \Sigma m \Delta_{f(products)} G° - \Sigma n \Delta_{f(reactants)} G°$

$\Delta_r G° = [(\Delta_f G° \text{ of } NO_2)] - [(\Delta_f G° \text{ of } NO) + (1/2)(\Delta_f G° \text{ of } O_2)]$

$\Delta_r G° = [(51 \text{ kJ/mol})] - [(86.60 \text{ kJ/mol}) + (1/2)(0 \text{ kJ/mol})] = -35.6 \text{ kJ/mol}$

$\Delta G° = -RT \ln K$

$\ln K = \dfrac{\Delta G°}{-RT} = \left(\dfrac{-35.6 \text{ kJ/mol}}{-(8.314 \text{ J/mol•K})(298 \text{ K})}\right)\left(\dfrac{10^3 \text{ J}}{1 \text{ kJ}}\right) = 14.3689$

$K = e^{14.3689} = 1.7391377 \times 10^6 = \mathbf{1.7 \times 10^6}$

b) $\Delta_r G° = [(\Delta_f G° \text{ of } H_2) + (\Delta_f G° \text{ of } Cl_2)] - [(2)(\Delta_f G° \text{ of } HCl)]$

$\Delta_r G° = [(0 \text{ kJ/mol}) + (0 \text{ kJ/mol})] - [(2)(-95.30 \text{ kJ/mol})] = 190.60 \text{ kJ/mol}$

$\ln K = \dfrac{\Delta G°}{-RT} = \left(\dfrac{190.60 \text{ kJ/mol}}{-(8.314 \text{ J/mol•K})(298 \text{ K})}\right)\left(\dfrac{10^3 \text{ J}}{1 \text{ kJ}}\right) = -76.930$

$K = e^{-76.930} = 3.88799 \times 10^{-34} = \mathbf{3.89 \times 10^{-34}}$

c) $\Delta_r G° = [(2)(\Delta_f G° \text{ of } CO)] - [(2)(\Delta_f G° \text{ of } C) + (\Delta_f G° \text{ of } O_2)]$

$\Delta_r G° = [(2)(-137.2 \text{ kJ/mol})] - [(2)(0 \text{ kJ/mol}) + (0 \text{ kJ/mol})] = 274.4 \text{ kJ/mol}$

$\ln K = \dfrac{\Delta G°}{-RT} = \left(\dfrac{-274.4 \text{ kJ/mol}}{-(8.314 \text{ J/mol•K})(298 \text{ K})}\right)\left(\dfrac{10^3 \text{ J}}{1 \text{ kJ}}\right) = 110.75359$

$K = e^{110.75359} = 1.2579778 \times 10^{48} = \mathbf{1.26 \times 10^{48}}$

Note: You may get a different answer depending on how you rounded in earlier calculations.

18.70 Plan: For each reaction, first find $\Delta G°$, then calculate K from $\Delta G° = -RT \ln K$. Calculate $\Delta G°$ using $\Delta_f G°$ values in the relationship $\Delta_r G° = \sum m \Delta_{f \text{(products)}} G° - \sum n \Delta_{f \text{(reactants)}} G°$.

Solution:

a) $\Delta_r G° = \sum m \Delta_{f \text{(products)}} G° - \sum n \Delta_{f \text{(reactants)}} G°$

$\Delta_r G° = [(2)(\Delta_f G° \text{ of } H_2O) + (2)(\Delta_f G° \text{ of } SO_2)]$

$\qquad\qquad - [(2)(\Delta_f G° \text{ of } H_2S) + (3)(\Delta_f G° \text{ of } O_2)]$

$\Delta_r G° = [(2)(-228.60 \text{ kJ/mol}) + (2)(-300.2 \text{ kJ/mol})] - [(2)(-33 \text{ kJ/mol}) + (3)(0 \text{ kJ/mol})]$

$\Delta_r G° = -991.6 \text{ kJ/mol}$

$\ln K = \dfrac{\Delta G°}{-RT} = \left(\dfrac{-991.6 \text{ kJ/mol}}{-(8.314 \text{ J/mol•K})(298 \text{ K})}\right)\left(\dfrac{10^3 \text{ J}}{1 \text{ kJ}}\right) = 400.2305$

$K = e^{400.2305} = 6.571696 \times 10^{173} = \mathbf{6.57 \times 10^{173}}$

Comment: Depending on how you round $\Delta_r G°$, the value for K can vary by a factor of 2 or 3 because the inverse natural log varies greatly with small changes in $\Delta_r G°$. Your calculator might register "error" when trying to calculate e^{400} because it cannot calculate exponents greater than 99. In this case, divide 400.2305 by 2 (= 200.115), and calculate $e^{200.115} e^{200.115} = (8.1066 \times 10^{86})^2 = (8.1066)^2 \times 10^{86 \times 2} = 65.71696 \times 10^{172}$ $= 6.5 \times 10^{173}$, which equals the first answer with rounding errors.

b) $\Delta_r G° = [(\Delta_f G° \text{ of } H_2O) + (\Delta_f G° \text{ of } SO_3)] - [(\Delta_f G° \text{ of } H_2SO_4)]$

$\Delta_r G° = [(-237.192 \text{ kJ/mol}) + (-371 \text{ kJ/mol})] - [(-690.059 \text{ kJ/mol})]$

$\Delta_r G° = 81.867 \text{ kJ/mol}$

$\ln K = \dfrac{\Delta G°}{-RT} = \left(\dfrac{81.867 \text{ kJ/mol}}{-(8.314 \text{ J/mol•K})(298 \text{ K})}\right)\left(\dfrac{10^3 \text{ J}}{1 \text{ kJ}}\right) = -33.0432$

$K = e^{-33.0432} = 4.4619 \times 10^{-15} = \mathbf{4.46 \times 10^{-15}}$

c) $\Delta_r G^\circ = [(\Delta_f G^\circ$ of NaCN$) + (\Delta_f G^\circ$ of H$_2$O$)]$

$$- [(\Delta_f G^\circ \text{ of HCN}) + (\Delta_f G^\circ \text{ of NaOH})]$$

NaCN(aq) and NaOH(aq) are not listed in Appendix B.
Converting the equation to net ionic form will simplify the problem:

$$\text{HCN}(aq) + \text{OH}^-(aq) \rightleftharpoons \text{CN}^-(aq) + \text{H}_2\text{O}(l)$$

$\Delta_r G^\circ = [(\Delta_f G^\circ$ of CN$^-) + (\Delta_f G^\circ$ of H$_2$O$)]$

$$- [(\Delta_f G^\circ \text{ of HCN}) + (\Delta_f G^\circ \text{ of OH}^-)]$$

$\Delta_r G^\circ = [(166 \text{ kJ/mol}) + (-237.192 \text{ kJ/mol})]$

$$- [(112 \text{ kJ/mol}) + (-157.30 \text{ kJ/mol})]$$

$\Delta_r G^\circ = -25.892 \text{ kJ/mol}$

$$\ln K = \frac{\Delta G^\circ}{-RT} = \left(\frac{-25.892 \text{ kJ/mol}}{-(8.314 \text{ J/mol·K})(298 \text{ K})}\right)\left(\frac{10^3 \text{ J}}{1 \text{ kJ}}\right) = 10.45055$$

$K = e^{10.45055} = 3.4563 \times 10^4 = \mathbf{3.46 \times 10^4}$

18.72 <u>Plan:</u> Write the balanced equation. First find ΔG°, then calculate K from $\Delta G^\circ = -RT \ln K$. Calculate ΔG° using

$\Delta_f G^\circ$ values in the relationship $\Delta_r G^\circ = \Sigma m \Delta_{f\,(\text{products})} G^\circ - \Sigma n \Delta_{f\,(\text{reactants})} G^\circ$.

<u>Solution:</u>
The solubility reaction for Ag$_2$S is

$$\text{Ag}_2\text{S}(s) + \text{H}_2\text{O}(l) \rightleftharpoons 2\text{Ag}^+(aq) + \text{HS}^-(aq) + \text{OH}^-(aq)$$

$\Delta_r G^\circ = \Sigma m \Delta_r G^\circ - \Sigma n \Delta_{f\,(\text{reactants})} G^\circ$

$\Delta_r G^\circ = [(2)(\Delta_f G^\circ$ of Ag$^+) + (\Delta_f G^\circ$ of HS$^-) + (\Delta_f G^\circ$ of OH$^-]$

$$- [(\Delta_f G^\circ \text{ of Ag}_2\text{S}) + (\Delta_f G^\circ \text{ of H}_2\text{O})]$$

$\Delta_r G^\circ = [(2)(77.111 \text{ kJ/mol}) + (12.6 \text{ kJ/mol}) + (-157.30 \text{ kJ/mol})]$

$$- [(-40.3 \text{ kJ/mol}) + (-237.192 \text{ kJ/mol})]$$

$\Delta_r G^\circ = 287.014 \text{ kJ/mol}$

$$\ln K = \frac{\Delta G^\circ}{-RT} = \left(\frac{287.014 \text{ kJ/mol}}{-(8.314 \text{ J/mol·K})(298 \text{ K})}\right)\left(\frac{10^3 \text{ J}}{1 \text{ kJ}}\right) = -115.8448675$$

$K = e^{-115.8448675} = 4.8889241 \times 10^{-51} = \mathbf{4.89 \times 10^{-51}}$

18.74 <u>Plan:</u> First find ΔG°, then calculate K from $\Delta G^\circ = -RT \ln K$. Calculate ΔG° using $\Delta_f G^\circ$ values in the relationship

$\Delta_r G^\circ = \Sigma m \Delta_{f\,(\text{products})} G^\circ - \Sigma n \Delta_{f\,(\text{reactants})} G^\circ$. Recognize that I$_2$($s$), not I$_2$($g$), is the standard state for iodine.

<u>Solution:</u>

$\text{I}_2(g) + \text{Cl}_2(g) \rightleftharpoons 2 \text{ ICl} g)$ $\quad \Delta_r G^\circ = \Sigma m \Delta_{f\,(\text{products})} G^\circ - \Sigma n \Delta_{f\,(\text{reactants})} G^\circ$

$\Delta_r G^\circ = [(2)(\Delta_f G^\circ$ of ICl$)] - [(\Delta_f G^\circ$ of I$_2) + (\Delta_f G^\circ$ of Cl$_2)]$

$\Delta_r G^\circ = [(2)(-6.075 \text{ kJ/mol})] - [(19.38 \text{ kJ/mol}) + (0 \text{ kJ/mol})]$

$\Delta_r G^\circ = -31.53 \text{ kJ/mol}$

$$\ln K = \frac{\Delta G^\circ}{-RT} = \left(\frac{-31.53 \text{ kJ/mol}}{-(8.314 \text{ J/mol·K})(298 \text{ K})}\right)\left(\frac{10^3 \text{ J}}{1 \text{ kJ}}\right) = 12.726169$$

$K = e^{12.726169} = 3.3643794 \times 10^5 = \mathbf{3.36 \times 10^5}$

18.76   Plan: The equilibrium constant, K, is related to $\Delta G°$ through the equation $\Delta G° = -RT \ln K$.
Solution:
$\Delta G° = -RT \ln K = -(8.314 \text{ J/mol•K})(298 \text{ K}) \ln (1.7\text{x}10^{-5}) = 2.72094\text{x}10^4 \text{ J/mol} = \textbf{2.7x10}^4 \textbf{ J/mol}$
The large positive $\Delta G°$ indicates that it would not be possible to prepare a solution with the concentrations of lead and chloride ions at the standard-state concentration of 1 mol/L. A Q calculation using 1 mol/L solutions will confirm this: $PbCl_2(s) \rightleftharpoons Pb^{2+}(aq) + 2Cl^{-}(aq)$

$$Q = [Pb^{2+}][Cl^{-}]^2$$
$$= (1 \text{ mol/L})(1 \text{ mol/L})^2$$
$$= 1$$

Since $Q > K_{sp}$, it is impossible to prepare a standard-state solution of $Pb^{2+}(aq)$ and $Cl^{-}(aq)$.

18.78   Plan: The equilibrium constant, K, is related to $\Delta G°$ through the equation $\Delta G° = -RT \ln K$. ΔG is found by using the relationship $\Delta G = \Delta G° + RT \ln Q$.
Solution:
a) $\Delta G° = -RT \ln K = -(8.314 \text{ J/mol•K})(298 \text{ K}) \ln (9.1\text{x}10^{-6}) = 2.875776\text{x}10^4 \text{ J/mol} = \textbf{2.9x10}^4 \textbf{ J/mol}$

b) Since $\Delta_r G°$ is positive, the reaction direction as written is nonspontaneous. The reverse direction, formation of reactants, is spontaneous, so the reaction proceeds to the left.

c) Calculate the value for Q and then use it to find ΔG.

$$Q = \frac{\left[Fe^{2+}\right]^2 \left[Hg^{2+}\right]^2}{\left[Fe^{3+}\right]^2 \left[Hg_2^{2+}\right]} = \frac{[0.010]^2 [0.025]^2}{[0.20]^2 [0.010]} = 1.5625\text{x}10^{-4}$$

$\Delta_{298} G = \Delta G° + RT \ln Q = 2.875776\text{x}10^4 \text{ J/mol} + (8.314 \text{ J/mol•K})(298 \text{ K}) \ln (1.5625\text{x}10^{-4})$
$\quad = 7.044187\text{x}10^3 \text{ J/mol} = \textbf{7.0x10}^3 \textbf{ J/mol}$
Because $\Delta_{298} G > 0$ and $Q > K$, the reaction proceeds to the left to reach equilibrium.

18.80   Plan: To decide when production of ozone is favored, both the signs of $\Delta_r H°$ and $\Delta_r S°$ for ozone are needed. The values of $\Delta_f H°$ and $S°$ can be used. Once $\Delta_r H°$ and $\Delta_r S°$ are known, $\Delta G°$ can be calculated with the relationship $\Delta_r G° = \Delta_r H° - T\Delta_r S°$. $\Delta_r S°$ values in J/mol•K must be converted to units of kJ/mol•K to match the units of $\Delta_r H°$. ΔG is found by using the relationship $\Delta G = \Delta G° + RT \ln Q$.

Solution:
a) Formation of O_3 from O_2 : $3O_2(g) \rightleftharpoons 2O_3(g)$ or per mole of ozone: $3/2 O_2(g) \rightleftharpoons O_3(g)$.

$\Delta_r H° = \Sigma m \Delta_{f \text{(products)}} H° - \Sigma n \Delta_{f \text{(reactants)}} H°$

$\Delta_r H° = [(1 \text{ mol } O_3)(\Delta_f H° \text{ of } O_3)] - [(3/2 \text{ mol } O_2)(\Delta_f H° \text{ of } O_2)]$

$\Delta_r H° = [(143 \text{ kJ/mol}] - [(3/2)(0 \text{ kJ/mol})] = 143 \text{ kJ/mol}$

$\Delta_r S° = \Sigma m S°_{\text{products}} - \Sigma n S°_{\text{reactants}}$

$\Delta_r S° = [(S° \text{ of } O_3)] - [(3/2)(S° \text{ of } O_2)]$

$\Delta_r S° = [(238.82 \text{ J/mol•K}] - [(3/2)(205.0 \text{ J/mol•K})] = -68.68 \text{ J/mol•K} = -0.06868 \text{ kJ/mol•K}$

The positive sign for $\Delta_r H°$ and the negative sign for $\Delta_r S°$ indicates the formation of ozone is favored at **no temperature**. The reaction is not thermodynamically allowed at any temperature.

b) $\Delta_r G° = \Delta_r H° - T\Delta_r S°$

$\Delta_r G° = 143 \text{ kJ/mol} - [(298 \text{ K})(-0.06868 \text{ J/mol•K })] = 163.46664 \text{ kJ/mol} = \textbf{163 kJ/mol}$ for the formation of one mole of O_3.

c) Calculate the value for Q and then use to find ΔG.

$$Q = \frac{p_{O_3}}{p_{O_2}^{3/2}} = \frac{\left(5\times10^{-7}\ \text{bar}\right)}{\left(0.21\ \text{bar}\right)^{3/2}} = 5.195664\times10^{-6}$$

$\Delta G = \Delta G^\circ + RT \ln Q = 163$ kJ/mol $+ (8.314$ J/mol•K$)(298$ K$)(1$ kJ$/10^3$ J$) \ln (5.195664\times10^{-6})$
$= 132.85368$ kJ/mol$= \mathbf{1\times10^2\ kJ/mol}$

18.83

	$\Delta_r S$	$\Delta_r H$	$\Delta_r G$	Comment
(a)	+	–	–	**Thermodynamically allowed**
(b)	(+)	0	–	**Thermodynamically allowed**
(c)	–	+	(+)	**Not thermodynamically allowed**
(d)	0	(–)	–	**Thermodynamically allowed**
(e)	(–)	0	+	**Not thermodynamically allowed**
(f)	+	+	(–)	$T\Delta S > \Delta H$

a) The reaction is always thermodynamically allowed when $\Delta_r G < 0$, so there is no need to look at the other values other than to check the answer.
b) Because $\Delta_r G = \Delta H - T\Delta S = -T\Delta S$, ΔS must be positive for $\Delta_r G$ to be negative.
c) The reaction is always nonspontaneous when $\Delta_r G > 0$, so there is no need to look at the other values other than to check the answer.
d) Because $\Delta_r G = \Delta H - T\Delta S = \Delta H$, ΔH must be negative for $\Delta_r G$ to be negative.
e) Because $\Delta_r G = \Delta H - T\Delta S = -T\Delta S$, ΔS must be negative for $\Delta_r G$ to be positive.
f) Because $T\Delta S > \Delta H$, the subtraction of a larger positive term causes $\Delta_r G$ to be negative.

18.87 Plan: Write the equilibrium expression for the reaction. The equilibrium constant, K, is related to ΔG° through the equation $\Delta G^\circ = -RT \ln K$. Once K is known, the ratio of the two species is known.
Solution:

a) For the reaction, $K = \dfrac{[\text{Hb•CO}][O_2]}{[\text{Hb•}O_2][\text{CO}]}$. Since the problem states that $[O_2] = [\text{CO}]$, we can use the K_c as the

thermodymic equilibrium constant; the K expression simplifies to: $K = \dfrac{[\text{Hb•CO}]}{[\text{Hb•}O_2]}$

$$\ln K = \frac{\Delta G^\circ}{-RT} = \left(\frac{-14\ \text{kJ/mol}}{-(8.314\ \text{J/mol•K})((273+37)\text{K})}\right)\left(\frac{10^3\ \text{J}}{1\ \text{kJ}}\right) = 5.431956979$$

$$K = e^{5.431956979} = 228.596 = \mathbf{2.3\times10^2} = \frac{[\text{Hb•CO}]}{[\text{Hb•}O_2]}$$

b) By increasing the concentration of oxygen, the equilibrium can be shifted in the direction of Hb•O_2. Administer oxygen-rich air to counteract the CO poisoning.

18.89 Plan: Sum the two reactions to yield an overall reaction. Use the relationship $\Delta_r G^\circ = \Delta_r H^\circ - T\Delta_r S^\circ$ to calculate $\Delta_r G^\circ$. $\Delta_r H^\circ$ and $\Delta_r S^\circ$ will have to be calculated first.
Solution:

$$UO_2(s) + 4HF(g) \rightarrow \cancel{UF_4(s)} + 2H_2O(g)$$
$$\underline{\cancel{UF_4(s)} + F_2(g) \rightarrow UF_6(s)}$$
$$UO_2(s) + 4\ HF(g) + F_2(g) \rightarrow UF_6(g) + 2H_2O(g) \text{ (overall process)}$$

$\Delta_r H^\circ = \sum m \Delta_{f\,(\text{products})} H^\circ - \sum n \Delta_{f\,(\text{reactants})} H^\circ$

$\Delta_r H^\circ = [(\Delta_f H^\circ \text{ of } UF_6) + (2)(\Delta_f H^\circ \text{ of } H_2O)]$

$\qquad - [(\Delta_f H^\circ \text{ of } UO_2) + (4)(\Delta_f H^\circ \text{ of } HF) + (\Delta_f H^\circ \text{ of } F_2)]$

$\Delta_r H^\circ = [(-2197 \text{ kJ/mol}) + (2)(-241.826 \text{ kJ/mol})]$

$\qquad - [(-1085 \text{ kJ/mol}) + (4)(-273 \text{ kJ/mol}) + (0 \text{ kJ/mol})]$

$\Delta_r H^\circ = -503.652 \text{ kJ/mol}$

$\Delta_r S^\circ = \sum m\, S^\circ_{products} - \sum n\, S^\circ_{reactants}$

$\Delta_r S^\circ = [(S^\circ \text{ of } UF_6) + (2)(S^\circ \text{ of } H_2O)]$

$\qquad - [(S^\circ \text{ of } UO_2) + (4)(S^\circ \text{ of } HF) + (S^\circ \text{ of } F_2)]$

$\Delta_r S^\circ = [(225 \text{ J/mol•K}) + (2)(188.72 \text{ J/mol•K})]$

$\qquad - [(77.0 \text{ J/mol•K}) + (4)(173.67 \text{ J/mol•K}) + (202.7 \text{ J/mol•K})]$

$\Delta_r S^\circ = -371.94 \text{ J/mol•K}$

$\Delta_r G^\circ = \Delta_r H^\circ - T\Delta_r S^\circ = (-503.652 \text{ kJ/mol}) - ((273 + 85)\text{K})(-371.94 \text{ J/mol•K})(\text{kJ}/10^3 \text{ J}) = -370.497 \text{ kJ/mol}$

$\qquad = \mathbf{-370. \ kJ/mol}$

18.91 Plan: $\Delta_r G^\circ$ can be calculated with the relationship $\sum m\, \Delta_{f\,(products)}G^\circ - \sum n\, \Delta_{f\,(reactants)}G^\circ$. ΔG is found by using the relationship $\Delta G = \Delta G^\circ + RT \ln Q$.
Solution:
a) $2N_2O_5(g) + 6F_2(g) \rightarrow 4NF_3(g) + 5O_2(g)$
b) $\Delta_r G^\circ = \sum m\, \Delta_{f\,(products)}G^\circ - \sum n\, \Delta_{f\,(reactants)}G^\circ$

$\Delta_r G^\circ = [(4)(\Delta_f G^\circ \text{ of } NF_3) + (5)(\Delta_f G^\circ \text{ of } O_2)]$

$\qquad - [(2)(\Delta_f G^\circ \text{ of } N_2O_5)) + (6)(\Delta_f G^\circ \text{ of } F_2)]$

$\Delta_r G^\circ = [(4)(-83.3 \text{ kJ/mol})) + (5)(0 \text{ kJ/mol})] - [(2)(118 \text{ kJ/mol}) + (6)(0 \text{ kJ/mol})]$

$\Delta_r G^\circ = -569.2 \text{ kJ/mol} = \mathbf{-569 \ kJ/mol}$

c) Calculate the value for Q and then use to find ΔG.

$$Q = \frac{p^4_{NF_3}\, p^5_{O_2}}{p^2_{N_2O_5}\, p^6_{F_2}} = \frac{(0.25 \text{ bar})^4 (0.50 \text{ bar})^5}{(0.20 \text{ bar})^2 (0.20 \text{ bar})^6} = 47.6837$$

$\Delta G = \Delta G^\circ + RT \ln Q = -569.2 \text{ kJ/mol} + (1 \text{ kJ}/10^3 \text{ J})(8.314 \text{ J/mol•K})(298 \text{ K}) \ln (47.6837)$

$\qquad = -559.625 \text{ kJ/mol} = \mathbf{-5.60 \times 10^2 \ kJ/mol}$

18.93 Plan: $\Delta_r H^\circ$ can be calculated from the individual $\Delta_f H^\circ$ values of the reactants and products by using the relationship $\Delta_r H^\circ = \sum m\, \Delta_{f\,(products)}H^\circ - \sum n\, \Delta_{f\,(reactants)}H^\circ$. $\Delta_r S^\circ$ can be calculated from the individual S° values of the reactants and products by using the relationship $\Delta_r S^\circ = \sum m\, S^\circ_{products} - \sum n\, S^\circ_{reactants}$. $\Delta_r G^\circ$ can be calculated with the relationship $\sum m\, \Delta_{f\,(products)}G^\circ - \sum n\, \Delta_{f\,(reactants)}G^\circ$.
Solution:
The reaction for the hydrogenation of ethene is $C_2H_4(g) + H_2(g) \rightarrow C_2H_6(g)$.

$\Delta_r H^\circ = \sum m\, \Delta_{f\,(products)}H^\circ - \sum n\, \Delta_{f\,(reactants)}H^\circ$

$\Delta_r H^\circ = [(\Delta_f H^\circ \text{ of } C_2H_6)] - [(\Delta_f H^\circ \text{ of } C_2H_4) + (\Delta_f H^\circ \text{ of } H_2)]$

$\qquad = \mathbf{[(-84.667 \ kJ/mol)] - [(52.47 \ kJ/mol) + (0 \ kJ/mol)] = -137.137 \ kJ/mol = -137.14 \ kJ/mol}$

$\Delta_r S^\circ = \sum m\, S^\circ_{products} - \sum n\, S^\circ_{reactants}$

$\Delta_r S° = [(S° \text{ of } C_2H_6)] - [(S° \text{ of } C_2H_4)) + (S° \text{ of } H_2)]$

$= [(229.5 \text{ J/mol•K})] - [(219.22 \text{ J/mol•K}) + (130.6 \text{ J/mol•K})] = -120.32 \text{ J/mol•K} = \mathbf{-120.3 \text{ J/mol•K}}$

$\Delta_r G° = \sum m \Delta_{f(products)}G° - \sum n \Delta_{f(reactants)}G°$

$\Delta_r G° = [(\Delta_f G° \text{ of } C_2H_6))] - [(\Delta_f G° \text{ of } C_2H_4) + (\Delta_f G° \text{ of } H_2)]$

$= (-32.89 \text{ kJ/mol})] - [(68.36 \text{ kJ/mol}) + (0 \text{ kJ/mol})] = \mathbf{-101.25 \text{ kJ/mol}}$

18.101 Plan: Use the relationship $\Delta G_8° = -RT \ln K$ to calculate $\Delta G°$. Use the relationship $\Delta G = \Delta G° + RT \ln Q$ to calculate ΔG.

Solution:

The given equilibrium is: G6P $\rightleftharpoons$ F6P $K = 0.510$ at 298 K

a) $\Delta G° = -RT \ln K$

$= - (8.314 \text{ J/mol•K})(298 \text{ K}) \ln (0.510) = 1.6682596 \times 10^3 \text{ J/mol} = \mathbf{1.67 \times 10^3 \text{ J/mol}}$

b) $Q = [\text{F6P}]/[\text{G6P}] = 10.0$

$\Delta G = \Delta G° + RT \ln Q$

$\Delta G = 1.6682596 \times 10^3 \text{ J/mol} + (8.314 \text{ J/mol•K})(298 \text{ K}) \ln 10.0$

$\Delta G = 7.3730799 \times 10^3 \text{ J/mol} = \mathbf{7.37 \times 10^3 \text{ J/mol}}$

c) Repeat the calculation in part b) with $Q = 0.100$

$\Delta G = 1.6682596 \times 10^3 \text{ J/mol} + (8.314 \text{ J/mol•K})(298 \text{ K}) \ln 0.100$

$\Delta G = -4.0365607 \times 10^3 \text{ J/mol} = \mathbf{-4.04 \times 10^3 \text{ J/mol}}$

d) $\Delta G = \Delta G° + RT \ln Q$

$(-2.50 \text{ kJ/mol})(10^3 \text{ J/1 kJ}) = 1.6682596 \times 10^3 \text{ J/mol} + (8.314 \text{ J/mol•K})(298 \text{ K}) \ln Q$

$(-4.1682596 \times 10^3 \text{ J/mol}) = (8.314 \text{ J/mol•K})(298 \text{ K}) \ln Q$

$\ln Q = (-4.1682596 \times 10^3 \text{ J/mol})/[(8.314 \text{ J/mol•K})(298 \text{ K})] = -1.68239696$

$Q = 0.18592778 = \mathbf{0.19}$

18.105 Plan: First calculate $\Delta H°$ and $\Delta S°$. According to the relationship $\ln K = \dfrac{\Delta G°}{-RT}$, since $\ln K = 0$ when $K = 1.00$,

$\Delta G° = 0$. Use the relationship $\Delta G° = 0 = \Delta H° - T\Delta S°$ to find the temperature. For part b), calculate $\Delta G°$ at the

higher temperature with the relationship $\Delta G° = \Delta H° - T\Delta S°$ and then calculate K with $\ln K = \dfrac{\Delta G°}{-RT}$.

Solution:

a) $\Delta H° = \sum m \Delta_{f(products)}H° - \sum n \Delta_{f(reactants)}H°$

$\Delta H° = [(2)(\Delta_f H° \text{ of } NH_3)] - [(\Delta_f H° \text{ of } N_2) + (3)(\Delta_f H° \text{ of } H_2)]$

$\Delta H° = [(2)(-45.9 \text{ kJ/mol})] - [(0 \text{ kJ/mol}) + (3)(0 \text{ kJ/mol})] = -91.8 \text{ kJ/mol}$

$\Delta S° = \sum m S°_{products} - \sum n S°_{reactants}$

$\Delta S° = [(2)(S° \text{ of } NH_3)] - [(S° \text{ of } N_2) + (3)(S° \text{ of } H_2)]$

$\Delta S° = [(2)(193 \text{ J/mol•K})] - [(191.50 \text{ J/mol•K}) + (3)(130.6 \text{ J/mol•K})]$

$\Delta S° = -197.3 \text{ J/mol•K}$

$\ln K = \dfrac{\Delta G°}{-RT}$

Since $\ln K = 0$ when $K = 1.00$, $\Delta G° = 0$.

$\Delta G° = 0 = \Delta H° - T\Delta S°$

$\Delta H° = T\Delta S°$

$$T = \frac{\Delta H^{\circ}}{\Delta S^{\circ}} = \frac{-91.8 \text{ kJ/mol}}{-197.3 \text{ J/K}\cdot\text{mol}}\left(\frac{10^3 \text{ J}}{1 \text{ kJ}}\right) = 465.281 \text{ K} = \mathbf{465\ K}$$

b) $\Delta G^{\circ} = \Delta H^{\circ} - T\Delta S^{\circ} = (-91.8 \text{ kJ/mol})(10^3 \text{ J}/1 \text{ kJ}) - (673 \text{ K})(-197.3 \text{ J/mol}\cdot\text{K}) = 4.09829\text{x}10^4 \text{ J/mol}$

$$\ln K = \frac{\Delta G^{\circ}}{-RT} = \left(\frac{4.09829\text{x}10^4 \text{ J/mol}}{-(8.314 \text{ J/mol}\cdot\text{K})(673 \text{ K})}\right) = -7.32449$$

$$K = e^{-7.32449} = 6.591958\text{x}10^{-4} = \mathbf{6.59\text{x}10^{-4}}$$

c) The reaction rate is higher at the higher temperature. The time required (kinetics) overshadows the lower yield (thermodynamics).

CHAPTER 19 ELECTROCHEMISTRY: CHEMICAL CHANGE AND ELECTRICAL WORK

CHEMICAL CONNECTIONS BOXED READING PROBLEMS

B19.1   Plan: Reduction is the gain of electrons while oxidation is the loss of electrons.
Solution:
a) Reduction: $Fe^{3+} + e^- \rightarrow Fe^{2+}$
   Oxidation: $Cu^+ \rightarrow Cu^{2+} + e^-$

b) Overall: $Fe^{3+} + Cu^+ \rightarrow Fe^{2+} + Cu^{2+}$

END–OF–CHAPTER PROBLEMS

19.1   Oxidation is the loss of electrons (resulting in a higher oxidation number), while reduction is the gain of electrons (resulting in a lower oxidation number). In an oxidation-reduction reaction, electrons transfer from the oxidized substance to the reduced substance. The oxidation number of the reactant being oxidized increases while the oxidation number of the reactant being reduced decreases.

19.3   **No**, one half-reaction cannot take place independently of the other because there is always a transfer of electrons from one substance to another. If one substance loses electrons (oxidation half-reaction), another substance must gain those electrons (reduction half-reaction).

19.6   To remove protons from an equation, add an equal number of hydroxide ions to both sides to neutralize the H^+ and produce water: $H^+(aq) + OH^-(aq) \rightarrow H_2O(l)$.

19.8   (a) Spontaneous reactions, $\Delta_{sys}G < 0$, take place in voltaic cells, which are also called galvanic cells.
(b) Nonspontaneous reactions take place in electrolytic cells and result in an increase in the free energy of the cell ($\Delta_{sys}G > 0$).

19.10   Plan: Assign oxidation numbers; the species with an atom whose oxidation number has increased is being oxidized and is the reducing agent. The species with an atom whose oxidation number has decreased is being reduced and is the oxidizing agent. Electrons flow from the reducing agent to the oxidizing agent. To write the molecular equation, pair K^+ ions with anions and SO_4^{2-} ions with cations to form neutral molecules.
Solution:

$$\overset{-8}{}$$
$$\overset{+1}{} \quad \overset{+7 \; -2}{} \qquad \overset{-1}{} \qquad \overset{+2}{} \qquad \overset{0}{} \qquad \overset{+2}{\overset{+1 \; -2}{}}$$
$$16H^+(aq) + 2MnO_4^-(aq) + 10Cl^-(aq) \rightarrow 2Mn^{2+}(aq) + 5Cl_2(g) + 8H_2O(l)$$

a) To decide which reactant is oxidized, look at oxidation numbers. **Cl⁻** is oxidized because its oxidation number increases from –1 in Cl^- to 0 in Cl_2.
b) **MnO_4^-** is reduced because the oxidation number of Mn decreases from +7 in MnO_4^- to +2 in Mn^{2+}.
c) The oxidizing agent is the substance that causes the oxidation by accepting electrons. The oxidizing agent is the substance reduced in the reaction, so **MnO_4^-** is the oxidizing agent.
d) **Cl⁻** is the reducing agent because it loses the electrons that are gained in the reduction.
e) **From Cl⁻**, which is losing electrons, **to MnO_4^-**, which is gaining electrons.
f) $8H_2SO_4(aq) + 2KMnO_4(aq) + 10KCl(aq) \rightarrow 2MnSO_4(aq) + 5Cl_2(g) + 8H_2O(l) + 6K_2SO_4(aq)$

19.12   Plan: Divide the reaction into the two half-reactions, balance elements other than oxygen and hydrogen, and then balance oxygen by adding H_2O and hydrogen by adding H^+. Balance the charge by adding electrons and multiply each half-reaction by an integer so that the number of electrons lost equals the number of electrons gained. Add the half-reactions together, canceling substances that appear on both sides. For basic solutions, add one OH⁻ ion to each side of the equation for every H⁺ ion present to form H_2O and cancel excess H_2O molecules. The substance that gains electrons is the oxidizing agent while the substance that loses electrons is the reducing agent.

Solution:

a) Divide into half-reactions:

$ClO_3^-(aq) \rightarrow Cl^-(aq)$

$I^-(aq) \rightarrow I_2(s)$

Balance elements other than O and H:

$ClO_3^-(aq) \rightarrow Cl^-(aq)$	chlorine is balanced
$2I^-(aq) \rightarrow I_2(s)$	iodine now balanced

Balance O by adding H_2O:

$ClO_3^-(aq) \rightarrow Cl^-(aq) + 3H_2O(l)$	add three waters to add three O atoms to product
$2I^-(aq) \rightarrow I_2(s)$	no change

Balance H by adding H⁺:

$ClO_3^-(aq) + 6H^+(aq) \rightarrow Cl^-(aq) + 3H_2O(l)$	add six H⁺ to reactants
$2I^-(aq) \rightarrow I_2(s)$	no change

Balance charge by adding e⁻:

$ClO_3^-(aq) + 6H^+(aq) + 6e^- \rightarrow Cl^-(aq) + 3\ H_2O(l)$	add 6e⁻ to reactants for a –1 charge on each side
$2I^-(aq) \rightarrow I_2(s) + 2e^-$	add 2e⁻ to products for a –2 charge on each side

Multiply each half-reaction by an integer to equalize the number of electrons:

$ClO_3^-(aq) + 6H^+(aq) + 6e^- \rightarrow Cl^-(aq) + 3H_2O(l)$	multiply by one to give 6e⁻
$3\{2I^-(aq) \rightarrow I_2(s) + 2e^-\}$ or	multiply by three to give 6e⁻
$6I^-(aq) \rightarrow 3I_2(s) + 6e^-$	

Add half-reactions to give balanced equation in acidic solution:

$ClO_3^-(aq) + 6H^+(aq) + 6I^-(aq) \rightarrow Cl^-(aq) + 3H_2O(l) + 3I_2(s)$

Check balancing:

	Reactants:		Products:	
		1 Cl		1 Cl
		3 O		3 O
		6 H		6 H
		6 I		6 I
		–1 charge		–1 charge

Oxidizing agent is ClO_3^- and reducing agent is I^-.

b) Divide into half-reactions:

$MnO_4^-(aq) \rightarrow MnO_2(s)$

$SO_3^{2-}(aq) \rightarrow SO_4^{2-}(aq)$

Balance elements other than O and H:

$MnO_4^-(aq) \rightarrow MnO_2(s)$	Mn is balanced
$SO_3^{2-}(aq) \rightarrow SO_4^{2-}(aq)$	S is balanced

Balance O by adding H_2O:

$MnO_4^-(aq) \rightarrow MnO_2(s) + 2H_2O(l)$	add two H_2O to products
$SO_3^{2-}(aq) + H_2O(l) \rightarrow SO_4^{2-}(aq)$	add one H_2O to reactants

Balance H by adding H⁺:

$MnO_4^-(aq) + 4H^+(aq) \rightarrow MnO_2(s) + 2H_2O(l)$	add four H⁺ to reactants
$SO_3^{2-}(aq) + H_2O(l) \rightarrow SO_4^{2-}(aq) + 2H^+(aq)$	add two H⁺ to products

Balance charge by adding e⁻:

$MnO_4^-(aq) + 4H^+(aq) + 3e^- \rightarrow MnO_2(s) + 2H_2O(l)$	add 3e⁻ to reactants for a 0 charge on each side
$SO_3^{2-}(aq) + H_2O(l) \rightarrow SO_4^{2-}(aq) + 2H^+(aq) + 2e^-$	add 2e⁻ to products for a –2 charge on each side

Multiply each half-reaction by an integer to equalize the number of electrons:

$2\{MnO_4^-(aq) + 4H^+(aq) + 3e^- \rightarrow MnO_2(s) + 2H_2O(l)\}$ or	multiply by two to give 6e⁻
$2MnO_4^-(aq) + 8H^+(aq) + 6e^- \rightarrow 2MnO_2(s) + 4H_2O(l)$	
$3\{SO_3^{2-}(aq) + H_2O(l) \rightarrow SO_4^{2-}(aq) + 2H^+(aq) + 2e^-\}$ or	multiply by three to give 6e⁻
$3SO_3^{2-}(aq) + 3H_2O(l) \rightarrow 3SO_4^{2-}(aq) + 6H^+(aq) + 6e^-$	

Add half-reactions and cancel substances that appear as both reactants and products:

$2 \text{MnO}_4^-(aq) + \cancel{8\text{H}^+}(aq) + 3\text{SO}_3^{2-}(aq) + \cancel{3\text{H}_2\text{O}(l)} \rightarrow 2\text{MnO}_2(s) + 4\text{H}_2\text{O}(l) + 3\text{SO}_4^{2-}(aq) + \cancel{6\text{H}^+(aq)}$

The balanced equation in acidic solution is:

$2\text{MnO}_4^-(aq) + 2\text{H}^+(aq) + 3\text{SO}_3^{2-}(aq) \rightarrow 2\text{MnO}_2(s) + \text{H}_2\text{O}(l) + 3\text{SO}_4^{2-}(aq)$

To change to basic solution, add OH⁻ to both sides of equation to neutralize H⁺

$2\text{MnO}_4^-(aq) + 2\text{H}^+(aq) + 2\text{OH}^-(aq) + 3\text{SO}_3^{2-}(aq) \rightarrow 2\text{MnO}_2(s) + \text{H}_2\text{O}(l) + 3\text{SO}_4^{2-}(aq) + 2\text{OH}^-(aq)$

$2\text{MnO}_4^-(aq) + \cancel{2}\text{H}_2\text{O}(l) + 3\text{SO}_3^{2-}(aq) \rightarrow 2\text{MnO}_2(s) + \cancel{\text{H}_2\text{O}(l)} + 3\text{SO}_4^{2-}(aq) + 2\text{OH}^-(aq)$

Balanced equation in basic solution:

$2\text{MnO}_4^-(aq) + \text{H}_2\text{O}(l) + 3\text{SO}_3^{2-}(aq) \rightarrow 2\text{MnO}_2(s) + 3\text{SO}_4^{2-}(aq) + 2\text{OH}^-(aq)$

Check balancing:

	Reactants:		Products:	
		2 Mn		2 Mn
		18 O		18 O
		2 H		2 H
		3 S		3 S
		−8 charge		−8 charge

Oxidizing agent is MnO_4^- and reducing agent is SO_3^{2-}.

c) Divide into half-reactions:

$\text{MnO}_4^-(aq) \rightarrow \text{Mn}^{2+}(aq)$

$\text{H}_2\text{O}_2(aq) \rightarrow \text{O}_2(g)$

Balance elements other than O and H:

$\text{MnO}_4^-(aq) \rightarrow \text{Mn}^{2+}(aq)$ Mn is balanced

$\text{H}_2\text{O}_2(aq) \rightarrow \text{O}_2(g)$ No other elements to balance

Balance O by adding H_2O:

$\text{MnO}_4^-(aq) \rightarrow \text{Mn}^{2+}(aq) + 4\text{H}_2\text{O}(l)$ add four H_2O to products

$\text{H}_2\text{O}_2(aq) \rightarrow \text{O}_2(g)$ O is balanced

Balance H by adding H^+:

$\text{MnO}_4^-(aq) + 8\text{H}^+(aq) \rightarrow \text{Mn}^{2+}(aq) + 4\text{H}_2\text{O}(l)$ add eight H^+ to reactants

$\text{H}_2\text{O}_2(aq) \rightarrow \text{O}_2(g) + 2\text{H}^+(aq)$ add two H^+ to products

Balance charge by adding e⁻:

$\text{MnO}_4^-(aq) + 8\text{H}^+(aq) + 5\text{e}^- \rightarrow \text{Mn}^{2+}(aq) + 4\text{H}_2\text{O}(l)$ add 5e⁻ to reactants for +2 on each side

$\text{H}_2\text{O}_2(aq) \rightarrow \text{O}_2(g) + 2\text{H}^+(aq) + 2\text{e}^-$ add 2e⁻ to products for 0 charge on each side

Multiply each half-reaction by an integer to equalize the number of electrons:

$2\{\text{MnO}_4^-(aq) + 8\text{H}^+(aq) + 5\text{e}^- \rightarrow \text{Mn}^{2+}(aq) + 4\text{H}_2\text{O}(l)\}$ or   multiply by two to give 10e⁻

$2\text{MnO}_4^-(aq) + 16\text{H}^+(aq) + 10\text{e}^- \rightarrow 2\text{Mn}^{2+}(aq) + 8\text{H}_2\text{O}(l)$

$5\{\text{H}_2\text{O}_2(aq) \rightarrow \text{O}_2(g) + 2\text{H}^+(aq) + 2\text{e}^-\}$ or   multiply by five to give 10e⁻

$5\text{H}_2\text{O}_2(aq) \rightarrow 5\text{O}_2(g) + 10\text{H}^+(aq) + 10\text{e}^-$

Add half-reactions and cancel substances that appear as both reactants and products:

$2\text{MnO}_4^-(aq) + \cancel{16}\text{H}^+(aq) + 5\text{H}_2\text{O}_2(aq) \rightarrow 2\text{Mn}^{2+}(aq) + 8\text{H}_2\text{O}(l) + 5\text{O}_2(g) + \cancel{10\text{H}^+(aq)}$

The balanced equation in acidic solution:

$2\text{MnO}_4^-(aq) + 6\text{H}^+(aq) + 5\text{H}_2\text{O}_2(aq) \rightarrow 2\text{Mn}^{2+}(aq) + 8\text{H}_2\text{O}(l) + 5\text{O}_2(g)$

Check balancing:

	Reactants:		Products:	
		2 Mn		2 Mn
		18 O		18 O
		16 H		16 H
		+4 charge		+4 charge

Oxidizing agent is MnO_4^- and reducing agent is H_2O_2.

19.14   <u>Plan:</u> Divide the reaction into the two half-reactions, balance elements other than oxygen and hydrogen, and then balance oxygen by adding H_2O and hydrogen by adding H^+. Balance the charge by adding electrons and multiply each half-reaction by an integer so that the number of electrons lost equals the number of electrons gained. Add the half-reactions together, canceling substances that appear on both sides. For basic solutions, add one OH⁻ ion to each side of the equation for every H^+ ion present to form H_2O and cancel excess H_2O molecules. The substance that gains electrons is the oxidizing agent while the substance that loses electrons is the reducing agent.

Solution:
a) Balance the reduction half-reaction:

$$Cr_2O_7^{2-}(aq) \rightarrow 2Cr^{3+}(aq)$$ balance Cr

$$Cr_2O_7^{2-}(aq) \rightarrow 2Cr^{3+}(aq) + 7H_2O(l)$$ balance O by adding H_2O

$$Cr_2O_7^{2-}(aq) + 14H^+(aq) \rightarrow 2Cr^{3+}(aq) + 7H_2O(l)$$ balance H by adding H^+

$$Cr_2O_7^{2-}(aq) + 14H^+(aq) + 6e^- \rightarrow 2Cr^{3+}(aq) + 7H_2O(l)$$ balance charge by adding $6e^-$

Balance the oxidation half-reaction:

$$Zn(s) \rightarrow Zn^{2+}(aq) + 2e^-$$ balance charge by adding $2e^-$

Add the two half-reactions multiplying the oxidation half-reaction by three to equalize the electrons:

$$Cr_2O_7^{2-}(aq) + 14H^+(aq) + 6e^- \rightarrow 2Cr^{3+}(aq) + 7H_2O(l)$$

$$3Zn(s) \rightarrow 3Zn^{2+}(aq) + 6e^-$$

Add half-reactions and cancel substances that appear as both reactants and products:

$$Cr_2O_7^{2-}(aq) + 14H^+(aq) + 3Zn(s) \rightarrow 2Cr^{3+}(aq) + 7H_2O(l) + 3Zn^{2+}(aq)$$

Oxidizing agent is $Cr_2O_7^{2-}$ and reducing agent is Zn.

b) Balance the reduction half-reaction:

$$MnO_4^-(aq) \rightarrow MnO_2(s) + 2H_2O(l)$$ balance O by adding H_2O

$$MnO_4^-(aq) + 4H^+(aq) \rightarrow MnO_2(s) + 2H_2O(l)$$ balance H by adding H^+

$$MnO_4^-(aq) + 4H^+(aq) + 3e^- \rightarrow MnO_2(s) + 2H_2O(l)$$ balance charge by adding 3 e^-

Balance the oxidation half-reaction:

$$Fe(OH)_2(s) + H_2O(l) \rightarrow Fe(OH)_3(s)$$ balance O by adding H_2O

$$Fe(OH)_2(s) + H_2O(l) \rightarrow Fe(OH)_3(s) + H^+(aq)$$ balance H by adding H^+

$$Fe(OH)_2(s) + H_2O(l) \rightarrow Fe(OH)_3(s) + H^+(aq) + e^-$$ balance charge by adding $1e^-$

Add half-reactions after multiplying oxidation half-reaction by 3:

$$MnO_4^-(aq) + 4H^+(aq) + 3e^- \rightarrow MnO_2(s) + 2H_2O(l)$$

$$3Fe(OH)_2(s) + 3H_2O(l) \rightarrow 3Fe(OH)_3(s) + 3H^+(aq) + 3e^-$$

Add half-reactions and cancel substances that appear as both reactants and products:

$$MnO_4^-(aq) + 4H^+(aq) + 3Fe(OH)_2(s) + 3H_2O(l) \rightarrow MnO_2(s) + 2H_2O(l) + 3Fe(OH)_3(s) + 3H^+(aq)$$

$$MnO_4^-(aq) + H^+(aq) + 3Fe(OH)_2(s) + H_2O(l) \rightarrow MnO_2(s) + 3Fe(OH)_3(s)$$

Add OH^- to both sides to neutralize the H^+ and convert $H^+ + OH^- \rightarrow H_2O$:

$$MnO_4^-(aq) + H^+(aq) + OH^-(aq) + 3Fe(OH)_2(s) + H_2O(l) \rightarrow MnO_2(s) + 3Fe(OH)_3(s) + OH^-(aq)$$

$$MnO_4^-(aq) + 3Fe(OH)_2(s) + 2H_2O(l) \rightarrow MnO_2(s) + 3Fe(OH)_3(s) + OH^-(aq)$$

Oxidizing agent is MnO_4^- and reducing agent is $Fe(OH)_2$.

c) Balance the reduction half-reaction:

$$2NO_3^-(aq) \rightarrow N_2(g)$$ balance N

$$2NO_3^-(aq) \rightarrow N_2(g) + 6H_2O(l)$$ balance O by adding H_2O

$$2NO_3^-(aq) + 12H^+(aq) \rightarrow N_2(g) + 6H_2O(l)$$ balance H by adding H^+

$$2NO_3^-(aq) + 12H^+(aq) + 10e^- \rightarrow N_2(g) + 6H_2O(l)$$ balance charge by adding $10e^-$

Balance the oxidation half-reaction:

$$Zn(s) \rightarrow Zn^{2+}(aq) + 2e^-$$ balance charge by adding $2e^-$

Add the half-reactions after multiplying the reduction half-reaction by one and the oxidation half-reaction by five:

$$2NO_3^-(aq) + 12H^+(aq) + 10e^- \rightarrow N_2(g) + 6H_2O(l)$$

$$5Zn(s) \rightarrow 5Zn^{2+}(aq) + 10e^-$$

Add half-reactions and cancel substances that appear as both reactants and products:

$$2NO_3^-(aq) + 12H^+(aq) + 5Zn(s) \rightarrow N_2(g) + 6H_2O(l) + 5Zn^{2+}(aq)$$

Oxidizing agent is NO_3^- and reducing agent is Zn.

19.16   Plan: Divide the reaction into the two half-reactions, balance elements other than oxygen and hydrogen, and then balance oxygen by adding H_2O and hydrogen by adding H^+. Balance the charge by adding electrons and multiply each half-reaction by an integer so that the number of electrons lost equals the number of electrons gained. Add the half-reactions together, canceling substances that appear on both sides. For basic solutions, add one OH^- ion to each side of the equation for every H^+ ion present to form H_2O and cancel excess H_2O molecules. The substance that gains electrons is the oxidizing agent while the substance that loses electrons is the reducing agent.

Solution:
a) Balance the reduction half-reaction:

$NO_3^-(aq) \rightarrow NO(g) + 2H_2O(l)$ balance O by adding H_2O

$NO_3^-(aq) + 4H^+(aq) \rightarrow NO(g) + 2H_2O(l)$ balance H by adding H^+

$NO_3^-(aq) + 4H^+(aq) + 3e^- \rightarrow NO(g) + 2H_2O(l)$ balance charge by adding $3e^-$

Balance oxidation half-reaction:

$4Sb(s) \rightarrow Sb_4O_6(s)$ balance Sb

$4Sb(s) + 6H_2O(l) \rightarrow Sb_4O_6(s)$ balance O by adding H_2O

$4Sb(s) + 6H_2O(l) \rightarrow Sb_4O_6(s) + 12H^+(aq)$ balance H by adding H^+

$4Sb(s) + 6H_2O(l) \rightarrow Sb_4O_6(s) + 12H^+(aq) + 12e^-$ balance charge by adding $12e^-$

Multiply each half-reaction by an integer to equalize the number of electrons:

$4\{NO_3^-(aq) + 4H^+(aq) + 3e^- \rightarrow NO(g) + 2H_2O(l)\}$ multiply by four to give $12e^-$

$1\{4Sb(s) + 6H_2O(l) \rightarrow Sb_4O_6(s) + 12H^+(aq) + 12e^-\}$ multiply by one to give $12e^-$

This gives:

$4NO_3^-(aq) + 16H^+(aq) + 12e^- \rightarrow 4NO(g) + 8H_2O(l)$

$4Sb(s) + 6H_2O(l) \rightarrow Sb_4O_6(s) + 12H^+(aq) + 12e^-$

Add half-reactions. Cancel common reactants and products:

$4 NO_3^-(aq) + \cancel{16}H^+(aq) + 4Sb(s) + \cancel{6H_2O}(l) \rightarrow 4NO(g) + \cancel{8}H_2O(l) + Sb_4O_6(s) + \cancel{12H^+(aq)}$

Balanced equation in acidic solution:

$4NO_3^-(aq) + 4H^+(aq) + 4Sb(s) \rightarrow 4NO(g) + 2H_2O(l) + Sb_4O_6(s)$

Oxidizing agent is NO_3^- and reducing agent is Sb.

b) Balance reduction half-reaction:

$BiO_3^-(aq) \rightarrow Bi^{3+}(aq) + 3H_2O(l)$ balance O by adding H_2O

$BiO_3^-(aq) + 6H^+(aq) \rightarrow Bi^{3+}(aq) + 3H_2O(l)$ balance H by adding H^+

$BiO_3^-(aq) + 6H^+(aq) + 2e^- \rightarrow Bi^{3+}(aq) + 3H_2O(l)$ balance charge to give +3 on each side

Balance oxidation half-reaction:

$Mn^{2+}(aq) + 4H_2O(l) \rightarrow MnO_4^-(aq)$ balance O by adding H_2O

$Mn^{2+}(aq) + 4H_2O(l) \rightarrow MnO_4^-(aq) + 8H^+(aq)$ balance H by adding H^+

$Mn^{2+}(aq) + 4H_2O(l) \rightarrow MnO_4^-(aq) + 8H^+(aq) + 5e^-$ balance charge to give +2 on each side

Multiply each half-reaction by an integer to equalize the number of electrons:

$5\{BiO_3^-(aq) + 6H^+(aq) + 2e^- \rightarrow Bi^{3+}(aq) + 3H_2O(l)\}$ multiply by five to give $10e^-$

$2\{Mn^{2+}(aq) + 4H_2O(l) \rightarrow MnO_4^-(aq) + 8H^+(aq) + 5e^-\}$ multiply by two to give $10e^-$

This gives:

$5BiO_3^-(aq) + 30H^+(aq) + 10e^- \rightarrow 5Bi^{3+}(aq) + 15H_2O(l)$

$2Mn^{2+}(aq) + 8H_2O(l) \rightarrow 2MnO_4^-(aq) + 16H^+(aq) + 10e^-$

Add half-reactions. Cancel H_2O and H^+ in reactants and products:

$5BiO_3^-(aq) + \cancel{30}H^+(aq) + 2Mn^{2+}(aq) + \cancel{8H_2O}(l) \rightarrow 5Bi^{3+}(aq) + \cancel{15}H_2O(l) + 2MnO_4^-(aq) + \cancel{16H^+(aq)}$

Balanced reaction in acidic solution:

$5BiO_3^-(aq) + 14H^+(aq) + 2Mn^{2+}(aq) \rightarrow 5Bi^{3+}(aq) + 7H_2O(l) + 2MnO_4^-(aq)$

BiO_3^- is the oxidizing agent and Mn^{2+} is the reducing agent.

c) Balance the reduction half-reaction:

$Pb(OH)_3^-(aq) \rightarrow Pb(s) + 3H_2O(l)$ balance O by adding H_2O

$Pb(OH)_3^-(aq) + 3H^+(aq) \rightarrow Pb(s) + 3H_2O(l)$ balance H by adding H^+

$Pb(OH)_3^-(aq) + 3H^+(aq) + 2e^- \rightarrow Pb(s) + 3H_2O(l)$ balance charge to give 0 on each side

Balance the oxidation half-reaction:

$Fe(OH)_2(s) + H_2O(l) \rightarrow Fe(OH)_3(s)$ balance O by adding H_2O

$Fe(OH)_2(s) + H_2O(l) \rightarrow Fe(OH)_3(s) + H^+(aq)$ balance H by adding H^+

$Fe(OH)_2(s) + H_2O(l) \rightarrow Fe(OH)_3(s) + H^+(aq) + e^-$ balance charge to give 0 on each side

Multiply each half-reaction by an integer to equalize the number of electrons:

$1\{Pb(OH)_3^-(aq) + 3H^+(aq) + 2e^- \rightarrow Pb(s) + 3H_2O(l)\}$ multiply by 1 to give $2e^-$

$2\{Fe(OH)_2(s) + H_2O(l) \rightarrow Fe(OH)_3(s) + H^+(aq) + e^-\}$ multiply by 2 to give $2e^-$

This gives:

$Pb(OH)_3^-(aq) + 3H^+(aq) + 2e^- \rightarrow Pb(s) + 3H_2O(l)$

$2Fe(OH)_2(s) + 2H_2O(l) \rightarrow 2Fe(OH)_3(s) + 2H^+(aq) + 2e^-$

Add the two half-reactions. Cancel H_2O and H^+:

$Pb(OH)_3^-(aq) + \cancel{3H^+}(aq) + 2Fe(OH)_2(s) + \cancel{2H_2O}(l) \rightarrow Pb(s) + 3H_2O(l) + 2Fe(OH)_3(s) + \cancel{2H^+}(aq)$

$Pb(OH)_3^-(aq) + H^+(aq) + 2Fe(OH)_2(s) \rightarrow Pb(s) + H_2O(l) + 2Fe(OH)_3(s)$

Add one OH^- to both sides to neutralize H^+:

$Pb(OH)_3^-(aq) + H^+(aq) + OH^-(aq) + 2Fe(OH)_2(s) \rightarrow Pb(s) + H_2O(l) + 2\,Fe(OH)_3(s) + OH^-(aq)$

$Pb(OH)_3^-(aq) + \cancel{H_2O}(l) + 2Fe(OH)_2(s) \rightarrow Pb(s) + \cancel{H_2O}(l) + 2Fe(OH)_3(s) + OH^-(aq)$

Balanced reaction in basic solution:

$Pb(OH)_3^-(aq) + 2Fe(OH)_2(s) \rightarrow Pb(s) + 2Fe(OH)_3(s) + OH^-(aq)$

$Pb(OH)_3^-$ is the oxidizing agent and $Fe(OH)_2$ is the reducing agent.

19.18   Plan: Divide the reaction into the two half-reactions, balance elements other than oxygen and hydrogen, and then balance oxygen by adding H_2O and hydrogen by adding H^+. Balance the charge by adding electrons and multiply each half-reaction by an integer so that the number of electrons lost equals the number of electrons gained. Add the half-reactions together, canceling substances that appear on both sides. For basic solutions, add one OH^- ion to each side of the equation for every H^+ ion present to form H_2O and cancel excess H_2O molecules. The substance that gains electrons is the oxidizing agent while the substance that loses electrons is the reducing agent.

Solution:

a) Balance reduction half-reaction:

$MnO_4^-(aq) \rightarrow Mn^{2+}(aq) + 4H_2O(l)$	balance O by adding H_2O
$MnO_4^-(aq) + 8H^+(aq) \rightarrow Mn^{2+}(aq) + 4H_2O(l)$	balance H by adding H^+
$MnO_4^-(aq) + 8H^+(aq) + 5e^- \rightarrow Mn^{2+}(aq) + 4H_2O(l)$	balance charge by adding $5e^-$

Balance oxidation half-reaction:

$As_4O_6(s) \rightarrow 4AsO_4^{3-}(aq)$	balance As
$As_4O_6(s) + 10H_2O(l) \rightarrow 4AsO_4^{3-}(aq)$	balance O by adding H_2O
$As_4O_6(s) + 10H_2O(l) \rightarrow 4AsO_4^{3-}(aq) + 20H^+(aq)$	balance H by adding H^+
$As_4O_6(s) + 10H_2O(l) \rightarrow 4AsO_4^{3-}(aq) + 20H^+(aq) + 8e^-$	balance charge by adding $8e^-$

Multiply reduction half-reaction by 8 and oxidation half-reaction by 5 to transfer 40 e^- in overall reaction.

$8MnO_4^-(aq) + 64H^+(aq) + 40e^- \rightarrow 8Mn^{2+}(aq) + 32H_2O(l)$

$5As_4O_6(s) + 50H_2O(l) \rightarrow 20AsO_4^{3-}(aq) + 100H^+(aq) + 40e^-$

Add the half-reactions and cancel H_2O and H^+:

$5As_4O_6(s) + 8MnO_4^-(aq) + \cancel{64H^+}(aq) + \cancel{50}H_2O(l) \rightarrow 20AsO_4^{3-}(aq) + 8Mn^{2+}(aq) + \cancel{32H_2O}(l) + \cancel{100}H^+(aq)$

Balanced reaction in acidic solution:

$5As_4O_6(s) + 8MnO_4^-(aq) + 18H_2O(l) \rightarrow 20AsO_4^{3-}(aq) + 8Mn^{2+}(aq) + 36H^+(aq)$

Oxidizing agent is MnO_4^- and reducing agent is As_4O_6.

b) The reaction gives only one reactant, P_4. Since both products contain phosphorus, divide the half-reactions so each includes P_4 as the reactant.

Balance reduction half-reaction:

$P_4(s) \rightarrow 4PH_3(g)$	balance P
$P_4(s) + 12H^+(aq) \rightarrow 4PH_3(g)$	balance H by adding H^+
$P_4(s) + 12H^+(aq) + 12e^- \rightarrow 4PH_3(g)$	balance charge by adding 12 e^-

Balance oxidation half-reaction:

$P_4(s) \rightarrow 4HPO_3^{2-}(aq)$	balance P
$P_4(s) + 12H_2O(l) \rightarrow 4HPO_3^{2-}(aq)$	balance O by adding H_2O
$P_4(s) + 12H_2O(l) \rightarrow 4HPO_3^{2-}(aq) + 20H^+(aq)$	balance H by adding H^+
$P_4(s) + 12H_2O(l) \rightarrow 4HPO_3^{2-}(aq) + 20H^+(aq) + 12e^-$	balance charge by adding 12 e^-

Add two half-reactions and cancel H^+:

$2P_4(s) + \cancel{12H^+}(aq) + 12H_2O(l) \rightarrow 4HPO_3^{2-}(aq) + 4PH_3(g) + \cancel{20}H^+(aq)$

Balanced reaction in acidic solution:

$2P_4(s) + 12H_2O(l) \rightarrow 4HPO_3^{2-}(aq) + 4PH_3(g) + 8H^+(aq)$ or

$P_4(s) + 6H_2O(l) \rightarrow 2HPO_3^{2-}(aq) + 2PH_3(g) + 4H^+(aq)$

P_4 is both the oxidizing agent and reducing agent.

c) Balance the reduction half-reaction:

$MnO_4^-(aq) \rightarrow MnO_2(s) + 2H_2O(l)$ balance O by adding H_2O

$MnO_4^-(aq) + 4H^+(aq) \rightarrow MnO_2(s) + 2H_2O(l)$ balance H by adding H^+

$MnO_4^-(aq) + 4H^+(aq) + 3e^- \rightarrow MnO_2(s) + 2H_2O(l)$ balance charge by adding $3e^-$

Balance oxidation half-reaction:

$CN^-(aq) + H_2O(l) \rightarrow CNO^-(aq)$ balance O by adding H_2O

$CN^-(aq) + H_2O(l) \rightarrow CNO^-(aq) + 2H^+(aq)$ balance H by adding H^+

$CN^-(aq) + H_2O(l) \rightarrow CNO^-(aq) + 2H^+(aq) + 2e^-$ balance charge by adding $2e^-$

Multiply the oxidation half-reaction by three and reduction half-reaction by two to transfer $6e^-$ in overall reaction.

$2MnO_4^-(aq) + 8H^+(aq) + 6e^- \rightarrow 2MnO_2(s) + 4H_2O(l)$

$3CN^-(aq) + 3H_2O(l) \rightarrow 3CNO^-(aq) + 6H^+(aq) + 6e^-$

Add the two half-reactions. Cancel the H_2O and H^+:

$2MnO_4^-(aq) + 3CN^-(aq) + \cancel{8}H^+(aq) + \cancel{3H_2O}(l) \rightarrow 2MnO_2(s) + 3CNO^-(aq) + \cancel{6H^+(aq)} + 4H_2O(l)$

$2MnO_4^-(aq) + 3CN^-(aq) + 2H^+(aq) \rightarrow 2MnO_2(s) + 3CNO^-(aq) + H_2O(l)$

Add 2 OH^- to both sides to neutralize H^+ and form H_2O:

$2MnO_4^-(aq) + 3CN^-(aq) + 2H^+(aq) + 2OH^-(aq) \rightarrow 2MnO_2(s) + 3CNO^-(aq) + H_2O(l) + 2OH^-(aq)$

$2MnO_4^-(aq) + 3CN^-(aq) + \cancel{2}H_2O(l) \rightarrow 2MnO_2(s) + 3CNO^-(aq) + \cancel{H_2O(l)} + 2OH^-(aq)$

Balanced reaction in basic solution:

$2MnO_4^-(aq) + 3CN^-(aq) + H_2O(l) \rightarrow 2MnO_2(s) + 3CNO^-(aq) + 2OH^-(aq)$

Oxidizing agent is MnO_4^- and reducing agent is CN^-.

19.21 a) Balance reduction half-reaction:

$NO_3^-(aq) \rightarrow NO_2(g) + H_2O(l)$ balance O by adding H_2O

$NO_3^-(aq) + 2H^+(aq) \rightarrow NO_2(g) + H_2O(l)$ balance H by adding H^+

$NO_3^-(aq) + 2H^+(aq) + e^- \rightarrow NO_2(g) + H_2O(l)$ balance charge to give 0 on each side

Balance oxidation half-reaction:

$Au(s) + 4Cl^-(aq) \rightarrow AuCl_4^-(aq)$ balance Cl

$Au(s) + 4Cl^-(aq) \rightarrow AuCl_4^-(aq) + 3e^-$ balance charge to –4 on each side

Multiply each half-reaction by an integer to equalize the number of electrons:

$3\{NO_3^-(aq) + 2H^+(aq) + e^- \rightarrow NO_2(g) + H_2O(l)\}$ multiply by three to give $3e^-$

$1\{Au(s) + 4Cl^-(aq) \rightarrow AuCl_4^-(aq) + 3e^-\}$ multiply by one to give $3e^-$

This gives:

$3NO_3^-(aq) + 6H^+(aq) + 3e^- \rightarrow 3NO_2(g) + 3H_2O(l)$

$Au(s) + 4Cl^-(aq) \rightarrow AuCl_4^-(aq) + 3e^-$

Add half-reactions:

$Au(s) + 3NO_3^-(aq) + 4Cl^-(aq) + 6H^+(aq) \rightarrow AuCl_4^-(aq) + 3NO_2(g) + 3H_2O(l)$

b) Oxidizing agent is NO_3^- and reducing agent is **Au**.

c) The HCl provides chloride ions that combine with the unstable gold ion to form the stable ion, $AuCl_4^-$.

19.22 Plan: The oxidation half-cell (anode) is shown on the left while the reduction half-cell (cathode) is shown on the right. Remember that oxidation is the loss of electrons and electrons leave the oxidation half-cell and move towards the positively charged cathode. If a metal is reduced, it will plate out on the cathode.

Solution:

a) **A** is the anode because by convention the anode is shown on the left.

b) **E** is the cathode because by convention the cathode is shown on the right.

c) **C** is the salt bridge providing electrical connection between the two solutions.

d) **A** is the anode, so oxidation takes place there. Oxidation is the loss of electrons, meaning that electrons are leaving the anode.

e) **E** is assigned a positive charge because it is the cathode.

f) **E** gains mass because the reduction of the metal ion produces the solid metal which plates out on E.

19.25 (a) An active electrode is a reactant or product in the cell reaction, whereas an inactive electrode is neither a reactant nor a product. (b) An inactive electrode is present only to conduct electricity when the half-cell reaction does not include a metal. (c) Platinum and graphite are commonly used as inactive electrodes.

19.26   a) The metal **A** is being oxidized to form the metal cation. To form positive ions, an atom must always lose electrons, so this half-reaction is always an oxidation.
b) The metal ion **B** is gaining electrons to form the metal **B**, so it is displaced.
c) The anode is the electrode at which oxidation takes place, so metal **A** is used as the anode.
d) Acid oxidizes metal **B** and metal **B** oxidizes metal **A**, so acid will oxidize metal **A** and **bubbles will form** when metal **A** is placed in acid. The same answer results if strength of reducing agents is considered. The fact that metal **A** is a better reducing agent than metal **B** indicates that if metal **B** reduces acid, then metal **A** will also reduce acid.

19.27   Plan: The anode, at which the oxidation takes place, is the negative electrode. Electrons flow from the anode to the cathode. Anions from the salt bridge flow into the oxidation half-cell, while cations from the salt bridge flow into the reduction half-cell.
Solution:
a) If the zinc electrode is negative, it is the anode and oxidation takes place at the zinc electrode:
$$Zn(s) \rightarrow Zn^{2+}(aq) + 2e^-$$
Reduction half-reaction: $Sn^{2+}(aq) + 2e^- \rightarrow Sn(s)$
Overall reaction: $Zn(s) + Sn^{2+}(aq) \rightarrow Zn^{2+}(aq) + Sn(s)$
b)

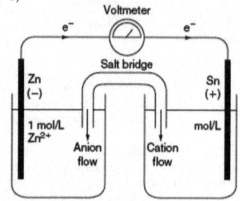

19.29   Plan: The oxidation half-cell (anode) is shown on the left while the reduction half-cell (cathode) is shown on the right. Remember that oxidation is the loss of electrons and electrons leave the oxidation half-cell and move towards the positively charged cathode. Anions from the salt bridge flow into the oxidation half-cell, while cations from the salt bridge flow into the reduction half-cell.
Solution:
a) Electrons flow from the anode to the cathode, so **from the iron half-cell to the nickel half-cell**, left to right in the figure. By convention, the anode appears on the left and the cathode on the right.
b) Oxidation occurs at the anode, which is the electrode in the **iron** half-cell.
c) Electrons enter the reduction half-cell, the **nickel** half-cell in this example.
d) Electrons are consumed in the reduction half-reaction. Reduction takes place at the cathode, **nickel** electrode.
e) The anode is assigned a negative charge, so the **iron** electrode is negatively charged.
f) Metal is oxidized in the oxidation half-cell, so the **iron** electrode will decrease in mass.
g) The solution must contain nickel ions, so any nickel salt can be added. **1 mol/L NiSO₄** is one choice.
h) KNO_3 is commonly used in salt bridges, the ions being **K^+ and NO_3^-**. Other salts are also acceptable answers.
i) **Neither**, because an inactive electrode could not replace either electrode since both the oxidation and the reduction half-reactions include the metal as either a reactant or a product.
j) Anions will move towards the half-cell in which positive ions are being produced. The oxidation half-cell produces Fe^{2+}, so salt bridge anions move **from right** (nickel half-cell) **to left** (iron half-cell).
k)   Oxidation half-reaction: $Fe(s) \rightarrow Fe^{2+}(aq) + 2e^-$
    Reduction half-reaction: $Ni^{2+}(aq) + 2e^- \rightarrow Ni(s)$
    Overall cell reaction: $Fe(s) + Ni^{2+}(aq) \rightarrow Fe^{2+}(aq) + Ni(s)$

19.31   Plan: The cathode, at which the reduction takes place, is the positive electrode. Electrons flow from the anode to the cathode. Anions from the salt bridge flow into the oxidation half-cell, while cations from the salt bridge flow into the reduction half-cell.

<u>Solution:</u>
a) The cathode is assigned a positive charge, so the iron electrode is the cathode.

Reduction half-reaction: $Fe^{2+}(aq) + 2e^- \rightarrow Fe(s)$
Oxidation half-reaction: $Mn(s) \rightarrow Mn^{2+}(aq) + 2e^-$
Overall cell reaction: $Fe^{2+}(aq) + Mn(s) \rightarrow Fe(s) + Mn^{2+}(aq)$

b)

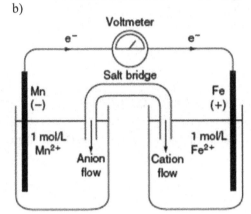

19.33   <u>Plan:</u> In cell notation, the oxidation components of the anode compartment are written on the left of the salt bridge and the reduction components of the cathode compartment are written to the right of the salt bridge. A double vertical line separates the anode from the cathode and represents the salt bridge. A single vertical line separates species of different phases. Anode || Cathode
<u>Solution:</u>
a) Al is oxidized, so it is the anode and appears first in the cell notation. There is a single vertical line separating the solid metals from their solutions.

$Al(s) \mid Al^{3+}(aq) \parallel Cr^{3+}(aq) \mid Cr(s)$

b) Cu^{2+} is reduced, so Cu is the cathode and appears last in the cell notation. The oxidation of SO_2 does not include a metal, so an inactive electrode must be present. Hydrogen ion must be included in the oxidation half-cell.

$Pt \mid SO_2(g) \mid SO_4{}^{2-}(aq), H^+(aq) \parallel Cu^{2+}(aq) \mid Cu(s)$

19.36   (a) A negative $E°_{cell}$ indicates that the cell reaction is not spontaneous, $\Delta G° > 0$. (b) The reverse reaction is spontaneous with $E°_{cell} > 0$.

19.37   (a) Similar to other state functions, the sign of $E°$ changes when a reaction is reversed. (b) Unlike $\Delta G°$, $\Delta H°$ and $S°$, $E°$ is an intensive property, the ratio of energy to charge. When the coefficients in a reaction are multiplied by a factor, the values of $\Delta G°$, $\Delta H°$ and $S°$ are multiplied by the same factor. However, $E°$ does not change because both the energy and charge are multiplied by the factor and their ratio remains unchanged.

19.38   <u>Plan:</u> Divide the balanced equation into reduction and oxidation half-reactions and add electrons. Add water and hydroxide ion to the half-reaction that includes oxygen. Use the relationship $E°_{cell} = E°_{cathode} - E°_{anode}$ to find the unknown $E°$ value.
<u>Solution:</u>
a) Oxidation: $Se^{2-}(aq) \rightarrow Se(s) + 2e^-$
Reduction: $2SO_3{}^{2-}(aq) + 3H_2O(l) + 4e^- \rightarrow S_2O_3{}^{2-}(aq) + 6OH^-(aq)$

b) $E°_{cell} = E°_{cathode} - E°_{anode}$

$E°_{anode} = E°_{cathode} - E°_{cell} = -0.57 \text{ V} - 0.35 \text{ V} = \mathbf{-0.92 \text{ V}}$

19.40 <u>Plan:</u> The greater (more positive) the reduction potential, the greater the strength as an oxidizing agent.
<u>Solution:</u>
a) From Appendix D:

$Fe^{3+}(aq) + e^- \rightarrow Fe^{2+}(aq)$ $\qquad\qquad$ $E° = 0.77$ V
$Br_2(l) + 2e^- \rightarrow 2Br^-(aq)$ $\qquad\qquad$ $E° = 1.07$ V
$Cu^{2+}(aq) + e^- \rightarrow Cu(s)$ $\qquad\qquad$ $E° = 0.34$ V

When placed in order of decreasing strength as oxidizing agents: $\mathbf{Br_2 > Fe^{3+} > Cu^{2+}}$.
b) From Appendix D:

$Ca^{2+}(aq) + 2e- \rightarrow Ca(s)$ $\qquad\qquad$ $E° = -2.87$ V
$Cr_2O_7^{2-}(aq) + 14H^+(aq)\ 6e^- \rightarrow 2Cr^{3+}(aq) + 7H_2O(l)$ $\qquad$ $E° = 1.33$ V
$Ag^+(aq) + e^- \rightarrow Ag(s)$ $\qquad\qquad$ $E° = 0.80$ V

When placed in order of increasing strength as oxidizing agents: $\mathbf{Ca^{2+} < Ag^+ < Cr_2O_7^{2-}}$.

19.42 <u>Plan:</u> Use the relationship $E°_{cell} = E°_{cathode} - E°_{anode}$. $E°$ values are found in Appendix D. Spontaneous reactions have $E°_{cell} > 0$.
<u>Solution:</u>

a) $\qquad$ Oxidation: $\qquad$ $Co(s) \rightarrow Co^{2+}(aq) + 2e^-$ $\qquad\qquad$ $E° = -0.28$ V
$\qquad$ Reduction: $\qquad$ $2H^+(aq) + 2e^- \rightarrow H_2(g)$ $\qquad\qquad$ $E° = 0.00$ V
$\qquad$ Overall reaction: $\quad$ $Co(s) + 2H^+(aq) \rightarrow Co^{2+}(aq) + H_2(g)$

$$E°_{cell} = 0.00 \text{ V} - (-0.28 \text{ V}) = \mathbf{0.28 \text{ V}}$$

$\qquad$ Reaction is **spontaneous** under standard-state conditions because $E°_{cell}$ is positive.

b) $\qquad$ Oxidation: $2\{Mn^{2+}(aq) + 4H_2O(l) \rightarrow MnO_4^-(aq) + 8H^+(aq) + 5e^-\}$ $\qquad$ $E° = +1.51$ V
$\qquad$ Reduction: $\qquad\qquad$ $5\{Br_2(l) + 2e^- \rightarrow 2\ Br^-(aq)\}$ $\qquad\qquad$ $E° = +1.07$ V
$\qquad$ Overall: $2Mn^{2+}(aq) + 5Br_2(l) + 8H_2O(l) \rightarrow 2MnO_4^-(aq) + 10Br^-(aq) + 16H^+(aq)$

$$E°_{cell} = 1.07 \text{ V} - 1.51 \text{ V} = \mathbf{-0.44 \text{ V}}$$

$\qquad$ Reaction is **not spontaneous** under standard-state conditions with $E°_{cell} < 0$.

c) $\qquad$ Oxidation: $\qquad$ $Hg_2^{2+}(aq) \rightarrow 2Hg^{2+}(aq) + 2e^-$ $\qquad\qquad$ $E° = +0.92$ V
$\qquad$ Reduction: $\qquad$ $Hg_2^{2+}(aq) + 2e^- \rightarrow 2Hg(l)$ $\qquad\qquad$ $E° = +0.85$ V
$\qquad$ Overall: $\qquad$ $2Hg_2^{2+}(aq) \rightarrow 2Hg^{2+}(aq) + 2Hg(l)$
$\qquad\qquad\qquad$ or $Hg_2^{2+}(aq) \rightarrow Hg^{2+}(aq) + Hg(l)$ $\qquad$ $E°_{cell} = 0.85$ V $- 0.92$ V $= \mathbf{-0.07 \text{ V}}$

$\qquad$ Negative $E°_{cell}$ indicates reaction is **not spontaneous** under standard-state conditions.

19.44 <u>Plan:</u> Use the relationship $E°_{cell} = E°_{cathode} - E°_{anode}$. $E°$ values are found in Appendix D. Spontaneous reactions have $E°_{cell} > 0$.
<u>Solution:</u>

a) $\qquad$ Oxidation: $\qquad$ $2\{Ag(s) \rightarrow Ag^+(aq) + e^-\}$ $\qquad\qquad$ $E° = +0.80$ V
$\qquad$ Reduction: $\qquad$ $Cu^{2+}(aq) + 2e^- \rightarrow Cu(s)$ $\qquad\qquad$ $E° = +0.34$ V
$\qquad$ Overall: $2Ag(s) + Cu^{2+}(aq) \rightarrow 2Ag^+(aq) + Cu(s)$

$$E°_{cell} = +0.34 \text{ V} - 0.80 \text{ V} = \mathbf{-0.46 \text{ V}}$$

$\qquad$ The reaction is **not spontaneous**.

b) $\qquad$ Oxidation: $\qquad$ $3\{Cd(s) \rightarrow Cd^{2+}(aq) + 2e^-\}$ $\qquad\qquad$ $E° = -0.40$ V
$\qquad$ Reduction: $Cr_2O_7^{2-}(aq) + 14H^+(aq) + 6e^- \rightarrow 2Cr^{3+}(aq) + 7H_2O(l)$ $\qquad$ $E° = +1.33$ V
$\qquad$ Overall: $Cr_2O_7^{2-}(aq) + 3Cd(s) + 14H^+(aq) \rightarrow 2Cr^{3+}(aq) + 3Cd^{2+}(aq) + 7H_2O(l)$

$$E°_{cell} = +1.33 \text{ V} - (-0.40 \text{ V}) = \mathbf{+1.73 \text{ V}}$$

$\qquad$ The reaction is **spontaneous**.

c)   Oxidation: $Pb(s) \rightarrow Pb^{2+}(aq) + 2e^-$ $E° = -0.13$ V
       Reduction: $Ni^{2+}(aq) + 2e^- \rightarrow Ni(s)$ $E° = -0.25$ V
       Overall: $Pb(s) + Ni^{2+}(aq) \rightarrow Pb^{2+}(aq) + Ni(s)$

$$E°_{cell} = -0.25 \text{ V} - (-0.13 \text{ V}) = \textbf{-0.12 V}$$

The reaction is **not spontaneous**.

19.46 Plan: Spontaneous reactions have $E°_{cell} > 0$. All three reactions are written as reductions. When two half-reactions are paired, one half-reaction must be reversed and written as an oxidation. Reverse the half-reaction that will result in a positive value of $E°_{cell}$ using the relationship $E°_{cell} = E°_{cathode} - E°_{anode}$. To balance each reaction, multiply each half-reaction by an integer so that the number of electrons lost equals the number of electrons gained and then add the half-reactions. The greater (more positive) the reduction potential, the greater the strength as an oxidizing agent.
Solution:
Adding (1) and (2) to give a spontaneous reaction involves converting (1) to oxidation:
Oxidation: $2\{Al(s) \rightarrow Al^{3+}(aq) + 3e^-\}$ $E° = -1.66$ V
Reduction: $3\{N_2O_4(g) + 2e^- \rightarrow 2NO_2^-(aq)\}$ $E° = +0.867$ V
$3N_2O_4(g) + 2Al(s) \rightarrow 6NO_2^-(aq) + 2Al^{3+}(aq)$

$$E°_{cell} = 0.867 \text{ V} - (-1.66 \text{ V}) = \textbf{2.53 V}$$

Oxidizing agents: $N_2O_4 > Al^{3+}$; reducing agents: $Al > NO_2^-$
Adding (1) and (3) to give a spontaneous reaction involves converting (1) to oxidation:
Oxidation: $2\{Al(s) \rightarrow Al^{3+}(aq) + 3e^-\}$ $E° = -1.66$ V
Reduction: $3\{SO_4^{2-}(aq) + H_2O(l) + 2e^- \rightarrow SO_3^{2-}(aq) + 2OH^-(aq)\}$ $E° = +0.93$ V
$2Al(s) + 3SO_4^{2-}(aq) + 3H_2O(l) \rightarrow 2Al^{3+}(aq) + 3SO_3^{2-}(aq) + 6OH^-(aq)$

$$E°_{cell} = 0.93 \text{ V} - (-1.66 \text{ V}) = \textbf{2.59 V}$$

Oxidizing agents: $SO_4^{2-} > Al^{3+}$; reducing agents: $Al > SO_3^{2-}$
Adding (2) and (3) to give a spontaneous reaction involves converting (2) to oxidation:
Oxidation: $2NO_2^-(aq) \rightarrow N_2O_4(g) + 2e^-$ $E° = 0.867$ V
Reduction: $SO_4^{2-}(aq) + H_2O(l) + 2e^- \rightarrow SO_3^{2-}(aq) + 2OH^-(aq)$ $E° = 0.93$ V
$SO_4^{2-}(aq) + 2NO_2^-(aq) + H_2O(l) \rightarrow SO_3^{2-}(aq) + N_2O_4(g) + 2OH^-(aq)$

$$E°_{cell} = 0.93 \text{ V} - 0.867 \text{ V} = \textbf{0.06 V}$$

Oxidizing agents: $SO_4^{2-} > N_2O_4$; reducing agents: $NO_2^- > SO_3^{2-}$
Rank oxidizing agents (substance being reduced) in order of increasing strength:
    $\textbf{Al}^{3+} < \textbf{N}_2\textbf{O}_4 < \textbf{SO}_4^{2-}$
Rank reducing agents (substance being oxidized) in order of increasing strength:
    $\textbf{SO}_3^{2-} < \textbf{NO}_2^- < \textbf{Al}$

19.48 Plan: Spontaneous reactions have $E°_{cell} > 0$. All three reactions are written as reductions. When two half-reactions are paired, one half-reaction must be reversed and written as an oxidation. Reverse the half-reaction that will result in a positive value of $E°_{cell}$ using the relationship $E°_{cell} = E°_{cathode} - E°_{anode}$. To balance each reaction, multiply each half-reaction by an integer so that the number of electrons lost equals the number of electrons gained and then add the half-reactions. The greater (more positive) the reduction potential, the greater the strength as an oxidizing agent.
Solution:
Adding (1) and (2) to give a spontaneous reaction involves converting (2) to oxidation:
Oxidation: $Pt(s) \rightarrow Pt^{2+}(aq) + 2e^-$ $E° = +1.20$ V
Reduction: $2HClO(aq) + 2H^+(aq) + 2e^- \rightarrow Cl_2(g) + 2H_2O(l)$ $E° = +1.63$ V
    $2HClO(aq) + Pt(s) + 2H^+(aq) \rightarrow Cl_2(g) + Pt^{2+}(aq) + 2H_2O(l)$

$$E°_{cell} = 1.63 \text{ V} - 1.20 \text{ V} = \textbf{0.43 V}$$

Oxidizing agents: $HClO > Pt^{2+}$; reducing agents: $Pt > Cl_2$
Adding (1) and (3) to give a spontaneous reaction involves converting (3) to oxidation:

Oxidation: $Pb(s) + SO_4^{2-}(aq) \rightarrow PbSO_4(s) + 2e^-$ $E° = -0.31$ V
Reduction: $2HClO(aq) + 2H^+(aq) + 2e^- \rightarrow Cl_2(g) + 2H_2O(l)$ $E° = +1.63$ V
        $2HClO(aq) + Pb(s) + SO_4^{2-}(aq) + 2H^+(aq) \rightarrow Cl_2(g) + PbSO_4(s) + 2H_2O(l)$

         $E°_{cell} = 1.63$ V $- (-0.31$ V$) = $ **1.94 V**

         Oxidizing agents: $HClO > PbSO_4$; reducing agents: $Pb > Cl_2$

Adding (2) and (3) to give a spontaneous reaction involves converting (3) to oxidation:
Oxidation: $Pb(s) + SO_4^{2-}(aq) \rightarrow PbSO_4(s) + 2e^-$ $E° = -0.31$ V
Reduction: $Pt^{2+}(aq) + 2e^- \rightarrow Pt(s)$ $E° = 1.20$ V
        $Pt^{2+}(aq) + Pb(s) + SO_4^{2-}(aq) \rightarrow Pt(s) + PbSO_4(s)$

         $E°_{cell} = 1.20$ V $- (-0.31$ V$) = $ **1.51 V**

         Oxidizing agents: $Pt^{2+} > PbSO_4$; reducing agents: $Pb > Pt$

Order of increasing strength as oxidizing agent: **$PbSO_4 < Pt^{2+} < HClO$**
Order of increasing strength as reducing agent: **$Cl_2 < Pt < (Pb + SO_4^{2-})$**

19.50   Metal A + Metal B salt → solid coloured product on metal A
         Conclusion: Product is solid metal B. B is undergoing reduction and plating out on A. A is a better
         reducing agent than B.
     Metal B + acid → gas bubbles
         Conclusion: Product is H_2 gas produced as result of reduction of H^+. B is a better reducing agent than
         acid.
     Metal A + Metal C salt → no reaction
         Conclusion: C is not undergoing reduction. C must be a better reducing agent than A.
     Since C is a better reducing agent than A, which is a better reducing agent than B and B reduces acid, then **C
     would also reduce acid to form H_2 bubbles**.
     The order of strength of reducing agents is: **C > A > B**.

19.53   At the negative (anode) electrode, oxidation occurs so the overall cell reaction is
     $A(s) + B^+(aq) \rightarrow A^+(aq) + B(s)$ with $Q = [A^+]/[B^+]$.
     a) The reaction proceeds to the right because with $E_{cell} > 0$ (voltaic cell), the spontaneous reaction occurs. As the
     cell operates, **$[A^+]$ increases and $[B^+]$ decreases**.
     b) E_{cell} **decreases** because the cell reaction takes place to approach equilibrium, $E_{cell} = 0$.

     c) E_{cell} and $E°_{cell}$ are related by the Nernst equation: $E_{cell} = E°_{cell} - \dfrac{RT}{zF} \ln \dfrac{\left[A^+\right]}{\left[B^+\right]}$.

     $E_{cell} = E°_{cell}$ when $\dfrac{RT}{zF} \ln \dfrac{\left[A^+\right]}{\left[B^+\right]} = 0$. This occurs when $\ln \dfrac{\left[A^+\right]}{\left[B^+\right]} = 0$. Recall that $e^0 = 1$, so **$[A^+]$ must equal $[B^+]$**

     for E_{cell} to equal $E°_{cell}$.

     d) **Yes**, it is possible for E_{cell} to be less than $E°_{cell}$ when **$[A^+] > [B^+]$**.

19.55   In a concentration cell, the overall reaction takes place to decrease the concentration of the more concentrated
     electrolyte. The more concentrated electrolyte is reduced, so it is in the **cathode** compartment.

19.56   <u>Plan:</u> The equilibrium constant can be found by using $\ln K = \dfrac{zFE°_{cell}}{RT}$. Use $E°$ values from Appendix D to

     calculate $E°_{cell}$ ($E°_{cell} = E°_{cathode} - E°_{anode}$) and then calculate K. The substances given in the problem must be the
     reactants in the equation.
     <u>Solution:</u>
     a) Oxidation: $Ni(s) \rightarrow Ni^{2+}(aq) + 2e^-$ $E° = -0.25$ V
        Reduction: $2\{Ag^+(aq) + 1e^- \rightarrow Ag(s)\}$ $E° = +0.80$ V

$$Ni(s) + 2Ag^+(aq) \rightarrow Ni^{2+}(aq) + 2Ag(s)$$

$E^\circ_{cell} = E^\circ_{cathode} - E^\circ_{anode} = 0.80\ V - (-0.25\ V) = 1.05\ V$; two electrons are transferred.

$$\ln K = \frac{zFE^\circ_{cell}}{RT} = \frac{2(96485\ C/mol\ e^-)(1.05\ V)}{(8.314\ J/mol \cdot K)(298\ K)} = 81.78107$$

$K = e^{81.78107}$

$K = 3.28904 \times 10^{35} = \mathbf{3 \times 10^{35}}$

b) Oxidation: $3\{Fe(s) \rightarrow Fe^{2+}(aq) + 2e^-\}$ $E^\circ = -0.44\ V$

  Reduction: $2\{Cr^{3+}(aq) + 3e^- \rightarrow Cr(s)\}$ $E^\circ = -0.74\ V$

$$3Fe(s) + 2Cr^{3+}(aq) \rightarrow 3Fe^{2+}(aq) + 2Cr(s)$$

$E^\circ_{cell} = E^\circ_{cathode} - E^\circ_{anode} = -0.74\ V - (-0.44\ V) = -0.30\ V$; six electrons are transferred.

$$\ln K = \frac{zFE^\circ_{cell}}{RT} = \frac{6(96485\ C/mol\ e^-)(-0.30\ V)}{(8.314\ J/mol \cdot K)(298\ K)} = -70.09806$$

$K = e^{-70.09806}$

$K = 3.604 \times 10^{-31} = \mathbf{4 \times 10^{-31}}$

19.58   <u>Plan:</u> The equilibrium constant can be found by using $\ln K = \dfrac{zFE^\circ_{cell}}{RT}$. Use E° values from Appendix D to calculate E°_{cell} ($E^\circ_{cell} = E^\circ_{cathode} - E^\circ_{anode}$) and then calculate K. The substances given in the problem must be the reactants in the equation.

<u>Solution:</u>

a) Oxidation: $2\{Ag(s) \rightarrow Ag^+(aq) + 1e^-\}$ $E^\circ = +0.80\ V$

  Reduction: $Mn^{2+}(aq) + 2e^- \rightarrow Mn(s)$ $E^\circ = -1.18\ V$

$$2Ag(s) + Mn^{2+}(aq) \rightarrow 2Ag^+(aq) + Mn(s)$$

$E^\circ_{cell} = E^\circ_{cathode} - E^\circ_{anode} = -1.18\ V - (0.80\ V) = -1.98\ V$; two electrons are transferred.

$$\ln K = \frac{zFE^\circ_{cell}}{RT} = \frac{2(96485\ C/mol\ e^-)(-1.98\ V)}{(8.314\ J/mol \cdot K)(298\ K)} = -154.2157$$

$K = e^{-154.2157}$

$K = 1.05914 \times 10^{-67} = \mathbf{1 \times 10^{-67}}$

b) Oxidation: $2Br^-(aq) \rightarrow Br_2(l) + 2e^-$ $E^\circ = 1.07\ V$

  Reduction: $Cl_2(g) + 2e^- \rightarrow 2Cl^-(aq)$ $E^\circ = 1.36\ V$

$$2Br^-(aq) + Cl_2(g) \rightarrow Br_2(l) + 2Cl^-(aq)$$

$E^\circ_{cell} = E^\circ_{cathode} - E^\circ_{anode} = 1.36\ V - 1.07\ V = 0.29\ V$; two electrons transferred.

$$\ln K = \frac{zFE^\circ_{cell}}{RT} = \frac{2(96485\ C/mol\ e^-)(0.29\ V)}{(8.314\ J/mol \cdot K)(298\ K)} = 22.58715$$

$K = e^{22.58715}$ $K = 6.44876 \times 10^9 = \mathbf{6 \times 10^9}$

19.60   <u>Plan:</u> Use $\Delta G^\circ = -nFE^\circ_{cell}$ to calculate ΔG°. Substitute J/C for V in the unit for E°_{cell}. The units of ΔG° remain as J/mol as a reminder that the value is for a reaction as written.

<u>Solution:</u>

a) $\Delta G^\circ = -zFE^\circ_{cell} = -(2\ mol\ e^-)(96,485\ C/mol\ e^-)(1.05\ J/C) = -2.026185 \times 10^5\ J = \mathbf{-2.03 \times 10^5\ J/mol}$

b) $\Delta G^\circ = -zFE^\circ_{cell} = -(6\ mol\ e^-)(96,485\ C/mol\ e^-)(-0.30\ J/C) = 1.73673 \times 10^5\ J = \mathbf{1.7 \times 10^5\ J/mol}$

19.62   Plan: Use $\Delta G° = -zFE°_{cell}$ to calculate $\Delta G°$. Substitute J/C for V in the unit for $E°_{cell}$. The units of $\Delta G°$ remain as J/mol as a reminder that the value is for a reaction as written.

Solution:

a) $\Delta G° = -zFE°_{cell} = -$ (2 mol e⁻)(96,485 C/mol e⁻)(−1.98 J/C) = 3.820806x10⁵ J= **3.82x10⁵ J/mol**

b) $\Delta G° = -zFE°_{cell} = -$ (2 mol e⁻)(96,485 C/mol e⁻)(0.29 J/C) = −5.59613x10⁴ J= **−5.6x10⁴ J/mol**

19.64   Plan: Use $E°_{cell} = \dfrac{RT}{zF} \ln K$ to find $E°_{cell}$ and then $\Delta G° = -RT \ln K$ to find $\Delta G°$.

Solution:

$T = (273 + 25)\text{K} = 298$ K

$E°_{cell} = \dfrac{RT}{zF} \ln K = \dfrac{(8.314 \text{ J/mol} \cdot \text{K})(298 \text{ K})}{(1)(96485 \text{ C/mol})} \ln\left(5.0\text{x}10^4\right) = 0.277834$ V= **0.28 V**

$\Delta G° = -RT \ln K = -$ (8.314 J/mol•K)(298 K) ln (5.0x10⁴) = −2.68067797x10⁴ J/mol= **−2.7x10⁴ J/mol**

19.66   Plan: Use $E°_{cell} = \dfrac{RT}{zF} \ln K$ to find $E°_{cell}$ and then $\Delta G° = -RT \ln K$ to find $\Delta G°$.

Solution:

$T = (273 + 25)\text{K} = 298$ K

$E°_{cell} = \dfrac{RT}{zF} \ln K = \dfrac{(8.314 \text{ J/mol} \cdot \text{K})(298 \text{ K})}{(2)(96485 \text{ C/mol})} \ln(65) = 0.0535956$ V= **0.054 V**

$\Delta G° = -RT \ln K = -$ (8.314 J/mol•K)(298 K) ln (65) = −1.03423x10⁴ J/mol= **−1.0x10⁴ J/mol**

19.68   Plan: The standard reference half-cell is the H_2/H^+ cell. Since this is a voltaic cell, a spontaneous reaction is occurring. For a spontaneous reaction between H_2/H^+ and Cu/Cu^{2+}, Cu^{2+} must be reduced and H_2 must be oxidized. Write the balanced reaction and calculate $E°_{cell}$. Use the Nernst equation, $E_{cell} = E°_{cell} - \dfrac{RT}{zF} \ln Q$, to find $[Cu^{2+}]$ when $E_{cell} = 0.22$ V.

Solution:

Oxidation: $H_2(g) \rightarrow 2H^+(aq) + 2e^-$ $\qquad\qquad$ $E° = 0.00$ V

Reduction: $Cu^{2+}(aq) + 2e^- \rightarrow Cu(s)$ $\qquad\qquad$ $E° = 0.34$ V

$\qquad$ $Cu^{2+}(aq) + H_2(g) \rightarrow Cu(s) + 2H^+(aq)$

$E°_{cell} = E°_{cathode} - E°_{anode} = 0.34$ V − 0.00 V = 0.34 V

$E_{cell} = E°_{cell} - \dfrac{RT}{zF} \ln Q$

$E_{cell} = E°_{cell} - \dfrac{RT}{zF} \ln \dfrac{\left[H^+\right]^2}{\left[Cu^{2+}\right] p_{H_2}}$

$\qquad$ For a standard hydrogen electrode $[H^+] = 1.0$ mol/L and $p_{H_2} = 1.0$ bar.

0.22 V = 0.34 V $- \dfrac{(8.314 \text{ J/mol} \cdot \text{K})(298 \text{ K})}{(2)(96485 \text{ C/mol})} \ln \dfrac{1.0}{\left[Cu^{2+}\right] 1.0}$

0.22 V $- 0.34$ V = $- \dfrac{(8.314 \text{ J/mol} \cdot \text{K})(298 \text{ K})}{(2)(96485 \text{ C/mol})} \ln \dfrac{1.0}{\left[Cu^{2+}\right] 1.0}$

-0.12 V = $- \dfrac{(8.314 \text{ J/mol} \cdot \text{K})(298 \text{ K})}{(2)(96485 \text{ C/mol})} \ln \dfrac{1.0}{\left[Cu^{2+}\right] 1.0}$

$$9.34641 = \ln \frac{1.0}{\left[Cu^{2+}\right]1.0} \qquad \text{Raise each side to } e^x.$$

$$1.14576 \times 10^4 = \frac{1}{\left[Cu^{2+}\right]}$$

$$[Cu^{2+}] = 8.72783 \times 10^{-5} = \mathbf{8.7 \times 10^{-5} \ mol/L}$$

19.70 Plan: Since this is a voltaic cell, a spontaneous reaction is occurring. For a spontaneous reaction between Ni/Ni^{2+} and Co/Co^{2+}, Ni^{2+} must be reduced and Co must be oxidized. Write the balanced reaction and calculate E°_{cell}.

Use the Nernst equation, $E_{cell} = E^\circ_{cell} - \frac{RT}{zF} \ln Q$, to find E_{cell} at the given ion concentrations. Then

the Nernst equation can be used to calculate $[Ni^{2+}]$ at the given E_{cell}. To calculate equilibrium concentrations, recall that at equilibrium $E_{cell} = 0.00$.

Solution:

a) Oxidation: $Co(s) \rightarrow Co^{2+}(aq) + 2e^-$ $E^\circ = -0.28$ V

Reduction: $Ni^{2+}(aq) + 2e^- \rightarrow Ni(s)$ $E^\circ = -0.25$ V

$$Ni^{2+}(aq) + Co(s) \rightarrow Ni(s) + Co^{2+}(aq)$$

$$E^\circ_{cell} = E^\circ_{cathode} - E^\circ_{anode} = -0.25 \ V - (-0.28 \ V) = 0.03 \ V$$

$$E_{cell} = E^\circ_{cell} - \frac{RT}{zF} \ln Q$$

$$E_{cell} = E^\circ_{cell} - \frac{RT}{zF} \ln \frac{\left[Co^{2+}\right]}{\left[Ni^{2+}\right]} \qquad z = 2e^-$$

$$E_{cell} = 0.03 \ V - \frac{(8.314 \ J/mol \cdot K)(298 \ K)}{(2)(96485 \ C/mol)} \ln \left(\frac{0.20}{0.80} \right)$$

$$E_{cell} = 0.04779885 \ V = \mathbf{0.05 \ V}$$

b) From part a), notice that an increase in $[Co^{2+}]$ leads to a decrease in cell potential. Therefore, the concentration of cobalt ion must increase further to bring the potential down to 0.03 V. Thus, the new concentrations will be $[Co^{2+}] = 0.20 \ mol/L + x$ and $[Ni^{2+}] = 0.80 \ mol/L - x$ (there is a 1:1 mole ratio).

$$E_{cell} = E^\circ_{cell} - \frac{RT}{zF} \ln \frac{\left[Co^{2+}\right]}{\left[Ni^{2+}\right]}$$

$$0.03 \ V = 0.03 \ V - \frac{(8.314 \ J/mol \cdot K)(298 \ K)}{(2)(96485 \ C/mol)} \ln \left(\frac{0.20 + x}{0.80 - x} \right)$$

$$0 = -\frac{(8.314 \ J/mol \cdot K)(298 \ K)}{(2)(96485 \ C/mol)} \ln \left(\frac{0.20 + x}{0.80 - x} \right)$$

$$0 = \ln \frac{(0.20 + x)}{(0.80 - x)} \qquad \text{Raise each side to } e^x.$$

$$e^0 = 1 = \frac{(0.20 + x)}{(0.80 - x)}$$

$$0.20 + x = 0.80 - x$$

$$x = 0.30 \ mol/L$$

$$[Ni^{2+}] = 0.80 - x = 0.80 - 0.30 = \mathbf{0.50 \ mol/L}$$

c) At equilibrium $E_{cell} = 0.00$; to decrease the cell potential to 0.00, $[Co^{2+}]$ increases and $[Ni^{2+}]$ decreases.

$$0.00 \ V = 0.03 \ V - \frac{(8.314 \ J/mol \cdot K)(298 \ K)}{(2)(96485 \ C/mol)} \ln \left(\frac{0.20 + x}{0.80 - x} \right)$$

$$-0.03\ \text{V} = -\frac{(8.314\ \text{J/mol}\cdot\text{K})(298\ \text{K})}{(2)(96485\ \text{C/mol})}\ln\left(\frac{0.20+x}{0.80-x}\right)$$

$$2.3366 = \ln\left(\frac{0.20+x}{0.80-x}\right) \qquad \text{Raise each side to } e^x.$$

$$10.3460 = \left(\frac{0.20+x}{0.80-x}\right)$$

$x = 0.71186 \qquad [Co^{2+}] = 0.20 + 0.71186 = 0.91186 = \textbf{0.91 mol/L}$
$[Ni^{2+}] = 0.80 - 0.71186 = 0.088135 = \textbf{0.09 mol/L}$

19.72 <u>Plan:</u> The overall cell reaction proceeds to increase the 0.10 mol/L H^+ concentration and decrease the 2.0 mol/L H^+ concentration. Use the Nernst equation to calculate E_{cell}. E°_{cell} = 0 V for a concentration cell since the half-reactions are the same.
<u>Solution:</u>
Half-cell **A is the anode** because it has the lower concentration.
Oxidation: $H_2(g; 0.95\ \text{bar}) \rightarrow 2H^+(aq; 0.10\ \text{mol/L}) + 2e^-$ $\qquad E^{\circ} = 0.00\ \text{V}$
Reduction: $2H^+(aq; 2.0\ \text{mol/L}) + 2e^- \rightarrow H_2(g; 0.60\ \text{bar})$ $\qquad E^{\circ} = 0.00\ \text{V}$
$\qquad\quad 2H^+(aq; 2.0\ \text{mol/L}) + H_2(g; 0.95\ \text{bar}) \rightarrow 2H^+(aq; 0.10\ \text{mol/L}) + H_2(g; 0.60\ \text{bar})$

$$E^{\circ}_{cell} = 0.00\ \text{V} \qquad z = 2e^-$$

$$E_{cell} = E^{\circ}_{cell} - \frac{RT}{zF}\ln Q$$

Q for the cell equals $\dfrac{\left[H^+\right]^2_{anode}\ p_{H_2(cathode)}}{\left[H^+\right]^2_{cathode}\ p_{H_2(anode)}} = \dfrac{(0.10)^2(0.60)}{(2.0)^2(0.95)} = 0.00157895$

$$E_{cell} = 0.00\ \text{V} - \frac{(8.314\ \text{J/mol}\cdot\text{K})(298\ \text{K})}{(2)(96485\ \text{C/mol})}\ln(0.00157895) = 0.082821\ \text{V} = \textbf{0.083 V}$$

19.74 Electrons flow from the anode, where oxidation occurs, to the cathode, where reduction occurs. The electrons always flow from the anode to the cathode, no matter what type of cell.

19.76 A D-sized battery is much larger than an AAA-sized battery, so the D-sized battery contains a greater amount of the cell components. (a) The potential, however, is an intensive property and does not depend on the amount of the cell components. (Note that amount is different from concentration.) (b) The total amount of charge a battery can produce does depend on the amount of cell components, so the D-sized battery produces more charge than the AAA-sized battery.

19.78 The Teflon spacers keep the two metals separated so the copper cannot conduct electrons that would promote the corrosion of the iron skeleton. Oxidation of the iron by oxygen causes rust to form and the metal to corrode.

19.81 <u>Plan:</u> Sacrificial anodes are metals with E° values that are more negative than that for iron, –0.44 V, so they are more easily oxidized than iron.
<u>Solution:</u>
a) E°(aluminum) = –1.66 V. Yes, except aluminum resists corrosion because once a coating of its oxide covers it, no more aluminum corrodes. Therefore, it would not be a good choice.
b) E°(magnesium) = –2.37 V. Yes, magnesium is appropriate to act as a sacrificial anode.
c) E°(sodium) = –2.71 V. Yes, except sodium reacts with water, so it would not be a good choice.
d) E°(lead) = –0.13 V. No, lead is not appropriate to act as a sacrificial anode because its E° value is too high.
e) E°(nickel) = –0.25 V. No, nickel is inappropriate as a sacrificial anode because its E° value is too high.
f) E°(zinc) = –0.76 V. Yes, zinc is appropriate to act as a sacrificial anode.
g) E°(chromium) = –0.74 V. Yes, chromium is appropriate to act as a sacrificial anode.

19.83 $3Cd^{2+}(aq) + 2Cr(s) \rightarrow 3Cd(s) + 2Cr^{3+}(aq)$

$E^{\circ}_{cell} = -0.40$ V $- (-0.74$ V$) = 0.34$ V

To reverse the reaction requires 0.34 V with the cell in its standard state. A 1.5 V supplies more than enough potential, so the cadmium metal oxidizes to Cd^{2+} and chromium plates out.

19.85 The oxidation number of nitrogen in the nitrate ion, NO_3^-, is +5 and cannot be oxidized further since nitrogen has only five electrons in its outer level. In the nitrite ion, NO_2^-, on the other hand, the oxidation number of nitrogen is +3, so it can be oxidized at the anode to the +5 state.

19.87 Plan: Oxidation occurs at the anode, while reduction occurs at the cathode.
Solution:
a) At the anode, bromide ions are oxidized to form bromine (**Br₂**). $2Br^-(l) \rightarrow Br_2(l) + 2e^-$
b) At the cathode, sodium ions are reduced to form sodium metal (**Na**). $Na^+(l) + e^- \rightarrow Na(s)$

19.89 Plan: Oxidation occurs at the anode, while reduction occurs at the cathode. Decide which anion is more likely to be oxidized and which cation is more likely to be reduced. The less electronegative anion holds its electrons less tightly and is more likely to be oxidized; the cation with the higher ionization energy has the greater attraction for electrons and is more likely to be reduced.
Solution:
Either iodide ions or fluoride ions can be oxidized at the anode. The ion that more easily loses an electron will form. Since I is less electronegative than F, I^- will more easily lose its electron and be oxidized at the anode. The product at the **anode is I₂** gas. The iodine is a gas because the temperature is high to melt the salts.
Either potassium or magnesium ions can be reduced at the cathode. Magnesium has greater ionization energy than potassium because magnesium is located up and to the right of potassium on the periodic table. The greater ionization energy means that magnesium ions will more readily add an electron (be reduced) than potassium ions. The product at the cathode is **magnesium** (liquid).

19.91 Plan: Oxidation occurs at the anode, while reduction occurs at the cathode. Decide which anion is more likely to be oxidized and which cation is more likely to be reduced. The less electronegative anion holds its electrons less tightly and is more likely to be oxidized; the cation with the higher ionization energy has the greater attraction for electrons and is more likely to be reduced.
Solution:
Bromine gas forms at the anode because the electronegativity of bromine is less than that of chlorine. **Calcium** metal forms at the cathode because its ionization energy is greater than that of sodium.

19.93 Plan: Compare the electrode potentials of the species with those of water. The reduction half-reaction with the more positive electrode potential occurs at the cathode, and the oxidation half-reaction with the more negative electrode potential occurs at the anode.
Solution:
Possible reductions:

$Cu^{2+}(aq) + 2e^- \rightarrow Cu(s)$	$E^{\circ} = +0.34$ V
$Ba^{2+}(aq) + 2e^- \rightarrow Ba(s)$	$E^{\circ} = -2.90$ V
$Al^{3+}(aq) + 3e^- \rightarrow Al(s)$	$E^{\circ} = -1.66$ V
$2H_2O(l) + 2e^- \rightarrow H_2(g) + 2OH^-(aq)$	$E = -1$ V with overvoltage

Copper can be prepared by electrolysis of its aqueous salt since its reduction half-cell potential is more positive than the potential for the reduction of water. The reduction of copper is more spontaneous than the reduction of water. Since the reduction potentials of Ba^{2+} and Al^{3+} are more negative and therefore less spontaneous than the reduction of water, these ions cannot be reduced in the presence of water since the water is reduced instead.
Possible oxidations:

$2Br^-(aq) \rightarrow Br_2(l) + 2e^-$	$E^{\circ} = +1.07$ V
$2H_2O(l) \rightarrow O_2(g) + 4H^+(aq) + 4e^-$	$E = 1.4$ V with overvoltage

Bromine can be prepared by electrolysis of its aqueous salt because its reduction half-cell potential is more negative than the potential for the oxidation of water with overvoltage. The more negative reduction potential for Br^- indicates that its oxidation is more spontaneous than the oxidation of water.

19.95 **Plan:** Compare the electrode potentials of the species with those of water. The reduction half-reaction with the more positive electrode potential occurs at the cathode, and the oxidation half-reaction with the more negative electrode potential occurs at the anode.

Solution:

Possible reductions:

$Li^+(aq) + e^- \rightarrow Li(s)$ $E° = -3.05$ V

$Zn^{2+}(aq) + 2e^- \rightarrow Zn(s)$ $E° = -0.76$ V

$Ag^+(aq) + e^- \rightarrow Ag(s)$ $E° = 0.80$ V

$2H_2O(l) + 2e^- \rightarrow H_2(g) + 2OH^-(aq)$ $E = -1$ V with overvoltage

Zinc and silver can be prepared by electrolysis of their aqueous salt solutions since their reduction half-cell potentials are more positive than the potential for the reduction of water. The reduction of zinc and silver is more spontaneous than the reduction of water. Since the reduction potential of Li^+ is more negative and therefore less spontaneous than the reduction of water, this ion cannot be reduced in the presence of water since the water is reduced instead.

Possible oxidations:

$2I^-(aq) \rightarrow I_2(l) + 2e^-$ $E° = +0.53$ V

$2H_2O(l) \rightarrow O_2(g) + 4H^+(aq) + 4e^-$ $E = 1.4$ V with overvoltage

Iodine can be prepared by electrolysis of its aqueous salt because its reduction half-cell potential is more negative than the potential for the oxidation of water with overvoltage. The more negative reduction potential for I^- indicates that its oxidation is more spontaneous than the oxidation of water.

19.97 **Plan:** Compare the electrode potentials of the species with those of water. The reduction half-reaction with the more positive electrode potential occurs at the cathode, and the oxidation half-reaction with the more negative electrode potential occurs at the anode.

Solution:

a) Possible oxidations:

   $2H_2O(l) \rightarrow O_2(g) + 4H^+(aq) + 4e^-$ $E = 1.4$ V with overvoltage

   $2F^- \rightarrow F_2(g) + 2e^-$ $E° = 2.87$ V

Since the reduction potential of water is more negative than the reduction potential for F^-, the oxidation of water is more spontaneous than that of F^-. The oxidation of water produces oxygen gas (**O_2**), and hydronium ions (**H_3O^+**) at the anode.

Possible reductions:

   $2H_2O(l) + 2e^- \rightarrow H_2(g) + 2OH^-(aq)$ $E = -1$ V with overvoltage

   $Li^+(aq) + e^- \rightarrow Li(s)$ $E° = -3.05$ V

Since the reduction potential of water is more positive than that of Li^+, the reduction of water is more spontaneous than the reduction of Li^+. The reduction of water produces **H_2** gas and **OH^-** at the cathode.

b) Possible oxidations:

   $2H_2O(l) \rightarrow O_2(g) + 4H^+(aq) + 4e^-$ $E = 1.4$ V with overvoltage

The oxidation of water produces oxygen gas (**O_2**), and hydronium ions (**H_3O^+**) at the anode.

The SO_4^{2-} ion cannot oxidize as S is already in its highest oxidation state in SO_4^{2-}.

Possible reductions:

   $2H_2O(l) + 2e^- \rightarrow H_2(g) + 2OH^-(aq)$ $E = -1$ V with overvoltage

   $Sn^{2+}(aq) + 2e^- \rightarrow Sn(s)$ $E° = -0.14$ V

   $SO_4^{2-}(aq) + 4H^+(aq) + 2e^- \rightarrow SO_2(g) + 2H_2O(l)$ $E = -0.63$ V (approximate)

The potential for sulfate reduction is estimated from the Nernst equation using standard-state concentrations and pressures for all reactants and products except H^+, which in pure water is 1×10^{-7} mol/L.

   $E = 0.20$ V $- (0.0592$ V$/2)$ ln $[1/(1 \times 10^{-7})^4] = -0.6288$ V $= -0.63$ V

The most easily reduced ion is Sn^{2+} with the most positive reduction potential, so **tin metal** forms at the cathode.

19.99 **Plan:** Compare the electrode potentials of the species with those of water. The reduction half-reaction with the more positive electrode potential occurs at the cathode, and the oxidation half-reaction with the more negative electrode potential occurs at the anode.

Solution:

a) Possible oxidations:

   $2H_2O(l) \rightarrow O_2(g) + 4H^+(aq) + 4e^-$ $E = 1.4$ V with overvoltage

The oxidation of water produces oxygen gas (O_2), and hydronium ions (H_3O^+) at the anode.
NO_3^- cannot oxidize since N is in its highest oxidation state in NO_3^-.
Possible reductions:

$$2H_2O(l) + 2e^- \rightarrow H_2(g) + 2OH^-(aq) \qquad E = -1 \text{ V with overvoltage}$$
$$Cr^{3+}(aq) + 3e^- \rightarrow Cr(s) \qquad E^\circ = -0.74 \text{ V}$$
$$NO_3^-(aq) + 4H^+(aq) + 3e^- \rightarrow NO(g) + 2H_2O(l) \qquad E = +0.13 \text{ V (approximate)}$$

The potential for nitrate reduction is estimated from the Nernst equation using standard-state concentrations and pressures for all reactants and products except H^+, which in pure water is 1×10^{-7} mol/L.

$$E = 0.96 \text{ V} - (0.0592 \text{ V}/2) \log [1/(1 \times 10^{-7})^4] = 0.1312 \text{ V} = 0.13 \text{ V}$$

The most easily reduced ion is NO_3^-, with the most positive reduction potential so **NO gas** is formed at the cathode.

b) Possible oxidations:

$$2H_2O(l) \rightarrow O_2(g) + 4H^+(aq) + 4e^- \qquad E = 1.4 \text{ V with overvoltage}$$
$$2Cl^-(aq) \rightarrow Cl_2(g) + 2e^- \qquad E^\circ = 1.36 \text{ V}$$

The oxidation of chloride ions to produce **chlorine gas** occurs at the anode. Cl^- has a more negative reduction potential showing that it is more easily oxidized than water.
Possible reductions:

$$2H_2O(l) + 2e^- \rightarrow H_2(g) + 2OH^-(aq) \qquad E = -1 \text{ V with overvoltage}$$
$$Mn^{2+}(aq) + 2e^- \rightarrow Mn(s) \qquad E^\circ = -1.18 \text{ V}$$

It is easier to reduce water than to reduce manganese ions, so **hydrogen gas and hydroxide ions** form at the cathode. The reduction potential of Mn^{2+} is more negative than that of water showing that its reduction is less spontaneous than that of water.

19.101   Plan: Write the half-reaction for the reduction of Mg^{2+}. Convert mass of Mg to amount (mol) and use the mole ratio in the balanced reaction to find the amount (mol) of electrons required for every mole of Mg produced. The Faraday constant is used to find the charge of the electrons in coulombs. To find the current, the charge is divided by the time in seconds.
Solution:
$$Mg^{2+} + 2e^- \rightarrow Mg$$

a) Amount (mol) of electrons $= \left(45.6 \text{ g Mg}\right)\left(\dfrac{1 \text{ mol Mg}}{24.31 \text{ g Mg}}\right)\left(\dfrac{2 \text{ mol e}^-}{1 \text{ mol Mg}}\right) = 3.751542575 \text{ mol} = \textbf{3.75 mol e}^-$

b) Charge $= \left(3.751542575 \text{ mol e}^-\right)\left(\dfrac{96,485 \text{ C}}{\text{mol e}^-}\right) = 3.619676 \times 10^5 \text{ C} = \textbf{3.62} \times \textbf{10}^5 \textbf{ C}$

c) Current $= \left(\dfrac{3.619676 \times 10^5 \text{ C}}{3.50 \text{ h}}\right)\left(\dfrac{1 \text{ h}}{3600 \text{ s}}\right)\left(\dfrac{A}{C/s}\right) = 28.727587 \text{ A} = \textbf{28.7 A}$

19.103   Plan: Write the half-reaction for the reduction of Ra^{2+}. Use the Faraday constant to convert charge in coulombs to amount (mol) of electrons provided; the balanced reduction reaction converts amount (mol) of electrons to amount (mol) of radium produced. Multiply amount (mol) of radium by its molar mass to obtain grams.
Solution:
$$Ra^{2+} + 2e^- \rightarrow Ra$$
In the reduction of radium ions, Ra^{2+}, to radium metal, the transfer of two electrons occurs.

Mass (g) of Ra $= \left(235 \text{ C}\right)\left(\dfrac{1 \text{ mol e}^-}{96,485 \text{ C}}\right)\left(\dfrac{1 \text{ mol Ra}}{2 \text{ mol e}^-}\right)\left(\dfrac{226 \text{ g Ra}}{1 \text{ mol Ra}}\right) = 0.275224 \text{ g} = \textbf{0.275 g Ra}$

19.105   Plan: Write the half-reaction for the reduction of Zn^{2+}. Convert mass of Zn to amount (mol)s and use the mole ratio in the balanced reaction to find the amount (mol) of electrons required for every mole of Zn produced. The Faraday constant is used to find the charge of the electrons in coulombs. To find the time, the charge is divided by the current.

Solution:

$Zn^{2+} + 2e^- \rightarrow Zn$

$$\text{Time (s)} = \left(65.5 \text{ g Zn}\right)\left(\frac{1 \text{ mol Zn}}{65.41 \text{ g Zn}}\right)\left(\frac{2 \text{ mol } e^-}{1 \text{ mol Zn}}\right)\left(\frac{96,485 \text{ C}}{1 \text{ mol } e^-}\right)\left(\frac{1}{21.0 \text{ A}}\right)\left(\frac{1 \text{ A}}{C/s}\right) = 9.20169 \times 10^3 \text{ s} = \mathbf{9.20 \times 10^3 \text{ s}}$$

19.107 a) The sodium sulfate ionizes to produce Na^+ and SO_4^{2-} ions which make the water conductive; therefore the current will flow through the water to complete the circuit, increasing the rate of electrolysis. Pure water, which contains very low (10^{-7} mol/L) concentrations of H^+ and OH^-, conducts electricity very poorly.
b) The reduction of H_2O has a more positive half-potential (–1 V) than the reduction of Na^+ (–2.71 V); the more spontaneous reduction of water will occur instead of the less spontaneous reduction of sodium ion. The oxidation of H_2O is the only oxidation possible because SO_4^{2-} cannot be oxidized under these conditions. In other words, it is easier to reduce H_2O than Na^+ and easier to oxidize H_2O than SO_4^{2-}.

19.109 Plan: Write the half-reaction for the reduction of Zn^{2+}. Find the charge in coulombs by multiplying the current by the time in units of seconds. Use the Faraday constant to convert charge in coulombs to amount (mol) of electrons provided; the balanced reduction reaction converts amount (mol) of electrons to amount (mol) of zinc produced. Multiply amount (mol) of zinc by its molar mass to obtain grams.
Solution:

$Zn^{2+} + 2e^- \rightarrow Zn$

$$\text{Mass (g) of Zn} = \left(0.855 \text{ A}\right)\left(\frac{C/s}{A}\right)\left(2.50 \text{ day}\right)\left(\frac{24 \text{ h}}{1 \text{ day}}\right)\left(\frac{3600 \text{ s}}{1 \text{ h}}\right)\left(\frac{1 \text{ mol } e^-}{96,485 \text{ C}}\right)\left(\frac{1 \text{ mol Zn}}{2 \text{ mol } e^-}\right)\left(\frac{65.41 \text{ g Zn}}{1 \text{ mol Zn}}\right)$$

$$= 62.59998 \text{ g} = \mathbf{62.6 \text{ g Zn}}$$

19.111 Plan: Write the reduction half-reaction for H^+. Use the ideal gas law to find the amount (mol) of H_2 produced. The mole ratio in the balanced reduction reaction gives the moles of electrons required for that amount of H_2 and the Faraday constant converts the amount (mol) of electrons to charge in coulombs. To convert coulombs to energy in joules, remember that 1 V equals 1 J/C; multiply the charge in coulombs by volts to obtain joules. Convert this energy to units of kilojoules and use the given conversion factor between mass of oil and energy to find the mass of oil combusted to provide the needed amount of energy.
Solution:
The half-reaction is: $2H^+(aq) + 2e^- \rightarrow H_2(g)$
a) First, find the amount (mol) of hydrogen gas.

$$n = \frac{PV}{RT} = \frac{\left(12.0 \text{ bar}\right)\left(3.5 \times 10^6 \text{ L}\right)}{\left(0.08314 \frac{L \cdot bar}{mol \cdot K}\right)\left((273 + 25)K\right)} = 1.695208 \times 10^6 \text{ mol } H_2$$

Then, find the coulombs knowing that there are two electrons transferred per mol of H_2.

$$\text{Coulombs} = \left(1.695208 \times 10^6 \text{ mole } H_2\right)\left(\frac{2 \text{ mol } e^-}{1 \text{ mol } H_2}\right)\left(\frac{96485 \text{ C}}{1 \text{ mol } e^-}\right) = 3.27124287760 \times 10^{11} = \mathbf{3.3 \times 10^{11} \text{ C}}$$

b) Energy (J) $= \left(\frac{1.44 \text{ J}}{C}\right)\left(3.27124287760 \times 10^{11} \text{ C}\right) = 4.71058974 \times 10^{11} = \mathbf{4.7 \times 10^{11} \text{ J}}$

c) Mass (kg) $= \left(4.71058974 \times 10^{11} \text{ J}\right)\left(\frac{1 \text{ kJ}}{10^3 \text{ J}}\right)\left(\frac{1 \text{ kg}}{4.0 \times 10^4 \text{ kJ}}\right) = 1.177647 \times 10^4 = \mathbf{1.2 \times 10^4 \text{ kg}}$

19.114 Plan: Write balanced half-reactions for the reduction of each metal ion. From the current, 65.0% of the amount (mol) of product will be copper and 35.0% zinc. Assume a current of exactly 100 C. The amount of current used to generate copper would be (65.0%/100%)(100 C) = 65.0 C, and the amount of current used to generate zinc would be (35.0%/100%)(100 C) = 35.0 C. Convert each coulomb amount to amount (mol) of electrons using the Faraday constant and use the balanced reduction reactions to convert the amount (mol) of electrons to amount (mol) and then mass of each metal. Divide the mass of copper produced by the total mass of both metals produced and multiply by 100 to obtain mass percent.

Solution:

The half-reactions are: $Cu^{2+}(aq) + 2e^- \rightarrow Cu(s)$ and $Zn^{2+}(aq) + 2e^- \rightarrow Zn(s)$

$$\text{Mass (g) of copper} = \left(65.0 \text{ C}\right)\left(\frac{1 \text{ mol } e^-}{96,485 \text{ C}}\right)\left(\frac{1 \text{ mol Cu}}{2 \text{ mol } e^-}\right)\left(\frac{63.55 \text{ g Cu}}{1 \text{ mol Cu}}\right) = 0.021406177 \text{ g Cu}$$

$$\text{Mass (g) of zinc} = \left(35.0 \text{ C}\right)\left(\frac{1 \text{ mol } e^-}{96,485 \text{ C}}\right)\left(\frac{1 \text{ mol Zn}}{2 \text{ mol } e^-}\right)\left(\frac{65.41 \text{ g Zn}}{1 \text{ mol Zn}}\right) = 0.01186376 \text{ g Zn}$$

$$\text{Mass \% of copper} = \frac{0.021406177 \text{ g Cu}}{0.021406177 \text{ g Cu} + 0.01186376 \text{ g Zn}}(100\%) = 64.340900 \% = \textbf{64.3\% Cu}$$

19.115 Plan: Write the reduction half-reaction for Au^{3+}. Use the equation for the volume of a cylinder to find the volume of gold required; use the density to convert volume of gold to mass and then amount (mol) of gold. The mole ratio in the balanced reduction reaction is used to convert the amount (mol) of gold to amount (mol) of electrons required and the Faraday constant is used to convert amount (mol) of electrons to coulombs. Divide the coulombs by the current to obtain time in seconds, which is converted to time in days. To obtain the cost, start by multiplying the amount (mol) of gold from part a) by four to get the amount (mol) of gold needed for the earrings. Convert this amount (mol) to grams, then to troy ounces, and finally to dollars.

Solution:

The reaction is: $Au^{3+}(aq) + 3e^- \rightarrow Au(s)$

a) $V = \pi r^2 h$

$$V \text{ (cm}^3) = \pi \left(\frac{4.00 \text{ cm}}{2}\right)^2 (0.25 \text{ mm})\left(\frac{10^{-3} \text{ m}}{1 \text{ mm}}\right)\left(\frac{1 \text{ cm}}{10^{-2} \text{ m}}\right) = 0.314159265 \text{ cm}^3$$

$$\text{Amount (mol) of Au} = \left(0.314159265 \text{ cm}^3\right)\left(\frac{19.3 \text{ g Au}}{1 \text{ cm}^3}\right)\left(\frac{1 \text{ mol Au}}{197.0 \text{ g Au}}\right) = 0.03077804 \text{ mol Au}$$

$$\text{Time (days)} = \left(0.03077804 \text{ mol Au}\right)\left(\frac{3 \text{ mol } e^-}{1 \text{ mol Au}}\right)\left(\frac{96,485 \text{ C}}{1 \text{ mol } e^-}\right)\left(\frac{A}{C/s}\right)\left(\frac{1}{0.013 \text{ A}}\right)\left(\frac{1 \text{ h}}{3600 \text{ s}}\right)\left(\frac{1 \text{ day}}{24 \text{ h}}\right)$$

$$= 7.931675 \text{ days} = \textbf{8 days}$$

b) The time required doubles once for the second earring of the pair and doubles again for the second side, thus it will take four times as long as one side of one earring.

$$\text{Time} = (4)(7.931675 \text{ days}) = 31.7267 \text{ days} = \textbf{32 days}$$

c) $$\text{Cost} = \left(4\right)\left(0.03077804 \text{ mol Au}\right)\left(\frac{197.0 \text{ g Au}}{1 \text{ mol Au}}\right)\left(\frac{1 \text{ troy oz}}{31.10 \text{ g}}\right)\left(\frac{\$1615}{\text{troy oz}}\right) = \$1259.45 = \textbf{\$1300}$$

19.118 Plan: Write the half-reactions and cell reaction for the silver battery. Convert mass of zinc to amount (mol) of zinc, keeping in mind that only 80% of the zinc will react; from the amount (mol) of zinc, the amount (mol) of electrons required is obtained. The Faraday constant is used to convert the amount (mol) of electrons to charge in coulombs which is divided by the current to obtain the time in seconds. The amount (mol) of zinc is also used to find the amount (mol) of Ag_2O consumed and the amount of Ag needed for that amount of Ag_2O. Convert this mass of silver to troy ounces and then to dollars.

Solution:

The half-reactions and the cell reaction are:

$$Zn(s) + \cancel{2OH^- (aq)} \rightarrow ZnO(s) + \cancel{H_2O(l)} + 2e^-$$
$$\underline{Ag_2O(s) + \cancel{H_2O(l)} + 2e^- \rightarrow 2Ag(s) + \cancel{2OH^- (aq)}}$$
$$Zn(s) + Ag_2O(s) \rightarrow ZnO(s) + 2Ag(s)$$

$$\text{Amount (mol) of Zn} = \left(0.75 \text{ g Zn}\right)\left(\frac{80\%}{100\%}\right)\left(\frac{1 \text{ mol Zn}}{65.41 \text{ g Zn}}\right) = 0.00917291 \text{ mol Zn}$$

a) Time (days) = $(0.00917291 \text{ mol Zn})\left(\dfrac{2 \text{ mol e}^-}{1 \text{ mol Zn}}\right)\left(\dfrac{96,485 \text{C}}{1 \text{ mol e}^-}\right)\left(\dfrac{\text{A}}{\text{C}/\text{s}}\right)\left(\dfrac{1 \text{ } \mu\text{A}}{10^{-6} \text{ A}}\right)\left(\dfrac{1}{0.85 \text{ } \mu\text{A}}\right)\left(\dfrac{1 \text{ h}}{3600 \text{ s}}\right)\left(\dfrac{1 \text{ day}}{24 \text{ h}}\right)$

$= 2.410262 \times 10^4 \text{ days} = \mathbf{2.4 \times 10^4 \text{ days}}$

b) Mass (g) of Ag = $(0.00917291 \text{ mol Zn})\left(\dfrac{1 \text{ mol Ag}_2\text{O}}{1 \text{ mol Zn}}\right)\left(\dfrac{100\%}{95\%}\right)\left(\dfrac{2 \text{ mol Ag}}{1 \text{ mol Ag}_2\text{O}}\right)\left(\dfrac{107.9 \text{ g Ag}}{1 \text{ mol Ag}}\right)$

$= 2.0836989 \text{ g} = \mathbf{2.1 \text{ g Ag}}$

c) Cost = $(2.0836989 \text{ g Ag})\left(\dfrac{95\%}{100\%}\right)\left(\dfrac{1 \text{ troy oz}}{31.10 \text{ g Ag}}\right)\left(\dfrac{\text{CAD } 27.48}{\text{troy oz}}\right)\left(\dfrac{1}{2.410262 \times 10^4 \text{ days}}\right)$

$= 7.25689 \times 10^{-5} = \mathbf{CAD \text{ } 7.3 \times 10^{-5}/\text{day}}$

19.121 Plan: Since the cells are voltaic cells, the reactions occurring are spontaneous and will have a positive E°_{cell}. Write the two half-reactions. When two half-reactions are paired, one half-reaction must be reversed and written as an oxidation. Reverse the half-reaction that will result in a positive value of E°_{cell} using the relationship $E^\circ_{\text{cell}} = E^\circ_{\text{cathode}} - E^\circ_{\text{anode}}$. E° values are found in Appendix D. The oxidation occurs at the negative electrode (the anode). Use the Nernst equation to find cell potential at concentrations other than 1 mol/L.
Solution:
a) Cell with SHE and Pb/Pb^{2+}:

Oxidation: $\text{Pb}(s) \rightarrow \text{Pb}^{2+}(aq) + 2\text{e}^-$ $E^\circ = -0.13 \text{ V}$

Reduction: $2\text{H}^+(aq) + 2\text{e}^- \rightarrow \text{H}_2(g)$ $E^\circ = 0.0 \text{ V}$

$E^\circ_{\text{cell}} = E^\circ_{\text{cathode}} - E^\circ_{\text{anode}} = 0.0 \text{ V} - (-0.13 \text{ V}) = \mathbf{0.13 \text{ V}}$
Cell with SHE and Cu/Cu^{2+}:

Oxidation: $\text{H}_2(g) \rightarrow 2\text{ H}^+(aq) + 2\text{e}^-$ $E^\circ = 0.0 \text{ V}$

Reduction: $\text{Cu}^{2+}(aq) + 2\text{e}^- \rightarrow \text{Cu}(s)$ $E^\circ = 0.34 \text{ V}$

$E^\circ_{\text{cell}} = E^\circ_{\text{cathode}} - E^\circ_{\text{anode}} = 0.34 \text{ V} - 0.00 \text{ V} = \mathbf{0.34 \text{ V}}$
b) The anode (negative electrode) for the cell with SHE and Pb/Pb^{2+} is **Pb**.
The anode for the cell with SHE and Cu/Cu^{2+} is **platinum** in the SHE.
c) The precipitation of PbS decreases [Pb^{2+}]. Use Nernst equation to see how this affects potential. Cell reaction is:

$\text{Pb}(s) + 2\text{H}^+(aq) \rightarrow \text{Pb}^{2+}(aq) + \text{H}_2(g)$ $E_{\text{cell}} = E^\circ_{\text{cell}} - \dfrac{(8.314 \text{ J/mol} \cdot \text{K})(298 \text{ K})}{z(96485 \text{ C/mol})} \ln Q$

$E_{\text{cell}} = E^\circ_{\text{cell}} - \dfrac{(8.314 \text{ J/mol} \cdot \text{K})(298 \text{ K})}{(2)(96485 \text{ C/mol})} \ln \dfrac{[\text{Pb}^{2+}]p_{\text{H}_2}}{[\text{H}^+]^2}$ $z = 2\text{e}^-$

Decreasing the concentration of lead ions makes the following term more negative:

$\dfrac{(8.314 \text{ J/mol} \cdot \text{K})(298 \text{ K})}{(2)(96485 \text{ C/mol})} \ln \dfrac{[\text{Pb}^{2+}]p_{\text{H}_2}}{[\text{H}^+]^2}$

When this more negative value is subtracted from E°_{cell}, cell potential **increases**.
d) The [H$^+$] = 1.0 mol/L , [Cu^{2+}] = 1×10^{-16} mol/L and the H$_2$ = 1 bar in the SHE.

Cell reaction: $\text{Cu}^{2+}(aq) + \text{H}_2(g) \rightarrow \text{Cu}(s) + 2\text{H}^+(aq)$

$E_{\text{cell}} = E^\circ_{\text{cell}} - \dfrac{(8.314 \text{ J/mol} \cdot \text{K})(298 \text{ K})}{z(96485 \text{ C/mol})} \ln Q$

$$E_{cell} = E^\circ_{cell} - \frac{(8.314 \text{ J/mol} \cdot \text{K})(298 \text{ K})}{(2)(96485 \text{ C/mol})} \ln \frac{[H^+]^2}{[Cu^{2+}]p_{H_2}} \qquad z = 2e^-$$

$$E_{cell} = 0.34 \text{ V} - \frac{(8.314 \text{ J/mol} \cdot \text{K})(298 \text{ K})}{(2)(96485 \text{ C/mol})} \ln \frac{(1)^2}{(1 \times 10^{-16})(1)}$$

$$E_{cell} = -0.133012 \text{ V} = \textbf{--0.13 V}$$

19.124 The three steps equivalent to the overall reaction $M^+(aq) + e^- \to M(s)$ are:

     1) $M^+(aq) \to M^+(g)$ Energy is $-\Delta_{hydration}H$
     2) $M^+(g) + e^- \to M(g)$ Energy is $-IE$ or $-\Delta_{ionization}H$
     3) $M(g) \to M(s)$ Energy is $-\Delta_{atomization}H$

The energy for step 3 is similar for all three elements, so the difference in the energy for the overall reaction depends on the values for $-\Delta_{hydration}H$ and $-IE$. The lithium ion has a more negative hydration energy than Na^+ and K^+ because it is a smaller ion with large charge density that holds the water molecules more tightly. The amount of energy required to remove the waters surrounding the lithium ion offsets the lower ionization energy to make the overall energy for the reduction of lithium larger than expected.

19.125 The key factor is that the table deals with electrode potentials in aqueous solution. The very high and low standard electrode potentials involve extremely reactive substances, such as F_2 (a powerful oxidant), and Li (a powerful reductant). These substances react directly with water, rather than according to the desired half-reactions. An alternative (essentially equivalent) explanation is that any aqueous cell with a voltage of more than 1.23 V has the ability to electrolyze water into hydrogen and oxygen. When two electrodes with 6 V across them are placed in water, electrolysis of water will occur.

19.127 Plan: Write the half-reaction for the reduction of Al^{3+}. Convert mass of Al to amount (mol) and use the mole ratio in the balanced reaction to find the amount (mol) of electrons required for every mole of Al produced. The Faraday constant is used to find the charge of the electrons in coulombs. To find the time, the charge is divided by the current. To calculate the electrical power, multiply the time by the current and voltage, remembering that 1 A = 1 C/s (thus, 100,000 A is 100,000 C/s) and 1 V = 1 J/C (thus, 5.0 V = 5.0 J/C). Change units of J to kW • h. To find the cost of the electricity, use the kW • h per 1000 kg of aluminum calculated in part b) to find the power (kW • h) for the mass of aluminum, keeping in mind the 90.% efficiency.
Solution:
a) Aluminum half-reaction: $Al^{3+}(aq) + 3 e^- \to Al(s)$, so $n = 3$. Remember that 1 A = 1 C/s.

$$\text{Time (s)} = (1000 \text{ kg Al})\left(\frac{10^3 \text{ g}}{1 \text{ kg}}\right)\left(\frac{1 \text{ mol Al}}{26.98 \text{ g Al}}\right)\left(\frac{3 \text{ mol e}^-}{1 \text{ mol Al}}\right)\left(\frac{96,485 \text{ C}}{1 \text{ mol e}^-}\right)\left(\frac{A}{C/s}\right)\left(\frac{1}{100,000 \text{ A}}\right)$$

      $= 1.0728503 \times 10^5 \text{ s} = \textbf{1} \times \textbf{10}^5 \textbf{ s}$
The mass and current limit the answer to 1 significant figure.
b) 5 V = 5 J/C

$$\text{Power} = (1.0728503 \times 10^5 \text{ s})\left(\frac{100,000 \text{ C}}{s}\right)\left(\frac{5.0 \text{ J}}{C}\right)\left(\frac{1 \text{ kJ}}{10^3 \text{ J}}\right)\left(\frac{1 \text{ kW} \cdot \text{h}}{3.6 \times 10^3 \text{ kJ}}\right) = 1.4900699 \times 10^4 = \text{kW} \cdot \text{h} \ \textbf{1.5} \times \textbf{10}^4 \textbf{ kW} \cdot \textbf{h}$$

c) $\text{Cost} = (454 \text{ g Al})\left(\dfrac{1 \text{ kg}}{1000 \text{ g}}\right)\left(\dfrac{1.4900699 \times 10^4 \text{ kW} \cdot \text{h}}{1000 \text{ kg Al}}\right)\left(\dfrac{\text{CAD } 0.177}{1 \text{ kW} \cdot \text{h}}\right)\left(\dfrac{100\%}{90.\%}\right) = \$1.3304 = \textbf{\$1.3}$

19.129 Plan: When considering two substances, the stronger reducing agent will reduce the other substance.
Solution:
Statement: Metal D + hot water → reaction   Conclusion: D reduces water to produce $H_2(g)$. D is a stronger reducing agent than H^+.
Statement: D + E salt → no reaction   Conclusion: D does not reduce E salt, so E reduces D salt. E is better reducing agent than D.

Statement: D + F salt → reaction   Conclusion: D reduces F salt. D is better reducing agent than F.
If E metal and F salt are mixed, the salt F would be reduced producing F metal because E has the greatest reducing strength of the three metals (E is stronger than D and D is stronger than F). The ranking of increasing reducing strength is **F < D < E**.

19.131 Plan: Examine the change in oxidation numbers in the equations to find n, the amount (mol) of electrons transferred. Use $\Delta G = -nFE$ to calculate ΔG. Substitute J/C for V in the unit for E. Convert ΔG to units of kJ and divide by the

total mass of reactants to obtain the ratio.
Solution:
a) Cell I: Oxidation number (O.N.) of H changes from 0 to +1, so one electron is lost from each of four hydrogen atoms for a total of four electrons. O.N. of oxygen changes from 0 to –2, indicating that two electrons are gained by each of the two oxygen atoms for a total of four electrons. There is a transfer of **four mole of electrons** in the reaction.

$$\Delta G = -zFE = -(4 \text{ mol e}^-)(96{,}485 \text{ C/mol e}^-)(1.23 \text{ J/C}) = -4.747062 \times 10^5 \text{ J/mol} = \mathbf{-4.75 \times 10^5 \text{ J/mol}}$$

Cell II: In $Pb(s) \rightarrow PbSO_4$, O.N. of Pb changes from 0 to +2 and in $PbO_2 \rightarrow PbSO_4$, O.N. of Pb changes from +4 to +2. There is a transfer of **two mole of electrons** in the reaction.

$$\Delta G = -zFE = -(2 \text{ mol e}^-)(96{,}485 \text{ C/mol e}^-)(2.04 \text{ J/C}) = -3.936588 \times 10^5 \text{ J/mol} = \mathbf{-3.94 \times 10^5 \text{ J/mol}}$$

Cell III: O.N. of each of two Na atoms changes from 0 to +1 and O.N. of Fe changes from +2 to 0. There is a transfer of **two mole of electrons** in the reaction.

$$\Delta G = -zFE = -(2 \text{ mol e}^-)(96{,}485 \text{ C/mol e}^-)(2.35 \text{ J/C}) = -4.534795 \times 10^5 \text{ J/mol} = \mathbf{-4.53 \times 10^5 \text{ J/mol}}$$

b) Cell I: Mass of reactants $= \left(2 \text{ mol H}_2\right)\left(\dfrac{2.016 \text{ g H}_2}{1 \text{ mol H}_2}\right) + \left(1 \text{ mol O}_2\right)\left(\dfrac{32.00 \text{ g O}_2}{1 \text{ mol O}_2}\right) = 36.032 \text{ g}$

$$\frac{w_{max}}{\text{reactant mass}} = \left(\frac{-4.747062 \times 10^5 \text{ J}}{36.032 \text{ g}}\right)\left(\frac{1 \text{ kJ}}{10^3 \text{ J}}\right) = -13.17457 \text{ kJ/g} = \mathbf{-13.2 \text{ kJ/g}}$$

Cell II: Mass of reactants =

$$\left(1 \text{ mol Pb}\right)\left(\frac{207.2 \text{ g Pb}}{1 \text{ mol Pb}}\right) + \left(1 \text{ mol PbO}_2\right)\left(\frac{239.2 \text{ g PbO}_2}{1 \text{ mol PbO}_2}\right) + \left(2 \text{ mol H}_2SO_4\right)\left(\frac{98.09 \text{ g H}_2SO_4}{1 \text{ mol H}_2SO_4}\right)$$
$$= 642.58 \text{ g}$$

$$\frac{w_{max}}{\text{reactant mass}} = \left(\frac{-3.936588 \times 10^5 \text{ J}}{642.58 \text{ g}}\right)\left(\frac{1 \text{ kJ}}{10^3 \text{ J}}\right) = -0.612622 \text{ kJ/g} = \mathbf{-0.613 \text{ kJ/g}}$$

Cell III: Mass of reactants $= \left(2 \text{ mol Na}\right)\left(\dfrac{22.99 \text{ g Na}}{1 \text{ mol Na}}\right) + \left(1 \text{ mol FeCl}_2\right)\left(\dfrac{126.75 \text{ g FeCl}_2}{1 \text{ mol FeCl}_2}\right) = 172.73 \text{ g}$

$$\frac{w_{max}}{\text{reactant mass}} = \left(\frac{-4.534795 \times 10^5 \text{ J}}{172.73 \text{ g}}\right)\left(\frac{1 \text{ kJ}}{10^3 \text{ J}}\right) = -2.625366 \text{ kJ/g} = \mathbf{-2.63 \text{ kJ/g}}$$

Cell I has the highest ratio (most energy released per gram) because the reactants have very low mass while Cell II has the lowest ratio because the reactants are very massive.

19.135 Plan: Write the balanced equation. Multiply the current and time to calculate total charge in coulombs. Remember that the unit 1 A is 1 C/s, so the time must be converted to seconds. From the total charge, the number of electrons transferred to form copper is calculated by dividing total charge by the Faraday constant. Each mole of copper deposited requires two moles of electrons, so divide the amount (mol) of electrons by two to get amount (mol) of copper. Then convert to grams of copper. The initial concentration of Cu^{2+} is 1.00 mol/L (standard condition) and initial volume is 345 mL. Use this to calculate the initial amount (mol) of copper ions, then subtract the amount (mol) of copper ions converted to copper metal and divide by the cell volume to find the remaining $[Cu^{2+}]$.
Solution:
a) Since the cell is a voltaic cell, write a spontaneous reaction. The reduction of Cu^{2+} is more spontaneous than the reduction of Sn^{2+}: $Cu^{2+}(aq) + Sn(s) \rightarrow Cu(s) + Sn^{2+}(aq)$

$$\text{Mass (g) of Cu} = \left(0.17 \text{ A}\right)\left(\frac{C/_s}{A}\right)\left(\frac{3600 \text{ s}}{1 \text{ h}}\right)\left(48.0 \text{ h}\right)\left(\frac{1 \text{ mol e}^-}{96,485 \text{ C}}\right)\left(\frac{1 \text{ mol Cu}}{2 \text{ mol e}^-}\right)\left(\frac{63.55 \text{ g Cu}}{1 \text{ mol Cu}}\right)$$

$$= 9.674275 \text{ g} = \textbf{9.7 g Cu}$$

b) Initial amount (mol) of $Cu^{2+} = \left(1.00 \frac{\text{mol Cu}^{2+}}{L}\right)\left(345 \text{ mL}\right)\left(\frac{10^{-3} \text{ L}}{1 \text{ mL}}\right) = 0.345 \text{ mol Cu}^{2+}$

Amount (mol) of Cu^{2+} reduced $= \left(9.674275 \text{ g Cu}\right)\left(\frac{1 \text{ mol Cu}}{63.55 \text{ g Cu}}\right) = 0.1522309205 \text{ mol Cu}^{2+}$

Remaining amount (mol) of Cu^{2+} = initial amount (mol) – amount (mol) reduced = 0.345 mol – 0.1522309205 mol = 0.1927691 mol Cu^{2+}

Concentration (mol/L) $Cu^{2+} = \dfrac{0.1927691 \text{ mol Cu}^{2+}}{\left(345 \text{ mL}\right)\left(\dfrac{10^{-3} \text{ L}}{1 \text{ mL}}\right)} = 0.558751 \text{ mol/L} = \textbf{0.56 mol/L Cu}^{2+}$

19.137 **Plan:** Examine each reaction to determine which reactant is the oxidizing agent; the oxidizing agent is the reactant that gains electrons in the reaction, resulting in a decrease in its oxidation number.
Solution:
From reaction between $U^{3+} + Cr^{3+} \rightarrow Cr^{2+} + U^{4+}$, find that Cr^{3+} oxidizes U^{3+}.
From reaction between $Fe + Sn^{2+} \rightarrow Sn + Fe^{2+}$, find that Sn^{2+} oxidizes Fe.
From the fact that there is no reaction that occurs between Fe and U^{4+}, find that Fe^{2+} oxidizes U^{3+}.
From reaction between $Cr^{3+} + Fe \rightarrow Cr^{2+} + Fe^{2+}$, find that Cr^{3+} oxidizes Fe.
From reaction between $Cr^{2+} + Sn^{2+} \rightarrow Sn + Cr^{3+}$, find that Sn^{2+} oxidizes Cr^{2+}.
Notice that nothing oxidizes Sn, so Sn^{2+} must be the strongest oxidizing agent. Both Cr^{3+} and Fe^{2+} oxidize U^{3+}, so U^{4+} must be the weakest oxidizing agent. Cr^{3+} oxidizes iron so Cr^{3+} is a stronger oxidizing agent than Fe^{2+}.
The half–reactions in order from strongest to weakest oxidizing agent:
$$Sn^{2+}(aq) + 2e^- \rightarrow Sn(s)$$
$$Cr^{3+}(aq) + e^- \rightarrow Cr^{2+}(aq)$$
$$Fe^{2+}(aq) + 2e^- \rightarrow Fe(s)$$
$$U^{4+}(aq) + e^- \rightarrow U^{3+}(aq)$$

19.141 **Plan:** Write a balanced equation that gives a positive E°_{cell} for a spontaneous reaction. Calculate the E°_{cell} and use the Nernst equation to find the silver ion concentration that results in the given E_{cell}.
Solution:
a) The calomel half-cell is the anode and the silver half-cell is the cathode. The overall reaction is:
$$2Ag^+(aq) + 2Hg(l) + 2Cl^-(aq) \rightarrow 2Ag(s) + Hg_2Cl_2(s)$$

$E^{\circ}_{cell} = E^{\circ}_{cathode} - E^{\circ}_{anode} = 0.80 \text{ V} - 0.24 \text{ V} = 0.56 \text{ V}$ with $z = 2$.

Use the Nernst equation to find $[Ag^+]$ when $E_{cell} = 0.060 \text{ V}$.

$$E_{cell} = E^{\circ}_{cell} - \frac{(8.314 \text{ J/mol} \cdot \text{K})(298 \text{ K})}{z(96485 \text{ C/mol})} \ln Q$$

$$0.060 \text{ V} = 0.56 \text{ V} - \frac{(8.314 \text{ J/mol} \cdot \text{K})(298 \text{ K})}{(2)(96485 \text{ C/mol})} \ln \frac{1}{\left[Ag^+\right]^2 \left[Cl^-\right]^2}$$

The problem suggests assuming that $[Cl^-]$ is constant. Assume it is 1.00 mol/L.

$$-0.50 \text{ V} = -\frac{(8.314 \text{ J/mol} \cdot \text{K})(298 \text{ K})}{(2)(96485 \text{ C/mol})} \ln \frac{1}{\left[Ag^+\right]^2 (1.00)^2}$$

$$38.94337 = \ln \frac{1}{\left[Ag^+ \right]^2 (1.00)^2}$$

$$e^{38.94337} = \frac{1}{\left[Ag^+ \right]^2}$$

$$8.18258 \times 10^{16} = \frac{1}{\left[Ag^+ \right]^2}$$

$8.18258 \times 10^{16} [Ag^+]^2 = 1$

$[Ag^+]^2 = 1.22211 \times 10^{-17}$

$[Ag^+] = 3.49587 \times 10^{-9}$ mol/L= **3.5×10^{-9} mol/L**

b) Again use the Nernst equation and assume $[Cl^-]$ = 1.00 mol/L.

$$E_{cell} = E^\circ_{cell} - \frac{(8.314 \text{ J/mol} \cdot \text{K})(298 \text{ K})}{(2)(96485 \text{ C/mol})} \ln \frac{1}{\left[Ag^+ \right]^2 \left[Cl^- \right]^2}$$

$$0.53 \text{ V} = 0.56 \text{ V} - \frac{(8.314 \text{ J/mol} \cdot \text{K})(298 \text{ K})}{(2)(96485 \text{ C/mol})} \ln \frac{1}{\left[Ag^+ \right]^2 \left[Cl^- \right]^2}$$

$$- 0.03 \text{ V} = - \frac{(8.314 \text{ J/mol} \cdot \text{K})(298 \text{ K})}{(2)(96485 \text{ C/mol})} \ln \frac{1}{\left[Ag^+ \right]^2 \left[Cl^- \right]^2}$$

$$2.33660 = \ln \frac{1}{\left[Ag^+ \right]^2 (1.00)^2}$$

$$e^{2.33660} = \frac{1}{\left[Ag^+ \right]^2}$$

$$10.3460 = \frac{1}{\left[Ag^+ \right]^2}$$

$10.3460 [Ag^+]^2 = 1$

$[Ag^+]^2 = 0.0966555$

$[Ag^+] = 0.31089$ mol/L = **0.3 mol/L**

19.143 <u>Plan:</u> Use the Nernst equation to write the relationship between E°_{cell} and the cell potential for both the waste stream and for the silver standard.
<u>Solution:</u>
a) The reaction is $Ag^+(aq) \rightarrow Ag(s) + 1e^-$

$$E_{cell} = E^\circ_{cell} - \frac{(8.314 \text{ J/mol} \cdot \text{K})(298 \text{ K})}{(z)(96485 \text{ C/mol})} \ln Q$$

Nonstandard cell: $\qquad E_{waste} = E^\circ_{cell} - \frac{(8.314 \text{ J/mol} \cdot \text{K})(298 \text{ K})}{(1)(96485 \text{ C/mol})} \ln \left[Ag^+ \right]_{waste}$

Standard cell: $\qquad E_{standard} = E^\circ_{cell} - \frac{(8.314 \text{ J/mol} \cdot \text{K})(298 \text{ K})}{(1)(96485 \text{ C/mol})} \ln \left[Ag^+ \right]_{standard}$

b) To find $[Ag^+]_{waste}$: $\qquad E^\circ_{cell} = E_{standard} + \frac{(8.314 \text{ J/mol} \cdot \text{K})(298 \text{ K})}{(1)(96485 \text{ C/mol})} \ln \left[Ag^+ \right]_{standard}$

$$= E_{waste} + \frac{(8.314 \text{ J/mol} \cdot \text{K})(298 \text{ K})}{(1)(96485 \text{ C/mol})} \ln \left[Ag^+ \right]_{waste}$$

$$E_{\text{standard}} - E_{\text{waste}} = \frac{(8.314 \text{ J/mol}\cdot\text{K})(298 \text{ K})}{(1)(96485 \text{ C/mol})} \left(\ln [\text{Ag}^+]_{\text{waste}} - \ln [\text{Ag}^+]_{\text{standard}} \right)$$

$$\frac{E_{\text{standard}} - E_{\text{waste}}}{0.0256783} = \left(\ln [\text{Ag}^+]_{\text{waste}} - \ln [\text{Ag}^+]_{\text{standard}} \right)$$

$$\ln [\text{Ag}^+]_{\text{waste}} = \frac{E_{\text{standard}} - E_{\text{waste}}}{0.0256783} + \ln [\text{Ag}^+]_{\text{standard}}$$

$$[\text{Ag}^+]_{\text{waste}} = \left[e^{\left(\frac{E_{\text{standard}} - E_{\text{waste}}}{0.0256783} \right)} \right] \left(\left[\text{Ag}^+ \right]_{\text{standard}} \right)$$

c) Convert mol/L to ng/L for both $[\text{Ag}^+]_{\text{waste}}$ and $[\text{Ag}^+]_{\text{standard}}$:

$$E_{\text{waste}} - E_{\text{standard}} = -\frac{(8.314 \text{ J/mol}\cdot\text{K})(298 \text{ K})}{(1)(96485 \text{ C/mol})} \ln \frac{[\text{Ag}^+]_{\text{waste}}}{[\text{Ag}^+]_{\text{standard}}} \quad \text{Remember: } \ln A - \ln B = \ln (A/B)$$

If both silver ion concentrations are in the same units, in this case ng/L, the "conversions" cancel and the equation derived in part b) applies if the standard concentration is in ng/L.

$$[\text{Ag}^+]_{\text{waste}} = \left[e^{\left(\frac{E_{\text{standard}} - E_{\text{waste}}}{0.0256783} \right)} \right] \left(\left[\text{Ag}^+ \right]_{\text{standard}} \right)$$

d) Plug the values into the answer for part c).

$$[\text{Ag}^+]_{\text{waste}} = \left[e^{\left(\frac{-0.003}{0.0256783} \right)} \right] (1000. \text{ ng/L}) = 889.7363 \text{ ng/L} = \textbf{900 ng/L}$$

e) Temperature is included in the RT/zF term, in which we have been using T = 298 K. To account for different temperatures, insert the required T value in RT/zF term.

$$E_{\text{standard}} + \left(\frac{RT_{\text{standard}}}{zF} \right) \ln [\text{Ag}^+]_{\text{standard}} = E_{\text{waste}} + \left(\frac{RT_{\text{waste}}}{zF} \right) \ln [\text{Ag}^+]_{\text{waste}}$$

$$E_{\text{standard}} - E_{\text{waste}} = \frac{RT_{\text{waste}}}{zF} \ln [\text{Ag}^+]_{\text{waste}} - \frac{RT_{\text{standard}}}{zF} \ln [\text{Ag}^+]_{\text{standard}}$$

$$E_{\text{standard}} - E_{\text{waste}} = \frac{R}{zF} \left(T_{\text{waste}} \ln [\text{Ag}^+]_{\text{waste}} - T_{\text{standard}} \ln [\text{Ag}^+]_{\text{standard}} \right)$$

$$(E_{\text{standard}} - E_{\text{waste}}) \left(\frac{zF}{R} \right) = T_{\text{waste}} \ln [\text{Ag}^+]_{\text{waste}} - T_{\text{standard}} \ln [\text{Ag}^+]_{\text{standard}}$$

$$(E_{\text{standard}} - E_{\text{waste}}) \left(\frac{zF}{R} \right) + T_{\text{standard}} \ln [\text{Ag}^+]_{\text{standard}} = T_{\text{waste}} \ln [\text{Ag}^+]_{\text{waste}}$$

$$\ln [\text{Ag}^+]_{\text{waste}} = \left(\frac{(E_{\text{standard}} - E_{\text{waste}})(zF/R) + T_{\text{standard}} \ln \left[\text{Ag}^+ \right]_{\text{standard}}}{T_{\text{waste}}} \right)$$

$$[\text{Ag}^+]_{\text{waste}} = e^{\left(\frac{(E_{\text{standard}} - E_{\text{waste}})(zF/R) + T_{\text{standard}} \ln \left[\text{Ag}^+ \right]_{\text{standard}}}{T_{\text{waste}}} \right)}$$

19.145 Plan: Multiply the current in amperes by the time in seconds to obtain coulombs. Convert coulombs to amount (mol) of electrons with the Faraday constant and use the mole ratio in the balanced half-reactions to convert amount (mol) of electrons to amount (mol) and then mass of reactants. Divide the total mass of reactants by the mass of the battery to find the mass percentage that consists of reactants.

Solution:

a) Determine the total charge the cell can produce.

$$\text{Capacity (C)} = \left(300.\ \text{mA} \cdot \text{h}\right)\left(\frac{10^{-3}\ \text{A}}{1\ \text{mA}}\right)\left(\frac{3600\ \text{s}}{1\ \text{h}}\right)\left(\frac{1\ \text{C}}{1\ \text{A} \cdot \text{s}}\right) = \mathbf{1.08 \times 10^3\ C}$$

b) The half-reactions are:

$Cd^0 \rightarrow Cd^{2+} + 2e^-$ and $NiO(OH) + H_2O(l) + e^- \rightarrow Ni(OH)_2 + OH^-$

Assume 100% conversion of reactants.

$$\text{Mass (g) of Cd} = \left(1080\ \text{C}\right)\left(\frac{1\ \text{mol}\ e^-}{96,485\ \text{C}}\right)\left(\frac{1\ \text{mol Cd}}{2\ \text{mol}\ e^-}\right)\left(\frac{112.4\ \text{g Cd}}{1\ \text{mol Cd}}\right) = 0.62907\ \text{g} = \mathbf{0.629\ g\ Cd}$$

$$\text{Mass (g) of NiO(OH)} = \left(1080\ \text{C}\right)\left(\frac{1\ \text{mol}\ e^-}{96,485\ \text{C}}\right)\left(\frac{1\ \text{mol NiO(OH)}}{1\ \text{mol}\ e^-}\right)\left(\frac{91.70\ \text{g NiO(OH)}}{1\ \text{mol NiO(OH)}}\right)$$
$$= 1.026439\ \text{g} = \mathbf{1.03\ g\ NiO(OH)}$$

$$\text{Mass (g) of H}_2\text{O} = \left(1080\ \text{C}\right)\left(\frac{1\ \text{mol}\ e^-}{96,485\ \text{C}}\right)\left(\frac{1\ \text{mol H}_2\text{O}}{1\ \text{mol}\ e^-}\right)\left(\frac{18.02\ \text{g H}_2\text{O}}{1\ \text{mol H}_2\text{O}}\right) = 0.20170596\ \text{g} = \mathbf{0.202\ g\ H_2O}$$

Total mass of reactants = 0.62907 g Cd + 1.026439 g NiO(OH) + 0.20170596 g H_2O
= 1.857215 g = **1.86 g reactants**

c) Mass % reactants = $\dfrac{1.85721\ \text{g}}{18.3\ \text{g}}(100\%) = 10.14872\ \% = \mathbf{10.1\%}$

19.147 Plan: For a list of decreasing reducing strength, place the elements in order of increasing (more positive) $E°$. Metals with potentials lower than that of water (–0.83 V) can displace hydrogen from water by reducing the hydrogen in water. Metals with potentials lower than that of hydrogen (0.00 V) can displace hydrogen from acids by reducing the H^+ in acid. Metals with potentials above that of hydrogen (0.00 V) cannot displace (reduce) hydrogen.

Solution:

Reducing agent strength: Li > Ba > Na > Al > Mn > Zn > Cr > Fe > Ni > Sn > Pb > Cu > Ag > Hg > Au

These can displace H_2 from water: Li, Ba, Na, Al, and Mn.

These can displace H_2 from acid: Li, Ba, Na, Al, Mn, Zn, Cr, Fe, Ni, Sn, and Pb.

These cannot displace H_2: Cu, Ag, Hg, and Au.

19.150 a) The reference half-reaction is: $Cu^{2+}(aq) + 2e^- \rightarrow Cu(s)$ $E° = 0.34$ V

Before the addition of the ammonia, $E_{cell} = 0$. The addition of ammonia lowers the concentration of copper ions through the formation of the complex $Cu(NH_3)_4^{2+}$. The original copper ion concentration is $[Cu^{2+}]_{original}$, and the copper ion concentration in the solution containing ammonia is $[Cu^{2+}]_{ammonia}$.

The Nernst equation is used to determine the copper ion concentration in the cell containing ammonia.

The reaction is $Cu^{2+}_{initial}(aq) + Cu(s) \rightarrow Cu(s) + Cu^{2+}_{ammonia}(aq)$.

The half-cell with the larger concentration of copper ion (no ammonia added) is the reduction and the half-cell with the lower concentration of copper ion due to the addition of ammonia and formation of the complex is the oxidation.

$$E_{cell} = E°_{cell} - \frac{(8.314\ \text{J/mol} \cdot \text{K})(298\ \text{K})}{(z)(96485\ \text{C/mol})}\ln Q$$

$$0.129\ \text{V} = 0.00\ \text{V} - \frac{(8.314\ \text{J/mol} \cdot \text{K})(298\ \text{K})}{(2)(96485\ \text{C/mol})}\ln\frac{\left[Cu^{2+}\right]_{ammonia}}{\left[Cu^{2+}\right]_{original}}$$

$$0.129 \text{ V} = -\frac{(8.314 \text{ J/mol}\cdot\text{K})(298 \text{ K})}{(2)(96485 \text{ C/mol})} \ln \frac{\left[\text{Cu}^{2+}\right]_{\text{ammonia}}}{\left[\text{Cu}^{2+}\right]_{\text{original}}}$$

$$-10.04739 = \ln \frac{\left[\text{Cu}^{2+}\right]_{\text{ammonia}}}{(0.0100)}$$

$$4.329865\text{x}10^{-5} = \frac{\left[\text{Cu}^{2+}\right]_{\text{ammonia}}}{(0.0100)}$$

$[\text{Cu}^{2+}]_{\text{ammonia}} = 4.329865\text{x}10^{-7}$ mol/L

This is the concentration of the copper ion that is not in the complex. The concentration of the complex and of the uncomplexed ammonia must be determined before K_f may be calculated.

The original amount (mol) of copper and the original amount (mol) of ammonia are found from the original volumes and concentrations:

$$\text{Original amount (mol) of copper} = \left(\frac{0.0100 \text{ mol Cu(NO}_3)_2}{\text{L}}\right)\left(\frac{1 \text{ mol Cu}^{2+}}{1 \text{ mol Cu(NO}_3)_2}\right)\left(\frac{10^{-3} \text{ L}}{1 \text{ mL}}\right)(90.0 \text{ mL})$$

$$= 9.00\text{x}10^{-4} \text{ mol Cu}^{2+}$$

$$\text{Original amount (mol) of ammonia} = \left(\frac{0.500 \text{ mol NH}_3}{\text{L}}\right)\left(\frac{10^{-3} \text{ L}}{1 \text{ mL}}\right)(10.0 \text{ mL}) = 5.00\text{x}10^{-3} \text{ mol NH}_3$$

Determine the amount (mol) of copper still remaining uncomplexed.

$$\text{Remaining amount (mol) of copper} = \left(\frac{4.329865\text{x}10^{-7} \text{ mol Cu}^{2+}}{\text{L}}\right)\left(\frac{10^{-3} \text{ L}}{1 \text{ mL}}\right)(100.0 \text{ mL})$$

$$= 4.329865\text{x}10^{-8} \text{ mol Cu}$$

The difference between the original amount (mol) of copper and the copper ion remaining in solution is the copper in the complex (= amount (mol) of complex). The concentration (mol/L) of the complex may now be found.

Amount (mol) of copper in complex = $(9.00\text{x}10^{-4} - 4.329865\text{x}10^{-8})$ mol Cu^{2+} = $8.9995670\text{x}10^{-4}$ mol Cu^{2+}

$$\text{Concentration (mol/L) of complex} = \left(\frac{8.9995670\text{x}10^{-4} \text{ mol Cu}^{2+}}{100.0 \text{ mL}}\right)\left(\frac{1 \text{ mol Cu(NH}_3)_4^{2+}}{1 \text{ mol Cu}^{2+}}\right)\left(\frac{1 \text{ mL}}{10^{-3} \text{ L}}\right)$$

$$= 8.9995670\text{x}10^{-3} \text{ mol/L Cu(NH}_3)_4^{2+}$$

The concentration of the remaining ammonia is found as follows:

Concentration (mol/L) of ammonia =

$$\left(\frac{\left(5.00\text{x}10^{-3} \text{ mol NH}_3\right)-\left(8.9995670\text{x}10^{-4} \text{ mol Cu}^{2+}\right)\left(\dfrac{4 \text{ mol NH}_3}{1 \text{ mol Cu}^{2+}}\right)}{100.0 \text{ mL}}\right)\left(\frac{1 \text{ mL}}{10^{-3} \text{ L}}\right)$$

$$= 0.014001732 \text{ mol/L ammonia}$$

The K_f equilibrium is:

$$\text{Cu}^{2+}(aq) + 4\text{NH}_3(aq) \leftrightharpoons \text{Cu(NH}_3)_4^{2+}(aq)$$

$$K_f = \frac{\left[\text{Cu(NH}_3)_4^{2+}\right]}{\left[\text{Cu}^{2+}\right]\left[\text{NH}_3\right]^4} = \frac{\left[8.9995670\text{x}10^{-3}\right]}{\left[4.329865\text{x}10^{-7}\right]\left[0.014001732\right]^4} = 5.407795\text{x}10^{11} = \mathbf{5.4\text{x}10^{11}}$$

b) The K_f will be used to determine the new concentration of free copper ions.

Amount(mol) of uncomplexed ammonia before the addition of new ammonia =

$(0.014001732 \text{ mol NH}_3/\text{L})(10^{-3} \text{ L/1 mL})(100.0 \text{ mL}) = 0.0014001732 \text{ mol NH}_3$

Amount(mol) of ammonia added = $5.00\text{x}10^{-3}$ mol NH$_3$ (same as original amount (mol) of ammonia)

From the stoichiometry:

$$Cu^{2+}(aq) \quad + \quad 4NH_3(aq) \quad \rightarrow \quad Cu(NH_3)_4^{2+}(aq)$$

	$Cu^{2+}(aq)$	$4NH_3(aq)$	$Cu(NH_3)_4^{2+}(aq)$
Initial amount (mol)	4.329865×10^{-8} mol	0.0014001732 mol	8.9995670×10^{-4} mol
Added amount (mol)		5.00×10^{-3} mol	
Cu^{2+} is limiting	$-(4.329865\times10^{-8}$ mol$)$	$-4(4.329865\times10^{-8}$ mol$)$	$+(4.329865\times10^{-8}$ mol$)$
After the reaction	0	0.006400 mol	9.00000×10^{-4} mol

Determine concentrations before equilibrium:

$[Cu^{2+}] = 0$

$[NH_3] = (0.006400$ mol $NH_3/110.0$ mL$)(1$ mL$/10^{-3}$ L$) = 0.0581818$ mol/L NH_3

$[Cu(NH_3)_4^{2+}] = (9.00000\times10^{-4}$ mol $Cu(NH_3)_4^{2+}/110.0$ mL$)(1$ mL$/10^{-3}$ L$)$
        $= 0.008181818$ mol/L $Cu(NH_3)_4^{2+}$

Now allow the system to come to equilibrium:

	$Cu^{2+}(aq)$	$+$	$4NH_3(aq)$	$\leftrightarrows$	$Cu(NH_3)_4^{2+}(aq)$
Initial molarity	0		0.0581818		0.008181818
Change	+x		+4x		−x
Equilibrium	x		0.0581818 + 4 x		0.008181818 − x

$$K_f = \frac{\left[Cu(NH_3)_4^{2+}\right]}{\left[Cu^{2+}\right]\left[NH_3\right]^4} = \frac{[0.008181818 - x]}{[x][0.0581818 + 4x]^4} = 5.34072\times10^{11}$$

Assume $-x$ and $+4x$ are negligible when compared to their associated numbers:

$$K_f = 5.34072\times10^{11} = \frac{[0.008181818]}{[x][0.0581818]^4}$$

$x = [Cu^{2+}] = 1.3369\times10^{-9}$ mol/L Cu^{2+}

Use the Nernst equation to determine the new cell potential:

$$E = 0.00\ V - \frac{(8.314\ J/mol\cdot K)(298\ K)}{(2)(96485\ C/mol)} \ln \frac{\left[Cu^{2+}\right]_{ammonia}}{\left[Cu^{2+}\right]_{original}}$$

$$E = -\frac{(8.314\ J/mol\cdot K)(298\ K)}{(2)(96485\ C/mol)} \ln \left(\frac{1.3369\times10^{-9}}{0.0100} \right)$$

$E = 0.203215\ V = \mathbf{0.20\ V}$

c) The first step will be to do a stoichiometry calculation of the reaction between copper ions and hydroxide ions.

$$\text{Amount (mol) of } OH^- = \left(\frac{0.500\ mol\ NaOH}{L} \right)\left(\frac{1\ mol\ OH^-}{1\ mol\ NaOH} \right)\left(\frac{10^{-3}\ L}{1\ mL} \right)(10.0\ mL) = 5.00\times10^{-3}\ mol\ OH^-$$

The initial moles of copper ions were determined earlier: 9.00×10^{-4} mol Cu^{2+}
The reaction:

	$Cu^{2+}(aq)$	$+$	$2OH^-(aq)$	$\rightarrow$	$Cu(OH)_2(s)$
Initial amount (mol)	9.00×10^{-4} mol		5.00×10^{-3} mol		
Cu^{2+} is limiting	$-(9.00\times10^{-4}$ mol$)$		$-2(9.00\times10^{-4}$ mol$)$		
After the reaction	0		0.0032 mol		

Determine concentrations before equilibrium:

$[Cu^{2+}] = 0$

$[NH_3] = (0.0032$ mol $OH^-/100.0$ mL$)(1$ mL$/10^{-3}$ L$) = 0.032$ mol/L OH^-

Now allow the system to come to equilibrium:

	$Cu(OH)_2(s)$	$\leftrightarrows$	$Cu^{2+}(aq)$	$+$	$2OH^-(aq)$
Initial molarity			0.0		0.032
Change			+x		+2x
Equilibrium			x		0.032 + 2 x

$K_{sp} = 2.2\times10^{-20} = [Cu^{2+}][OH^-]^2$

$K_{sp} = 2.2\times10^{-20} = [x][0.032 + 2x]^2$

Assume 2x is negligible compared to 0.032 mol/L.

$K_{sp} = 2.2 \times 10^{-20} = [x][0.032]^2$

$x = [Cu^{2+}] = 2.1484375 \times 10^{-17} = 2.1 \times 10^{-17}$ mol/L

Use the Nernst equation to determine the new cell potential:

$$E = 0.00 \text{ V} - \frac{(8.314 \text{ J/mol} \cdot \text{K})(298 \text{ K})}{(2)(96485 \text{ C/mol})} \ln \frac{\left[Cu^{2+} \right]_{hydroxide}}{\left[Cu^{2+} \right]_{original}}$$

$$E = - \frac{(8.314 \text{ J/mol} \cdot \text{K})(298 \text{ K})}{(2)(96485 \text{ C/mol})} \ln \left(\frac{2.1484375 \times 10^{-17}}{0.0100} \right)$$

$$E = 0.433630 \text{ V} = \mathbf{0.43 \text{ V}}$$

d) Use the Nernst equation to determine the copper ion concentration in the half-cell containing the hydroxide ion.

$$E = 0.00 \text{ V} - \frac{(8.314 \text{ J/mol} \cdot \text{K})(298 \text{ K})}{(2)(96485 \text{ C/mol})} \ln \frac{\left[Cu^{2+} \right]_{hydroxide}}{\left[Cu^{2+} \right]_{original}}$$

$$0.340 = - \frac{(8.314 \text{ J/mol} \cdot \text{K})(298 \text{ K})}{(2)(96485 \text{ C/mol})} \ln \frac{\left[Cu^{2+} \right]_{hydroxide}}{(0.0100)}$$

$$-26.48149 = \ln \frac{\left[Cu^{2+} \right]_{hydroxide}}{(0.0100)}$$

$$3.15671 \times 10^{-12} = \frac{\left[Cu^{2+} \right]_{hydroxide}}{(0.0100)}$$

$[Cu^{2+}]_{hydroxide} = 3.15671 \times 10^{-14}$ mol/L

Now use the K_{sp} relationship:

$K_{sp} = [Cu^{2+}][OH^-]^2 = 2.2 \times 10^{-20}$

$K_{sp} = 2.2 \times 10^{-20} = [3.2622257 \times 10^{-14}][OH^-]^2$

$[OH^-]^2 = 6.96928 \times 10^{-7}$

$[OH^-] = 8.3482 \times 10^{-4} = 8.3 \times 10^{-4}$ mol/L $OH^- = \mathbf{8.3 \times 10^{-4} \text{ mol/L NaOH}}$

19.153 a) The chemical equation for the combustion of octane is:

$2C_8H_{18}(l) + 25O_2(g) \rightarrow 16CO_2(g) + 18H_2O(g)$

The heat of reaction may be determined from heats of formation.

$$\Delta_r H^\circ = \Sigma m \Delta_{f \text{(products)}} H^\circ - \Sigma n \Delta_{f \text{(reactants)}} H^\circ$$

$$\Delta_r H^\circ = [(16)(\Delta_f H^\circ \text{ of } CO_2) + (18)(\Delta_f H^\circ \text{ of } H_2O)]$$

$$- [(2)(\Delta_f H^\circ \text{ of } C_8H_{18}) + (25)(\Delta_f H^\circ \text{ of } O_2)]$$

$$\Delta_r H^\circ = [(16)(-393.5 \text{ kJ/mol}) + (18)(-241.826 \text{ kJ/mol})]$$

$$- [(2)(-250.1 \text{ kJ/mol}) + (25)(0 \text{ kJ/mol})]$$

$$\Delta_r H^\circ = -10148.868 \text{ kJ/mol} = -10148.9 \text{ kJ per two moles of octane}$$

The energy from 4.00 L of gasoline is:

$$\text{Energy (kJ)} = (4.00 \text{ L}) \left(\frac{1 \text{ mL}}{10^{-3} \text{ L}} \right) \left(\frac{0.7028 \text{ g}}{\text{mL}} \right) \left(\frac{1 \text{ mol } C_8H_{18}}{114.22 \text{ g } C_8H_{18}} \right) \left(\frac{-10148.9 \text{ kJ}}{2 \text{ mol } C_8H_{18}} \right)$$

$$= -1.2489313 \times 10^5 = \mathbf{-1.25 \times 10^5 \text{ kJ}}$$

b) The energy from the combustion of hydrogen must be found using the balanced chemical equation and the heats of formation.

$$H_2(g) + 1/2O_2(g) \rightarrow H_2O(g)$$

With the reaction written this way, the heat of reaction is simply the heat of formation of water vapour (since the heats of formation of the pure elements are zero). .

$$\Delta H^\circ = -241.826 \text{ kJ/mol}$$

The amount (mol) of hydrogen needed to produce the energy from part a) is:

$$\text{Amount (mol) of } H_2 = \left(-1.2489313 \times 10^5 \text{ kJ / mol}\right)\left(\frac{1 \text{ mol } H_2}{-241.826 \text{ kJ / mol}}\right) = 516.45867 \text{ mol}$$

Finally, use the ideal gas equation to determine the volume.

$$V = \frac{nRT}{p} = \frac{\left(516.45867 \text{ mol } H_2\right)\left(0.08314 \dfrac{L \cdot bar}{mol \cdot K}\right)\left((273 + 25)K\right)}{(1.00 \text{ bar})} = 1.27956 \times 10^4 = \mathbf{1.28 \times 10^4 \text{ L}}$$

c) This part of the problem requires the half-reaction for the electrolysis of water to produce hydrogen gas.

$$2H_2O(l) + 2e^- \rightarrow H_2(g) + 2OH^-(aq)$$

Use 1 A = 1 C/s

$$\text{Time (s)} = \left(516.45867 \text{ mol } H_2\right)\left(\frac{2 \text{ mol } e^-}{1 \text{ mol } H_2}\right)\left(\frac{96,485 \text{ C}}{1 \text{ mol } e^-}\right)\left(\frac{s}{1.00 \times 10^3 C}\right) = 9.966103 \times 10^4 = \mathbf{9.97 \times 10^4 \text{ seconds}}$$

d) Find the coulombs involved in the electrolysis of 516 moles of H_2.

$$\text{Coulombs} = \left(516.45867 \text{ mol } H_2\right)\left(\frac{2 \text{ mol } e^-}{1 \text{ mol } H_2}\right)\left(\frac{96485 \text{ C}}{1 \text{ mol } e^-}\right) = 99,661,030 \text{ C}$$

$$\text{Joules} = C \times V = 99,661,030 \text{ C} \times 6.00 \text{ V} = 597,966,177 \text{ J}$$

$$\text{Power (kW} \cdot \text{h)} = \left(597,966,177 \text{ J}\right)\left(\frac{1 \text{ kW} \cdot h}{3.6 \times 10^6 \text{ J}}\right) = 166.102 \text{ kW} \cdot h = \mathbf{166 \text{ kW} \cdot h}$$

e) The process is only 88.0% efficient, additional electricity is necessary to produce sufficient hydrogen. This is the purpose of the (100%/88.0%) factor.

$$\text{Cost} = \left(166.102 \text{ kW} \cdot h\right)\left(\frac{100\%}{88\%}\right)\left(\frac{\$0.123}{1 \text{ kW} \cdot h}\right) = \$23.2165 = \mathbf{\$23.2}$$

19.154   Plan: Write the half-reactions and the overall reaction. Calculate E°_{cell} by using $E^\circ_{cell} = E^\circ_{cathode} - E^\circ_{anode}$ and then use the Nernst equation to find $[H^+]$ at a cell potential of 0.915 V. pH is obtained from $[H^+]$.
Solution:
The half-reactions are (from the Appendix):

Oxidation:	$H_2(g) \rightarrow 2H^+(aq) + 2e^-$	$E^\circ = 0.00$ V
Reduction:	$2(Ag^+(aq) + 1e^- \rightarrow Ag(s))$	$E^\circ = 0.80$ V
Overall:	$2Ag^+(aq) + H_2(g) \rightarrow 2Ag(s) + 2H^+(aq)$	$E^\circ_{cell} = 0.80$ V $- 0.0$ V $= 0.80$ V

The hydrogen ion concentration can now be found from the Nernst equation.

$$E_{cell} = E^\circ_{cell} - \frac{(8.314 \text{ J/mol} \cdot K)(298 \text{ K})}{(2)(96485 \text{ C/mol})} \ln Q$$

$$0.915 \text{ V} = 0.80 \text{ V} - \frac{(8.314 \text{ J/mol} \cdot K)(298 \text{ K})}{(2)(96485 \text{ C/mol})} \ln \frac{\left[H^+\right]^2}{\left[Ag^+\right]^2 p_{H_2}}$$

$$0.915 \text{ V} - 0.80 \text{ V} = - \frac{(8.314 \text{ J/mol} \cdot K)(298 \text{ K})}{(2)(96485 \text{ C/mol})} \ln \frac{\left[H^+\right]^2}{(0.100)^2 (1.00)}$$

$$0.115 \text{ V} = -\frac{(8.314 \text{ J/mol} \cdot \text{K})(298 \text{ K})}{(2)(96485 \text{ C/mol})} \ln \frac{\left[\text{H}^+\right]^2}{(0.100)^2 (1.00)}$$

$$-8.9570 = \ln \frac{\left[\text{H}^+\right]^2}{(0.0100)}$$

$$1.28835 \times 10^{-4} = \frac{\left[\text{H}^+\right]^2}{(0.0100)}$$

$[\text{H}^+] = 1.135 \times 10^{-3}$ mol/L

pH $= -\log [\text{H}^+] = -\log (1.1413851 \times 10^{-3}) = 2.94498 =$ **2.94**

CHAPTER 20 ORGANIC COMPOUNDS AND THE ATOMIC PROPERTIES OF CARBON

END–OF–CHAPTER PROBLEMS

20.2   a) Carbon's electronegativity is midway between the most metallic and nonmetallic elements of Period 2. To attain a filled outer shell, carbon forms covalent bonds to other atoms in molecules (e.g., methane, CH_4), network covalent solids (e.g., diamond), and polyatomic ions (e.g., carbonate, CO_3^{2-}).
b) Since carbon has four valence electrons, it forms four covalent bonds to attain an octet.
c) Two noble gas configurations, He and Ne, are equally near carbon's configuration. To reach the He configuration, the carbon atom must lose four electrons, requiring too much energy to form the C^{4+} cation. This is confirmed by the fact that the value of the ionization energy for carbon is very high. To reach the Ne configuration, the carbon atom must gain four electrons, also requiring too much energy to form the C^{4-} anion. The fact that a carbon anion is unlikely to form is supported by carbon's electron affinity. The other possible ions would not have a stable noble gas configuration.
d) Carbon is able to bond to itself extensively because carbon's small size allows for closer approach and greater orbital overlap. The greater orbital overlap results in a strong, stable bond.
e) The C–C bond is short enough to allow the sideways overlap of unhybridized p orbitals on neighboring C atoms. The sideways overlap of p orbitals results in double and triple bonds.

20.3   a) The elements that most frequently bond to carbon are other carbon atoms, hydrogen, oxygen, nitrogen, phosphorus, sulfur, and the halogens, F, Cl, Br, and I.

b) In organic compounds, heteroatoms are defined as atoms of any element other than carbon and hydrogen. The elements **O, N, P, S, F, Cl, Br,** and **I** listed in part a) are heteroatoms.

c) Elements more electronegative than carbon are **N, O, F, Cl,** and **Br**. Elements less electronegative than carbon are **H** and **P**. Sulfur and iodine have the same electronegativity as carbon.

d) The more types of atoms that can bond to carbon, the greater the variety of organic compounds that are possible.

20.6   <u>Plan:</u> Chemical reactivity occurs when unequal sharing of electrons in a covalent bond results in regions of high and low electron density.

<u>Solution:</u>
The C–H and the C–C bonds are unreactive because electron density is shared equally between the two atoms. The C-I bond is reactive because it is long and weak. The **C=O** bond is reactive because oxygen is more electronegative than carbon and the electron rich π bond is above and below the C–O bond axis, making it very attractive to electron-poor atoms. The **C–Li** bond is also reactive because the bond polarity results in an electron-rich region around carbon and an electron-poor region around Li.

20.7   a) An alkane is an organic compound consisting of carbon and hydrogen in which there are no multiple bonds between carbon atoms, only single bonds. A cycloalkane is an alkane in which the carbon chain is arranged in a ring.

b) The general formula for an alkane is C_nH_{2n+2}. The general formula for a cycloalkane is C_nH_{2n}. (elimination of two hydrogen atoms is required to form the additional bond between carbon atoms in the ring).

20.9   <u>Plan:</u> The longest chain is named. Then we find the lowest branch numbers by counting C atoms from the end closer to a branch. Name each branch (root- + -*yl*) and put the names alphabetically before the chain name.
<u>Solution:</u>
a) Octane denotes an eight carbon alkane chain. A methyl group (–CH$_3$) is located at the second and third carbon position from the left.

$$CH_3-\underset{\underset{CH_3}{|}}{CH}-\underset{\underset{CH_3}{|}}{\overset{\overset{CH_3}{|}}{CH}}-CH_2-CH_2-CH_2-CH_2-CH_3$$

b) Cyclohexane denotes a six-carbon ring containing only single bonds. Numbering of the carbon atoms on the ring could start at any point, but typically, numbering starts at the top carbon atom of the ring for convenience. The ethyl group (–CH$_2$CH$_3$) is located at position 1 and the methyl group is located at position 3.

c) The longest continuous chain contains seven carbon atoms, so the root name is "hept." The molecule contains only single bonds, so the suffix is "ane." Numbering the carbon chain from the left results in side groups (methyl groups) at positions 3 and 4. Numbering the carbon chain from the other end will result in side groups at positions 4 and 5. Since the goal is to obtain the lowest numbering position for a side group, the correct name is **3,4-dimethylheptane**. Note that the prefix "di" is used to denote that two methyl side groups are present in this molecule.

d) This molecule is a 4–carbon chain, with two methyl groups (dimethyl) located at the position 2. The correct name is **2,2-dimethylbutane**.

20.11   <u>Plan:</u> The longest chain is named. Then we find the lowest branch numbers by counting C atoms from the end closer to a branch. Name each branch (root- + -*yl*) and put the names alphabetically before the chain name.
<u>Solution:</u>
a) 4-methylhexane means a 6 C chain with a methyl group on the 4th carbon:

$$\underset{6}{CH_3}-\underset{5}{CH_2}-\underset{4}{CH_2}-\underset{3}{\overset{\overset{CH_3}{|}}{CH}}-\underset{2}{CH_2}-\underset{1}{CH_3}$$

Numbering from the end carbon to give the lowest value for the methyl group gives the correct name of **3-methylhexane**.
b) 2-ethylpentane means a five-carbon chain with an ethyl group on the second carbon:

$$\underset{1}{CH_3}-\underset{2}{\overset{\overset{CH_3}{|}}{\underset{|}{\overset{|}{CH}}}}-\underset{3}{CH_2}-\underset{4}{CH_2}-\underset{5}{CH_3}$$

Numbering the longest chain gives the correct name, **3-methylhexane**.

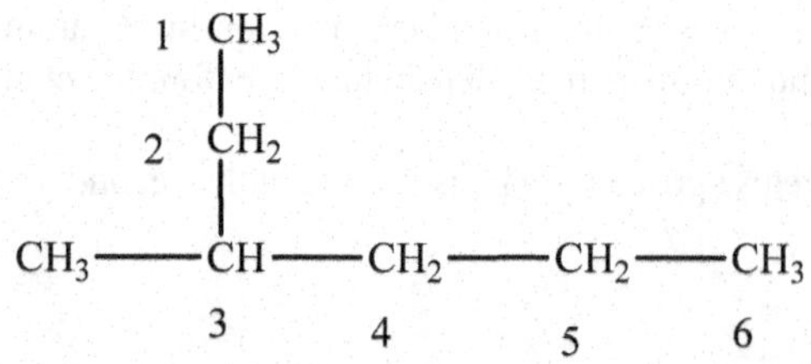

c) 2-methylcyclohexane means a 6 C ring with a methyl group on carbon #2:

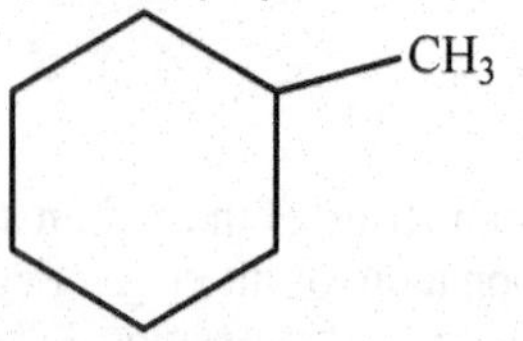

In a ring structure, whichever carbon is bonded to the methyl group is automatically assigned as carbon #1. Since this is automatic, it is not necessary to specify 1-methyl in the name. Correct name is **methylcyclohexane**.

d) 3,3-methyl-4-ethyloctane means an 8 C chain with 2 methyl groups attached to the 3rd carbon and one ethyl group to the 4th carbon.

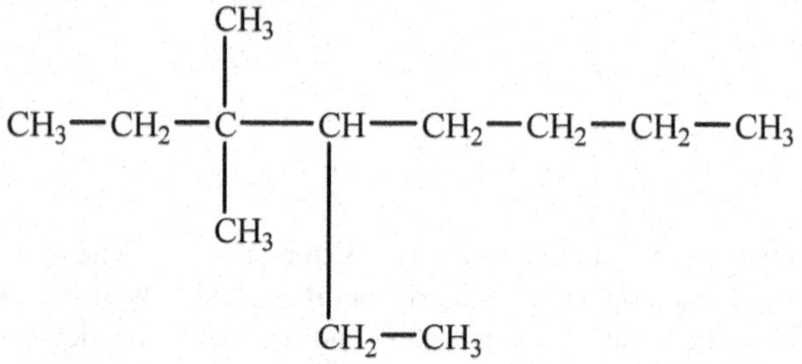

Numbering is good for this structure, but the fact that there are two methyl groups must be indicated by the prefix di- in addition to listing 3,3. The branch names appear in alphabetical order. Correct name is **4-ethyl-3,3-dimethyloctane**.

20.13   All non-numbered carbon atoms are secondary (2). All other carbon atoms are identified as primary (1), tertiary (3) or quaternary (4). Note that this notation is not used for carbon atoms participating in double or triple bonds.

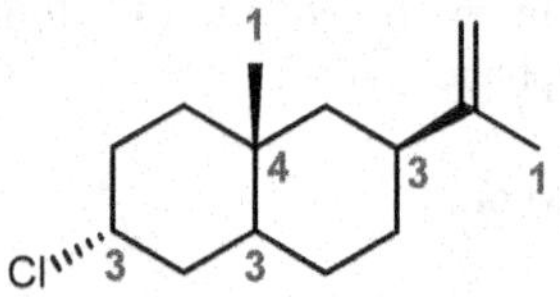

20.15

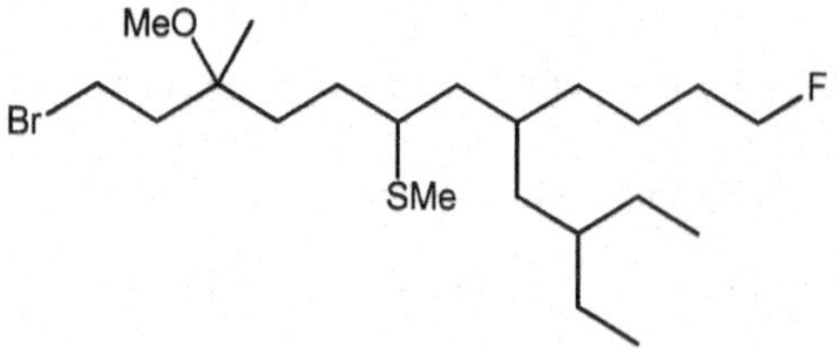

20.18   **B** is the most stable as it minimizes the interaction between the largest substituents (methyl groups)

20.20

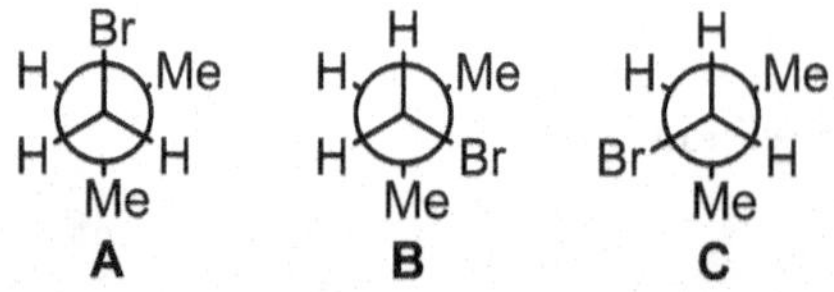

B is the least stable. A and C are equally stable.

20.22

Carbon skeleton: 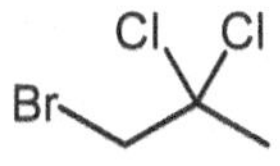   Fischer projection:

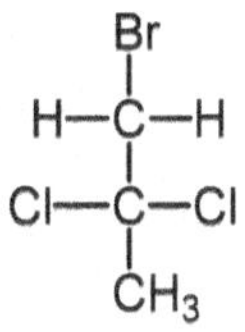

20.23

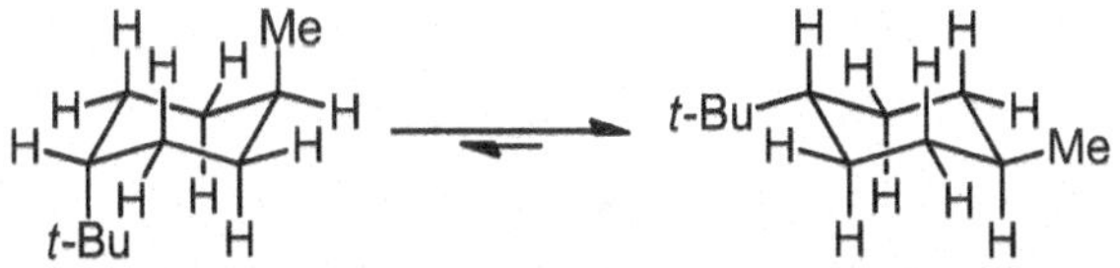

Structure B is more stable as the bulky groups (*tert*-butyl and methyl) are in the equatorial position, which reduces the 1,3-diaxial interactions.

20.25   a) Constitutional isomers are those with different sequences of bonded atoms.
b) Geometric isomers are those where the connectivity between the atoms is the same, but have a different spatial arrangement of the atoms. Geometric isomers differ in the geometric arrangement of the groups attached to the double bond or to the ring.
c) Optical isomers are a type of stereoisomerism that arises when a molecule and its mirror image cannot be superimposed on each other. They rotate the plane of polarized light in opposite direction.

Configurational and conformational isomers are are stereoisomers. Constitutional isomers are not stereoisomers.

20.28   a) *trans* (with respect to longest chain) but labelled **Z**
b) *trans* (with respect to longest chain) but labelled **E.**
As you can see from above E/Z and *cis-trans* nomenclature becomes more complicated with double bonds having more than 2 substituents. In general, we need to specify what the reference point is when talking about *cis* and *trans*. In this case we used the longest carbon chain. Moreover, for double bonds with 2 or more substituents the E/Z nomenclature is preferred.

20.32   **H < D < O < P < Br < I**

20.33   Plan: An asymmetric molecule has no plane of symmetry.
Solution:
a) A circular clock face numbered 1 to 12 o'clock is **asymmetric**. Imagine that the clock is cut in half, from 12 to 6 or from 9 to 3. The one-half of the clock could never be superimposed on the other half, so the halves are not identical. Another way to visualize symmetry is to imagine cutting an object in half and holding the half up to a mirror. If the original object is "re-created" in the mirror, then the object has a plane of symmetry.

b) A football is **symmetric** and has two planes of symmetry — one axis along the length and one axis along the fattest part of the football.

c) A dime is **asymmetric**. Either cutting it in half or slicing it into two thin diameters results in two pieces that cannot be superimposed on one another.

d) A brick, assuming that it is perfectly shaped, is **symmetric** and has three planes of symmetry at right angles to each other.

e) A hammer is **symmetric** and has one plane of symmetry, slicing through the metal head and down through the handle.

f) A spring is **asymmetric**. Every coil of the spring is identical to the one before it, so a spring can be cut in half and the two pieces can be superimposed on one another by sliding (not flipping) the second half over the first. However, if the cut spring is held up to a mirror, the resulting image is not the same as the uncut spring. Disassemble a ballpoint pen and cut the spring inside to verify this explanation.

20.36   The compound 2-methylhex-3-ene has *cis-trans* isomers.

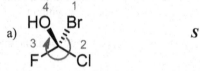

cis-2-methylhex-3-ene   *trans*-2-methylhex-3-ene

The compound 2-methylhex-2-ene does not have *cis-trans* isomers because the #2 carbon atom is attached to two identical methyl ($-CH_3$) groups:

2-methylhex-2-ene

20.38   <u>Plan</u>: Use the Cahn-Ingold-Prelog rules to evaluate each structure.
In the case of a chiral centre, orient the molecule such that the lowest priority of the four substituents is pointed away from the viewer. If the priority of the remaining three substituents decreases in a clockwise direction, the carbon is labeled R. If the priority of the substituents decreases in a counterclockwise direction, the carbon is labeled S.
For double bonds, look at the atoms directly attached to each carbon of the double bond. Rank them according to decreasing atomic number. If two atoms are identical, look at all the atoms directly attached to these atoms. If the high priority groups are on the same side, then the alkene is Z (i.e., German for "together") and if the high priority groups are on the opposite side, then the alkene is E (i.e., German for "opposite"). If there is more than one double bond, then the location needs to be included with the locant (e.g., 2E or 4Z).

a)   *S*

In the molecule above, the lowest priority of the four substituents (4) is pointed towards the viewer and the priority of the remaining three substituents decreases in a clockwise direction. However, if we invert the molecule, the lowest priority of the four substituents is pointed away from the viewer and we get exactly the opposite: the priority of the substituents decreases in a counterclockwise direction. That is why the stereogenic centre is S.

b)   *R* and **E**

c) 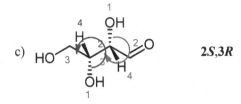   **2S,3R**

20.41   Plan: In common names, the positions of two groups are indicated by *o-* (*ortho*) for groups in positions 1 and 2, *m-* (*meta*) for groups in positions 1 and 3, and *p-* (*para*) for groups in positions 1 and 4.
Solution:

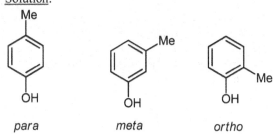

para   meta   ortho

20.44   Plan: A carbon atom is chiral if it is attached to four different groups.
Solution:
The circled atoms below are chiral.

(a)   (b)

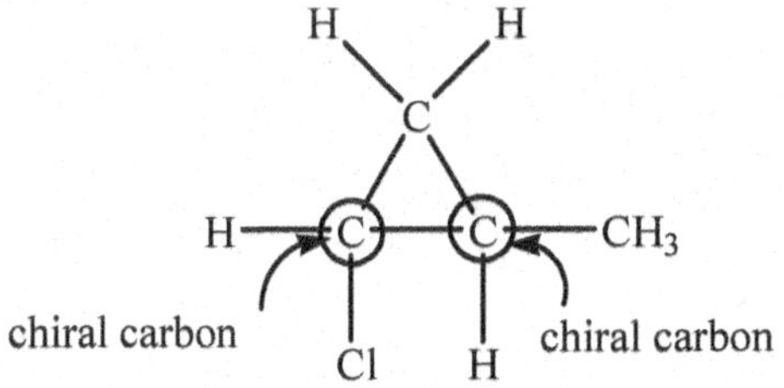

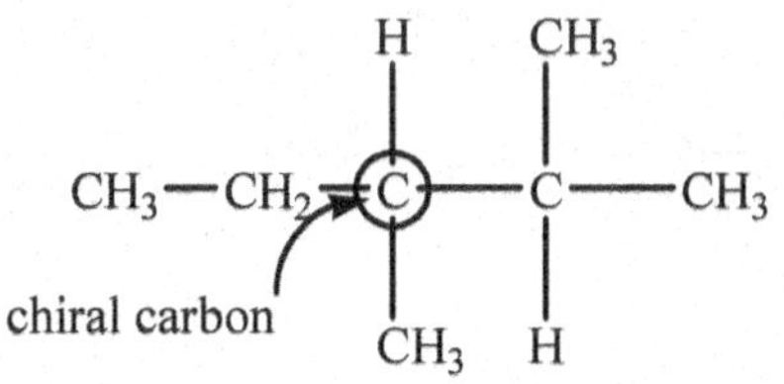

20.46   Plan: The longest chain is named. Then we find the lowest branch numbers by counting C atoms from the end closer to a branch. Name each branch (root- + -*yl*) and put the names alphabetically before the chain name. An optically active compound contains at least one chiral center, a carbon with four distinct groups bonded to it.

Solution: a) This compound is a six-carbon chain with a Br on the third carbon. 3-bromohexane is optically active because carbon #3 has four distinct groups bonded to it: 1) –Br, 2) –H, 3) –CH₂CH₃, 4) –CH₂CH₂CH₃.

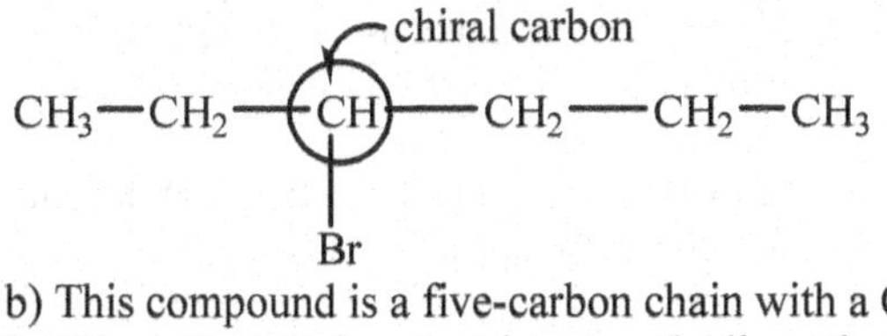

b) This compound is a five-carbon chain with a Cl and a methyl (CH₃) group on the third carbon. 3-Chloro-3-methylpentane is not optically active because no carbon has four distinct groups. The third carbon has three distinct groups: 1) –Cl, 2) –CH₃, 3) two –CH₂CH₃ groups.

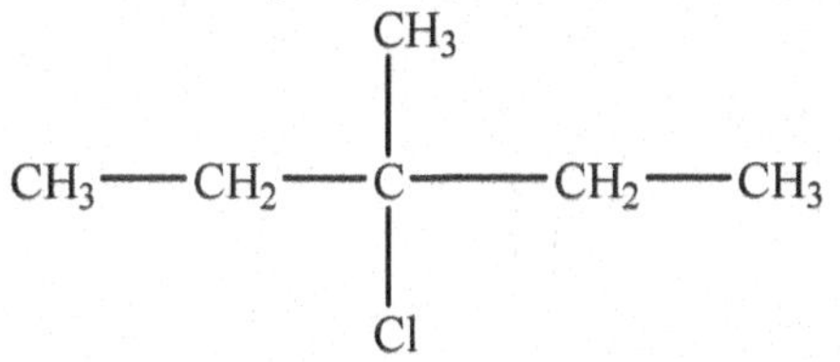

c) This compound is a four-carbon chain with Br atoms on the first and second carbon atoms and a methyl group on the second carbon. 1,2-dibromo-2-methylbutane is optically active because the second carbon is chiral, bonded to the four groups: 1) –CH_2Br, 2) –CH_3, 3) –Br, 4) –CH_2CH_3.

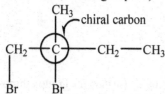

20.48   <u>Plan:</u> Geometric isomers are defined as compounds with the same atom sequence but different arrangements of the atoms in space. The *cis-trans* geometric isomers occur when rotation is restricted around a bond, as in a double bond or a ring structure, and when two different groups are bonded to each atom in the restricted bond.
<u>Solution:</u>
a) Both carbon atoms in the double bond are bonded to two distinct groups, so geometric isomers will occur. The double bond occurs at position 2 in a five-carbon chain.

cis-pent-2-ene   *trans*-pent-2-ene

b) *Cis-trans* geometric isomerism occurs about the double bond. The ring is named as a side group (cyclohexyl) occurring at position 1 on the propene main chain.

cis-cyclohexylprop-1-ene   *trans*-cyclohexylprop-1-ene

c) No geometric isomers occur because the left carbon participating in the double bond is attached to two identical methyl (–CH_3) groups.

20.50   <u>Plan:</u> Geometric isomers are defined as compounds with the same atom sequence but different arrangements of the atoms in space. The *cis-trans* geometric isomers occur when rotation is restricted around a bond, as in a double bond or a ring structure, and when two different groups are bonded to each atom in the restricted bond.
<u>Solution:</u>
a) The structure of propene is CH_2=CH–CH_3. The first carbon that is involved in the double bond is bonded to two of the same type of group, hydrogen. Geometric isomers will not occur in this case.

b) The structure of hex-3-ene is CH_3CH_2CH=$CHCH_2CH_3$. Both carbon atoms in the double bond are bonded to two distinct groups, so geometric isomers will occur.

cis-hex-3-ene   *trans*-hex-3-ene

c) The structure of 1,1-dichloroethene is $CCl_2{=}CH_2$. Both carbon atoms in the double bond are bonded to two identical groups, so no geometric isomers occur.

d) The structure of 1,2-dichloroethene is $CHCl{=}CHCl$. Each carbon in the double bond is bonded to two distinct groups, so geometric isomers do exist.

cis-1,2-dichloroethene   trans-1,2-dichloroethene

20.52   a) An alkene is a hydrocarbon with at least one double bond between two carbon atoms. An alkyne is a hydrocarbon with at least one triple bond between two carbon atoms.

b) For an alkene, assuming only one double bond, the general formula is C_nH_{2n}. When a double bond is formed in an alkane, two hydrogen atoms are removed.
For an alkyne, assuming only one triple bond, the general formula is C_nH_{2n-2}. Forming a triple bond from a double bond causes the loss of two hydrogen atoms.

20.53   Plan: To draw the possible skeletons, it is useful to have a systematic approach to make sure no structures are missed. Draw the chain or ring and then draw structures with branches or a double bond at different points along the chain.
Solution:
a) Since there are seven C atoms but only a six-carbon chain, there is one C branch off of the chain. First, draw the skeleton with the double bond between the first and second carbons and place the branched carbon in all possible positions starting with C #2. Then move the double bond to between the second and third carbon and place the branched carbon in all possible positions. Then move the double bond to between the third and fourth carbons and place the branched carbon in all possible positions. The double bond does not need to be moved further in the chain since the placement between the second and third carbon is equivalent to placement between the fourth and fifth carbons and placement between the first and second carbons is equivalent to placement between the fifth and sixth carbons. The other position to consider for the double bond is between the branched carbon and the six-carbon chain.
Double bond between first and second carbons:

Double bond between second and third carbons:

Double bond between third and fourth carbons:

```
C——C——C═══C——C——C          C——C——C═══C——C——C
    |                                      |
    C                                      C
```

Double bond between branched carbon and chain:

```
C——C——C——C——C——C
       ‖
       C
```

The total number of unique skeletons is eleven. To determine if structures are the same, build a model of one skeleton and see if you can match the structure of the other skeleton by rotating the model and without breaking any bonds. If bonds must be broken to make the other skeleton, the structures are not the same.

b) The same approach can be used here with placement of the double bond first between C #1 and C #2, then between C #2 and C #3. Since there are seven C atoms but only five C atoms in the chain, there are two C branches.

Double bond between first and second carbons:

```
C═══C——C——C——C            C═══C——C——C——C
    |   |                      |       |
    C   C                      C       C
        |
        C
```

```
C═══C——C——C——C            C═══C——C——C——C
    |                          |       |
    C                          C       C
    |
    C
```

```
    C
    |
C═══C——C——C——C            C═══C——C——C——C
        |                      |
        C                      C——C
```

Double bond between second and third carbons:

```
C——C═══C——C——C            C——C═══C——C——C
   |   |                     |       |
   C   C                     C       C
```

```
                                          C
                                          |
C——C═══C——C——C            C——C═══C——C——C
   |   |                     |
   C   C                     C
```

```
C——C═══C——C——C
   |
   C——C
```

c) Five of the carbons are in the ring and two are branched off the ring. Remember that all the carbons in the ring are equivalent and there are two groups bonded to each carbon in the ring.

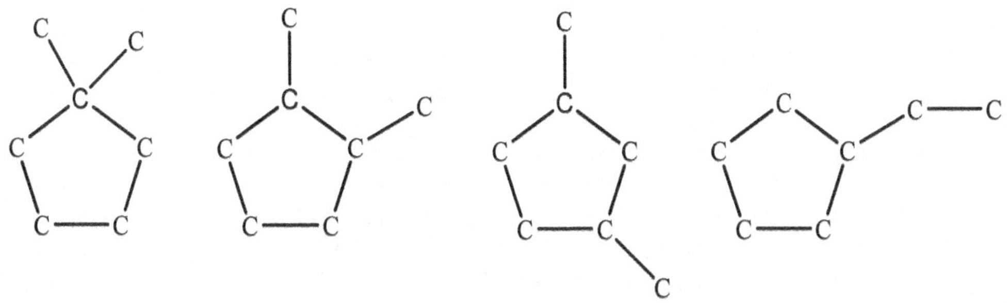

(structures of four substituted cyclopentane rings with carbon-only skeletal drawings shown at top of page)

20.55 <u>Plan:</u> Add hydrogen atoms to make a total of four bonds to each carbon.
<u>Solution:</u>
a)

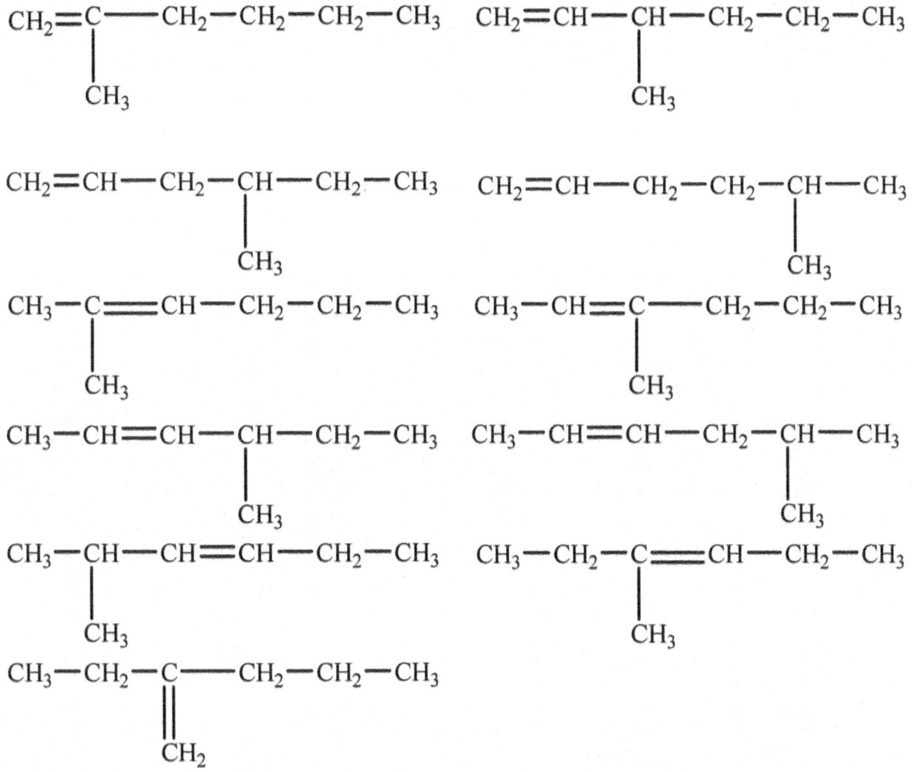

$CH_2{=}C{-}CH_2{-}CH_2{-}CH_2{-}CH_3$
   |
   CH_3

$CH_2{=}CH{-}CH{-}CH_2{-}CH_2{-}CH_3$
    |
    CH_3

$CH_2{=}CH{-}CH_2{-}CH{-}CH_2{-}CH_3$
      |
      CH_3

$CH_2{=}CH{-}CH_2{-}CH_2{-}CH{-}CH_3$
        |
        CH_3

$CH_3{-}C{=}CH{-}CH_2{-}CH_2{-}CH_3$
   |
   CH_3

$CH_3{-}CH{=}C{-}CH_2{-}CH_2{-}CH_3$
    |
    CH_3

$CH_3{-}CH{=}CH{-}CH{-}CH_2{-}CH_3$
      |
      CH_3

$CH_3{-}CH{=}CH{-}CH_2{-}CH{-}CH_3$
        |
        CH_3

$CH_3{-}CH{-}CH{=}CH{-}CH_2{-}CH_3$
   |
   CH_3

$CH_3{-}CH_2{-}C{=}CH{-}CH_2{-}CH_3$
     |
     CH_3

$CH_3{-}CH_2{-}C{-}CH_2{-}CH_2{-}CH_3$
     ‖
     CH_2

b)

$CH_2{=}C{-}CH{-}CH_2{-}CH_3$
   | |
   CH_3 CH_3

$CH_2{=}C{-}CH_2{-}CH{-}CH_3$
   | |
   CH_3 CH_3

     CH_3
     |
$CH_2{=}CH{-}C{-}CH_2{-}CH_3$
     |
     CH_3

$CH_2{=}CH{-}CH{-}CH{-}CH_3$
    | |
    CH_3 CH_3

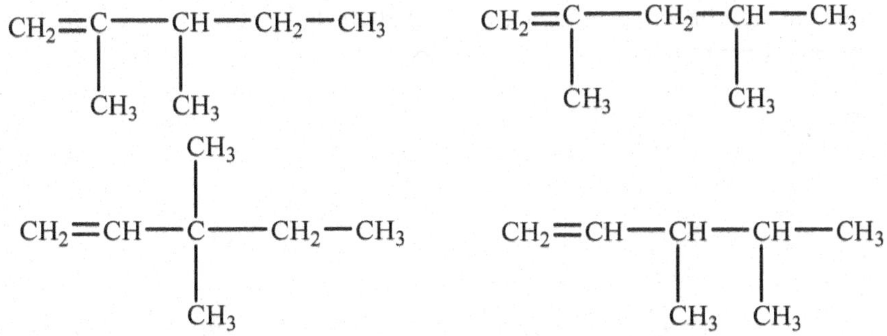

$$CH_2\!=\!CH\!-\!CH_2\!-\!\underset{\underset{CH_3}{|}}{\overset{\overset{CH_3}{|}}{C}}\!-\!CH_3$$

$$CH_2\!=\!CH\!-\!\underset{\underset{CH_2\!-\!CH_3}{|}}{CH}\!-\!CH_2\!-\!CH_3$$

$$CH_3\!-\!C\!=\!\underset{}{C}\!-\!CH_2\!-\!CH_3 \quad (\text{with } CH_3 \text{ on both central C})$$

$$CH_3\!-\!\underset{\underset{CH_3}{|}}{C}\!=\!CH\!-\!\underset{\underset{CH_3}{|}}{CH}\!-\!CH_3$$

$$CH_3\!-\!CH\!=\!\underset{\underset{CH_3}{|}}{C}\!-\!\underset{\underset{CH_3}{|}}{CH}\!-\!CH_3$$

$$CH_3\!-\!CH\!=\!CH\!-\!\underset{\underset{CH_3}{|}}{\overset{\overset{CH_3}{|}}{C}}\!-\!CH_3$$

$$CH_3\!-\!CH\!=\!\underset{\underset{CH_2\!-\!CH_3}{|}}{C}\!-\!CH_2\!-\!CH_3$$

c)

$$\begin{array}{c}CH_3 \quad CH_3\\ \diagdown\ \diagup\\ C\\ CH_2\ \ CH_2\\ CH_2\!-\!CH_2\end{array}$$

$$\begin{array}{c}CH_3\\ |\\ CH\ \ \ CH_3\\ CH_2\ \ \ CH\\ CH_2\!-\!CH_2\end{array}$$

$$\begin{array}{c}CH_3\\ |\\ CH\\ CH_2\ \ \ CH_2\\ CH_2\!-\!CH\\ \quad CH_3\end{array}$$

$$\begin{array}{c}CH_2\ \ CH_2\!-\!CH_3\\ CH_2\ \ \ CH\\ CH_2\!-\!CH_2\end{array}$$

20.57   <u>Plan:</u> Remember that each C must have 4 bonds.
<u>Solution:</u>
a) The first carbon in the chain has five bonds, so remove one of the hydrogen atoms on this carbon.

$$H_2C\!=\!CH\!-\!CH_2\!-\!CH_3$$

b) The second carbon in the chain has five bonds, so move the ethyl group from the second carbon to the third. To do this, a hydrogen atom must be removed from the third carbon atom.

$$HC\!\equiv\!C\!-\!\underset{\underset{\underset{\underset{CH_3}{|}}{CH_2}}{|}}{CH}\!-\!CH_3$$

c) Structure is correct.

20.59   Due to resonance structures, all the bonds in benzene are equivalent and the same, having partial double bond and partial single bond characteristic.

20.62.   A) **Methyl:** *ortho*
         B) **Hydroxy:** *para*
         C) **Bromo:** *meta*
         D) **Chloro:** *meta*
         E) **Fluoro:** *ortho*

20.64   Plan: Identify the parent compound based on the substituents attached to the benzene ring. Note the following common names: toluene (methylbenzene); phenol (hydroxyl group on benzene ring); aniline (NH_2 group on benzene ring). Ethenylbenzene is also known as vinylbenzene or styrene; however no substitution is allowed when using styrene.
         Solution:
         a) **2-bromo-4-methylphenol**
         b) **5-bromo-2-chloro-3-methylaniline**
         c) **1-bromo-2,6-dichloro-3-fluoro-5-methyl-4-ethenylbenzene**

20.65   **A** has a positively charged carbon and two double bonds. $4n+2 = 4$; $n = \frac{1}{2}$. The molecule is not aromatic.
         B has three double bonds and a carbon with a lone pair which is delocalized in the ring. $4n+2 = 8$; $n = 1.5$. **B** is **not aromatic**.
         C is fully conjugated molecule. The N atoms are using their one p orbital for the electrons in the double bond and their lone pair of electrons are not π electrons; therefore, the total of π electrons is 6. Applying Hückel's rule, we find that n = 1. Since the molecule follows all criteria for aromaticity, we conclude that **C is aromatic**.
         In **D**, the top carbon is sp^3 hybridized, so the molecule is **not aromatic**.

20.68   a) **4,4-dimethylpent-2-yne**

         b) **(2Z,5E)-hepta-2,5-diene** (if counted from right to left) or (2E,5Z)-hepta-2,5-diene (if counted from left to right)

         c) (*E*)-5-bromopent-3-en-1-yne

20.69   Plan: Benzene is a planar, aromatic hydrocarbon. It is commonly depicted as a hexagon with a circle in the middle to indicate that the π bonds are delocalized around the ring and that all ring bonds are identical. With two groups attached to the ring, number the C atoms so that a group is attached to ring C-1. Alternatively, the *ortho* (*o*-), *meta* (*m*-), and *para* (*p*-) naming system is used to denote the location of attached groups in benzene compounds only, not other ring structures like the cycloalkanes.
         Solution:

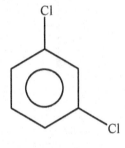   

1,2-dichlorobenzene   1,3-dichlorobenzene   1,4-dichlorobenzene
(*o*-dichlorobenzene)   (*m*-dichlorobenzene)   (*p*-dichlorobenzene)

20.71 Plan: Analyzing the name gives benzene as the base structure with the following groups bonded to it: 1) on carbon #1 a hydroxy group, –OH; 2) on carbon atoms #2 and #6 a *tert*-butyl group, –C(CH$_3$)$_3$; and 3) on carbon #4 a methyl group, –CH$_3$.

Solution:

20.72 From lowest to highest, the predicted boiling point order is: **C < B < D < A.** Boiling point increases with molecular weight (therefore **C** is lowest, followed by **B**). Long chains have higher boiling points than branched species since they are able to form stronger intermolecular interactions. **D** is more hindered than **A** and therefore is less able to make hydrogen bonds (therefore **D** is lower than **A**)

20.75 Plan: Refer to the Table of Functional Groups in the chapter.

Solution:

a) Halogens, except iodine, differ from carbon in electronegativity and form a single bond with carbon. The organic compound is a **haloalkane**.

b) Carbon forms triple bonds with itself and nitrogen. For the bond to be polar, it must be between carbon and nitrogen. The compound is a **nitrile**.

c) **Carboxylic acids** contain a double bond to oxygen and a single bond to oxygen. Carboxylic acids dissolve in water to give acidic solutions.

d) Oxygen is commonly double bonded to carbon. A carbonyl group (C=O) that is at the end of a chain is found in an **aldehyde**.

20.77

e)

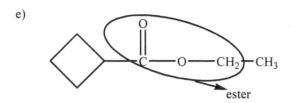

ester

20.80   Aldehydes:

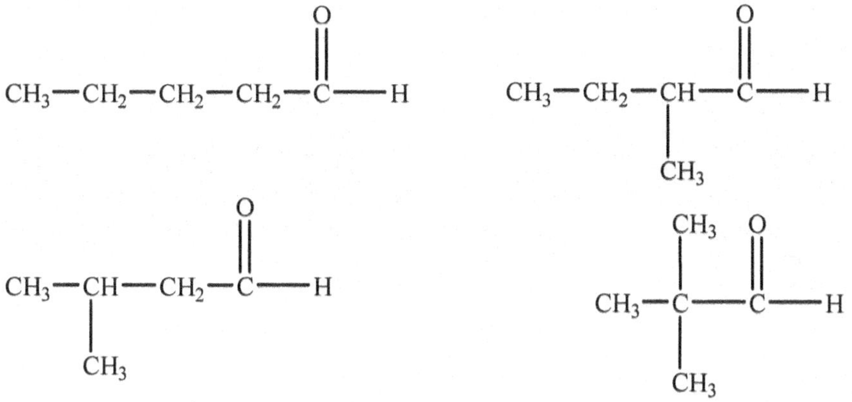

CH₃—CH₂—CH₂—CH₂—C(=O)—H

CH₃—CH₂—CH(CH₃)—C(=O)—H

CH₃—CH(CH₃)—CH₂—C(=O)—H

CH₃—C(CH₃)(CH₃)—C(=O)—H

Ketones:

CH₃—C(=O)—CH₂—CH₂—CH₃

CH₃—CH₂—C(=O)—CH₂—CH₃

CH₃—C(=O)—CH(CH₃)—CH₃

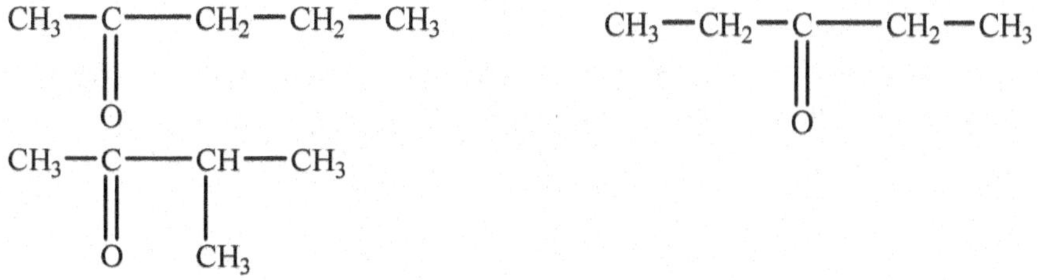

20.81   <u>Plan:</u> First, draw all primary amines (formula R–NH₂). Next, draw all secondary amines (formula R–NH–R').
There is only one possible tertiary amine structure (formula R₃–N). Eight amines with the formula $C_4H_{11}N$ exist.
<u>Solution:</u>

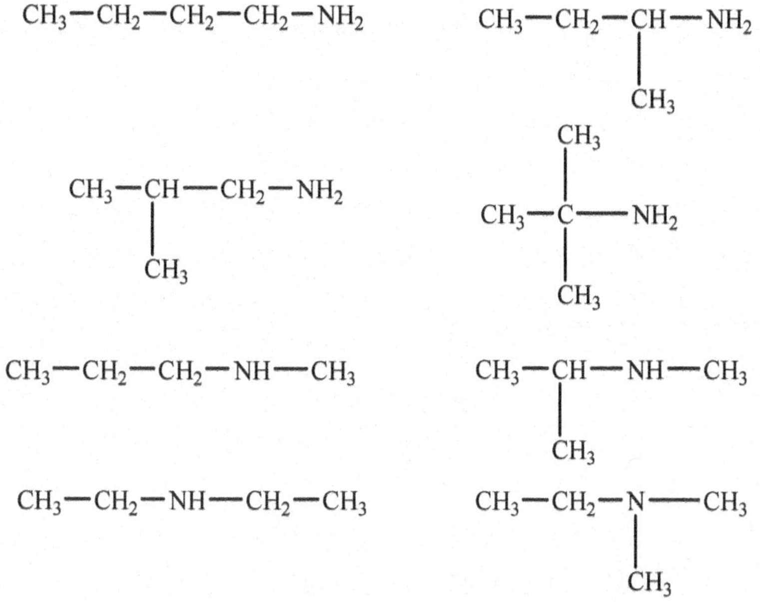

CH₃—CH₂—CH₂—CH₂—NH₂

CH₃—CH₂—CH(CH₃)—NH₂

CH₃—CH(CH₃)—CH₂—NH₂

CH₃—C(CH₃)(CH₃)—NH₂

CH₃—CH₂—CH₂—NH—CH₃

CH₃—CH(CH₃)—NH—CH₃

CH₃—CH₂—NH—CH₂—CH₃

CH₃—CH₂—N(CH₃)—CH₃

20.84   Plan: We can calculate the degrees of unsaturation from the following general formula:

$$DU = \frac{2C + N - H - X + 2}{2}$$

where C = number of carbon atoms, N = number of nitrogen atoms, X = number of halogens and H = number of hydrogen atoms.
Solution:

$$DU = \frac{2(13) + 0 - 16 - 0 + 2}{2} = 6$$

20.86 $DU = \dfrac{2(6) + 2 - 6 - 2 + 2}{2} = 4$

20.89. $DU = \dfrac{2(7) + 0 - 6 - 0 + 2}{2} = 5$

With a degree of unsaturation equal to 5, the molecule could have five double bonds, a triple bond and three double bonds, two triple bonds and a double bond or a ring and four double bonds, as shown below (recall that an acid reacts with a base to form a salt).

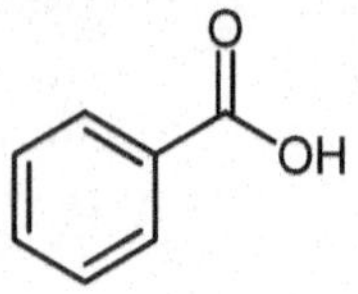

$C_7H_6O_2$

20.93   Plan: The general formula C_nH_{2n} refers to alkenes so we can now draw and name all of our possible structures of C_5H_{10} making sure that all carbon and hydrogen atoms are present.

Solution:

pent-1-ene 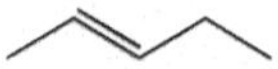   pent-2-ene 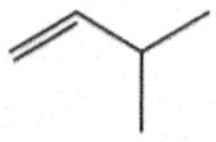   3-methylbut-1-ene 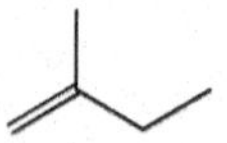   2-methylbut-1-ene 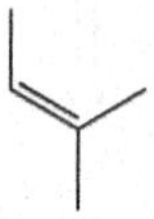   2-methylbut-2-ene

Two of the possible isomers are geometric isomers and we can name them using E/Z nomenclature from Section 20.5

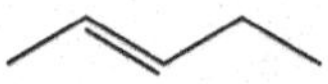

(E)-pent-2-ene 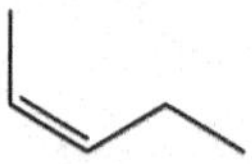   (Z)-pent-2-ene

Geometric Isomers

20.95   <u>Plan:</u> Using the formula from Section 20.6 we can determine the degree of unsaturation the formula $C_7H_{10}O_2$ has. We can then draw the structures using the rules from 20.6, for the aromatic structure we must check any structures we draw using Hückel's rule (Section 20.5)

<u>Solution:</u>

$$DU = \frac{2C - N - H - X - 2}{2} = \frac{2(7) - 0 - 10 - 0}{2} = 2$$

For DU = 2, we can have 2 rings or two double bonds or 1 triple bond or 1 ring and 1 double bond in our final structure.

Below are several possible structures containing the required functional groups and following the formula $C_7H_{10}O_2$. The ring structure below has n = 1 and therefore satisfies the Hückel rule meaning it is aromatic.

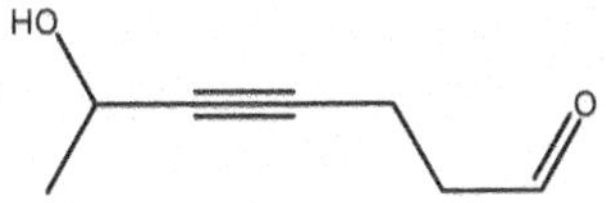

aldehyde

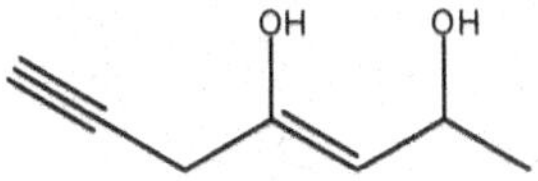

alkyne

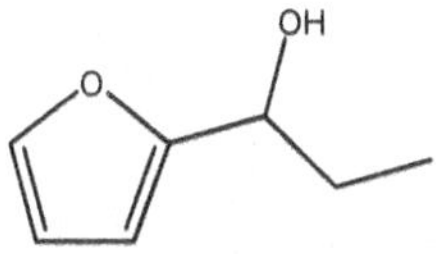

aromatic ring

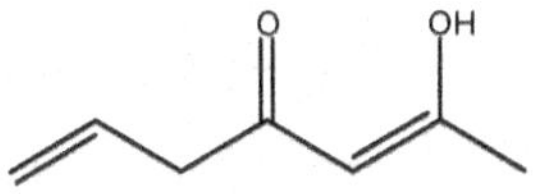

ketone

It is not possible to create a molecule containing all of the functional groups as it would require a DU of at least 6.

20.96   <u>Plan:</u> We know from Section 20.3 that the most stable conformation will be the one that has the most number of groups in the equatorial position and that groups which are larger will take precedent over smaller groups.

<u>Solution:</u>
The first structure has a *tert*-butyl group equatorial and a methyl group axial, the *tert*-butyl group defines the most stable conformation.

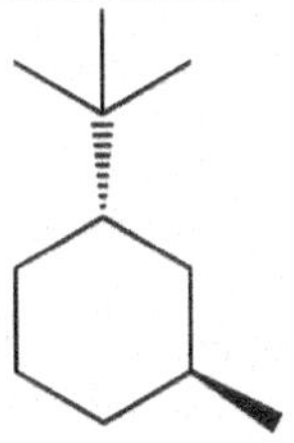

(*trans*)-1-*tert*-butyl-3-methylcyclohexane 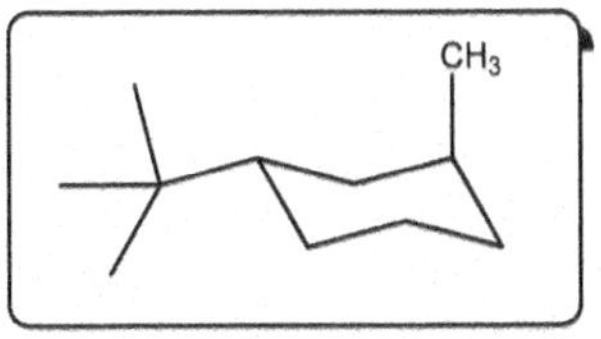   **Most Stable**

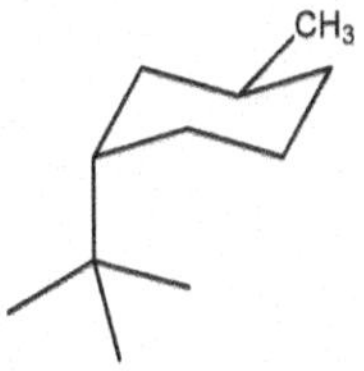

The second moleculehas one conformation in which both groups are equatorial, therefore this is the most stable.

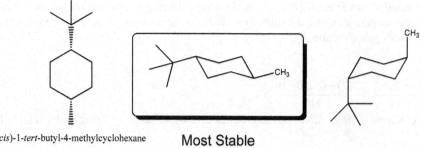

(*cis*)-1-*tert*-butyl-4-methylcyclohexane   **Most Stable**

The third structure will always have one group axial and one group equatorial, therefore both conformations are equally stable.

(*trans*)-1,3-dimethylcyclohexane   **Equally Stable**

CHAPTER 21 ORGANIC REACTION MECHANISMS

END–OF–CHAPTER PROBLEMS

21.4   <u>Plan:</u> Look for a change in the number of atoms bonded to carbon. In an addition reaction, more atoms become bonded to carbon; in an elimination reaction, fewer atoms are bonded to carbon, while in a substitution reaction, the product has the same number of atoms bonded to carbon.
<u>Solution:</u>
a)   HBr is removed from the reactant so that there are fewer bonds to carbon in the product. This is an **elimination reaction**, and an unsaturated product is formed.
b)   Hydrogen is added to the double bond, resulting in the product having two more atoms bonded to carbons. This is an **addition reaction**, resulting in a saturated product.

21.6   <u>Plan:</u> In an addition reaction, atoms are added to the carbons in a double bond. Atoms are removed in an elimination reaction, resulting in a product with a double bond. In a substitution reaction, an atom or group of atoms substitutes for another one in the reactant.

<u>Solution:</u>
a) Water (H_2O or H and OH) is added to the double bond:

$$CH_3CH_2CH{=}CHCH_2CH_3 + H_2O \xrightarrow{\ \ H^+\ \ } CH_3CH_2CH_2\underset{\underset{OH}{|}}{C}HCH_2CH_3$$

b) H and Br are eliminated from the molecule, resulting in a double bond:
$CH_3CHBrCH_3 + CH_3CH_2OK \rightarrow CH_3CH{=}CH_2 + CH_3CH_2OH + KBr$

c) Two chlorine atoms are substituted for two hydrogen atoms in ethane:

$$CH_3CH_3 + 2Cl_2 \xrightarrow{\ \ h\upsilon\ \ } CHCl_2CH_3 + 2HCl$$

21.8   <u>Plan:</u> To decide whether an organic compound is oxidized or reduced in a reaction, rely on the rules in the chapter:
A C atom is oxidized when it forms more bonds to O or fewer bonds to H because of the reaction.
A C atom is reduced when it forms fewer bonds to O or more bonds to H because of the reaction.

<u>Solution:</u>
a) The C atom is **oxidized** because it forms more bonds to O.
b) The C atom is **reduced** because it forms more bonds to H.
c) The C atom is **reduced** because it forms more bonds to H.

21.10   <u>Plan:</u> A C atom is oxidized when it forms more bonds to O or fewer bonds to H because of the reaction. A C atom is reduced when it forms fewer bonds to O or more bonds to H because of the reaction.
<u>Solution:</u>
a) The reaction $CH_3CH{=}CHCH_2CH_2CH_3 \xrightarrow[\text{cold OH}]{KM_nO_4} CH_2CH(OH){-}CH(OH)CH_2CH_2CH_3$ shows the second and third carbon atoms in the chain gaining a bond to oxygen: C–O–H. Therefore, the hex-2-ene compound has been **oxidized**.

b) The reaction shows that each carbon atom in the cyclohexane loses a bond to hydrogen to form benzene. Fewer bonds to hydrogen in the product indicates **oxidation**.

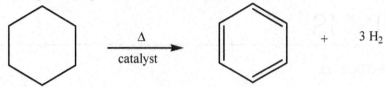

21.12   *Step 1* **substitution**   *Step 2* **addition**

21.13   The answer is (c). A concerted process occurs in one step (i.e., one hump) and in an exothermic reaction the products have lower energy than the reactants.

21.14   a) **stepwise**
        b) **exothermic**
        c) **step A**

21.16   Plan:When the electrons in the bond are equally divided, we call it a **homolytic cleavage**, while when the bond is unequally divided, the more electronegative atom gets the electrons, and we call it a **heterolytic cleavage**
        Solution:
        a) **heterolytic**
        b) **homolytic**
        c) **heterolytic**

21.18   (b) is the most nucleophilic. Nucleophilicity of the same atom type roughly follow the basicity of the atom. Methanol is more basic than the mildly acidic phenol (a) or the more acidic carboxylic acid (c) or sulfonic acid (d)

21.24   **(b)**. As S_N1 reactions are a stepwise process, they generate an intermediate carbocation. The generation of this carbocation is the rate determining step – therefore substrates which generate a more stable carbocation will have lower activation energies for the formation of this carbocation. As methyl groups are electron releasing (due to hyperconjugation) the most substituted carbocation will be the most stable.

21.27   As the reaction goes by an S_N1 mechanism, there is a planar carbocation intermediate which can be attacked from either side giving both enantiomers and resulting in a racemic mixture.

21.29   **(b)**. The azide (N_3^-) is negatively charged (making it highly nucleophilic). In addition, as the azide is linear shape it is less sterically hindered than the other two nucleophiles.

21.32

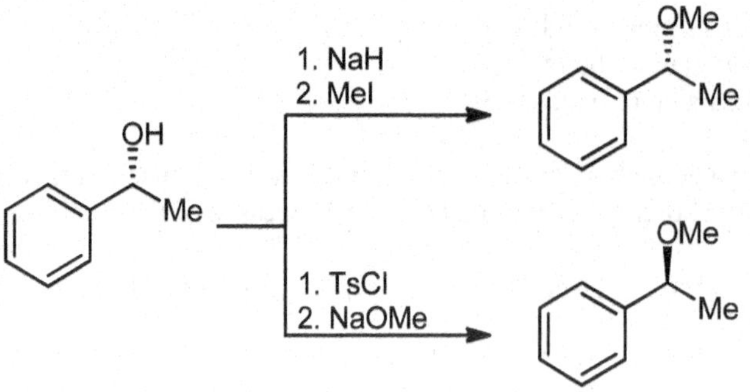

Importantly, to maintain the stereochemical information, a series of S_N2 reactions should be proposed. In the first reaction, the alcohol is deprotonated and reacted with methyl iodide via an S_N2 reaction. In the second case, we get inversion of the configuration by converting the alcohol into a good leaving group, by conversion to the tosylate, followed by an S_N2 reaction with sodium methoxide. Other methods for activation of the alcohol are acceptable, however acidic conditions will lead to racemization due to the competitive S_N1 reaction.

21.33 a)

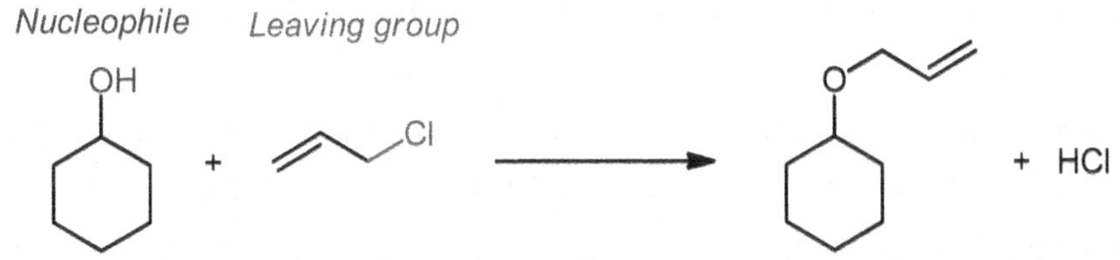

Nucleophile   *Leaving group*

+   HCl

b)

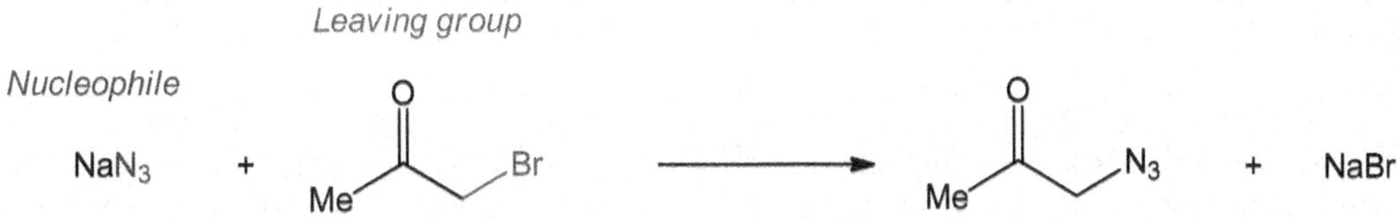

Leaving group

Nucleophile

NaN$_3$ +   (structure)   ⟶   (structure)   +   NaBr

c)

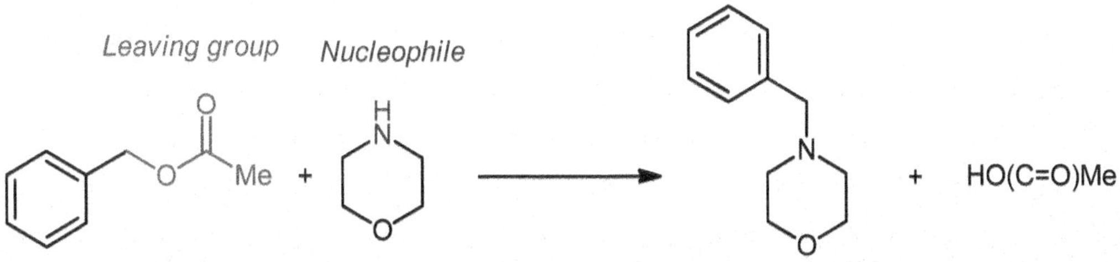

Leaving group   *Nucleophile*

(structure)   +   (structure)   ⟶   (structure)   +   HO(C=O)Me

d)

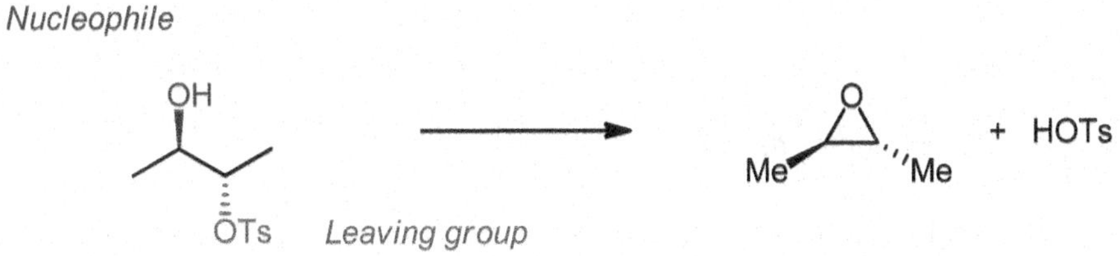

Nucleophile

+   HOTs

OTs   *Leaving group*

e)

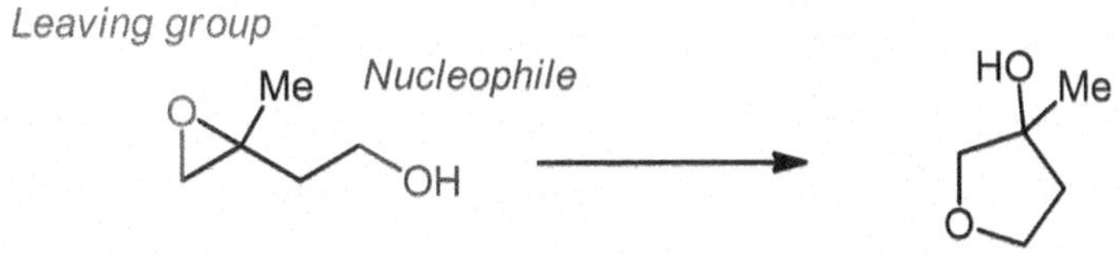

Leaving group

Me   *Nucleophile*

21.37 a)

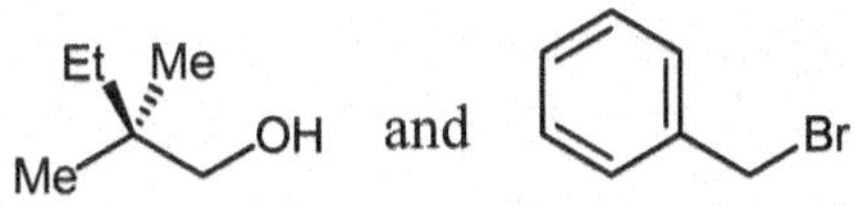

and   (structure with Br)

b)

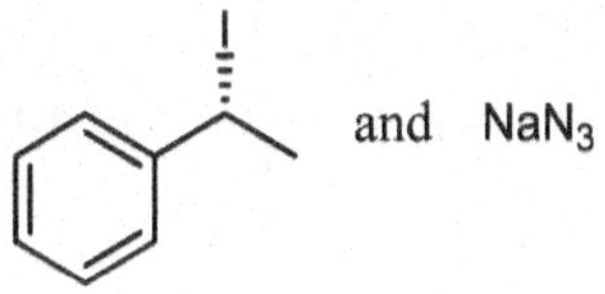

(structure)   and   NaN$_3$

c)

OH

(structure)   and   Me—I

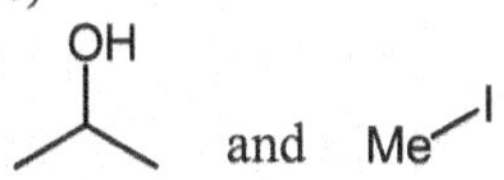

21.38 **(b):** E1 reactions require substrates that can form a stabilized carbocation (compare with the S_N1 reaction). Of the three examples given (a) would generate a primary carbocation (the least stable), (c) would generate a secondary carbocation (middle stability), and (b) would generate an allylic carbocation, which is stabilized by resonance and is the most stable.

21.41 **(b).** Steric hindrance is an important consideration in E2 reactions. Molecule (a) is highly sterically congested and is therefore an E2 type elimination would be difficult. In (c) the proton is more acidic due to the phenyl ring, but only one proton is available for deprotonation and therefore the rate of elimination would be slower than in (b) where deprotonation of any of the 6 available protons would lead to an E2 elimination. In addition, (b) is also a good E1 substrate due to the stability of the carbocation. Therefore low temperatures would help to favor an E2 type mechanism.

21.43 The most basic is (b), the least basic is (d). Basicity is linked to the stability of the anion. Molecules (c) and (d) are stabilized by resonance making them the most stable. The acid (d) has multiple heteroatoms to delocalize the charge, making it the most stable and therefore the least basic. Molecules (a) and (b) lack any resonance forms. As methyl groups release electron density through hyperconjugation, the anion in (b) is less stable than the one in (a).

21.47 **(a).** In the reaction with the unhindered base (MeO⁻) the S_N2 reaction will dominate. In (b), and (c), the hindered base favors elimination.

21.49

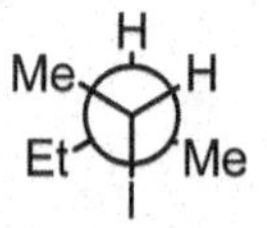

Anti-periplanar conformation

The major product we would expect is the more hindered double bond as the only conformation which allows elimination (antiperiplanar) leads to this product. It is worth noting that often due to the higher temperatures that are required to favor elimination, significant equilibration to the less hindered diastereomer can occur.

21.51

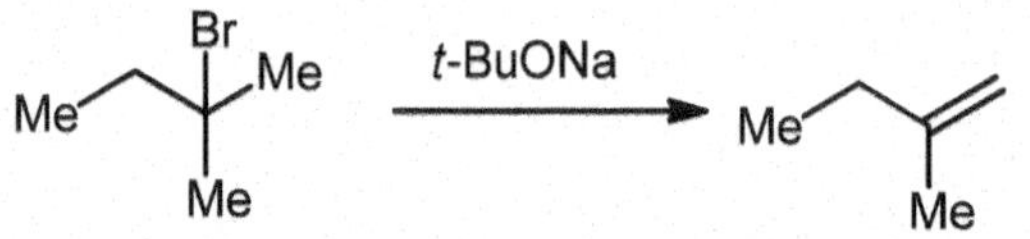

The sterically hindered base will abstract the more accessible proton.

21.53 Fill in each blank with a general formula for the type of compound formed:

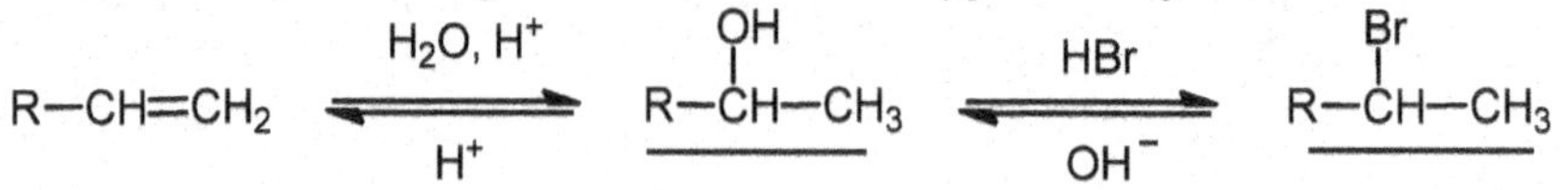

21.56 B > C > A > D. Reactivity order is based on which ring is most electron rich (from the most activating effect to the most deactivating effect).

21.57   Give the products of the following reactions.

a) 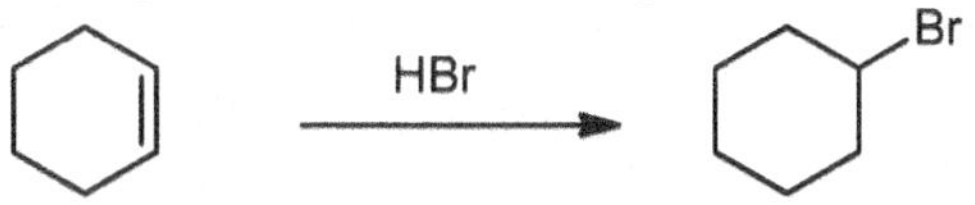 HBr → (bromocyclohexane)

b) 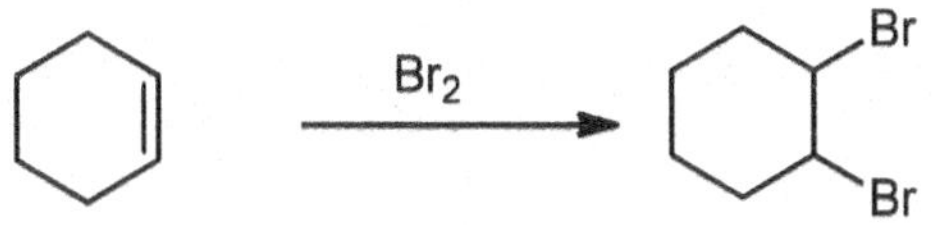 Br$_2$ → (1,2-dibromocyclohexane)

c) 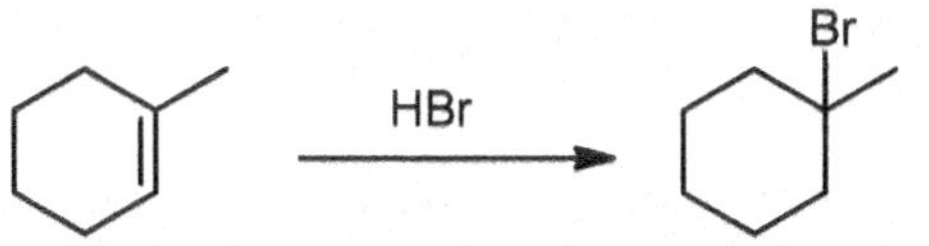 HBr → (1-bromo-1-methylcyclohexane)

d) 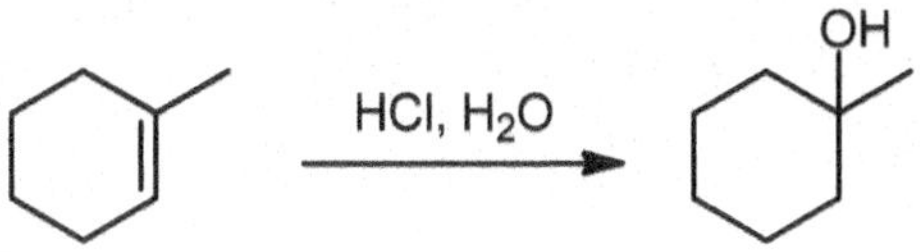 HCl, H$_2$O → (1-methylcyclohexanol)

21.60   The reagents indicate the substitution of an H with a Br. Methyl groups are ortho/para directing.

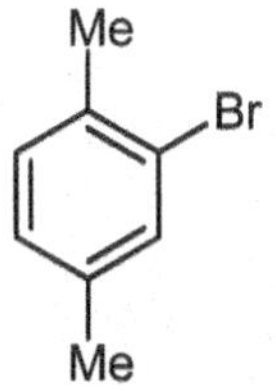

21.61

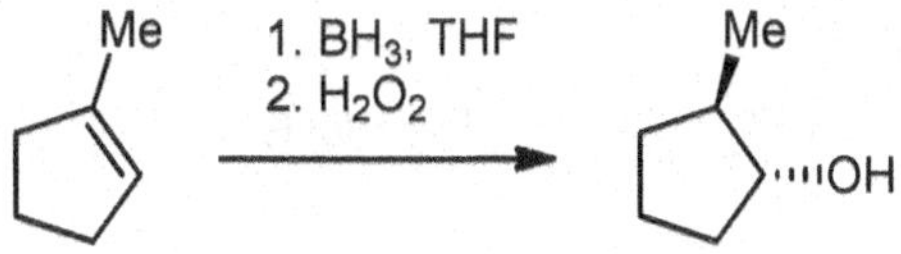

1. BH$_3$, THF
2. H$_2$O$_2$

21.63

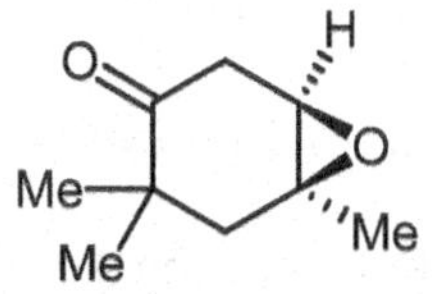

21.66

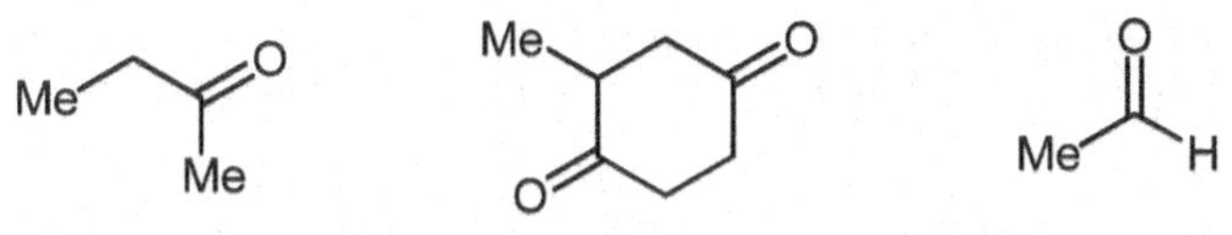

21.68   Aromatic molecules behave differently than other compounds with C=C bonds. In general, aromatic rings are much less reactive (more stable) than compounds with isolated C=C double bonds because of their delocalized π electrons. The benzene ring can undergo electrophilic substitution, nucleophilic substitution, elimination, and addition reactions, while the alkenes mainly undergo addition reactions. There are reactions that alkenes undergo pretty easily, but benzene does not. For example, bromine, Br$_2$ adds easily across alkene double bonds. Ethene (CH$_2$=CH$_2$) would add bromine to form dibromoethane, BrCH$_2$-CH$_2$Br. As a result, the red-brown colour of bromine disappears instantly if it is added to an alkene, because the bromine is rapidly consumed. Benzene can be halogenated, but is more difficult. For example, the aromatic halogenation of benzene with bromine, chlorine, or iodine needs the help of a catalyst (an iron salt or aluminum trihalide).

21.73   The aniline is a good ortho/para director and under weak acidic conditions (right hand arrow) dominates the course of the reaction. Under strongly acidic conditions, the aniline is protonated, making it a weak meta director, and the methyl group and protonated aniline give the alternative product (left hand arrow).

21.74   The C=C bond is nonpolar while the C=O bond is polar, since oxygen is more electronegative than carbon. Both bonds react by addition. In the case of addition to a C=O bond, an electron-rich group will bond to the carbon and an electron-poor group will bond to the oxygen, resulting in one product. In the case of addition to an alkene, the carbons are identical, or nearly so, so there will be no preference for which carbon bonds to the electron-poor group and which bonds to the electron-rich group. This may lead to two isomeric products, depending on the structure of the alkene.

When water is added to a double bond, the hydrogen is the electron-poor group and the hydroxyl is the electron-rich group. For a compound with a carbonyl group, only one product results as H bonds to the O atom in the double bond and –OH bonds to the carbon atom in the double bond:

However, when water adds to a C=C, two products result since the OH can bond to either carbon in the double bond:

In this reaction, very little of the second product forms.

21.78   Alcohols undergo substitution at a saturated carbon while acids undergo substitution at the carboxyl carbon.

21.81   Plan: These reactions are dehydration-condensation reactions, in which H and OH groups on the two reactant molecules react to form water and a new bond is formed between the two reactants.
        Solution:
        a) This reaction is a dehydration-condensation reaction to form an amide.

b) An alcohol and a carboxylic acid undergo dehydration-condensation to form an ester.

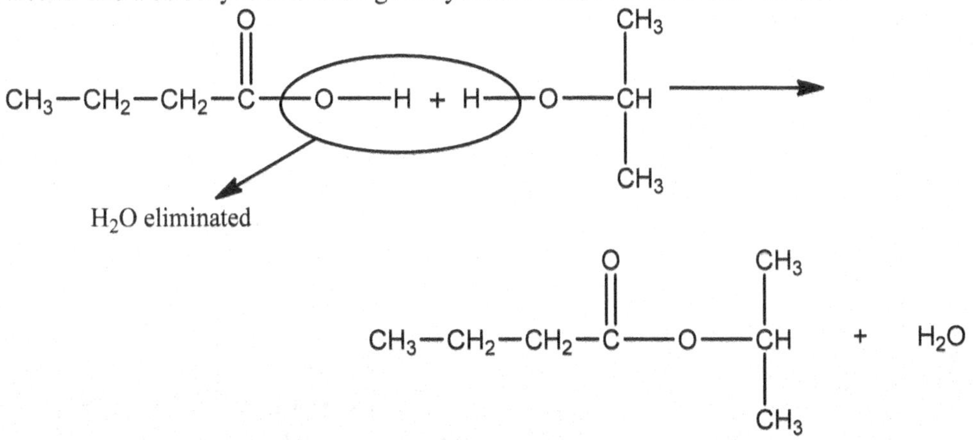

$$CH_3-CH_2-CH_2-\overset{\overset{O}{\|}}{C}\underbrace{-O-H + H-O}-\overset{\overset{CH_3}{|}}{\underset{\underset{CH_3}{|}}{CH}} \longrightarrow$$

H$_2$O eliminated

$$CH_3-CH_2-CH_2-\overset{\overset{O}{\|}}{C}-O-\overset{\overset{CH_3}{|}}{\underset{\underset{CH_3}{|}}{CH}} \quad + \quad H_2O$$

c) This reaction is ester formation through dehydration-condensation.

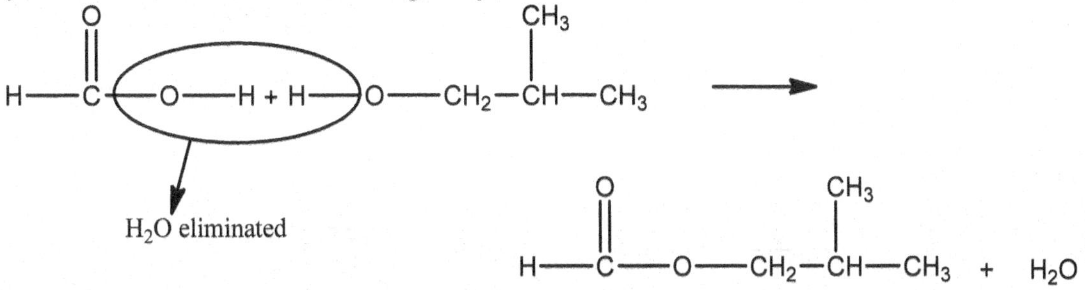

$$H-\overset{\overset{O}{\|}}{C}\underbrace{-O-H + H-O}-CH_2-\overset{\overset{CH_3}{|}}{CH}-CH_3 \longrightarrow$$

H$_2$O eliminated

$$H-\overset{\overset{O}{\|}}{C}-O-CH_2-\overset{\overset{CH_3}{|}}{CH}-CH_3 \quad + \quad H_2O$$

21.84 a)

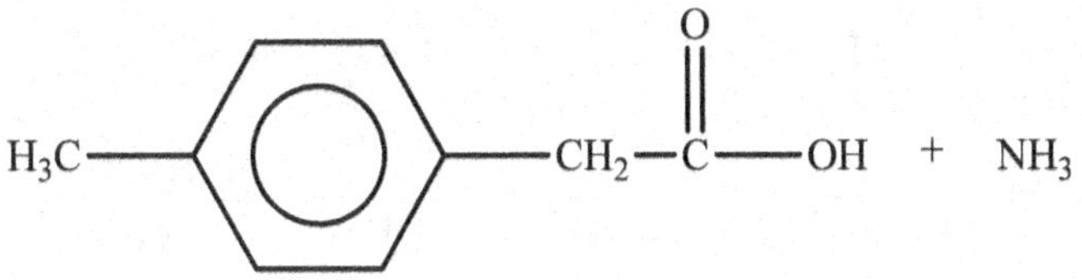

$$H_3C-\text{(benzene ring)}-CH_2-\overset{\overset{O}{\|}}{C}-OH \quad + \quad NH_3$$

b)

$$CH_3-\overset{\overset{CH_3}{|}}{CH}-\overset{\overset{O}{\|}}{C}-OH \quad + \quad H-\overset{}{\underset{\underset{CH_3}{|}}{N}}-CH_2-CH_3$$

c)

$$H-\overset{\overset{O}{\|}}{C}-OH \quad + \quad H-\overset{}{\underset{\underset{H}{|}}{N}}-\text{(benzene ring)}$$

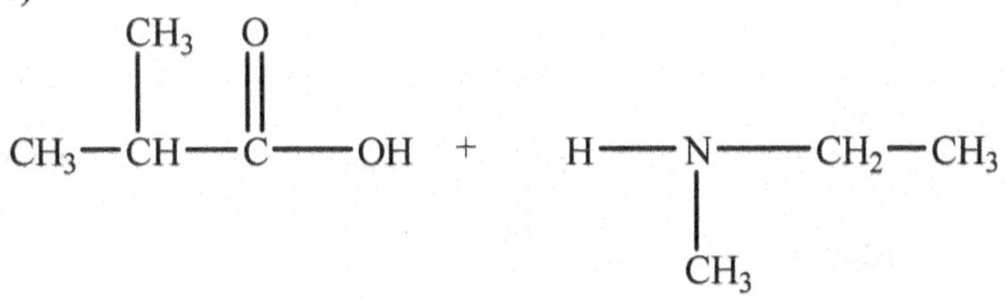

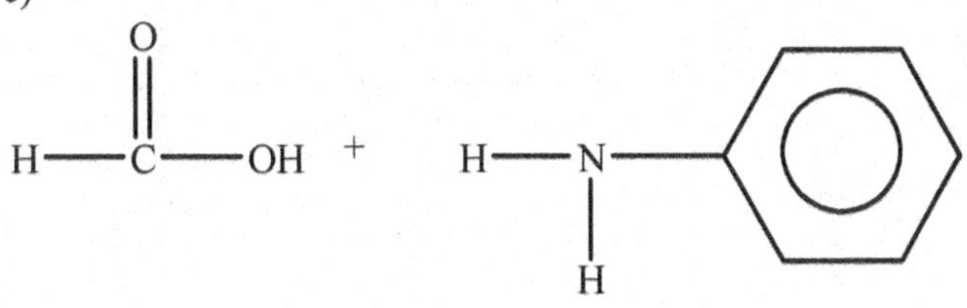

21.85 a) Substitution of Br⁻ occurs by the stronger base, OH⁻. Then a substitution reaction between the alcohol and carboxylic acid produces an ester:

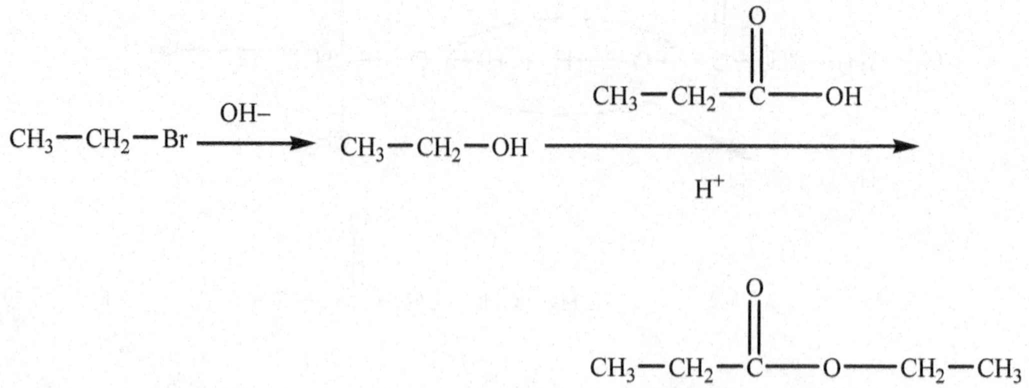

$$CH_3-CH_2-Br \xrightarrow{OH-} CH_3-CH_2-OH \xrightarrow[H^+]{CH_3-CH_2-\overset{\overset{\displaystyle O}{\|}}{C}-OH}$$

$$CH_3-CH_2-\overset{\overset{\displaystyle O}{\|}}{C}-O-CH_2-CH_3$$

b) The strong base, CN⁻, substitutes for Br. The nitrile is then hydrolyzed to a carboxylic acid.

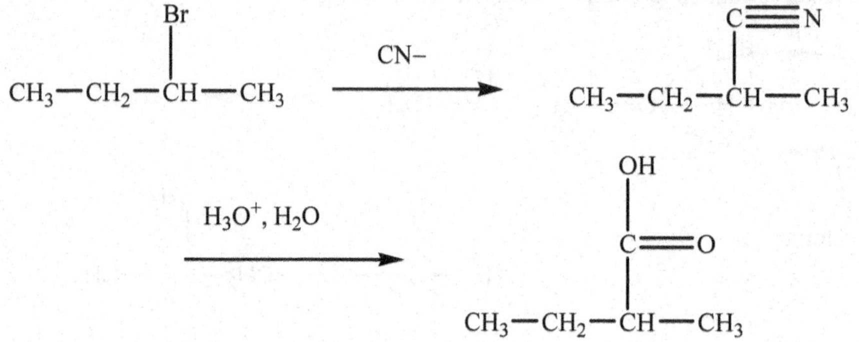

$$CH_3-CH_2-\overset{\overset{\displaystyle Br}{|}}{CH}-CH_3 \xrightarrow{CN-} CH_3-CH_2-\overset{\overset{\displaystyle C\equiv N}{|}}{CH}-CH_3$$

$$\xrightarrow{H_3O^+, H_2O} CH_3-CH_2-\overset{\overset{\displaystyle \overset{\overset{\displaystyle OH}{|}}{C}=O}{|}}{CH}-CH_3$$

21.91 a) Symbolize the monoprotic acid as HA. Then, the balanced chemical equation will be:

$$NaOH(aq) + HA(aq) \rightarrow NaA(aq) + H_2O(l)$$

$$\text{Molar mass (g/mol)} = (0.2003 \text{ g HA})\left(\frac{1 \text{ mol NaOH}}{1 \text{ mol HA}}\right)\left(\frac{1L \text{ NaOH}}{0.03811 \text{ mol NaOH}}\right)\left(\frac{1 \text{ mL NaOH}}{10^{-3} \text{ L NaOH}}\right)\left(\frac{1}{45.25 \text{ mL NaOH}}\right)$$

$$= 116.1511 = \textbf{116.2 g HA/mol}$$

b) To convert an alcohol to an acid, the alcohol loses two hydrogen atoms and gains an oxygen atom. This process must be reversed to get to the original alcohol:

Molar mass (g/mol) = (116.1511 g/mol) + 2(1.008 g H/mol) – (16.00 g O/mol) = 102.1671 = **102.2 g/mol**

21.92 a) $CH_3CHO + C_6H_5-MgBr \rightarrow C_6H_5CH(OH)CH_3$

b)

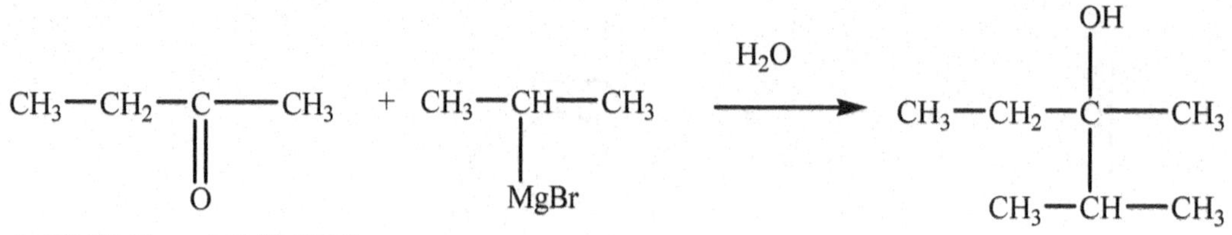

$$CH_3-CH_2-\overset{\overset{\displaystyle }{\underset{\underset{\displaystyle O}{\|}}{C}}}{}-CH_3 \; + \; CH_3-\overset{\overset{\displaystyle }{\underset{\underset{\displaystyle MgBr}{|}}{CH}}}{}-CH_3 \xrightarrow{H_2O} CH_3-CH_2-\overset{\overset{\displaystyle \overset{\displaystyle OH}{|}}{C}}{\underset{\underset{\displaystyle CH_3-CH-CH_3}{|}}{}}-CH_3$$

c) **CH₃MgBr and C₆H₅CHO**

d) **HCHO** (methanal, also known as formaldehyde)

e)

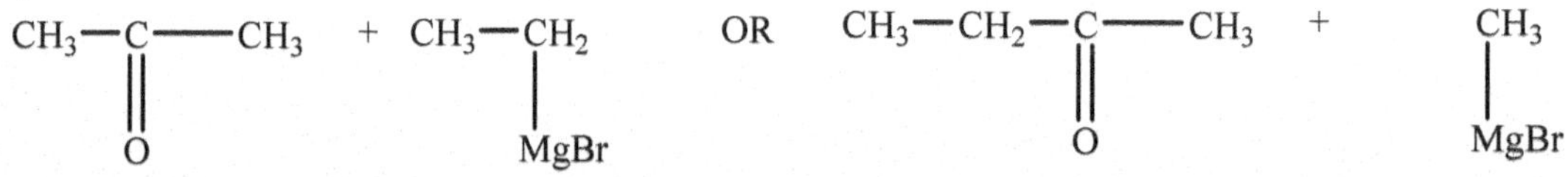

$$CH_3-\overset{\overset{\displaystyle }{\underset{\underset{\displaystyle O}{\|}}{C}}}{}-CH_3 \; + \; CH_3-\overset{\overset{\displaystyle }{\underset{\underset{\displaystyle MgBr}{|}}{CH_2}}}{} \quad \text{OR} \quad CH_3-CH_2-\overset{\overset{\displaystyle }{\underset{\underset{\displaystyle O}{\|}}{C}}}{}-CH_3 \; + \; \overset{\overset{\displaystyle CH_3}{}}{\underset{\underset{\displaystyle MgBr}{|}}{}}$$

21.93 a)The functional group in ibuprofen is the carboxylic acid group COOH. The chiral center is RC*H(CH₃)COOH.

$$CH_3$$
$$\text{(structure of ibuprofen)}$$

b) React the aldehyde with methyl Grignard reagent, CH_3MgBr to get the alcohol.

$$R\text{——}CHO + CH_3MgBr \xrightarrow{\ H_2O\ } R\text{—}CH\overset{CH_3}{\underset{OH}{\diagup}}$$

React the alcohol with HBr to get the brominated product.

$$R\text{—}CH\overset{CH_3}{\underset{OH}{\diagup}} + HBr \longrightarrow R\text{—}CH\overset{CH_3}{\underset{Br}{\diagup}} + H_2O$$

React the bromide with cyanide ion to produce the nitrile.

$$R\text{—}CH\overset{CH_3}{\underset{Br}{\diagup}} + NaCN \longrightarrow R\text{—}CH\overset{CH_3}{\underset{C\equiv N}{\diagup}} + NaBr$$

Then hydrolyze the nitrile with aqueous HCl to get the carboxylic acid.

$$R\text{—}CH\overset{CH_3}{\underset{C\equiv N}{\diagup}} + HCl(aq) \longrightarrow R\text{—}CH\overset{CH_3}{\underset{COOH}{\diagup}}$$

21.94 a) Perform an acid-catalyzed dehydration of the alcohol (elimination), followed by bromination of the double bond (addition of Br_2):

$$CH_3\text{—}CH_2\text{—}CH_2\text{—}OH \xrightarrow{\ H^+\ } CH_3\text{—}CH\text{=}CH_2$$

$$CH_3\text{—}CH\text{=}CH_2 + Br_2 \longrightarrow CH_3\text{—}\underset{Br}{CH}\text{—}\underset{Br}{CH_2}$$

b) The product is an ester, so a carboxylic acid is needed to prepare the ester. First, oxidize one mole of ethanol to ethanoic acid (acetic acid):

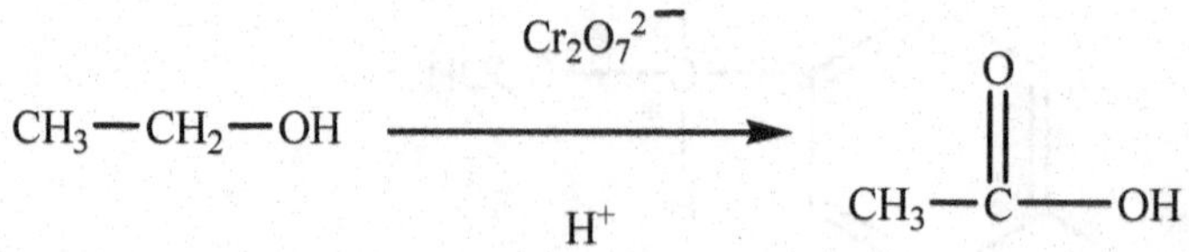

$$CH_3-CH_2-OH \xrightarrow[\;H^+\;]{\;Cr_2O_7^{2-}\;} CH_3-\overset{\overset{\displaystyle O}{\|}}{C}-OH$$

Then, react one mole of ethanoic acid with a second mole of ethanol to form the ester:

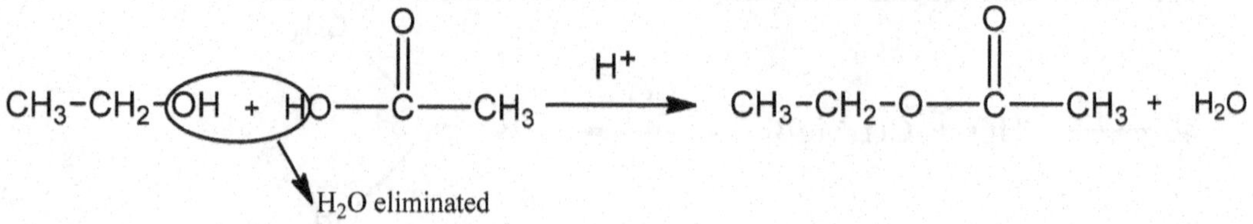

$$CH_3-CH_2-OH \; + \; HO-\overset{\overset{\displaystyle O}{\|}}{C}-CH_3 \xrightarrow{\;H^+\;} CH_3-CH_2-O-\overset{\overset{\displaystyle O}{\|}}{C}-CH_3 \; + \; H_2O$$

H₂O eliminated

21.97   Plan: In order to answer these questions we must recognize which mechanisms are occurring in each case. The first reaction depicts an E2 elimination reaction which must pass through an anti-periplanar transition state. The second reaction is an electrophilic halogenation reaction which results in an anti-addition product. Finally the third reaction is an epoxidation reaction which should result in a syn- product.

Solution:
a) The 2-chlorobutane will adopt an anti-periplanar arrangement in which the methyl groups are in an anti-arrangement (see Section 20.3 for a review). The minor product will occur when the two methyl groups are in a gauche configuration. Since this is a higher energy conformation it will be less likely to form.

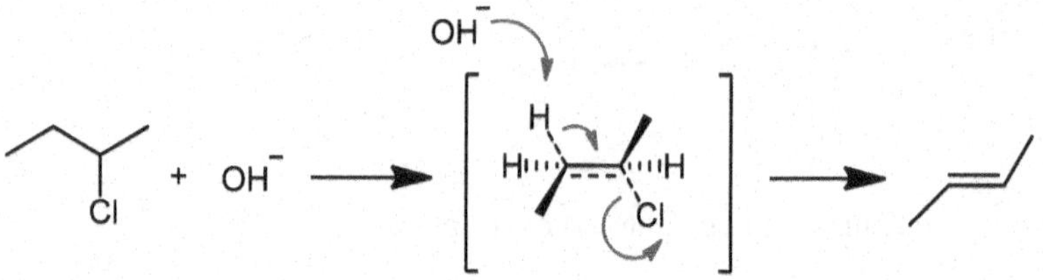

b) Since the addition of Br₂ can only generate the anti-product, there will be only one major product, which is shown below.

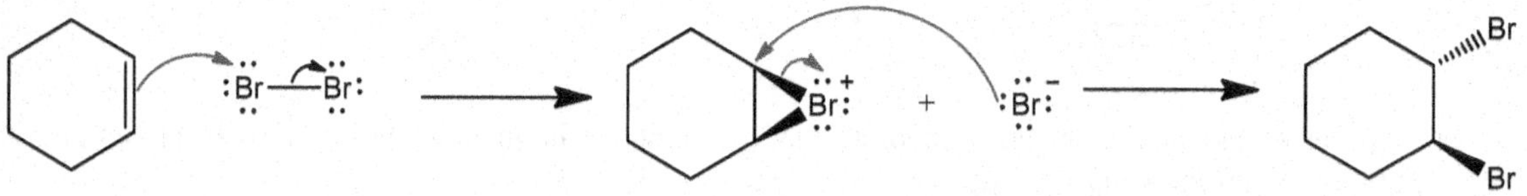

c) The epoxidation mechanism is concerted and results in a syn- product only. Furthermore, the depicted minor structure would not be physically possible since the oxygen could not exist both above and below the plane of the molecule as depicted by the stereo-bonds.

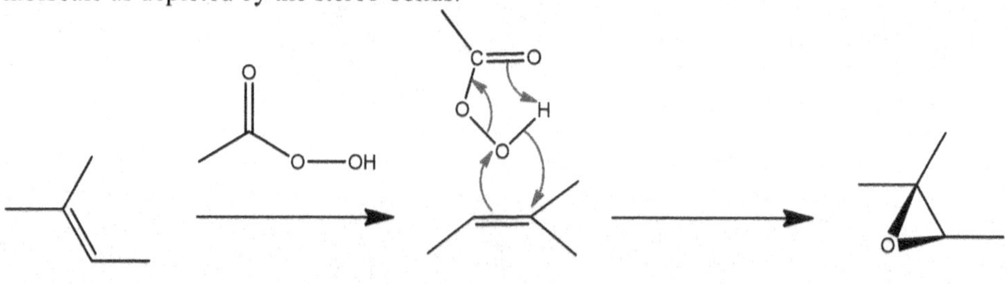

21.99   Plan: Identifying the type of reaction will allow us to determine the common reagents used and the likely nature of the other molecules. The first reaction (a) produces an ester using an alcohol as one of the reagents, the second reaction (b) appears to be a nucleophilic substitution reaction and the final reaction (c) is an elimination reaction.

Solution:
a) As we studied in Section 21.7, esters can be formed by the reaction of carboxylic acids with alcohols in an acidic medium. Therefore if we have the final product (an ester) and the reagent (an alcohol), the starting material must be an acid. This reaction is catalyzed by acids.

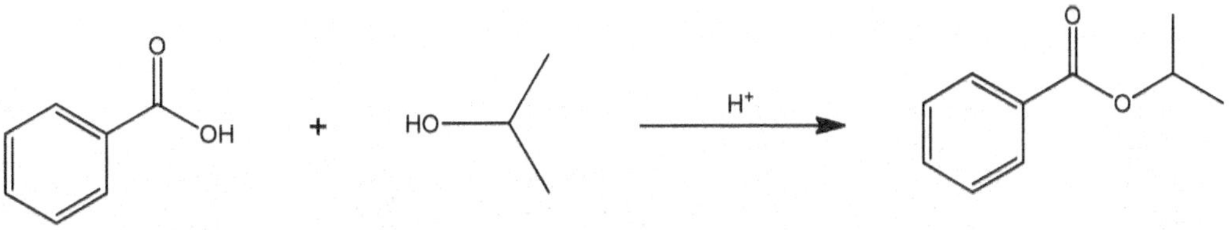

esterification

b) This is a substitution reaction and since it is occurring at a 1° carbon it must follow the S_N2 mechanism. OH⁻ is an ideal nucleophile for S_N2 reactions making it a likely reagent.

substitution (S_N2)

c) This is an elimination reaction but it does not follow Zaitsev's rule (Section 21.4). In order to violate Zaitsev's rule a bulky base must be used so that protons are only removed from the least sterically hindered carbon.

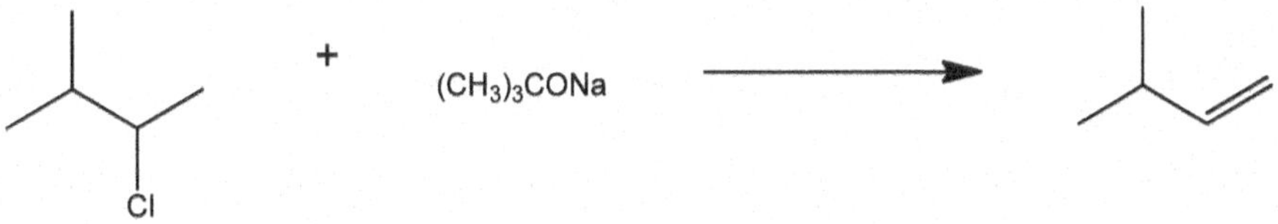

elimination (E2)

21.101 Plan: Given that we know that the starting material is a 3 carbon haloalkane and that the one product we are provided has 3 carbon atoms in it we can work backwards (retrosynthesis) to figure out all the missing reagents

Solution:
3-methyl-N-propylbutanamide is an amide and we know from section 21.7 that amides can be formed by the reaction of an amine and an acyl chloride. This allows us to predict the structure of the acyl chloride as being 3-methylbutanoyl chloride, which means that the other reagent must be prop-1-amine. The S_N2 substitution reaction of 1-bromopropane in liquid ammonia would generate the prop-1-amine

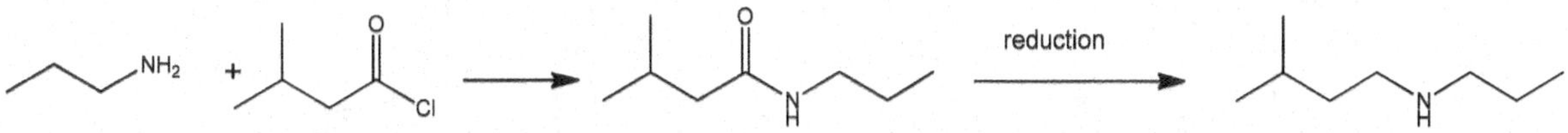

21.104 Plan: As we know what the starting material and final product are and all of the reagents in between, we need to figure out the product for each reaction, starting with the reaction of the bromoalkene with methyllithium.

Solution:
a) In the first step the methyl group replaces the bromine in a substitution reaction. The second reaction is an acid catalyzed electrophilic hydration of the alkene and generates the Markovnikov product. Reaction of p-tosyl chloride with an alcohol generates a p-toluenesulfonate which is a very good leaving group.

21-11

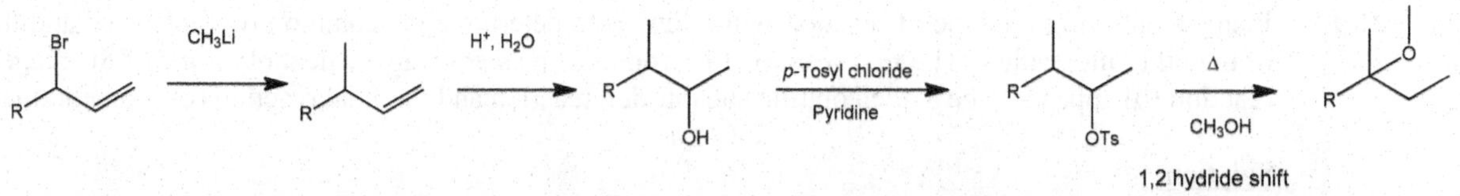

Br → CH₃Li → H⁺, H₂O → p-Tosyl chloride / Pyridine → Δ / CH₃OH → 1,2 hydride shift

(reaction scheme at top with labels: Br, R; CH₃Li; H⁺, H₂O; OH; p-Tosyl chloride, Pyridine; OTs; Δ, CH₃OH; 1,2 hydride shift)

The polar protic solvent (CH₃OH) and a good leaving group allows the reaction to follow an S_N1 pathway as shown below, thus leading to the final product.

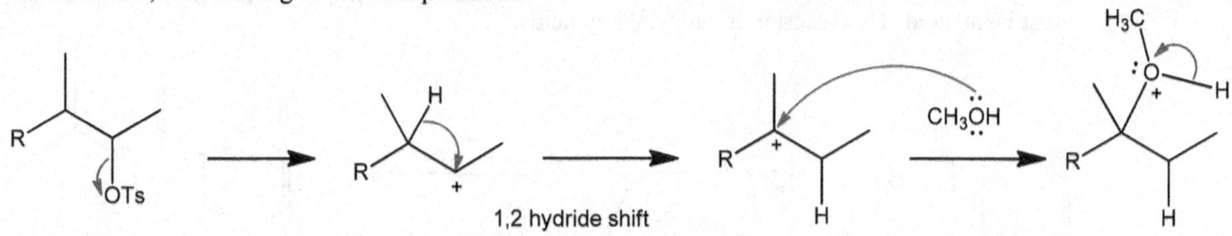

(second reaction scheme with labels: OTs; 1,2 hydride shift; CH₃OH; H₃C, O, H)

b) Doubling the concentration of CH₃Li would double the reaction rate since it is an S_N2 reaction.
c) Halving the concentration of CH₃OH in the final step would have no effect as it is a S_N1 reaction.

21.106

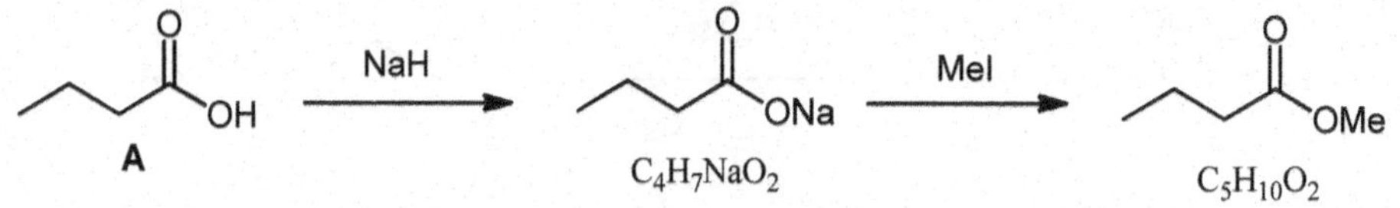

(reaction scheme: **A** with OH → NaH → ONa, $C_4H_7NaO_2$ → MeI → OMe, $C_5H_{10}O_2$)

21.108

(reaction scheme: **A** cyclopentanone → MeMgBr → cyclopentanol with OH and Me, $C_6H_{12}O$)

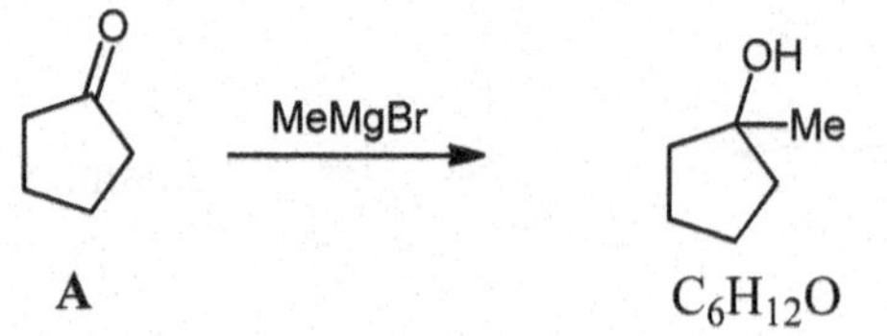

21.110   Plan: Refer to the Table of Functional Groups in Chapter 20. Carbon atoms surrounded by four electron regions (four single bonds) are sp^3 hybridized. Carbon atoms surrounded by three electron regions (two single bonds and one double bond) are sp^2 hybridized. A carbon atom is chiral if it is attached to four different groups.
Solution:
a) Functional groups in jasmolin II:

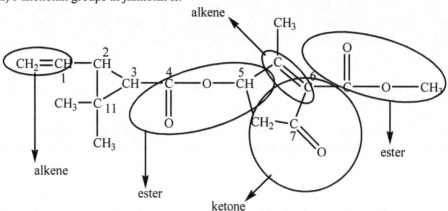

b) Carbon 1 is sp^2 hybridized.   Carbon 2 is sp^3 hybridized.
   Carbon 3 is sp^3 hybridized.   Carbon 4 is sp^2 hybridized.
   Carbon 5 is sp^3 hybridized.   Carbon 6 and 7 are sp^2 hybridized.

c) Carbon atoms 2, 3, and 5 are chiral centers as they are each bonded to four different groups.

CHAPTER 22 SPECIAL TOPICS IN ORGANIC CHEMISTRY

CHEMICAL CONNECTIONS BOXED READING PROBLEMS

B22.1 Plan: When a ddNTP is incorporated into the growing DNA chain, polymerization stops since no more phosphodiester bonds can be formed. When ddATP is added, the chain stops as each base T is encountered (base A pairs with base T); when ddCTP is added, the chain stops as each base G is encountered (base C pairs with base G).
Solution:
With ddATP, the chain stops at each base T:
TACAGGTTCAGT
ddATP will give four complementary chain pieces: A, AGTCA, AAGTCA, ATGTCCAAGTCA.
With ddCTP, the chain stops at each base G:
TACAGGTTCAGT
ddCTP will give three complementary chain pieces: CA, CAAGTCA, CCAAGTCA

END–OF–CHAPTER PROBLEMS

22.1 Plan: The molar mass of a polymer chain ($\mathcal{M}_{polymer}$, in g/mol) depends on the molar mass of the repeat unit ($\mathcal{M}_{repeat}$) and the **degree of polymerization (n)**, the number of repeat units in the chain: $\mathcal{M}_{polymer} = \mathcal{M}_{repeat} \times n$. (Use Table 22.3 to determine the repeat unit for the specified polymer).
Solution: Polyethylene is made up of ethene (ethylene) repeating units, whose molar mass is 28 g/mol. If an individual polyethylene chain has a degree of polymerization of 6600, the molar mass of this chain is:
$\mathcal{M}_{polymer} = \mathcal{M}_{repeat} \times n = (28 \text{ g/mol}) \times (6.6 \times 10^3) = 184800 \text{ g/mol} = \textbf{1.8} \times \textbf{10}^5 \textbf{ g/mol}$

22.5 Plan: The length of an *extended* backbone is simply the number of repeat units (degree of polymerization, n) times the length of each repeat unit (l_0).
Solution: The number of repeat units in question 22.1 is 6600 and each unit is approximately 250 pm, therefore,
250 pm × 6600 = 1.65 x10^6 pm = **1.7 x10^6 pm**

22.8 Plan: The size of the coiled chain is expressed by its **radius of gyration (Rg)**, the average distance from the centre of mass of the molecule to the outer edge of the coil. The mathematical expression for the radius of gyration includes the length of each repeat unit and the degree of polymerization:

$$R_g = \sqrt{\frac{n l_o^2}{6}}$$

Solution:

$$R_g = \sqrt{\frac{(6600)(250)^2}{6}} = 8291.56 = \textbf{8292 pm}$$

22.11 The glass transition temperature is the midpoint of the range of temperatures when a semicrystalline substance, like a polymer, changes from a molten or rubber-like substance into a hard brittle solid. The glass transition temperature for the polymer given is 6°C.

22.13 Both branching and crosslinking are bifurcations in a linear polymer, where instead of extending in only one linear direction, now two or more chains exist. In cross-linked polymers, these branches connect two chains together, whereas in a normal branched polymer they do not connect chains together. In a branched polymer, this leads to more difficulty in packing and therefore leads to a flexible polymer with low crystallinity. In a cross-linked polymer, the addition covalent linkages between chains make the polymer more rigid and strong.

22.15 A block polymer is a special type of copolymer consisting of a larger polymer made up from blocks of polymerized monomer units. Therefore the chain consists of a number of repeats of one monomer unit followed by a number of repeats of a second different monomer unit. An ABA block copolymer can be represented as:

A-A-A-A-A-A-A-A-A-A-A-A-A-B-B-B-B-B-B-B-B-B-B-B-A-A-A-A-A-A-A-A-A-A-A-A

22.21 Nylon is formed by the condensation reaction between an **amine and a carboxylic acid** resulting in an amide bond. Polyester is formed by the condensation reaction between a **carboxylic acid and an alcohol** to form an ester bond.

22.23 <u>Plan:</u> Both PVC and polypropylene are addition polymers. To draw the repeat unit, replace the double bond with a single bond, draw an additional single bond to each carbon atom, draw brackets around the molecule, and use a subscript n to denote that the monomer is repeated n times to form the polymer.
<u>Solution:</u>
a)

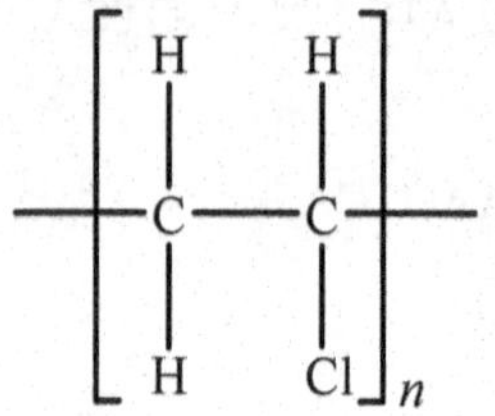

b)

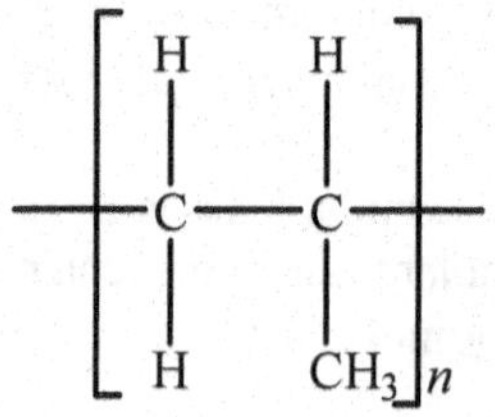

22.26

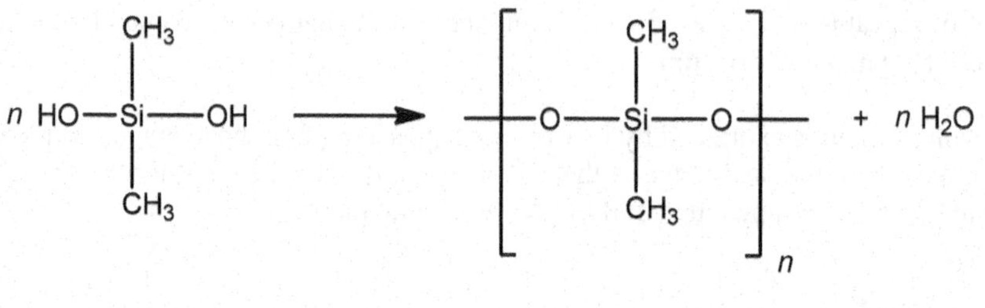

22.28 a) To prepare a polymer with a benzene containing backbone, styrene, C_6H_5–CH=CH_2 can be used to produce polystyrene, – (–$CH(C_6H_5)$ –CH_2–)–$_n$.

b) p-diethenylbenzene can be used to crosslink the polymer.

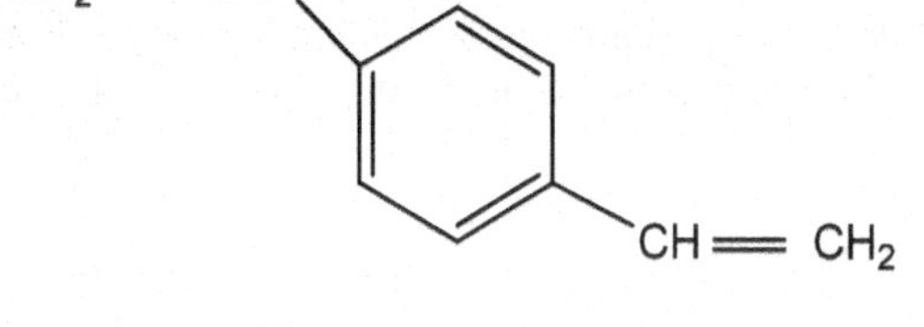

22.32 Isotatic has a regular structure making its solid form more regular and semicrystalline. As this makes the solid more stable it will have a higher melting point than the atatic variant.

22.34   **Polyamide** condensation bonds should have a higher glass transition temperature. As amides have bond hydrogen bond donor and acceptor functionality (they have parts with lone pairs and other parts with hydrogen connected to a heteroatom) they are capable of making intermolecular hydrogen bonds. Esters on the other hand, lack the N-H (hydrogen connected to a heteroatom) and therefore are less able to make intermolecular hydrogen bonds. These hydrogen bonds stabilize the solid form and raise the glass transition temperature.

22.36   a) Amino acids form **condensation** polymers, called proteins.
b) Alkenes form **addition** polymers, the simplest of which is polyethylene.
c) Simple sugars form **condensation** polymers, called polysaccharides.
d) Mononucleotides form **condensation** polymers, called nucleic acids.

22.42   Plan: A tripeptide contains three amino acids and two peptide (amide) bonds. Find the structures of the amino acids in Figure 22.8 (the common amino acids). Join the three acids to give the tripeptide; water is produced.
Solution:

aspartic acid   histidine   tryptophan

22-3

b) Repeat the preceding procedure, with charges on the terminal groups as are found in cell fluid.

glycine   cysteine   tyrosine

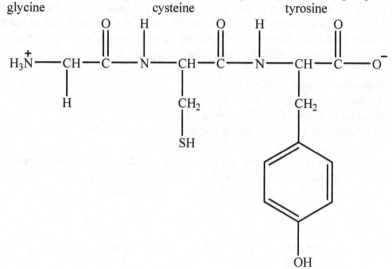

22.44   <u>Plan:</u> Base A always pairs with Base T; Base C always pairs with Base G.
         <u>Solution:</u>
         a) Complementary DNA strand is **AATCGG**.
         b) Complementary DNA strand is **TCTGTA**

22.48   <u>Plan:</u> Convert each mass to moles, and divide the moles by the smallest number to determine molar ratio, and thus
         relative numbers of the amino acids. To find the minimum molar mass, add the products of the moles of each
         amino acid and its molar mass.
         <u>Solution:</u>
         a) The hydrolysis process requires the addition of water to break the peptide bonds.
         b)   (3.00 g gly)/(75.07 g/mol) = 0.0399627 mol glycine
                 (0.90 g ala)/(89.10 g/mol) = 0.010101010 mol alanine
                 (3.70 g val)/(117.15 g/mol) = 0.0315834 mol valine
                 (6.90 g pro)/(115.13 g/mol) = 0.0599323 mol proline
                 (7.30 g ser)/(105.10 g/mol) = 0.0694577 mol serine
                 (86.00 g arg)/(174.21 g/mol) = 0.493657 mol arginine
         Divide by the smallest value (0.010101010 mol alanine), and round to a whole number.
                 (0.0399627 mol glycine)/(0.010101010 mol) = **4**
                 (0.010101010 mol alanine)/(0.010101010 mol) = **1**
                 (0.0315834 mol valine)/(0.010101010 mol) = **3**
                 (0.0599323 mol proline)/(0.010101010 mol) = **6**
                 (0.0694577 mol serine)/(0.010101010 mol) = **7**
                 (0.493657 mol arginine)/(0.010101010 mol) = **49**
         c) Minimum $\mathcal{M}$= (4 × 75.07 g/mol) + (1 × 89.09 g/mol) + (3 × 117.15 g/mol) + (6 × 115.13 g/mol)
                 + (7 × 105.10 g/mol) + (49 × 174.21 g/mol) = **10,700 g/mol**

22.52 Nucleoside = sugar + nucleobase
Nucleotide = sugar + nucleobase + phosphate

Nucleobase   **Nucleoside**   **Nucleotide**

22.55 The nitrogen-containing bases form hydrogen bonds to their complimentary bases. The flat, N-containing bases stack above each other, which allow extensive interaction through dispersion forces. The exterior negatively charged sugar-phosphate chains form ion-dipole and hydrogen bonds to the aqueous surroundings, but this is of minor importance to the structure.

22.58 Dispersion forces are present between the nonpolar portions of the molecules within the bilayer. Polar groups are present to hydrogen bond or to form ion-dipole interactions with the aqueous surroundings.

22.61 β-Pleated sheets are a type of secondary structural element.

22.64 <u>Plan:</u> Refer to Figure 22.8 in the chapter. The types of forces operating in proteins were discussed in Section 22.4. Disulfide bonds form between sulfur atoms, salt links form between $-COO^-$ and $-NH_3^+$ groups, and hydrogen bonding occurs between NH– and –OH groups. Nonpolar chains interact through dispersion forces.
<u>Solution:</u>
a) Both side chains are part of the amino acid **cysteine**. Two cysteine R groups can form a **disulfide bond** (covalent bond).
b) The R group ($-(CH_2)_4-NH_3^+$) is found in the amino acid **lysine** and the R group ($-CH_2COO^-$) is found in the amino acid **aspartic acid**. The positive charge on the amine group in lysine is attracted to the negative charge on the acid group in aspartic acid to form a **salt link**.
c) The R group in the amino acid **asparagine** and the R group in the amino acid **serine**. The –NH– and –OH groups will **hydrogen bond**.
d) Both the R group $-CH(CH_3)-CH_3$ from **valine** and the R group $C_6H_5-CH_2-$ from **phenylalanine** are nonpolar, so their interaction is through **dispersion forces**.

22. 66 The resonance structures show that the bond between carbon and nitrogen will have some double bond character that restricts rotation around the bond.

$$:\!O\!: \quad H \qquad\qquad\qquad\qquad :\!O\!:^{-} \quad H$$
$$\underset{|}{\overset{\parallel}{\underset{|}{C}}}\!-\!\underset{\cdot\cdot}{N}\!- \qquad \longleftrightarrow \qquad \underset{|}{C}\!=\!\underset{|}{\overset{+}{N}}\!-$$

22.71 As chlorine is a highly electronegative atom, it increases the positive charge on the carbon of the carbonyl compared to acetone. This in turn makes the carbonyl more polarized and increases the bond strength. As stronger bonds vibrate at larger wavenumbers, it increases the frequency of the absorption.

propan-2-one (acetone)   ethanoyl chloride(acetyl chloride)

22.77　Plan: The number of peaks corresponds to the number of protons with different environments. Therefore, the first step will be to draw the structure of benzaldehyde.
Solution:

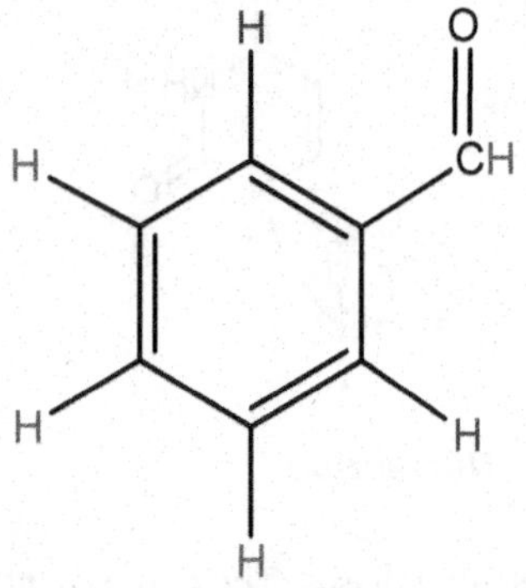

The total number of sets of peaks would be **four**. The H's represent the protons with different environment (five types of ^1H environments).

22.80　The circled methyl will have the highest shift because it is attached to an electronegative atom, making it electron deficient. Due to the lack of electron density it will appear at a higher ppm. These protons are the most deshielded ones.

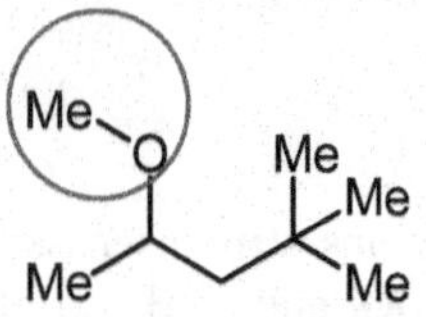

22.81　O-H bonds are readily exchangeable in $CDCl_3$. The protons attached to the hydroxyl groups are clearly seen. When the sample is shaken with D_2O, the deuterium in the D_2O can exchange with OH groups of the sample, converting them to OD groups. As deuterium atoms cannot be seen in ^1H NMR, the OD groups can no longer been seen.

22.83　Plan: The number of peaks corresponds to the number of carbon atoms with different environments. Therefore, the first step will be to draw the structure of propan-2-one (acetone).
Solution:

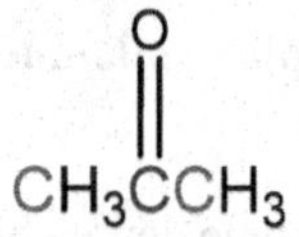

Since there are two types of carbon environments, we would expect to see two peaks.

22.86　Plan: After drawing the structure of the N,N-diethylethanamine (triethylamine), we identify the protons with different environments and their neighbouring spin-coupled nuclei.
Solution:

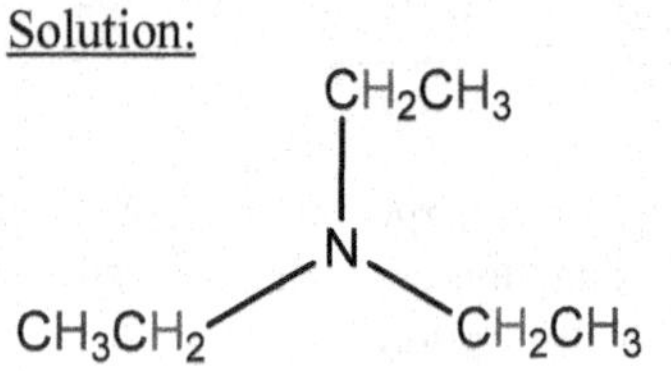

There are two peaks (two types of ^1H environments)
1 high medium shifted peak (approx. 2.5 ppm), multiplicity is a quartet (the CH_2)
1 high low shifted peak (approx. 1.0 ppm), multiplicity is a triplet (the CH_3)

22.90   Kevlar is formed from 1,4-phenylenediamine with terephthaloyl chloride.

This type of reaction would be consistent with chapter 21, where amides were described as being formed by acid chlorides and amines.

22.95   Plan: Since we are given the DNA sequence we can form the complementary sequence knowing that A and T are complementary and G and C are also complementary and that RNA molecules do not contain U instead of T.

Solution:
a) The complementary sequence to GATCGACTA would be: CTAGCTGAT. The RNA sequence would be different since RNA contains U instead of T, therefore the sequence would be: CUAGCUGAU.

b) It requires 3 bases in order to code for one amino acid, therefore this sequence could code for 3 amino acids.

c) GC would not be a good technique to separate this nucleotide sequence from a mixture of other nucleotides since the molecular weight of the sequence and polarity mean that the nucleotide is not volatile enough. Liquid chromatography or better yet gel electrophoresis would be better separation techniques.

22.97   Plan: Using our knowledge of polymer reactions we can draw the mechanism which will then show the type of reaction. We are given that the T_g of the material is 50 °C so we must then rationalize whether this material would be a good material for gloves knowing that it will be below the T_g in most applications (ie. room temperature = 25 °C).

Solution: a) This type of polymerization is a condensation polymerization (shown below) in which the monomers lost HCl during the process.

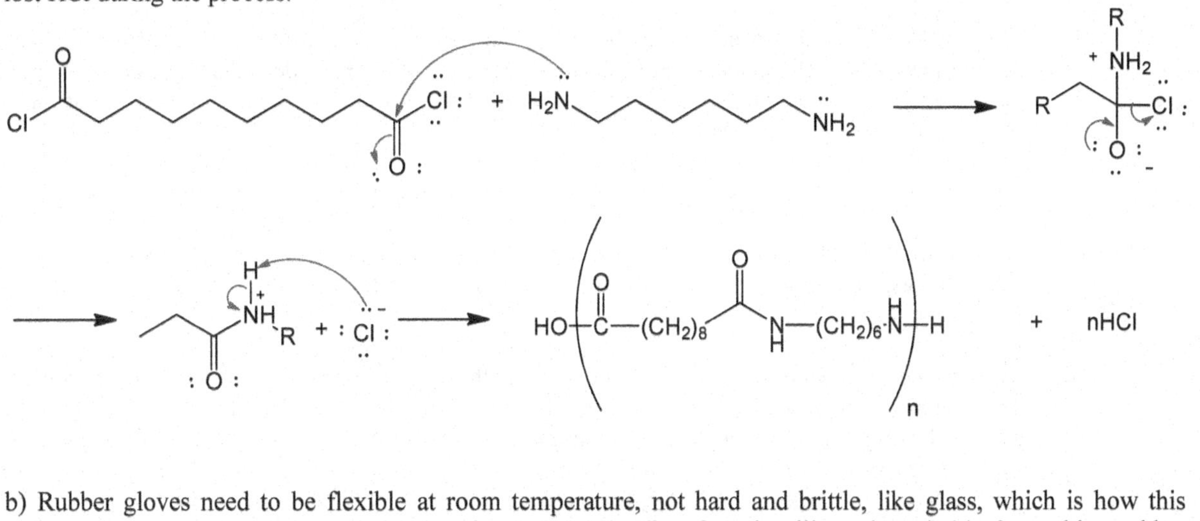

b) Rubber gloves need to be flexible at room temperature, not hard and brittle, like glass, which is how this polymer becomes when it is cooled below its T_g (50 °C). Therefore, it will not be suitable for making rubber gloves.
c) Since this is a polymer, Size Exclusion Chromatography (SEC) would likely be the best technique to analyze it, though it might also be possible to use liquid chromatography.

CHAPTER 23 THE ELEMENTS IN NATURE AND INDUSTRY

CHEMICAL CONNECTIONS BOXED READING PROBLEMS

B23.2   a) (1) $NO + O_3 \rightarrow XO + O_2$ [slow]
         (2) $XO + O \rightarrow X + O_2$ [fast]
    b) The rate-determining step is the slow step. The rate law for that is:
    rate = $k[NO][O_3]$
         = $(6 \times 10^{-15}$ cm^3/molecule•s)$(5 \times 10^{12}$ molecule/cm^3)$(1.0 \times 10^9$ molecule/cm^3)
         = 3×10^7 molecule/cm^3•s

END–OF–CHAPTER PROBLEMS

23.2   Iron forms iron(III) oxide, Fe_2O_3 (commonly known as hematite). Calcium forms calcium carbonate, $CaCO_3$, (commonly known as limestone). Sodium is commonly found in sodium chloride (halite), NaCl. Zinc is commonly found in zinc sulfide (sphalerite), ZnS.

23.3   a) Differentiation refers to the processes involved in the formation of Earth into regions (core, mantle, and crust) of differing composition. Substances separated according to their densities, with the more dense material in the core and less dense in the crust.
    b) The four most abundant elements are oxygen, silicon, aluminum, and iron in order of decreasing abundance.
    c) Oxygen is the most abundant element in the crust and mantle but is not found in the core. Silicon, aluminum, calcium, sodium, potassium, and magnesium are also present in the crust and mantle but not in the core.

23.7   Plants produced O_2, slowly increasing the oxygen concentration in the atmosphere and creating an oxidative environment for metals. Evidence of Fe(II) deposits pre-dating Fe(III) deposits suggests this hypothesis is true. The decay of plant material and its incorporation into the crust increased the concentration of carbon in the crust and created large fossil-fuel deposits.

23.9   Fixation refers to the process of converting a substance in the atmosphere into a form more readily usable by organisms. Examples are the fixation of carbon by plants in the form of carbon dioxide and of nitrogen by bacteria in the form of nitrogen gas. Fixation of carbon dioxide gas by plants converts the CO_2 into carbohydrates during photosynthesis. Fixation of nitrogen gas by nitrogen-fixing bacteria involves the conversion of N_2 to ammonia and ammonium ions.

23.12   Atmospheric nitrogen is utilized by three fixation pathways: atmospheric, industrial, and biological. Atmospheric fixation requires high-temperature reactions (e.g., lightning) to convert N_2 into NO and other oxidized species. Industrial fixation involves mainly the formation of ammonia, NH_3, from N_2 and H_2. Biological fixation occurs in nitrogen-fixing bacteria that live in the roots of legumes. "Human activity" is referred to as "industrial fixation." Human activity is a significant factor, contributing about 17% of the nitrogen removed.

23.14   a) No gaseous phosphorus compounds are involved in the phosphorus cycle, so the atmosphere is not included in the phosphorus cycle.
    b) Two roles of organisms in phosphorus cycle: 1) Plants excrete acid from their roots to convert PO_4^{3-} ions into more soluble $H_2PO_4^-$ ions, which the plant can absorb. 2) Through excretion and decay after death, organisms return soluble phosphate compounds to the cycle.

23.17   Plan: First determine the moles of F present in 100. kg of fluorapatite, using the molar mass of $Ca_5(PO_4)_3F$ (504.31 g/mol); take 15% of this amount. Convert mol F to mol SiF_4, and use the ideal gas law to determine the volume of the SiF_4 gas. For part b), convert moles of SiF_4 to moles of Na_2SiF_6 using the mole ratio in the given equation and convert moles of Na_2SiF_6 to moles and then mass of F. The definition of ppm ("parts per million") states that 1 ppm $F^- = (1 \text{ g } F^-/(10^6 \text{ g } H_2O))$. Find the volume of water that can be fluoridated with the calculated mass of F.

<u>Solution:</u>
a) Moles of F =

$$\left(100. \text{ kg } Ca_5(PO_4)_3F\right)\left(\frac{10^3 \text{ g } Ca_5(PO_4)_3F}{1 \text{ kg } Ca_5(PO_4)_3F}\right)\left(\frac{1 \text{ mol } Ca_5(PO_4)_3F}{504.31 \text{ g } Ca_5(PO_4)_3F}\right)\left(\frac{1 \text{ mol } F}{1 \text{ mol } Ca_5(PO_4)_3F}\right)\left(\frac{15\%}{100\%}\right)$$

$$= 29.74361 \text{ mol F}$$

Moles of $SiF_4 = \left(29.74361 \text{ mol F}\right)\left(\frac{1 \text{ mol } SiF_4}{4 \text{ mol F}}\right) = 7.43590 \text{ mol } SiF_4$

$pV = nRT$

$$V\text{(L)} = \frac{nRT}{p} = \frac{\left(7.43590 \text{ mol } SiF_4\right)\left(8.31446\frac{\text{L}\cdot\text{kPa}}{\text{mol}\cdot\text{K}}\right)\left((273 + 1450.)\text{K}\right)}{\left(101.3 \text{ kPa}\right)} = 1051.58267 = \mathbf{1.1x10^3 \text{ L}}$$

b) Moles of $Na_2SiF_6 = \left(7.43590 \text{ mol } SiF_4\right)\left(\frac{1 \text{ mol } Na_2SiF_6}{2 \text{ mol } SiF_4}\right) = 3.71795 \text{ mol } Na_2SiF_6$

Mass (g) of $F^- = \left(3.71795 \text{ mol } Na_2SiF_6\right)\left(\frac{6 \text{ mol } F^-}{1 \text{ mol } Na_2SiF_6}\right)\left(\frac{19.00 \text{ g } F^-}{1 \text{ mol } F^-}\right) = 423.8463 \text{ g} = 4.2x10^2 \text{ g } F^-$

If 1 g F^- will fluoridate 10^6 g H_2O to a level of 1 ppm, how many grams (converted to mL using density, then converted from mL to L to m^3) of water can 423.8463 g F^- fluoridate to the 1 ppm level? Necessary conversion factors: $1 \text{ m}^3 = 1000$ L, density of water = 1.00 g/mL .

$$\text{Volume (m}^3) = \left(423.8463 \text{ g } F^-\right)\left(\frac{10^6 \text{ g } H_2O}{1 \text{ g } F^-}\right)\left(\frac{\text{mL } H_2O}{1.00 \text{ g } H_2O}\right)\left(\frac{1 \text{ cm}^3}{1 \text{ mL}}\right)\left(\frac{10^{-2} \text{ m}}{1 \text{ cm}}\right)^3 = 423.8463 \text{ m}^3 = \mathbf{4.2x10^2 \text{ m}^3}$$

23.18   <u>Plan:</u> Since the 50. t contains 2.0% Fe_2O_3 by mass, $100 - 2.0 = 98\%$ by mass of the 50. t contains $Ca_3(PO_4)_2$. Find the moles of $Ca_3(PO_4)_2$ in the sample and convert moles of $Ca_3(PO_4)_2$ to moles and then mass of P_4, remembering that the production of P_4 has a 90% yield.
<u>Solution:</u>
a) The iron ions form an insoluble salt, $Fe_3(PO_4)_2$, that decreases the yield of phosphorus. This salt is of limited value.
b) Use the conversion factor 1 metric tonne (t) = $1x10^3$ kg.

$$\text{Moles of } Ca_3(PO_4)_2 = \left(50. \text{ t}\right)\left(\frac{98\%}{100\%}\right)\left(\frac{10^3 \text{ kg}}{1 \text{ t}}\right)\left(\frac{10^3 \text{ g}}{1 \text{ kg}}\right)\left(\frac{1 \text{ mol } Ca_3(PO_4)_2}{310.18 \text{ g } Ca_3(PO_4)_2}\right) = 157972.79 \text{ mol } Ca_3(PO_4)_2$$

Reaction: $2Ca_3(PO_4)_2(s) + 10C(s) + 6SiO_2(s) \rightarrow 6CaSiO_3(s) + 10CO(g) + P_4(s)$ (section 23.3)

Mass (metric tonnes) of P_4 =

$$\left(157972.79 \text{ mol } Ca_3(PO_4)_2\right)\left(\frac{1 \text{ mol } P_4}{2 \text{ mol } Ca_3(PO_4)_2}\right)\left(\frac{123.88 \text{ g } P_4}{1 \text{ mol } P_4}\right)\left(\frac{1 \text{ kg}}{10^3 \text{ g}}\right)\left(\frac{1 \text{ t}}{10^3 \text{ kg}}\right)\left(\frac{90.\%}{100\%}\right)$$

$$= 8.80635 \text{ t} = \mathbf{8.8 \text{ t } P_4}$$

23.20   a) Roasting involves heating the mineral in air (O_2) at high temperatures to convert the mineral to the oxide.
b) Smelting is the reduction of the metal oxide to the free metal using heat and a reducing agent such as coke.
c) Flotation is a separation process in which the ore is removed from the gangue by exploiting the different abilities of the two to interact with detergent. The gangue sinks to the bottom and the lighter ore-detergent mix is skimmed off the top.
d) Refining is the final step in the purification process to yield the pure metal with no impurities.

23.25 a) Slag is a waste product of iron metallurgy formed by the reaction:
$$CaO(s) + SiO_2(s) \rightarrow CaSiO_3(l)$$
In other words, slag is a by-product of steelmaking and contains the impurity SiO_2.
b) Pig iron, used to make cast iron products, is the impure product of iron metallurgy (containing 3–4% C) that is purified to steel.
c) Steel refers to the products of iron metallurgy, specifically alloys of iron containing small amounts of other elements including 1–1.5% carbon.
d) Basic-oxygen process refers to the process used to purify pig iron to form steel. The pig iron is melted and oxygen gas under high pressure is passed through the liquid metal. The oxygen oxidizes impurities to their oxides, which then react with calcium oxide to form a liquid that is decanted. Molten steel is left after the basic-oxygen process.

23.27 Iron and nickel are more easily oxidized than copper, so they are separated from the copper in the roasting step and conversion to slag. In the electrorefining process, all three metals are oxidized into solution, but only Cu^{2+} ions are reduced at the cathode to form $Cu(s)$.

23.30 The potassium in the molten potassium salt is reduced by molten sodium. Ordinarily, sodium would not be a good reducing agent for the more active potassium. But the reduction is carried out above the boiling point of potassium, producing gaseous potassium:
$$Na(l) + K^+(l) \rightarrow Na^+(l) + K(g)$$
The potassium gas is removed as it is produced. Le Châtelier's principle states that the system shifts toward formation of more K as the gaseous metal leaves the cell.

23.31 a) Aqueous salt solutions are mixtures of ions and water. When two half-reactions are possible at an electrode, the one with the more positive electrode potential occurs. In this case, the two half-reactions are:

$M^+ + e^- \rightarrow M^0$ $E°_{red} = -3.05$ V, -2.93 V, and -2.71 V for Li^+, K^+, and Na^+, respectively

$2H_2O + 2e^- \rightarrow H_2 + 2OH^-$ $E_{red} = -0.42$ V, with an overvoltage of about -1 V

In all of these cases, it is energetically more favorable to reduce H_2O to H_2 than to reduce M^+ to M.
b) The question asks if Ca could chemically reduce RbX, i.e., convert Rb^+ to Rb^0. In order for this to occur, Ca^0 loses two electrons ($Ca^0 \rightarrow Ca^{2+} + 2e^-$) and each Rb^+ gains an electron ($2Rb^+ + 2e^- \rightarrow 2Rb^0$). The reaction is written as follows:
$$2RbX + Ca \rightarrow CaX_2 + 2Rb$$
where $\Delta H = IE_1(Ca) + IE_2(Ca) - 2IE_1(Rb) = 590 + 1145 - 2(403) = +929$ kJ/mol.
Recall that Ca^0 acts as a *reducing agent* for the Rb^+ ion because it *oxidizes*. The energy required to remove an electron is the ionization energy. It requires more energy to ionize calcium's electrons, so it seems unlikely that Ca^0 could reduce Rb^+. Based on values of IE and a positive ΔH for the forward reaction, it seems more reasonable that Rb^0 would reduce Ca^{2+}.
c) If the reaction is carried out at a temperature greater than 688°C (the boiling point of rubidium), the product mixture will contain gaseous Rb. This can be removed from the reaction vessel, causing a shift in the equilibrium to form more Rb product. If the reaction is carried out between 688°C and 1484°C (bpt for Ca), then Ca remains in the molten phase and remains separated from gaseous Rb.
d) The reaction of calcium with molten CsX is written as follows:
$$2CsX + Ca \rightarrow CaX_2 + 2Cs$$
where $\Delta H = IE_1(Ca) + IE_2(Ca) - 2IE_1(Cs) = 590 + 1145 - 2(376) = +983$ kJ/mol. This reaction is more unfavorable than for Rb, but Cs has a lower boiling point of 671°C. If the reaction is carried out between 671°C and 1484°C, then calcium can be used to separate gaseous Cs from molten CsX.

23.32 <u>Plan:</u> Write the balanced equation for the process. For every two moles of Na metal produced, one mole of Cl_2 is produced. Calculate the amount of chlorine gas from the reaction stoichiometry, then use the ideal gas law to find the volume of chlorine gas. For part b), write the balanced equation for the oxidation of Cl^- to Cl_2; convert moles of Cl_2 produced to moles of electrons required and then convert to coulomb with the conversion factor 96,485 C = 1 mole of e^-. Convert electric charge to time with the conversion factor 1 C = 1 A•s.

Solution:

a) $2NaCl(l) \rightarrow 2Na(l) + Cl_2(g)$

Moles of $Cl_2 = (31.0 \text{ kg Na})\left(\dfrac{10^3 \text{ g}}{1 \text{ kg}}\right)\left(\dfrac{1 \text{ mol Na}}{22.99 \text{ g Na}}\right)\left(\dfrac{1 \text{ mol Cl}_2}{2 \text{ mol Na}}\right) = 674.2062 \text{ mol Cl}_2$

$pV = nRT$

$V(L) = \dfrac{nRT}{p} = \dfrac{(674.2062 \text{ mol Cl}_2)\left(8.31446\dfrac{\text{L} \cdot \text{kPa}}{\text{mol} \cdot \text{K}}\right)((273 + 540.)\text{K})}{(101.3 \text{ kPa})} = 4.49892 \times 10^4 \text{ L} = \mathbf{4.5 \times 10^4 \text{ L}}$

b) Two moles of electrons are passed through the cell for each mole of Cl_2 produced:

$$2Cl^-(l) \rightarrow Cl_2(g) + 2e^-$$

Electric charge $= (674.2062 \text{ mol Cl}_2)\left(\dfrac{2 \text{ mol e}^-}{1 \text{ mol Cl}_2}\right)\left(\dfrac{96,485 \text{ C}}{1 \text{ mol e}^-}\right) = 1.30101570 \times 10^8 \text{ C} = \mathbf{1.30 \times 10^8 \text{ C}}$

c) Time (s) $= (1.30101570 \times 10^8 \text{ C})\left(\dfrac{\text{A} \cdot \text{s}}{1 \text{ C}}\right)\left(\dfrac{1}{77.0 \text{ A}}\right) = 1.689631 \times 10^6 \text{ s} = \mathbf{1.69 \times 10^6 \text{ s}}$

23.35   a) Mg^{2+} is more difficult to reduce than H_2O, so $H_2(g)$ would be produced instead of Mg metal. $Cl_2(g)$ forms at the anode due to overvoltage.

b) The $\Delta_f H^\circ$ for $MgCl_2(s)$ is –641.6 kJ/mol: $Mg(s) + Cl_2(g) \rightarrow MgCl_2(s) + \text{heat}$.

High temperature favors the reverse reaction (which is endothermic), so high temperatures favor the formation of magnesium metal and chlorine gas.

23.37   a) Sulfur dioxide is the reducing agent and is oxidized to the +6 state (as sulfate ion, SO_4^{2-}).

b) The sulfate ion formed reacts as a base in the presence of acid to form the hydrogen sulfate ion.

$SO_4^{2-}(aq) + H^+(aq) \rightarrow HSO_4^-(aq)$

c) Skeleton redox equation: $SO_2(g) + H_2SeO_3(aq) \rightarrow Se(s) + HSO_4^-(aq)$

Reduction half-reaction: $H_2SeO_3(aq) \rightarrow Se(s)$

balance O and H $H_2SeO_3(aq) + 4H^+(aq) \rightarrow Se(s) + 3H_2O(l)$

balance charge $H_2SeO_3(aq) + 4H^+(aq) + 4e^- \rightarrow Se(s) + 3H_2O(l)$

Oxidation half-reaction: $SO_2(g) \rightarrow HSO_4^-(aq)$

balance O and H $SO_2(g) + 2H_2O(l) \rightarrow HSO_4^-(aq) + 3H^+(aq)$

balance charge $SO_2(g) + 2H_2O(l) \rightarrow HSO_4^-(aq) + 3H^+(aq) + 2e^-$

Multiply oxidation half-reaction by 2 $2SO_2(g) + 4H_2O(l) \rightarrow 2HSO_4^-(aq) + 6H^+(aq) + 4e^-$

Add the two half-reactions:

$H_2SeO_3(aq) + 4H^+(aq) + 4e^- \rightarrow Se(s) + \cancel{3}H_2O(l)$

$2SO_2(g) + 4H_2O(l) \rightarrow 2HSO_4^-(aq) + \cancel{6}H^+(aq) + \cancel{4e^-}$

$\overline{H_2SeO_3(aq) + 2SO_2(g) + H_2O(l) \rightarrow Se(s) + 2HSO_4^-(aq) + 2H^+(aq)}$

23.42   a) The oxidation state of copper in Cu_2S is +1 (sulfur is –2).

The oxidation state of copper in Cu_2O is +1 (oxygen is –2).

The oxidation state of copper in Cu is 0 (oxidation state is always 0 in the elemental form).

b) The reducing agent is the species that is *oxidized*. Sulfur changes oxidation state from –2 in Cu_2S to +4 in SO_2. Therefore, Cu_2S is the reducing agent, leaving Cu_2O as the oxidizing agent.

23.44   a) Use the surface area and thickness of the film to calculate its volume. Multiply the volume by the density to find the mass of the aluminum oxide. Convert mass to moles of aluminum oxide. The oxidation of aluminum involves the loss of three electrons for each aluminum atom or six electrons for each Al_2O_3 compound formed. From this, find the number of electrons produced and multiply by Faraday's constant to find the electric charge (coulomb).

Moles of $Al_2O_3 = (2.5 \text{ m}^2)(23 \times 10^{-6} \text{ m})\left(\dfrac{1 \text{ cm}}{10^{-2} \text{ m}}\right)^3 \left(\dfrac{3.97 \text{ g Al}_2O_3}{\text{cm}^3}\right)\left(\dfrac{1 \text{ mol Al}_2O_3}{101.96 \text{ g Al}_2O_3}\right)$

$$= 2.2388682 \text{ mol Al}_2O_3$$

$$\text{Electric charge (C)} = (2.2388682 \text{ mol Al}_2O_3)\left(\frac{6 \text{ mol e}^-}{1 \text{ mol Al}_2O_3}\right)\left(\frac{96,485 \text{ C}}{1 \text{ mol e}^-}\right) = 1.296103 \times 10^6 \text{ C} = \mathbf{1.3 \times 10^6 \text{ C}}$$

b) Current in amps can be found by dividing charge in coulombs by the time in seconds.
$$[(1.296103 \times 10^6 \text{ C})/[15 \text{ min } (60 \text{ s/min})] \times (1 \text{ A/(C/s))} = 1200 \text{ A} = \mathbf{1.2 \times 10^3 \text{ A}}$$

23.47   Plan: Free energy, ΔG°, is the measure of the ability of a reaction to proceed spontaneously. ΔG° can be calculated with the relationship $\sum m \Delta_{f \text{ (products)}} G^\circ - \sum n \Delta_{f \text{ (reactants)}} G^\circ$.
Solution:
The direct reduction of ZnS follows the reaction:
$2ZnS(s) + C(\text{graphite}) \rightarrow 2Zn(s) + CS_2(g)$
$\Delta_r G^\circ = 2(\Delta_f G^\circ \text{ of Zn}) + (\Delta_f G^\circ \text{ of } CS_2)]$

$$- [2(\Delta_f G^\circ \text{ of ZnS}) + (\Delta_f G^\circ \text{ of C})]$$

$\Delta_r G^\circ = [2(0 \text{ kJ/mol}) + (66.9 \text{ kJ/mol})] - [2(-198 \text{ kJ/mol}) + (0 \text{ kJ/mol})]$

$\Delta_r G^\circ = 462.9 \text{kJ/mol} = +463 \text{ kJ/mol}$

Since $\Delta_r G^\circ$ is positive, this reaction is not spontaneous at standard-state conditions. The stepwise reduction involves the conversion of ZnS to ZnO, followed by the final reduction step:
$2ZnO(s) + C(s) \rightarrow 2Zn(s) + CO_2(g)$
$\Delta_r G^\circ = [2(\Delta_f G^\circ \text{ of Zn}) + (\Delta_f G^\circ \text{ of } CO_2)]$

$$- [2(\Delta_f G^\circ \text{ of ZnO}) + (\Delta_f G^\circ \text{ of C})]$$

$\Delta_r G^\circ = [2(0 \text{ kJ/mol}) + (-394.4 \text{ kJ/mol})] - [2(-318.2 \text{ kJ/mol}) + (0 \text{ kJ/mol})]$

$\Delta_r G^\circ = +242.0 \text{ kJ /mol}$
This reaction is also not spontaneous, but the oxide reaction is less unfavorable.

23.48   The formation of sulfur trioxide is very slow at ordinary temperatures. Increasing the temperature can speed up the reaction, but the reaction is exothermic, so increasing the temperature decreases the yield. Recall that yield, or the extent to which a reaction proceeds, is controlled by the thermodynamics of the reaction. Adding a catalyst increases the rate of the formation reaction but does not impact the thermodynamics, so a lower temperature can be used to enhance the yield. Catalysts are used in such a reaction to allow control of both rate and yield of the reaction.

23.51   a) The chlor-alkali process yields Cl_2, H_2, and NaOH.
b) The mercury-cell process yields higher purity NaOH, but produces Hg-polluted waters that are discharged into the environment.

23.52   Plan: ΔG° at 25°C can be calculated with the relationship $\sum m \Delta_{f \text{ (products)}} G^\circ - \sum n \Delta_{f \text{ (reactants)}} G^\circ$. Calculate ΔG° at 500.°C with the relationship $\Delta_r G^\circ = \Delta_r H^\circ - \Delta_r S^\circ$. $\Delta_r H^\circ$ and $\Delta_r S^\circ$ must be calculated first. The equilibrium constant K is calculated by using $\Delta G^\circ = -RT \ln K$. Finally, to find the temperature at which the reaction becomes spontaneous, use $\Delta_r G^\circ = 0 = \Delta_{rxn} H^\circ - \Delta_r S^\circ$ and solve for temperature.
Solution:
a) The balanced equation for the oxidation of SO_2 to SO_3 is $2SO_2(g) + O_2(g) \rightarrow 2SO_3(g)$.
$\Delta_r G^\circ = \sum m \Delta_{f \text{ (products)}} G^\circ - \sum n \Delta_{f \text{ (reactants)}} G^\circ$

$\Delta_r G^\circ = [2(\Delta_f G^\circ \text{ of } SO_3)] - [2(\Delta_f G^\circ \text{ of } SO_2) + (\Delta_f G^\circ \text{ of } O_2)]$

$\Delta_r G^\circ = [2(-371 \text{ kJ/mol})] - [2(-300.2 \text{ kJ/mol}) + (0 \text{ kJ/mol})]$

$\Delta_r G^\circ = -141.6 \text{ kJ/mol} = -142 \text{ kJ/mol}$

Since $\Delta_r G°$ is negative, the reaction is spontaneous at 25°C.

b) The rate of the reaction is very slow at 25°C, so the reaction does not produce significant amounts of SO_3 at room temperature.

c) $\Delta_r H° = \sum m \Delta_{f(products)} H° - \sum n \Delta_{f(reactants)} H°$

$\Delta_r H° = [2(\Delta_f H° \text{ of } SO_3)] - [2(\Delta_f H° \text{ of } SO_2) + (\Delta_f H° \text{ of } O_2)]$

$\Delta_r H° = [2(-396 \text{ kJ/mol})] - [2(-296.8 \text{ kJ/mol}) + (0 \text{ kJ/mol})]$

$\Delta_r H° = -198.4 \text{ kJ/mol} = -198 \text{ kJ/mol}$

$\Delta_r S° = \sum m S°_{products} - \sum n S°_{reactants}$

$\Delta_r S° = [2(S° \text{ of } SO_3)] - [2(S° \text{ of } SO_2) + (S° \text{ of } O_2)]$

$\Delta_r S° = [2(256.66 \text{ J/mol•K})] - [2(248.1 \text{ J/mol•K}) + (205.0 \text{ J/mol•K})]$

$\Delta_r S° = -187.88 \text{ J/K•mol} = -187.9 \text{ J/K•mol}$

$\Delta_{500°C} G° = \Delta_r H° - T \Delta_r S° = -198.4 \text{ kJ•mol} - ((273 + 500.) \text{ K})(-187.88 \text{ J/K•mol})(1 \text{ kJ}/10^3 \text{ J})$

$\qquad = -53.16876 \text{ kJ/mol} = -53 \text{ kJ/mol}$

The reaction is spontaneous at 500°C since free energy is negative.

d) The equilibrium constant at 500°C is smaller than the equilibrium constant at 25°C because the free energy at 500°C indicates the reaction does not go as far to completion as it does at 25°C.

Equilibrium constants can be calculated from $\Delta G° = -RT \ln K$.

At 25°C: $\ln K = \dfrac{\Delta G°}{-RT} = -\dfrac{(-142 \text{ kJ})\left(\dfrac{10^3 \text{ J}}{1 \text{ kJ}}\right)}{(8.314 \text{ J/mol•K})((273 + 25)\text{K})} = 57.31417694$

$K_{25°C} = e^{57.31417694} = 7.784501 \times 10^{24} = 7.8 \times 10^{24}$

At 500°C: $\ln K = \dfrac{\Delta G°}{-RT} = -\dfrac{(-53 \text{ kJ})\left(\dfrac{10^3 \text{ J}}{1 \text{ kJ}}\right)}{(8.314 \text{ J/mol•K})((273 + 500)\text{K})} = 8.246817$

$K_{500°C} = e^{8.246817} = 3.815 \times 10^3 = 3.8 \times 10^3$

e) Temperature below which the reaction is spontaneous at standard state can be calculated by setting $\Delta G°$ equal to zero and using the enthalpy and entropy values at 25°C to calculate the temperature.

$\Delta_r G° = 0 = \Delta_r H° - T \Delta_r S°$

$\Delta_r H° = T \Delta_r S°$

$T = \dfrac{\Delta H°}{\Delta S°} = \dfrac{-198 \text{ kJ}}{-187.9 \text{ J/K}\left(\dfrac{1 \text{ kJ}}{10^3 \text{ J}}\right)} = 1.05375 \times 10^3 \text{ K} = \mathbf{1.05 \times 10^3 \text{ K or } 780°C}$

23.53   Plan: This problem deals with the stoichiometry of electrolysis. The balanced oxidation half-reaction for the chlor-alkali process is given in the chapter:

$\qquad 2Cl^-(aq) \rightarrow Cl_2(g) + 2e^-$

Use the Faraday constant, F, $(1 \; F = 9.6485 \times 10^4 \text{ C/mol e}^-)$ and the fact that one mol of Cl_2 produces two mol e^- or $2 \; F$, to convert coulombs to moles of Cl_2.

Solution:

$\text{Mass (kg) of } Cl_2 = \left(3 \times 10^4 \text{ A}\right)\left(\dfrac{C/s}{A}\right)\left(\dfrac{3600 \text{ s}}{1 \text{ h}}\right)(8 \text{ h})\left(\dfrac{1 \text{ mol e}^-}{96,485 \text{ C}}\right)\left(\dfrac{1 \text{ mol } Cl_2}{2 \text{ mol e}^-}\right)\left(\dfrac{70.90 \text{ g } Cl_2}{1 \text{ mol } Cl_2}\right)\left(\dfrac{1 \text{ kg}}{10^3 \text{ g}}\right)$

$\qquad = 317.46 \text{ kg} = \mathbf{3 \times 10^2 \text{ kg } Cl_2}$

23.56   Plan: Write the balanced equation. Use the stoichiometry in the equation to find the moles of H_3PO_4 produced by the reaction of the given amount of P_4O_{10}. Divide moles of H_3PO_4 by the volume to obtain its concentration (mol/L). Since H_3PO_4 is a weak acid, use its equilibrium expression to find the $[H_3O^+]$ and then pH.
Solution:
a) Because P_4O_{10} is a drying agent, water is incorporated in the formation of phosphoric acid, H_3PO_4.

$$P_4O_{10}(s) + 6H_2O(l) \rightarrow 4H_3PO_4(l)$$

b) Moles of $H_3PO_4 = \left(8.5 \text{ g } P_4O_{10}\right)\left(\dfrac{1 \text{ mol } P_4O_{10}}{283.88 \text{ g } P_4O_{10}}\right)\left(\dfrac{4 \text{ mol } H_3PO_4}{1 \text{ mol } P_4O_{10}}\right) = 0.11976892 \text{ mol } H_3PO_4$

Concentration of $H_3PO_4 = \left(\dfrac{0.11976892 \text{ mol } H_3PO_4}{0.750 \text{ L}}\right) = 0.1596919 \text{ mol/L } H_3PO_4$

Phosphoric acid is a weak acid and only partly dissociates to form H_3O^+ in water, based on its K_a. Since $K_{a1} \gg K_{a2} \gg K_{a3}$, assume that the H_3O^+ contributed by the second and third dissociation is negligible in comparison to the H_3O^+ contributed by the first dissociation.

$$H_3PO_4(l) + H_2O(l) \rightarrow H_3O^+(aq) + H_2PO_4^-(aq)$$

$$K_a = 7.2 \times 10^{-3} = \dfrac{\left[H_3O^+\right]\left[H_2PO_4^-\right]}{\left[H_3PO_4\right]}$$

$$K_a = 7.2 \times 10^{-3} = \dfrac{[x][x]}{(0.1596919 - x)} \qquad \text{Assume x is small compared to 0.1596919.}$$

$$K_a = 7.2 \times 10^{-3} = \dfrac{[x][x]}{(0.1596919)}$$

x = 0.0339084 mol/L
Check assumption that x is small compared to 0.1596919:

$$\dfrac{0.0339084}{0.1596919}(100) = 21\% \text{ error, so the assumption is not valid.}$$

The problem will need to be solved as a quadratic.
$x^2 = (7.2 \times 10^{-3})(0.1596919 - x) = 1.14978 \times 10^{-3} - 7.2 \times 10^{-3}x$
$x^2 + 7.2 \times 10^{-3}x - 1.14978 \times 10^{-3} = 0$

$$a = 1 \qquad b = 7.2 \times 10^{-3} \qquad c = -1.14978 \times 10^{-3}$$

$$x = \dfrac{-7.2 \times 10^{-3} \pm \sqrt{\left(7.2 \times 10^{-3}\right)^2 - 4(1)\left(-1.14978 \times 10^{-3}\right)}}{2(1)}$$

$x = 3.049897 \times 10^{-2}$ mol/L H_3O^+
pH $= -\log[H_3O^+] = -\log(3.049897 \times 10^{-2}) = 1.51571 = \mathbf{1.52}$

23.58   Plan: Write a balanced equation for the production of iron and use the reaction stoichiometry to calculate the amount of CO_2 produced when the given amount of Fe is produced. Then write a balanced equation for the combustion of gasoline (C_8H_{18}.) Find the total volume of gasoline, use the density to convert volume to mass of gasoline, and use the reaction stoichiometry to calculate the amount of CO_2 produced.

Solution:
a) The reaction taking place in the blast furnace to produce iron is:

$$Fe_2O_3(s) + 3CO(g) \rightarrow 2Fe(s) + 3CO_2(g)$$

Mass (g) of $CO_2 = \left(7620.t \text{ Fe}\right)\left(\dfrac{8 \times 10^6 \text{ g}}{t}\right)\left(\dfrac{1 \text{ mol Fe}}{55.85 \text{ g Fe}}\right)\left(\dfrac{3 \text{ mol } CO_2}{2 \text{ mol Fe}}\right)\left(\dfrac{44.01 \text{ g } CO_2}{1 \text{ mol } CO_2}\right)$

$= 9.006881 \times 10^9$ g $= \mathbf{9.007 \times 10^9}$ g $\mathbf{CO_2}$
b) Combustion reaction for octane:

$$2C_8H_{18}(l) + 25O_2(g) \rightarrow 16CO_2(g) + 18H_2O(l)$$

Mass (g) of CO_2 =

$$\left(1.0 \times 10^6 \text{ autos}\right)\left(\frac{19 \text{ L}}{1 \text{ auto}}\right)\left(\frac{1 \text{ mL}}{10^{-3} \text{ L}}\right)\left(\frac{0.74 \text{ g}}{\text{mL}}\right)\left(\frac{1 \text{ mol } C_8H_{18}}{114.22 \text{ g } C_8H_{18}}\right)\left(\frac{16 \text{ mol } CO_2}{2 \text{ mol } C_8H_{18}}\right)\left(\frac{44.01 \text{ g } CO_2}{1 \text{ mol } CO_2}\right)$$

$$= 4.33396 \times 10^{10} \text{ g} = 4.3 \times 10^{10} \text{ g } CO_2$$

The CO_2 production by automobiles is much greater than that from steel production.

23.60   Plan: Step 2 of "Isolation of Magnesium" in Section 23.4 describes this reaction. Sufficient OH^- must be added to precipitate $Mg(OH)_2$. The necessary amount of OH^- can be determined from the K_{sp} of $Mg(OH)_2$. For part b), use the K_{sp} of $Ca(OH)_2$ to determine the amount of OH^- that a saturated solution of $Ca(OH)_2$ provides. Substitute this amount into the K_{sp} expression for $Mg(OH)_2$ to determine how much Mg^{2+} remains in solution with this amount of OH^-.

Calculate the fraction of $[Mg^{2+}]$ remaining and subtract from 1 to obtain the fraction of $[Mg^{2+}]$ that precipitated.

Solution:

a) $Mg(OH)_2(s) \rightarrow Mg^{2+}(aq) + 2OH^-(aq)$

$K_{sp} = 6.3 \times 10^{-10} = [Mg^{2+}][OH^-]^2$

$$[OH^-] = \sqrt{\frac{6.3 \times 10^{-10}}{[Mg^{2+}]}} = \sqrt{\frac{6.3 \times 10^{-10}}{0.052}} = 1.100699 \times 10^{-4} \text{ mol/L} = 1.1 \times 10^{-4} \text{ mol/L}$$

Thus, if $[OH^-] > 1.1 \times 10^{-4}$ mol/L (i.e., if pH > 10.04), $Mg(OH)_2$ will precipitate.

b) $Ca(OH)_2(s) \rightarrow Ca^{2+}(aq) + 2OH^-(aq)$

$K_{sp} = 6.5 \times 10^{-6} = [Ca^{2+}][OH^-]^2 = (x)(2x)^2 = 4x^3$

$x = 0.011756673$; $[OH^-] = 2x = 0.023513347$ mol/L

$K_{sp} (Mg(OH)_2) = 6.3 \times 10^{-10} = [Mg^{2+}][OH^-]^2$

$$[Mg^{2+}] = \frac{6.3 \times 10^{-10}}{(0.023513347)^2} = 1.1394930 \times 10^{-6} \text{ mol/L}$$

This concentration is the amount of the original 0.052 mol/L Mg^{2+} that was not precipitated. The percent precipitated is the difference between the remaining $[Mg^{2+}]$ and the initial $[Mg^{2+}]$ divided by the initial concentration.

Fraction Mg^{2+} remaining = $(1.1394930 \times 10^{-6}$ mol/L)/(0.052 mol/L) = 2.19134×10^{-5}

Mg^{2+} precipitated = $1 - 2.19134 \times 10^{-5} = 0.9999781 = 1$ (To the limit of the significant figures, all the magnesium has precipitated.)

23.61   Plan: The equation $\Delta_r G° = \Delta_r H° - T\Delta_r S°$ will be used to calculate $\Delta_r G°$ at the two temperatures. $\Delta_r H°$ and $\Delta_r S°$ will have to be calculated first. Then use $\Delta G° = -RT \ln K$ to determine K. Subscripts indicate the temperature, and (1) or (2) indicate the reaction.

Solution:

For the first reaction (1):

$\Delta_r H° = \Sigma m \Delta_{f \text{ (products)}} H° - \Sigma n \Delta_{f \text{ (reactants)}} H°$

$\Delta_r H° = [4(\Delta_f H° \text{ of NO}) + 6(\Delta_f H° \text{ of } H_2O)]$

$\qquad\qquad\qquad\qquad - [4(\Delta_f H° \text{ of } NH_3) + 5(\Delta_f H° \text{ of } O_2)]$

$\Delta_r H° = [4(90.29 \text{ kJ/mol}) + 6(-241.826 \text{ kJ/mol})] - [4(-45.9 \text{ kJ/mol}) + 5(0 \text{ kJ/mol})]$

$\Delta_r H° = -906.196 \text{ kJ /mol}$

$\Delta_r S° = [4(S° \text{ of NO}) + 6(S° \text{ of } H_2O)]$

$\qquad\qquad\qquad\qquad - [4(S° \text{ of } NH_3) + 5(S° \text{ of } O_2)]$

$\Delta_r S° = [4(210.65 \text{ J/K•mol}) + 6(188.72 \text{ J/K•mol})]$

$\qquad\qquad\qquad\qquad - [4(193 \text{ J/K•mol}) + 5(205.0 \text{ J/K•mol})](1 \text{ kJ}/10^3 \text{ J})$

$\Delta_r S° = 0.17792 \text{ kJ/K •mol}$

$$\Delta_r G^\circ = \Delta_r H^\circ - T \Delta_r S^\circ$$

$$\Delta_{25^\circ C} G^\circ = -906.196 \text{ kJ/mol} - [(273 + 25)K(\ 0.17792 \text{ kJ/K} \bullet \text{mol}) = -959.216 \text{ kJ}$$

$$\Delta_{900^\circ C} G^\circ = -906.196 \text{ kJ/mol} - [(273 + 900.)K(\ 0.17792 \text{ kJ/K} \bullet \text{mol}) = -1114.896 \text{ kJ/mol}$$

For the second reaction (2):

$$\Delta_r H^\circ = [2(\Delta_f H^\circ \text{ of N}_2) + 6(\Delta_f H^\circ \text{ of H}_2\text{O})]$$
$$- [4(\Delta_f H^\circ \text{ of NH}_3) + 3(\Delta_f H^\circ \text{ of O}_2)]$$

$$\Delta_r H^\circ = [2(0 \text{ kJ/mol}) + 6(-241.826 \text{ kJ/mol})] - [4(-45.9 \text{ kJ/mol}) + 3(0 \text{ kJ/mol})]$$

$$\Delta_r H^\circ = -1267.356 \text{ kJ /mol}$$

$$\Delta_r S^\circ = [2(S^\circ \text{ of N}_2) + 6(S^\circ \text{ of H}_2\text{O})]$$
$$- [4(S^\circ \text{ of NH}_3) + 3(S^\circ \text{ of O}_2)]$$

$$\Delta_r S^\circ = [2(191.5 \text{ J/K} \bullet \text{mol}) + 6(188.72 \text{ J/K} \bullet \text{mol})]$$
$$- [4(193 \text{ J/K} \bullet \text{mol}) + 3(205.0 \text{ J/K} \bullet \text{mol})](1 \text{ kJ/10}^3 \text{ J})$$

$$\Delta_r S^\circ = 0.12832 \text{ J/K} \bullet \text{mol}$$

$$\Delta_r G^\circ = \Delta_r H^\circ - \Delta_r S^\circ$$

$$\Delta_{25^\circ C} G^\circ = -1267.356 \text{ kJ/mol} - [(273 + 25)K](0.12832 \text{ kJ/K} \bullet \text{mol}) = -1305.595 \text{ kJ/mol}$$

$$\Delta_{900^\circ C} G^\circ = -1267.356 \text{ kJ/mol} - [(273 + 900.)K](0.12832 \text{ kJ/K} \bullet \text{mol}) = -1417.875 \text{ kJ/mol}$$

a) $\ln K_{25^\circ C}(1) = \dfrac{\Delta G^\circ}{-RT} = -\dfrac{(-959.216 \text{ kJ/mol})}{(8.314 \text{ J/mol} \bullet \text{K})((273 + 25)K)}\left(\dfrac{10^3 \text{ J}}{1 \text{ kJ}}\right) = 387.15977$

$$K_{25^\circ C}(1) = 1.38 \times 10^{168} = 1 \times 10^{168}$$

$\ln K_{25^\circ C}(2) = \dfrac{\Delta G^\circ}{-RT} = -\dfrac{(-1305.595 \text{ kJ/mol})}{(8.314 \text{ J/mol} \bullet \text{K})((273 + 25)K)}\left(\dfrac{10^3 \text{ J}}{1 \text{ kJ}}\right) = 526.9655$

$$K_{25^\circ C}(2) = 7.2146 \times 10^{228} = 7 \times 10^{228}$$

b) $\ln K_{900^\circ C}(1) = \dfrac{\Delta G^\circ}{-RT} = -\dfrac{(-1114.896 \text{ kJ/mol})}{(8.314 \text{ J/mol} \bullet \text{K})((273 + 900)K)}\left(\dfrac{10^3 \text{ J}}{1 \text{ kJ}}\right) = 114.3210817$

$$K_{900^\circ C}(1) = 4.4567 \times 10^{49} = 4.5 \times 10^{49}$$

$\ln K_{900^\circ C}(2) = \dfrac{\Delta G^\circ}{-RT} = -\dfrac{(-1417.875 \text{ kJ/mol})}{(8.314 \text{ J/mol} \bullet \text{K})((273 + 900)K)}\left(\dfrac{10^3 \text{ J}}{1 \text{ kJ}}\right) = 145.388$

$$K_{900^\circ C}(2) = 1.38422 \times 10^{63} = 1.4 \times 10^{63}$$

c) Cost (\$) Pt $= \left(6.6 \text{x} 10^6 \text{ t HNO}_3\right)\left(\dfrac{175 \text{ mg Pt}}{1 \text{ t HNO}_3}\right)\left(\dfrac{10^{-3} \text{ g}}{1 \text{ mg}}\right)\left(\dfrac{1 \text{ kg}}{10^3 \text{ g}}\right)\left(\dfrac{32.15 \text{ oz t}}{1 \text{ kg}}\right)\left(\dfrac{\$1557}{1 \text{ oz t}}\right)$

$$= \$5.781647 \times 10^7 = \$5.8 \times 10^7$$

d) Cost (\$) Pt $= \left(6.6 \text{x} 10^6 \text{ t HNO}_3\right)\left(\dfrac{175 \text{ mg Pt}}{1 \text{ t HNO}_3}\right)\left(\dfrac{72\%}{100\%}\right)\left(\dfrac{10^{-3} \text{ g}}{1 \text{ mg}}\right)\left(\dfrac{1 \text{ kg}}{10^3 \text{ g}}\right)\left(\dfrac{32.15 \text{ oz t}}{1 \text{ kg}}\right)\left(\dfrac{\$1557}{1 \text{ oz t}}\right)$

$$= \$4.1627856 \times 10^7 = \$4.2 \times 10^7$$

23.64   Plan: Balance each reaction. Acidity is a measure of the concentration of H_3O^+ (H^+), so any reaction that produces H^+ will increase the acidity.
Solution:
a) $2H_2O(l) + 2FeS_2(s) + 7O_2(g) \rightarrow 2Fe^{2+}(aq) + 4SO_4^{2-}(aq) + 4H^+(aq)$ Increases acidity.
b) $4H^+(aq) + 4Fe^{2+}(aq) + O_2(g) \rightarrow 4Fe^{3+}(aq) + 2H_2O(l)$
c) $Fe^{3+}(aq) + 3H_2O(l) \rightarrow Fe(OH)_3(s) + 3H^+(aq)$ Increases acidity.
d) $8H_2O(l) + FeS_2(s) + 14Fe^{3+}(aq) \rightarrow 15Fe^{2+}(aq) + 2SO_4^{2-}(aq) + 16H^+(aq)$ Increases acidity.

23.65   Plan: The carbon fits into interstitial positions. The cell size will increase slightly to accommodate the carbons atoms. The increase in size is assumed to be negligible. The mass of the carbon added depends upon the carbon in the unit cell.
Solution:
Ferrite:

$$\left(\frac{7.86\ g}{cm^3}\right) + \left(\frac{7.86\ g}{cm^3}\right)\left(\frac{0.0218\%}{100\%}\right) = 7.86171\ \text{g/cm}^3 = \textbf{7.86 g/cm}^3$$

Austenite:

$$\left(\frac{7.40\ g}{cm^3}\right) + \left(\frac{7.40\ g}{cm^3}\right)\left(\frac{2.08\%}{100\%}\right) = 7.55392\ \text{g/cm}^3 = \textbf{7.55 g/cm}^3$$

23.67   Plan: Decide what is reduced and what is oxidized of the two ions present in molten NaOH. Then, write half-reactions and balance them.   Then write the overall equation for the electrolysis of NaOH and also for the reaction of Na with water. Examine the molar ratios involving water and Na in these equations.
Solution:
a) At the cathode, sodium ions are reduced: $Na^+(l) + e^- \rightarrow Na(l)$
At the anode, hydroxide ions are oxidized: $4OH^-(l) \rightarrow O_2(g) + 2H_2O(g) + 4e^-$
b) The overall cell reaction is $4Na^+(l) + 4OH^-(l) \rightarrow 4Na(l) + O_2(g) + 2H_2O(g)$ and the reaction between sodium metal and water is $2Na(l) + 2H_2O(g) \rightarrow 2NaOH(l) + H_2(g)$.
For each mole of water produced, two moles of sodium are produced, but for each mole of water that reacts only one mole of sodium reacts.
Since 1/2 of the Na reacts with H_2O, the maximum efficiency is 1/2 mol Na/mol e^-, or **50%**.

23.70   Plan: Convert mass of CO_2 to moles of O_2 using the reaction stoichiometry in the balanced equation. $pV = nRT$ is used to convert moles of O_2 to volume. Temperature must be in units of Kelvin.
Solution:
a) The reaction for the fixation of carbon dioxide includes CO_2 and H_2O as reactants and $(CH_2O)_n$ and O_2 as products. The balanced equation is: $nCO_2(g) + nH_2O(l) \rightarrow (CH_2O)_n(s) + nO_2(g)$
b) The moles of carbon dioxide fixed equal the moles of O_2 produced.

$$\text{Mole } O_2\text{/day} = \left(\frac{48\ g\ CO_2}{day}\right)\left(\frac{1\ mol\ CO_2}{44.01\ g\ CO_2}\right)\left(\frac{1\ mol\ O_2}{1\ mol\ CO_2}\right) = 1.090661\ \text{mol } O_2\text{/day}$$

To find the volume of oxygen, use the ideal gas equation. Temperature must be converted to K.
T (in K) = 25.6 °C + 273.15 = 25.6 °C + 273.15 = 298.75 K
$pV = nRT$

$$V = \frac{nRT}{p} = \frac{(1.090661\ mol\ O_2)(8.31446\ L \cdot kPa/mol \cdot K)(298.75\ K)}{(101.3\ kPa)} = 26.7437\ L = \textbf{27 L}$$

c) The moles of air containing 1.090661 mol of CO_2 are:

$$\text{Mole } CO_2\text{/day} = \left(\frac{48\ g\ CO_2}{day}\right)\left(\frac{1\ mol\ CO_2}{44.01\ g\ CO_2}\right)\left(\frac{100\ mol\ \%\ air}{0.035\ mol\ \%\ CO_2}\right) = 3.11617\text{x}10^3\ \text{mol air/day}$$

$$V = \frac{nRT}{p} = \frac{(3.11617\text{x}10^3\ mol\ air)(8.31446\ L \cdot kPa/mol \cdot K)(298.75\ K)}{(101.3\ kPa)} = 7.64106\text{x}10^4\ L = \textbf{7.6x10}^4\ \textbf{L}$$

23.71 This problem requires a series of conversion steps:
Concentration =

$$\left(\frac{210. \text{ kg (NH}_4)_2\text{SO}_4}{1000. \text{ m}^3}\right)\left(\frac{10^3 \text{ g}}{1 \text{ kg}}\right)\left(\frac{1 \text{ mol (NH}_4)_2\text{SO}_4}{132.15 \text{ g (NH}_4)_2\text{SO}_4}\right)\left(\frac{2 \text{ mol NO}_3^-}{1 \text{ mol (NH}_4)_2\text{SO}_4}\right)\left(\frac{37\%}{100\%}\right)\left(\frac{62.01 \text{ g NO}_3^-}{1 \text{ mol NO}_3^-}\right)\left(\frac{1 \text{ mg}}{10^{-3} \text{ g}}\right)\left(\frac{10^{-3} \text{ m}^3}{1 \text{ L}}\right)$$

= 72.9198 mg/L= **73 mg/L**

This assumes the plants in the field absorb none of the fertilizer.

23.72 <u>Plan:</u> Write a balanced equation. Determine which one of the three reactants is the limiting reactant by determining the amount of cryolite produced by each reactant. The amount of Al(OH)$_3$ requires conversion of kg to g; the amount of NaOH requires conversion from amount of solution to mass in grams by using the density; the amount of HF requires conversion from volume to moles using the ideal gas law.
<u>Solution:</u>
The balanced chemical equation for this reaction is:

$6HF(g) + Al(OH)_3(s) + 3NaOH(aq) \rightarrow Na_3AlF_6(aq) + 6H_2O(l)$

a) Assuming Al(OH)$_3$ is the limiting reactant:

$$\text{Moles of Na}_3\text{AlF}_6 = \left(365 \text{ kg Al(OH)}_3\right)\left(\frac{10^3 \text{ g}}{1 \text{ kg}}\right)\left(\frac{1 \text{ mol Al(OH)}_3}{78.00 \text{ g Al(OH)}_3}\right)\left(\frac{1 \text{ mol Na}_3\text{AlF}_6}{1 \text{ mol Al(OH)}_3}\right)$$

$= 4.6795 \times 10^3 \text{ mol Na}_3\text{AlF}_6$

b) Assuming NaOH is the limiting reactant:
Moles of Na$_3$AlF$_6$ =

$$\left(1.20 \text{ m}^3\right)\left(\frac{1 \text{ L}}{10^{-3} \text{ m}^3}\right)\left(\frac{1 \text{ mL}}{10^{-3} \text{ L}}\right)\left(\frac{1.53 \text{ g}}{\text{mL}}\right)\left(\frac{50.0\% \text{ NaOH}}{100\%}\right)\left(\frac{1 \text{ mol NaOH}}{40.00 \text{ g NaOH}}\right)\left(\frac{1 \text{ mol Na}_3\text{AlF}_6}{3 \text{ mol NaOH}}\right)$$

$= 7.650 \times 10^3 \text{ mol Na}_3\text{AlF}_6$

c) Assuming HF is the limiting reactant:
$pV = nRT$

$$\text{Moles of HF} = \frac{PV}{RT} = \frac{(305 \text{ kPa})(265 \text{ m}^3)}{(8.31446 \text{ L} \cdot \text{kPa/mol} \cdot \text{K})((273.2 + 91.5)\text{K})}\left(\frac{1 \text{ L}}{10^{-3} \text{ m}^3}\right)$$

$= 26{,}654.83 \text{ mol HF}$

$$\text{Moles of Na}_3\text{AlF}_6 = \left(26{,}654.83 \text{ mol HF}\right)\left(\frac{1 \text{ mol Na}_3\text{AlF}_6}{6 \text{ mol HF}}\right) = 4.4425 \times 10^3 \text{ mol Na}_3\text{AlF}_6$$

Because the 265 m^3 of HF produces the smallest amount of Na$_3$AlF$_6$, it is the limiting reactant. Convert moles Na$_3$AlF$_6$ to g Na$_3$AlF$_6$, using the molar mass, convert to kg, and multiply by 95.6% to determine the final yield.

$$\text{Mass (g) of cryolite} = \left(4.4425 \times 10^3 \text{ mol Na}_3\text{AlF}_6\right)\left(\frac{209.95 \text{ g Na}_3\text{AlF}_6}{1 \text{ mol Na}_3\text{AlF}_6}\right)\left(\frac{1 \text{ kg}}{10^3 \text{ g}}\right)\left(\frac{95.6\%}{100\%}\right)$$

$= 891.658 \text{ kg} = $ **892 kg Na$_3$AlF$_6$**

23.73 <u>Plan:</u> The rate of effusion is inversely proportional to the square root of the molar mass of the molecule (Graham's law).
<u>Solution:</u>

a) $\dfrac{\text{Rate}_H}{\text{Rate}_D} = \sqrt{\dfrac{\text{molar mass}_D}{\text{molar mass}_H}} = \sqrt{\dfrac{4.00 \text{ g/mol}}{2.016 \text{ g/mol}}} = 1.40859$

The time for D$_2$ to effuse is 1.41 times greater than that for H$_2$.
$\text{Time}_{D_2} = (1.40859)(16.5 \text{ min}) = 23.2417 \text{ min} = $ **23.2 min**

b) Set x equal to the number of effusion steps. The ratio of mol H$_2$ to mol D$_2$ is 99:1.
Set up the equation to solve for x: $99/1 = (1.40859)^x$.
When solving for an exponent, take the log of both sides.
$\log (99) = \log (1.40859)^x$

Remember that log (a^b) = b log (a)

$$\log (99) = x \log (1.40859)$$
$$x = 13.4129$$

To separate H_2 and D_2 to 99% purity requires **13 effusion steps**.

23.75   Plan: Use the stoichiometric relationships found in the balanced chemical equation to find the mass of Al_2O_3, mass of graphite, and moles of CO_2. Use the ideal gas law to convert moles of CO_2 into volume.
Solution:
a) $2Al_2O_3(\text{in } Na_3AlF_6) + 3C(\text{graphite}) \rightarrow 4Al(l) + 3CO_2(g)$

Mass (t) of Al_2O_3 =

$$(1 \text{ t Al})\left(\frac{10^3 \text{ kg}}{1 \text{ t}}\right)\left(\frac{10^3 \text{g}}{1 \text{ kg}}\right)\left(\frac{1 \text{ mol Al}}{26.98 \text{ g Al}}\right)\left(\frac{2 \text{ mol Al}_2O_3}{4 \text{ mol Al}}\right)\left(\frac{101.96 \text{ g Al}_2O_3}{1 \text{ mol Al}_2O_3}\right)\left(\frac{1 \text{ kg}}{10^3 \text{ g}}\right)\left(\frac{1 \text{ t}}{10^3 \text{ kg}}\right)$$

$$= 1.8895478t = \textbf{1.890 t Al}_2\textbf{O}_3$$

Therefore, **1.890 t of Al_2O_3** are consumed in the production of 1 t of pure Al.

b) Mass (t) of C = $(1 \text{ t Al})\left(\frac{10^3 \text{ kg}}{1 \text{ t}}\right)\left(\frac{10^3 \text{g}}{1 \text{ kg}}\right)\left(\frac{1 \text{ mol Al}}{26.98 \text{ g Al}}\right)\left(\frac{3 \text{ mol C}}{4 \text{ mol Al}}\right)\left(\frac{12.01 \text{ g C}}{1 \text{ mol C}}\right)\left(\frac{1 \text{ kg}}{10^3 \text{ g}}\right)\left(\frac{1 \text{ t}}{10^3 \text{ kg}}\right)$

$$= 0.3338584 \text{ t} = \textbf{0.3339 t C}$$

Therefore, **0.3339 t of C** is consumed in the production of 1 t of pure Al, assuming 100% efficiency.
c) The percent yield with respect to Al_2O_3 is **100%** because the actual plant requirement of 1.89 t Al_2O_3 equals the theoretical amount calculated in part a).
d) The amount of graphite used in reality to produce 1 t of Al is greater than the amount calculated in part b). In other words, a 100% efficient reaction takes only 0.3339 t of graphite to produce a metric tonne of Al, whereas real production requires more graphite and is less than 100% efficient. Calculate the efficiency using a simple ratio:

$$(0.45 \text{ t})(x) = (0.3338584 \text{ t})(100\%)$$
$$x = 74.19076 \% = \textbf{74\%}$$

e) For every four moles of Al produced, three moles of CO_2 are produced.

Moles of C = $(1 \text{ t Al})\left(\frac{10^3 \text{ kg}}{1 \text{ t}}\right)\left(\frac{10^3 \text{ g}}{1 \text{ kg}}\right)\left(\frac{1 \text{ mol Al}}{26.98 \text{ g Al}}\right)\left(\frac{3 \text{ mol CO}_2}{4 \text{ mol Al}}\right) = 2.7798 \times 10^4 \text{ mol CO}_2$

The problem states that 101.3 kPa is exact. Use the ideal gas law to calculate volume, given moles, temperature, and pressure.

$pV = nRT$

$$V = \frac{nRT}{p} = \left(\frac{\left(2.7798 \times 10^4 \text{ mol CO}_2\right)(8.31446 \text{ L} \cdot \text{kPa/mol} \cdot \text{K})\left((273 + 960.) \text{K}\right)}{101.3 \text{ kPa}}\right)\left(\frac{10^{-3} \text{ m}^3}{1 \text{ L}}\right)$$

$$= 2.813204 \times 10^3 \text{ m}^3 = \textbf{2.813} \times \textbf{10}^3 \textbf{ m}^3$$

23.80   Plan: Solubility of a salt can be calculated from its K_{sp}. K_{sp} for $Ca_3(PO_4)_2$ is 1.2×10^{-29}. Phosphate is derived from a weak acid, so the pH of the solution impacts exactly where the acid-base equilibrium lies. Phosphate can gain one H^+ to form HPO_4^{2-}. Gaining another H^+ gives $H_2PO_4^-$ and a last H^+ added gives H_3PO_4. The K_a values for phosphoric acid are $K_{a1} = 7.2 \times 10^{-3}$, $K_{a2} = 6.3 \times 10^{-8}$, $K_{a3} = 4.2 \times 10^{-13}$. To find the ratios of the various forms of phosphate, use the equilibrium expressions and the concentration of H^+.
Solution:

a) $Ca_3(PO_4)_2(s) \rightarrow 3Ca^{2+}(aq) + 2PO_4^{3-}(aq)$

Initial	—	0	0
Change	–x	+3x	+2x
Equilibrium	—	3x	2x

$K_{sp} = 1.2 \times 10^{-29} = [Ca^{2+}]^3[PO_4^{3-}]^2 = (3x)^3(2x)^2 = 108x^5$
$x = 6.4439 \times 10^{-7} = \textbf{6.4} \times \textbf{10}^{-7} \textbf{ mol/L } Ca_3(PO_4)_2$

b) $[H_3O^+] = 10^{-4.5} = 3.162 \times 10^{-5}$ mol/L

$$H_3PO_4(aq) + H_2O(l) \rightarrow H_2PO_4^-(aq) + H_3O^+(aq)$$

$$K_{a1} = \frac{\left[H_2PO_4^-\right]\left[H_3O^+\right]}{\left[H_3PO_4\right]}$$

$$\frac{\left[H_2PO_4^-\right]}{\left[H_3PO_4\right]} = \frac{K_{a1}}{\left[H_3O^+\right]} = \frac{7.2 \times 10^{-3}}{3.162 \times 10^{-5}} = 227.70$$

$$H_2PO_4^-(aq) + H_2O(l) \rightleftharpoons HPO_4^{2-}(aq) + H_3O^+(aq)$$

$$K_{a2} = \frac{\left[HPO_4^{2-}\right]\left[H_3O^+\right]}{\left[H_2PO_4^-\right]}$$

$$\frac{\left[HPO_4^{2-}\right]}{\left[H_2PO_4^-\right]} = \frac{K_{a2}}{\left[H_3O^+\right]} = \frac{6.3 \times 10^{-8}}{3.162 \times 10^{-5}} = 1.9924 \times 10^{-3}$$

$$HPO_4^{2-}(aq) + H_2O(l) \rightleftharpoons PO_4^{3-}(aq) + H_3O^+(aq)$$

$$K_{a3} = \frac{\left[PO_4^{3-}\right]\left[H_3O^+\right]}{\left[HPO_4^{2-}\right]}$$

$$\frac{\left[PO_4^{3-}\right]}{\left[HPO_4^{2-}\right]} = \frac{K_{a3}}{\left[H_3O^+\right]} = \frac{4.2 \times 10^{-13}}{3.162 \times 10^{-5}} = 1.32827 \times 10^{-8}$$

From the ratios, the concentration of $H_2PO_4^-$ is at least 100 times more than the concentration of any other species, so assume that dihydrogen phosphate is the dominant species and find the value for $[PO_4^{3-}]$.

$$\frac{\left[PO_4^{3-}\right]}{\left[HPO_4^{2-}\right]} = 1.32827 \times 10^{-8} \quad \text{and} \quad \frac{\left[HPO_4^{2-}\right]}{\left[H_2PO_4^-\right]} = 1.9924 \times 10^{-3}$$

$[PO_4^{3-}] = (1.32827 \times 10^{-8})[HPO_4^{2-}]$ and $[HPO_4^{2-}] = (1.9924 \times 10^{-3})[H_2PO_4^-]$
$[PO_4^{3-}] = (1.32827 \times 10^{-8})[HPO_4^{2-}] = (1.32827 \times 10^{-8})(1.9924 \times 10^{-3})[H_2PO_4^-]$
$[PO_4^{3-}] = (2.6464 \times 10^{-11})[H_2PO_4^-]$

Substituting this into the K_{sp} expression gives

$K_{sp} = [Ca^{2+}]^3[PO_4^{3-}]^2 = 1.2 \times 10^{-29}$
$K_{sp} = [Ca^{2+}]^3\{(2.6464 \times 10^{-11})[H_2PO_4^-]\}^2$

Rearranging gives

$K_{sp}/(2.6464 \times 10^{-11})^2 = [Ca^{2+}]^3[H_2PO_4^-]^2$

The concentration of calcium ions is still represented as 3x and the concentration of dihydrogen phosphate ion as 2x, since each $H_2PO_4^-$ comes from one PO_4^{3-}.

$K_{sp}/(2.6464 \times 10^{-11})^2 = (3x)^3(2x)^2$
$(1.2 \times 10^{-29})/(2.6464 \times 10^{-11})^2 = 108x^5$
$x = 1.0967 \times 10^{-2} = \mathbf{1.1 \times 10^{-2}}$ **mol/L**

Acid rain increases the leaching of PO_4^{3-} into the groundwater, due to the protonation of PO_4^{3-} to form HPO_4^{2-} and $H_2PO_4^-$. As shown in calculations a) and b), solubility increases from 6.4×10^{-7} mol/L (in pure water) to 1.1×10^{-2} mol/L (in acidic rainwater).

23.81   a) The mole % of oxygen missing may be estimated from the discrepancy between the actual and ideal formula.

$$\text{Mol \% O missing} = \left(\frac{(2.000 - 1.98)\,\text{mol O}}{2.000\,\text{mol O}}\right) \times 100\% = \mathbf{1.00\%}$$

b) The molar mass is determined like a normal molar mass except that the quantity of oxygen is not an integer value.

Molar mass = 1 mol Pb (207.2 g/mol) + 1.98 mol O (16.00 g/mol) = 238.88 g/mol = **238.9 g/mol**

22.83   <u>Plan:</u> Convert the unit cell edge length to cm and cube that length to obtain the volume of the cell. A face-centered cubic structure contains four atoms of silver. Divide that number by Avogadro's number to find the moles of silver in the cell and multiply by the molar mass to obtain the mass of silver in the cell. Density is obtained by dividing the mass of silver by the volume of the cell. The calculation will now be repeated replacing the atomic mass of silver with the "atomic mass" of sterling silver. The "atomic mass" of sterling silver is simply a weighted average of the masses of the atoms present (Ag and Cu).
<u>Solution:</u>

Edge length (cm) = $\left(408.6 \text{ pm}\right)\left(\dfrac{10^{-12} \text{ m}}{1 \text{ pm}}\right)\left(\dfrac{1 \text{ cm}}{10^{-2} \text{ m}}\right) = 4.086 \times 10^{-8}$ cm

Volume (cm^3) of cell = $(4.086 \times 10^{-8} \text{ cm})^3 = 6.82174 \times 10^{-23}$ cm^3

Mass (g) of silver = $\left(\dfrac{4 \text{ Ag atoms}}{\text{unit cell}}\right)\left(\dfrac{1 \text{ mol Ag}}{6.022 \times 10^{23} \text{ Ag atoms}}\right)\left(\dfrac{107.9 \text{ g Ag}}{1 \text{ mol Ag}}\right) = 7.1671 \times 10^{-22}$ g

Density of silver = $\dfrac{7.1671 \times 10^{-22} \text{ g}}{6.82174 \times 10^{-23} \text{ cm}^3} = 10.506264$ g/cm³ = **10.51 g/cm^3**

Atomic mass of sterling silver = $\left(\dfrac{107.9 \text{ g}}{\text{mol}}\right)\left(\dfrac{(100.0 - 7.5)\%}{100\%}\right) + \left(\dfrac{63.55 \text{ g}}{\text{mol}}\right)\left(\dfrac{7.5\%}{100\%}\right) = 104.57375$ g/mol

Mass (g) of sterling silver = $\left(\dfrac{4 \text{ Ag atoms}}{\text{unit cell}}\right)\left(\dfrac{1 \text{ mol Ag}}{6.022 \times 10^{23} \text{ Ag atoms}}\right)\left(\dfrac{104.57375 \text{ g Ag}}{1 \text{ mol Ag}}\right) = 6.946 \times 10^{-22}$ g

Density of sterling silver = $\dfrac{6.9461 \times 10^{-22} \text{ g}}{6.82174 \times 10^{-23} \text{ cm}^3} = 10.1823$ g/cm³ = **10.2 g/cm^3**

CHAPTER 24 THE TRANSITION ELEMENTS AND THEIR COORDINATION COMPOUNDS

END–OF–CHAPTER PROBLEMS

24.2 a) All transition elements in Period 5 will have a "base" configuration of [Kr]$5s^2$, and will differ in the number of d electrons (x) that the configuration contains. Therefore, the general electron configuration is **$1s^22s^22p^63s^23p^64s^23d^{10}4p^65s^24d^x$**.
b) A general electron configuration for Period 6 transition elements includes f subshell electrons, which are lower in energy than the d subshell. The configuration is **$1s^22s^22p^63s^23p^64s^23d^{10}4p^65s^24d^{10}5p^66s^24f^{14}5d^x$**.

24.4 (a) The maximum number of unpaired d electrons is **five** since there are five d orbitals. (b) An example of an atom with five unpaired d electrons is Mn with electron configuration [Ar]$3d^54s^2$. An ion with five unpaired electrons is Mn^{2+} with electron configuration [Ar]$3d^5$.

24.6 a) One would expect that the elements would increase in size as they increase in mass from Period 5 to 6. Because there are fourteen inner transition elements in Period 6, the effective nuclear charge increases significantly. As effective charge increases, the atomic size decreases or "contracts." This effect is significant enough that Zr^{4+} and Hf^{4+} are almost the same size but differ greatly in atomic mass.
b) The size increases from Period 4 to 5, but stays fairly constant from Period 5 to 6.
c) Atomic mass increases significantly from Period 5 to 6, but atomic radius (and thus volume) hardly increases, so Period 6 elements are very dense.

24.9 a) A paramagnetic substance is attracted to a magnetic field, while a diamagnetic substance is slightly repelled by one.
b) Ions of transition elements often have unfilled d orbitals whose unpaired electrons make the ions paramagnetic. Ions of main-group elements usually have a noble gas configuration with no partially filled levels. When orbitals are filled, electrons are paired and the ion is diamagnetic.
c) The d orbitals in the transition element ions are not filled, which allows an electron from a lower energy d orbital to move to a higher energy d orbital. The energy required for this transition is relatively small and falls in the visible wavelength range. All orbitals are filled in a main-group element ion, so enough energy would have to be added to move an electron to a higher energy level, not just another orbital within the same energy level. This amount of energy is relatively large and outside the visible range of wavelengths.

24.10 <u>Plan:</u> The transition elements in Periods 4 and 5 have a general electron configuration of [noble gas] $(n-1)d^x ns^2$. Transition elements in Periods 6 and 7 have a general electron configuration of [noble gas] $(n-2)f^{14} (n-1)d^x ns^2$.
<u>Solution:</u>
a) Vanadium is in Period 4 and Group 5. Electron configuration of V is **$1s^22s^22p^63s^23p^64s^23d^3$** or **[Ar]$3d^74s^2$**.
b) Yttrium is in Period 5 and Group 3. Electron configuration of Y is **$1s^22s^22p^63s^23p^64s^23d^{10}4p^65s^24d^1$** or **[Kr]$5s^24d^15s^2$**.
c) Mercury is in Period 6 and Group 12. Electron configuration of Hg is **[Xe]$4f^{14}5d^{10}6s^2$**.

24.12 <u>Plan:</u> The transition elements in Periods 4 and 5 have a general electron configuration of [noble gas] $(n-1)d^x ns^2$. Transition elements in Periods 6 and 7 have a general electron configuration of [noble gas] $(n-2)f^{14} (n-1)d^x ns^2$.
<u>Solution:</u>
a) Osmium is in Period 6 and Group 8. Electron configuration of Os is **[Xe]$4f^{14}5d^66s^2$**.
b) Cobalt is in Period 4 and Group 9. Electron configuration of Co is **[Ar]$3d^74s^2$**.
c) Silver is in Period 5 and Group 11. Electron configuration of Ag is **[Kr]$4d^{10}5s^1$**. Note that the filled d orbital is the preferred arrangement, so the configuration is not $5s^24d^9$.

24.14   Plan: Write the electron configuration of the atom and then remove the electrons as indicated by the charge of the metal ion. Transition metals lose their ns orbital electrons first in forming cations. After losing the ns electrons, additional electrons may be lost from the $(n-1)d$ orbitals.
Solution:
a) The two $4s$ electrons and one $3d$ electron are removed to form Sc^{3+}:
Sc: $[Ar]3d^14s^2$; Sc^{3+}: $[Ar]$ or $1s^22s^22p^63s^23p^6$. There are **no unpaired electrons**.
b) The single $4s$ electron and one $3d$ electron are removed to form Cu^{2+}:
Cu: $[Ar]3d^{10}4s^1$; Cu^{2+}: $[Ar]3d^9$. There is **one unpaired electron**.
c) The two $4s$ electrons and one $3d$ electron are removed to form Fe^{3+}:
Fe: $[Ar]3d^64s^2$; Fe^{3+}: $[Ar]3d^5$. There are **five unpaired electrons** since each of the five d electrons occupies its own orbital.
d) The two $5s$ electrons and one $4d$ electron are removed to form Nb^{3+}:
Nb: $[Kr]4d^35s^2$; Nb^{3+}: $[Kr]4d^2$. There are **two unpaired electrons**.

24.16   Plan: For Groups 3 to 7, the highest oxidation state is equal to the group number. The highest oxidation state occurs when both ns electrons and all $(n-1)d$ electrons have been removed.
Solution:
a) Tantalum, Ta, is in Group 5, so the highest oxidation state is **+5**. The electron configuration of Ta is $[Xe]4f^{14}5d^36s^2$ with a total of five electrons in the $6s$ and $5d$ orbitals.
b) Zirconium, Zr, is in Group 4, so the highest oxidation state is **+4**. The electron configuration of Zr is $[Kr]4d^25s^2$ with a total of four electrons in the $5s$ and $4d$ orbitals.
c) Manganese, Mn, is in Group 7, so the highest oxidation state is **+7**. The electron configuration of Mn is $[Ar]3d^54s^2$ with a total of seven electrons in the $4s$ and $3d$ orbitals.

24.18   Plan: For Groups 3 to 7, the highest oxidation state is equal to the group number. The highest oxidation state occurs when both ns electrons and all $(n-1)d$ electrons have been removed.
Solution:
The elements in Group 6 exhibit an oxidation state of +6. These elements have a total of six electrons in the outermost s orbital and d orbital: $(n-1)d^5 ns^1$. These elements include **Cr, Mo, and W**. Sg (Seaborgium) is also in Group 6, but its lifetime is so short that chemical properties, like oxidation states within compounds, are impossible to measure.

24.20   Plan: Transition elements in their lower oxidation states act more like metals.
Solution:
The oxidation state of chromium in CrF_2 is +2 and in CrF_6 is +6 (use –1 oxidation state of fluorine to find oxidation state of Cr). **CrF_2** exhibits greater metallic behavior than CrF_6 because the chromium is in a lower oxidation state in CrF_2 than in CrF_6.

24.22   While atomic size increases slightly down a group of transition elements, the nuclear charge increases much more, so the first ionization energy generally increases. The reduction potential for Mo is lower, so **it is more difficult to oxidize Mo** than Cr. In addition, the ionization energy of Mo is higher than that of Cr, so it is more difficult to remove electrons from, i.e., oxidize, Mo.

24.24   Plan: Oxides of transition metals become less basic (or more acidic) as oxidation state increases.
Solution:
The oxidation state of chromium in CrO_3 is +6 and in CrO is +2, based on the –2 oxidation state of oxygen. The oxide of the higher oxidation state, **CrO_3**, produces a more acidic solution.

24.28   a) The f block contains **seven** orbitals, so if one electron occupied each orbital, a maximum of **seven** electrons would be unpaired.
b) The maximum number of unpaired electrons corresponds to a half-filled f subshell.

24.30   Plan: The inner transition elements have a general electron configuration of [noble gas] $(n-2)f^x (n-1)d^0 ns^2$. Inner transition metals lose their ns orbital electrons first in forming cations. After losing the ns electrons, additional electrons may be lost from the $(n-1)d$ orbitals.

Solution:
a) Lanthanum is a transition element in Period 6 with atomic number 57. La: $[Xe]5d^1 6s^2$
b) Cerium is in the lanthanide series in Period 6 with atomic number 58. Ce: $[Xe]4f^1 5d^1 6s^2$, so Ce^{3+}: $[Xe]4f^1$.
Note that cerium is one of the three lanthanide elements that have one electron in a $5d$ orbital.
c) Einsteinium is in the actinide series in Period 7 with atomic number 99. Es: $[Rn]5f^{11}7s^2$
d) Uranium is in the actinide series in Period 7 with atomic number 92. U: $[Rn]5f^3 6d^1 7s^2$. Removing four electrons gives U^{4+} with configuration $[Rn]5f^2$.

24.32   Plan: Write the electron configuration of the atom and then remove electrons as indicated by the charge of the metal ion. Electrons are removed first from the $6s$ orbital and then from the $4f$ orbital.
Solution:
a) Europium is in the lanthanide series with atomic number 63. The configuration of Eu is $[Xe]4f^7 6s^2$. The stability of the half-filled f subshell explains why the configuration is not $[Xe]4f^6 5d^1 6s^2$. The two $6s$ electrons are removed to form the Eu^{2+} ion, followed by electron removal in the f block to form the other two ions:
> Eu^{2+}: $[Xe]4f^7$
> Eu^{3+}: $[Xe]4f^6$
> Eu^{4+}: $[Xe]4f^5$
The stability of the half-filled f subshell makes Eu^{2+} most stable.
b) Terbium is in the lanthanide series with atomic number 65. The configuration of Tb is $[Xe]4f^9 6s^2$. The two $6s$ electrons are removed to form the Tb^{2+} ion, followed by electron removal in the f block to form the other two ions:
> Tb^{2+}: $[Xe]4f^9$
> Tb^{3+}: $[Xe]4f^8$
> Tb^{4+}: $[Xe]4f^7$
Tb would demonstrate a +4 oxidation state because it has the half-filled subshell.

24.34   The lanthanide element **gadolinium, Gd**, has electron configuration $[Xe]4f^7 5d^1 6s^2$ with **eight** unpaired electrons. The ion Gd^{3+} has **seven** unpaired electrons: $[Xe]4f^7$.

24.37   The coordination number indicates the number of ligand atoms bonded to the central metal ion. The oxidation number represents the number of electrons lost to form the ion. The coordination number is unrelated to the oxidation number.

24.39   Coordination number of two indicates **linear** geometry.
Coordination number of four indicates either **tetrahedral** or **square planar** geometry.
Coordination number of six indicates **octahedral** geometry.

24.42   The *-ate* ending signifies that the complex ion has a negative charge.

24.45   Plan: Use the naming rules for coordination compounds given in the text.
Solution:
a) The oxidation state of nickel is found from the total charge on the ion (+2 because two Cl^- charges equals –2) and the charge on ligands:
> charge on nickel = +2 – 6(0 charge on water) = +2
Name nickel as nickel(II) to indicate oxidation state. Ligands are six (hexa-) waters (aqua). Put together with chloride anions to give **hexaaquanickel(II) chloride**.
b) The cation is $[Cr(en)_3]^{n+}$ and the anion is ClO_4^-, the perchlorate ion. The charge on the cation is +3 to make a neutral salt in combination with the –3 charge of the three perchlorate ions. The ligand is ethylenediamine, which has 0 charge. The charge of the cation equals the charge on chromium ion, so chromium(III) is included in the name. The three ethylenediamine ligands, abbreviated en, are indicated by the prefix tris- because the name of the ligand includes a numerical indicator, di-. The complete name is **tris(ethylenediamine)chromium(III) perchlorate**.
c) The cation is K^+ and the anion is $[Mn(CN)_6]^{4-}$. The charge of 4– is deduced from the four potassium +1 ions in the formula. The oxidation state of Mn is $-4 - \{6(-1)\} = +2$. The name of CN^- ligand is cyano and six ligands are represented by the prefix hexa-. The name of manganese anion is manganate(II). The -ate suffix on the complex ion is used to indicate that it is an anion. The full name of compound is **potassium hexacyanomanganate(II)**.

24.47   Plan: The charge of the central metal atom was determined in Problem 24.45 because the Roman numeral indicating oxidation state is part of the name. The coordination number, or number of ligand atoms bonded to the metal ion, is found by examining the bonded entities inside the square brackets to determine if they are unidentate, bidentate, or polydentate.
Solution:
a) The Roman numeral "II" indicates a +2 oxidation state. There are six water molecules bonded to Ni and each ligand is unidentate, so the coordination number is **6**.
b) The Roman numeral "III" indicates a +3 oxidation state. There are three ethylenediamine molecules bonded to Cr, but each ethylenediamine molecule contains two donor N atoms (bidentate). Therefore, the coordination number is **6**.
c) The Roman numeral "II" indicates a +2 oxidation state. There are six unidentate cyano molecules bonded to Mn, so the coordination number is **6**.

24.49   Plan: Use the naming rules for coordination compounds given in the text.
Solution:
a) The cation is K^+, potassium. The anion is $[Ag(CN)_2]^-$ with the name dicyanoargentate(I) ion for the two cyanide ligands and the name of silver in an anion, argentate(I). The Roman numeral (I) indicates the oxidation number on Ag. O.N. for Ag $= -1 - \{2(-1)\} = +1$ since the complex ion has a charge of -1 and the cyanide ligands are also -1. The complete name is **potassium dicyanoargentate(I)**.
b) The cation is Na^+, sodium. Since there are two +1 sodium ions, the anion is $[CdCl_4]^{2-}$ with a charge of 2–. The anion is the tetrachlorocadmate(II) ion. With four –1 chloride ligands, the oxidation state of cadmium is +2 and the name of cadmium in an anion is cadmate. The complete name is **sodium tetrachlorocadmate(II)**.
c) The cation is $[Co(NH_3)_4(H_2O)Br]^{2+}$. The +2 charge is deduced from the two Br^- ions. The cation has the name tetraammineaquabromocobalt(III) ion, with four ammonia ligands (tetraammine), one water ligand (aqua) and one bromide ligand (bromo). The oxidation state of cobalt is +3: $2 - \{4(0) + 1(0) + 1(-1)\}$. The oxidation state is indicated by (III), following cobalt in the name. The anion is Br^-, bromide. The complete name is **tetraammineaquabromocobalt(III) bromide**.

24.51   Plan: The charge of the central metal atom was determined in Problem 24.49 because the Roman numeral indicating oxidation state is part of the name. The coordination number, or number of ligand atoms bonded to the metal ion, is found by examining the bonded entities inside the square brackets to determine if they are unidentate, bidentate, or polydentate.
Solution:
a) The counter ion is K^+, so the complex ion is $[Ag(CN)_2]^-$. Each cyano ligand has a –1 charge, so silver has a **+1** charge: $+1 + 2(-1) = -1$. Each cyano ligand is unidentate, so the coordination number is **2**.
b) The counter ion is Na^+, so the complex ion is $[CdCl_4]^{2-}$. Each chloride ligand has a –1 charge, so Cd has a **+2** charge: $+2 + 4(-1) = -2$. Each chloride ligand is unidentate, so the coordination number is **4**.
c) The counter ion is Br^-, so the complex ion is $[Co(NH_3)_4(H_2O)Br]^{2+}$. Both the ammine and aqua ligands are neutral. The bromide ligand has a –1 charge, so Co has a **+3** charge: $+3 + 4(0) + 0 + (-1) = +2$. Each ligand is unidentate, so the coordination number is **6**.

24.53   Plan: Use the rules given in the chapter.
Solution:
a) The cation is tetramminezinc ion. The tetraammine indicates four NH_3 ligands. Zinc has an oxidation state of +2, so the charge on the cation is +2. The anion is SO_4^{2-}. Only one sulfate is needed to make a neutral salt. The formula of the compound is **[Zn(NH_3)_4]SO_4**.
b) The cation is pentaamminechlorochromium(III) ion. The ligands are five NH_3 from pentaammine, and one chloride from chloro. The chromium ion has a charge of +3, so the complex ion has a charge equal to +3 from chromium, plus 0 from ammonia, plus –1 from chloride for a total of +2. The anion is chloride, Cl^-. Two chloride ions are needed to make a neutral salt. The formula of compound is **[Cr(NH_3)_5Cl]Cl_2**.
c) The anion is bis(thiosulfato)argentate(I). Argentate(I) indicates silver in the +1 oxidation state, and bis(thiosulfato) indicates two thiosulfate ligands, $S_2O_3^{2-}$. The total charge on the anion is +1 plus $2(-2)$ to equal –3. The cation is sodium, Na^+. Three sodium ions are needed to make a neutral salt. The formula of compound is **Na_3[Ag(S_2O_3)_2]**.

24.55   <u>Plan:</u> The coordination number, or number of ligand atoms bonded to the metal ion, is found by examining the bonded entities inside the square brackets to determine if they are unidentate, bidentate, or polydentate. Coordination compounds act like electrolytes, i.e., they dissolve in water to yield charged species, the counter ion, and the complex ion. However, the complex ion itself does not dissociate. The "number of individual ions per formula unit" refers to the number of ions that would form per coordination compound upon dissolution in water.
   <u>Solution:</u>
   a) The counter ion is SO_4^{2-}, so the complex ion is $[Zn(NH_3)_4]^{2+}$. Each ammine ligand is unidentate, so the coordination number is **4**. Each molecule dissolves in water to form one SO_4^{2-} ion and one $[Zn(NH_3)_4]^{2+}$ ion, so **two ions** form per formula unit.
   b) The counter ion is Cl^-, so the complex ion is $[Cr(NH_3)_5Cl]^{2+}$. Each ligand is unidentate, so the coordination number is **6**. Each molecule dissolves in water to form two Cl^- ions and one $[Cr(NH_3)_5Cl]^{2+}$ ion, so **three ions** form per formula unit.
   c) The counter ion is Na^+, so the complex ion is $[Ag(S_2O_3)_2]^{3-}$. Assuming that the thiosulfate ligand is unidentate, the coordination number is **2**. Each molecule dissolves in water to form three Na^+ ions and one $[Ag(S_2O_3)_2]^{3-}$ ion, so **four ions** form per formula unit.

24.57   <u>Plan:</u> Follow the naming rules given in the chapter.
   <u>Solution:</u>
   a) The cation is hexaaquachromium(III) with the formula $[Cr(H_2O)_6]^{3+}$. The total charge of the ion equals the charge on chromium because water is a neutral ligand. Six water ligands are indicated by a *hexa* prefix to aqua. The anion is SO_4^{2-}. To make the neutral salt requires three sulfate ions for two cations. The compound formula is $\mathbf{[Cr(H_2O)_6]_2(SO_4)_3}$.
   b) The anion is tetrabromoferrate(III) with the formula $[FeBr_4]^-$. The total charge on the ion equals +3 charge on iron plus 4×-1 charge on each bromide ligand for –1 overall. The cation is barium, Ba^{2+}. Two anions are needed for each barium ion to make a neutral salt. The compound formula is $\mathbf{Ba[FeBr_4]_2}$.
   c) The cation is bis(ethylenediamine)platinum(II) ion. Charge on platinum is +2 and this equals the total charge on the complex ion because ethylenediamine is a neutral ligand. The *bis* preceding ethylenediamine indicates two ethylenediamine ligands, which are represented by the abbreviation "en." The cation is $[Pt(en)_2]^{2+}$. The anion is CO_3^{2-}. One carbonate combines with one cation to produce a neutral salt. The compound formula is $\mathbf{[Pt(en)_2]CO_3}$.

24.59   <u>Plan:</u> The coordination number, or number of ligand atoms bonded to the metal ion, is found by examining the bonded entities inside the square brackets to determine if they are unidentate, bidentate, or polydentate. Coordination compounds act like electrolytes, i.e., they dissolve in water to yield charged species, the counter ions, and the complex ion. However, the complex ion itself does not dissociate. The "number of individual ions per formula unit" refers to the number of ions that would form per coordination compound upon dissolution in water.
   <u>Solution:</u>
   a) The counter ion is SO_4^{2-}, so the complex ion is $[Cr(H_2O)_6]^{3+}$. Each aqua ligand is unidentate, so the coordination number is **6**. Each molecule dissolves in water to form three SO_4^{2-} ions and two $[Cr(H_2O)_6]^{3+}$ ions, so **five ions** form per formula unit.
   b) The counter ion is Ba^{2+}, so the complex ion is $[FeBr_4]^-$. Each bromo ligand is unidentate, so the coordination number is **4**. Each molecule dissolves in water to form one Ba^{2+} ion and two $[FeBr_4]^-$ ions, so **three ions** form per formula unit.
   c) The counter ion is CO_3^{2-}, so the complex ion is $[Pt(en)_2]^{2+}$. Each ethylenediamine ligand is bidentate, so the coordination number is **4**. Each molecule dissolves in water to form one CO_3^{2-} ion and one $[Pt(en)_2]^{2+}$ ion, so **two ions** form per formula unit.

24.61   <u>Plan:</u> Ligands that form linkage isomers have two different possible donor atoms.
   <u>Solution:</u>
   a) The nitrite ion **forms linkage isomers** because it can bind to the metal ion through the lone pair on the N atom or any lone pair on either O atom. Resonance Lewis structures are:

$$\left[\ddot{O}\!=\!\ddot{N}\!-\!\ddot{O}\!:\right]^{-} \longleftrightarrow \left[:\!\ddot{O}\!-\!\ddot{N}\!=\!\ddot{O}\!:\right]^{-}$$

b) Sulfur dioxide molecules **form linkage isomers** because the lone pair on the S atom or any lone pair on either O atom can bind the central metal ion.

c) Nitrate ions have an N atom with no lone pair and three O atoms, all with lone pairs than can bond to the metal ion. But all of the O atoms are equivalent so these ions **do not form linkage isomers**.

24.63   Plan: Types of isomers for coordination compounds are coordination isomers with different arrangements of ligands and counter ions, linkage isomers with different donor atoms from the same ligand bound to the metal ion, geometric isomers with differences in ligand arrangement relative to other ligands, and optical isomers with mirror images that are not superimposable.
Solution:
a) Platinum ion, Pt^{2+}, is a d^8 ion so the ligand arrangement is square planar. Cis and trans geometric isomers exist for this complex ion:

cis isomer   trans isomer

No optical isomers exist because the mirror images of both compounds are superimposable on the original molecules. In general, a square planar molecule is superimposable on its mirror image.
b) Cis and trans geometric isomers exist for this complex ion. No optical isomers exist because the mirror images of both compounds are superimposable on the original molecules.

cis isomer   trans isomer

c) Three geometric isomers exist for this molecule, although they are not named *cis* or *trans* because all the ligands are different. A different naming system is used to indicate the relation of one ligand to another.

24.65   Plan: Types of isomers for coordination compounds are coordination isomers with different arrangements of ligands and counter ions, linkage isomers with different donor atoms from the same ligand bound to the metal ion, geometric isomers with differences in ligand arrangement relative to other ligands, and optical isomers with mirror images that are not superimposable.

Solution:
a) Platinum ion, Pt^{2+}, is a d^8 ion, so the ligand arrangement is square planar. The ligands are two Cl^- and two Br^-, so the arrangement can be either both ligands *trans* or both ligands *cis* to form geometric isomers.

b) The complex ion can form linkage isomers with the NO_2 ligand. Either the N or an O may be the donor.

c) In the octahedral arrangement, the two iodide ligands can be either *trans* to each other, 180° apart, or *cis* to each other, 90° apart.

24.67   The traditional formula does not correctly indicate that at least some of the chloride ions serve as counter ions. The NH_3 molecules serve as ligands, so *n* could equal 6 to satisfy the coordination number requirement. This complex has the formula $[Cr(NH_3)_6]Cl_3$. This is a correct formula because the name "chromium(III)" means that the chromium has a +3 charge, and this balances with the −3 charge provided by the three chloride counter ions. However, when this compound dissociates in water, it produces four ions ($[Cr(NH_3)_6]^{3+}$ and three Cl^-, whereas

NaCl only produces two ions. Other possible compounds are $n = 5$, $CrCl_3 \cdot 5NH_3$, with formula $[Cr(NH_3)_5Cl]Cl_2$; $n = 4$, $CrCl_3 \cdot 4NH_3$, with formula $[Cr(NH_3)_4Cl_2]Cl$; $n = 3$, $CrCl_3 \cdot 3NH_3$, with formula $[Cr(NH_3)_3Cl_3]$. The compound **$[Cr(NH_3)_4Cl_2]Cl$** has a coordination number equal to 6 and produces two ions when dissociated in water, so it has an electrical conductivity similar to an equimolar solution of NaCl.

24.69   Plan: First find the charge on the palladium ion, then arrange ligands and counter ions to form the complex.
Solution:
a) Charge on palladium = $-[(+1$ on $K^+) + (0$ on $NH_3) + 3(-1$ on $Cl^-)] = +2$
Palladium(II) forms four-coordinate complexes. The four ligands in the formula are one NH_3 and three Cl^- ions. The formula of the complex ion is $[Pd(NH_3)Cl_3]^-$. Combined with the potassium cation, the compound formula is **$K[Pd(NH_3)Cl_3]$**.
b) Charge on palladium = $-[2(-1$ on $Cl^-) + 2(0$ on $NH_3)] = +2$
Palladium(II) forms four-coordinate complexes. The four ligands are two chloride ions and two ammonia molecules. The formula is **$[PdCl_2(NH_3)_2]$**.
c) Charge on palladium = $-[2(+1$ on $K^+) + 6(-1$ on $Cl^-)] = +4$
Palladium(IV) forms six-coordinate complexes. The six ligands are the six chloride ions. The formula is **$K_2[PdCl_6]$**.
d) Charge on palladium = $-[4(0$ on $NH_3) + 4(-1$ on $Cl^-)] = +4$
Palladium(IV) forms six-coordinate complexes. The ammonia molecules have to be ligands. The other two ligand bonds are formed with two of the chloride ions. The remaining two chloride ions are the counter ions. The formula is **$[Pd(NH_3)_4Cl_2]Cl_2$**.

24.71   a) Four empty orbitals of equal energy are "created" to receive the donated electron pairs from four ligands. The four orbitals are hybridized from an s, two p, and one d orbital from the previous n level to form four **dsp^2** orbitals.
b) One s and three p orbitals become four **sp^3** hybrid orbitals.

24.74   Absorption of **orange** or **yellow** light gives a blue solution.

24.75   a) The crystal field splitting energy is the energy difference between the two sets of d orbitals that result from the bonding of ligands to a central transition metal atom.
b) In an octahedral field of ligands, the ligands approach along the x, y, and z axes. The $d_{x^2-y^2}$ and d_{z^2} orbitals are located along the x, y, and z axes, so ligand interaction is higher in energy than the other orbital-ligand interactions. The other orbital-ligand interactions are lower in energy because the d_{xy}, d_{yz}, and d_{xz} orbitals are located between the x, y, and z axes.
c) In a tetrahedral field of ligands, the ligands do not approach along the x, y, and z axes. The ligand interaction is greater for the d_{xy}, d_{yz}, and d_{xz} orbitals and lesser for the $d_{x^2-y^2}$ and d_{z^2} orbitals. The crystal field splitting is reversed, and the d_{xy}, d_{yz}, and d_{xz} orbitals are higher in energy than the $d_{x^2-y^2}$ and d_{z^2} orbitals.

24.78   If Δ is greater than $E_{pairing}$, electrons will preferentially pair spins in the lower energy d orbitals before adding as unpaired electrons to the higher energy d orbitals. If Δ is less than $E_{pairing}$, electrons will preferentially add as unpaired electrons to the higher d orbitals before pairing spins in the lower energy d orbitals. The first case gives a complex that is low-spin and less paramagnetic than the high-spin complex formed in the latter case.

24.80   Plan: To determine the number of d electrons in a central metal ion, first write the electron configuration for the metal atom. Examine the formula of the complex to determine the charge on the central metal ion, and then write the ion's configuration by removing the correct number of electrons, beginning with the ns electrons and then the $(n-1)d$ electrons.
Solution:
a) Electron configuration of Ti: $[Ar]3d^24s^2$
          Charge on Ti: Each chloride ligand has a -1 charge, so Ti has a $+4$ charge $\{+4 + 6(-1)\} = $ -2- ion.
Both of the $4s$ electrons and both $3d$ electrons are removed.
          Electron configuration of Ti^{4+}: $[Ar]$
          Ti^{4+} has **no d electrons**.
b) Electron configuration of Au: $[Xe]4f^{14}5d^{10}6s^1$

Charge on Au: The complex ion has a –1 charge ([AuCl$_4$]$^-$) since K has a +1 charge. Each chloride ligand has a –1 charge, so Au has a +3 charge {+3 + 4(–1)} = -1 ion. The 6s electron and two d electrons are removed.

Electron configuration of Au^{3+}: [Xe]$4f^{14}5d^8$

Au^{3+} has **eight d electrons**.

c) Electron configuration of Rh: [Kr]$4d^75s^2$

Charge on Rh: Each chloride ligand has a –1 charge, so Rh has a +3 charge {+3 + 6(–1)} = -3 ion. The 5s electrons and one 4d electron are removed.

Electron configuration of Rh^{3+}: [Kr]$4d^6$ Rh^{3+} has **six d electrons**.

24.82   <u>Plan:</u> To determine the number of d electrons in a central metal ion, first write the electron configuration for the metal atom. Examine the formula of the complex to determine the charge on the central metal ion, and then write the ion's configuration by removing the correct number of electrons, beginning with the ns electrons and then the $(n – 1)d$ electrons.

<u>Solution:</u>

a) [(+2 on Ca^{2+}) + 6(–1 on F$^-$) + Ir = 0]

Charge on iridium = – [(+2 on Ca^{2+}) + 6(–1 on F$^-$)] = +4

Configuration of Ir is [Xe]$4f^{14}5d^76s^2$.

Configuration of Ir^{4+} is [Xe]$4f^{14}5d^5$. **Five d electrons in Ir^{4+}.**

b) [Hg + 4(–1 on I$^-$)] = –2

Charge on mercury = – [4(–1 on I$^-$)] – 2 = +2

Configuration of Hg is [Xe]$4f^{14}5d^{10}6s^2$.

Configuration of Hg^{2+} is [Xe]$4f^{14}5d^{10}$. **Ten d electrons in Hg^{2+}.**

c) [Co + (–4 on EDTA)] = – 2

Charge on cobalt = – [–4 on EDTA] – 2 = +2

Configuration of Co is [Ar]$3d^74s^2$.

Configuration of Co^{2+} is [Ar]$3d^7$. **Seven d electrons in Co^{2+}.**

24.84

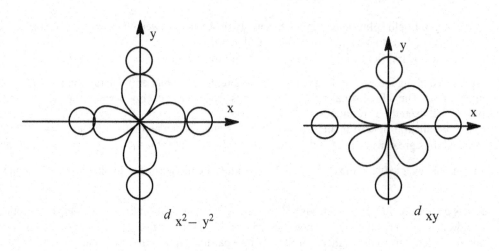

In an octahedral field of ligands, the ligands approach along the x, y, and z axes. The $d_{x^2-y^2}$ orbital is located *along* the x and y axes, so ligand interaction is greater. The d_{xy} orbital is offset from the x and y axes by 90°, so ligand interaction is less. The greater interaction of the $d_{x^2-y^2}$ orbital results in its higher energy.

24.86   <u>Plan:</u> Determine the electron configuration of the ion, which gives the number of d electrons. If there are only 1, 2, or 3 d electrons, the complex is always high-spin since there are not enough electrons to pair. If there are 8 or 9 d electrons, the complex is always high-spin since the higher energy d orbitals will always contain two (d^8) or one (d^9) unpaired electrons.

Solution:

a) Ti: $[Ar]3d^24s^2$. The electron configuration of Ti^{3+} is $[Ar]3d^1$. With only one electron in the d orbitals, the titanium(III) ion **cannot form** high- and low-spin complexes — all complexes will contain one unpaired electron and have the same spin.

b) Co: $[Ar]3d^74s^2$. The electron configuration of Co^{2+} is $[Ar]3d^7$ and will form high- and low-spin complexes with seven electrons in the d orbital.

c) Fe: $[Ar]3d^64s^2$. The electron configuration of Fe^{2+} is $[Ar]3d^6$ and will form high- and low-spin complexes with six electrons in the d orbital.

d) Cu: $[Ar]3d^{10}4s^1$. The electron configuration of Cu^{2+} is $[Ar]3d^9$, so in complexes with both strong- and weak-field ligands, one electron will be unpaired and the spin in both types of complexes is identical. Cu^{2+} **cannot form** high- and low-spin complexes.

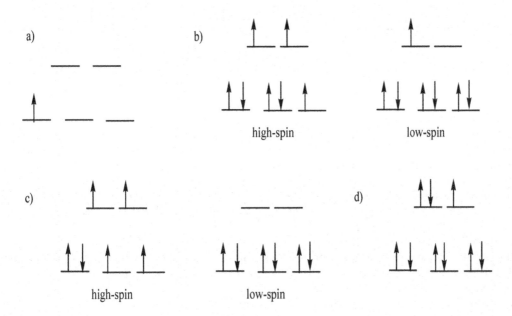

24.88   Plan: To draw the orbital-energy splitting diagram, first determine the number of d electrons in the transition metal ion. Examine the formula of the complex ion to determine the electron configuration of the metal ion, remembering that the ns electrons are lost first. Determine the coordination number from the number of ligands, recognizing that six ligands result in an octahedral arrangement and four ligands result in a tetrahedral or square planar arrangement. Weak-field ligands give the maximum number of unpaired electrons (high-spin) while strong-field ligands lead to electron pairing (low-spin).

Solution:

a) Electron configuration of Cr: $[Ar]3d^54s^1$

Charge on Cr: The aqua ligands are neutral, so the charge on Cr is +3.

Electron configuration of Cr^{3+}: $[Ar]3d^3$

Six ligands indicate an octahedral arrangement. Using Hund's rule, fill the lower energy t_{2g} orbitals first, filling empty orbitals before pairing electrons within an orbital.

b) Electron configuration of Cu: $[Ar]3d^{10}4s^1$

Charge on Cu: The aqua ligands are neutral, so Cu has a +2 charge.

Electron configuration of Cu^{2+}: $[Ar]3d^9$

Four ligands and a d^9 configuration indicate a square planar geometry (only filled d subshell ions exhibit tetrahedral geometry). Use Hund's rule to fill in the nine d electrons. Therefore, the correct orbital-energy splitting diagram shows one unpaired electron.

c) Electron configuration of Fe: $[Ar]3d^64s^2$

Charge on Fe: Each fluoride ligand has a -1 charge for a total charge of -6, so Fe has a +3 charge to make the overall complex charge equal to -3.

Electron configuration of Fe^{3+}: $[Ar]3d^5$
Six ligands indicate an octahedral arrangement. Use Hund's rule to fill the orbitals.
F^- is a weak-field ligand, so the splitting energy, Δ, is not large enough to overcome the resistance to electron pairing. The electrons remain unpaired, and the complex is called high-spin.

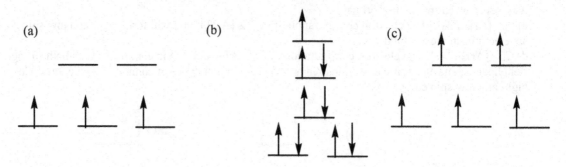

(a)   (b)   (c)

24.90   Plan: To draw the orbital-energy splitting diagram, first determine the number of d electrons in the transition metal ion. Examine the formula of the complex ion to determine the electron configuration of the metal ion, remembering that the ns electrons are lost first. Determine the coordination number from the number of ligands, recognizing that six ligands result in an octahedral arrangement and four ligands result in a tetrahedral or square planar arrangement. Weak-field ligands give the maximum number of unpaired electrons (high-spin) while strong-field ligands lead to electron pairing (low-spin).
Solution:
a) Electron configuration of Mo: $[Kr]4d^55s^1$
Charge on Mo: Each chloride ligand has a -1 charge for a total charge of -6, so Mo has a $+3$ charge to make the overall complex charge equal to -3.
Electron configuration of Mo^{3+}: $[Kr]4d^3$
Six ligands indicate an octahedral arrangement. Using Hund's rule, fill the lower energy t_{2g} orbitals first, filling empty orbitals before pairing electrons within an orbital. (Refer to diagram below.)
b) Electron configuration of Ni: $[Ar]3d^84s^2$
Charge on Ni: The aqua ligands are neutral, so the charge on Ni is $+2$.
Electron configuration of Ni^{2+}: $[Ar]3d^8$
Six ligands indicate an octahedral arrangement. Use Hund's rule to fill the orbitals.
H_2O is a weak-field ligand, so the splitting energy, Δ, is not large enough to overcome the resistance to electron pairing. One electron occupies each of the five d orbitals before pairing in the t_{2g} orbitals, and the complex is called high-spin.
c) Electron configuration of Ni: $[Ar]3d^84s^2$
Charge on Ni: Each cyanide ligand has a -1 charge for a total charge of -4, so Ni has a $+2$ charge to make the overall complex charge equal to -2.
Electron configuration of Ni^{2+}: $[Ar]3d^8$
The coordination number is 4 and most d^8 metal ions form square planar complex ions (Figure 24.7B).
The complex is low-spin because CN^- is a strong-field ligand. Electrons pair in one set of orbitals before occupying orbitals of higher energy.

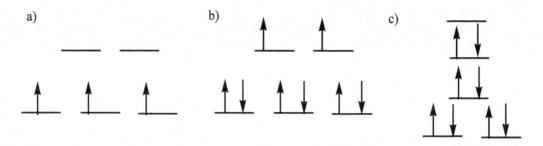

a)   b)   c)

24.92   <u>Plan:</u> The spectrochemical series describes the spectrum of splitting energy, Δ. The greater the crystal field strength of the ligand, the greater the crystal field splitting energy, Δ, and the greater the energy of light absorbed.
<u>Solution:</u>
NO_2^- is a stronger field ligand than NH_3, which is a stronger field ligand than H_2O. NO_2^- produces the largest Δ, followed by NH_3, and then H_2O with the smallest Δ value. The energy of light absorbed increases as Δ increases since more energy is required to excite an electron from a lower energy orbital to a higher energy orbital when Δ is very large.

$$[Cr(H_2O)_6]^{3+} < [Cr(NH_3)_6]^{3+} < [Cr(NO_2)_6]^{3-}$$

24.94   <u>Plan:</u> A weaker field ligand will result in a smaller Δ in the complex and lower energy light absorbed. When a particular colour of light is absorbed, the complementary colour is seen.
<u>Solution:</u>
A violet complex absorbs yellow-green light. The light absorbed by a complex with a weaker ligand would be at a lower energy and longer wavelength. Light of lower energy than yellow-green light is yellow, orange, or red light. The colour observed would be **blue** or **green**.

24.97   <u>Plan:</u> A weaker field ligand will result in a smaller Δ in the complex and lower energy light absorbed. When a particular colour of light is absorbed, the complementary colour is seen.
<u>Solution:</u>
The aqua ligand is weaker than the ammine ligand. The weaker ligand results in a lower splitting energy and absorbs a lower energy of visible light. The green hexaaqua complex appears green because it absorbs red light (opposite side of the colour wheel). The hexaammine complex appears violet because it absorbs yellow light, which is higher in energy (shorter λ) than red light.

24.101   The electron configuration of Hg is $[Xe]4f^{14}5d^{10}6s^2$ and that of Hg^+ is $[Xe]4f^{14}5d^{10}6s^1$. The electron configuration of Cu is $[Ar]3d^{10}4s^1$ and that of Cu^+ is $[Ar]3d^{10}$. In the mercury(I) ion, there is one electron in the $6s$ orbital that can form a covalent bond with the electron in the $6s$ orbital of another Hg^+ ion. In the copper(I) ion, there are no electrons in the s orbital to bond with another copper(I) ion.

24.102   <u>Plan:</u> The coordination number, or number of ligand atoms bonded to the metal ion, is found by examining the bonded entities inside the square brackets to determine if they are unidentate, bidentate, or polydentate. The oxidation of the central metal ion is found by determining the charges of the ligands and insuring that the charges of the metal ion, ligands, and counter ion add to zero. Coordination compounds act like electrolytes, i.e., they dissolve in water to yield charged species, the counter ions and the complex ion. However, the complex ion itself does not dissociate. The "number of individual ions per formula unit" refers to the number of ions that would form per coordination compound upon dissolution in water.
<u>Solution:</u>
a) The coordination number of cobalt is **6**. The two Cl^- ligands are unidentate and the two ethylenediamine ligands are bidentate (each en ligand forms two bonds to the metal), so a total of six ligand atoms are connected to the central metal ion.
b) The counter ion is Cl^-, so the complex ion is $[Co(en)_2Cl_2]^+$. Each chloride ligand has a -1 charge and each en ligand is neutral, so cobalt has a **+3** charge: $+3 + 2(0) + 2(-1) = +1$.
c) One mole of complex dissolves in water to yield one mole of $[Co(en)_2Cl_2]^+$ ions and one mole of Cl^- ions. Therefore, each formula unit yields **two** individual ions.
d) One mole of compound dissolves to form one mole of Cl^- ions, which reacts with the Ag^+ ion (from $AgNO_3$) to form **one mole of AgCl precipitate**.

24.109   <u>Plan:</u> Types of isomers for coordination compounds include: (i) *coordination isomers* with different arrangements of ligands and counter ions; (ii), *linkage isomers* with different donor atoms from the same ligand bound to the metal ion; (iii) *geometric isomers* with differences in ligand arrangement relative to other ligands; and (iv) *optical isomers* with mirror images that are not superimposable.
<u>Solution:</u>
This compound exhibits geometric (*cis-trans*) and linkage isomerism. The SCN^- ligand can bond to the metal through either the S atom or the N atom.

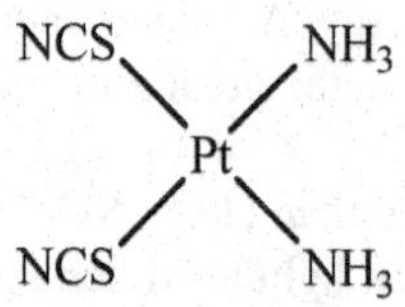

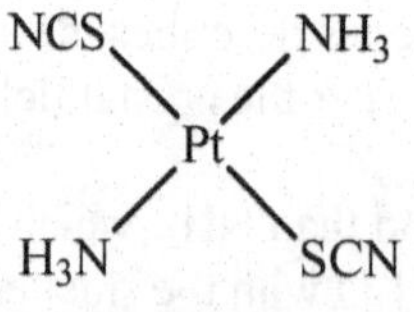

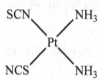

NCS, NH₃
    Pt
NCS   NH₃

cis-diamminedithiocyanatoplatinum(II)

NCS, NH₃
    Pt
H₃N   SCN

trans-diamminedithiocyanatoplatinum(II)

SCN, NH₃
    Pt
SCN   NH₃

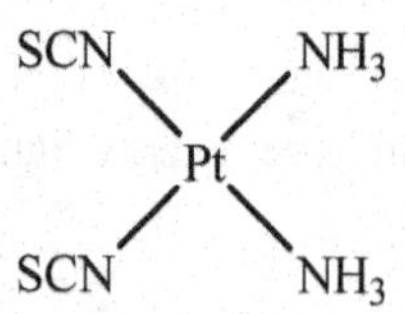

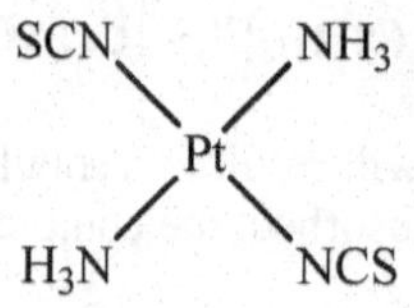

cis-diamminediisothiocyanatoplatinum(II)

SCN, NH₃
    Pt
H₃N   NCS

trans-diamminediisothiocyanatoplatinum(II)

SCN, NH₃
    Pt
NCS   NH₃

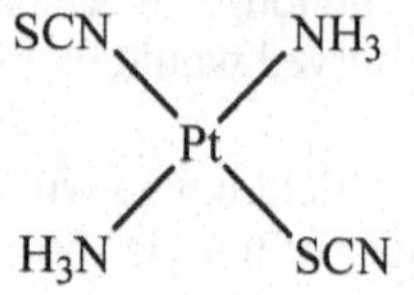

cis-diamminethiocyanatoisothiocyanatoplatinum(II)

SCN, NH₃
    Pt
H₃N   SCN

trans-diamminethiocyanatoisothiocyanatoplatinum(II)

24.110   <u>Plan:</u> Types of isomers for coordination compounds are coordination isomers with different arrangements of ligands and counter ions, linkage isomers with different donor atoms from the same ligand bound to the metal ion, geometric isomers with differences in ligand arrangement relative to other ligands, and optical isomers with mirror images that are not superimposable.

<u>Solution:</u>

(a) $[Co(NH_3)_4(H_2O)Cl]^{2+}$ tetraammineaquachlorocobalt(III) ion
         2 geometric isomers

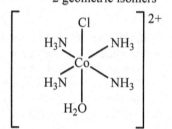

trans Cl and H₂O

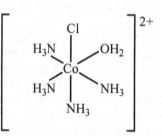

cis Cl and NH₃

(b) $[Cr(H_2O)_3Br_2Cl]$ triaquadibromochlorochromium(III)
         3 geometric isomers

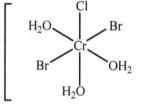

Br's *trans*

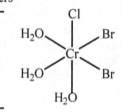

Br's *cis*
H₂O's facial

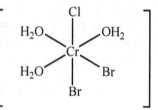

Br's *cis*
H₂O's meridional

(Unfortunately *meridional* and *facial* isomers are not covered in the text. *Facial (fac) isomers* have three adjacent corners of the octahedron occupied by similar groups. *Meridional (mer) isomers* have three similar groups around the outside of the complex.)

(c) $[Cr(NH_3)_2(H_2O)_2Br_2]^+$ diamminediaquadibromochromium(III) ion
         6 isomers (5 geometric)

24-13

All pairs are *trans* (top left)

Only NH$_3$'s are *trans* (top right)

Only H$_2$O's are *trans* (middle left)

Only Br's are *trans* (middle right)

All pairs are *cis*. These are optical isomers of each other.

24.115 Plan: Sketch the structure of each complex ion and look for a plane of symmetry. A complex ion with a plane of symmetry does not have optical isomers.
Solution:
a) A plane that includes both ammonia ligands and the zinc ion is a plane of symmetry. The complex **does not have optical isomers** because it has a plane of symmetry.
b) The Pt^{2+} ion is d^8, so the complex is square planar. Any square planar complex has a plane of symmetry, so the complex **does not have optical isomers**.
c) The *trans* octahedral complex has the two chloride ions opposite each other. A plane of symmetry can be passed through the two chlorides and platinum ion, so the *trans* complex **does not have optical isomers**.
d) **No optical isomers** for same reason as in part c).
e) The *cis* isomer does not have a plane of symmetry, so it **does have optical isomers**.

24.116 Plan: Assume a 100-g sample (making the percentages of each element equal to the mass present in grams) and convert the mass of each element to the amount (mol) using the element's molar mass. Divide each mole amount by the smallest mole amount to determine whole-number ratios of the elements to determine the empirical formula.
Once the empirical formula is known, use the formula of the triethylphosphine to deduce the molecular formula.
Solution:

$$\text{Amount (mol) of Pt} = \left(38.8 \text{ g Pt}\right)\left(\frac{1 \text{ mol Pt}}{195.1 \text{ g Pt}}\right) = 0.198872 \text{ mol Pt}; \qquad \frac{0.198872}{0.198872} = 1$$

$$\text{Amount (mol) of Cl} = \left(14.1 \text{ g Cl}\right)\left(\frac{1 \text{ mol Cl}}{35.45 \text{ g Cl}}\right) = 0.397743 \text{ mol Cl}; \qquad \frac{0.397743}{0.198872} = 2$$

$$\text{Amount (mol) of C} = \left(28.7 \text{ g C}\right)\left(\frac{1 \text{ mol C}}{12.01 \text{ g C}}\right) = 2.389675 \text{ mol C}; \qquad \frac{2.389675}{0.198872} = 12$$

$$\text{Amount (mol) of P} = \left(12.4 \text{ g P}\right)\left(\frac{1 \text{ mol P}}{30.97 \text{ g P}}\right) = 0.400387 \text{ mol P}; \qquad \frac{0.400387}{0.198872} = 2$$

$$\text{Amount (mol) of H} = \left(6.02 \text{ g H}\right)\left(\frac{1 \text{ mol H}}{1.008 \text{ g H}}\right) = 5.972222 \text{ mol H}; \qquad \frac{5.972222}{0.198872} = 30$$

The empirical formula for the compound is $PtCl_2C_{12}P_2H_{30}$. Each triethylphosphine ligand, $P(C_2H_5)_3$ accounts for one phosphorus atom, six carbon atoms, and fifteen hydrogen atoms. According to the empirical formula, there are two triethylphosphine ligands: 2 $P(C_2H_5)_3$ "equals" $C_{12}P_2H_{30}$. The compound must have two $P(C_2H_5)_3$ ligands and two chloro ligands per Pt ion. The formula is $[Pt[P(C_2H_5)_3]_2Cl_2]$. The central Pt ion has four ligands and is square planar, existing as either a *cis* or *trans* compound.

cis-dichlorobis(triethylphosphine)platinum(II)   *trans*-dichlorobis(triethylphosphine)platinum(II)

24.118 Plan: A reaction is favored in terms of entropy if there is an increase in entropy. Entropy increases if the amount (mol) of product is larger than the amount (mol) of the reactant.
Solution:
a) The first reaction shows no change in the number of particles. In the second reaction, the number of reactant particles is greater than the number of product particles. A decrease in the number of particles means a decrease in entropy, while no change in number of particles indicates little change in entropy. Based on entropy change only, the first reaction is favored.
b) The ethylenediamine complex is more stable with respect to ligand exchange with water because the entropy change is unfavorable.

CHAPTER 25 NUCLEAR REACTIONS AND THEIR APPLICATIONS

CHEMICAL CONNECTIONS BOXED READING PROBLEMS

B25.1   In the s-process, a nucleus captures a neutron sometime over a long period of time. Then the nucleus emits a beta particle to form another element. The stable isotopes of most heavy elements up to ^{209}Bi form by the s-process. The r-process very quickly forms less stable isotopes and those with A greater than 230 by multiple neutron captures, followed by multiple beta decays.

B25.3   The simultaneous fusion of three nuclei is a termolecular process. Termolecular processes have a very low probability of occurring. The bimolecular fusion of ^{8}Be with ^{4}He is more likely.

B25.4   Plan: In a balanced nuclear equation, the total of mass numbers and the total of charges on the left side and the right side must be equal.
Solution:

$$^{210}_{83}\text{Bi} \rightarrow {}^{210}_{84}\text{Po} + {}^{0}_{-1}\beta \qquad\qquad {}^{210}_{84}\text{Po is nuclide A}$$

$$^{210}_{84}\text{Po} \rightarrow {}^{206}_{82}\text{Pb} + {}^{4}_{2}\alpha \qquad\qquad {}^{206}_{82}\text{Pb is nuclide B}$$

$$^{206}_{82}\text{Pb} + 3\,{}^{1}_{0}\text{n} \rightarrow {}^{209}_{82}\text{Pb} \qquad\qquad {}^{209}_{82}\text{Pb is nuclide C}$$

$$^{209}_{82}\text{Pb} \rightarrow {}^{210}_{83}\text{Bi} + {}^{0}_{-1}\beta \qquad\qquad {}^{210}_{83}\text{Bi is nuclide D}$$

END–OF–CHAPTER PROBLEMS

25.1   a) Chemical reactions are accompanied by relatively small changes in energy while nuclear reactions are accompanied by relatively large changes in energy.
b) Increasing temperature increases the rate of a chemical reaction but has no effect on a nuclear reaction.
c) Both chemical and nuclear reaction rates increase with higher reactant concentrations.
d) If the reactant is limiting in a chemical reaction, then more reactant produces more product and the yield increases in a chemical reaction. The presence of more radioactive reagent results in more decay product, so a higher reactant concentration increases the yield in a nuclear reaction.

25.2   a) The percentage of sulfur atoms that are sulfur-32 is 95.02%, the same as the relative abundance of ^{32}S.
b) The atomic mass is larger than the isotopic mass of ^{32}S. Sulfur-32 is the lightest isotope, as stated in the problem, so the other 5% of sulfur atoms are heavier than 31.972070 u. The average mass of all the sulfur atoms will therefore be greater than the mass of a sulfur-32 atom.

25.4   Plan: Radioactive decay that produces a different element requires a change in *atomic number* (Z, number of protons).
Solution:

$\qquad\qquad {}^{A}_{Z}\text{X} \qquad A$ = mass number (protons + neutrons)

$\qquad\qquad\qquad\quad Z$ = number of protons (positive charge)

$\qquad\qquad\qquad\quad$ X = symbol for the particle

$\qquad\qquad\qquad\quad N = A - Z$ (number of neutrons)

a) Alpha decay produces an atom of a different element, i.e., a daughter with two less protons and two less neutrons.

$$^{A}_{Z}\text{X} \rightarrow {}^{A-4}_{Z-2}\text{Y} + {}^{4}_{2}\text{He} \qquad \text{2 fewer protons, 2 fewer neutrons}$$

b) Beta decay produces an atom of a different element, i.e., a daughter with one more proton and one less neutron. A neutron is converted to a proton and β particle in this type of decay.

$$^{A}_{Z}\text{X} \rightarrow {}^{A}_{Z+1}\text{Y} + {}^{0}_{-1}\beta \qquad \text{1 more proton, 1 less neutron}$$

c) Gamma decay does not produce an atom of a different element and Z and N remain unchanged.

$$_{Z}^{A}X^{*} \rightarrow _{Z}^{A}X + _{0}^{0}\gamma \qquad (_{Z}^{A}X^{*} = \text{energy rich state}), \text{ no change in number of protons or neutrons.}$$

d) Positron emission produces an atom of a different element, i.e., a daughter with one less proton and one more neutron. A proton is converted into a neutron and positron in this type of decay.

$$_{Z}^{A}X \rightarrow _{Z-1}^{A}Y + _{+1}^{0}\beta \qquad \text{1 less proton, 1 more neutron}$$

e) Electron capture produces an atom of a different element, i.e., a daughter with one less proton and one more neutron. The net result of electron capture is the same as positron emission, but the two processes are different.

$$_{Z}^{A}X + _{-1}^{0}e \rightarrow _{Z-1}^{A}Y \qquad \text{1 less proton, 1 more neutron}$$

A different element is produced in all cases except (c).

25.6   A neutron-rich nuclide decays to convert neutrons to protons while a neutron-poor nuclide decays to convert protons to neutrons. The conversion of neutrons to protons occurs by beta decay:

$$_{0}^{1}n \rightarrow _{1}^{1}p + _{-1}^{0}\beta$$

The conversion of protons to neutrons occurs by either positron decay:

$$_{1}^{1}p \rightarrow _{0}^{1}n + _{1}^{0}\beta$$

or electron capture:

$$_{1}^{1}p + _{-1}^{0}e \rightarrow _{0}^{1}n$$

Neutron-rich nuclides, with a high N/Z, undergo β decay. Neutron-poor nuclides, with a low N/Z, undergo positron decay or electron capture.

25.8   Plan: In a balanced nuclear equation, the total of mass numbers and the total of charges on the left side and the right side must be equal.
Solution:
a) The process involves the loss of an α particle from the nucleus. For each α particle emitted, the mass number decreases by four and the atomic number decreases by two.

$$_{92}^{234}U \rightarrow _{2}^{4}He + _{90}^{230}Th \qquad \text{Mass: } 234 = 4 + 230; \qquad \text{Charge: } 92 = 2 + 90$$

b) The electron captured by the nucleus combines with a proton to form a neutron, so mass number is constant

$$_{93}^{232}Np + _{-1}^{0}e \rightarrow _{92}^{232}U \qquad \text{Mass: } 232 + 0 = 232; \qquad \text{Charge: } 93 + (-1) = 92$$

c) Positron emission decreases atomic number by one, but not mass number.

$$_{7}^{12}N \rightarrow _{1}^{0}\beta + _{6}^{12}C \qquad \text{Mass: } 12 = 0 + 12; \qquad \text{Charge: } 7 = 1 + 6$$

25.10   Plan: In a balanced nuclear equation, the total of mass numbers and the total of charges on the left side and the right side must be equal.
Solution:
a) The process converts a neutron to a proton, so the mass number is the same, but the atomic number increases by one.

$$_{12}^{27}Mg \rightarrow _{-1}^{0}\beta + _{13}^{27}Al \qquad \text{Mass: } 27 = 0 + 27; \qquad \text{Charge: } 12 = -1 + 13$$

b) Positron emission decreases atomic number by one, but not mass number.

$$_{12}^{23}Mg \rightarrow _{1}^{0}\beta + _{11}^{23}Na \qquad \text{Mass: } 23 = 0 + 23; \qquad \text{Charge: } 12 = 1 + 11$$

c) The electron captured by the nucleus combines with a proton to form a neutron, so mass number is constant, but atomic number decreases by one.

$$_{46}^{103}Pd + _{-1}^{0}e \rightarrow _{45}^{103}Rh \qquad \text{Mass: } 103 + 0 = 103; \qquad \text{Charge: } 46 + (-1) = 45$$

25.12   Plan: In a balanced nuclear equation, the total of mass numbers and the total of charges on the left side and the right side must be equal.
Solution:
a) In other words, an unknown nuclide decays to give Ti-48 and a positron.

$$_{23}^{48}V \rightarrow _{22}^{48}Ti + _{1}^{0}\beta \qquad \text{Mass: } 48 = 48 + 0; \qquad \text{Charge: } 23 = 22 + 1$$

b) In other words, an unknown nuclide captures an electron to form Ag-107.

$$_{48}^{107}Cd + _{-1}^{0}e \rightarrow _{47}^{107}Ag \qquad \text{Mass: } 107 + 0 = 107; \qquad \text{Charge: } 48 + (-1) = 47$$

c) In other words, an unknown nuclide decays to give Po-206 and an alpha particle.

$$^{210}_{86}Rn \rightarrow {}^{206}_{84}Po + {}^{4}_{2}He \qquad \text{Mass: } 210 = 206 + 4; \qquad \text{Charge: } 86 = 84 + 2$$

25.14   Plan: In a balanced nuclear equation, the total of mass numbers and the total of charges on the left side and the right side must be equal.
Solution:
a) In other words, an unknown nuclide captures an electron to form Ir-186.

$$^{186}_{78}Pt + {}^{0}_{-1}e \rightarrow {}^{186}_{77}Ir \qquad \text{Mass: } 186 + 0 = 186; \qquad \text{Charge: } 78 + (-1) = 77$$

b) In other words, an unknown nuclide decays to give Fr-221 and an alpha particle.

$$^{225}_{89}Ac \rightarrow {}^{221}_{87}Fr + {}^{4}_{2}He \qquad \text{Mass: } 225 = 221 + 4; \qquad \text{Charge: } 89 = 87 + 2$$

c) In other words, an unknown nuclide decays to give I-129 and a beta particle.

$$^{129}_{52}Te \rightarrow {}^{129}_{53}I + {}^{0}_{-1}\beta \qquad \text{Mass: } 129 = 129 + 0; \qquad \text{Charge: } 52 = 53 + (-1)$$

25.16   Plan: Look at the N/Z ratio, the ratio of the number of neutrons to the number of protons. If the N/Z ratio falls in the band of stability, the nuclide is predicted to be stable. For stable nuclides of elements with atomic number greater than 20, the ratio of number of neutrons to number of protons (N/Z) is greater than one. In addition, the ratio increases gradually as atomic number increases. Also check for exceptionally stable numbers of neutrons and/or protons – the *magic numbers* of 2, 8, 20, 28, 50, 82, and ($N = 126$). Also, even numbers of protons and or neutrons are related to stability whereas odd numbers are related to instability.
Solution:
a) $^{20}_{8}O$ appears stable because its Z (8) value is a *magic number*, but its N/Z ratio $(20 - 8)/8 = 1.50$ is too high and this nuclide is above the band of stability; $^{20}_{8}O$ is unstable.

b) $^{59}_{27}Co$ might look unstable because its Z value is an odd number, but its N/Z ratio $(59 - 27)/27 = 1.19$ is in the band of stability, so $^{59}_{27}Co$ appears stable.

c) $^{9}_{3}Li$ appears unstable because its N/Z ratio $(9 - 3)/3 = 2.00$ is too high and is above the band of stability.

25.18   Plan: Look at the N/Z ratio, the ratio of the number of neutrons to the number of protons. If the N/Z ratio falls in the band of stability, the nuclide is predicted to be stable. For stable nuclides of elements with atomic number greater than 20, the ratio of number of neutrons to number of protons (N/Z) is greater than one. In addition, the ratio increases gradually as atomic number increases. Also check for exceptionally stable numbers of neutrons and/or protons – the *magic numbers* of 2, 8, 20, 28, 50, 82, and ($N = 126$). Also, even numbers of protons and or neutrons are related to stability whereas odd numbers are related to instability.
Solution:
a) For the element iodine $Z = 53$. For iodine-127, $N = 127 - 53 = 74$. The N/Z ratio for ^{127}I is $74/53 = 1.4$. Of the examples of stable nuclides given in the book, ^{107}Ag has the closest atomic number to iodine. The N/Z ratio for ^{107}Ag is 1.3. Thus, it is likely that iodine with six additional protons is stable with an N/Z ratio of 1.4.
b) Tin is element number 50 ($Z = 50$). The N/Z ratio for ^{106}Sn is $(106 - 50)/50 = 1.1$. The nuclide ^{106}Sn is unstable with an N/Z ratio that is too low.
c) For ^{68}As, $Z = 33$ and $N = 68 - 33 = 35$ and $N/Z = 1.1$. The ratio is within the range of stability, but the nuclide is most likely unstable because there is an odd number of both protons and neutrons.

25.20   Plan: Calculate the N/Z ratio for each nuclide. A neutron-rich nuclide decays to convert neutrons to protons while a neutron-poor nuclide decays to convert protons to neutrons. Neutron-rich nuclides, with a high N/Z, undergo β decay. Neutron-poor nuclides, with a low N/Z, undergo positron decay or electron capture. For $Z < 20$, β^+ emission is more common; for $Z > 80$, e^- capture is more common. Alpha decay is the most common means of decay for a heavy, unstable nucleus ($Z > 83$).
Solution:
a) $^{238}_{92}U$: Nuclides with $Z > 83$ decay through α decay.

b) The N/Z ratio for $^{48}_{24}Cr$ is $(48 - 24)/24 = 1.00$. This number is below the band of stability because N is too low and Z is too high. To become more stable, the nucleus decays by converting a proton to a neutron, which is positron decay. Alternatively, a nucleus can capture an electron and convert a proton into a neutron through electron capture.

c) The N/Z ratio for $^{50}_{25}$Mn is $(50 - 25)/25 = 1.00$. This number is below the band of stability, so the nuclide undergoes positron decay or electron capture.

25.22   Plan: Calculate the N/Z ratio for each nuclide. A neutron-rich nuclide decays to convert neutrons to protons while a neutron-poor nuclide decays to convert protons to neutrons. Neutron-rich nuclides, with a high N/Z, undergo β decay. Neutron-poor nuclides, with a low N/Z, undergo positron decay or electron capture. For $Z < 20$, $β^+$ emission is more common; for $Z > 80$, e^- capture is more common. Alpha decay is the most common means of decay for a heavy, unstable nucleus ($Z > 83$).

Solution:

a) For carbon-15, $N/Z = 9/6 = 1.5$, so the nuclide is neutron-rich. To decrease the number of neutrons and increase the number of protons, carbon-15 decays by beta decay.

b) The N/Z ratio for ^{120}Xe is $66/54 = 1.2$. Around atomic number 50, the ratio for stable nuclides is larger than 1.2, so ^{120}Xe is proton-rich. To decrease the number of protons and increase the number of neutrons, the xenon-120 nucleus either undergoes positron emission or electron capture.

c) Thorium-224 has an N/Z ratio of $134/90 = 1.5$. All nuclides of elements above atomic number 83 are unstable and decay to decrease the number of both protons and neutrons. Alpha decay by thorium-224 is the most likely mode of decay.

25.24   Plan: Stability results from a favorable N/Z ratio, even numbers of N and/or Z, and the occurrence of *magic numbers*.

Solution:

The N/Z ratio of $^{52}_{24}$Cr is $(52 - 24)/24 = 1.17$, which is within the band of stability. The fact that Z is even does not account for the variation in stability because all isotopes of chromium have the same Z. However, $^{52}_{24}$Cr has 28 neutrons, so N is both an even number and a *magic number* for this isotope only.

25.28   The equation for the nuclear reaction is $^{235}_{92}$U $\rightarrow$ $^{207}_{82}$Pb $+$ ___$^{0}_{-1}$β $+$ ___$^{4}_{2}$He

To determine the coefficients, notice that the beta particles will not impact the mass number. Subtracting the mass number for lead from the mass number for uranium will give the total mass number for the alpha particles released, $235 - 207 = 28$. Each alpha particle is a helium nucleus with mass number 4. The number of helium atoms is determined by dividing the total mass number change by 4, $28/4 = 7$ helium atoms or seven alpha particles. The equation is now

$$^{235}_{92}\text{U} \rightarrow {}^{207}_{82}\text{Pb} + \_\_{}^{0}_{-1}\beta + 7{}^{4}_{2}\text{He}$$

To find the number of beta particles released, examine the difference in number of protons (atomic number) between the reactant and products. Uranium, the reactant, has 92 protons. The atomic number in the products, lead atom and 7 helium-4 nuclei, total 96. To balance the atomic numbers, four electrons (beta particles) must be emitted to give the total atomic number for the products as $96 - 4 = 92$, the same as the reactant. In summary, seven alpha particles and four beta particles are emitted in the decay of uranium-235 to lead-207.

$$^{235}_{92}\text{U} \rightarrow {}^{207}_{82}\text{Pb} + 4{}^{0}_{-1}\beta + 7{}^{4}_{2}\text{He}$$

25.31   No, it is not valid to conclude that $t_{1/2}$ equals 1 min because the number of nuclei is so small (six nuclei). Decay rate is an average rate and is only meaningful when the sample is macroscopic and contains a large number of nuclei, as in the second case. Because the second sample contains 6×10^{12} nuclei, the conclusion that $t_{1/2} = 1$ min is valid.

25.33   Plan: Specific activity of a radioactive sample is its decay rate per gram. Calculate the specific activity by dividing the number of particles emitted per second (disintegrations per second = dps) by the mass of the sample. Convert disintegrations per second to Ci by using the conversion factor between the two units.

Solution:

$1 \text{ Ci} = 3.70 \times 10^{10}$ dps

Specific activity (Ci/g) $= \left(\dfrac{1.56 \times 10^6 \text{ dps}}{1.65 \text{ mg}} \right) \left(\dfrac{1 \text{ mg}}{10^{-3} \text{ g}} \right) \left(\dfrac{1 \text{ Ci}}{3.70 \times 10^{10} \text{ dps}} \right) = 2.55528 \times 10^{-2}$ Ci/g $= \mathbf{2.56 \times 10^{-2}}$ **Ci/g**

25.35 Plan: Specific activity of a radioactive sample is its decay rate per gram. Calculate the specific activity by dividing the number of particles emitted per second (disintegrations per second = dps) by the mass of the sample. Convert disintegrations per second to Bq by using the conversion factor between the two units.
Solution:
A becquerel is a disintegration per second (dps).

$$\text{Specific activity (Bq/g)} = \dfrac{\left(\left(\dfrac{7.4 \times 10^4\ d}{min}\right)\left(\dfrac{1\ min}{60\ s}\right)\right)}{8.58\ \mu g\left(\dfrac{10^{-6}\ g}{1\ \mu g}\right)}\left(\dfrac{1\ Bq}{1\ dps}\right) = 1.43745 \times 10^8\ \text{Bq/g} = \mathbf{1.4 \times 10^8\ Bq/g}$$

25.37 Plan: The decay constant is the rate constant for the first-order reaction.
Solution:

$$\text{Decay rate} = -\frac{\Delta \mathcal{N}}{\Delta t} = k\mathcal{N}$$

$$-\frac{-1\ \text{atom}}{\text{day}} = k(1 \times 10^{12}\ \text{atom})$$

$$k = \mathbf{1 \times 10^{-12}\ d^{-1}}$$

25.39 Plan: The rate constant, k, relates the number of radioactive nuclei to their decay rate through the equation $\mathcal{A} = kN$. The number of radioactive nuclei is calculated by converting moles to atoms using Avogadro's number. The decay rate is 1.39×10^5 atoms/yr or more simply, $1.39 \times 10^5\ \text{yr}^{-1}$ (the disintegrations are assumed).
Solution:

$$\text{Decay rate} = \mathcal{A} = -\frac{\Delta \mathcal{N}}{\Delta t} = k\mathcal{N}$$

$$-\frac{-1.39 \times 10^5\ \text{atoms}}{1.00\ \text{yr}} = k\left(\frac{1.00 \times 10^{-12}\ \text{mol}}{}\right)\left(\frac{6.022 \times 10^{23}\ \text{atoms}}{1\ \text{mol}}\right)$$

1.39×10^5 atom/yr = $k(6.022 \times 10^{11}$ atom)
$k = (1.39 \times 10^5$ atom/yr)/6.022×10^{11} atom
$k = 2.30820 \times 10^{-7}\ \text{yr}^{-1} = \mathbf{2.31 \times 10^{-7}\ yr^{-1}}$

25.41 Plan: Radioactive decay is a first-order process, so the integrated rate law is $\ln \mathcal{N}_t = \ln \mathcal{N}_0 - kt$
First find the value of k from the half-life and use the integrated rate law to find $\mathcal{N}_t$. The time unit in the time and the k value must agree.
Solution:
$t_{1/2} = 1.01\ \text{yr} \qquad t = 3.75 \times 10^3\ \text{h}$

$$t_{1/2} = \frac{\ln 2}{k} \quad \text{or}\ k = \frac{\ln 2}{t_{1/2}}$$

$$k = \frac{\ln 2}{1.01\ \text{yr}} = 0.686284\ \text{yr}^{-1}$$

$\ln \mathcal{N}_t = \ln \mathcal{N}_0 - kt$

$$\ln \mathcal{N}_t = \ln [2.00\ \text{mg}] - (0.686284\ \text{yr}^{-1})(3.75 \times 10^3\ \text{h})\left(\frac{1\ d}{24\ h}\right)\left(\frac{1\ yr}{365\ d}\right)$$

$\ln \mathcal{N}_t = 0.399361$
$\mathcal{N}_t = e^{0.399361}$
$\mathcal{N}_t = 1.49087\ \text{mg} = \mathbf{1.49\ mg}$

25.43   Plan: Lead-206 is a stable daughter of ^{238}U. Since all of the ^{206}Pb came from ^{238}U, the starting amount of ^{238}U was (270 μmol + 110 μmol) = 380 μmol = N_0. The amount of ^{238}U at time t (current) is 270 μmol = N_t. Find k from the first-order rate expression for half-life, and then substitute the values into the integrated rate law and solve for t.
Solution:

$$t_{1/2} = \frac{\ln 2}{k} \quad \text{or} \quad k = \frac{\ln 2}{t_{1/2}}$$

$$k = \frac{\ln 2}{4.5 \times 10^9 \text{ yr}} = 1.540327 \times 10^{-10} \text{ yr}^{-1}$$

$$\ln N_t = \ln N_0 - kt \qquad \text{or} \qquad \ln \frac{N_0}{N_t} = kt$$

$$\ln \frac{380 \text{ μmol}}{270 \text{ μmol}} = (1.540327 \times 10^{-10} \text{ yr}^{-1})(t)$$

$$0.3417492937 = (1.540327 \times 10^{-10} \text{ yr}^{-1})(t)$$

$$t = 2.21868 \times 10^9 \text{ yr} = \mathbf{2.2 \times 10^9 \text{ yr}}$$

25.45   Plan: The specific activity of the potassium-40 is the decay rate per mL of milk. Use the conversion factor 1 Ci = 3.70×10^{10} disintegrations per second (dps) to find the disintegrations per mL per s; convert the time unit to min.
Solution:

$$\text{Activity} = \left(\frac{6 \times 10^{-11} \text{ mCi}}{\text{mL}} \right)\left(\frac{10^{-3} \text{ Ci}}{1 \text{ mCi}} \right)\left(\frac{3.70 \times 10^{10} \text{ dps}}{1 \text{ Ci}} \right)\left(\frac{60 \text{ s}}{1 \text{ min}} \right)\left(\frac{1000 \text{ mL}}{1 \text{ L}} \right)(0.2 \text{ L}) = 26.64 \text{ dpm} = \mathbf{27 \text{ dpm}}$$

25.47   Plan: Both N_t and N_0 are given: the number of nuclei present currently, N_t, is found from the moles of ^{232}Th. Each fission track represents one nucleus that disintegrated, so the number of nuclei disintegrated is added to the number of nuclei currently present to determine the initial number of nuclei, N_0. The rate constant, k, is calculated from the half-life. All values are substituted into the first-order decay equation to find t.
Solution:

$$t_{1/2} = \frac{\ln 2}{k} \quad \text{or} \quad k = \frac{\ln 2}{t_{1/2}}$$

$$k = \frac{\ln 2}{1.4 \times 10^{10} \text{ yr}} = 4.95105129 \times 10^{-11} \text{ yr}^{-1}$$

$$N_t = \left(3.1 \times 10^{-15} \text{ mol Th} \right)\left(\frac{6.022 \times 10^{23} \text{ Th atoms}}{1 \text{ mol Th}} \right) = 1.86682 \times 10^9 \text{ atoms Th}$$

$$N_0 = 1.86682 \times 10^9 \text{ atoms} + 9.5 \times 10^4 \text{ atoms} = 1.866915 \times 10^9 \text{ atoms}$$

$$\ln N_t = \ln N_0 - kt \qquad \text{or} \qquad \ln \frac{N_0}{N_t} = kt$$

$$\ln \frac{1.866915 \times 10^9 \text{ atoms}}{1.86682 \times 10^9 \text{ atoms}} = (4.95105129 \times 10^{-11} \text{ yr}^{-1})(t)$$

$$5.088738 \times 10^{-5} = (4.95105129 \times 10^{-11} \text{ yr}^{-1})(t)$$

$$t = 1.027809 \times 10^6 \text{ yr} = \mathbf{1.0 \times 10^6 \text{ yr}}$$

25.50   Both gamma radiation and neutron beams have no charge, so neither is deflected by electric or magnetic fields. Neutron beams differ from gamma radiation in that a neutron has mass approximately equal to that of a proton. Researchers observed that a neutron beam could induce the emission of protons from a substance. Gamma rays do not cause such emissions.

25.52   Protons are repelled from the target nuclei due to the interaction of like (positive) charges. Higher energy is required to overcome the repulsion.

25.53   <u>Plan</u>: In a balanced nuclear equation, the total of mass numbers and the total of charges on the left side and the right side must be equal. In the shorthand notation, the nuclide to the left of the parentheses is the reactant while the nuclide written to the right of the parentheses is the product. The first particle inside the parentheses is the projectile particle while the second substance in the parentheses is the ejected particle.
<u>Solution</u>:
a) An alpha particle is a reactant with ^{10}B and a neutron is one product. The mass number for the reactants is $10 + 4 = 14$. So, the missing product must have a mass number of $14 - 1 = 13$. The total atomic number for the reactants is $5 + 2 = 7$, so the atomic number for the missing product is 7.

$$^{10}_{5}B + {}^{4}_{2}He \rightarrow {}^{1}_{0}n + {}^{13}_{7}N$$

b) A deuteron (^{2}H) is a reactant with ^{28}Si and ^{29}P is one product. For the reactants, the mass number is $28 + 2 = 30$ and the atomic number is $14 + 1 = 15$. The given product has mass number 29 and atomic number 15, so the missing product particle has mass number 1 and atomic number 0. The particle is thus a neutron.

$$^{28}_{14}Si + {}^{2}_{1}H \rightarrow {}^{1}_{0}n + {}^{29}_{15}P$$

c) The products are two neutrons and ^{244}Cf with a total mass number of $2 + 244 = 246$, and an atomic number of 98. The given reactant particle is an alpha particle with mass number 4 and atomic number 2. The missing reactant must have mass number of $246 - 4 = 242$ and atomic number $98 - 2 = 96$. Element 96 is Cm.

$$^{242}_{96}Cm + {}^{4}_{2}He \rightarrow 2\,{}^{1}_{0}n + {}^{244}_{98}Cf$$

25.58   Ionizing radiation is more dangerous to children because their rapidly dividing cells are more susceptible to radiation than an adult's slowly dividing cells.

25.60   <u>Plan</u>: The rad is the amount of radiation energy absorbed in J per body mass in kg: 1 rad = 0.01 J/kg. The conversion factor between rad and gray is 1 rad = 0.01 Gy.
<u>Solution</u>:
a) Dose (rad) $= \left(\dfrac{3.3 \times 10^{-7}\,J}{61.2\,kg}\right)\left(\dfrac{1\,rad}{1 \times 10^{-2}\,J/kg}\right) = 5.39 \times 10^{-7}\,rad = \mathbf{5.4 \times 10^{-7}\ rad}$

b) Gray (rad) $= \left(5.39 \times 10^{-7}\,rad\right)\left(\dfrac{0.01\,gy}{1\,rad}\right) = 5.39 \times 10^{-9}\,Gy = \mathbf{5.4 \times 10^{-9}\ Gy}$

25.62   <u>Plan</u>: Multiply the number of particles by the energy of one particle to obtain the total energy absorbed. Convert the energy to dose in grays with the conversion factor 1 rad = 0.01 J/kg = 0.01 Gy. To find the millirems, convert grays to rads and multiply rads by RBE (relative biological effectiveness) to find rems. Convert rems to mrems. Convert the dose to sieverts with the conversion factor 1 rem = 0.01 Sv.
<u>Solution</u>:
a) Energy (J) absorbed $= \left(6.0 \times 10^{5}\,\beta\right)\left(8.74 \times 10^{-14}\,J/\beta\right) = 5.244 \times 10^{-8}\,J$

Dose (Gy) $= \dfrac{5.244 \times 10^{-8}\,J}{70.\,kg}\left(\dfrac{1\,rad}{0.01\,J/kg}\right)\left(\dfrac{0.01\,Gy}{1\,rad}\right) = 7.4914 \times 10^{-10}\,Gy = \mathbf{7.5 \times 10^{-10}\ Gy}$

b) rems = rads x RBE $= \left(7.4914 \times 10^{-10}\,Gy\right)\left(\dfrac{1\,rad}{0.01\,Gy}\right)(1.0)\left(\dfrac{1\,mrem}{10^{-3}\,rem}\right) = 7.4914 \times 10^{-5}\,mrem = \mathbf{7.5 \times 10^{-5}\ mrem}$

sieverts $= \left(7.4914 \times 10^{-5}\,mrem\right)\left(\dfrac{10^{-3}\,rem}{1\,mrem}\right)\left(\dfrac{0.01\,Sv}{1\,rem}\right) = 7.4914 \times 10^{-10}\,Sv = \mathbf{7.5 \times 10^{-10}\ Sv}$

25.65   Use the time and disintegrations per second (Bq) to find the number of ^{60}Co atoms that disintegrate, which equals the number of β particles emitted. The dose in rad is calculated as energy absorbed per body mass.

Dose $= \left(\dfrac{475\,Bq}{1.858\,g}\right)\left(\dfrac{10^{3}\,g}{1\,kg}\right)\left(\dfrac{1\,dps}{1\,Bq}\right)\left(\dfrac{5.05 \times 10^{-14}\,J}{1\,disint.}\right)(24.0\,min)\left(\dfrac{60\,s}{1\,min}\right)\left(\dfrac{1\,rad}{0.01\,J/kg}\right)$

$= 1.8591 \times 10^{-3}\,rad = \mathbf{1.86 \times 10^{-3}\ rad}$

25.67   NAA does not destroy the sample while chemical analysis does. Neutrons bombard a non-radioactive sample, "activating" or energizing individual atoms within the sample to create radioisotopes. The radioisotopes decay back to their original state (thus, the sample is not destroyed) by emitting radiation that is different for each isotope.

25.73   Energy is released when a nuclide forms from nucleons. The nuclear binding energy is the amount of energy holding the nucleus together. Energy is absorbed to break the nucleus into nucleons and is released when nucleons "come together."

25.75   Plan: The conversion factors are: 1 MeV $= 10^6$ eV and 1 eV $= 1.602 \times 10^{-19}$ J.
Solution:

a) Energy (eV) $= (0.01861 \text{ MeV}) \left(\dfrac{10^6 \text{ eV}}{1 \text{ MeV}} \right) = \mathbf{1.861 \times 10^4}$ **eV**

b) Energy (J) $= (0.01861 \text{ MeV}) \left(\dfrac{10^6 \text{ eV}}{1 \text{ MeV}} \right) \left(\dfrac{1.602 \times 10^{-19} \text{ J}}{1 \text{ eV}} \right) = 2.981322 \times 10^{-15}$ J $= \mathbf{2.981 \times 10^{-15}}$ **J**

25.77   Plan: Convert moles of ^{239}Pu to atoms of ^{239}Pu using Avogadro's number. Multiply the number of atoms by the energy per atom (nucleus) and convert the MeV to J using the conversion 1 eV $= 1.602 \times 10^{-19}$ J.
Solution:

Number of atoms $= (1.5 \text{ mol}^{239}\text{Pu}) \left(\dfrac{6.022 \times 10^{23} \text{ atoms}}{\text{mol}} \right) = 9.033 \times 10^{23}$ atoms

Energy (J) $= (9.033 \times 10^{23} \text{ atoms}) \left(\dfrac{5.243 \text{ MeV}}{1 \text{ atom}} \right) \left(\dfrac{10^6 \text{ eV}}{1 \text{ MeV}} \right) \left(\dfrac{1.602 \times 10^{-19} \text{ J}}{1 \text{ eV}} \right) = 7.587075 \times 10^{11}$ J $= \mathbf{7.6 \times 10^{11}}$ **J**

25.79   Plan: Oxygen-16 has eight protons and eight neutrons. First find the Δm for the nucleus by subtracting the given mass of one oxygen atom from the sum of the masses of eight ^{1}H atoms and eight neutrons. Use the conversion factor 1 u $= 931.5$ MeV to convert Δm to binding energy in MeV and divide the binding energy by the total number of nucleons (protons and neutrons) in the oxygen nuclide to obtain binding energy per nucleon. Convert Δm of one oxygen atom to MeV using the conversion factor for binding energy/atom. To obtain binding energy per mole of oxygen, use the relationship $\Delta E = \Delta mc^2$. Δm must be converted to units of kg/mol.
Solution:
Mass of 8 ^{1}H atoms $= 8 \times 1.007825$ u $= 8.062600$ u
Mass of 8 neutrons $= 8 \times 1.008665$ u $= 8.069320$ u
Total mass $= 16.131920$ u
$\Delta m = (16.131920 - 15.994915)$u $= 0.137005$ u/^{16}O $= 0.137005$ g/mol ^{16}O

a) Binding energy (MeV/nucleon) $= \left(\dfrac{0.137005 \text{ u}^{16}\text{O}}{16 \text{ nucleons}} \right) \left(\dfrac{931.5 \text{ MeV}}{1 \text{ u}} \right) = 7.976259844$ MeV/nucleon
   $= \mathbf{7.976}$ **MeV/nucleon**

b) Binding energy (MeV/atom) $= \left(\dfrac{0.137005 \text{ u}^{16}\text{O}}{1 \text{ atom}} \right) \left(\dfrac{931.5 \text{ MeV}}{1 \text{ u}} \right) = 127.6201575$ MeV/atom
   $= \mathbf{127.6}$ **MeV/atom**

c) $\Delta E = \Delta mc^2$

Binding energy (kJ/mol) $= \left(\dfrac{0.137005 \text{ g}^{16}\text{O}}{\text{mol}} \right) \left(\dfrac{1 \text{ kg}}{10^3 \text{ g}} \right) (2.99792 \times 10^8 \text{ m/s})^2 \left(\dfrac{1 \text{ J}}{\text{kg} \bullet \text{m}^2 / \text{s}^2} \right) \left(\dfrac{1 \text{ kJ}}{10^3 \text{ J}} \right)$

   $= 1.23133577 \times 10^{10}$ kJ/mol $= \mathbf{1.23134 \times 10^{10}}$ **kJ/mol**

25.81   Plan: Cobalt-59 has 27 protons and 32 neutrons. First find the Δm for the nucleus by subtracting the given mass of one cobalt atom from the sum of the masses of 27 ^{1}H atoms and 32 neutrons. Use the conversion factor 1 u = 931.5 MeV to convert Δm to binding energy in MeV and divide the binding energy by the total number of nucleons (protons and neutrons) in the cobalt nuclide to obtain binding energy per nucleon.   Convert Δm of one cobalt atom to MeV using the conversion factor for binding energy/atom. To obtain binding energy per mole of cobalt, use the relationship $\Delta E = \Delta mc^2$. Δm must be converted to units of kg/mol.
Solution:
Mass of 27 ^{1}H atoms = 27 x 1.007825 u = 27.211275 u
Mass of 32 neutrons = 32 x 1.008665 u = 32.27728 u
Total mass = 59.488555 u
Δm = (59.488555 – 58.933198)u = 0.555357 u/^{59}Co = 0.555357 g/mol ^{59}Co

a) Binding energy (MeV/nucleon) = $\left(\dfrac{0.555357 \text{ u}^{59}\text{Co}}{59 \text{ nucleons}}\right)\left(\dfrac{931.5 \text{ MeV}}{1 \text{ u}}\right)$ = 8.768051619 MeV/nucleon

   = 8.768 MeV/nucleon

b) Binding energy (MeV/atom) = $\left(\dfrac{0.555357 \text{ u}^{59}\text{Co}}{1 \text{ atom}}\right)\left(\dfrac{931.5 \text{ MeV}}{1 \text{ u}}\right)$ = 517.3150 MeV/atom= **517.3 MeV/atom**

c) Use $\Delta E = \Delta mc^2$

Binding energy (kJ/mol) = $\left(\dfrac{0.555357 \text{ g}^{59}\text{Co}}{\text{mol}}\right)\left(\dfrac{1 \text{ kg}}{10^3 \text{ g}}\right)\left(2.99792 \times 10^8 \text{ m/s}\right)^2\left(\dfrac{1 \text{ J}}{\text{kg}\cdot\text{m}^2\big/\text{s}^2}\right)\left(\dfrac{1 \text{ kJ}}{10^3 \text{ J}}\right)$

   = 4.9912845x10^{10} kJ/mol = **4.99128x10^{10} kJ/mol**

25.85   In both radioactive decay and fission, radioactive particles are emitted, but the process leading to the emission is different. Radioactive decay is a spontaneous process in which unstable nuclei emit radioactive particles and energy. Fission occurs as the result of high-energy bombardment of nuclei with small particles that cause the nuclides to break into smaller nuclides, radioactive particles, and energy. In a chain reaction, all fission events are not the same. The collision between the small particle emitted in the fission and the large nucleus can lead to splitting of the large nuclei in a number of ways to produce several different products.

25.88   The water serves to slow the neutrons so that they are better able to cause a fission reaction. Heavy water ($^{2}_{1}$H$_2$O or D$_2$O) is a better moderator because it does not absorb neutrons as well as light water ($^{1}_{1}$H$_2$O) does, so more neutrons are available to initiate the fission process. However, D$_2$O does not occur naturally in great abundance, so production of D$_2$O adds to the cost of a heavy water reactor. In addition, if heavy water does absorb a neutron, it becomes *tritiated*, i.e., it contains the isotope tritium, $^{3}_{1}$H , which is radioactive.

25.93   Plan: Use the masses given in the problem to calculate the mass change (reactant – products) for the reaction. The conversion factor between u and kg is 1 u = 1.66054x10^{-27} kg. Use the relationship $E = \Delta mc^2$ to convert the mass change to energy.
Solution:
a) $^{243}_{96}\text{Cm} \rightarrow {}^{239}_{94}\text{Pu} + {}^{4}_{2}\text{He}$
Δm (u) = 243.0614 u – (4.0026 + 239.0522) u = 0.0066 u

Δm (kg) = $\left(0.0066 \text{ u}\right)\left(\dfrac{1.66054 \times 10^{-24} \text{ g}}{1 \text{ u}}\right)\left(\dfrac{1 \text{ kg}}{10^3 \text{ g}}\right)$ = 1.095956x10^{-29} kg = **1.1x10^{-29} kg**

b) $E = \Delta mc^2 = \left(1.09626 \times 10^{-29} \text{ kg}\right)\left(2.99792 \times 10^8 \text{ m/s}\right)^2\left(\dfrac{1 \text{ J}}{\text{kg}\cdot\text{m}^2\big/\text{s}^2}\right)$ = 9.85266x10^{-13} J = **9.9x10^{-13} J**

c) E released $= \left(\dfrac{9.85266 \times 10^{-13}\ \text{J}}{\text{reaction}}\right)\left(\dfrac{6.022 \times 10^{23}\ \text{reactions}}{\text{mol}}\right)\left(\dfrac{1\ \text{kJ}}{10^3\ \text{J}}\right) = 5.93317 \times 10^8\ \text{kJ/mol} = \textbf{5.9} \times \textbf{10}^{\textbf{8}}\ \textbf{kJ/mol}$

This is approximately one million times larger than a typical heat of reaction.

25.95   <u>Plan:</u> Determine k for ^{14}C using the half-life (5730 yr). Determine the mass of carbon in 4.58 g of CaCO$_3$. Divide the given activity of the C in d/min by the mass of carbon to obtain the activity in d/min•g; this is $\mathcal{A}_t$ and is compared to the activity of a living organism ($\mathcal{A}_0 = 15.3$ d/min•g) in the integrated rate law, solving for t.

<u>Solution:</u>

$k = \dfrac{\ln 2}{t_{1/2}} = \dfrac{\ln 2}{5730\ \text{yr}} = 1.2096809 \times 10^{-4}\ \text{yr}^{-1}$

Mass (g) of C $= \left(4.58\ \text{g CaCO}_3\right)\left(\dfrac{1\ \text{mol CaCO}_3}{100.09\ \text{g CaCO}_3}\right)\left(\dfrac{1\ \text{mol C}}{1\ \text{mol CaCO}_3}\right)\left(\dfrac{12.01\ \text{g C}}{1\ \text{mol C}}\right) = 0.5495634\ \text{g C}$

$\mathcal{A}_t = \dfrac{3.2\ \text{d/min}}{0.5495634\ \text{g}} = 5.8228\ \text{d/min•g}$

Using the integrated rate law:

$\ln\left(\dfrac{\mathcal{A}_t}{\mathcal{A}_0}\right) = -kt \qquad \mathcal{A}_0 = 15.3$ d/min•g (the ratio of ^{12}C:^{14}C in living organisms)

$\ln\left(\dfrac{5.8228\ \text{d/min•g}}{15.3\ \text{d/min•g}}\right) = -(1.2096809 \times 10^{-4}\ \text{yr}^{-1})(t)$

$t = 7986.17$ yr $= \textbf{8.0} \times \textbf{10}^{\textbf{3}}$ **yr**

25.96   Find the rate constant from the rate of decay and the initial number of atoms. Use rate constant to calculate half life.

Initial number of atoms:

Ra atoms $= \left(5.4\ \mu\text{g RaCl}_2\right)\left(\dfrac{10^{-6}\ \text{g}}{1\ \mu\text{g}}\right)\left(\dfrac{1\ \text{mol RaCl}_2}{297\ \text{g RaCl}_2}\right)\left(\dfrac{1\ \text{mol Ra}}{1\ \text{mol RaCl}_2}\right)\left(\dfrac{6.022 \times 10^{23}\ \text{Ra atoms}}{1\ \text{mol Ra}}\right)$

$= 1.09490909 \times 10^{16}$ Ra atoms

$\mathcal{A} = k\mathcal{N} \quad$ or $\quad k = \dfrac{\mathcal{A}}{\mathcal{N}}$

$k = \left(\dfrac{1.5 \times 10^5\ \text{Bq}}{1.09490909 \times 10^{16}\ \text{Ra atoms}}\right)\left(\dfrac{1\,\text{d}/\text{s}}{\text{Bq}}\right) = 1.36997675 \times 10^{-11}\ \text{s}^{-1}$

$t_{1/2} = \dfrac{\ln 2}{k} = \dfrac{\ln 2}{1.36997675 \times 10^{-11}\ \text{s}^{-1}} = 5.05955 \times 10^{10}\ \text{s} = \textbf{5.1} \times \textbf{10}^{\textbf{10}}$ **s**

25.98   <u>Plan:</u> Determine the amount of AgCl (grams) dissolved in 1 mL of solution. The activity of the radioactive Ag$^+$ indicates how much AgCl dissolved, given a starting sample with a specific activity (175 nCi/g). Convert g/mL to mol/L (molar solubility) using the molar mass of AgCl.

<u>Solution:</u>

Concentration $= \left(\dfrac{1.25 \times 10^{-2}\ \text{Bq}}{\text{mL}}\right)\left(\dfrac{1\ \text{dps}}{1\ \text{Bq}}\right)\left(\dfrac{1\ \text{Ci}}{3.70 \times 10^{10}\ \text{dps}}\right)\left(\dfrac{1\ \text{nCi}}{10^{-9}\ \text{Ci}}\right)\left(\dfrac{1\ \text{g AgCl}}{175\ \text{nCi}}\right) = 1.93050 \times 10^{-6}$ g AgCl/mL

Concentration (mol/L) $= \left(\dfrac{1.93050 \times 10^{-6}\ \text{g AgCl}}{\text{mL}}\right)\left(\dfrac{1\ \text{mol AgCl}}{143.4\ \text{g AgCl}}\right)\left(\dfrac{1\ \text{mL}}{10^{-3}\ \text{L}}\right)$

$= 1.34623 \times 10^{-5}$ mol/L $= \textbf{1.35} \times \textbf{10}^{\textbf{-5}}$ **mol/L AgCl**

25.100 Plan: Determine the value of k from the half-life. Then determine the fraction from the integrated rate law.
Solution:

$$k = \frac{\ln 2}{t_{1/2}} = \frac{\ln 2}{7.0 \times 10^8 \text{ yr}} = 9.90210 \times 10^{-10} \text{ yr}^{-1}$$

$$\ln \frac{N_0}{N_t} = kt = (9.90210 \times 10^{-10} \text{ yr}^{-1})(2.8 \times 10^9 \text{ yr}) = 2.772588$$

$$\frac{N_0}{N_t} = 15.99998844$$

$$\frac{N_t}{N_0} = 0.062500 = \mathbf{6.2 \times 10^{-2}}$$

25.102 Plan: Find the rate constant, k, using any two data pairs (the greater the time between the data points, the greater the reliability of the calculation). Calculate $t_{1/2}$ using k. Once k is known, use the integrated rate law to find the percentage lost after 2 h. The percentage of isotope *remaining* is the fraction remaining after 2.0 h (N_t where $t = 2.0$ h) divided by the initial amount (N_0), i.e., fraction remaining is N_t/N_0. Solve the first-order rate expression for N_t/N_0, and then subtract from 100% to get fraction *lost*.
Solution:

a) $\ln \dfrac{N_t}{N_0} = -kt$

$$\ln \left(\frac{495 \text{ photons/s}}{5000 \text{ photons/s}} \right) = -k(20 \text{ h})$$

$$-2.312635 = -k(20 \text{ h})$$
$$k = 0.11563 \text{ h}^{-1}$$

$$t_{1/2} = \frac{\ln 2}{k} = \frac{\ln 2}{0.11563 \text{ h}^{-1}} = 5.9945 \text{ h} = \mathbf{5.99 \text{ h}}$$ (Assuming the times are exact, and the emissions have three significant figures.)

b) $\ln \dfrac{N_t}{N_0} = -kt$

$$\ln \frac{N_t}{N_0} = -(0.11563 \text{ h}^{-1})(2.0 \text{ h}) = -0.23126$$

$$\frac{N_t}{N_0} = 0.793533 \qquad\qquad \frac{N_t}{N_0} \times 100\% = 79.3533\%$$

The fraction lost upon preparation is $100\% - 79.3533\% = 20.6467\% = \mathbf{21\%}$.

25.104 Plan: Use the given relationship for the fraction remaining after time t, where $t = 10.0$ yr, 10.0×10^3 yr, and 10.0×10^4 yr.
Solution:

a) (i) Fraction remaining after 10.0 yr $= \left(\frac{1}{2}\right)^{t/t_{1/2}} = \left(\frac{1}{2}\right)^{10.0/5730} = 0.998791 = \mathbf{0.999}$

(ii) Fraction remaining after 10.0×10^3 yr $= \left(\frac{1}{2}\right)^{10.0 \times 10^3/5730} = 0.298292 = \mathbf{0.298}$

(iii) Fraction remaining after 10.0×10^4 yr $= \left(\frac{1}{2}\right)^{10.0 \times 10^4/5730} = 5.5772795 \times 10^{-6} = \mathbf{5.58 \times 10^{-6}}$

b) Radiocarbon dating is more reliable for (ii) because a significant quantity of ^{14}C has decayed and a significant quantity remains. Therefore, a change in the amount of ^{14}C would be noticeable. For the fraction in (i), very little ^{14}C has decayed and for (iii) very little ^{14}C remains. In either case, it will be more difficult to measure the change so the error will be relatively large.

25.106 Plan: At one half-life, the fraction of sample is 0.500. Find n for which $(0.900)^n = 0.500$.
Solution:
$(0.900)^n = 0.500$
$n \ln (0.900) = \ln (0.500)$
$n = (\ln 0.500)/(\ln 0.900) = 6.578813 \text{ h} = \mathbf{6.579 \text{ h}}$

25.110 Plan: The *production rate* of radon gas (volume/hour) is also the *decay rate* of ^{226}Ra. The decay rate, or activity, is proportional to the number of radioactive nuclei decaying, or the number of atoms in 1.000 g of ^{226}Ra, using the relationship $\mathcal{A} = k\mathcal{N}$. Calculate the number of atoms in the sample, and find k from the half-life. Convert the activity in units of nuclei/time (also disintegrations per unit time) to volume/time using the ideal gas law.
Solution:
$$^{226}_{88}\text{Ra} \rightarrow \,^{4}_{2}\text{He} + \,^{222}_{86}\text{Rn}$$

$$k = \frac{\ln 2}{t_{1/2}} = \frac{\ln 2}{1599 \text{ yr}} = 4.33879178 \times 10^{-4} \text{ yr}^{-1}(1 \text{ yr}/8766 \text{ h}) = 4.94510515 \times 10^{-8} \text{ h}^{-1}$$

The mass of ^{226}Ra is 226.025402 u/atom or 226.025402 g/mol.

$$\mathcal{N} = \left(1.000 \text{ g Ra}\right)\left(\frac{1 \text{ mol Ra}}{226.025402 \text{ g Ra}}\right)\left(\frac{6.022 \times 10^{23} \text{ Ra atoms}}{1 \text{ mol Ra}}\right) = 2.6643023 \times 10^{21} \text{ Ra atoms}$$

$\mathcal{A} = k\mathcal{N} = (4.94510515 \times 10^{-8} \text{ h}^{-1})(2.6643023 \times 10^{21} \text{ Ra atoms}) = 1.3175255 \times 10^{14} \text{ Ra atoms/h}$

This result means that 1.318×10^{14} ^{226}Ra nuclei are decaying into ^{222}Rn nuclei every hour. Convert atoms of ^{222}Rn into volume of gas using the ideal gas law.

$$\text{Moles of Rn/h} = \left(\frac{1.3175255 \times 10^{14} \text{ Ra atoms}}{h}\right)\left(\frac{1 \text{ atom Rn}}{1 \text{ atom Ra}}\right)\left(\frac{1 \text{ mol Rn}}{6.022 \times 10^{23} \text{ Rn atoms}}\right)$$

$$= 2.1878537 \times 10^{-10} \text{ mol Rn/h}$$

$$V = \frac{nRT}{p} = \frac{\left(2.1878537 \times 10^{-10} \text{ mol Rn/h}\right)\left(8.31446 \frac{\text{kPa} \cdot \text{L}}{\text{mol} \cdot \text{K}}\right)(273.15 \text{ K})}{100 \text{ kPa}}$$

$$= 4.96882305 \times 10^{-9} \text{ L/h} = \mathbf{4.969 \times 10^{-9} \text{ L/h}}$$

Therefore, radon gas is produced at a rate of 4.904×10^{-9} L/h. Note: Activity could have been calculated as decay in moles/time, removing Avogadro's number as a multiplication and division factor in the calculation.

25.113 Plan: Determine k from the half-life and then use the integrated rate law, solving for time.
Solution:
$$k = \frac{\ln 2}{t_{1/2}} = \frac{\ln 2}{29 \text{ yr}} = 0.0239016 \text{ yr}^{-1}$$

$$\ln \frac{\mathcal{N}_t}{\mathcal{N}_0} = -kt$$

$$\ln \left(\frac{1.0 \times 10^4 \text{ particles}}{7.0 \times 10^4 \text{ particles}}\right) = -(0.0239016 \text{ yr}^{-1})(t)$$

$$-1.945910 = -(0.0239016 \text{ yr}^{-1})(t)$$

$$t = 81.413378 \text{ yr} = \mathbf{81 \text{ yr}}$$

25.115 Plan: Convert pCi to Bq using the conversion factors 1 Ci = 3.70×10^{10} Bq and 1 pCi = 10^{-12} Ci. For part b), use the first-order integrated rate law to find the activity at the later time ($t = 9.5$ days). You will first need to calculate k from the half-life expression. For part c), solve for the time at which $\mathcal{N}_t$ = the level recommended by Health Canada.
Solution:

a) Activity (Bq/L) = $\left(\frac{4.0 \text{ pCi}}{L}\right)\left(\frac{10^{-12} \text{ Ci}}{1 \text{ pCi}}\right)\left(\frac{3.70 \times 10^{10} \text{ Bq}}{1 \text{ Ci}}\right) = 0.148 \text{ Bq/L} = 0.15 \text{ Bq/L}$

The safe level is **0.15 Bq/L**.

b) $k = \dfrac{\ln 2}{t_{1/2}} = \dfrac{\ln 2}{3.82 \text{ d}} = 0.181452 \text{ d}^{-1}$

$\ln \dfrac{N_t}{N_0} = -kt$

$\ln \dfrac{N_t}{41.5 \text{ pCi/L}} = -(0.181452 \text{ d}^{-1})(9.5 \text{ d}) = -1.723794$

$\dfrac{N_t}{41.5 \text{ pCi/L}} = 0.17838806$

$N_t = 7.403104 \text{ pCi/L}$

Activity (Bq/L) $= \left(\dfrac{7.403104 \text{ pCi}}{L} \right)\left(\dfrac{10^{-12} \text{ Ci}}{1 \text{ pCi}} \right)\left(\dfrac{3.70 \times 10^{10} \text{ Bq}}{1 \text{ Ci}} \right) = 0.2739148 \text{ Bq/L} = \textbf{0.27 Bq/L}$

c) The desired activity is 0.15 Bq/L, however, the room air currently contains 0.27 Bq/L.

$\ln \dfrac{N_t}{N_0} = -kt$

$\ln \dfrac{0.15 \text{ Bq/L}}{0.2739148 \text{ Bq/L}} = -(0.181452 \text{ d}^{-1})(t)$

$-0.602182 = -(0.181452 \text{ d}^{-1})(t)$

$t = 3.318685 \text{ d} = \textbf{3.3 d}$

It takes 3.3 d more to reach the recommended EPA level. A total of 12.8 (3.3 + 9.5) d is required to reach recommended levels when the room was initially measured at 41.5 pCi/L.

25.118   Plan: Convert mCi to Ci to disintegrations per second; multiply the dps by the energy of each disintegration in MeV and convert to energy in J. Recall that 1 rad = 0.01 J/kg.
Solution:

Energy (J/s) $= (1.0 \text{ mCi})\left(\dfrac{10^{-3} \text{ Ci}}{1 \text{ mCi}} \right)\left(\dfrac{3.70 \times 10^{10} \text{ dps}}{1 \text{ Ci}} \right)\left(\dfrac{5.59 \text{ MeV}}{1 \text{ disint.}} \right)\left(\dfrac{1.602 \times 10^{-13} \text{ J}}{1 \text{ MeV}} \right) = 3.3134166 \times 10^{-5} \text{ J/s}$

Time for 1.0 mrad to be absorbed:

Time (s) $= (1.0 \text{ mrad})\left(\dfrac{10^{-3} \text{ rad}}{1 \text{ mrad}} \right)\left(\dfrac{0.01 \text{ J/kg}}{1 \text{ rad}} \right)\left(\dfrac{24.5 \text{ kg}}{3.3134166 \times 10^{-5} \text{ J/s}} \right) = 7.3941804 \text{ s} = \textbf{7.4 s}$

25.121   Because the 1941 wine has a little over twice as much tritium in it, just over one half-life has passed between the two wines. Therefore, the older wine was produced before 1929 (1941 – 12.26) but not much earlier than that. To find the number of years back in time, use the first-order rate expression, where $N_0 = 2.32 \, N$, $N_t = N$ and $t =$ years transpired between the manufacture date and 1941.

$k = \dfrac{\ln 2}{t_{1/2}} = \dfrac{\ln 2}{12.26 \text{ yr}} = 0.05653729 \text{ yr}^{-1}$

$\ln \dfrac{N_t}{N_0} = -kt$

$\ln \dfrac{N}{2.32 \, N} = -(0.05653729 \text{ yr}^{-1})(t)$

$-0.841567 = -(0.05653729 \text{ yr}^{-1})(t)$

$t = 14.92857 \text{ yr} = 14.9 \text{ yr}$

The wine was produced in (1941 – 15) = **1926**.

25.124   Plan: Determine the change in mass for the reaction by subtracting the masses of the products from the masses of the reactants. Use conversion factors to convert the mass change in u to energy in eV and then to J.
Solution:
Δm = mass of reactants − mass of products = $(14.003074 + 1.008665)u − (14.003241 + 1.007825)u = 0.000673$ u

$$\text{Energy (eV)} = (0.000673 \text{ u})\left(\frac{931.5 \text{ MeV}}{1 \text{ u}}\right)\left(\frac{10^6 \text{ eV}}{1 \text{ MeV}}\right) = 6.268995 \times 10^5 \text{ eV} = \mathbf{6.27 \times 10^5 \text{ eV}}$$

$$\text{Energy (kJ/mol)} = (6.268995 \times 10^5 \text{ eV})\left(\frac{1.602 \times 10^{-19} \text{ J}}{1 \text{ eV}}\right)\left(\frac{1 \text{ kJ}}{10^3 \text{ J}}\right)\left(\frac{6.022 \times 10^{23}}{1 \text{ mol}}\right)$$

$$= 6.0478524 \times 10^7 \text{ kJ/mol} = \mathbf{6.05 \times 10^7 \text{ kJ/mol}}$$

25.130   Plan: The difference in the energies of the two α particles gives the energy of the γ ray released to get from excited state I to the ground state. Use $E = hc/\lambda$ to determine the wavelength. The energy of the gamma ray must be converted from MeV to J. The energy of the 2% α particle is equal to the highest energy α particle minus the energy of the two γ rays (the rays are from excited state II to excited state I, and from excited state I to the ground state).
Solution:
a) Energy of the γ ray = $(4.816 − 4.773)$ MeV = **0.043 MeV**

$$\lambda = \frac{hc}{E} = \frac{(6.626 \times 10^{-34} \text{ J}\bullet\text{s})(2.99792 \times 10^8 \text{ m/s})}{(0.043 \text{ MeV})}\left(\frac{1 \text{ MeV}}{1.602 \times 10^{-13} \text{ J}}\right) = 2.8836 \times 10^{-11} \text{ m} = \mathbf{2.9 \times 10^{-11} \text{ m}}$$

b) $(4.816 − 0.043 − 0.060)$ MeV = **4.713 MeV**

25.134   Plan: Multiply each of the half-lives by 20 (the number of half-lives is considered to be exact).
Solution:
a) ^{242}Cm $20(163 \text{ d}) = \mathbf{3.26 \times 10^3 \text{ d}}$
b) ^{214}Po $20(1.6 \times 10^{-4} \text{ s}) = \mathbf{3.2 \times 10^{-3} \text{ s}}$
c) ^{232}Th $20(1.39 \times 10^{10} \text{ yr}) = \mathbf{2.78 \times 10^{11} \text{ yr}}$

25.136   a) When 1.00 kg of antimatter annihilates 1.00 kg of matter, the change in mass is:
         $\Delta m = 0 − 2.00$ kg $= −2.00$ kg. The energy released is calculated from $\Delta E = \Delta mc^2$.
         $\Delta E = (−2.00 \text{ kg})(2.99792 \times 10^8 \text{ m/s})^2(\text{J}/(\text{kg}\bullet\text{m}^2/\text{s}^2)) = −1.7975049 \times 10^{17} \text{ J} = \mathbf{−1.80 \times 10^{17} \text{ J}}$
The negative value indicates the energy is released.
b) Assuming that four hydrogen atoms fuse to form the two protons and two neutrons in one helium atom and release two positrons, the energy released can be calculated from the binding energy of helium-4.
         $4\,_{1}^{1}\text{H} \rightarrow \,_{2}^{4}\text{He} + 2\,_{+1}^{0}\beta$
         $\Delta m = [4(1.007825 \text{ u})] − [4.00260 \text{ u} + 2(0.000549 \text{ u})]$
            $= 0.02760$ u per $_{2}^{4}\text{He}$ formed

$$\text{Total } \Delta m = (1.00 \times 10^5 \text{ H atoms})\left(\frac{0.02760 \text{ u}}{^4\text{He}}\right)\left(\frac{1\,^4\text{He}}{4 \text{ H atoms}}\right) = 6.90 \times 10^2 \text{ u}$$

$$\text{Energy} = (6.90 \times 10^2 \text{ u})\left(\frac{931.5 \text{ MeV}}{1 \text{ u}}\right)\left(\frac{1.602 \times 10^{-16} \text{ kJ}}{1 \text{ MeV}}\right) = 1.02966 \times 10^{-10} \text{ kJ per antiH collision}$$

$$\text{AntiH atoms} = (1.00 \text{ kg})\left(\frac{10^3 \text{ g}}{1 \text{ kg}}\right)\left(\frac{1 \text{ mol antiH}}{1.008 \text{ g antiH}}\right)\left(\frac{6.022 \times 10^{23} \text{ antiH}}{1 \text{ mol antiH}}\right) = 5.9742 \times 10^{26} \text{ antiH}$$

$$\text{Energy released} = \left(\frac{1.02966 \times 10^{-10} \text{ kJ}}{\text{antiH}}\right)(5.9742 \times 10^{26} \text{ antiH}) = 6.15139 \times 10^{16} \text{ kJ} = \mathbf{6.15 \times 10^{16} \text{ kJ}}$$

c) From the above calculations, the procedure in part b) with excess hydrogen produces more energy per kilogram of antihydrogen.

25.137 <u>Plan:</u> Einstein's equation is $E = mc^2$, which is modified to $E = \Delta mc^2$ to reflect a mass difference. The speed of light, c, is 2.99792×10^8 m/s. The mass of exactly 1 u is 1.66054×10^{-27} kg (inside back cover of text). When the quantities are multiplied together, the unit will be kg•m^2/s^2, which is also J. Convert J to MeV using the conversion factor 1.602×10^{-13} J = 1 MeV.

<u>Solution:</u>

$\Delta E = (\Delta m)c^2$

$$\Delta E = \left[(1\,u) \left(\frac{1.66054 \times 10^{-27} \text{ kg}}{1 \text{ u}} \right) \right] (2.99792 \times 10^8 \text{ m/s})^2 \left(\frac{\text{J}}{\text{kg•m}^2 \Big/ \text{s}^2} \right) \left(\frac{1 \text{ MeV}}{1.602 \times 10^{-13} \text{ J}} \right)$$

$= 9.3159448 \times 10^2$ MeV = **9.316 \times 10^2 MeV**

25.141 <u>Plan:</u> The rate of formation of plutonium-239 depends on the rate of decay of neptunium-239 with a half-life of 2.35 d. Calculate k from the half-life equation and use the integrated rate law to find the time necessary to react 90% of the neptunium-239 (10% left).

<u>Solution:</u>

$k = \dfrac{\ln 2}{t_{1/2}} = \dfrac{\ln 2}{2.35 \text{ d}} = 0.294956 \text{ d}^{-1}$

$\ln \dfrac{N_t}{N_0} = -kt$

$\ln \left(\dfrac{(1.00 \text{ kg})\left(10.\% \Big/ 100\%\right)}{1.00 \text{ kg}} \right) = -(0.294956 \text{ d}^{-1})(t)$

$-2.3025851 = -(0.294956 \text{ d}^{-1})(t)$

$t = 7.806538$ d = **7.81 d**